1966
COMET, FALCON, FAIRLANE and MUSTANG

SHOP MANUAL

 SERVICE PUBLICATIONS

FIRST PRINTING—AUGUST, 1965

© 1965 FORD MOTOR COMPANY, DEARBORN, MICHIGAN

VEHICLE IDENTIFICATION	1
BRAKES	2
SUSPENSION, STEERING, WHEELS AND TIRES	3
REAR AXLE	4
DRIVE SHAFT AND CLUTCH	5
MANUAL SHIFT TRANSMISSION	6
AUTOMATIC TRANSMISSION	7
ENGINE	8
IGNITION SYSTEM	9
FUEL SYSTEM	10
COOLING SYSTEM	11
EXHAUST SYSTEM	12
CHARGING SYSTEM	13
STARTING SYSTEM	14
LIGHTING SYSTEM, HORNS AND INSTRUMENTS	15
VENTILATING, HEATING AND ACCESSORIES	16
BODY, DOORS AND WINDOWS	17
TRIM, SEATS AND CONVERTIBLE TOP	18
MAINTENANCE SCHEDULE	19
MAINTENANCE OPERATIONS	20
LUBRICATION CHARTS AND SPECIFICATIONS	21
SCHEMATICS	22

SPECIFICATIONS AND SPECIAL SERVICE TOOLS AT END OF EACH GROUP

FOREWORD

This shop manual provides the Service Technician with complete information for the proper servicing of the 1966 Comet, Falcon, Fairlane and Mustang cars.

The information is grouped according to the type of work being performed, such as diagnosis and testing, frequently performed adjustments and repairs, in-vehicle adjustments, overhaul, etc. Specifications and recommended special tools are included.

Refer to the opposite page for important vehicle identification data.

The descriptions and specifications in this manual were in effect at the time this manual was approved for printing. The Ford Motor Company reserves the right to discontinue models at any time, or change specifications or design, without notice and without incurring obligation.

 SERVICE PUBLICATIONS

VEHICLE IDENTIFICATION

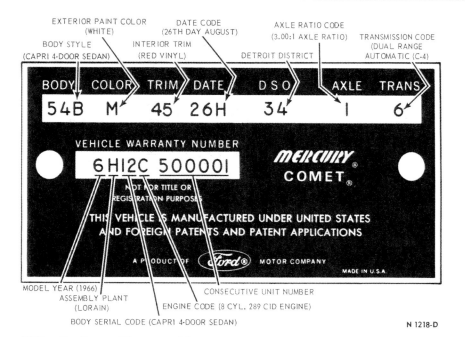

FIG. 1—Comet Warranty Plate

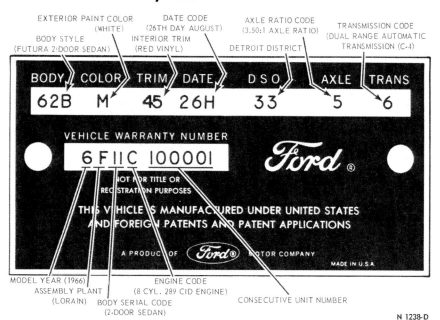

FIG. 2—Falcon Warranty Plate

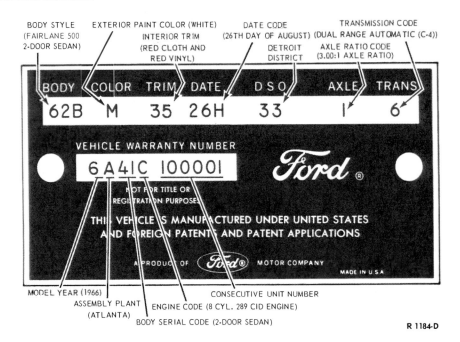

FIG. 3—Fairlane Warranty Plate

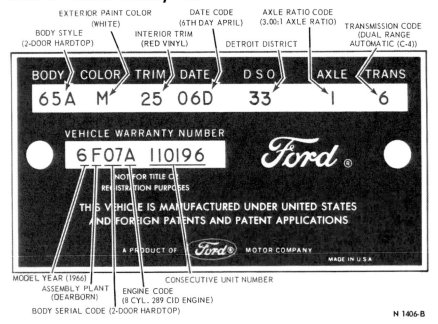

FIG. 4—Mustang Warranty Plate

FIG. 5—Vehicle Identification Number Location—Comet, Falcon and Mustang

FIG. 6—Vehicle Identification Number Location—Fairlane

Figures 1, 2, 3 and 4 illustrate the Comet, Falcon, Fairlane and Mustang Warranty Plates. The warranty plate is located on the rear face (lock face) of the left front door.

The official Vehicle Identification Number, for title and registration purposes, is stamped on the top upper flange of the left front fender apron for Falcon. Comet and Mustang (Fig. 5) and on the vertical face of the left front fender apron near the top for the Fairlane (Fig. 6). Do not use the Vehicle Warranty Number, which appears on the warranty plate, for title or registration purposes.

VEHICLE DATA

The vehicle data appears in a line across the top of the warranty plate (Figs. 1, 2, 3 and 4). The first two letters and a number identify the Body Style. The following one or two letters identify the Exterior Paint Color. The next code consisting of two numbers, or a letter and a number, identifies the Interior Trim. The Date Code showing the date the car was manufactured, follows the Trim Code and consists of two numbers and a letter. The next code gives the district in which the car was ordered and consists of two numbers. The next to the last code is the Axle Ratio Code and is designated by a number for a conventional axle or a letter for an Equa-Lock axle. The last code in the vehicle data is the Transmission Code and consists of one number. The charts that follow, list in detail the various vehicle data codes.

VEHICLE WARRANTY NUMBER

The vehicle warranty number is the second line of numbers and letters appearing on the Warranty Plate (Figs. 1, 2, 3 and 4). The first number indicates the model year. The letter following the model year indicates the assembly plant at which the car was manufactured. The next two numbers designate the Body Serial Code. The letter following the Body Serial Code designates the Engine Code. The remaining numbers indicate the Consecutive Unit Number. The charts that follow, list the various Vehicle Warranty Number codes.

BODY SERIAL AND STYLE CODES

The two-digit numeral which follows the assembly plant code identifies the body series. This two-digit number is used in conjunction with the Body Style Code, in the Vehicle Data, which consists of a two-digit number with a letter Suffix. The following chart lists the Body Series Codes, Body Style Codes and the Model.

COMET

Body Serial Code	Body Style Code	Body Type	Model
02	54A	4-Door Sedan①	Comet
01	62A	2-Door Sedan①	202
06	71A	4-Door Wagon①	
12	54B	4-Door Sedan①	Capri
13	63B	2-Door Hardtop①	
16	71C	4-Door (Villager) Wagon①	
22	54D	4-Door Sedan①	
23	63C	2-Door Hardtop②	Comet
23	63D	2-Door Hardtop①	Caliente
25	76B	2-Door Convertible②	
25	76D	2-Door Convertible①	
27	63E	2-Door Hardtop②	Cyclone
27	63H	2-Door Hardtop② (GT)	
29	76C	2-Door Convertible	
29	76H	2-Door Convertible② (GT)	

①Bench Seat
②Bucket Seats

FALCON

Body Serial Code	Body Style Code	Body Type	Model
02	54A	4-Door Sedan	Standard
01	62A	2-Door Sedan	Sedan
12	54B	4-Door Sedan (Bench)	
11	62B	2-Door Sedan (Bench)	Futura
14	62C	2-Door Sport Coupe (Bucket)	
22	71A	4-Door Wagon	Station
24	71B	4-Door Wagon Deluxe	Wagon
27	66A	2-Door Standard Ranchero	
27	66B	2-Door Deluxe Ranchero	Ranchero
27	66D	2-Door Standard (RPO Bucket W/Console)	

FAIRLANE

Body Serial Code	Body Style Code	Body Type	Model
31	62A	2-Door Coupe	Fairlane
32	54A	4-Door Club Coupe	
41	62B	2-Door Sedan	Fairlane
42	54B	4-Door Sedan	500
43	63B	2-Door Hardtop	
45	76B	2-Door Convertible	
46	63C	2-Door Hardtop①	Fairlane
47	76C	2-Door Convertible①	500 XL
40	63D	2-Door Hardtop①	Fairlane
44	76D	2-Door Convertible①	500 GT
38	71D	4-Door Ranch Wagon	Station
48	71B	4-Door Cust. Ranch Wagon	Wagons
49	71E	4-Door Squire	

①Bucket Seats

MUSTANG

Body Serial Code	Body Style Code	Body Type	Model
09	63A	2-Door Fastback①	Mustang
07	65A	2-Door Hardtop①	
08	76A	2-Door Convertible①	
09	63B	2-Door Fastback②	
07	65B	2-Door Hardtop②	
08	76B	2-Door Convertible②	
07	65C	2-Door Hardtop③	
08	76C	2-Door Convertible③	

①Std. Bucket Seats
②Luxury Bucket Seats
③Std. Bench Seats

EXTERIOR PAINT COLOR CODES

A single letter code designates a solid body color and two letters denote a two-tone—the first letter, the lower color and the second letter, the upper color.

Code	M-30J M-32-J#	Color
A	1724-A	Black
F	1226-A	Lt. Blue
H	1912-A	Lt. Beige
K	1903-A	Dk. Blue Met.
M	1619-A	White
P	1910-A	Med. Palomino Met.
R	1879-A	Dk. Green Met.
T	2008-A	Red
U	1070-A	Med. Turquoise Met.
V	1921-A	Emberglo Met.
X	1632-A	Maroon Met.
Y	1269-A	Lt. Blue Met.
Z	1915-A	Med. Sage Gold Met.
4	1901-A	Med. Silver Met.
5	2025-A	Red
8	1955-A	Yellow

INTERIOR TRIM CODES

Code	Trim Schemes
11	Silver Cloth and Black Vinyl
12	Blue Cloth and Blue Vinyl
15	Red Cloth and Red Vinyl
17	Aqua Cloth and Aqua Vinyl
22	Blue Vinyl
25	Red Vinyl
26	Black Vinyl
27	Aqua Vinyl
32	Blue Cloth and Blue Vinyl
35	Red Cloth and Red Vinyl
36	Black Vinyl
37	Aqua Cloth and Aqua Vinyl
38	Ivy Gold Cloth and Ivy Gold Vinyl
42	Blue Vinyl
44	Emberglo Vinyl
45	Red Vinyl
46	Black Vinyl
47	Aqua Vinyl
48	Ivy Gold Vinyl
52	Blue Cloth and Blue Vinyl
55	Red Cloth and Red Vinyl
57	Aqua Cloth and Aqua Vinyl
62	Blue Vinyl
64	Emberglo Vinyl
65	Red Vinyl
66	Black Vinyl
67	Aqua Vinyl
68	Ivy Gold Vinyl
82	Blue Vinyl
84	Emberglo Vinyl
85	Red Vinyl
86	Black Vinyl
87	Aqua Vinyl
88	Ivy Gold Vinyl
1D	Parchment Cloth and Parchment Vinyl
2D	Parchment Vinyl
3D	Parchment Cloth and Parchment Vinyl
4D	Parchment Vinyl
5D	Parchment Cloth and Parchment Vinyl
0D	Parchment Vinyl
B1	Parchment Vinyl W/Silver
B2	Parchment Vinyl W/Blue
B4	Parchment Vinyl W/Emberglo
B5	Parchment Vinyl W/Red
B6	Parchment Vinyl W/Black
B7	Parchment Vinyl W/Aqua
B8	Parchment Vinyl W/Ivy Gold
B9	Parchment Vinyl W/Palomino
C2	Parchment Vinyl W/Blue
C3	Parchment Vinyl W/Burgundy
C4	Parchment Vinyl W/Emberglo
C6	Parchment Vinyl W/Black
C7	Parchment Vinyl W/Aqua
C8	Parchment Vinyl W/Gold
C9	Parchment Vinyl W/Palomino
D2	Parchment Vinyl W/Blue
D3	Parchment Vinyl W/Burgundy
D4	Parchment Vinyl W/Emberglo
D6	Parchment Vinyl W/Black
D7	Parchment Vinyl W/Aqua
D8	Parchment Vinyl W/Gold
D9	Parchment Vinyl W/Palomino
F2	Parchment Vinyl W/Blue
F3	Parchment Vinyl W/Burgundy
F4	Parchment Vinyl W/Emberglo
F6	Parchment Vinyl W/Black
F7	Parchment Vinyl W/Aqua
F8	Parchment Vinyl W/Ivy Gold
F9	Parchment Vinyl W/Palomino
H1	White Vinyl W/Silver
H2	White Vinyl W/Blue
H4	White Vinyl W/Emberglo

INTERIOR TRIM CODES (Cont'd.)

Code	Trim Schemes
H5	White Vinyl W/Red
H6	White Vinyl W/Black
H7	White Vinyl W/Aqua
H8	White Vinyl W/Palomino

DATE CODES

A number signifying the date precedes the month code letter. A second-year code letter will be used if the model exceeds 12 months.

Month	Code First Year	Code Second Year
January	A	N
February	B	P
March	C	Q
April	D	R
May	E	S
June	F	T
July	G	U
August	H	V
September	J	W
October	K	X
November	L	Y
December	M	Z

DISTRICT CODES (DSO)

Units built on a Domestic Special Order, Foreign Special Order, or other special orders will have the complete order number in this space. Also to appear in this space is the two-digit code number of the District which ordered the unit. If the unit is a regular production unit, only the District code number will appear.

COMET

Code	District	Code	District
11	Boston	34	Detroit
16	Philadelphia	41	Chicago
15	New York	42	St. Louis
17	Washington	46	Twin Cities
21	Atlanta	51	Denver
22	Dallas	52	Los Angeles
23	Jacksonville	53	Oakland
26	Memphis	54	Seattle
31	Buffalo	81	Ford of Canada
32	Cincinnati	84	Home Office Reserve
33	Cleveland	90-99	Export

FALCON, FAIRLANE AND MUSTANG

Code	District	Code	District
11	Boston	45	Davenport
12	Buffalo	51	Denver
13	New York	52	Des Moines
14	Pittsburgh	53	Kansas City
15	Newark	54	Omaha
21	Atlanta	55	St. Louis
22	Charlotte	61	Dallas
23	Philadelphia	62	Houston
24	Jacksonville	63	Memphis
25	Richmond	64	New Orleans
26	Washington	65	Oklahoma City
31	Cincinnati	71	Los Angeles
32	Cleveland	72	San Jose
33	Detroit	73	Salt Lake City
34	Indianapolis	74	Seattle
35	Lansing	81	Ford of Canada
36	Louisville	83	Government
41	Chicago	84	Home Office Reserve
42	Fargo	85	American Red Cross
43	Rockford	89	Transportation Services
44	Twin Cities	90-99	Export

REAR AXLE RATIO CODES

A number designates a conventional axle, while a letter designates a Locking differential.

Code	Ratio	Code	Ratio
1	3.00:1	A	3.00:1
2	2.83:1	L	2.83:1
3	3.20:1	C	3.20:1
4	3.25:1	D	3.25:1
5	3.50:1	E	3.50:1
6	2.80:1	F	2.80:1
8	3.89:1	H	3.89:1

TRANSMISSION CODES

Code	Type
1	3-Speed Manual
4	Dual Range Automatic (C-6)
5	4-Speed Manual
6	Dual Range Automatic (C-4)

MODEL YEAR CODE

The number 6 designates 1966

ASSEMBLY PLANT CODES

Code Letter	Assembly Plant	Code Letter	Assembly Plant
A	Atlanta	L	Michigan Truck
B	Oakville (Canada)	N	Norfolk
C	Ontario Truck	P	Twin Cities
D	Dallas	R	San Jose
E	Mahwah	S	Pilot Plant
F	Dearborn	T	Metuchen
G	Chicago	U	Louisville
H	Lorain	W	Wayne
J	Los Angeles	Y	Wixom
K	Kansas City	Z	St. Louis

ENGINE CODES

Code	Engine
A	8 Cyl. 289 Cu. In. (4V Prem.)
C	8 Cyl. 289 Cu. In. (2V)
K	8 Cyl. 289 Cu. In. (4V Hi-Perf.)
T	6 Cyl. 200 Cu. In. (1V)
Y	8 Cyl. 390 Cu. In. (2V)
Z	8 Cyl. 390 Cu. In. (4V)
2	6 Cyl. ①200 Cu. In. (1V)
3	8 Cyl. ①289 Cu. In. (2V)

①Low Compression

CONSECUTIVE UNIT NUMBER

Each model year, each assembly plant begins production with the number 100001 (Falcon, Fairlane or Mustang) or 500001 (Comet) and continues on for each unit built.

BRAKES

GROUP 2

PART 2-1   **PAGE**
GENERAL BRAKE SERVICE 2-1

PART 2-3   **PAGE**
SPECIFICATIONS 2-39

PART 2-2
BRAKE SYSTEM 2-8

PART 2-1 GENERAL BRAKE SERVICE

Section	Page
1 Diagnosis and Testing	2-1
Preliminary Tests	2-1
Road Test	2-1
Disc Brake Trouble Symptoms and Possible Causes	2-2
Drum Brake Trouble Symptoms and Possible Causes	2-3
Booster Diagnosis Guide	2-4
2 Common Adjustments and Repairs	2-4

Section	Page
Parking Brake Linkage Adjustment	2-4
Power Brake Master Cylinder Push Rod Adjustment	2-4
Hydraulic System Bleeding	2-4
3 Cleaning and Inspection	2-6
Disc Brakes	2-6
Drum Brakes	2-7
Booster Unit	2-7

1 DIAGNOSIS AND TESTING

PRELIMINARY TESTS

FLUID LEVEL

Check the fluid in the master cylinder, and add Rotunda (R-103-A (B7AZ-19542-A) heavy-duty brake fluid.

AUTOMATIC ADJUSTERS

Push the brake pedal down as far as it will go while the car is standing. If the car is equipped with power brakes, the engine should be running while making this test. If the brake pedal travels more than half-way between the released position and the floor, check the automatic adjusters for being inoperative. To check adjuster operation, inspect the brake shoes and the adjuster components for binding or improper installation and follow the procedure described under Brake Shoe Adjustments in Part 2-2, Section 2.

Make several reverse stops to ensure uniform adjustment at all wheels.

HYDRAULIC SYSTEM

If the car is equipped with power brakes, shut off the engine and exhaust all vacuum from the booster system before performing this test.

Depress the brake pedal and hold it in the applied position. If the pedal gradually falls away under this pressure, the hydraulic system is leaking. Check all tubing, hoses, and connections for leaks.

If the brake pedal movement feels spongy, bleed the hydraulic system to remove air from the lines and cylinder. See Hydraulic System Bleeding, Section 2. Also, check for leaks or insufficient fluid.

BOOSTER

With the transmission in neutral, stop the engine and apply the parking brake. Depress the service brake pedal several times to exhaust all vacuum in the system. Then, depress the pedal and hold it in the applied position. Start the engine. If the vacuum system is operating, the pedal will tend to fall away under foot pressure and less pressure will be required to hold the pedal in the applied position. If no action is felt, the vacuum booster system is not functioning. Follow the procedures in the Booster Diagnosis Guide.

For booster removal and installation procedures, refer to Part 2-2, Section 3. For disassembly and assembly procedures, refer to Part 2-2 Section 4. For cleaning and inspection refer to Part 2-1, Section 3.

LOCKED BRAKES

Should one of the brakes be locked and the car must be moved, open the brake cylinder bleeder screw long enough to let out a few drops of brake fluid. **This bleeding operation will release the brakes, but it will not correct the cause of the trouble.**

ROAD TEST

The car should be road tested only if the brakes will safely stop the car. Apply the brakes at a speed of 25-30 mph to check for the existence of the trouble symptoms listed in Table 1, with the exception of those resolved in the preliminary tests and brake chatter. For each of the symptoms encountered, check and eliminate the causes which are also listed in Table 1. To check for brake chatter or surge, apply the brakes lightly from approximately 50 mph.

TABLE 1—Disc Brake Trouble Symptoms and Possible Causes

Possible Causes of Trouble Symptoms	TROUBLE SYMPTOMS								
	Excessive Pedal Travel	Brake Roughness or Chatter (Pedal Pumping)	Excessive Pedal Effort	Pull	Rattle	Brakes Heat Up During Driving and Fail to Release	Leaky Wheel Cylinder	Grabbing or Uneven Braking Action	No Braking Effect When Pedal is Depressed
Shoe and Lining Knock-back after violent cornering or rough road travel	X								
Piston and Shoe and Lining Assembly Not Properly Seated or Positioned	X								X
Air Leak or Insufficient Fluid in System or Caliper	X								X
Loose Wheel Bearing Adjustment	X								
Damaged or Worn Caliper Piston Seal	X						X		X
Excessive Lateral Run-out of Rotor		X							
Rotor Excessively Out of Parallel		X							
Frozen or Seized Pistons			X	X		X		X	
Brake Fluid, Oil or Grease on Linings			X	X			X	X	
Shoe and Lining Worn Below Specifications			X						
Proportioning Valve Malfunction			X						
Caliper Out of Alignment with Rotor				X				X	
Loose Caliper Attachment		X		X				X	
Shoe Hold-Down Clips Missing or Improperly Positioned					X				
Operator Riding Brake Pedal						X			
Scores in the Cylinder Bore							X		
Corrosion Build-up in the Cylinder Bore or on the Piston Surface			X				X		
Bleeder Screw Still Open	X							X	X
Lines From Master Cylinder to Proportioning Valve Interchanged						X			

TABLE 2—Drum Brake Trouble Symptoms and Possible Causes

Possible Causes of Trouble Symptoms	TROUBLE SYMPTOMS												
	One Brake Drags	All Brakes Drag	Hard Pedal	Spongy Pedal	Car Pulls to One Side	One Wheel Locks	Brakes Chatter	Excessive Pedal Travel	Pedal Gradually Goes to Floor	Brakes Uneven	Shoe Click Release	Noisy or Grabbing Brakes	Brakes Do Not Apply
Mechanical Resistance at Pedal or Shoes — Damaged Linkage		X	X										
Brake Line Restricted	X	X	X		X					X			
Leaks or Insufficient Fluid				X				X	X				X
Improper Tire Pressure					X					X			
Improperly Adjusted or Worn Wheel Bearing	X				X								
Distorted or Improperly Adjusted Brake Shoe	X	X	X		X	X		X		X		X	
Faulty Retracting Spring	X				X					X			
Drum Out of Round	X					X							
Linings Glazed or Worn			X		X	X		X					X
Oil or Grease in Lining			X		X	X	X			X		X	X
Loose Carrier Plate	X				X	X	X			X		X	
Loose Lining					X		X			X			
Scored Drum										X		X	
Dirt on Drum-Lining Surface										X		X	
Faulty Wheel Cylinder					X	X						X	
Dirty Brake Fluid	X	X								X			X
Faulty Master Cylinder		X		X				X	X				X
Air in Hydraulic System				X				X					X
Self Adjusters Not Operating					X			X		X	X		
Insufficient Shoe-to-Carrier Plate Lubrication	X										X		
Tire Tread Worn						X							
Poor Lining to Drum Contact							X						
Loose Front Suspension							X			X			
"Threads" Left by Drum Turning Tool — Pull Shoes Sideways											X		
Cracked Drum							X						
Sticking Booster Control Valve		X										X	

BRAKE BOOSTER TROUBLE DIAGNOSIS GUIDE

BOOSTER INOPERATIVE— HARD PEDAL	If the preliminary tests show that the booster is inoperative or if a hard pedal condition still exists after eliminating the causes of Hard Pedal listed in Table 2, the trouble may be caused by vacuum leakage. Disconnect the vacuum line (two lines if equipped with an automatic transmission) at the booster, remove the vacuum manifold and check valve assembly, and look for a sticking or faulty check valve. Check all vacuum connections for leakage or obstruction. Check all hoses for a	leaking or collapsed condition. Repair or replace parts as necessary. If the foregoing procedure does not eliminate the trouble, remove the booster from the car. Separate the booster body from the end plate, and check the bellows, booster body, and diaphragm assembly for damage that would cause leaks. When assembling, be sure that the diaphragm assembly is properly positioned. Improper location could cause leakage between the vacuum and atmospheric sides of the diaphragm.
BRAKES DRAG OR GRAB	If the brakes still drag or grab after eliminating the causes listed in Table 1, the condition is probably caused by a sticking valve plunger	assembly. Remove and disassemble the booster. Clean, inspect, and replace parts as necessary.
SELF APPLICATION OF BRAKES WHEN ENGINE STARTS	Remove and disassemble the booster. Check the diaphragm for being out of locating radii in the housing. Check for a sticking or un-	seated atmospheric valve. Clean, inspect, and replace parts as necessary. Be sure that the diaphragm is properly located when assembling.

2 COMMON ADJUSTMENTS AND REPAIRS

PARKING BRAKE LINKAGE ADJUSTMENT

MUSTANG

Check the parking brake cables when the brakes are fully released. If the cables are loose, adjust them as follows:

1. Fully release the parking brake by turning the handle counterclockwise and pushing it inward.

2. Pull the parking brake handle outward to the third notch from its normal released position.

3. Raise the car.

4. Turn the locking adjustment nut forward against the equalizer (Fig. 1) until a moderate drag is felt when turning the rear wheels in the direction of forward rotation.

5. Release the parking brake, and make sure that the brake shoes return to the fully released position and no drag is felt when turning the rear wheels.

COMET—FALCON—FAIRLANE

Check the parking brake cables when the brakes are fully released. If the cables are loose, adjust them as follows:

1. Fully release the parking brake pedal.

2. Depress the parking brake pedal one notch from its normal released position.

3. Raise the car.

4. Loosen the equalizer lock nut and turn the adjusting nut forward against the equalizer until a moderate drag is felt when turning the rear wheels (Fig. 2). Tighten the lock nut.

5. Release the parking brake, and make sure that the brake shoes return to the fully released position.

POWER BRAKE MASTER CYLINDER PUSH ROD ADJUSTMENT

The push rod is provided with an adjustment screw to maintain the correct relationship between the booster control valve plunger and the master cylinder piston. Failure to maintain this relationship will prevent the master cylinder piston from completely releasing hydraulic pressure and can cause the brakes to drag, or cause excessive brake pedal travel.

To check the adjustment of the screw, fabricate a gauge of the dimension shown in Fig. 3. Then place the gauge against the master cylinder mounting surface of the booster body as shown in Fig. 4 or 5. The push rod screw should be adjusted so that the end of the screw just touches the inner edge of the slot in the gauge. Do not set up side forces on the push rod. Side forces may break the valve plunger.

This is an approximate adjustment only. The push rod should not move more than 0.015 inch as it contacts the master cylinder piston. No movement (exact contact) is ideal.

HYDRAULIC SYSTEM BLEEDING

When any part of the hydraulic system has been disconnected for repair or replacement, air may get into the lines and cause spongy pedal action. Bleed the hydraulic system after it has been properly connected to be sure that all air is expelled from the brake cylinders or disc brake calipers, and lines.

The hydraulic system can be bled manually or with pressure bleeding equipment.

With disc brakes, more pumping of the pedal is required and more frequent checking of the master cylinder may be necessary while bleeding.

On a car *with disc brakes*, remove the front wheels and tires to gain access to the bleeder fitting on the disc brake calipers.

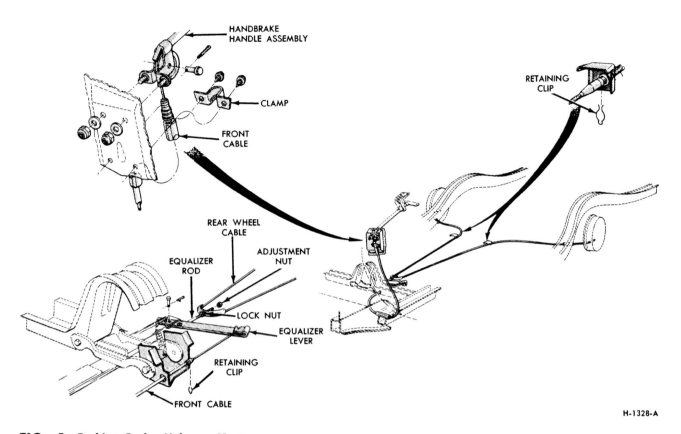

FIG. 1—Parking Brake Linkage—Mustang

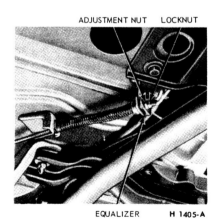

FIG. 2—Parking Brake Linkage Adjustment Comet—Fairlane—Falcon

MANUAL BLEEDING

Bleed the longest lines first. Keep the master cylinder reservoir filled with new Rotunda R-103-A (B7AZ-19542-A) brake fluid during the bleeding operation.

Never use brake fluid which has been drained from the hydraulic system.

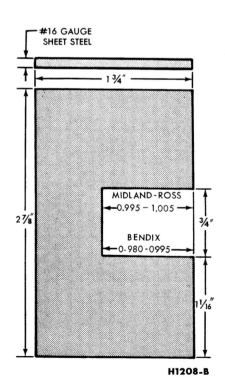

FIG. 3—Push Rod Gauge Dimensions

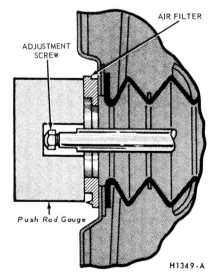

FIG. 4—Push Rod Adjustment —Midland-Ross

1. Position a bent ⅜-inch box wrench on the bleeder fitting on the right rear brake wheel cylinder (Fig. 6). Attach a rubber drain tube to the bleeder fitting. **The end of the tube should fit snugly around the bleeder fitting.**

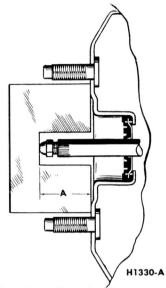

FIG. 5—Push-Rod Adjustment—Bendix

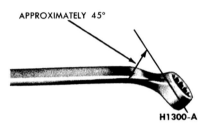

FIG. 6—Brake Bleeder Wrench

2. Submerge the free end of the tube in a container partially filled with clean brake fluid. Loosen the bleeder fitting approximately ¾ turn.

3. Push the brake pedal down slowly through its full travel. Close the bleeder fitting, then return the pedal to the fully-released position. Repeat this operation until air bubbles cease to appear at the submerged end of the tube.

4. When the fluid is completely free of air bubbles, close the bleeder fitting and remove the drain tube.

5. Repeat this procedure on the brake cylinders or disc calipers at each wheel in order: left rear, right front, and left front. Refill the master cylinder reservoir after each brake cylinder is bled and when the bleeding operation is completed. The fluid level should be within ⅜ inch of the top of the reservoir. The diaphragm-type gasket should be properly positioned in the reservoir cap before the cap is installed.

6. On a car with disc brakes, pump the brake pedal until the front brake pistons are returned to their normal positions and that the shoe and lining assemblies are properly seated.

7. Before driving the car, check the operation of the brakes and be sure that a firm pedal is obtained.

PRESSURE BLEEDING

Bleed the longest lines first. **Never use brake fluid which has been drained from the hydraulic system.**

The bleeder tank should contain enough new heavy-duty brake fluid to complete the bleeding operation, and it should be charged with 10-30 pounds of air pressure.

1. Clean all dirt from the master cylinder reservoir cap.

2. Remove the master cylinder reservoir cap, install an adapter cap to the reservoir, and attach the bleeder tank hose to the fitting on the adapter cap.

An adapter cap can be fabricated by cutting a hole in the center of a reservoir cap and smoldering a fitting at the hole. The adapter cap must be securely seated and completely

sealed on the master cylinder or leakage will occur.

3. Position a ⅜-inch box wrench on the bleeder fitting on the right rear brake wheel cylinder (Fig. 6). Attach a rubber drain tube to the bleeder fitting. **The end of the tube should fit snugly around the bleeder fitting.**

4. Open the valve on the bleeder tank to admit pressurized brake fluid to the master cylinder reservoir.

5. Submerge the free end of the tube in a container partially filled with clean brake fluid, and loosen the bleeder fitting.

6. When air bubbles cease to appear in the fluid at the submerged end of the drain tube, close the bleeder fitting and remove the tube.

7. Repeat this procedure on the brake cylinder or disc caliper at each wheel in order: left rear, right front, and left front. Refill the master cylinder reservoir after each brake cylinder is bled.

8. When the bleeding operation is completed, close the bleeder tank valve and remove the tank hose from the adapter fitting.

9. Remove the adapter cap, refill the master cylinder reservoir to within ⅜-inch from the top of the reservoir. Be sure that the diaphragm-type gasket is properly positioned in the reservoir cap, and then install the cap.

10. On a car with disc brakes, pump the brake pedal until the front brake pistons are returned to their normal positions and the shoe and lining assemblies are properly seated.

11. Before driving the car, check the operation of the brakes and be sure that a firm pedal is obtained.

---

3 CLEANING AND INSPECTION

DISC BRAKES

1. Remove the wheel and tire, caliper splash shield, and the shoes and linings as outlined in Part 2-2, Section 2.

2. Make three thickness measurements with a micrometer across the middle section of the shoe and lining. Take one reading at each side and one in the center. If the assembly has worn to a thickness of 0.195-inch (shoe and lining together) at any one of the three measuring locations, replace all (4) shoe and lining assemblies on both front wheels.

3. With the shoe and lining assemblies installed, insert a feeler gauge between the lining and rotor. If the clearnace is not within 0.002-0.010-inch, check for shoe and lining assemblies not being properly seated on the caliper bridges, for a piston pushed back in the cylinder bore, for a seized piston, or for malfunction of a piston seal.

Ordinarily, the clearance should be 0.002-0.010 inch. However, if the car was stopped by a brake application just prior to checking the clearance, the brakes may drag slightly.

4. To check rotor runout, first eliminate the wheel bearing end play by tightening the adjusting nut. After tightening the nut make certain that the rotor can still be rotated.

5. Clamp a dial indicator to the caliper housing so that the stylus contacts the rotor at a point approximately 1 inch from the outer edge. Rotate the rotor and take an indicator reading. If the reading exceeds 0.0025 inch total indicator runout, replace the rotor. **Do not attempt to refinish a rotor that indicates runout**

in excess of specification. When the runout check is finished be sure to adjust the bearings as outlined in Group 3, in order to prevent bearing failure.

6. Check the rotor for scoring. Minor scores can be removed with a fine emery cloth. If the rotor is excessively scored, replace it.

7. Visually check the caliper. If it is cracked it should be replaced. If leakage or seized pistons is evident, disassemble and repair the caliper as required.

8. If upon disassembly the caliper is found to be distorted or damaged, or if the cylinder bores are scored or excessively worn, replace the assembly.

The two halves of the caliper assembly should never be separated. Damage or failure of one requires replacement of both as a unit.

DRUM BRAKES

1. Remove the wheel from the drum, and remove the drum as outlined in Part 2-2, Section 2. Wash all the parts except the brake shoes in a cleaning fluid and dry with compressed air.

2. Brush all dust from the carrier plate and interior of the brake drum.

3. Inspect the brake shoes for excessive lining wear or shoe damage. If the lining is worn to within $1/32$ inch of the rivet heads or if the shoes are damaged, they must be replaced. Replace any lining that has been oil saturated. Replace the lining in axle sets. Prior to replacement of the lining, the drum diameter should be checked to determine if oversize linings must be installed.

4. Check the condition of the brake shoes, retracting springs, and drum for signs of overheating. If the shoes have a slight blue coloring, or if the springs show a change in free length, indicating overheating, replacement of the retracting and hold down springs is necessary. **Overheated springs lose their force and could cause the new lining to wear prematurely if they are not replaced.**

5. If the car has 30,000 or more miles of operation on the brake linings, or signs of overheating are present when relining brakes, the wheel cylinders should be disassembled and inspected for wear and dirt in the cylinder. The cylinder cups and other parts contained in the overhaul kit should be replaced, thus avoiding future problems.

6. Inspect all other brake parts

and replace any that are worn or damaged.

7. Inspect the brake drums and, if necessary, refinish. Refer to Part 2-2, Section 4 for refinishing.

BOOSTER UNITS

Disassembled views of the brake booster are shown in Figs. 40, 49 and 50, Part 2-2.

After disassembly, immerse all metal parts in a suitable solvent. Use only alcohol on rubber parts or parts containing rubber. After the parts have been thoroughly cleaned and rinsed in cleaning solvent, the metal parts which come in contact with hydraulic brake fluid or rubber parts should be rewashed in clean alcohol before assembly. Use an air hose to blow dirt and cleaning fluid from the recesses and internal passages. When overhauling a power booster, use all parts furnished in the repair kit. **Discard all old rubber parts.**

Inspect all other parts for damage or excessive wear. Replace damaged or excessively worn parts. If the inside of the booster body is rusted or corroded, polish it with steel wool or fine emery cloth.

PART 2-2

BRAKE SYSTEM

Section	Page
1 Description and Operation	2-8
Hydraulic Self-Adjusting Brake System	2-8
Disc Brake Assemblies	2-8
Booster System—Bendix	2-11
Booster System—Midland-Ross	2-13
Parking Brake	2-14
2 In-Car Adjustments and Repairs	2-16
Brake Shoe Adjustments	2-16
Front Brake Drum	2-17
Rear Brake Drum	2-17
Brake Shoes and Adjusting Screw	2-17
Disc Brake Shoe and Lining Replacement	2-18
Disc Brake Caliper Assembly	2-19
Front Wheel Hub and Rotor Assembly—Disc Brakes	2-19
Disc Brake Rotor Splash Shield	2-20
Proportioning Valve	2-20
Wheel Cylinder Repair	2-21
Wheel Cylinder Replacement	2-21
Brake Carrier Plate Replacement	2-24

Section	Page
Hydraulic Lines	2-24
Brake Tube Replacement	2-24
Brake Hose Replacement	2-24
3 Removal and Installation	2-24
Master Cylinder—Standard Brakes	2-24
Master Cylinder—Power Brakes	2-24
Booster Unit	2-25
Brake Pedal—Manual Shift Transmission	2-25
Brake Pedal—Automatic Transmission	2-27
Parking Brake Control Assembly	2-27
Parking Brake Equalizer to Control Cable	2-27
Parking Brake Equalizer to Rear Wheel Cable	2-30
4 Major Repair Operations	2-31
Brake Drum Refinishing	2-31
Brake Shoe Relining	2-31
Master Cylinder	2-31
Disassembly of Bendix Type Booster	2-33
Assembly of Bendix Type Booster	2-34
Disassembly of Midland-Ross Type Booster	2-35
Assembly of Midland-Ross Type Booster	2-36

1 DESCRIPTION AND OPERATION

Disc brakes are available as optional equipment for the front wheels on Mustang 8-cylinder cars. The hydraulic brake system employs duo-servo single anchor, internal expanding and self-adjusting drum brake assemblies on the rear wheels of cars with disc brakes, and of front and rear wheels of all others.

A vacuum booster is available as optional eqipment on all models except Mustangs equipped with disc brakes.

The master cylinder converts physical force from the brake pedal (and booster if so equipped) into hydraulic pressure against the pistons in the calipers (disc brakes) or in the wheel cylinders (drum brakes). The pistons in turn convert hydraulic pressure back into physical force at the brake shoes.

SELF ADJUSTING DRUM BRAKE ASSEMBLIES

The self-adjusting brake mechanism consists of a cable, cable guide, adjusting lever, and adjuster spring (Fig. 1 and 2). The cable is hooked over the anchor pin at the top and is connected to the lever at the bottom. The cable is connected to the sec-

ondary brake shoe by means of the cable guide. The adjuster spring is hooked to the primary brake shoe and to the lever. The automatic adjuster operates only when the brakes are applied while the car is moving rearward and only when the secondary shoe is free to move toward the drum beyond a predetermined point.

With the car moving rearward and the brakes applied, the wrap-around action of the shoes following the drum forces the upper end of the primary shoe against the anchor pin. The action of the wheel cylinder moves the upper end of the secondary shoe away from the anchor pin. The movement of the secondary shoe causes the cable to pull the adjusting lever upward and against the end of a tooth on the adjusting screw star-wheel. The upward travel of the lever increases as lining wear increases. When the lever can move upward far enough, it passes over the end of the tooth and engages the tooth. When the brakes are released, the adjusting spring pulls the lever downward causing the star-wheel to turn and expand the shoes. The star-wheel is turned one tooth at a time as the linings pro-

gressively wear.

With the car moving forward and the brakes applied, the secondary shoe is against the anchor pin and the primary shoe is moved toward the drum. Therefore, the adjuster does not operate.

The rear brake assembly is basically the same as the front brake. The conventional parking brake lever, link, and spring are used in the rear brake.

The anchor pins on all brakes are fixed and are non-adjustable.

DISC BRAKE ASSEMBLIES

RELATION AND FUNCTION OF COMPONENT PARTS

The disc brake is a fixed caliper, opposed piston, non-energized, ventilated disc type, actuated by a hydraulic system (Fig. 3). There is no lateral movement of either the disc (rotor) or the caliper. The caliper assembly consists of two caliper housings bolted together with each half containing two cylinder bores of $1^{15}/_{16}$ inch diameter. Each cylinder bore contains a piston with an attached molded rubber dust boot to

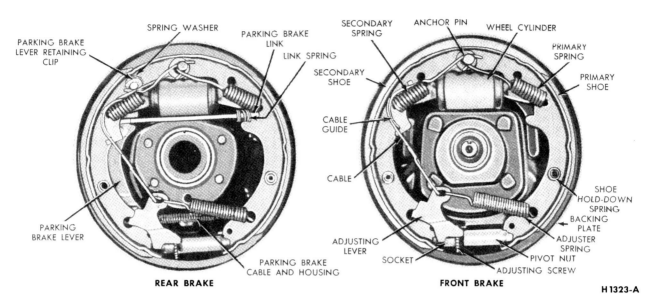

FIG. 1—Self-Adjusting Brake Assemblies—9 Inch Drum

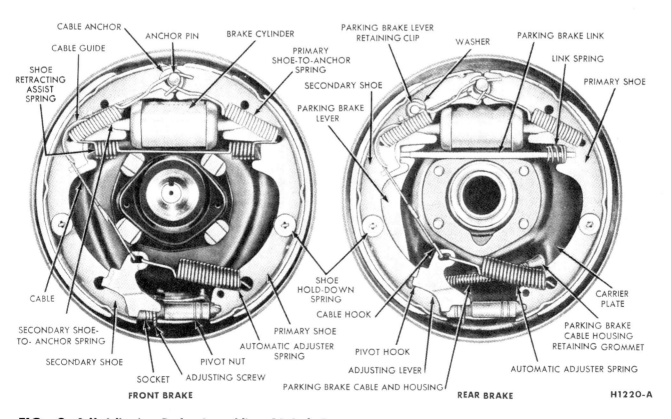

FIG. 2—Self Adjusting Brake Assemblies—10 Inch Drum

seal the cylinder bore from contamination. (Fig. 4). Square-section rubber piston seals are positioned in grooves in the cylinder bores.

The piston seals perform three important tasks:

1. They provide hydraulic sealing between the cylinders and pistons.

2. They return the pistons to released position, when hydraulic pressure is released.

3. They maintain the shoes in correct adjustment at all times (comparable to the automatic adjusters in drum-type brakes).

The cylinders are conneced hy-

draulically by means of internal passages in the caliper housing and an external transfer tube between the two halves of the caliper assembly. One bleeder screw and fluid inlet fitting is provided on each caliper assembly.

The shoe and lining assemblies are

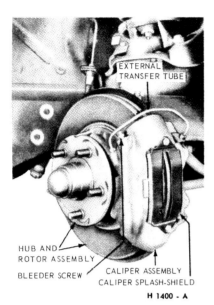

H 1400 - A

FIG. 3—Typical Disc Brake Assembly

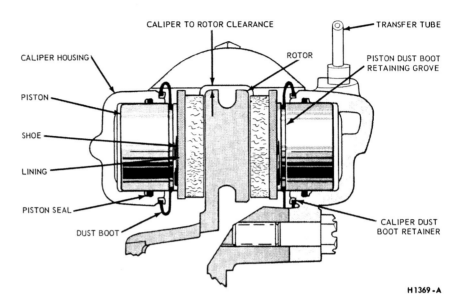

H1369-A

FIG. 4—Typical Caliper Assembly—Sectional View

located between parallel machined abutments within the caliper, and are supported radially by tabs on the outer ends of the shoe assemblies (Fig. 35). The shoes slide axially in the caliper abutments by means of the tabs which ride on machined ledges (bridges) when hydraulic pressure is applied to the piston (Fig. 19). A shoe and lining assembly consists of friction material bonded to a metal plate called the shoe. It is replaced as a unit. Brake torque is absorbed by the mating of the shoe end against the caliper abutments (Fig. 35). A splash shield is attached to the top of the caliper to retain the shoe and lining assemblies and reduce contamination. The caliper assembly is mounted to a bracket located between the spindle and rotor splash shield, to the front of the wheel vertical centerline.

The cast iron disc is of the ventilated rotor type incorporating forty fins and is staked to, and rotates with, the wheel hub. The outside diameter of the rotor is 11.375 inches and the inside diameter is 7.375 inches. This type of design increases cooling area and permits circulation of air through the rotor resulting in more rapid cooling of the brake. A splash shield bolted to the spindle is used primarily to prevent road contaminants from contacting the inboard rotor and lining surfaces (Fig. 20). The wheel provides protection for the outboard surface of the rotor.

OPERATION

As the brake pedal is depressed, hydraulic pressure from the master cylinder forces the pistons out of the caliper bores against their respective shoe and lining assemblies. The force of the pistons against the shoes moves the linings against both sides of the revolving rotor to effect braking action.

During brake application, the rubber seal on each piston stretches as the piston moves against the shoe (Fig. 5). When the hydraulic pressure against the piston is released, the seal relaxes or rolls back. This roll-back action pulls the piston away from the shoe approximately 0.005 inch to relieve the force of the lining against the rotor and, thereby, provide the required running clearance. Also, inherent rotor runout contributes to the maintenance of running clearance. Automatic adjustment is achieved by the pistons sliding in the seals outward from the cylinder bores. The piston gradually changes its position relative to the seal as the lining wears and, thus, maintains the correct adjustment location at all times.

When the brakes are in the unapplied position, there is no hydraulic pressure to the calipers because the fluid source at the master cylinder by-passes the residual check valve.

A warning sound feature is incorporated in the design of the brake shoes. Metal tabs on the ends of the shoes create an audible metallic, scraping noise, when the linings become worn enough to allow the tabs to contact the rotor. This metal-to-metal contact warns the driver that the shoes need replacing and is not detrimental to the function of the disc brake.

A proportioning valve located be-

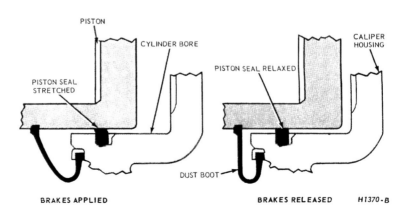

FIG. 5—Function of Piston Seal

tween the master cylinder and the rear brake wheel cylinders provides balanced braking action between the front and the rear brakes under a wide range of braking conditions. (Fig. 21). By regulating the hydraulic pressure applied to the rear wheel cylinders, the valve limits rear braking action when high pressures are required at the front brakes. In this manner, premature rear wheel skid is prevented. The proportioning valve is serviced as an assembly and is never adjusted or overhauled.

BOOSTER SYSTEM—BENDIX TYPE

The diaphragm type brake booster is a self contained vacuum-hydraulic braking unit mounted on the engine side of the dash panel.

The vacuum power chamber consists of a front and rear shell locked together. Within the vacuum chamber are the rubber diaphragm and the integral valve hub and diaphragm plate. The rubber diaphragm fits over the plate, and the outer bead of the diaphragm is locked between the front and rear shells (Fig. 6). The diaphragm return spring is located between the diaphragm plate and the front shell.

The valve hub section of the diaphragm plate protrudes from the

rear shell. A synthetic rubber seal is used between the valve hub and the rear shell. The seal and the valve hub are protected from dirt by a rubber guard connected between the air filter at the end of the hub and a flange on the rear shell. The control valve assembly fits into the hub and is connected to the brake pedal by the valve operating rod. The control valve assembly consists of a plunger, a valve body which supports a single poppet of flexible rubber, and two return springs. When the brake pedal is in the released position the valve return spring holds the valve assembly and operating rod away from the diaphragm plate. In this position, the poppet on the valve body is off the vacuum port seat which is a part of the diaphragm plate. The poppet return spring likewise holds the poppet against the atmospheric port seat which is a part of the plunger.

The hydraulic master cylinder which contains all of the components of the conventional master cylinder is bolted to the booster front shell. The hydraulic push rod forms the link between the master cylinder piston and the vacuum power diaphragm assembly. The end of the push rod, that enters the master cylinder piston, is equipped with a self-locking adjusting screw. The oppo-

site end has a piston head which enters the diaphragm plate. A seal, located in the front shell, seals the opening between the hydraulic push rod and the shell.

Engine manifold vacuum is supplied to the booster through a vacuum check valve located in the front shell. Air is admitted through the air filter located at the end of the valve hub. The hydraulic push rod is actuated by pedal pressure assisted by the diaphragm, which derives power from the pressure differential existing between the vacuum on its front side and atmospheric pressure on its rear side. A passage in the diaphragm plate permits vacuum to pass from the front to the rear side of the diaphragm when the vacuum port opens as the brakes are released.

RELEASED POSITION

With the engine running and the brakes released (Fig. 7), vacuum from the intake manifold is admitted through the check valve to the front (constant vacuum) chamber of the power unit. In the released position (no pressure applied to the brake pedal), the valve operating rod and valve plunger are held to the rear in the valve hub by the valve return spring to CLOSE the atmospheric

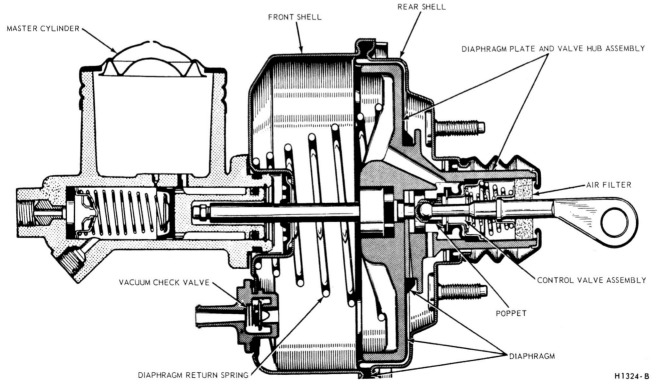

FIG. 6—Cutaway View of Vacuum Booster—Bendix-Type

H1324-B

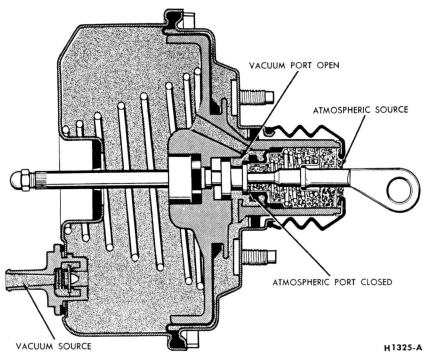

H1325-A

FIG. 7—Booster in Released Position—Bendix-Type

port and OPEN the vacuum port. With the valve in this position, the rear (control vacuum) chamber is also open to vacuum through the porting in the diaphragm and valve hug assembly. The diaphragm is then balanced or suspended in vacuum, since vacuum is present on both sides of the power diaphragm. With the power diaphragm balanced in vacuum, the diaphragm return spring holds the diaphragm and hydraulic push rod in the fully released position. With the hydraulic push rod in this position, the hydraulic compensating port in the hydraulic master cylinder is OPEN. The open port permits brake fluid to either return from the brake system to the fluid reservoir or enter the brake system from the fluid reservoir to compensate for any gain or loss in fluid volume.

APPLIED POSITION

When the brakes are applied (Fig. 8), the valve operating rod and valve plunger move forward in the valve hub section of the diaphragm plate to compress the valve return spring and force the poppet against the vacuum valve seat in the diaphragm plate to CLOSE the vacuum port. Any additional movement of the valve operating rod in the applied direction moves the valve plunger away from the poppet valve to OPEN the atmospheric port and

admit atmosphere through the air cleaner and passages in the diaphragm plate to the rear side of the power chamber. With vacuum present on the front side of the diaphragm and valve housing and atmospheric pressure present on the rear side of the diaphragm, a force is developed to move the vacuum power diaphragm assembly, hydraulic

push rod and master cylinder piston forward to close the compensating port and force hydraulic fluid under pressure through the residual check valve and brake tubes into the brake wheel cylinders. As hydraulic pressure is developed in the brake master cylinder, a counter force (to the rear) acting through the hydraulic push rod, sets up a reaction force against the power diaphragm assembly and valve plunger through the rubber reaction disc (located at the end of the hydraulic push rod). The rubber reaction disc acts similar to a column of fluid to distribute the pressure between the vacuum power diaphragm assembly and the valve plunger in proportion to their respective contact areas. The pressure acting against the valve plunger and valve hub assembly to close off the the valve plunger slightly to the rear in relation to the diaphragm and valve hub assembly to close off the atmospheric port. The driver is thus assured a feel of the brake, since part of the counter force reacts through the valve plunger, valve operating rod, and pedal linkage against the driver's foot. This reaction force is in direct proportion to the hydraulic pressure developed within the brake system.

HOLDING POSITION

During brake application, the reaction force which opposes the

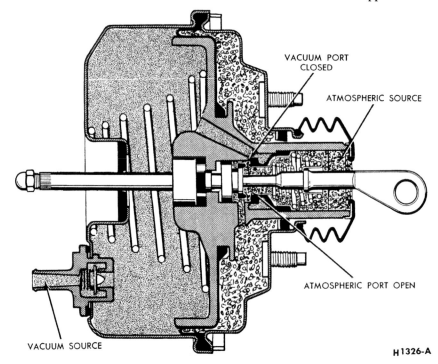

H1326-A

FIG. 8—Booster in Applied Position—Bendix-Type

force applied by the driver, tends to close the atmospheric port. When both atmospheric and vacuum ports are CLOSED, the booster is said to be in the holding position (Fig. 9).

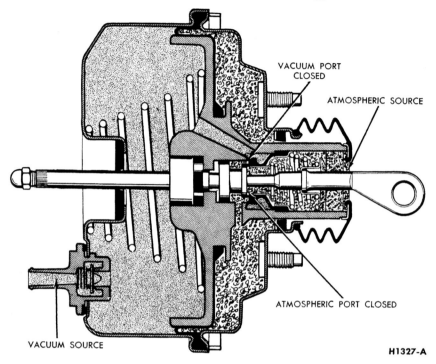

FIG. 9—Booster in Holding Position—Bendix-Type

With both valves closed, any degree of brake application attained will be held until either the atmospheric port is **reopened** by an increase in pedal pressure to further increase the brake application or by a decrease in pedal pressure to **reopen** the vacuum port to decrease the brake application. Whenever the pressure applied to the brake pedal is held constant for a moment, the valve returns to its holding position. However, upon reaching the fully applied position the force applied to the brake pedal overrules the reaction force. In this position the valve plunger and atmospheric valve seat are held away from the valve poppet to admit maximum atmospheric pressure to the rear chamber. With the front chamber open to manifold vacuum, full power application is attained which is referred to as the run-out of the power unit. Any increase in hydraulic pressure beyond this point must be supplied by physical effort of the driver.

NO POWER CONDITION

It should be noted that in case of engine failure and consequent loss of engine vacuum, at least one full

power brake application may be made from the vacuum in the booster. With the engine off and no vacuum in the power system, the brakes can be applied in the conventional manner by applying more physical effort to the brake pedal.

BOOSTER SYSTEM— MIDLAND-ROSS

The optional power brake booster is installed on the engine side of the dash panel and is connected to the brake pedal through a lever assembly and push rod link.

The booster consists of a vacuum chamber, atmospheric valve, control valve plunger assembly, diaphragm, and an atmospheric chamber (Figs. 10, 11 and 12).

Atmospheric pressure is present at all times in the atmospheric chamber at the front side of the atmospheric valve. The air intake to the atmospheric chamber is protected by an air filter. The atmospheric chamber is separated from the vacuum chamber by the bellows assembly within the vacuum chamber.

Vacuum is present at all times in that area of the vacuum chamber forward of the diaphragm. Vacuum is supplied through a hose from the intake manifold to the vacuum manifold and check valve on the booster body. With this integral check valve

and vacuum chamber, it is possible to obtain several power assisted brake applications with the engine shut off. This arrangement makes a vacuum reservoir unnecessary.

Wither vacuum from the forward side of the diaphragm or air from the bellows (atmospheric chamber) can be connected to the rear side of the diaphragm through porting in the control valve hub and the plunger assembly.

APPLYING POSITION

As the brake pedal is depressed, the valve operating rod and valve plunger assembly move forward compressing the plunger return spring (Fig. 10). The initial movement of the plunger closes the porting from the vacuum chamber preventing further evacuation of the area back of the diaphragm. Further movement of the plunger forces the atmospheric valve off its seat so that atmospheric pressure from the bellows can enter the hub porting that leads to the rear side of the diaphragm.

With vacuum on the front side of the diaphragm and atmospheric pressure on the back side of the diaphragm, a force is developed to move the diaphragm, push rod and master cylinder piston forward to close the compensating port and force hydraulic fluid under pressure through the residual pressure check valve and brake tubes to the wheel brakes. As hydraulic pressure is developed in the hydraulic system, a reaction counter-force acts against the reaction lever and ring assembly. This reaction lever and ring assembly is designed to transmit the reaction forces back through the actuating control valve assembly to the brake pedal and provide the driver with a resistance that is in proportion to the brake hydraulic apply forces. This is the means of providing the proper driver feel to the power brake unit.

HOLDING POSITION

When the forward motion of the brake pedal is stopped and held, the valve operating rod ceases to move the control valve plunger forward. However, the unbalanced forces of atmospheric pressure and vacuum on each side of the diaphragm will continue to move the outer sleeve of the control valve plunger forward keeping the vacuum porting closed. At the same time, the reaction force

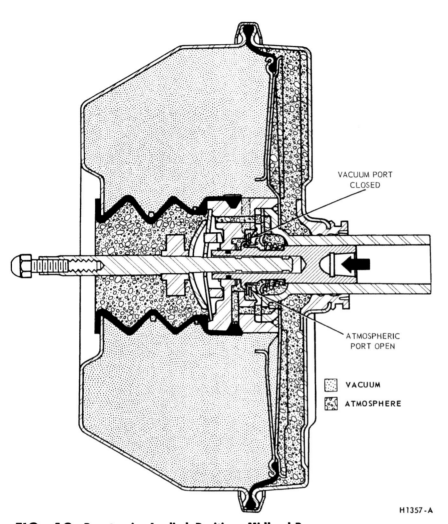

VACUUM PORT
CLOSED

ATMOSPHERIC
PORT OPEN

⬚ VACUUM

▨ ATMOSPHERE

H1357-A

FIG. 10—Booster in Applied Position—Midland-Ross

acting through the reaction ring and lever assembly will tend to move the atmospheric valve to the closed position (Fig. 11). When these combined forces balance, the porting to the vacuum supply will remain closed and the atmospheric valve will cut off any further passage of atmospheric pressure to the area behind the diaphragm. Therefore, the power assist force acting on the master cylinder piston will stabilize and the hydraulic force applying the brakes will be maintained at a constant level.

RELEASED POSITION

When the pedal pressure is released from the valve operating rod and plunger assembly, the plunger return spring moves the plunger away from the atmospheric valve allowing the valve to seat against the hub (Fig. 12). This seating of the

valve closes off the bellows chamber from the hub porting that connects to the rear side of the diaphragm. At the same time, the rearward movement of the plunger opens the porting from the vacuum chamber and draws out the air from the rear side of the power diaphragm. With vacuum on both sides of the diaphragm, the assist force against the master cylinder push rod is eliminated.

Also, a pressure differential is created by the presence of vacuum on the rear (small diameter) side of the valve hub and atmospheric (bellows) pressure on the front (large diameter) side. This pressure differential moves the valve hub and, with it, the valve plunger and diaphragm assembly back to the released position. This releasing action permits the brake shoe retracting springs, acting through the wheel cylinder pistons

and the hydraulic fluid, to return the master cylinder piston and push rod to the released positioned.

With the piston and push rod in the released position, the hydraulic compensating port in the master cylinder is open. The open port permits fluid to either return from the brake system to the fluid reservoir, or enter the brake system from the reservoir.

PARKING BRAKES—MUSTANG

An independent hand-operated parking brake control actuates the rear wheel brake shoes through a cable linkage. The operating cable is routed from the parking brake control assembly to the equalizer lever which is attached to the equalizer assembly. The rear brake cables connect the equalizer assembly to the parking brake lever at each rear secondary shoe as shown in Figs. 1 and 2.

When the handle is pulled the primary and secondary brake shoes are forced against the rear brake drums. The handle is held in the applied position by the engagement of a spring loaded pawl with a ratchet. Turning the handle counterclockwise disengages the pawl from the ratchet to release the brakes.

**PARKING BRAKE
COMET, FAIRLANE AND
FALCON**

An independent foot-operated parking brake control actuates the rear wheel brake shoes through a cable linkage. The operating cable is routed from the parking brake control assembly to the equalizer. The rear brake cables connect the equalizer assembly to the parking brake lever at each rear secondary shoe (Fig. 1).

When the pedal is depressed the secondary brake shoes are forced against the rear brake drums. The pedal is held in the applied position by the engagement of a spring-loaded pawl with a ratchet in the control assembly (Fig. 29).

The parking brake control assembly is mounted to the cowl inner side panel. The pedal pivots on a stationary pedal mount. A spring-loaded pawl and a release lever are assembled to the pedal. A ratchet is assembled to the upper end of the pedal. The pawl contacts the rachet at such an angle that the rachet teeth will slide over the pawl as the pedal is depressed; however, when

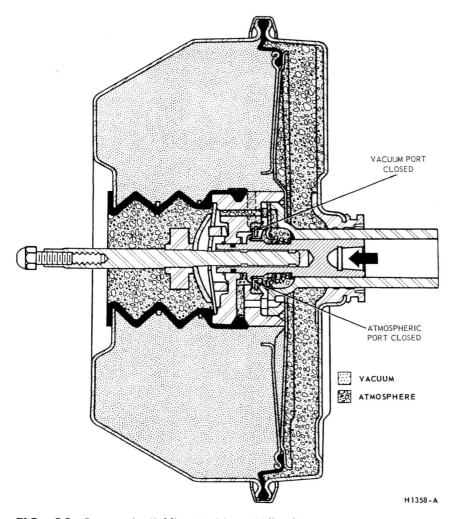

VACUUM PORT
CLOSED

ATMOSPHERIC
PORT CLOSED

VACUUM

ATMOSPHERE

H1358-A

FIG. 11—Booster in Holding Position—Midland-Ross

the applying motion stops and the pedal starts to release, the pawl engages the ratchet and thus locks the brakes in the applied position.

When the manual release lever is pulled back, (Fig. 29), the cam action of the lever on the pawl cam pin will disengage the pawl from the ratchet to release the brakes.

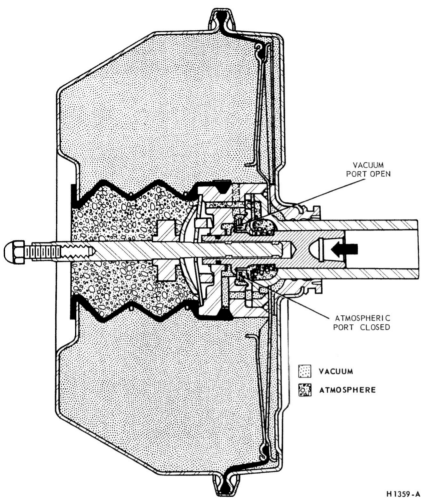

H 1359-A

FIG. 12—Booster in Released Position—Midland-Ross

2   IN-CAR ADJUSTMENTS AND REPAIRS

BRAKE SHOE ADJUSTMENTS

The hydraulic service brakes are self-adjusting and require a manual adjustment only after the brake shoes have been relined, replaced, or when the length of the adjusting screw has been changed while performing some other service operation. **The manual adjustment is performed with the drums removed, using the tool and the procedure detailed below.**

In case a brake drum cannot be removed in the normal manner, an access knock-out slug is provided in the brake carrier plate. Knock the slug out with a punch and then release the brake shoe as detailed under **Brake Drum-Removal.** Re-

move the drum and knock-out slug. (Install a standard adjusting hole cover in the carrier plate when assembling).

When adjusting the rear brake shoes, check the parking brake cables for proper adjustment. Make sure that the equalizer operates freely.

To adjust the brake shoes:

1. Using Rotunda Tool HRE 8650, (Fig. 13) determine the inside diameter of the drum braking surface.

2. Reverse the tool as shown in Fig. 14 and adjust the brake shoe diameter to fit the gauge. Hold the automatic adjusting lever out of engagement while rotating the adjust-

H 1411-A

FIG. 13—Measuring Drum

ing screw, to prevent burring *the* screw slots. Make sure the adjusting screw rotates freely. If neces-

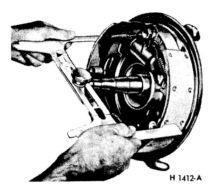

FIG. 14—Measuring Shoes

sary, lubricate the adjusting screw threads with a thin, uniform coating of C1AZ-19590-B Grease.

3. Rotate Tool HRE 8650 around the brake shoes to be sure of the setting.

4. Apply a **small** quantity of high temperature grease to the points where the shoes contact the carrier plate, being careful not to get the lubricant on the linings.

5. Install the wheel on the drum and tighten the mounting nuts to specification.

6. Complete the adjustment by applying the brakes several times while backing the car.

7. After the brake shoes have been properly adjusted, check the operation of the brakes by making several stops while operating in a forward direction.

FRONT BRAKE DRUM

REMOVAL

1. Raise the car until the wheel and tire clear the floor. Remove the wheel cover or hub cap, and remove the wheel and tire from the drum.

2. Remove the drum. If the drum will not come off, knock the access slug out of the brake carrier plate, using a punch. Insert a narrow screwdriver through the slot and disengage the adjusting lever from the adjusting screw. While holding the adjusting lever away from the screw, back off the adjusting screw with the brake adjusting tool (Fig. 15). **Be very careful not to burr, chip, or damage the notches in the adjusting screws; otherwise the self-adjusting mechanism will not function properly.**

3. Remove the grease cap from the hub. Remove the cotter pin, nut lock, adjusting nut, and flat washer from the spindle. Remove the outer bearing cone and roller assembly.

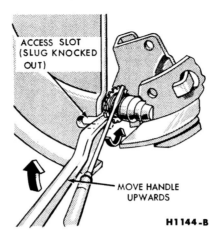

FIG. 15—Backing Off Brake Adjustment

4. Pull the hub and drum assembly off the wheel spindle.

INSTALLATION

1. If the drum is being replaced, remove the protective coating from the new drum with carburetor degreaser. Install new bearings and grease retainer. Soak the new grease retainer in light engine oil at least 30 minutes before installation if retainer is of a leather composition. Rubber seals need not be treated with oil before installation. Pack the wheel bearings, install the inner bearing cone and roller assembly in the inner cup, and install the new grease retainer. See Part 3-5, Section 4 for procedure.

If the original drum is being installed, make sure that the grease in the hub is clean and adequate.

2. Adjust the brakes and install the drum assembly as outlined under "Brake Shoe Adjustments" in this section.

3. Install the outer wheel bearing, washer and adjusting nut.

4. Adjust the wheel bearing as outlined in Part 3-5, Section 2, then install the cotter pin grease cap. Install the wheel and hub cap.

REAR BRAKE DRUM

REMOVAL

1. Raise the car so that the wheel is clear of the floor.

2. Remove the hub cap and wheel. Remove the three Tinnerman nuts and remove the brake drum. If the drum will not come off, knock the excess slug out of the brake carrier plate, using a punch. Insert a narrow screwdriver through the

hole in the carrier plate, and disengage the adjusting lever from the adjusting screw. While holding the adjusting lever away from the adjusting screw, back off the adjusting screw with the brake adjusting tool (Fig. 15). **Be very careful not to burr, chip or damage the notches in the adjusting screw; otherwise, the self-adjusting mechanism will not function properly.**

If the adjustment was backed off, make sure that the adjuster lever is properly seated in the shoe web.

INSTALLATION

1. Remove the protective coating from a new drum with carburetor degreaser.

2. Adjust the brakes as outlined under Brake Shoe Adjustments in this section.

3. Place the drum over the brake assembly and into position. Install the three Tinnerman nuts and tighten them securely. Install the wheel on the axle shaft flange studs against the drum, and tighten the attaching nuts to specifications.

BRAKE SHOES AND ADJUSTING SCREW

REMOVAL

1. With the wheel and drum removed, install a clamp over the ends of the wheel cylinder as shown in Fig. 16.

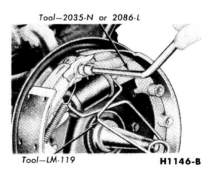

FIG. 16—Retracting Spring Removal—Typical

2. Remove the brake retracting springs using Tool 2035-N or 2086-L (Fig. 16).

3. Disconnect the brake shoe holddown springs and remove the brake shoe assemblies along with the complete automatic adjustment mechanism.

4. Disassemble the brake shoes.

5. On rear brakes, remove the parking brake link and spring from

the brake assemblies. Disconnect the parking brake cable from the parking brake lever.

6. After removing the rear brake shoes disassemble the parking brake lever from the secondary shoe by removing the retaining clip and spring washer (Fig. 1 and 2).

INSTALLATION

1. Before installing the rear brake shoes, assemble the parking brake lever to the secondary shoe and secure it with the spring washer and retaining clip.

2. Apply a light coating of high-temperature grease at the points where the brake shoes contact the backing plate.

3. Position the brake shoes on the backing plate and secure them with the hold down springs. On the rear brake, install the parking brake link and spring. Connect the parking brake cable to the parking brake lever.

Install the cable guide on the secondary shoe web with the flanged hole properly fitted into the hole in the secondary shoe web. Install the secondary shoe to anchor spring (Figs. 1 and 2).

5. Place the cable eye over the anchor pin with the crimped side toward the backing plate. Install the primary shoe to anchor spring with the tool shown in Fig. 17.

Tool—2035-N or 2086-L

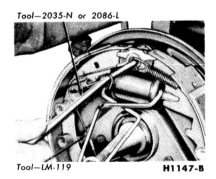

Tool—LM-119   **H1147-B**

FIG. 17—Retracting Spring Installation—Typical

6. Thread the cable around the cable guide groove.

It is imperative that the cable be positioned in this groove and not between the guide and the shoe web. Be certain that the cable eye is not cocked or binding on the anchor pin when installed. All parts should be flat on the anchor pin. Remove the brake cylinder clamp.

7. Apply a small amount of high-temperature grease to the threads and the socket end of the adjusting screw. Turn the adjusting screw into the adjusting pivot nut to the limit of the threads and then back off ½ turn.

Interchanging the brake shoe adjusting screw assemblies from one side of the car to the other would cause the brake shoes to retract rather than expand each time the automatic adjusting mechanism operated. To prevent accidental installation of the adjusting screw on the wrong side of the car the socket end of the adjusting screw is stamped with an R or L (Fig. 18). The ad-

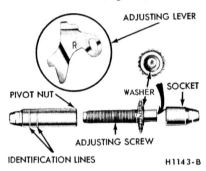

FIG. 18—Adjusting Screw and Lever Identification

justing pivot nuts can be distinguished by the number of grooves machined around the body of the nut. Two grooves indicate a right-hand nut: one groove indicates a left-hand nut.

8. Place the adjusting socket on the screw and install this assembly between the shoe ends with the adjusting screw toothed wheel nearest the secondary shoe.

9. Hook the cable hook into the hole in the adjusting lever. The adjusting levers are stamped with an R or L to indicate their installation on a right or left brake assembly (Fig. 18).

10. Position the hooked end of the adjuster spring completely into the large hole in the primary shoe web. The last coil of the spring should be at the edge of the hole. Connect the loop end of the spring to the adjuster lever hole (Figs. 1 and 2).

11. Pull the adjuster lever, cable and automatic adjuster spring down and toward the rear to engage the pivot hook in the large hole in the secondary shoe web.

12. After installation, check the

action of the adjuster by pulling the section of the cable between the cable guide and the adjusting lever toward the secondary shoe web far enough to lift the lever past a tooth on the adjusting screw wheel. The lever should snap into position behind the next tooth, and release of the cable should cause the adjuster spring to return the lever to its original position. This return action of the lever will turn the adjusting screw one tooth.

If pulling the cable does not produce the action described, or if the lever action is sluggish instead of positive and sharp, check the position of the lever on the adjusting screw toothed wheel. With the brake in a vertical position (anchor at the top), the lever should contact the adjusting wheel $3/16$ inch (plus or minus $1/32$ inch) above the centerline of the screw. If the contact point is below the centerline, the lever will not lock on the teeth in the adjusting screw wheel, and the screw will not be turned as the lever is actuated by the cable.

To determine the cause of this condition:

a. Check the cable end fittings. The cable should completely fill or extend slightly beyond the crimped section of the fittings. If it does not meet this specification, possible damage is indicated and the cable assembly should be replaced.

b. Check the cable length. The cable should measure $8 3/16$ inches on 9 inch brakes or $10 1/8$ inches on 10 inch brakes from the end of the cable anchor to the end of the cable hook.

c. Check the cable guide for damage. The cable groove should be parallel to the shoe web, and the body of the guide should lie flat against the web. Replace the guide if it shows damage.

d. Check the pivot hook on the lever. The hook surfaces should be square with the body of the lever for proper pivoting. Replace the lever if the hook shows damage.

e. See that the adjusting screw socket is properly seated in the notch in the shoe web.

DISC BRAKE SHOE AND LINING REPLACEMENT

After any brake service work, pump the brake pedal to obtain a firm pedal before moving the car. Riding the brake pedal (common on left foot applications) should be avoided when driving the car.

REMOVAL

1. Remove the wheel and tire from the hub and rotor assembly. **Be careful to avoid damage or interference with the caliper splash shield, bleeder screw fitting or transfer tube.**

2. Remove the two bolts that attach the caliper splash shield, and remove the shield (Fig. 3).

3. To facilitate removal and installation of the shoe and lining assemblies, the pistons must be pushed into their bores. Apply a steady inward pressure against each shoe and lining assembly toward its respective caliper housing on each side of the rotor (Fig. 4). Maintain the pressure for at least a minute. If the pistons will not go in easily, force them in with water pump pliers.

4. Grasp the metal flange on the outer end of the shoe with two pairs of pliers and pull the shoe out of the caliper (Fig. 19).

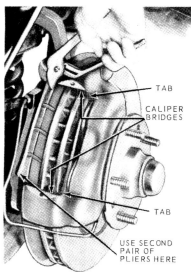

H 1366 - A

FIG. 19—Removing Disc Brake Shoe and Lining Assembly—Typical

CLEANING AND INSPECTION

When the shoe and lining assemblies are replaced, remove the dust boots from the pistons. Check the condition of the boots, and inspect each piston surface for damage or corrosion. Thoroughly clean each dust boot and surrounding area before installing.

INSTALLATION

1. Position a new shoe and lining assembly on each side of the rotor so that the lining faces the rotor. Be sure that the tabs on the shoe flanges seat fully against the caliper bridges (Fig. 19).

2. Install the caliper splash shield and secure the shield to the caliper with two retaining bolts (Fig 3).

3. Pump the brake pedal several times until a firm pedal is obtained and the shoe and lining assemblies are properly seated.

4. Install the wheel and tire on the hub and rotor assembly.

5. Check and refill the master cylinder reservoir with specified brake fluid as required.

6. Road test the car.

It should not be necessary to bleed the system after a shoe and lining replacement.

DISC BRAKE CALIPER ASSEMBLY

REMOVAL

1. Remove the wheel and tire from the hub and rotor assembly. **Be careful to avoid damage or interference with the caliper splash shield, bleeder screw fitting or transfer tube.**

2. Disconnect the front brake flexible hose from the brake tube at the bracket on the frame (Fig. 24).

3. Remove the two bolts that attach the caliper to the mounting bracket.

Take care to avoid loosening the bridge bolts that hold the two halves of the caliper together.

4. Lift the caliper assembly off the rotor.

INSTALLATION

1. Position the caliper assembly on the rotor, and mate the mounting bolt holes in the caliper with those in the spindle. It may be necessary to push the caliper pistons into the cylinder bores to obtain clearance between the shoe and lining assemblies and the rotor. The shoe and lining assemblies should be seated properly on the bridges.

2. Install the caliper to mounting bracket attaching bolts and torque to specification. Check to insure that the rotor runs squarely and centrally between the two halves of the caliper. There should be approximately 0.090-0.120 inch clearance between the caliper and the rotor outside diameter (Fig. 4).

3. Connect the front wheel brake flexible hose to the brake tube at the bracket on the frame (Fig. 24). The

hose should be checked for correct routing.

4. Bleed the brake system as outlined in Section 2-1. Check the master cylinder fluid level, and the specified brake fluid as required.

5. **Pump the brake pedal several times to actuate the piston seals and to position the shoe and lining assemblies.**

6. Install the wheel and tire.

7. Road test the car.

FRONT WHEEL HUB AND ROTOR ASSEMBLY—DISC BRAKES

REMOVAL

1. Remove the wheel and tire from the hub and rotor assembly (Fig. 20). **Be careful to avoid damage or interference with the caliper splash shield, bleeder screw fitting or transfer tube.**

2. Remove the caliper assembly from the spindle and the rotor. If the caliper does not require servicing, it is not necessary to disconnect the brake hose or remove the caliper from the car. Position the caliper out of the way, and support it with a wire to avoid damaging the caliper or stretching the hose. Insert a **clean** cardboard spacer between the linings to prevent the pistons from coming out of the cylinder bores while the caliper is removed.

Handle the rotor and caliper assemblies in such a way as to avoid deformation of the rotor and nicking or scratching of the brake linings.

3. Remove the grease cap from the hub. Remove the cotter pin, nut lock, adjusting nut, and flat washer from the spindle. Remove the outer bearing cone and roller assembly.

4. Remove the hub and rotor assembly from the spindle.

INSTALLATION

1. If the rotor is being replaced, remove the protective coating from the new rotor with carburetor degreaser. Pack a new set of bearings with specified grease, and install the inner bearing cone and roller assembly in the inner cup. Pack grease lightly between the lips of a new grease retainer and install the retainer (Fig. 20).

If the original rotor is being installed, make sure that the grease in the hub is clean and adequate, that the inner bearing and grease retainer are lubricated and in good condition, and that the rotor braking surfaces are clean.

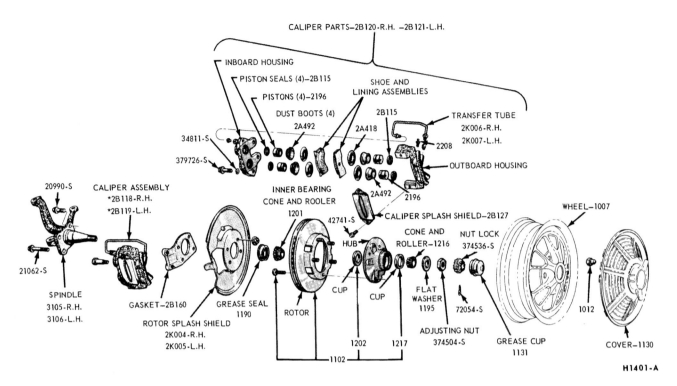

CALIPER PARTS—2B120-R.H. —2B121-L.H.

INBOARD HOUSING
PISTON SEALS (4)—2B115
PISTONS (4)—2196
SHOE AND LINING ASSEMBLIES
DUST BOOTS (4) 2A492   2B115
34811-S   2A418
379726-S   2208
                                            TRANSFER TUBE
                                            2K006-R.H.
                                            2K007-L.H.
                                            OUTBOARD HOUSING
20990-S   CALIPER ASSEMBLY   INNER BEARING
           *2B118-R.H.   CONE AND ROOLER   2A492 2196
           *2B119-L.H.   1201   WHEEL—1007
                                          42741-S   CALIPER SPLASH SHIELD—2B127
                                                CONE AND   NUT LOCK
21062-S   HUB ROLLER—1216 374536-S
                                          CUP   CUP
SPINDLE   FLAT   72054-S   1012
3105-R.H.   GASKET—2B160   GREASE SEAL   ROTOR   WASHER
3106-L.H.   1190   1195   GREASE CUP   COVER—1130
           ROTOR SPLASH SHIELD   ADJUSTING NUT   1131
           2K004-R.H.   1202   1217   374504-S
           2K005-L.H.   1102

H1401-A

FIG. 20—Disc Brake Disassembled

2. Install the hub and rotor assembly on the spindle.

3. Lubricate and install the outer wheel bearing, washer and adjusting nut.

4. Adjust the wheel bearings to specification, and then install the nut lock, cotter pin, and grease cap. **The wheel bearing adjustment is especially important with disc brakes.**

5. Mount the caliper assembly on the mounting bracket and torque the two mounting bolts to specification. If necessary, push the caliper pistons into the cylinder bores to obtain clearance between the shoe and lining assemblies and the rotor. Be sure that the shoe and lining assemblies are seated on the bridges. Check the flexible hose for correct routing.

6. Install the wheel and tire on the hub and rotor assembly.

DISC BRAKE ROTOR SPLASH SHIELD

REMOVAL

1. Remove the caliper and the hub and rotor assembly as outlined under Removal in the foregoing procedure.

2. Remove the four nuts that attach the splash shield to the mounting bracket and remove the shield (Fig. 20).

3. Remove the gasket.

INSTALLATION

1. Install the gasket.

2. If the shield is bent, straighten it out before installation. Position the shield to the mounting bracket, install the attaching nuts, and torque to specification (Fig. 20).

3. Install the hub and rotor assembly and the caliper as outlined under Installation in the foregoing procedure.

PROPORTIONING VALVE

The proportioning valve is serviced as an assembly and is never adjusted or overhauled.

REMOVAL

1. Disconnect and remove the Master cylinder - to - proportioning valve brake tube (Fig. 23).

2. Disconnect the front-to-rear brake tube from the proportioning valve.

3. Working underneath the left fender, remove the bolt that attaches the porportioning valve to the fender apron and remove the valve through the access hole (Fig. 21).

INSTALLATION

1. From underneath the left fender, install the proportioning valve through the access hole in the fender apron. Position the valve to the

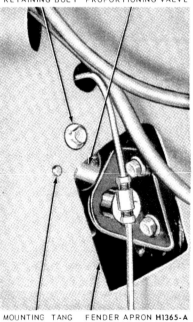

RETAINING BOLT   PROPORTIONING VALVE

MOUNTING TANG   FENDER APRON H1365-A

FIG. 21—Removing or Installing Proportioning Valve

apron so that the mounting tang extends through the hole in the fender apron as shown in Fig. 21. Install the attaching bolt.

2. Connect the front-to-rear brake tube to the valve (Fig. 23).

3. Position and connect the master cylinder-to-proportioning valve brake tube.

4. Bleed the brake system.

WHEEL CYLINDER REPAIR

It is not necessary to remove the wheel cylinder from the backing plate to disassemble, inspect, or hone and overhaul it. Removal is necessary only when the cylinder is damaged or scored beyond repair.

DISASSEMBLY

1. With the wheel in a raised position, remove the wheel and the drum.

2. Place a clamp over the ends of the brake cylinder as shown in Fig. 16.

3. Remove the brake shoe assemblies following procedures outlined in this section.

4. The 6-cylinder Falcon and Mustang models are not provided with links. Remove the rubber boots from the ends of the piston.

On 8-cylinder models and on all Comets and Fairlanes, remove the links and rubber boots from the ends of the piston. Remove the pistons, cups, and return spring from the cylinder bore (Fig. 22).

5. Remove the bleeder screw from the cylinder.

INSPECTION

1. Wash all parts in clean denatured alcohol. If alcohol is not available, use specified brake fluid. Dry with compressed air.

2. Check all the internal parts for excessive wear or damage. **If any of**

the internal parts require replacing, all should be replaced.**

3. Inspect the cylinder bore for score marks or rust. If either condition is present, the cylinder bore must be honed. **However, the cylinder should not be honed more than 0.003 inch beyond its original diameter.** A baffle in the front wheel cylinder of the 6-cylinder Falcon and Mustang models prevents honing; therefore, the cylinder must be replaced.

4. Check the bleeder hole to be sure that it is open.

ASSEMBLY

1. Apply a coating of heavy-duty brake fluid to all internal parts.

2. Thread the bleeder screw into the cylinder and tighten securely.

3. Insert the return spring, cups, and pistons into their respective positions in the cylinder bore (Fig. 22). Place a boot over each end of the cylinder. On 8-cylinder model Mustangs and Falcons and all Comets and Fairlanes, install the links in the ends of the brake cylinders.

4. Install the shoe and adjuster assemblies, then adjust the shoes as outlined in this section.

5. Install the brake drum and wheel, then bleed the brakes as outlined in this section.

WHEEL CYLINDER REPLACEMENT

REMOVAL

1. With the wheel in a raised position, remove the wheel and the drum.

2. Place a clamp over the ends of the wheel cylinder as shown in Fig. 16.

3. Remove the brake shoe assemblies, following procedures outlined in this section.

4. Disconnect the brake line from the brake cylinder. **On a car with a vacuum brake booster, be sure the engine is stopped and there is no vacuum in the booster system before disconnecting the hydraulic lines.**

To disconnect the hose at a front cylinder, loosen the tube fitting that connects the opposite end of the hose to the brake tube at a bracket on the frame. Remove the horseshoe-type retaining clip from the hose and bracket, disengage the hose from the bracket, then unscrew the entire hose assembly from the front wheel cylinder.

At a rear cylinder, unscrew the tube fitting that connects the tube to the cylinder. **Do not pull the metal tube away from the cylinder. Pulling the tube out of the cylinder connection will bend the metal tube and make installation difficult.** The tube will separate from the cylinder when the cylinder is removed from the carrier plate.

5. Remove the wheel cylinder attaching bolts and lock washers and remove the cylinder.

INSTALLATION

Wipe the end(s) of the hydraulic line to remove any foreign matter before making connections.

1. **To install a front cylinder:**

a. Position the cylinder in place against the carrier plate. Install the two lock washers and attaching bolts. Torque them to specifications.

b. Install a new copper gasket over the hose fitting. Thread the hose assembly into the cylinder and tighten it securely.

c. Engage the opposite end of the hose to the bracket on the frame, install the horseshoe-type retaining clip, and connect the brake tube to the hose with the tube fitting nut. Tighten the nut to specifications.

2. **To install a rear cylinder:**

a. Position the rear wheel cylinder in place against the carrier plate. Enter the tubing into the cylinder, and start the tube fitting nut into the threads of the cylinder.

b. Secure the cylinder to the carrier plate with the attaching bolts and lock washers.

c. Tighten the tube fitting nut to specifications.

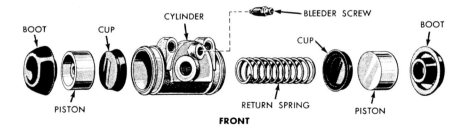

FRONT

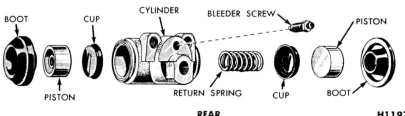

REAR   H1197-B

FIG. 22—Front and Rear Wheel Cylinders

H 1408-A

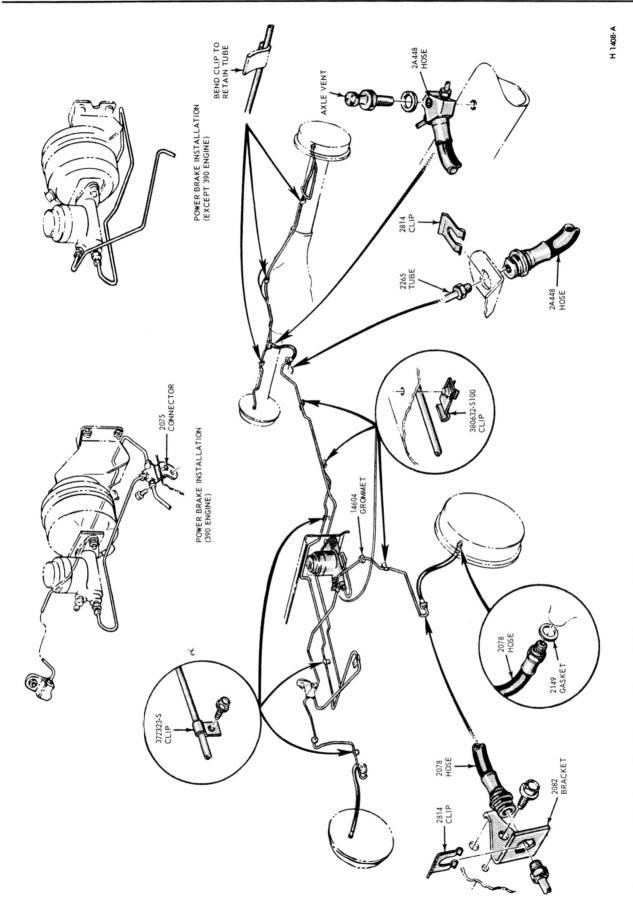

POWER BRAKE INSTALLATION
(EXCEPT 390 ENGINE)

BEND CLIP TO
RETAIN TUBE

AXLE VENT

2A448
HOSE

2814
CLIP

2265
TUBE

2A448
HOSE

380632-S100
CLIP

2075
CONNECTOR

POWER BRAKE INSTALLATION
(390 ENGINE)

14604
GROMMET

2078
HOSE

2149
GASKET

372323-S
CLIP

2078
HOSE

2814
CLIP

2082
BRACKET

FIG. 23—Hydraulic Brake System—Comet-Fairlane and Falcon

H 1407-A

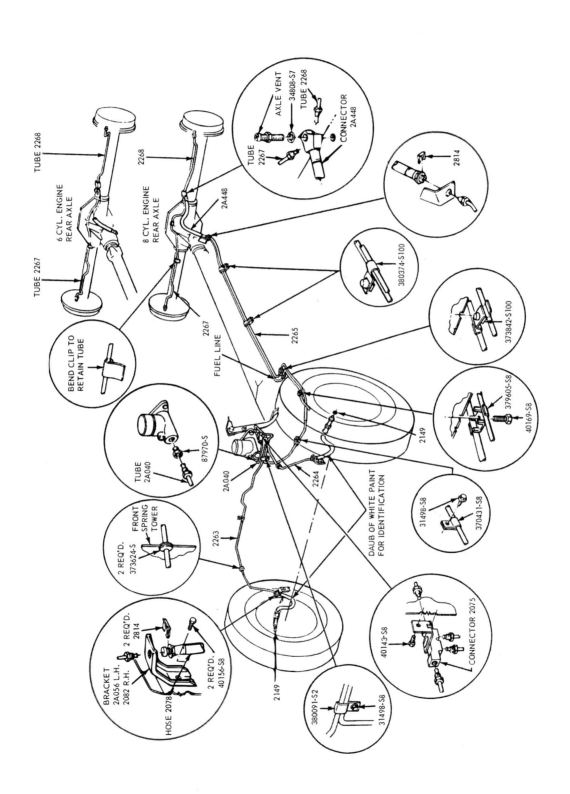

FIG. 24—Hydraulic Brake System—Mustang

3. Install the links in the ends of the wheel cylinder (8-cylinder models only on Falcon and Mustang and all Comet and Fairlane models).

4. Install the brake shoes as detailed in this section.

5. Adjust the brakes as detailed in Part 2-2, Section 2.

6. Install the brake drums and wheels.

7. Bleed the brakes as detailed in Part 2-1, Section 2.

BRAKE CARRIER PLATE REPLACEMENT

REMOVAL

1. Remove the wheel and brake drum. Disconnect the brake line from the brake cylinder.

2. Remove the brake shoe and adjuster assemblies and the wheel cylinder as outlined in this section. On the rear wheels, disconnect the parking brake lever from the cable.

3. If the rear carrier plate is being replaced, rotate the axle shaft so that the hole in the axle shaft flange lines up with the carrier plate retaining nuts and remove the nuts. Pull the axle shaft assembly out of the housing with tool 4235-C and a slide hammer (Part 4-2), then remove the carrier plate.

If the front carrier plate is being replaced, remove the bolts and nuts that secure the plate to the front wheel spindle and remove the plate.

INSTALLATION

1. Position a new rear carrier plate on the attaching bolts in the axle housing flange. Insert the axle shaft into the housing so that the splines engage the differential side gear with the bearing retainer sliding onto the retaining bolts and against the carrier plate. Install the attaching nuts through the access hole in the axle shaft flange.

Position a new **front** carrier plate to the wheel spindle and install the attaching bolts and nuts.

2. Install the wheel cylinder and connect the brake line as outlined in this section.

3. Install the brake shoe and adjuster assemblies as outlined in this section. On a rear brake, connect the parking brake cable to the lever.

4. Adjust the brake shoes (Section 2).

5. Install the brake drum and wheel and bleed the brake system as outlined in Part 2-1, Section 2.

HYDRAULIC LINES

Steel tubing is used throughout the brake system with the exception of the flexible hoses at the front wheels and at the rear axle housing brake tube connector (Figs. 23 and 24).

Always bleed the entire hydraulic system after any hose or line replacement.

BRAKE TUBE REPLACEMENT

If a section of the brake tubing becomes damaged, the entire section should be replaced with tubing of the same type, size, shape and length. **Copper tubing should not be used in a hydraulic system.** When bending brake tubing to fit underbody or rear axle contours, be careful not to kink or crack the tube.

All brake tubing should be flared properly to provide good leak-proof connections. Clean the brake tubing by flushing with clean denatured alcohol, before installation.

When connecting a tube to a hose, tube connector, disc caliper, or brake cylinder, tighten the tube fitting nut to specified torque with Milbar tool 1112-144 or equivalent.

BRAKE HOSE REPLACEMENT

A flexible brake hose should be replaced if it shows signs of softening, cracking, or other damage.

When installing a new front brake hose, position the hose to avoid contact with other chassis parts. Place a new copper gasket over the hose fitting and screw the hose assembly into the front brake cylinder. Engage the opposite end of the hose to the bracket on the frame. Install the horseshoe-type retaining clip, and connect the tube to the hose with the tube fitting nut.

A rear brake hose should be installed so that it does not touch the muffler outlet pipe or shock absorber.

Since the rear brake hose is integral with the rear brake tube connector, the entire hose and connector is replaced as an assembly. Mount the connector to the rear axle housing with the retaining bolt (axle vent) and lock washer. Connect the two rear wheel brake tubes to the connector.

3 REMOVAL AND INSTALLATION

MASTER CYLINDER— STANDARD BRAKES

REMOVAL

1. Disconnect the rubber boot from the rear end of the master cylinder in the passenger compartment.

2. Disconnect the brake line(s) from the master cylinder (Fig. 27)

3. Remove the bolts that secure the master cylinder to the dash panel and lift the cylinder out and away from the push rod. Remove the rubber boot from the push rod.

INSTALLATION

1. With the rubber boot on the push rod, guide the master cylinder over the end of the push rod, and position the cylinder against the dash panel.

2. Install and torque the mounting bolts to specification.

3. Connect the brake line(s) to the master cylinder fitting, but leave the brake line fitting(s) loose.

4. Fill the master cylinder reservoir with heavy-duty Rotunda brake fluid to within ⅜ inch of the top. Install and tighten the filler cap.

5. Bleed the master cylinder to let air escape from the cylinder at the brake line fitting(s). Then tighten the fitting(s).

6. Remove the filler cap and fill the reservoir to the level specified. Be sure that the diaphragm type gasket is properly seated in the cap. Install the cap and wipe off any *fluid* from the cylinder.

7. Connect the rubber boot to the master cylinder.

MASTER CYLINDER— POWER BRAKES

REMOVAL

1. Disconnect the hydraulic line(s) from the master cylinder.

2. Remove the two nuts and lock washers that attach the master cylinder to the booser.

3. Remove the master cylinder from the vacuum booster.

INSTALLATION

1. Before installing the master cylinder, check the distance from the outer end of the push rod to the master cylinder mounting surface at *at the end* of the vacuum cylinder (Fig. 4 or 5, Part 2-1). If the push rod dimension is not correct, see Master Cylinder Push Rod Adjust-

ment Part 2-1, Section 2.

2. Position the master cylinder over the push rod onto the two studs that are integral with the booster body.

3. Install, but do not tighten the attaching nuts and lock washers.

4. Connect the hydraulic line(s) to the master cylinder.

5. Tighten the two master cylinder attaching nuts.

6. Tighten all hydraulic line fittings.

7. Bleed the brake system. Fill the master cylinder to ⅜ inch from the top of the filler opening. Be sure that the diaphragm type gasket is properly seated in the reservoir cap, and install the cap.

BRAKE BOOSTER

REMOVAL

1. Working inside the car below the instrument panel, disconnect the stop light switch wires at the connector.

2. Remove the hairpin type retainer. Slide the stop light switch off the brake pedal pin **just far enough for the switch outer hole to clear the pin,** and then lower the switch away from the pin. Slide the master cylinder push rod link and the nylon washers and bushing off from the brake pedal pin (Fig. 25 or 26).

3. Working in the engine compartment, loosen the hose clamp, and disconnect the vacuum hose from the booster at the check valve.

4. Remove the two master cylinder attaching nuts and pull the master cylinder from the booster, **without disconnecting the hydraulic lines.** Secure the master cylinder out of the way.

5. Remove the four mounting bracket-to-dash panel attaching bolts.

6. Remove the booster and bracket assembly from the dash panel, sliding the push rod link out from the engine side of the dash panel.

INSTALLATION

1. Mount the booster and bracket assembly to the dash panel by sliding the push rod link in through the hole in the dash panel. Install the four attaching bolts.

2. Position the brake master cylinder to the booster assembly and install the attaching nuts.

3. Connect the vacuum hose to the booster at the check valve, and tighten the hose clamp.

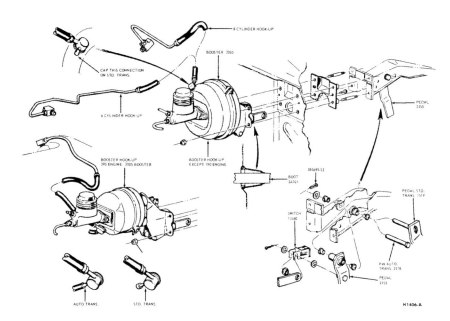

FIG. 25—Vacuum Booster Installation—Comet-Fairlane-Falcon

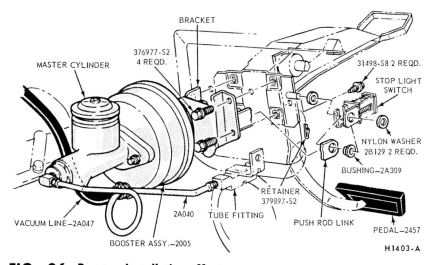

FIG. 26—Booster Installation—Mustang

4. Working from inside the car, install the inner nylon washer, the master cylinder push rod link, and the bushing on the brake pedal pin. Position the switch so that it straddles the push rod with the switch slot on the pedal pin and the switch outer hole just clearing the pin. Slide the switch completely onto the pin, and install the outer nylon washer as shown in Fig. 25 or 26. Secure these

parts to the pin with the hairpin type retainer.

5. Connect the stop light switch wires to the connector, and install the wires in the retaining clip.

BRAKE PEDAL—MANUAL SHIFT TRANSMISSION
REMOVAL

1. On a Falcon, Comet or Fairlane, remove the clutch pedal assist spring, (Fig. 27).

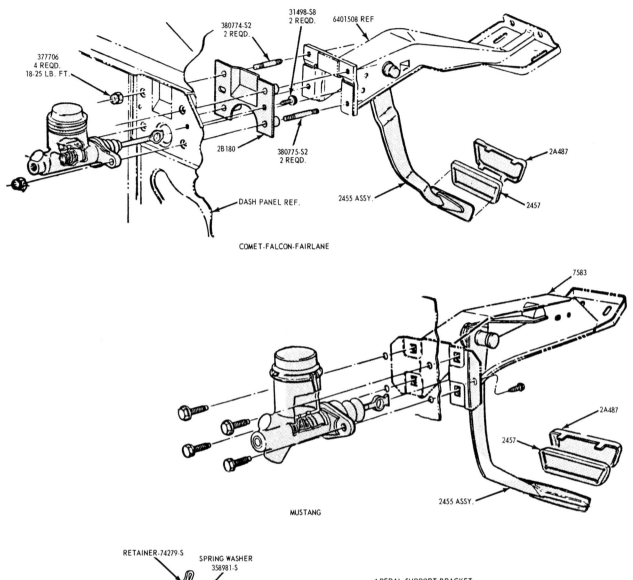

COMET-FALCON-FAIRLANE

MUSTANG

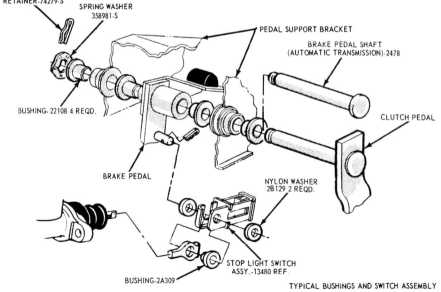

TYPICAL BUSHINGS AND SWITCH ASSEMBLY

H1361-B

FIG. 27—Master Cylinder, Brake Pedal and Related Parts—Falcon, Fairlane, Comet and Mustang

On a Mustang, remove the pedal bumper and bracket assembly from the pedal support bracket to relieve the tension on the assist spring, and then remove the spring.

2. Disconnect the clutch pedal-to-equalizer rod at the clutch pedal by removing the hairpin type retainer and bushing.

3. Disconnect the stop light switch wires at the connector.

4. Remove the switch retainer, and slide the stop light switch off the brake pedal pin just far enough for the switch outer hole to clear the pin. Then lower the switch away from the pin.

5. Slide the master cylinder push rod and the nylon washers and bushing off from the brake pedal pin (Fig. 27).

6. Remove the self-locking pin and washer from the clutch and brake pedal shaft, then remove the clutch pedal and shaft assembly, the brake pedal assembly, and the bushings from the pedal support bracket (Fig. 27).

INSTALLATION

1. Apply a coating of SAE 10 engine oil to the bushings and locate all bushings in their proper places on the clutch and brake pedal assemblies.

'2. Position the brake pedal to the support bracket, then install the clutch pedal and shaft assembly through the support bracket and brake pedal assembly. Install the spring washer and retainer. (Fig. 27).

3. Install the split bushing in the spring groove of the clutch pedal. Hook the clutch assist spring to the groove and to the spring retainer.

4. Connect the clutch pedal to equalizer rod to the clutch pedal assembly with the bushing and the hairpin retainer. Apply SAE 10 engine oil to the bushing.

5. Install the inner nylon washer, the master cylinder push rod, and the bushing on the brake pedal pin. Position the switch so that it straddles the push rod with the switch slot on the pedal pin and the switch outer hole just clearing the pin. Slide the switch completely onto the pin, and install the outer nylon washer as shown in Fig. 27. Secure these parts to the pin with the self-locking pin.

6. Connect the stop light switch wires to the connector, and install the wires to the retaining clip.

BRAKE PEDAL—AUTOMATIC TRANSMISSION

REMOVAL

1. Disconnect the stop light switch wires at the connector.

2. Remove the self-locking pin and slide the stop light switch off the brake pedal pin **just far enough for the switch outer hole to clear the pin.** Then lower the switch away from the pin. Slide the master cylinder push rod and the nylon washers and bushing off from the brake pedal pin (Fig. 27).

3. Remove the self-locking pin and washer from the brake pedal shaft, then remove the shaft, the brake pedal assembly and the bushings from the pedal support bracket.

INSTALLATION

1. Apply a coating of SAE10 engine oil to the bushings and locate all the bushings in their proper places on the pedal assembly and pedal support bracket. (Fig. 27).

2. Position the brake pedal assembly to the support bracket, then install the pedal shaft through the support bracket and brake pedal assembly. Install the washer and self-locking pin.

3. Install the inner nylon washer, the master cylinder push rod, and the bushing on the brake pedal pin. Position the switch so that it straddles the push rod with the switch slot on the pedal pin, and the switch outer hole just clearing the pin. Slide the switch completely onto the pin, and install the outer nylon washer as shown in Fig 27. Secure these parts to the pin with the self-locking pin.

4. Connect the stop light switch wires to the connector, and install the wires in the retaining clip.

PARKING BRAKE HANDLE—MUSTANG

REMOVAL

1. Remove the two screws that hold the handle bracket on the instrument panel. Remove the attaching screws and the insulator bracket (Fig. 28).

2. Remove the two nuts and lock washers that secure the control to the dash panel.

3. Remove the clevis pin that secures the pulley to the control handle assembly.

4. Disengage the locking rod and remove the ball on the cable from the slot in the control assembly.

INSTALLATION

1. Disengage the locking rod and connect the ball end of the cable to the slot on the control assembly.

2. Assemble the pulley to the control handle and the clevis pin.

3. Position the assembly against the dash panel and instrument panel. Secure the assembly to the instrument panel with the two screws.

4. Install the insulator bracket with the attaching screws (Fig. 28).

5. Working from under the left front fender, install the two lock washers and attaching nuts.

PARKING BRAKE CONTROL ASSEMBLY—FAIRLANE, FALCON, COMET

REMOVAL

1. Make sure the parking brake is completely released. Remove the 3 screws (Fig. 29) that attach the control assembly to the cowl inner side panel.

2. Pull the control away from the cowl panel and remove the hairpin lock retaining the parking brake cable housing to the control assembly.

3. Disconnect the ball-end of the parking brake cable from the control and remove the control assembly.

INSTALLATION

1. Connect the ball-end of the parking brake cable to the control.

2. Install the hair-pin cable housing retainer.

3. Position the control assembly to the cowl side panel and install the attaching screws. Torque to 12-20 ft-lb.

PARKING BRAKE EQUALIZER TO HANDLE CABLE—MUSTANG

REMOVAL

1. Remove the attaching screws and insulator-bracket from the dash panel (Fig. 28).

2. Remove the parking brake handle assembly and disengage the cable from the handle as outlined in this section.

3. Pull the cable down through the hole in the dash panel.

4. Remove the hairpin retainer, and disengage the cable and housing from the bracket on the crossmember.

5. Disconnect the cable ball from the equalizer lever, and remove the cable from the car.

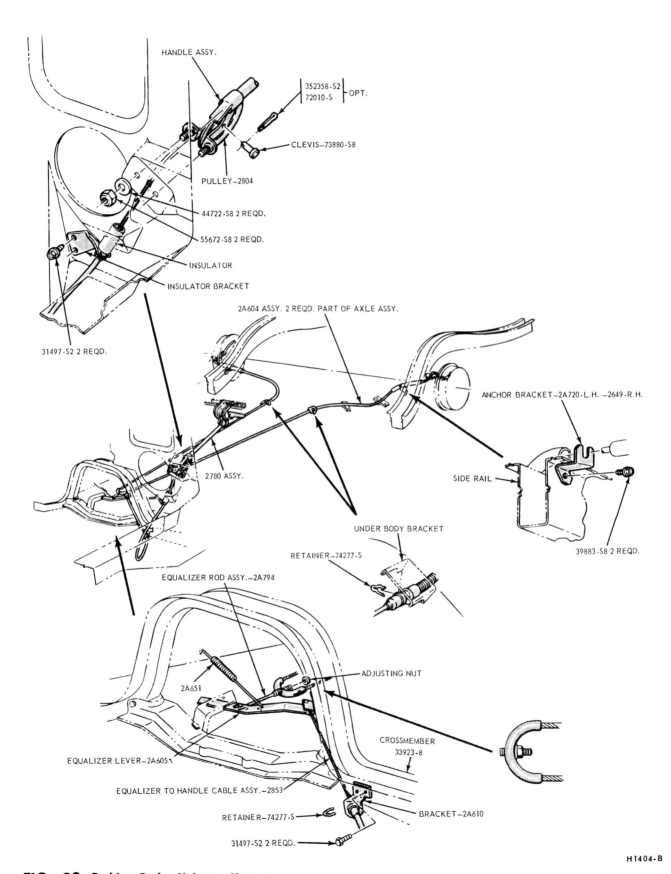

HANDLE ASSY.

352358-S2
72010-S   OPT.

CLEVIS—73880-S8

PULLEY—2804

44722-S8 2 REQD.

55672-S8 2 REQD.

INSULATOR

INSULATOR BRACKET

2A604 ASSY. 2 REQD. PART OF AXLE ASSY.

31497-S2 2 REQD.

ANCHOR BRACKET—2A720-L.H. —2649-R.H.

2780 ASSY.

SIDE RAIL

UNDER BODY BRACKET

RETAINER—74277-S

39883-S8 2 REQD.

EQUALIZER ROD ASSY.—2A794

2A651

ADJUSTING NUT

CROSSMEMBER
33923-8

EQUALIZER LEVER—2A605

EQUALIZER TO HANDLE CABLE ASSY.—2853

BRACKET—2A610

RETAINER—74277-S

31497-S2 2 REQD.

H1404-B

FIG. 28—Parking Brake Linkage—Mustang

H 1409-A

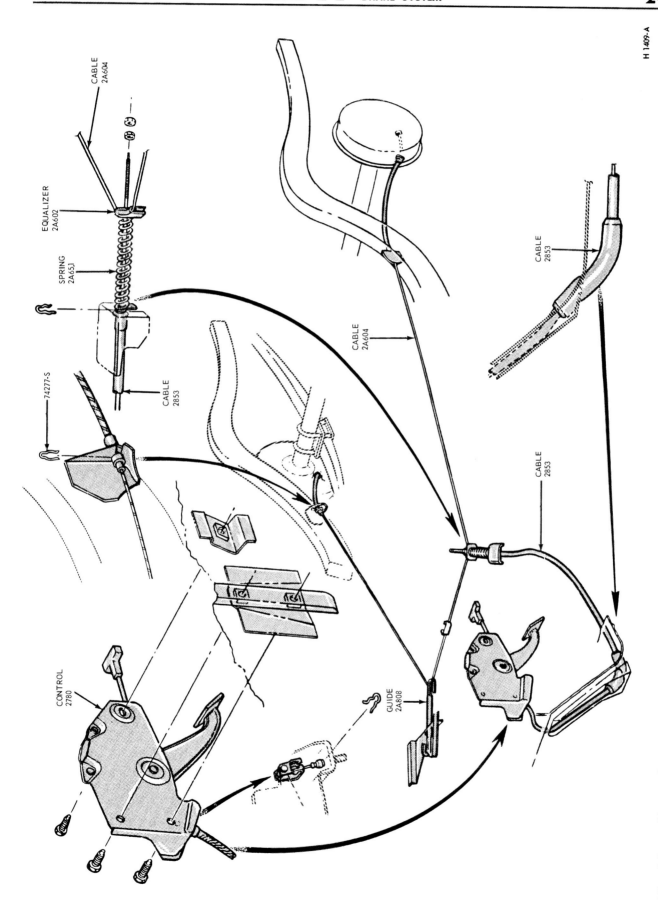

CABLE
2A604

EQUALIZER
2A602

SPRING
2A651

74277-S

CABLE
2853

CABLE
2A604

CABLE
2853

CABLE
2853

CONTROL
2780

GUIDE
2A808

FIG. 29—Parking Brake Linkage—Comet-Fairlane-Falcon

INSTALLATION

1. Connect the cable lower ball to the equalizer lever (Fig. 28).

2. Engage the cable and housing to the bracket on the crossmember and secure with the hairpin retainer.

3. Push the upper end of the cable up through the hole in the dash panel.

4. Connect the cable upper ball to the parking brake handle, and install the handle assembly as outlined in this section.

5. Install the insulator bracket to the dash panel and secure with the two attaching screws.

PARKING BRAKE EQUALIZER TO PEDAL CABLE—FAIRLANE, COMET, FALCON

REMOVAL

1. Remove the two nuts that attach the cable to the equalizer and remove the equalizer and spring (Fig. 29).

2. Remove the hair pin retainer holding the cable housing to the frame bracket at the equalizer.

3. Working from inside the car, remove the hair pin retainer holding the cable housing to the parking brake control assembly.

4. Disconnect the ball end of the cable from the parking brake control arm.

5. Remove the left front cowl side trim panel, roll back the floor mat and pull the cable assembly from the floor.

INSTALLATION

1. Position the cable housing through the opening in the floor and pull the grommet into position from under the car.

2. Install the ball-end of the cable in the parking brake control.

3. Install the hair pin retainer to lock the cable housing in position on the parking brake control.

4. Working from under the car, position the cable housing in the frame bracket and install the retainer.

5. Position the spring and equalizer on the cable and install the adjusting nut.

6. Apply the parking brake one notch from the released position.

7. Tighten the adjusting nut until a light to moderate drag is felt when the rear wheels are rotated.

8. Tighten the check nut securely.

9. Fully release the parking brake. No drag should be felt when the wheels are rotated.

10. Position the floor mat and install the cowl side trim panel.

PARKING BRAKE EQUALIZER TO REAR WHEEL CABLE

A single cable passing through the equalizer and cable guides connects both parking brake assemblies on Comet and Fairlane station wagons and on Falcon and Mustang passenger cars. Separate cables for each parking brake are used on Comet and Fairlane passenger cars.

FAIRLANE AND COMET PASSENGER CARS

REMOVAL

1. Remove the equalizer lock nut and adjusting nut, equalizer and spring.

2. With the cables slack, disconnect the ball-ends from the connector (Fig. 29).

3. Remove the cable from the guide, if required.

4. Remove the hair pin lock retaining the cable housing to the side rail bracket.

5. Remove the wheel and tire and the rear brake drum as outlined in Section 2.

6. Disconnect the rear end of the cable from the parking brake lever on the brake shoe. Disengage the cable housing retaining grommet from the carrier plate and withdraw the cable and housing from the inboard side of the carrier plate.

7. Slide the cable and housing out of the side rail bracket.

INSTALLATION

1. Insert the rear end of the cable through the side rail bracket and pull the cable and housing into position.

2. Insert the rear end of the cable and housing through the hole in the carrier plate from the inboard side.

3. Connect the cable to the parking brake lever on the brake shoe, and install the cable housing retaining the grommet in the carrier plate.

4. Position the cable housing in the side rail bracket and install the hair pin type retainer.

5. Position the cable in the guide and install the connector, thus hooking the two cables together.

6. Insert the cable into the equalizer and install the equalizer, spring, adjusting nut and lock nut to the front, parking brake control, cable.

7. Adjust the parking brake as directed in Part 2-1, Section 2.

FAIRLANE AND COMET STATION WAGONS AND FALCON PASSENGER CAR

REMOVAL AND INSTALLATION

1. Generally follow the procedure given above, omitting separation of the cables, since the hand brake cable supplied for these models is in one piece. Removal and installation of both rear wheels, tires and drums will also be required.

MUSTANG

REMOVAL

1. Remove the adjusting lock nut and cable yoke from the equalizer rod (Fig. 28), along with the rear cable assembly.

2. Remove the hairpin retainers and disengage the cable rear housings from the brackets on the underbody.

3. If an 8-cylinder model, remove the single bolt and clamp retaining the cable housing to the underbody immediately behind the cable housing bracket.

4. Remove the two bolts and clamp securing the cable housing to the underbody on all models.

5. Remove the wheels and tires and the rear brake drums as outlined in Section 2.

6. Disconnect the rear ends of the cable from the parking brake levers on the brake shoes. Disengage the cable housing retaining grommets from the carrier plates and withdraw the cable ends and housings from the inboard sides of the carrier plates.

7. Slide the cable housings out of the main side brackets and remove the cable assembly from the car.

INSTALLATION

1. Insert both cable ends and housings through the holes in the carrier plates from the inboard side.

2. Connect the cable ends to the parking brake levers on the brake shoes and engage the cable housing retaining grommets to the carrier plate.

3. Position the cable housings in the main side brackets and install the hairpin retainers.

4. Install the front clamp with one bolt, if an 8-cylinder model.

5. Install the rear clamp with two bolts.

6. Position the cable yoke and cable on the equalizer rod and install the adjusting locknut.

7. Adjust the parking brake as directed in Part 2-1, Section 2.

4 MAJOR REPAIR OPERATIONS

BRAKE DRUM REFINISHING

The 6-cylinder Falcon and Mustang models are equipped with 9-inch brake drums. All other models are equipped with 10-inch drums.

Minor scores on a brake drum can be removed with a fine emery cloth. A drum that is excessively scored or shows a total indicator runout of over 0.007 inch should be turned down. Remove only enough stock to eliminate the scores and true up the drum. The refinished diameter must not exceed 0.060 inch oversize.

If the drum diameter is less than 0.030 inch oversize (9.030 inches 6-cylinder Falcon or Mustang, or 10.030 inches on other models after refinishing, standard lining may be installed. If the drum diameter is more than 9.030 inches or 10.030 inches, oversize linings must be installed.

After a drum is turned down, wipe the refinished surface with a cloth soaked in clean denatured alcohol. If one drum is turned down, the opposite drum on the same axle should also be cut down to the same size.

BRAKE SHOE RELINING

Brake linings that are worn to within $1/32$ inch of any rivet or have been saturated with grease or oil should be replaced. Failure to replace worn linings will result in a scored drum. **When it is necessary to replace linings, they must also be replaced on the wheel on the opposite side of the car.**

Inspect brake shoes for distortion, cracks, or looseness. If this condition exists, the shoe should be discarded. **Do not repair a defective brake shoe.**

1. Wash the brake shoes thoroughly in a clean solvent. Remove all burrs or rough spots from the shoes.

2. Check the inside diameter of the brake drum. If the diameter is less than 9.030 or 10.030 inches, standard lining may be installed. If the diameter is 9.030 to 9.060 or 10.030 to 10.060 inches, oversize lining should be installed.

3. Position the new lining on the shoe. Starting in the center, insert and secure the rivets working alternately towards each end. Install all parts supplied in the kit. **Genuine replacement linings are ground and no further grinding is required.**

4. Check the clearance between the shoe and lining. The lining must seat tightly against the shoe with not more than .005 inch clearance between any two rivets.

MASTER CYLINDER—EXCEPT CARS WITH DISC BRAKES

DISASSEMBLY

1. Clean the outside of the cylinder, and remove the filler cap and gasket. Pour out any brake fluid that may remain in the cylinder or reservoir.

2. Remove the snap ring from the bore at the rear of the cylinder with tool 33621 (Fig. 32).

3. When disassembling a master cylinder used with the standard brake system, remove the piston assembly, cup, spring, check valve, and valve seat from the cylinder bore (Fig. 30).

When disassembling a master cylinder used with a booster, remove the piston assembly, cup, and the spring and check valve assembly from the cylinder bore. Remove the O-ring from the piston (Fig. 31).

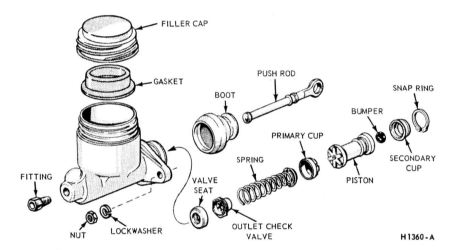

FIG. 30—Master Cylinder With Standard Brake System

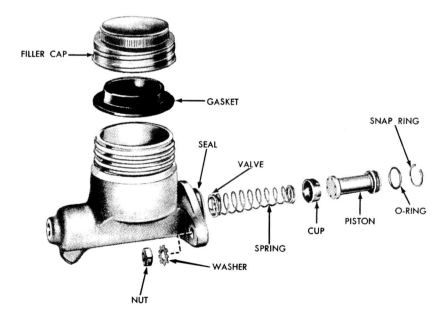

FIG. 31—Master Cylinder With Booster

ASSEMBLY

1. Dip all parts except the master cylinder body in clean Rotunda 103-A **heavy-duty brake fluid.**

2. Install the brake line fitting(s) on the cylinder and tighten them securely.

3. When assembling a master cylinder used with the standard brake system, install the valve seat, check valve, spring, cup, and piston assembly in the cylinder bore (Fig. 30).

When assembling a master cylinder used with a booster, install the O-ring on the piston. Install the spring and check valve assembly, cup, and piston in the cylinder bore (Fig. 31).

4. Install the snap-ring in the back of the bore (Fig. 32).

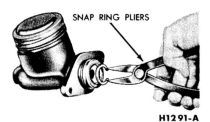

FIG. 32—Removing Snap Ring From Master Cylinder—Typical

MASTER CYLINDER— WITH DISC BRAKES

DISASSEMBLY

1. Press in against the piston while removing the snap ring retainer, and then remove the piston assembly, cup, spring, residual check valve and seat. (Fig. 33).

2. Remove secondary cup from the piston. Remove the cover by releasing the spring clips on the sides, and remove the diaphragm.

ASSEMBLY

1. Clamp the master cylinder housing in a vise. Dip the hydraulic cylinder parts in brake fluid and assemble the check valve seal, residual check valve, and piston return spring in the bore of the cylinder in the order shown in Fig. 33.

2. If the secondary piston cup was removed from the piston, dip the cup in brake fluid and assemble the cup in the groove of the piston with the lip of the cup as shown.

3. Place the primary cup on the end of the piston assembly, and guide it into the cylinder bore.

4. Press in against the piston to compress the spring while seating

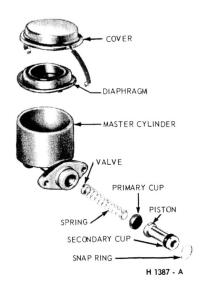

FIG. 33—Master Cylinder Used With Disc Brakes—Disassembled

the snap ring in the groove in the cylinder bore.

5. Install a new diaphragm (only if the old one is defective) in the cover, and attach the cover to the cylinder with the spring clips.

MASTER CYLINDER CLEANING AND INSPECTION

1. Clean all master cylinder parts in clean denatured alcohol, and inspect the parts for wear or damage, replacing them as required. **When using a master cylinder repair kit, install all of the parts supplied.**

2. Check the ports and vents in the master cylinder to make sure that all are open and free of foreign matter. Check the condition of the diaphragm type gasket.

3. A leaf-type valve is riveted to the front end of the piston in a master cylinder used with the standard brake system (Fig. 30). If this valve is loose or has moved so that the piston ports are open, replace the piston.

When inspecting a master cylinder used with a booster, check the ports in the piston to make sure that they are open and free of foreign material (Fig. 31).

4. Inspect the cylinder walls for scores or rust, and recondition them if necessary. **Hone the cylinder walls no more than necessary (0.003 inch maximum). Oversize pistons and cups are not available for excessively honed cylinders.**

5. Remove any burrs or loose metal that may have resulted from the honing operation, and clean the cylinder with denatured alcohol.

DISC BRAKE CALIPER

DISASSEMBLY

Do not remove the bridge bolts that hold the two halves of the caliper together. The two caliper housings are shown separated in Fig. 35 for illustration purposes only.

1. Remove the caliper assembly from the car as outlined in Section 2.

2. Remove the two retaining bolts and the caliper splash shield Fig. 35.

3. Remove the two shoe and lining assemblies.

4. Remove the flexible brake hose from the caliper.

5. Remove the external transfer tube.

6. Remove the four dust boots from the caliper housings and piston grooves.

7. Clamp the caliper in a vise and secure it by the mounting flanges on the inboard housing (Fig. 34).

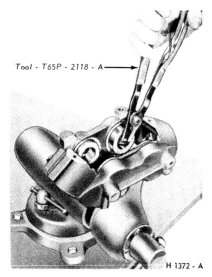

FIG. 34—Removing or Installing Pistons

8. Remove the four pistons from the cylinder bores with the special tool shown in Fig. 34. To prevent cocking with consequent damage to the piston or bore, rotate the piston with the tool while pulling it outward at the same time. **Be careful to avoid scratching or damaging the outside diameter surface or dust boot retaining groove of the piston. Such damage causes poor sealing.**

If a piston is so completely seized in the cylinder bore that it can not be removed with the special tool, *force the cylinder* out of the bore by positioning two screwdrivers in the piston dust boot retaining groove and prying outward. To prevent cocking, tap the end of the piston lightly around the circumference with a hammer, while the prying force is being applied. Be careful to avoid damaging the dust boot retainer in the caliper housing (Fig. 35). If this method of removal is used, the pistons must be replaced.

If the caliper dust boot retainer or retaining groove is damaged or scratched, pry the retainer out of the caliper housing with screwdrivers.

9. Remove the rubber piston seals from the grooves in the cylinder bores by carefully inserting the point of a small knife or other pointed instrument under the seal and raising the seal up far enough to be pulled out with the fingers.

CLEANING AND INSPECTION

Clean all metal parts with alcohol or a suitable solvent (Fig. 35). Use clean, dry compressed air to clean out and dry the grooves and passageways. Be sure that the caliper bore and component parts are completely free of any foreign material.

Check the cylinder bores and pistons for damage or excessive wear. Replace the piston if it is pitted, scored, or the chrome plating is worn

off. Check the caliper dust boot retainer for wear or damage.

ASSEMBLY

1. Clamp the caliper in a vise and secure it by the mounting flange on the inboard housing.

2. If a new caliper dust boot retainer is to be installed, thoroughly clean the contact area on the caliper housing and apply Loctite Sealant, Grade H to the retainer surface that seats in the housing. Install the retainer in the caliper housing.

3. Apply a film of clean brake fluid to **new** caliper piston seals and install them in the grooves of the cylinder bore. The seal should be positioned at one area in the groove and gently worked around. **Do not use the old seals.**

4. Coat the outside diameter of the pistons with brake fluid and install them in the cylinder bores so that the open end of the piston and the boot retaining groove face out of the bore. To avoid cocking, locate the piston squarely in the bore and apply a slow, steady pressure. If a piston will not easily go all the way into the bore, remove it and thoroughly inspect the cylinder bore, the

piston seal and the installation of the seal. If the piston still will not go in with bore in good condition and the piston seal properly installed, use the tool shown in Fig. 34. Rotate the piston with the tool while pushing it inward at the same time.

5. Carefully install four **new** dust boots on the caliper housings and pistons. Be sure that each boot is fully seated in the groove of its respective caliper housing and piston (Fig. 35). **Do not use the old dust boots.**

6. Install the external transfer tube.

7. Install the flexible brake hose to the caliper.

8. Install the caliper assembly on the spindle, and install the shoe and lining assemblies and the splash shield as outlined in Section 2.

9. Check the caliper for fluid leaks under maximum pedal pressures. **Do not move the car until a firm brake pedal is obtained.**

DISASSEMBLY OF BOOSTER—BENDIX TYPE

1. Remove the speed nuts that attach the mounting plate to the rear shell and remove the plate.

On a Mustang, remove the retaining nuts and lockwashers and remove the mounting brackets from the rear shell (Fig. 40.)

2. Pull the hydraulic push rod and front seal (Fig. 36) from the front shell.

3. Scribe an index mark across the front and rear shells.

4. Place the booster in a vise as shown in Fig. 37. Press downward on the rear shell and at the same time, turn it counterclockwise with a flat bar to release it from the front shell. Release the pressure on the rear shell slowly to prevent the dia-

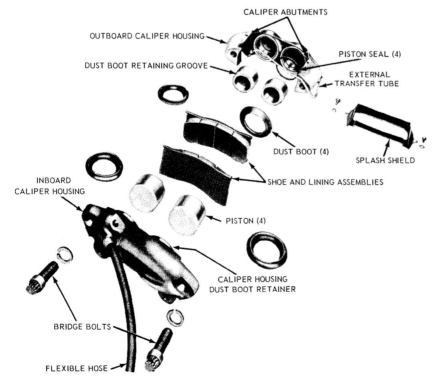

H1367-A

FIG. 35—Caliper Assembly—Disassembled

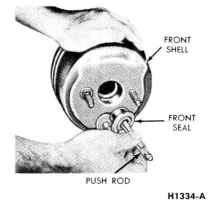

H1334-A

FIG. 36—Removing Front Seal and Push Rod—Bendix Booster

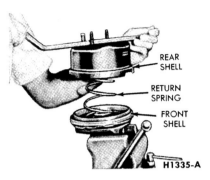

FIG. 37—Separating Booster Shells—Bendix Booster

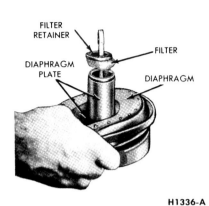

FIG. 38—Removing Diaphragm —Bendix Booster

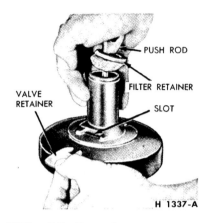

FIG. 39—Removing or Installing Valve Retainer—Bendix Booster

phragm plate return spring from flying out.

5. Separate the two shells and remove the return spring.

6. Withdraw the diaphragm plate and diaphragm from the rear shell. Remove the dust shield.

7. Remove the diaphragm from the diaphragm plate as shown in Fig. 38.

8. Pry the filter retainer off the diaphragm plate being careful not to chip or damage the plate.

9. Hold the diaphragm plate so that the valve retainer is facing downward. Press the valve push rod inward to release the tension on the retainer and allow it to drop out of the plate (Fig. 39).

10. Withdraw the valve and rod from the plate.

11. Press the reaction disc out of the diaphragm plate.

12. Drive the seal out of the rear

shell with a punch or screwdriver. (Fig. 40). Discard the seal.

13. Working from the inside of the front shell, cut the bead off the check valve grommet. Remove the check valve.

ASSEMBLY OF BOOSTER— BENDIX-TYPE

1. Place the rear shell on two

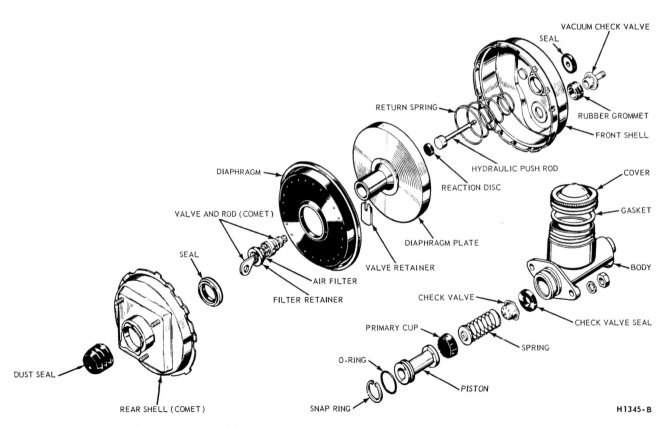

FIG. 40—Vacuum Booster Disassembled—Booster

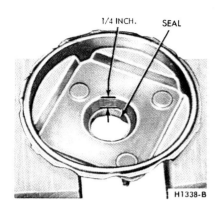

FIG. 41—Installing Rear Shell Seal—Bendix Booster

wood blocks as shown in Fig. 41. Press a new seal, plastic side first, into the recess on the inside of the shell to a depth of ¼ inch.

2. Dip a new check valve grommet (Fig. 40) in alcohol and install it in the front shell making sure that the beveled edge is toward the inside. Make sure that the grommet is seated. Dip the shoulder of the check valve in alcohol and install it in the grommet. Press the check valve into the grommet until the flange contacts the grommet.

3. Apply silicone grease to the outer surface of the diaphragm plate hub of the diaphragm plate. Push surfaces of the valve.

4. Insert the valve and rod into the hub of the diaphragm plate. Push the rod inward until the retaining groove is aligned with the slot, and then slide the retainer into the groove (Fig. 39).

5. Tuck the filter into place in the plate hub. Press the filter retainer onto the hub being careful not to chip or damage the plastic. (Fig. 38).

6. Install the diaphragm on the diaphragm plate, making sure that the diaphragm lip is tucked in all around the recess between the hub and the plate (Fig. 38).

7. Place the rear shell in a vise. Apply silicone lubricant generously to the top outer flange of the shell. Apply silicone grease to the seal in the rear shell.

8. Carefully guide the valve rod and diaphragm plate hub through the seal in the rear shell.

9. Center the large end of the return spring on the diaphragm plate.

10. Align the index mark on the front shell with the one on the rear shell. Place a flat bar on the front

shell and compress the spring until the tangs on the rear shell contact the notched sections of the front shell, and then rotate it clockwise to lock it in place.

11. Apply lubricant sparingly to the stem of the hydraulic push rod keeping it away from the adjusting screw area. Apply silicone grease liberally to the piston area of the push rod and to the reaction disc.

12. Center the reaction disc on the push rod piston. Guide the disc and push rod into the base of the diaphragm plate, and press the rod inward until the disc is bottomed (Fig. 42).

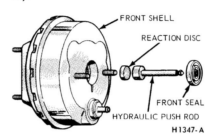

FIG. 42—Installing Reaction Disc, Push Rod and Front Seal—Bendix Booster

13. Press a new front seal into the front shell until it bottoms in the recess (Fig. 42).

14. Install a new dust seal over the push rod and onto the rear shell.

15. On a Comet, position the mounting plate on the rear shell and secure it in place with speed nuts.

On a Mustang, position the two mounting brackets on the rear shell studs, and install the retaining nuts and lock washers (Fig. 40).

DISASSEMBLY OF BOOSTER—MIDLAND-ROSS TYPE

REMOVAL OF EXTERNAL PARTS

1. Remove the two attaching nuts and lockwashers, and separate the master cylinder from the booster body.

2. Remove the air filter assembly from the booster body. Separate the cover and retainer, and remove the air filter (Fig. 49).

3. Remove the vacuum manifold and check valve assembly and the rubber grommet from the booster body (Fig. 49).

4. Disconnect the valve operating rod from the lever assembly by removing the retainer clip and connecting pin (Fig. 49).

5. Disconnect the lever assembly from the end plate brackets by removing the retainer clip and pivot pin.

6. Disconnect the push rod link from the lever assembly by removing the retainer and connecting pin.

7. Remove the attaching nuts, and disassemble the brackets from the end plate.

8. Remove the rubber boot from the valve operating rod.

SEPARATION OF MAJOR COMPONENTS

1. Scribe a line across the booster body, clamp band, and end plate.

2. Remove the clamp band screw and nut, and separate the clamp band, booster body, and end plate (Fig. 49).

3. Push the bellows assembly into the vacuum chamber (Fig. 43), and separate the bellows, control valve, diaphragm assembly, and end plate from the booster body.

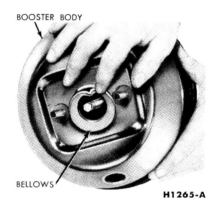

FIG. 43—Bellows to Booster Body Engagement—Midland-Ross

4. Push the valve, tail stock, and diaphragm assembly out of the end plate.

5. Remove the rear seal from the end plate (Fig. 44).

DISASSEMBLY OF BELLOWS, PUSH ROD AND VALVE ASSEMBLY FROM DIAPHRAGM

1. Remove the large bellows clamp and separate the bellows, bellows support rings, and bellows protector from the diaphragm and valve assembly (Fig. 45).

2. Remove the two support rings and the protector from the bellows.

3. Remove the push rod assembly and the reaction lever assembly from the control hub (Fig. 46).

FIG. 44—Removing or Installing Rear Seal to End Plate —Midland-Ross

FIG. 45—Removing or Installing the Bellows Assembly —Midland-Ross

4. Remove the two plastic guides from the push rod. Remove the reaction cone retainer and the cone from the push rod (Fig. 46).

5. Remove the valve operating rod from the plunger. To remove, hold the rod firmly and force the plunger off the rod breaking the plastic retainer. If the plunger is to be used again, remove all the broken pieces of the plastic retainer from the groove in the plunger.

6. Turn the control hub and plunger assembly clockwise to separate it from the diaphragm, and then remove the tail stock and O-ring from the diaphragm (Fig. 47).

7. Remove the retainer that holds the plunger to the control hub (Fig. 48). Separate the control hub and plunger assembly. **It may be necessary to file the burr from the pro-**

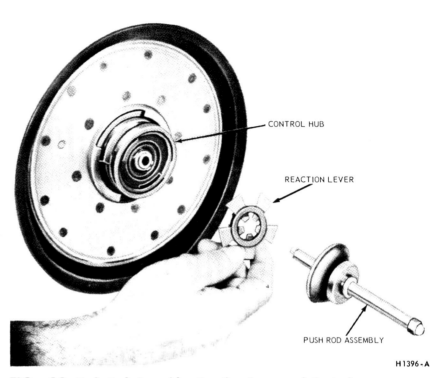

FIG. 46—Push Rod Assembly, Reaction Lever and Control Hub—Midland-Ross

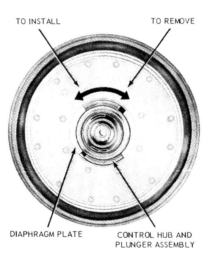

FIG. 47—Removing or Installing Control Hub and Plunger Assembly—Midland-Ross

truding end of the plunger before it can be separated from the control hub.

DISASSEMBLY OF CONTROL VALVE PLUNGER

1. Compress the spring towards the rubber valve and remove the spring retainer.

2. Remove the spring, valve plate,

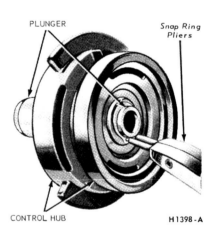

FIG. 48—Removing or Installing Plunger to Control Hub Retainer—Midland-Ross

rubber valve, O-ring, and fiber washer from the plunger (Fig. 49).

ASSEMBLY OF BOOSTER— MIDLAND-ROSS TYPE

CONTROL VALVE PLUNGER

1. Assemble the rubber valve, valve plate, spring, O-ring, and fiber washer on the plunger.

2. Compress the spring towards the rubber valve and assemble the spring retainer on the plunger with the flange towards the spring (Fig. 49).

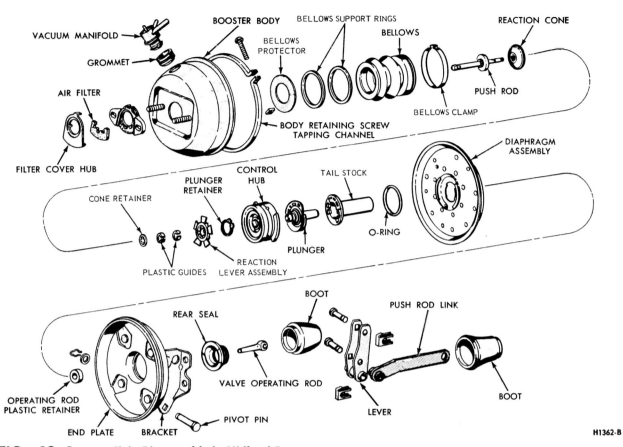

FIG. 49—Booster Unit Disassembled—Midland-Ross

ASSEMBLY OF VALVE ASSEMBLY, PUSH ROD, AND BELLOWS TO DIAPHRAGM

1. Assemble the control valve plunger assembly into the control hub so that the round holes in the rubber valve index with the raised projections on the hub, and the flat on the valve plate indexes with the flat projection on the hub (Fig. 50). Compress the valve spring, and install the retainer in the plunger groove to secure the control valve plunger to the control hub (Fig. 48).

2. Assemble the tail stock over the plunger with the flat on the tail stock indexing with the flat on the hub.

3. Assemble the O-ring over the tail stock and into the "V" groove formed by the tail stock and hub.

4. Assemble the tail stock and the plunger and control hub assembly to the diaphragm, and turn the hub counterclockwise to secure these parts together (Fig. 47).

5. Install the lever assembly in the control hub with the rubber protrusions toward the hub (Fig. 46).

6. Assemble the reaction cone, retainer, and two plastic push rod guides on the push rod. Install the push rod assembly in the valve hub so that the push rod indexes in the valve plunger.

7. Install the two bellows support rings and bellows protector on the bellows. The support rings are positioned in the two larger folds of the bellows and the protector in the smaller fold.

8. Assemble the bellows on the control hub so that the lip of the bellows indexes in the groove on the hub. Secure the bellows to the hub by assembling the large bellows clamp on the diaphragm end of bellows approximately $1/32$ inch from the end of the bellows (Fig. 45).

ASSEMBLY OF MAJOR COMPONENTS

1. Assemble the rear seal in the end plate (Fig. 44) and position the diaphragm, the control valve components, and the bellows as an assembly into the end plate.

2. Install the rubber grommet in the booster body with the large diameter side to be outside of the booster. Force the vacuum manifold and check valve assembly through the grommet (Fig. 49).

3. Assemble the booster body to the end plate. Make sure that the lip of the diaphragm is evenly positioned on the retaining radius of the end plate and the booster body. Pull the front lip of the bellows through the booster body and position it evenly around the hole in the booster body (Fig. 46).

4. Install the clamp band over the lips of the booster body and end plate. Align the scribe lines, compress the assembly together, and secure with the clamp and band bolt. Tap the clamp band with a fibre hammer around its circumference as the bolt is being tightened. Tighten to 15 inch-pounds of torque.

INSTALLATION OF EXTERNAL PARTS

1. Install the rubber boot to the valve operating rod and assemble the plastic retainer to the end of the rod. Insert the rod into the plunger so that the retainer engages the groove in the plunger. Install the lip of the boot in the groove of the rear seal (Fig. 49).

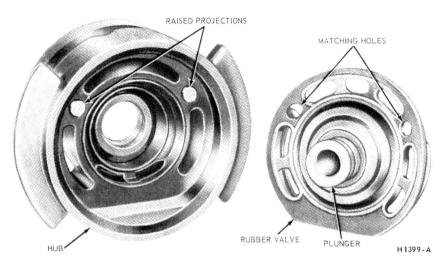

RAISED PROJECTIONS

MATCHING HOLES

HUB

RUBBER VALVE   PLUNGER

H1399-A

FIG. 50—Assembling Valve Plunger to Hub—Midland-Ross

2. Connect the valve operating rod to the upper end of the lever, and connect the push rod link to the center of the lever with the connecting pins and clips.

3. Position the mounting brackets to the end plate and install the retaining nuts.

4. Connect the lever assembly to the lower end of the mounting brackets with the pivot pin and clip.

5. Position the air filter in the plastic filter cover and then snap the cover and filter on the metal hub with the filter between.

6. Assemble the cover, filter, and hub assembly to the booster body with the metal hub against the booster body.

7. Assemble the master cylinder to the booster body. Torque the master cylinder mounting nuts to specification.

PART 2-3 SPECIFICATIONS

LINING DIMENSIONS—INCHES
FALCON

MODELS	POSITION	FRONT	REAR	COLOR CODE
Falcon Sedan & Hardtop—Six Cylinder	Primary Secondary	2.25 x 7.75 2.25 x 10.0	1.5 x 7.75 1.5 x 10.0	Red-Blue Green
Falcon Station Wagons—Six Cylinder	Primary Secondary	2.25 x 8.35 2.25 x 10.75	2.25 x 8.35 2.25 x 10.75	Silver Yellow-Black
Falcon Sedans—Eight Cylinder	Primary Secondary	2.25 x 8.35 2.25 x 10.75	1.75 x 8.35 1.75 x 10.75	Silver Yellow-White
Station Wagon—Eight Cylinder	Primary Secondary	2.50 x 8.35 2.50 x 10.75	2.00 x 8.35 2.00 x 10.75	Yellow-Black Black-Black

MUSTANG

MODELS	POSITION	FRONT	REAR	COLOR CODE
All Six Cylinder	Primary Secondary	2.25 x 7.75 2.25 x 10.0	1.5 x 7.75 1.5 x 10.0	Red-Blue Green
All Eight Cylinder	Primary Secondary	2.25 x 8.35 2.25 x 10.75	1.75 x 8.35 1.75 x 10.75	Silver Yellow-White
All Eight Cylinder	Disc	4.82 x 1.84	—	White

FAIRLANE AND COMET

MODELS	POSITION	FRONT	REAR	COLOR CODE
Fairlane & Comet 200 & 289 Passenger Cars	Primary Secondary	2.25 x 8.35 2.25 x 10.75	1.75 x 8.35 1.75 x 10.75	Silver Yellow-White
Fairlane & Comet LPO Police & 390 Passenger Cars Maximum Fade Resist.	Primary Secondary	2.50 x 8.35 2.50 x 10.75	2.00 x 8.35 2.00 x 10.75	Yellow-Black Black-Black
Fairlane & Comet LPO Taxi— Max. Wear Resist. (Bonded)	Primary Secondary	2.50 x 9.51 2.50 x 10.75	2.00 x 9.51 2.00 x 10.75	Red White
Station Wagons—Fairlane & Comet 200 & 289	Primary Secondary	2.50 x 8.35 2.50 x 10.75	2.00 x 8.35 2.00 x 10.75	Yellow-Black Black-Black
Station Wagon Fairlane & Comet 390	Primary Secondary	2.50 x 8.35 2.50 x 10.75	2.50 x 8.35 2.50 x 10.75	Yellow-Black Black-Black

CHECKS AND ADJUSTMENTS—INCHES
FALCON

Master Cylinder Bore Diameter Standard	1.000	Lining Maximum Wear Limit (From Top of Rivets)	0.031
Master Cylinder Maximum Allowable Hone	0.003	Lining Maximum Clearance to Shoe (Midway Between Rivets)	0.008
Front Wheel Cylinder Bore Diameter 9" Brake 10" Brake	 1.062 1.125		
Rear Wheel Cylinder Bore Diameter 9" Brake 10" Brake	 0.844 0.906	Pedal Travel—Standard Pedal Travel—Power Push Rod Adjustment—Power Brakes— Bendix—Midland-Ross	6.50 4.50 0.980-0.995 0.995-1.005
Wheel Cylinder Maximum Allowable Hone①	0.003	Hydraulic Line Diameter	0.188
Drum Diameter 9" Brake 10" Brake	 9.0 10.0	Parking Brake—Type Foot Operated with Pedal Mounted Below	
Drum Maximum Allowable Run-Out	0.007	Left Side of the Instrument Panel	
Drum Maximum Boring Diameter 9" Brake 10" Brake	 9.060 10.060		

①Front Wheel Brake Cylinders on Cars with 9" Brakes cannot be Honed

CHECKS AND ADJUSTMENTS—INCHES (Continued)

MUSTANG

Master Cylinder Bore Diameter
    Standard
    Power
	1.000
	0.875
		Lining Maximum Wear Limit
		(From Top of Rivets)
			0.031

Master Cylinder Maximum Allowable Hone	0.003	Lining Maximum Clearance to Shoe (Midway Between Rivets)	0.008

Front Wheel Cylinder Bore Diameter
    6 Cylinder Engine
    8 Cylinder Engine
	1.062
	1.125
		Pedal Ratio
		Pedal Travel—Standard
			6.3:1
			6.50

Rear Wheel Cylinder Bore Diameter
    6 Cylinder Engine
    8 Cylinder Engine
	0.844
	0.906
		Pedal Travel—Power
		Push Rod Adjustment—Power Brakes
		    Bendix
		    Midland-Ross
			3.54
			
			0.980-0.995
			0.995-1.005

Wheel Cylinder Maximum Allowable Hone①	0.003		

Drum Diameter:
    6 Cylinder Engine
    8 Cylinder Engine
	9.0
	10.0
		Hydraulic Line Diameter	0.188

Drum Maximum Allowable Run-Out	0.007	Parking Brake-Type
		    Hand Operated with Handle Mounted on Lower
		    Left Side of the Instrument Panel	

Drum Maximum Boring Diameter
    6 Cylinder Engine
    8 Cylinder Engine
	9.060
	10.060		

FRONT WHEEL DISC BRAKE (RPO—8 CYLINDER ENGINE)			
Master Cylinder Bore Diameter	0.938	Lining Thickness:	0.400 Nominal
Master Cylinder Maximum Allowable Hone	0.003		
Caliper Cylinder Bore Diameter	1.636	Lining Maximum Wear Limit (From Surface of Shoe)	0.030

Rotor Diameter:
    Outside
    Inside
	11.375
	7.375
		Lining to Rotor Clearance
		(Brakes Released)
			0.002-0.010

Rotor Thickness	0.810	Pedal Travel (Non Power)	6.50
Rotor Maximum Allowable Runout	0.002	Pedal Ratio	5.57:1
Lining Area	34.00 sq. in.		

①Front Wheel Brake Cylinders on 6 Cyl. Cars cannot be Honed

FAIRLANE AND COMET

Master Cylinder Bore Diameter	1.000	Lining Maximum Wear Limit (From Top of Rivets or Shoe Rim)	0.031
Master Cylinder Maximum Allowable Hone	0.003		

Front Wheel Cylinder Bore Diameter
    Passenger—200 & 289
    Station Wagon and 390 Car
	1.125
	1.094
		Lining Maximum Clearance to Shoe
		(Midway Between Rivets)
			0.008

Rear Wheel Cylinder Bore Diameter 390 Car
    Passenger—200 & 289
    Station Wagon—dll
	0.875
	0.906
	0.938
		Pedal Travel—Standard
		Pedal Travel—Power
			6.5
			4.5

LPO Maximum Fade & Maximum Wear Resistant
    Wheel Cylinders (200 & 289)
		Push Rod Adjustment—Power Brakes
		    Bendix
		    Midland-Ross
			0.980-0.995
			0.995-1.005

Front Wheel Cylinder Bore Diameter	1.094		
Rear Wheel Cylinder Bore Diameter	0.875	Hydraulic Line Diameter	0.188
Drum Diameter	10.0		

Drum Maximum Allowable Run-Out	0.007	Parking Brake—Type
		    Foot Operated With Pedal Mounted Below Left
		    Side of the Instrument Panel	

Drum Maximum Boring Diameter	10.060		

Drum Width—Front
    Passenger
    Station Wagon—Maximum Fade and Wear
    Resistant & 390 car
	2.25
	
	2.50		

Drum Width—Rear
    Passenger
    Station Wagon
    Maximum Fade & Maximum Wear Resistant
	1.75
	2.50
	2.00		

TORQUE LIMITS—BRAKES

Description	Falcon ft-lbs	Mustang ft-lbs	Comet and Fairlane ft-lbs
Brake Cylinder to Brake Carrier Plate Bolt	5-7	5-7	10-20
Parking Brake Control Assembly to Instrument Panel Bolt	15-20	8-12	15-20
Master Cylinder to Dash Panel Bolt	20-34	18-25	20-34
Tube Connector to Master Cylinder	6-12	6-12	6-12
Master Cylinder Cover	Finger Tight	Finger Tight	Finger Tight
Parking Brake Control Assembly to Dash Panel Bolt	15-20	8-12	15-20
Brake Hose Bolt	10-15	10-15	10-15
Brake Pedal Support Bracket to Dash Panel Bolt	20-34	20-34	20-34
Brake Pedal Support Bracket to Instrument Panel Nut	9-13	9-13	9-13
FRONT DRUM BRAKES ONLY	5 Lug—75-110	5 Lug—6 Cyl.	75-110
Wheel Assembly to Wheel Hub and Drum Assembly Nut	4 Lug—55-85	4 Lug—8 Cyl.	
Wheel, Hub and Drum Assembly to Wheel Spindle Nut①	17-25	17-25	17-25
Carrier Plate to Spindle Nut	25-45	25-45	25-45
REAR BRAKES ONLY	8 Cyl.—30-40	8 Cyl.—30-40	
Axle Housing to Carrier Plate Lock Nut	6 Cyl.—25-35	6 Cyl.—25-35	30-40
Drum to Axle Shaft Assembly Speednut	Hand Push Fit	Hand Push Fit	Hand Push Fit
Wheel Assembly to Axle Shaft to Drum Assembly Nut	4 Lug—55-85 5 Lug—75-110	4 Lug—55-85 5 Lug—75-110	75-110
Brake Line Connection to Axle Housing Bolt	12-18	12-18	
Bleeder Screw to Wheel Cylinder	50 in-lbs Max.	50 in-lbs Max.	55 in-lbs Max.
POWER BRAKES			
Vacuum Manifold to Booster Body Mounting Bolt	8-10		
Master Cylinder to Booster Body	10-13		
Brake Booster to Dash Panel	12-15		
Push Rod to Brake Pedal Bolt	10-15		

①.0005 to .0065 Bearing end play at assembly.

TORQUE LIMITS—DISC BRAKES

Description	ft-lbs
Caliper Assembly to Mounting Bracket	45-60
Mounting Bracket to Spindle	35-45
Caliper Bleeder Screw	10 (120 in-lbs maximum)— Must be leak proof
Caliper Splash Shield	7-9
Caliper Bridge Bolts	65-75
Rotor Splash Shield to Spindle	10-20
Hub and Rotor Assembly to Front Wheel Spindle	17-25—Rotate rotor while torquing.①
Wheel Assembly to Front Wheel Hub and Rotor Assembly	75-110 ft-lbs
Brake Tube Fitting Nuts to Propor- tioning Valve	70 in-lbs—maximum— Must be leak proof

①.0005" to .0065" maximum bearing end play with torque specification of 17-25 ft./lbs.

SUSPENSION, STEERING, WHEELS & TIRES

GROUP 3

PART 3-1   **PAGE**
SUSPENSION, STEERING, WHEELS
    AND TIRES GENERAL SERVICE 3-1

PART 3-2
SUSPENSION 3-11

PART 3-3
MANUAL STEERING 3-22

PART 3-4   **PAGE**
POWER STEERING 3-34

PART 3-5
WHEELS AND TIRES 3-44

PART 3-6
SPECIFICATIONS 3-49

PART 3-1   SUSPENSION, STEERING, WHEELS AND TIRES GENERAL SERVICE

Section   **Page**
1 Diagnosis and Testing 3-1
    Manual Steering 3-1
    Power Steering 3-1
    Front Wheel Alignment Checks 3-4
        Equipment Installation 3-4
        Caster 3-6
        Camber 3-6
        Toe-In 3-6
        Front Wheel Turning Angle 3-6
2 Common Adjustments and Repairs 3-6
    Caster and Camber Adjustments 3-6
        Mustang 3-6
        Comet, Falcon, and Fairlane 3-7
    Toe-In and Steering Wheel Alignment
        Adjustments 3-7

Section   **Page**
    Steering Gear Lubricant Checking
        Procedure 3-8
        Mustang 3-8
        Comet, Falcon, and Fairlane 3-8
3 Cleaning and Inspection 3-9
    Steering Gear Cleaning and Inspection 3-9
    Flushing the Power Steering System 3-9
    Front End General Inspection 3-9
    Wheel Inspection 3-9
    Upper Ball Joint Inspection 3-10
    Lower Ball Joint Inspection 3-10
    Shock Absorbers 3-10

1 DIAGNOSIS AND TESTING

MANUAL STEERING

Table 1 lists various steering gear and linkage trouble symptoms and possible causes. Several of these symptoms are also common to suspension frame, and wheel and tire troubles. For this reason, be sure that the cause of the trouble is in the steering gear or linkage before adjusting, repairing, or replacing any of the steering parts.

POWER STEERING

PRELIMINARY TESTS

The following preliminary checks should always be made before performing any trouble-shooting operations.

Check Pump Belt

If the pump belt is broken, glazed, or worn, replace with a new belt. **Use only the specified type of belt.**

Check The Belt Tension

If the belt is too loose or too tight, it should be adjusted to the proper tension as outlined in Part 3-4. **A "used belt" is one that has run 15 minutes or longer.**

Check Fluid Level

Start the engine, turn the steering wheel all the way to the left and right several times, and shut off the engine.

Check the fluid level in the reservoir. If the level is low, add enough fluid to raise the level to the base of the filler neck. **Do not overfill the reservoir.**

Check For Fluid Leaks

1. If the power steering fluid does not already include yellowish green dye, pre-mix one teaspoonful of oil-soluble aniline dye with 2 pints of automatic transmission fluid CIAZ-19582-A. Then refill the reservoir with the dye solution.

2. With the engine running at idle speed, turn the steering wheel all the way to the right stop and to the left stop several times to distribute the dye solution throughout the hydraulic system. Do not hold the wheel against each wheel stop for more than 3 to 5 seconds.

3. Shut off the engine, and check for leaks.

Fitting and Tube Seat Leak. Since most fluid leaks occur at the fittings and connections in a power steering hydraulic system, these parts should be checked before any other part is replaced.

1. With the engine running at idle speed, raise the car on a hoist.

2. Clean the outside of the control valve and the power cylinder, the bottom surfaces of the pump, and all lines and fittings. Dirt, oil, and grease should be removed from all areas where leaks may exist.

3. Tighten all fittings, using a special 5-flat tube wrench. **Do not tighten the fitting with a standard open end wrench.** If a properly tightened fitting leaks, replace the seat.

Pump, Control Valve, and Power Cylinder Leak. If the fittings and connections do not leak, check the other parts of the system.

Check the hose connection at the pump for leaks, and tighten the hose clamp if necessary.

Pump Leaks. If leakage occurs at the pump reservoir seal, pump outlet valve seals, or the support stud seal, check the torque of the outlet valve nut and the support stud nut. If torque is within specifications, replace the reservoir seal, outlet valve seals, or the support stud seal, whichever is required if leaks are evident other than the lines.

Control Valve Leaks. If the control valve is leaking (somewhere other than the tube seats), replace all the seals, using a control valve seal kit. Use all the parts in the kit, and be sure they are correctly installed. When assembling the new seals in the valve, an application of silicone grease to the internal parts will help to provide a better seal against future leakage. Apply grease to the centering spring area, especially on the cap and spacer mating surfaces. Coat the threads of the cap retaining bolts with grease. The rubber boot seals, the actuator assembly, and the metal cup seals in the control valve should also be coated with silicone grease.

Some oil remaining from the manufacturing processes may be found in the sleeve near the ball stud. Do not confuse this oil with leaking fluid from the hydraulic system.

Power Cylinder Leaks. The power cylinder may leak at the piston rod

seals. A power cylinder seal kit should be used to correct leakage. **Do not replace the power cylinder assembly unless the piston rod is scored or has a dull gray finish instead of a high luster chrome finish.**

Check Turning Effort

With the front wheels properly aligned and tire pressures correct, check the effort required to turn the steering wheel.

1. With the car on dry concrete, set the parking brakes.

2. With the engine warmed up and running at idle speed, turn the steering wheel to the left and right several times to warm the fluid.

3. Attach a torque wrench to the steering wheel hub. (Fig. 1). Check

Torque Wrench (In. Lb.) G 1270-B

FIG. 1—Checking Turning Effort—Typical

the effort required to turn the wheel at least one complete revolution in both directions. See Part 3-6 for the specified torque which should be approximately equal in both directions.

Pump-Fluid Pressure Test

A fluid pressure test will show whether the pump or some other unit in the power steering system is causing trouble in the system. Steps outlined below should be followed to determine the cause of the trouble.

1. Measure the pump belt tension. **When adjusting the belt tension on the power steering pump, do not pry against the pump to obtain the proper belt load.**

A half-inch cast boss has been incorporated on the front face of the pump cover plate onto which a $9/16$ inch open end wrench can be fitted to pry the pump and obtain the proper belt tension.

2. Disconnect the pressure line hose from the pump outlet, and install a 0-2000 psi pressure gauge and shut off valve between the end of the hose and the pump outlet (Fig. 2). **Be sure that the pressure gauge is between the pump and the shut off valve, all connections are tight, and the shut off valve is fully open.**

3. Connect a tachometer.

4. Start the engine and operate it at idle speed for at least two minutes to warm up the fluid.

5. Cycle the steering wheel from stop-to-stop several times to expel any

SHUT-OFF VALVE *Tool - T 56 L - 33610 - D*   PUMP OUTLET   PRESSURE LINE

G 1271 - A

FIG. 2—Pressure Testing Tool Installed—Typical

air from the system; stop the engine. Remove the reservoir filler cap and check the fluid level in the reservoir. If necessary, add lubricant CIAZ-19582-A to the proper level.

6. With the engine running at **approximately** 500 rpm and no steering effort applied, and the lubricant at normal operating temperature, the pressure gauge should show a pressure of less than **50** psi. If the pressure is higher, inspect the hoses for kinks and obstructions.

7. Increase the engine speed to 1000 rpm; then, slowly close the gauge shut-off valve. With the valve fully closed, the pump pressure should be 750 to 900 psi.

Do not close the valve for more than a few seconds (maximum 5 seconds), as this would abnormally increase the lubricant (fluid) temperature and cause undue pump and/or steering gear wear. Engine rpm should not exceed fast idle during this test.

If pressure is more or less than specification, replace the pump assembly. If pressure is as specified and steering efforts are heavy, the gear and/or control valve could be at fault.

STEERING TROUBLE DIAGNOSIS GUIDE

BINDING OR POOR RECOVERY	If the steering wheel binds or sticks when turned, or if poor recovery to the straight-ahead position occurs, check the Pitman arm ball stud in the control valve sleeve. If the ball stud is rubbing against the edge of the sleeve slot, the roll pin may be missing. If either of the idler arm bushings are worn or damaged, replace both bushings. Check the steering gear adjustment (Section 2). Check the operation of the control valve spool in the valve housing. If the spool is binding in the housing,	check the spool adjustment. If the adjustment is correct, overhaul or replace the control valve. Check the control valve travel regulator stop adjustment. If the stop is drawn up too tightly, the ball stud will bind in the seats. Adjust the stop as required. Check the control valve sleeve and the socket tube for damage. Replace parts that show signs of damage, and adjust the travel regulator stop. Check for possible interference between the steering wheel and the steering column.
HARD STEERING	If the effort required to turn the steering wheel is greater than normal for the entire travel of the front wheels, check the tire pressure then, test the fluid pressure. Be sure that there are no leaks, that the reservoir is properly filled, and that the belt is properly adjusted. If the pump output pressure is low, the pump may be defective and should be replaced. If the pressure test shows that the trouble is in the control valve or power cylinder, remove and inspect these units. Repair or replace any damaged parts. If the pressure test indicates that the pressures throughout the system are within specifications, check the following items in the order given: Check the control valve spool cen-	tering spring adjustment. Adjust if required (Section 2). Check the control valve spool for movement. If the spool does not move freely, check for, and eliminate, interference between the socket tube and the valve sleeve. If the spool is sticking in the housing, remove the spool and check the spool lands for burrs. Small burrs may be removed with crocus cloth if the edges of the valve lands are not rounded in the process. If the spool cannot be repaired, replace the control valve. Check the control valve ball stud for free movement in the ball stud seats. If the stud is binding in the seats, adjust the travel regulator stop. If the hard steering still persists, check the front end alignment.
EXCESSIVE FREE PLAY	If excessive free play or lost motion is noticed when steering, check the steering gear preload and mesh adjustment. Check for excessive clearance between the steering arm ball stud and the ball stud seats. If the ball stud is loose in the seats, adjust the control	valve travel regulator stop. Check the control valve centering spring adjustment. If the spring adjustment nut is loose, tighten the nut until it is snug, and then back off the nut not more than ¼ turn. **Excessive tightening may damage the stop pin.**

CONTINUED ON NEXT PAGE

STEERING TROUBLE DIAGNOSIS GUIDE (Continued)

NOISE	Check the pump belt tension. A loose or glazed belt can cause belt squeal. A glazed belt, even when properly adjusted, may slip. Excessive torque at the pressure line joints may distort the tube seats	and cause noise. Noise may result if the specified hose is not used or if it is improperly routed. If noise still exists with the specified hose properly installed and routed, the pump should be replaced.
STEERING CHATTER	A loose pump belt or air in the fluid can cause chatter against the wheel stops during an extremely sharp turn. Check the belt tension, and adjust it to specifications or fill the reservoir if necessary. Check for looseness in the idler arm rod connection. Looseness at this point may be due to worn mounting	bushings or improper mounting nut torque. Replace the bushings if worn. Torque the nut to specification. Check the power cylinder piston rod insulators for looseness. If the insulators are worn, replace them. If the mounting nut is loose, torque it to specification, and torque the locknut to specification.
RATTLES	Check the control valve spool centering spring adjustment. If the adjustment is loose, tighten the nut until snug, and then back off the nut not more than ¼ turn. **Excessive tighten-**	**ing may damage the stop pin.** Check for looseness between the control valve ball stud and the ball stud seats. If the stud is loose in the seats, adjust the travel regulator stop.
LOSS OF POWER ASSIST	Check the entire system for damage, replacing parts as necessary. Tighten a loose pump belt. Test the fluid pressure to determine whether the trouble is in the pump, the control valve, or the power cylinder. If the pressure test indicates that the pump is at fault, replace the pump. If the pressure test indicates that the control valve or power cylinder is at fault, check as follows: Disconnect the power cylinder piston rod from the idler arm bracket. Operate the piston by hand to check	for resistance to movement. If the piston moves easily with little or no resistance, the internal parts of the power cylinder are broken or damaged. Replace the power cylinder if broken or damaged. Maladjustment of the control valve spool centering spring can cause a loss of either right or left power assist. Check the adjustment, and readjust if necessary. Replace all defective parts. Check the operation of the control valve check valve. If the check valve does not operate freely, replace the check valve assembly.

FRONT WHEEL ALIGNMENT CHECKS

Do not attempt to check and adjust front wheel alignment without first making a preliminary inspection of the front-end parts.

Check all the factors of front wheel alignment except the turning angle before making any adjustments. The turning angle should be checked only after caster, camber, and toe-in have been adjusted to specification.

The front wheel alignment specifications, given in Part 3-6 are correct only when the car is at "Curb Height." Before checking or adjusting the alignment factors, the suspension alignment spacers (Tool T65P-3000-B or C) must be installed to obtain the curb heights.

EQUIPMENT INSTALLATION

Equipment used for front wheel alignment inspection must be accurate. Alignment height spacers (Figs. 3 and 4) are used to check caster, camber. The spacers should be omitted when checking toe-in.

1. Drive the car in a straight line far enough to establish the straight-ahead position of the front wheels, and mark the steering wheel hub and the steering column collar (Fig. 5). **Do not adjust the steering wheel spoke position at this time.** If the front wheels are turned at any time during the inspection, align the marks to bring the wheels back to the straight-ahead position.

2. With the car in position for the front end alignment inspection and

adjustment, install the alignment spacers as follows to establish the curb height.

Insert the pin in the spacer hole marked for the model being checked (Mustang rear does not use the pin). Raise the front of the car and position the alignment spacers between the suspension upper arm and the spring tower as shown in Fig. 3. The lower end of the spacer should be placed over the head of the ball joint front outside attaching rivet. Position the alignment spacers for the rear of the car between the rear axle and the side rail as shown in (Fig. 4).

3. Install the wheel alignment equipment on the car. Whichever type of equipment is used, follow the installation and inspection instruc-

TABLE 1—Trouble Symptoms and Possible Causes

POSSIBLE CAUSES OF TROUBLE

SYMPTOMS	Jerky Steering	Loose Steering	Hard Steering and/or Loss of Power Assist	Hard Turning When Stationary	Steering and Suspension Noises	Shimmy or Wheel Tramp	Pull to One Side	Side-to-Side Wander	Body Sway or Roll	Tire Squeal on Turns	Binding or Poor Recovery	Abnormal or Irregular Tire Wear	Sag at One Wheel	Hard or Rough Ride	Rear Suspension Misalignment (Dog-Tracking)
1. Incorrect Tire Pressure			X	X		X	X	X	X	X	X	X	X	X	
2. Tire Sizes Not Uniform			X	X			X	X		X		X	X		
3. Overloaded or Unevenly Loaded Vehicle							X	X				X	X	X	
4. Power Steering Fluid Level Low-Leak	X		X	X	X										
5. Sagging or Broken Spring						X	X	X	X			X	X	X	
6. Glazed, Loose or Broken Power Steering Pump Belt	X		X	X	X										
7. Rear Spring Tie Bolt Off Center							X					X			X
8. Broken Rear Spring Tie Bolts					X	X	X	X	X			X			X
9. Rear Spring Front Hanger Mislocated							X					X			X
10. Bent Spindle Arm							X	X		X		X			
11. Bent Spindle							X	X		X		X			
12. Lack of Lubrication			X	X	X						X			X	
13. Air in Power Steering System	X		X		X	X									
14. Obstruction in Power Steering Lines			X	X	X										
15. Loose or Weak Shock Absorber					X	X		X	X			X		X	
16. Loose or Worn Suspension Arm Bushings					X	X						X		X	
17. Binding Front Suspension Ball Joints or Steering Linkage	X		X	X	X						X			X	
18. Loose, Worn, or Damaged Steering Linkage or Connections	X	X				X	X		X		X	X			
19. Loose Steering Gear Mountings	X	X				X	X		X						
20. Insufficient Steering Pump Pressure			X	X							X				
21. Incorrect Steering Gear Adjustment	X	X	X	X	X	X		X	X		X	X			
22. Incorrect Brake Adjustment	X					X			X		X	X			
23. Incorrect Front Wheel Bearing Adjustment	X	X				X	X	X				X			
24. Wheel Out of Balance	X					X						X		X	
25. Incorrect Front Wheel Alignment			X			X	X	X	X		X	X			
26. Out-of-Round Wheel or Brake Drum						X						X		X	
27. Frame or Underbody Out of Alignment							X					X			X
28. Bent Rear Axle Housing					X		X					X			X
29. Excessive Wear of Steering Pump Internal Parts			X	X											
30. Steering Gear Valve Spool Binding or out of Adjustment			X	X			X				X				
31. Obstruction Within Steering Gear	X		X	X							X				

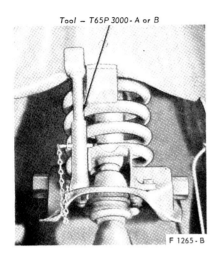

Tool — T65P 3000 - A or B

FIG. 3—Typical Front Alignment Spacer Installation

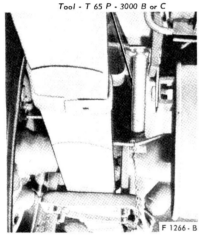

Tool - T 65 P - 3000 B or C

FIG. 4—Typical Rear Alignment Spacer Installation

tions provided by the equipment manufacturer.

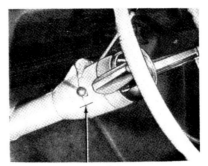

ALIGNMENT MARKS　　　F1267-B

FIG. 5—Straight Ahead Position Marks—Typical

CASTER

Check the caster angle at each front wheel.

Caster is the forward or rearward tilt of the top of the wheel spindle (Fig. 6). If the spindle tilts to the rear, caster is positive. If the spindle tilts to the front, caster is negative. The correct caster angle, or tilt, is specified in Part 3-6. The maximum difference between both front wheel caster angles should not exceed $\frac{1}{2}°$. However, a difference of not more than $\frac{1}{4}°$ is preferred.

CAMBER

Check the camber angle at each front wheel.

Camber is the amount the front wheels are tilted at the top (Fig. 6). If a wheel tilts outward, camber is positive. If a wheel tilts inward, camber is negative. The correct camber angle, or outward (positive) tilt, is specified in Part 3-6. The maximum difference between both front wheel camber angles should not exceed $\frac{1}{2}°$. However, a difference of not more than $\frac{1}{4}°$ is preferred.

TOE-IN

Alignment height spacers are not

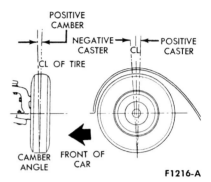

FIG. 6—Caster and Camber Angles

used to check and adjust toe-in. Toe-in should only be checked and adjusted after the caster and camber has been adjusted to specification.

Check the toe-in with the front wheels in the straight-ahead position. **Run the engine so that the power steering control valve will be in the center (neutral) position (if so equipped).** Measure the distance between the extreme front and also between the extreme rear of both front wheels. The difference between these two distances is the toe-in.

Correct toe-in, or inward pointing of both front wheels at the front, is specified in Part 3-6.

FRONT WHEEL TURNING ANGLE

When the inside wheel is turned 20°, the turning angle of the outside wheel should be as specified in Part 3-6. The turning angle cannot be adjusted directly, because it is a result of the combination of caster, camber, and toe-in adjustments and should, therefore, be measured only after these adjustments have been made. If the turning angle does not measure to specifications, check the spindle or other suspension parts for a bent condition.

2 COMMON ADJUSTMENTS AND REPAIRS

After front wheel alignment factors have been checked, make the necessary adjustments. **Do not attempt to adjust the front wheel alignment by bending the suspension or steering parts.**

CASTER AND CAMBER ADJUSTMENTS

MUSTANG

Be sure **all** the equipment listed in

Equipment Installation is installed before adjusting the caster and camber.

Caster and camber can be adjusted by removing or installing shims between the inner shaft of the front suspension upper arm and the underbody (Fig. 7).

Both caster and camber adjustment can be made at the same time by loosening the nuts on the two bolts that fasten the inner shaft to the underbody. After the required shims

have been removed or installed, torque the nuts to specification. Caster and camber adjusting shims are available in $\frac{1}{32}$-inch and $\frac{1}{8}$-inch thickness.

The $\frac{1}{32}$ inch shims should be placed against the fender housing sheet metal or between the $\frac{1}{8}$ inch shims.

CASTER

To adjust caster, remove or install

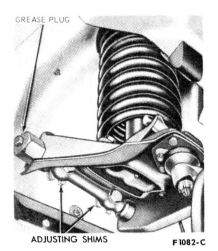

FIG. 7—Caster and Camber
Adjustments—Mustang

shims at either the front bolt or the
rear bolt (Fig. 7).

The removal of shims at the front
bolt or the installation of shims at the
rear bolt will cause the upper ball
joint to move forward. The removal
of shims at the rear bolt or the installation of shims at the front bolt will
cause the ball joint to move rearward.
A $1/32$-inch change of shim thickness
at either bolt will change the caster
angle approximately $1/2°$. The difference between the shim stack thickness at the two bolts should not exceed $1/16$ inch (Fig. 7).

CAMBER

To adjust camber, remove or install equal shim thickness at both
bolts (Fig. 7).

The removal of equal shims at both
bolts will move the upper ball joint
inward. The installation of equal
shims at both bolts will move the ball
joint outward. A $1/16$-inch change of
shim thickness at both bolts will
change the camber angle $1/3°$. The
total shim stack thickness at each
bolt should not exceed $9/16$-inch (Fig.
7).

COMET, FALCON, AND
FAIRLANE

Caster is controlled by the front
suspension strut (Fig. 8). To obtain
positive caster, loosen the strut front
nut and tighten the strut rear nut
against the bushing. To obtain negative caster, loosen the strut rear nut
and tighten the strut front nut against
the bushing.

Camber is controlled by the eccentric cam located at the lower arm
attachment to the side rail (Fig. 8).

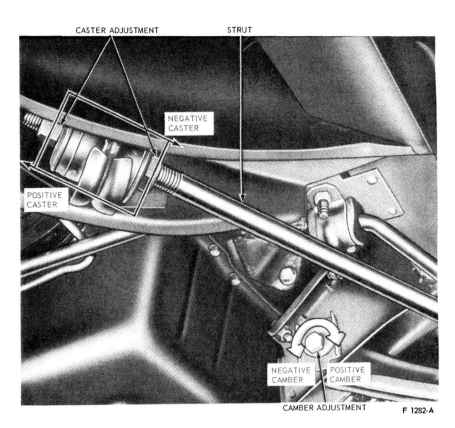

FIG. 8—Caster and Camber Adjustments—Comet, Falcon, and
Fairlane

To adjust the camber, loosen the eccentric bolt nut and rotate the bolt
and eccentric clockwise from the high
position to increase camber or counterclockwise to decrease camber.

After the caster and camber has
been adjusted to specification, torque
the lower arm eccentric bolt nut and
the strut front nut to specification.

TOE-IN AND STEERING WHEEL
ALIGNMENT ADJUSTMENTS

Check the steering wheel spoke position when the front wheels are in
the straight-ahead position. If the
spokes are not in their normal position, they can be properly adjusted
while toe-in is being adjusted.

1. Loosen the two clamp bolts on
each spindle connecting rod sleeve
(Fig. 9).

2. Adjust toe-in. If the steering
wheel spokes are in their normal position, lengthen or shorten both rods
equally to obtain correct toe-in (Fig.
10). If the steering wheel spokes are
not in their normal position, make the
necessary rod adjustments to obtain
correct toe-in and steering wheel

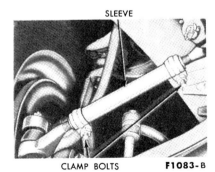

FIG. 9—Spindle Connecting
Rod Sleeve—Typical

spoke alignment (Figs. 11 and 12).

3. Recheck toe-in and steering
wheel spoke alignment. If toe-in is
correct and the steering wheel spokes
are still not in their normal position,
turn both connecting rod sleeves upward or downward the same number
of turns to move the steering wheel
spokes (Fig. 11 and 12).

4. When toe-in and steering wheel
spoke alignment are both correct,
torque the clamp bolts on both connecting rod sleeves to specification.

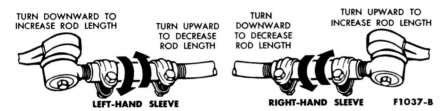

FIG. 10—Spindle Connecting Rod Adjustment

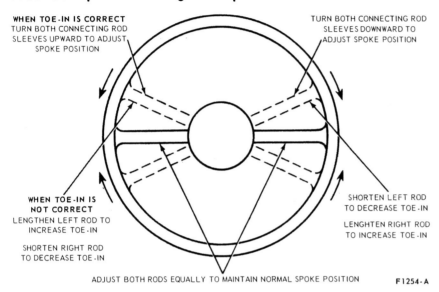

FIG. 11—Toe-In and Steering Wheel Spoke Adjustments—Comet, Falcon, and Fairlane

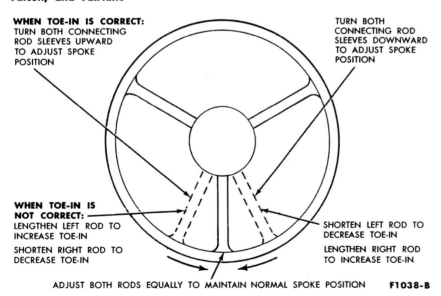

FIG. 12—Toe-In and Steering Wheel Spoke Adjustments—Mustang

The sleeve position should be as shown in Fig. 13 when the clamp bolts are tightened.

STEERING GEAR LUBRICANT CHECKING PROCEDURE

MUSTANG

1. Center the steering wheel.
2. Remove the steering gear housing filler plug.
3. Remove the **upper** cover-to-housing attaching bolt.
4. With a **clean** punch or like instrument, clean out or push inward the loose lubricant in the filler plug hole and cover to housing attaching bolt hole.
5. Slowly turn the steering wheel to the **right** stop, lubricant should rise within the **upper** cover bolt hole; then slowly turn the steering wheel to the **left** stop, lubricant should rise within the filler plug hole. If lubricant does not rise in both the cover bolt hole and the filler plug hole, add lubricant until it comes out both holes during this check.
6. Install the upper cover-to-housing attaching bolt.

COMET, FALCON, AND FAIRLANE

1. Center the steering wheel.
2. Remove the steering gear housing filler plug.
3. Remove the lower cover-to-housing attaching bolt.
4. With a **clean** punch or like instrument, clean out or push inward the loose lubricant in the filler plug hole and cover to housing attaching bolt hole.
5. Slowly turn the steering wheel to the **left** stop, lubricant should rise within the lower cover bolt hole; then slowly turn the steering wheel to the **right** stop, lubricant should rise within the filler plug hole. If lubricant does not rise in both the cover bolt hole and the filler plug hole, add lubricant until it comes out both holes during this check.
6. Install the lower cover-to-housing attaching bolt and the filler plug.

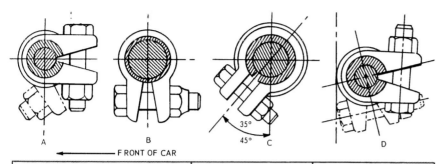

CAR	MANUAL STEERING		POWER STEERING	
	Right Side	Left Side	Right Side	Left Side
COMET – FALCON – FAIRLANE	D	A	D	A
MUSTANG	B	B	B	C

G 1379- A

FIG. 13—Spindle Connecting Rod Sleeve Clamp Position

3 CLEANING AND INSPECTION

STEERING GEAR CLEANING AND INSPECTION

Wash all parts in a cleaning solvent and dry with a lint-free cloth. **The bearing should not be spun dry with compressed air.** Inspect the shaft and worm for scoring, cracks or checks, and for straightness of the shaft. Check the splines and the threads on the sector shaft for wear and burrs. Inspect the gear teeth for scoring, pitting and other wear. Inspect the ball bearings for free movement, and the cups for wear or irregular surfaces. Check the housing for cracks and the sector shaft needle bearing for free movement or other wear.

Check the power steering pump pressures. If the pump pressures are not to specification and there are no external fluid leaks, replace the pump. If the pump has a visible leak, replace the reservoir seal, outlet valve seals, or support stud seal, whichever is required.

FLUSHING THE POWER STEERING SYSTEM

Should a power steering pump become inoperative, the shaft and pulley should be checked for freedom of rotation. If the pump shaft does not turn freely (binding), it is an indication that there is wear on the pump internal components and the need for flushing the steering system, when installing a **new** pump.

1. Remove the power steering pump and pulley as outlined in Part 3-4.

2. Install a new pump and connect only the pressure hose to the pump (Part 3-4).

3. Place the oil return line in a suitable container and plug the reservoir return pipe.

4. Fill the reservoir with lubricant CIAZ-19582-A.

5. Disconnect the coil wire to prevent the engine from starting and raise the front wheels off the ground.

6. While approximately two quarts of steering gear lubricant are being poured into the reservoir, turn the engine over using the ignition key, at the same time cycle the steering wheel from stop to stop.

7. As soon as all of the lubricant has been poured in, turn off the ignition key, and attach the coil wire.

8. Remove the plug from the reservoir return pipe, and attach the return hose to the reservoir.

9. Check the reservoir fluid level; if low add fluid to the proper level. **Do not overfill.**

10. Lower the car.

11. Start the engine and cycle the steering wheel from stop to stop to expel any trapped air from the system.

FRONT END GENERAL INSPECTION

Do not check and adjust front wheel alignment without first making the following inspection for front-end maladjustment, damage, or wear.

1. Check for specified air pressures in all four tires.

2. Raise the front of the car off the floor. Shake each front wheel grasping the upper and lower surfaces of the tire to check the front suspension ball joints and mountings for looseness, wear, and damage. Check the brake backing plate mountings. Torque all loose nuts and bolts to specifications. Replace all worn parts as outlined in Part 3-2.

3. Check the steering gear mountings and all steering linkage connections for looseness. Torque all mountings to specifications. If any of the linkage is worn or bent, replace the parts as outlined in Part 3-3.

4. Check the front wheel bearings. If any in-and-out free play is noticed, adjust the bearing to specification (Part 3-5). Replace worn or damaged bearings as outlined in Part 3-5.

5. Spin each front wheel with a wheel spinner, and check and balance each wheel as required.

6. Check the action of the shock absorbers. If the shock absorbers are not in good condition, the car may not settle in a normal, level position, and front wheel alignment may be affected.

WHEEL INSPECTION

Wheel lug nuts should be tightened to specification at the predelivery inspection. Loose wheel lug nuts may cause shimmy and vibration. Elongated stud holes in the wheels may also result from loose lug nuts.

Keep the wheels and hubs clean. Stones wedged between the wheel and drum and lumps of mud or grease can unbalance a wheel and tire.

Check for damage that would affect the runout of the wheels. Wobble or shimmy caused by a damaged wheel will cause premature tire wear and eventually damage the wheel bearings. Inspect the wheel rims for dents that could permit air to leak from the tires.

WHEEL BALANCING

See the instructions provided with the Rotunda Wheel Balancer.

UPPER BALL JOINT INSPECTION

1. Raise the car on a frame contact hoist or by floor jacks placed beneath the underbody until the wheel falls to the full down position as shown in Fig. 14. This will unload the upper ball joint.

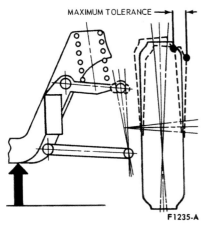

MAXIMUM TOLERANCE →

F1235-A

FIG. 14—Measuring Upper Ball Joint Radial Play

2. Adjust the wheel bearings as described in Part 3-5.

3. Attach a dial indicator to the upper arm. Position the indicator so that the plunger rests against the underside of the spindle at the upper ball joint stud.

4. With the dial indicator attached to the upper arm, position the indicator so that the plunger rests against the inner side of the wheel rim adjacent to the upper arm ball joint.

5. Grasp the tire at the top and bottom, and slowly move the tire in and out (Fig. 14). Note the reading (radial play) on the dial indicator. If the reading exceeds specifications (Part 3-6), replace the upper ball joint.

LOWER BALL JOINT INSPECTION

1. Raise the car on a frame contact hoist or by floor jacks placed beneath the underbody until the wheel falls to the full down position.

2. Ask an assistant to grasp the lower edge of the tire and move the wheel in and out.

3. As the wheel is being moved in and out, observe the lower end of the spindle and the lower arm.

4. Any movement between the lower end of the spindle and the lower arm indicates ball joint wear and loss of preload. If any such movement is observed, replace the lower arm.

During the foregoing check, the upper ball joint will be unloaded and may move. Disregard all such movement of the upper ball joint. Also, do not mistake loose wheel bearings for a worn ball joint.

SHOCK ABSORBERS

Passenger cars and station wagons are equipped with hydraulic shock absorbers of the direct-acting type and are nonadjustable and nonrefillable, and cannot be repaired.

Before replacing a shock absorber, check the action of the shock absorbers by grasping the bumper and jouncing the car up and down. If the shock absorbers are in good condition the car will immediately settle to a normal position after the bumper is released.

TESTING

To check a shock absorber removed from a car proceed as follows:

1. Hold the shock absorber in the vertical position with the piston in the same position, push in the piston rod until the shock is extended to its full length.

2. With the shock absorber held in the same position, push in the piston rod until the shock is compressed to its shortest length.

3. Repeat steps 1 and 2 several times until all the air is expelled.

4. Clamp the lower end (small diameter) in a vise in a vertical position.

5. Extend the shock to its full length and then compress it to its shortest length. There should be a constant drag during the complete cycle. Any sudden loss of drag indicates air in the system, loss of fluid, or faulty internal valve operation. Replace defective shock absorbers.

PART 3-2 SUSPENSION

Section	Page
1 Description and Operation	3-11
Front Suspension	3-11
Rear Suspension	3-12
2 In-Car Adjustments and Repairs	3-12
Upper Ball Joint Replacement	3-12
Upper Arm Shaft and/or Bushing Replacement	3-13
Stabilizer Replacement	3-13
Lower Arm Strut and/or Bushing Replacement	3-13
Mustang	3-13
Comet, Falcon, and Fairlane	3-14
3 Removal and Installation	3-14
Front Spring	3-14
Mustang	3-14
Comet, Falcon, and Fairlane	3-15

Section	Page
Front Suspension Upper Arm	3-15
Mustang	3-15
Comet, Falcon, and Fairlane	3-16
Front Suspension Lower Arm	3-17
Mustang	3-17
Comet, Falcon, and Fairlane	3-17
Front Wheel Spindle	3-18
Drum Brakes	3-18
Disc Brakes	3-18
Front Shock Absorber	3-19
Rear Shock Absorber	3-19
Mustang	3-19
Comet, Falcon, and Fairlane (Except Convertible)	3-20
Comet and Fairlane Convertible	3-21
Rear Spring and/or Bushing	3-21

1 DESCRIPTION AND OPERATION

FRONT SUSPENSION

Each front wheel rotates on a spindle. The upper and lower ends of the spindle are attached to upper and lower ball joints which are mounted to an upper and lower arm respectively. The upper arm pivots on a bushing and shaft assembly which is bolted to the underbody. The lower arm pivots on a bolt that is located in an underbody bracket (Figs. 1 and 14).

A coil spring seats between the upper arm and the top of the spring housing. A double acting shock absorber is bolted to the arm and the top of the spring housing.

The swiveling action of the ball joints allow the wheel and spindle assemblies to move up and down with changes in road surface. The swiveling ball joints also permit the spindles and wheels to be turned to the left or right by the steering gear and linkage.

The pivoting action of the suspension arms provides an **up and down** movement for the spindles and wheels as required by bumps or depressions in the road surface. The coil springs, shock absorbers and stabilizer bar control the front suspension up and down movements. The struts, which are connected between the suspension lower arms and the underbody prevent the suspension arms from moving forward and backward.

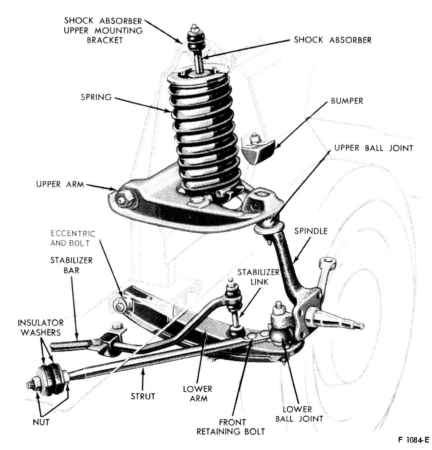

FIG. 1—Front Suspension—Typical

F 1084-E

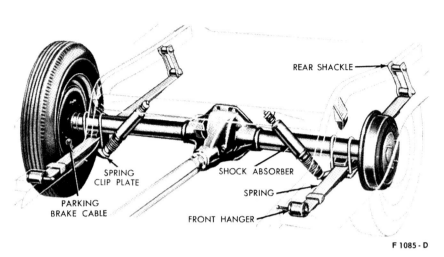

FIG. 2—Rear Suspension—Typical

REAR SUSPENSION

Each rear wheel, hub, and brake drum assembly is bolted to the rear axle shaft flange. The wheel and axle shaft assembly rotates in the rear axle housing. Two spring pads integral with the axle housing, rest on two leaf type springs. The axle housing is fastened to the springs by spring clips. (U-bolts), spring clip plates and nuts (Figs. 2 and 18). Each spring is suspended from the underbody side rail by a hanger at the front and a shackle at the rear. The upper end of each shock absorber is mounted to a bracket in the underbody. The lower end is mounted to the spring clip plate.

The springs and shock absorbers provide for up and down movement of the rear axle and wheels as required by changes in the road surface. They also cushion road shocks.

---

2 IN-CAR ADJUSTMENTS AND REPAIRS

HOISTING INSTRUCTIONS

Damage to suspension and/or steering linkage components may occur if care is not exercised when positioning the hoist adapters of 2 post hoists prior to lifting the car.

If a 2 post hoist is used to lift the car, place the adapters under the front suspension lower arms. **Do not allow the adapters to contact the steering linkage.**

UPPER BALL JOINT REPLACEMENT

1. Position a support between the upper arm and frame side rail as shown in Figs. 3 and 4; then, raise the car and position safety stands.

2. Remove the wheel and tire.

3. Remove the cotter pin and nut from the upper ball joint stud.

4. Position the ball joint remover tool as shown in Fig. 5. **The tool should seat firmly against the ends of both studs, and not against the lower stud nut.** It may be necessary to remove the lower ball joint cotter pin if it prevents the tool from seating on the lower stud.

5. Turn the tool with a wrench until both studs are under tension, and then, with a hammer, tap the spindle near the upper stud to loosen the stud from the spindle. **Do not loosen the stud with tool pressure alone.** Raise the stud out of the spindle bore.

6. Using a large chisel, cut off the

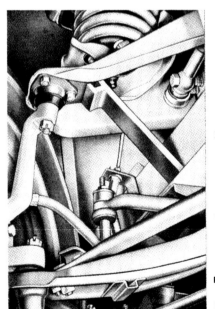
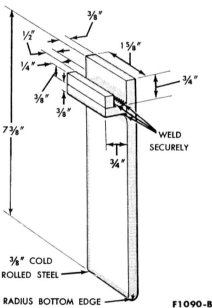

FIG. 3—Upper Arm Support—Mustang

three upper ball joint retaining rivets and remove the ball joint.

7. Clean the end of the arm, and remove all burrs from the hole edges. Check for cracks in the metal at the holes, and replace the arm if it is cracked.

8. Attach the new ball joint to the upper arm. **Use only the specified bolts, nuts, and washers. Do not rivet the new ball joint to the arm.** Torque the nuts to specification (Part 3-6).

9. Position the ball joint stud in the spindle bore, and torque the retaining nut to specification. Install a new cotter pin, tighten the nut if necessary to line up the cotter pin hole.

10. Lubricate the ball joint, and install the wheel and tire. Torque the lug nuts to specification (Part 3-6).

11. Remove the safety stands, and lower the car.

12. Remove the support from between the upper arm and frame.

13. Check and, if necessary, adjust caster, camber, and toe-in.

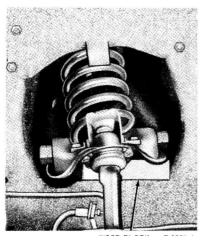

FIG. 4—Upper Arm Support —Comet, Falcon, and Fairlane

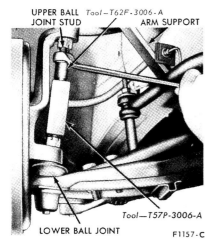

FIG. 5—Loosening Ball Joint Studs in Spindle—Typical

UPPER ARM SHAFT AND/OR BUSHING RELACEMENT

1. Remove the shock absorber and upper mounting bracket as an assembly.

2. Raise the car on a hoist, install safety stands, and remove the wheel cover or hub cap.

3. Remove the grease cap from the hub; then, remove the cotter pin, nut lock, adjusting nut and outer bearing from the hub.

4. Pull the wheel, tire, and the hub and drum off the spindle as an assembly.

5. Install the spring compressor, Tool T63P-5310-A or the Comet Tool 5310-C and compress the spring (Section 3).

6. Remove 2 upper arm to spring tower retaining nuts and swing the

upper arm outboard from the spring tower.

7. Rotate the inner shaft so that the retaining studs can be removed. Remove the retaining studs with a soft mallet (Mustang Only).

8. Unscrew the bushings from the shaft and suspension arm; then, remove the shaft from the arm.

9. Position the shaft in the arm, apply grease to the new bushings and O-rings, and install the bushings loose on the shaft and arm. **Turn the bushings so that the shaft is exactly centered in the arm.** The shaft will be properly centered when dimensions A and B in Fig. 6 are equal.

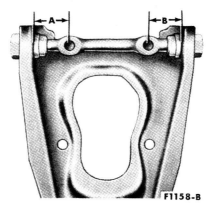

FIG. 6—Shaft Centered in Arm—Typical

10. Fabricate a spacer from a section of ¾-inch diameter pipe or metal of comparable size and strength. On a Mustang the spacer should be 7 $^{7}/_{16}$ inches long. On a Comet, Falcon, or Fairlane, the spacer should be 6 $^{15}/_{16}$ inches long.

11. Position the spacer parallel with the inner shaft, and force the spacer between the flanges of the upper arm (Fig. 7).

If the spacer can not be forced between the arm flanges due to excessive distortion, replace the upper arm assembly.

12. With the spacer positioned in the arm, torque the bushings to specification. Move the arm on the shaft to be sure that no binding exists, then remove the spacer.

13. Connect the suspension upper arm to the underbody. Install the adjusting shims (Mustang only) and release the front spring.

14. Remove the spring compressor and position the wheel, tire, and hub and drum on the spindle.

15. Install the bearing, washer, adjusting nut and nut lock. Adjust the wheel bearing as outlined in Part 3-5

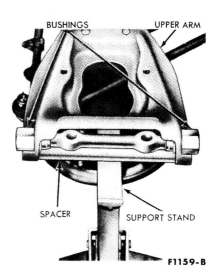

FIG. 7—Torque Upper Arm Inner Shaft Bushings—Typical

and install the cotter pin, grease cap and hub cap or wheel cover.

16. Lower the car and install the shock absorber and upper mounting bracket.

17. Check caster, camber, and toe-in and adjust as necessary (Part 3-1).

STABILIZER REPLACEMENT

1. Raise the car high enough to provide working space, and place supports under both front wheels.

2. Disconnect the stabilizer from each link. Disconnect both stabilizer retaining brackets, and remove the stabilizer.

3. Coat the necessary parts of the stabilizer with RUGLYDE or a comparable lubricant, and slide new insulators onto the stabilizer.

4. Connect the stabilizer retaining brackets, and connect the stabilizer to both links. Torque the bracket retaining screws and the link bolt nut to specification.

5. Remove the supports and lower the car.

LOWER ARM STRUT AND/OR BUSHING REPLACEMENT

MUSTANG

1. Position the block as shown in Fig. 3 under the upper arm for support.

2. Raise the car, position safety stands, and remove the wheel and tire.

3. Remove the strut - to - bracket forward retaining nut, washer and insulator bushings (Fig. 14).

4. Remove the 2 strut-to-lower arm retaining nuts and bolts; then,

lift the strut with rear insulator bushing and washer from the car.

5. Install the new rear washer and insulator bushing on the forward end of the strut rod.

6. Position the strut into the mounting bracket and to the lower suspension arm. Install the strut-to-arm retaining bolts and nuts, and torque to specification.

7. Install the forward insulator bushing, washer, and nut to the forward end of the strut and torque the strut rod nut to specification.

8. Install the wheel and tire, remove the safety stands and lower the

car. Remove the tool supporting the upper arm.

COMET, FALCON, AND FAIRLANE

Removal

1. Raise the car and install safety stands.

2. Remove the lower arm strut front retaining nut, washer and bushing at the frame bracket (14).

3. Remove 2 bolts and nuts attaching the strut to the lower arm and remove the strut.

4. Remove the bushing, washer and nut from the strut.

Installation

1. Install the nut, washer and bushing on the strut.

2. Position the strut to the front bushing bracket and to the lower arm. Install the strut to lower arm attaching bolts and nuts and torque to specification.

3. Position the strut front bushing and washer on the strut and install the adjusting nut.

4. Tighten the strut adjusting nuts against the strut frame bracket.

5. Lower the car and check caster, camber and toe-in and adjust as necessary.

---

3   REMOVAL AND INSTALLATION

HOISTING INSTRUCTIONS

Damage to suspension and / or steering linkage components may occur if care is not exercised when positioning the hoist adapters of 2 post hoists prior to lifting the car.

If a 2 post hoist is used to lift the car, place the adapters under the front suspension lower arms. **Do not allow the adapters to contact the steering linkage.**

FRONT SPRING

MUSTANG

Removal

1. Raise the front of the car, position safety stands under the frame, and lower the car slightly.

2. Remove the wheel and tire assembly.

3. Remove the shock absorber lower retaining nuts and washers.

4. Remove the shock absorber upper mounting bracket retaining nuts, and remove the shock absorber and bracket as an assembly (Fig. 15).

5. On all 8-cylinder cars, remove the air cleaner to obtain access for tool installation.

6. Position the upper plate (Tool T64K-5310-A) at the spring upper seat; place the bearing of tool T63P-5310-A on the plate and insert the tool shaft (detail A1) through the bearing and upper plate with the tool nut (detail A2) against the bearing as shown in Fig. 8.

7. Install the tool lower plate (detail A3) under the third coil from the bottom (Fig. 9). Secure the plate to the shaft screw (detail A1) with the retainer (detail A4). The retainer en-

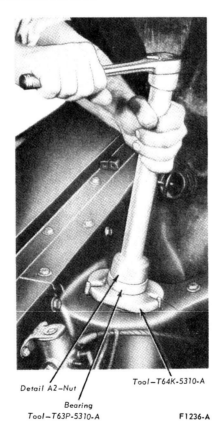

Detail A2—Nut

Bearing
Tool—T63P-5310-A

Tool—T64K-5310-A

F1236-A

FIG. 8—Compressing or Releasing Spring on Mustang—Upper View

gages the groove in the shaft screw below the plate as shown. The tang of the retainer engages the cut-out in the plate.

8. Insert a ½-inch square drive flexhandle wrench in the drive hole in the lower plate to prevent the tool and spring from turning (Fig. 9). While thus holding the tool, compress

Tool—T63P-5310-A
Detail A1—Shaft Screw   Detail A3—Lower Plate

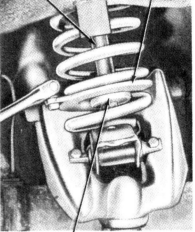

Detail A4—Retainer   F1237-A

FIG. 9—Compressing or Releasing Spring on Mustang—Lower View

the spring by turning the tool shaft nut clockwise (Fig. 8) until the spring clears the suspension upper arm.

9. Remove the upper suspension arm inner shaft retaining nuts from the engine compartment, and pull the arm, shaft, and retaining bolts away from the underbody. Measure and note the total shim thickness at each inner shaft retaining bolt. Swing the upper arm and shaft assembly 180° out to provide clearance for spring removal (Fig. 10).

10. Turn the tool shaft nut counterclockwise until the spring is released (Fig. 8). **Hold the tool lower plate from turning during spring release. Use a ½-inch square drive flexhandle wrench (Fig. 9).**

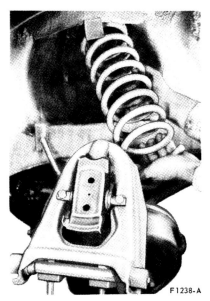

FIG. 10—Removing or Installing Spring—Mustang

11. Remove the components of the spring compressing tool; then, remove the spring as shown in Fig. 10.

Installation

1. With the upper arm turned out of the way for clearance, install the spring in the housing (Fig. 10).

2. Install the spring compressor tool and compress the spring.

3. Swing the suspension upper arm assembly inboard, and insert the arm inner shaft retaining bolts through the mounting holes in the underbody.

4. From inside the engine compartment, install but do not tighten the nuts and lockwashers on the two inner shaft retaining bolts. **The specified keystone type lock washers must be used.**

5. Install the adjusting shims on both bolts between the inner shaft and the underbody. **Install the same shim thicknesses that were removed from each bolt when the arm was disconnected.** Torque the inner shaft retaining nuts to specification.

6. Turn the tool shaft nut counterclockwise to release the spring (Fig. 8). As the spring is being released, guide the spring into its lower seat.

7. Remove the components of the spring tool.

8. Position the shock absorber in the spring housing so that the holes in the upper mounting bracket engage the upper retaining studs in the housing (Fig. 15). The lower retaining bolts go through the mounting holes in the spring lower seat.

9. Install the bracket retaining

nuts, and torque to specification. Install the shock absorber lower retaining nuts on the bolts at the underside of the spring lower seat and torque to specification.

10. Install the wheel and tire assembly, remove the safety stands and lower the car.

11. Check and, if necessary, adjust caster, camber, and toe-in.

COMET, FALCON, AND FAIRLANE

Removal

1. Remove the shock absorber and upper mounting bracket as an assembly.

2. Raise the car on a hoist, install safety stands, and remove the wheel cover or hub cap.

3. Remove the grease cap from the hub; then, remove the cotter pin, nut lock, adjusting nut and outer bearing from the hub.

4. Pull the wheel, tire and the hub and drum off the spindle as an assembly.

5. Install the spring compressor, Tool T63P-5310-A or the Comet Tool 5310-C (Fig. 11), and compress the spring (Figs. 9 and 12). Either tool can be used.

6. Remove 2 upper arm to spring

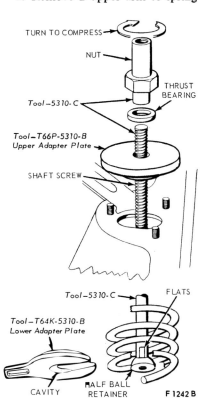

FIG. 11—Comet Spring Tool Installation

tower retaining nuts and swing the upper arm outboard from the spring tower (Fig. 13).

7. Release the spring compressor tool and remove the tool from the spring. Then, remove the spring from the car (Fig. 10).

Installation

1. Place the spring upper insulator on the spring and secure in place with tape.

2. Position the spring in the spring tower. Install the spring compressor, Tool T63P-5310-A and compress the spring.

3. Swing the upper arm inboard and insert the bolts through the holes in the side of the spring tower. Then, install the retaining nuts and torque them to specification.

4. Release the spring pressure and guide the spring into the upper arm spring seat. **The end of the spring must seat against the tab on the spring seat.**

5. Remove the spring compressor and position the wheel, tire, and hub and drum on the spindle.

6. Install the bearing, washer, adjusting nut and nut lock. Adjust the wheel bearing as outlined in Part 3-5 and install the cotter pin, grease cap, and hub cap or wheel cover.

7. Lower the car and install the shock absorber and upper mounting bracket.

8. Check caster, camber, and toe-in and adjust as necessary (Part 3-1).

FRONT SUSPENSION UPPER ARM

MUSTANG

Removal

1. Raise the front of the car, position safety stands under the frame, and lower the car slightly.

2. Remove the wheel and tire assembly.

3. Remove the shock absorber lower retaining nuts and washers.

4. Remove the shock absorber upper mounting bracket retaining nuts, and remove the shock absorber and bracket as an assembly (Fig. 15).

On all 8-cylinder cars, remove the air cleaner to obtain access for tool installation.

5. Install the spring compressor, Tools T63P-5310-A and T64K-5310-A and compress the spring (Figs. 8 and 9).

6. Position a safety stand under the lower arm.

7. Remove the cotter pin from the

T 63P-5310-A   T 66P-5310-A OR B   F 1288-A

FIG. 12—Spring Compressor Installed—Upper View—Comet, Falcon and Fairlane

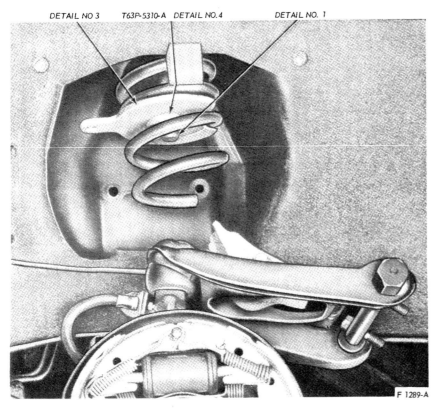

DETAIL NO 3   T63P-5310-A DETAIL NO. 4   DETAIL NO. 1

F 1289-A

FIG. 13—Compressing Spring—Lower View—Comet, Falcon, and Fairlane

nut on the upper ball joint stud, and loosen the nut one or two turns. **Do not remove the nut from the stud at this time.**

8. Position the ball joint remover tool between the upper and lower ball joint studs as shown in Fig. 5. **The tool should seat firmly against the ends of both studs and not against the stud nuts.**

9. Turn the tool with a wrench until the tool places the studs under tension; then, tap the spindle near the upper stud with a hammer to loosen the stud in the spindle. **Do not loosen the stud in the spindle with tool pressure only.** If both arms are being removed, loosen the lower stud in the same manner as the upper stud.

10. Remove the nut from the upper stud and lift the stud out of the spindle.

11. Remove the upper arm inner shaft retaining nuts from the engine compartment, and remove the upper arm. Measure and note the total shim thickness at each inner shaft bolt.

12. Wipe off all loose dirt from the upper arm parts. **Do not wash the ball joint with a solvent.**

Installation

1. Position the upper arm on the underbody mounting bracket, and install but do not tighten the nuts and lockwashers on the two inner shaft retaining bolts. **The specified keystone-type lockwashers must be used.**

2. Install the adjusting shims on both bolts between the inner shaft and the underbody. **Install the same shim thicknesses that were removed from both bolts during disassembly** (Fig. 7, Part 3-1). Torque the nuts to specification.

3. Position the upper ball joint stud in the top of the wheel spindle, and install the stud nut. Torque the nut to specification, and continue to tighten it until he cotter pin hole and slots line up. Install a new cotter pin.

4. Release the coil spring, remove the tool, and install the front shock absorber and the wheel and tire assembly.

COMET, FALCON, AND FAIRLANE

Removal

1. Remove the front shock absorber from the car.

2. Raise the car and install safety stands under the frame side rails.

3. Remove the hub cap or wheel cover and the wheel and tire.

4. Install the spring compressor,

Tools T63P-5310-A (Tool-5310-C-Comet), T64K5310-A or B, and T66P-5310-A or B and compress the spring (Fig. 13).

5. Remove the cotter pin from the upper ball joint stud and loosen the stud nut.

6. Position the ball joint remover tool as shown in Fig. 5. **The tool should seat firmly against the ends of both studs and not against the lower stud nut.** It may be necessary to remove the lower ball joint cotter pin if it prevents the tool from seating on the stud.

7. Turn the tool with a wrench until both studs are under tension; then, tap the spindle near the upper stud with a hammer to loosen the stud from the spindle. **Do not loosen the stud with tool pressure alone.**

8. Remove the ball joint remover tool and remove the ball joint stud nut from the stud.

9. Remove 2 nuts and washers retaining the upper arm to the spring tower. Pull the upper arm away from the spring tower, lift the ball joint stud from the spindle, and remove the upper arm from the car.

10. Remove 2 nuts and bolts and remove the spring pivot from the upper arm.

Installation

1. Position the spring pivot to the upper arm and install the 2 attaching bolts and nuts. Torque the nuts to specification.

2. Position the upper arm to the spring tower and the ball joint stud to the spindle. Install but do not tighten the ball joint stud nut.

3. Position the upper arm to spring tower and install the washers and retaining nuts. Torque the nuts to specification.

4. Release the spring compressor tool while aligning the spring with the upper arm spring pivot. Then, remove the tool.

5. Torque the ball joint stud nut to specification (Part 3-6). Continue to tighten the nut until the slots in the nut are in line with the hole in the ball joint stud. Then, install a new cotter pin.

6. Install the wheel and tire and the hub cap or wheel cover.

7. Remove the safety stands and lower the car.

8. Install the shock absorber.

FRONT SUSPENSION LOWER ARM

MUSTANG

Removal

1. Position a support between the upper arm and side rail as shown in Fig. 3.

2. Raise the car, position safety stands, and remove the wheel and tire.

3. Remove the stabilizer bar and link retaining nut, disconnect the bar from the link, and remove the link bolt.

4. Remove the strut to lower arm retaining nuts and bolts. Remove the steering arm stop from the strut.

5. Remove the cotter pin from the nut on the lower ball joint stud, and loosen the nut one or two turns. **Do not remove the nut from the stud at this time.**

6. Straighten the cotter pin on the upper ball joint stud nut. Position the ball joint remover tool between the upper and lower ball joint studs in the reverse position from that shown in Fig. 5. **The tool should seat firmly aginst the ends of both studs and not against the stud nuts.**

7. Turn the tool with a wrench until the tool places the studs under tension, and tap the spindle near the lower stud with a hammer to loosen the stud in the spindle. **Do not loosen the stud in the spindle with tool pressure only.** If both arms are being removed, loosen the upper stud in the same manner as the lower stud.

8. Remove the nut from the lower ball joint stud, and lower the arm.

9. Remove the lower arm to underbody pivot bolt, nut and washer. Remove the lower arm.

Installation

1. Position the lower arm to the underbody bracket and install the pivot bolt, washer, and nut loose.

2. Raise the lower arm, guide the lower ball joint stud into the spindle bore, and install the stud retaining nut loose.

3. Install the stabilizer link bolt, washers, bushings and spacer. Connect the stabilizer bar to the link. Install the retaining nut and torque to specifications (Fig. 14).

4. Position the strut and steering arm stop to the lower arm. Install the retaining bolts and nuts, and torque to specification.

5. Torque the lower ball joint stud nut to specification, continue to tighten the nut until the cotter pin hole

and slots are aligned, and install a new cotter pin.

6. Torque the lower arm-to-underbody pivot bolt and nut to specification.

7. Remove the safety stands and lower the car.

8. Remove the support from between the upper arm and frame.

9. **Check and, if necessary, adjust caster, camber, and toe-in.**

COMET, FALCON, AND FAIRLANE

Removal

1. Raise the car and position safety stands under the side rails.

2. Remove the hub cap or wheel cover.

3. Remove the wheel, tire, and hub and drum as an assembly.

4. Remove the stabilizer bar link retaining nut and remove the washers, bushings, spacer, and link bolt (Fig. 14).

5. Remove the 2 strut to lower arm attaching nuts and bolts.

6. Remove the lower ball joint stud nut cotter pin and loosen the nut one or two turns. **Do not remove the nut from the stud at this time.**

7. Position the ball joint remover tool between the upper and lower ball joint studs in the reverse position (upside down) from that shown in Fig. 14. **The tool should seat firmly against the ends of both studs and not against the stud nuts.**

8. Turn the tool with a wrench until the studs are under tension. Tap the spindle near the lower stud with a hammer to loosen the stud in the spindle. **Do not loosen the stud with tool pressure only.**

9. Remove the tool and remove the nut from the lower ball joint stud.

10. Mark the location of the eccentric and eccentric bolt at the lower arm to underbody attachment.

11. Remove the nut, bolt, and eccentrics attaching the lower arm to the underbody and remove the lower arm.

Installation

1. Position the lower arm to the underbody and install the bolt, eccentrics, and nut.

2. Position the ball joint stud in the spindle bore and install the retaining nut.

3. Adjust the eccentrics to the previous marked location and torque the nut to specification (Part 3-6).

4. Position the strut to the lower

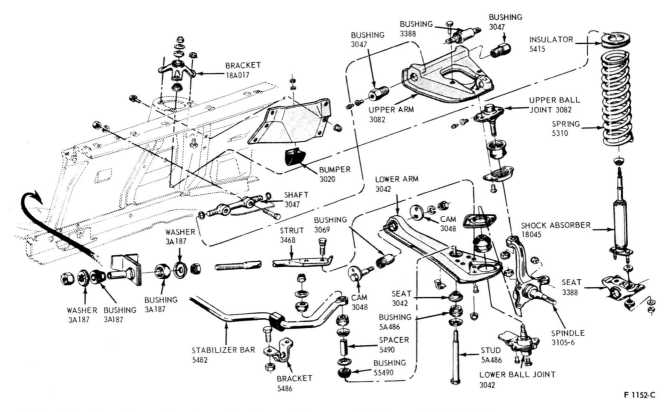

FIG. 14—Front Suspension Assembly—Comet, Falcon, and Fairlane—Typical of Mustang

arm and install the attaching bolts and nuts. Torque the nuts to specification (Part 3-6).

5. Position the stabilizer bar link to the lower arm and install the bolt, washers, bushings, spacer, and retaining nut. Torque the nut to specification (Part 3-6).

6. Torque the lower ball joint stud nut to specification (Part 3-6) and install the cotter pin.

7. Install the wheel, tire, and hub and drum on the spindle and adjust the wheel bearing (Part 3-5).

8. Install the hub cap or wheel cover, remove the safety stands, and lower the car.

9. Check caster, camber, and toe-in and adjust as necessary.

FRONT WHEEL SPINDLE
DRUM BRAKES
Removal

1. Position a support between the upper arm and frame as shown in Figs. 3 and 4; then, raise the car and position safety stands.

2. Remove the hub cap or wheel cover.

3. Remove the grease cap from the hub; then, remove the adjusting nut, washer, and outer bearing cone and roller assembly.

4. Pull the wheel, hub, and drum assembly off the wheel spindle.

5. Remove the brake carrier plate from the spindle. Support the plate to prevent damage to the brake hose.

6. Disconnect the spindle connecting rod end from the spindle arm using Tool 3290-C.

7. Remove the cotter pins from both ball joint stud nuts, and loosen the nuts one or two turns. **Do not remove the nuts from the studs at this time.**

8. Position the ball joint remover tool between the upper and lower ball joint studs (Fig. 5). **The tool should seat firmly against the ends of both studs and not against the stud nuts.**

9. Turn the tool with a wrench until the tool places the studs under tension, and, with a hammer, tap the spindle near the studs to loosen them in the spindle. **Do not loosen the studs in the spindle with tool pressure alone.**

10. Remove the stud nuts and remove the spindle from both studs.

Installation

1. Position the spindle on the lower ball joint stud and install the stud nut (Fig. 14).

2. Raise the lower suspension arm,

and guide the upper ball joint stud into the spindle. Install the stud nut.

3. Torque the upper stud nut and then the lower stud nut to specification. Continue to tighten both nuts until the cotter pin holes and slots line up. Install new cotter pins.

4. Connect the spindle connecting rod end to the spindle arm.

5. Install the brake carrier plate on the spindle, and torque the bolts to specification.

6. Install the wheel and drum and adjust the wheel bearing (Part 3-5).

7. Remove the safety stands, and lower the car.

8. Remove the support from between the upper arm and frame.

9. Check and, if necessary, adjust caster, camber, and toe-in.

DISC BRAKES
Removal

1. Remove the hub cap or wheel cover, and remove the wheel and tire from the hub.

2. Remove two bolts attaching the caliper to the caliper bracket. Remove the caliper from the rotor and wire it to the underbody to prevent damage to the brake hose.

3. Remove the grease cap from the hub, then, remove the adjusting nut, washer, and outer bearing cone and roller assembly.

4. Pull the hub and rotor assembly off the wheel spindle.

5. Remove four bolts and nuts and remove the splash shield and caliper bracket from the spindle.

6. Disconnect the spindle connecting rod end from the spindle arm using Tool-3290-C.

7. Remove the cotter pins from both ball joint stud nuts, and loosen the nuts one or two turns. **Do not remove the nuts from the studs at this time.**

8. Position the ball joint remover tool between the upper and lower ball joint studs (Fig. 5). **The tool should seat firmly against the ends of both studs and not against the stud nuts.**

9. Turn the tool with a wrench until the tool places the studs under tension, and, with a hammer, tap the spindle near the studs to loosen them in the spindle. **Do not loosen the studs in the spindle with tool pressure alone.**

10. Position a floor jack under the lower suspension arm.

11. Remove the upper and lower ball joint stud nuts; lower the jack and remove the spindle.

Installation

1. Position the spindle on the lower ball joint stud and install the stud nut (Fig 14). Torque the nut to specification and install the cotter pin.

2. Raise the lower suspension arm, and guide the upper ball joint stud into the spindle. Install the stud nut.

3. Torque the nut to specifications and install the cotter pin. Then, remove the floor jack.

4. Connect the spindle connecting rod end to the spindle arm and install the retaining nut. Torque the nut to specification and install the cotter pin.

5. Position the caliper bracket and splash shield to the spindle and install the attaching bolts and nuts. Torque the nuts and bolts to specification.

6. Install the hub and rotor on the spindle.

7. Position the caliper to the rotor and caliper bracket and install the attaching bolts.

8. Install the wheel and tire on the hub and adjust the wheel bearing (Part 3-5).

9. Install the hub cap or wheel cover.

10. Before driving the car, pump the brake pedal several times to obtain normal brake lining to rotor

clearance and restore normal brake pedal travel.

FRONT SHOCK ABSORBER

REMOVAL

1. Raise the hood and remove 3 shock absorber upper mounting bracket to spring tower retaining nuts.

2. Raise the front of the car and place safety stands under the lower arms.

3. Remove 2 shock absorber lower retaining nuts and washers (Fig. 15).

4. Lift the shock absorber and upper bracket from the spring tower (Fig. 15) and remove the bracket from the shock absorber.

UPPER MOUNTING BRACKET

LOWER RETAINING BOLTS   F1239-A

FIG. 15—Removing or Installing Front Shock Absorber—Typical

INSTALLATION

1. Install the upper mounting bracket on the shock absorber and torque to specification.

2. Position the shock absorber and upper mounting bracket in the spring tower, making sure the shock absorber lower studs are in the pivot plate holes.

3. Install the 2 washers and retaining nuts on the shock absorber lower studs and torque to specification.

4. Install the 3 shock absorber upper mounting bracket to spring tower retaining nuts and torque to specification. Then, remove the safety stands and lower the car.

REAR SHOCK ABSORBER—

MUSTANG

Removal

1. Disconnect the shock absorber from the spring clip plate (Fig. 18).

2. On the passenger car, remove the shock absorber access cover from the luggage compartment (Fig. 16).

SHOCK ABSORBER ACCESS COVER

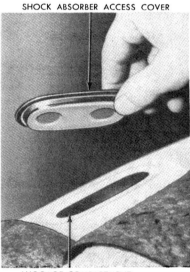

LUGGAGE COMPARTMENT
FLOOR PANEL   F1086-A

FIG. 16—Rear Shock Absorber Access Cover

On the Ranchero, remove the retaining screws, and lift the forward half of the floor panel from the body; then, remove the access cover from the opening in the floor pan over the shock absorber.

On station wagons, remove the access cover from the opening in the seat riser over the shock absorber.

3. Remove the shock absorber upper retaining nut.

4. Compress the shock absorber and remove it from the car. Remove the bushings and washers from the shock absorber studs.

Installation

1. Place the bushings and washers on the shock absorber studs.

2. Connect the upper stud to the

mounting, and install the bushing, washer, and nut on the stud. Torque the nut to specification, and install the cover (on a station wagon or car).

On the Ranchero, after installing the nut to specification, and install stall the forward half of the floor panel.

3. Connect the lower stud to the spring clip plate, and install the bushing, washer, and nut on the stud. **Be sure the spring clip plate is free of burrs.** Tighten the nut to specification.

COMET, FALCON, AND FAIRLANE (EXCEPT CONVERTIBLE)

Removal

1. Open the luggage compartment door, and remove the spare wheel and tire. On a station wagon, remove the floor bed panel (14 screws).

2. Fold back the floor mat and remove the shock absorber access cover from the floor pan. Remove the nut, outer washer, and rubber bushing that retain the shock absorber to the upper mounting in the floor pan (Fig. 17).

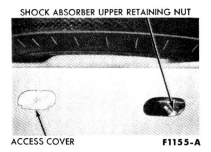

SHOCK ABSORBER UPPER RETAINING NUT

ACCESS COVER   F1155-A

FIG. 17—Rear Shock Absorber Upper Mounting

3. Raise the car and remove the retaining nut, outer washer and bushing from the shock absorber at the spring clip plate (Fig. 18). Compress the shock absorber and remove it from the car.

4. If the shock absorber is serviceable and requires new bushings remove the inner bushings and washers from the shock absorber studs.

Installation

1. Place the inner washer and bushing on each shock absorber stud.

2. Expand the shock absorber and position it to the spring clip plate and to the mounting in the floor pan.

3. Connect the lower stud to the spring clip plate, and install the bushing, washer, and nut on the stud (Fig. 18). **Be sure the spring clip plate is free of burrs.** Tighten the nut to specification.

4. From the luggage compartment, install the bushing washer and retaining nut to the upper mounting stud (Fig. 17). Torque to specifica-

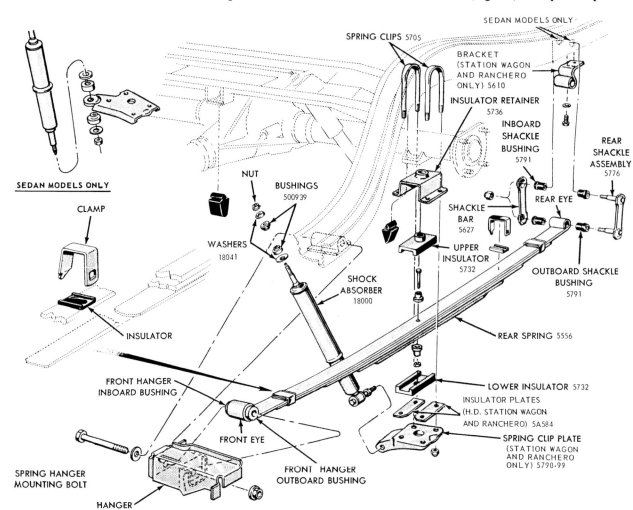

FIG. 18—Rear Spring and Shock Absorber—Typical

F 1153-C

tion. On a station wagon, replace the floor bed panel (14 screws).

5. Place the spare wheel and tire in the luggage compartment, and secure it in the storage position.

COMET AND FAIRLANE CONVERTIBLE

1. Remove the rear seat cushion and seat back.

2. Partially raise the car on a hoist. With an assistant under the car holding the shock absorber, remove the nut from the top of the shock absorber.

3. Remove the lower shock absorber attaching nut and remove the shock absorber.

4. Position the washers and bushings on the shock absorber and position the shock absorber to the lower attachment. Install the bushing, washer, and retaining nut and torque the nut to specification (Part 3-6).

5. Lower the car and install the bushing, washer, and retaining nut on the top of the shock absorber. Torque the nut to specification.

6. Install the rear seat back and seat cushion.

REAR SPRING AND/OR BUSHING

REMOVAL

1. Raise the car on a hoist and place supports beneath the underbody and under the axle.

2. Disconnect the lower end of the shock absorber from the spring clip plate, and push the shock out of the way.

3. Remove the spring clip plate nuts from the U-bolts; then, remove the plate (Fig. 18).

4. Remove the two retaining nuts, the rear shackle bar, and the two shackle inner bushings.

5. Remove the rear shackle assembly and the two outer bushings.

6. Remove the front hanger bolt, nut, and washer from the eye at the forward end of the spring. Lift out the spring assembly.

7. If the front bushing is being replaced, assemble the special tool combination to the bushing in the spring front eye as shown in Fig. 19.

8. While holding the tool nut, tighten the tool bolt against the tool thrust washer, the adapter, and detail A1. This operation will force the bushing out of the spring eye into detail A4 of the tool as shown.

INSTALLATION

1. Assemble the bushing and the

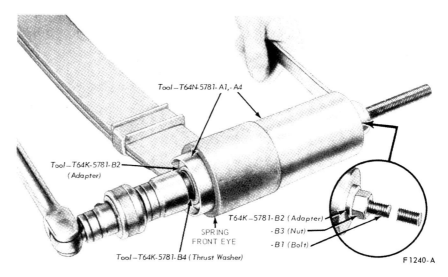

FIG. 19—Rear Spring Front Bushing Removal—Typical

special tool combination to the spring front eye as shown in Fig. 20.

2. While holding the tool nut, tighten the tool bolt against the tool thrust washer, adapter, and detail A4 to force the bushing into the spring eye as shown.

3. Position the spring under the rear axle and insert the shackle assembly into the rear hanger bracket and the rear eye of the spring.

4. Install the shackle inner bushings, the shackle plate, and the locknuts. Tighten the locknuts finger tight.

5. Position the spring front eye in the front hanger, slip the washer on the front hanger bolt, and (from the inboard side) insert the bolt through the hanger and eye. Install the lock

nut on the hanger bolt and tighten finger tight.

6. Torque the rear shackle locknuts to specification.

7. Lower the rear axle until it rests on the spring. Position the spring clip plate on the clips (U-bolts). Install the U-bolt nuts and torque to specification.

8. Connect the lower end of the shock absorber to the spring clip plate.

9. Place safety stands under the rear axle, lower the car until the spring is in the approximate curb load position, and then torque the front hanger stud locknut to specification.

10. Remove the safety stands and lower the car.

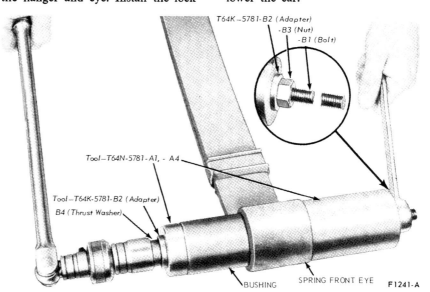

FIG. 20—Rear Spring Front Bushing Installation—Typical

PART 3-3 MANUAL STEERING

Section   **Page**

1 Description 3-22
2 In-Car Adjustment and Repairs 3-23
   Steering Gear Worm and Sector
     Adjustments 3-23
   Steering Wheel Spoke Position
     Adjustment 3-24
   Steering Wheel Replacement 3-24
   Steering Column Shift Tube
     Replacement 3-24
     Falcon With Standard Transmission—
      Comet and Fairlane With Standard
      Transmission and Standard Steering 3-24
     Comet and Fairlane With Standard
      Transmission and Power Steering 3-24
     Falcon With Automatic Transmission—
      Comet and Fairlane With Automatic
      Transmission and Standard Steering 3-25
     Comet and Fairlane With Automatic
      Transmission and Power Steering 3-26
   Steering Column Upper Bearing
     Replacement 3-26
     Comet and Fairlane With Power
      Steering 3-27
     All Models Except Comet and
      Fairlane With Power Steering 3-27

3 Removal and Installation 3-27
   Steering Gear 3-27
     Mustang 3-27
     Comet and Fairlane With Standard
      Steering (Except 390 C.I.D. Engine)
      and All Falcon 3-28
     Comet and Fairlane With Power
      Steering 3-29
     Comet and Fairlane with 390 C.I.D.
      Engine 3-29
4 Major Repair Operations 3-30
   Steering Gear 3-30
     Disassembly 3-30
     Assembly 3-30
5 Steering Linkage Repair 3-31
   Spindle Connecting Rod Replacement 3-31
   Spindle Sleeve Replacement 3-31
   Steering Arm-to-Idler Arm Rod
     Replacement 3-32
     Mustang—6 Cylinder 3-32
     Comet, Falcon, Fairlane and
      8 Cylinder Mustang 3-33
   Steering Idler Arm and/or Bushing 3-33

1 DESCRIPTION

The steering gear (Fig. 1) is of the worm and recirculating ball type. The sector shaft rotates in needle bearings that are pressed into the gear housing.

The worm bearing preload is controlled by the large bearing adjuster which is threaded into the housing. The sector shaft mesh load is controlled by an adjusting screw located in the housing cover.

A steering gear identification tag is provided under one of the cover attaching bolts (Fig. 2).

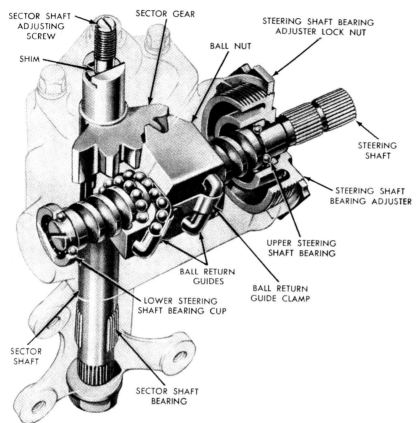

FIG. 1—Recirculating Ball Type Steering Gear—Typical

G1026-B

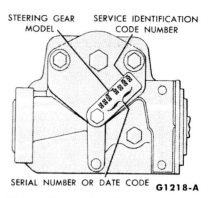

FIG. 2—Steering Gear Identification Tag

2 IN-CAR ADJUSTMENTS AND REPAIRS

HOISTING INSTRUCTIONS

Damage to suspension and/or steering linkage components may occur if care is not exercised when positioning the hoist adapters of 2 post hoists prior to lifting the car.

If a 2 post hoist is used to lift the car, place the adapters under the front suspension lower arms. **Do not allow the adapters to contact the steering linkage.**

STEERING GEAR WORM AND SECTOR ADJUSTMENTS

The ball nut assembly and the sector gear must be adjusted properly to maintain minimum steering shaft end play (a factor of preload adjustment) and minimum backlash between sector gear and ball nut. There are only two possible adjustments within the recirculating balltype steering gear, and **these should be made in the following order to avoid damage or gear failure.**

1. Disconnect the Pitman arm from the sector shaft.

2. Remove the steering wheel, spring and the centering cone from the shaft and note the relation of the shaft to the bearing.

3. If the shaft is not centered, attach a spring scale to it.

4. Center the shaft by pulling on the scale and note the reading.

5. If more than 20 lbs. pull is required to center the shaft, the steering column should be aligned as detailed in steering gear installation, before adjusting the preload and mesh load.

6. Loosen the nut which locks the sector adjusting screw (Fig. 3), and turn the adjusting screw counterclockwise.

7. Measure the worm bearing preload by attaching an in.-lb. torque wrench to the steering wheel nut (Fig. 4). With the steering wheel off center, read the pull required to rotate the input shaft approximately 1½ turns either side of center. If the torque or preload is not within specification

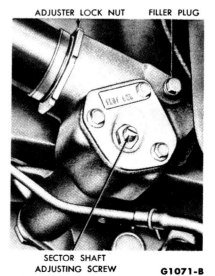

FIG. 3—Steering Gear Adjustments—Typical

(Part 3-6), adjust as explained in the next step.

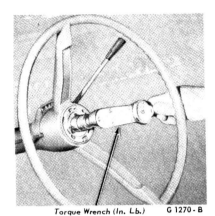

FIG. 4—Checking Pre-Load —Typical

8. Loosen the steering shaft bearing adjuster lock nut, and tighten or back off the bearing adjuster (Fig. 3) to bring the preload within the specified limits.

9. Tighten the steering shaft bearing adjuster lock nut, and recheck the preload.

10. Turn the steering wheel slowly to either stop. **Turn gently against the stop to avoid possible damage to the ball return guides.** Then rotate the wheel 2¼ turns to center the ball nut.

11. Turn the sector adjusting screw clockwise until the specified pull (Part 3-6) is necessary to rotate the worm past its center high spot (Fig. 4). **No perceptible backlash is permissable at 30° on either side of center.**

12. While holding the sector adjusting screw, tighten the locknut to specification and recheck the backlash adjustment.

13. Connect the Pitman arm to the sector shaft and torque to specification.

STEERING WHEEL SPOKE POSITION ADJUSTMENT

When the steering gear is on the high point, the front wheels should be in the straight-ahead position and the steering wheel spokes should be in their normal position with the Pitman arm pointing directly forward. If the spokes are not in their normal position, they can be adjusted without disturbing the toe-in adjustment (Refer to Part 3-1).

STEERING WHEEL REPLACEMENT

1. Remove the horn ring (or button) assembly and related parts.

2. Remove the steering wheel at-

taching nut and remove the steering wheel from the shaft, using the tool shown in Fig. 5.

FIG. 5—Removing Steering Wheel—Typical

3. With the front wheels straight forward, position the steering wheel on the steering shaft with the post on the steering wheel hub at the top.

4. Apply Loctite Sealer (C3AZ-19554-A) to the steering shaft threads and install the steering wheel nut on the shaft. Torque the nut to specification.

5. With the front wheels straight forward (post on steering wheel hub at the top), install the horn ring (or button) assembly and the related parts.

STEERING COLUMN SHIFT TUBE REPLACEMENT

FALCON WITH STANDARD TRANSMISSION—COMET AND FAIRLANE WITH STANDARD TRANSMISSION AND STANDARD STEERING

Removal

1. Open the hood and insert a fabricated alignment tool (Group 6) through the column tube and shift arms to retain the shift mechanism in neutral.

2. Disconnect the turn signal and horn wires at the steering column connectors.

3. Remove the horn ring and spring from the steering wheel.

4. Remove the steering wheel retaining nut and remove the steering wheel with Tool 3600-AA (Fig. 5).

5. Remove the trunnion and springs retaining the shift lever in the socket and remove the shift lever.

6. Remove the turn signal switch lever.

7. Remove 3 bearing retainer at-

taching screws and remove the bearing retainer and turn signal switch from the steering column (Fig. 6).

8. Lift the spring and centering sleeve from the steering shaft.

9. Loosen 2 flange bolt nuts retaining the flange to the steering column tube (Fig. 6).

10. Pull upward on the shift lever socket and remove the flange and shift lever socket from the steering column.

11. Lift the shift tube from the steering column.

Installation

1. Position the shift tube in the steering column and through the shift arms. **Be sure the shift tube is inserted through both shift arms.**

2. Position the shift lever socket on the steering column and engage it with the shift tube (Fig. 6).

3. Position the flange to the hub so that the heads of the 2 flange bolts engage in the slots of the steering column tube. Then, tighten the 2 flange bolt nuts.

4. Position the centering sleeve on the steering shaft and seat it into the flange bearing.

5. Feed the turn signal switch wires through the steering column and position the switch and bearing retainer to the flange.

6. Install the 3 bearing retainer attaching screws.

7. Position the shift lever to the shift lever socket and install the springs and trunnion.

8. Apply 2 drops of Loctite sealer (C3AZ-19554-A) to the threads of the turn signal switch lever and install the lever.

9. Position the spring and steering wheel on the steering shaft and install the retaining nut. Torque the nut to specification and apply 2 drops of Loctite sealer (C3AZ-19554-A) to the junction of the nut and steering shaft threads.

10. Install the spring and horn ring or button on the steering wheel and connect the turn signal and horn wires at the connectors.

11. Adjust the shift linkage, if required, and remove the alignment tool.

COMET AND FAIRLANE WITH STANDARD TRANSMISSION AND POWER STEERING

Removal

1. Open the hood and insert a fabricated alignment tool (Group 6) through the column tube and shift

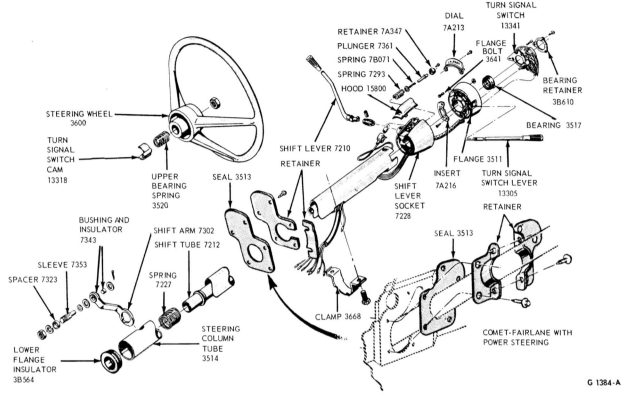

FIG. 6—Steering Column Disassembled—Typical

arms to retain the shift mechanism in neutral.

2. Disconnect the turn signal and horn wires at the steering column connectors.

3. Remove the horn ring and spring from the steering wheel.

4. Remove the steering wheel retaining nut and remove the steering wheel with Tool 3600-AA (Fig. 5).

5. Remove the trunnion and springs retaining the shift lever in the socket and remove the lever.

6. Remove the turn signal switch lever.

7. Remove 3 bearing retainer attaching screws and remove the bearing retainer and turn signal switch from the steering column (Fig. 6).

8. Remove the snap ring from the steering shaft.

9. Loosen 2 flange bolt nuts retaining the flange to the steering column tube (Fig. 6).

10. Pull upward on the shift lever socket and tap the end of the steering shaft with a soft hammer. This is to break the bearing loose from the shaft.

11. Remove the bearing, flange, and shift lever socket from the steering column.

12. Lift the shift tube from the steering column.

Installation

1. Position the shift tube in the steering column and through the shift arms and spacer. **Be sure the shift tube is inserted through both shift arms.**

2. Position the shift lever socket on the steering column and engage it with the shift tube (Fig. 6).

3. Position the flange to the hub so that the heads of the 2 flange bolts engage in the slots of the steering column tube. Then, tighten the 2 flange bolt nuts.

4. Position the bearing on the steering shaft and seat in the flange with Tool T62F-3576-A, if necessary.

5. Remove the tool and install the snap ring on the shaft.

6. Feed the turn signal switch wires through the steering column and position the switch and bearing retainer to the flange.

7. Install the 3 bearing retainer attaching screws.

8. Position the shift lever to the shift lever socket and install the roll pin.

9. Apply 2 drops of Loctite sealer (C3AZ-19554-A) to the threads of

the turn signal switch lever and install the lever.

10. Position the spring and steering wheel on the steering shaft and install the retaining nut. Torque the nut to specification and apply 2 drops of Loctite sealer (C3AZ-19554-A) to the junction of the nut and steering shaft threads.

11. Install the spring and horn ring (or button) on the steering wheel.

12. Adjust the shift linkage, if required, and remove the alignment pin from the shift arms and steering column.

13. Connect the turn signal and horn wires at the steering column connectors.

FALCON WITH AUTOMATIC TRANSMISSION COMET AND FAIRLANE WITH AUTOMATIC TRANSMISSION AND STANDARD STEERING

Removal

1. Open the hood and disconnect the shift rod from the steering column shift arm.

2. Loosen the steering gear to side rail retaining bolts.

3. Disconnect the turn signal and

horn wires at the steering column connectors.

4. Remove the horn ring (or button) and spring from the steering wheel.

5. Remove the steering wheel retaining nut and remove the steering wheel with Tool 3600-AA (Fig. 5).

6. Remove the insulation from the dash panel in the area of the steering column.

7. Remove 5 dash panel seal retainer attaching screws (Fig. 6) and remove the seal from the steering column opening. Then, slide the seal up the steering column.

8. Remove 2 bolts attaching the steering column to the instrument panel support.

9. Apply tape to the area around the instrument panel steering column opening to protect the finish on the panel.

10. Place the transmission selector lever in the low gear position.

11. Turn the steering column ¼ turn counterclockwise. Pull the steering column upward on the steering shaft until the shift arm contacts the dash panel in the engine compartment.

12. Rotate the steering column clockwise until the shift arm clears the opening in the dash panel. Then, pull upward on the column until the steering column attaching bracket clears the instrument panel. It may be necessary to apply a slight downward pressure on the steering column so the bracket will clear the instrument panel.

13. Rotate the steering column until the shift arm is pointing down and remove the column from the car.

14. Place the steering column on a bench and move the transmission selector lever to the neutral position.

15. Remove the shift tube to steering column hub retaining screw located on the underside of the hub.

16. Pull the shift tube out of the steering column from the lower end.

Installation

1. Position the shift tube in the steering column and install the retaining screw.

2. Place the steering column over the steering shaft with the shift arm pointing down.

3. Slide the steering column down on the steering shaft until the bracket is near the instrument panel opening.

4. Rotate the steering column about ½ turn until the top of the

steering column bracket is straight up and down on the left side of the column.

5. Slide the steering column down on the steering shaft until the shift arm contacts the dash panel. It may be necessary to apply a slight downward pressure to the steering column so the bracket will clear the instrument panel.

6. Rotate the steering column so the shift arm clears the dash panel opening and slide the column down until the shift arm is through the opening. Then, rotate the steering column so that the steering column bracket is in position at the instrument panel support bracket.

7. Loosely install the 2 steering column bracket to support bracket attaching bolts (Fig. 6).

8. Position the seal and retainer to the steering column and dash panel and install the attaching screws (Fig. 6).

9. Position the upper bearing sleeve and spring on the steering shaft.

10. Position the steering wheel on the steering shaft and install the retaining nut. Torque the nut to specification and apply 2 drops of Loctite sealer (C3AZ-19554-A) to the junction of the nut and steering shaft threads.

11. Install the spring and horn ring (or button) on the steering wheel.

12. Connect the horn and turn signal wires at the multiple connector.

13. Connect the shift linkage to the shift arm.

14. Torque the steering gear attaching bolts to specification.

15. Torque the steering column bracket to support brace attaching bolts to specification.

16. Check and adjust the shift linkage as required.

COMET AND FAIRLANE WITH AUTOMATIC TRANSMISSION AND POWER STEERING

Removal

1. Open the hood and disconnect the shift linkage from the steering column shift arm.

2. Remove 2 bolts and nuts retaining the flex coupling to the steering shaft.

3. Disconnect the turn signal and horn wires at the steering column connectors.

4. Remove the horn ring (or button) and spring from the steering wheel.

5. Remove the steering wheel retaining nut and remove the steering wheel with Tool 3600-AA (Fig. 5).

6. Remove the insulation from the dash panel in the area of the steering column.

7. Remove 2 screws clamping the dash panel seal retainer to the steering column. Then, remove 5 screws attaching the retainer to the dash panel and remove the retainer.

8. Remove 2 bolts attaching the steering column to the instrument panel support and remove the steering column from the car.

9. Remove the snap ring from the steering shaft and remove the steering shaft from the steering column.

10. Place the selector lever in the neutral position and remove the shift tube to steering column hub retaining screw located on the underside of the hub.

11. Pull the shift tube out of the lower end of the steering column.

Installation

1. Position the shift tube in the steering column and install the retaining screw.

2. Insert the steering shaft in the steering column and place the upper bearing sleeve on the upper end of the column. Install the spring and nut on the steering shaft to retain the shaft in the column.

3. Position the steering column in the car and loosely install the steering column to instrument panel support bolts.

4. Install the 2 bolts and nuts attaching the flex joint to the steering shaft.

5. Position the dash panel opening seal and retainer to the dash panel and install the 7 attaching screws.

6. Install the insulation to the dash panel in the area of the steering column.

7. Remove the nut from the steering shaft and position the steering wheel on the shaft. Install the retaining nut and torque to specification (Part 3-6).

8. Apply 2 drops of Loctite sealer (C3AZ-19554-A) to the junction of the steering shaft and nut threads.

9. Torque the steering column to instrument panel attaching bolts to specification (Part 3-6).

10. Install the horn ring and spring and connect the turn signal and horn wires at the connector.

11. Connect the shift linkage to

the steering column shift arm and adjust as required.

STEERING COLUMN UPPER BEARING REPLACEMENT

COMET AND FAIRLANE WITH POWER STEERING

1. Disconnect the horn wire and the turn indicator wires at the connectors. Remove the horn ring (or button) and the spring.

2. Remove the steering wheel attaching nut. Remove the steering wheel (Fig. 5) with a puller.

3. Remove the turn indicator lever. Remove the upper bearing retainer screws and move the turn signal switch to one side.

4. Remove 1 bolt clamping the flex coupling on the steering shaft.

5. Remove the snap ring from the steering shaft.

6. Pull up on the steering shaft to remove the bearing from the flange and remove the bearing from the steering shaft.

7. Lubricate the bearing and position it on the steering shaft. Use Tool T62F-3576-A to seat the bearing, if necessary.

8. Install the snap ring on the steering shaft.

9. Install the flex coupling clamp bolt.

10. Position the turn signal switch and bearing retainer to the flange and install the 3 retaining screws.

11. Apply 2 drops of Loctite sealer (C3AZ-19554-A) to the turn signal switch lever and install the lever.

ALL MODELS EXCEPT COMET AND FAIRLANE WITH POWER STEERING

1. Disconnect the horn wire and the turn indicator wires at the connectors. Remove the horn ring (or button) and the spring.

2. Remove the steering wheel attaching nut. Remove the steering wheel (Fig. 5) with a puller, Tool 3600-AA.

3. Remove the 3 bearing retainer screws and remove the bearing retainer.

4. Lift the turn signal switch up and over the steering shaft and position it to one side.

5. Remove the centering sleeve and spring from the steering shaft.

6. Remove 2 flange bolt nuts (Fig. 6) and lift the flange from the steering column.

7. Place a socket of the correct diameter in the steering shaft opening of the flange and drive the bearing out of the flange from the bottom side.

8. Position the 2 flange bolts in the flange holes. Start the flange bolt nuts on the flange bolts about 1½ turns.

9. Position the flange to the column so that the heads of the 2 flange bolts engage in the slots of the steering column tube. Then, tighten the 2 flange bolt nuts.

10. Lubricate the bearing and install it in the flange.

11. Position the turn signal switch and bearing retainer to the flange and install the 3 retaining screws.

12. Install the centering sleeve and spring on the steering shaft.

13. Position the steering wheel on the steering shaft and install the retaining nut. Torque the nut to specification and apply 2 drops of Loctite sealer (C3AZ-19554-A) to the junction of the nut and steering shaft threads.

14. Install the horn ring (or button) and spring on the steering wheel.

15. Connect the turn signal and horn wires at the connectors and check the operation of both units.

☰3 REMOVAL AND INSTALLATION

HOISTING INSTRUCTIONS

Damage to suspension and / or steering linkage components may occur if care is not exercised when positioning the hoist adapters of 2 post hoists prior to lifting the car.

If a 2 post hoist is used to lift the car, place the adapters under the front suspension lower arms. **Do not allow the adapters to contact the steering linkage.**

STEERING GEAR
MUSTANG
Removal

1. Disconnect the horn and turn indicator wires under the instrument panel. Also on a car with an automatic transmission, disconnect the neutral switch wires.

2. Remove the horn ring (or button). Remove the steering wheel retaining nut and the steering wheel (Fig. 5).

3. Remove the upper bearing centering sleeve and spring.

4. Remove the steering column clamp to instrument panel bolts and

remove the clamp and the insulator.

5. Pull the rubber seal up on the steering column, fold the floor mat aside, and move the dash panel insulation out of the way.

6. Remove the retaining screws from the steering column weather seal on the dash panel. Remove the steering column cover plates and gasket.

7. Slide the steering column tube assembly from the steering gear shaft, guiding the shift lever(s) up through the opening in the dash panel.

8. Raise the car and remove the clutch equalizer and bracket assembly from the frame side rail and engine if so equipped to obtain clearance.

9. On power steering equipped vehicles, remove pal nut attaching nut insulator and washer and remove the power steering cylinder rod from the bracket to obtain clearance for removal of Pitman arm.

10. Remove the inlet pipe from the manifold to obtain clearance.

11. Remove nut and washer. Install Tool T64P-3590-F and remove the Pitman arm from the sector shaft (Fig. 7).

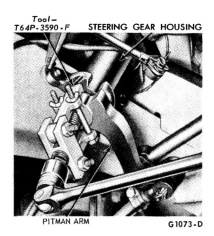

FIG. 7—Removing Pitman Arm—Typical

12. Remove steering gear retaining bolts.

13. Lower the car and disconnect

the wires from the left bank of spark plugs to prevent damaging them.

14. On vehicles equipped with column mounted shift mechanism, disconnect the transmission shift rod(s) at the gear shift lever(s).

15. Remove brake booster if necessary.

16. Remove the support rod from cowl to spring tower (except Comet).

17. Loosen air cleaner to obtain clearance if necessary.

18. Lift the steering gear and shaft assembly from the engine compartment by raising the gear up and forward past the engine and spring tower taking care not to soil or tear the front seat fabric with the end of the steering shaft.

Installation

1. Install the steering gear from engine side and guide the shaft through the dash panel being careful not to soil or tear the front seat fabric. Install the steering gear attaching bolts but do not tighten.

2. Center the steering shaft for straight ahead drive position.

3. Raise car on hoist and install clutch equalizer assembly to engine and underbody if car is so equipped.

4. Install inlet pipe to manifold.

5. Install Pitman arm to the sector shaft and install the lock washer and the torque nut to specification.

6. If equipped with power steering, install power cylinder rod to bracket and install insulator washer and nut to retain.

7. Partially lower car onto safety stands and install the steering column tube assembly over the steering shaft, guiding the shifting arms through the opening in the dash panel.

8. Position the steering column assembly and retaining clamp and insulator, and loosely install the attaching bolts and nuts.

9. Tighten the steering gear to side rail mounting bolts and column to instrument panel retaining bracket.

Check steering shaft to column upper bearing clearance. If the shaft does not touch the bearing, no further readjustment is required. If the shaft is touching the column upper bearing, it will be necessary to check the pull required to center the shaft in the column, using a fish scale. Where pull exceeds 20 lbs. at either plane to center the shaft in the column, the following correction must be made:

Vertical movement of the steering shaft can be accomplished by loosening the steering gear mounting bolts and pivoting the gear up and down.

Horizontal movement of the steering shaft can be accomplished by loosening the steering column to instrument panel retaining bracket and moving the column to the left or right.

Should additional horizontal movement be required to align the steering shaft, it will be necessary to insert shim(s) of proper thickness between the steering gear assembly and the vehicle side rail. Front end alignment shims can be used for this purpose. After the steering shaft is centered, torque all bolts to specification.

10. Position the upper bearing centering sleeve and spring. After applying Lubriplate to the upper surface of the steering shaft upper bearing and the horn switch brush plate, position the steering wheel on the steering shaft and install the retaining nut. Torque the nut to specification. Then, apply 2 drops of Loctite sealer (C3AZ-19554-A) to the junction of the steering shaft and the retaining nut threads.

Apply Loctite sealer sparingly to the turn indicator lever threads and install the lever.

11. Install the horn ring (or button) and spring, and steering wheel to the center point.

12. Set gap between column tube and steering wheel and tighten column to instrument panel.

13. Lower the car from the safety stands. Connect the horn, turn indicator wires, and (on a car with an automatic transmission) the neutral switch wires.

14. Position the steering column cover plates and gasket on the dash panel and install the retaining screws.

15. Position the dash panel insulation just above the steering column. Position the floor mat and push the rubber seal down to the floor mat.

16. Connect the transmission shift rods and correct adjustment of shift lever(s) and the neutral switch.

17. Connect ignition wires.

18. Connect cowl to spring tower support rod (except Comet).

19. Tighten the air cleaner.

COMET AND FAIRLANE WITH STANDARD STEERING (EXCEPT 390 C.I.D. ENGINE) AND ALL FALCON

Removal

1. Disconnect the turn signal and horn wires at the steering column connectors.

2. Remove the horn ring from the steering wheel.

3. Remove the steering wheel retaining nut and remove the steering wheel with Tool 3600-AA (Fig. 5).

4. Remove 5 steering column retainer attaching screws and remove the retainer from the steering column and dash panel (Fig. 6). Slide the seal up the steering column.

5. Remove the 2 steering column clamp to instrument panel support attaching bolts.

6. Remove the upper bearing centering sleeve and spring from the steering shaft.

7. Disconnect the shift linkage from the steering column shift arms.

8. Raise the car and remove the Pitman arm retaining nut and remove the Pitman arm with Tool T64P-3590-F (Fig. 7).

9. Remove the nut retaining the clutch release arm return spring bracket and remove the bracket and spring (Standard transmission cars only).

10. Remove the 3 steering gear to frame side rail attaching bolts.

11. Lower the car and remove the steering column from the steering shaft.

12. Remove the steering gear from the car.

Installation

1. Position the steering gear in the car and allow it to rest on the frame side rail.

2. Position the steering column over the steering shaft and through the hole in the dash panel.

3. Install the steering gear attaching bolts and the clutch release arm return spring, bracket, and nut.

4. Install the Pitman arm and retaining nut and washer on the sector shaft. Torque the nut to specification.

5. Position the steering column to the instrument panel and install the 2 retaining bolts. Do not tighten the bolts at this time.

6. Position the seal and retainer to the dash panel opening and install the attaching screws.

7. Position the upper bearing sleeve, spring, and steering wheel on the steering shaft and install the retaining nut (Fig. 6). Torque the nut to specification and apply 2 drops of Loctite sealer (C3AZ-19554-A) to the junction of the steering shaft and retaining nut threads.

8. Adjust the steering wheel to flange clearance to $3/64$ inch and tighten the steering column clamp to instrument panel attaching bolts. Torque the bolts to specification (Part 3-6).

9. Install the spring and horn ring (or button) on the steering wheel.

10. Connect the turn signal and horn wires at the steering column connectors.

11. Connect the shift rods to the steering column shift arms.

12. Torque the steering gear attaching bolts to specification (Part 3-6) and fill the steering gear with the specified lubricant to the correct level (Part 3-1).

COMET AND FAIRLANE WITH POWER STEERING

Removal

1. Open the hood and remove 2 bolts and nuts retaining the flex coupling to the steering shaft.

2. Raise the car and remove 3 bolts and a nut retaining the power cylinder bracket to the frame side rail. Separate the bracket from the side rail and allow the cylinder and bracket to hang.

3. Remove the Pitman arm retaining nut and washer and remove the Pitman arm from the sector shaft with Tool T64P-3590-F (Fig. 7).

4. Remove the nut retaining the clutch release arm return spring bracket and remove the bracket and spring (Standard transmission cars only).

5. Remove 3 steering gear attaching bolts and remove the steering gear.

Installation

1. Position the steering gear to the frame side rail and the flex coupling to the steering shaft and install the 3 steering gear attaching bolts. Torque the bolts to specification (Part 3-6).

2. Install the clutch release arm return spring and bracket (Standard transmission cars only).

3. Position the Pitman arm to the sector shaft and install the washer and retaining nut. Torque the nut to specification (Part 3-6).

4. Position the power cylinder bracket to the side rail and install the 3 retaining bolts and nut. Torque the bolts and nut to specification (Part 3-6).

5. Lower the car and install the 2 flex coupling to steering shaft retaining bolts and nuts.

6. Fill the steering gear with the specified lubricant to the correct level (Part 3-1).

COMET AND FAIRLANE WITH 390 C.I.D. ENGINE AND STANDARD STEERING

Removal

1. Raise the car and remove the Pitman arm retaining nut and washer.

2. Remove the Pitman arm from the sector shaft with the tool shown in Fig. 7.

3. Remove the 3 steering gear to side rail attaching bolts and disconnect the shift rods from the shift levers.

4. Lower the car and disconnect the horn and turn signal wires at the steering column multiple disconnects.

5. Remove the horn button or ring from the steering wheel, and remove the steering wheel retaining nut.

6. Remove the steering wheel from the steering shaft with Tool 3600-AA. Then, remove the tool from the steering wheel.

7. Remove 5 screws attaching the steering column opening seal and retainer to the dash panel. Remove the retainer and slide the seal up the steering column.

8. Remove 2 steering column clamp to instrument panel retaining bolts and lift the steering column from the steering shaft.

9. Open the hood and disconnect the master cylinder brake line from the junction block.

10. Remove the brake master cylinder attaching bolts and remove the master cylinder and brake line from the dash panel.

11. Disconnect the spark plug wires from numbers 5 through 8 spark plugs, and remove the rocker cover from the left cylinder head.

12. Remove 3 steering gear housing cover attaching bolts and remove the housing cover from the steering gear.

13. Remove the steering gear from the car as follows:

a. Place the steering gear output shaft against the fender apron.

b. Pull the steering gear up and over the spring tower and remove the steering gear from the car.

Installation

1. Remove the steering gear housing cover from the steering gear.

2. Position the steering gear in the car as follows:

a. Insert the steering shaft through the opening in the dash panel.

b. Point the output shaft toward the fender apron. Slide the gear downward and position it to the frame side rail.

3. Install the steering gear housing cover on the gear housing and adjust the steering gear (Section 2).

4. Position the steering column over the steering shaft and loosely install the steering column clamp to instrument panel retaining bolts.

5. Position the steering column opening seal and retainer to the dash panel and install the retaining screws.

6. Center the steering gear midway between a full right and full left turn and position the steering wheel on the steering shaft and install the retaining nut.

7. Torque the nut to specification and apply 2 drops of Loctite sealer (C3AZ-19554-A) to the junction of the nut and steering shaft threads.

8. Install the horn button or ring and the spring to the steering wheel.

9. Install the rocker cover on the left cylinder head and connect the spark plug wires to the spark plugs (Group 8).

10. Position the brake master cylinder to the dash panel and install the attaching bolts.

11. Connect the brake master cylinder line to the junction block.

12. Raise the car and install the steering gear to side rail retaining bolts. Torque the retaining bolts to specification (Part 3-6).

13. Position the Pitman arm to the sector shaft and install the retaining nut. Torque the nut to specification (Part 3-6).

14. Bleed the brake hydraulic system (Part 2-1).

15. Connect the shift rods to the shift levers.

16. Lower the car and torque the steering column clamp to instrument panel retaining bolts.

17. Connect the horn and turn signal wires at the steering column multiple connectors.

4 MAJOR REPAIR OPERATIONS

STEERING GEAR

DISASSEMBLY

1. Rotate the steering shaft approximately 2¼ turns from either stop.

2. After removing the sector adjusting screw locknut and the housing cover bolts, remove the sector shaft with the cover. Remove the cover from the shaft by turning the screw clockwise. **Keep the shim with the screw** (Fig. 8).

of wood (Fig. 9) to loosen it from the housing.

6. Remove the ball return guide clamp and the ball return guides from the ball nut. **Keep the ball nut clamp-side up until ready to remove the balls.**

7. Turn the ball nut over, and rotate the worm shaft from side to side until all balls (Mustang—62 balls; Comet, Falcon, and Fairlane—54 balls) have dropped out of the nut into a clean pan. With the balls re-

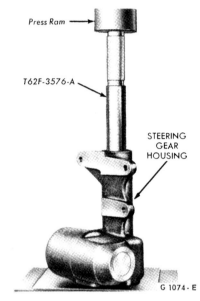

FIG. 10—Removing Sector Shaft Bearing

Press both sector shaft bearings out of the housing (Fig. 10). **Remove the seal and the bearings only if there is an indication of wear, damage, or bearing mislocation. Do not install a new bearing in a housing in which the bearing has turned or is found to be mislocated. A new housing must be used.**

ASSEMBLY

1. If the sector shaft bearings have been removed, press new bearings into the housing (Fig. 11).

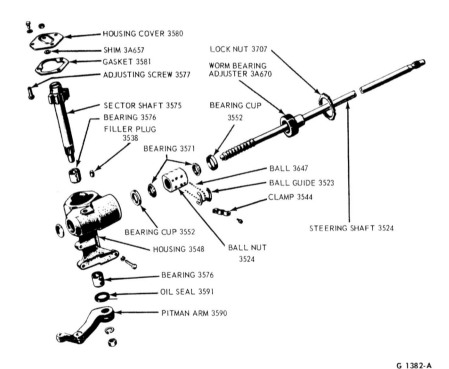

FIG. 8—Manual Steering Gear Disassembled

3. Loosen the worm bearing adjuster nut, and remove the adjuster assembly and the steering shaft upper bearing and cup.

4. Carefully pull the steering shaft and ball nut from the housing. **To avoid possible damage to the ball return guides, keep the ball nut from running down to either end of the worm.**

Disassemble the ball nut only if there is indication of binding or tightness.

5. Remove the lower bearing and cup from the housing. It may be necessary to tap the housing on a block

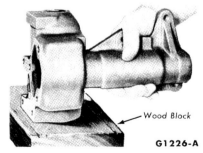

FIG. 9—Removing Lower Bearing Cup from Housing

moved, the ball nut will slide off the worm.

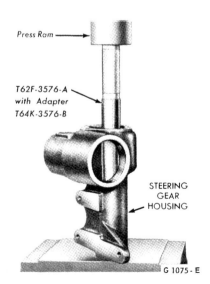

FIG. 11—Installing Sector Shaft Bearing

2. Position a bearing cup in the adjuster.

3. If the sector shaft oil seal has been removed, install a new oil seal.

4. Swab the inside diameter of the ball nut and the outside diameter of the worm with gear lubricant C3AZ-19578-A prior to assembly. Lay the steering shaft on a bench as shown in Fig. 12. After positioning the shaft, turn the ball nut to place the

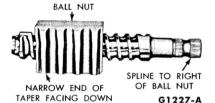

BALL NUT

NARROW END OF
TAPER FACING DOWN

SPLINE TO RIGHT
OF BALL NUT

G1227-A

FIG. 12—Positioning Ball Nut—Typical

guide holes in the up position. Align the grooves in the worm and in the ball nut by sighting through the ball guide holes.

5. Insert the ball guides into the holes of the ball nut, tapping them lightly with a wood handle of a screw driver if necessary to seat them.

6. Insert the balls (Mustang—62 balls; Comet, Falcon, and Fairlane—54 balls) into the hole in the top of each ball guide. It may be necessary to rotate the shaft slightly one way,

then in the opposite direction to distribute the balls in the circuit.

7. After the balls (Mustang—31 balls; Comet, Falcon, and Fairlane—27 balls) are installed, install the ball guide clamp. Check the ball nut to see that it rotates freely. Torque the screw to specification.

8. Coat the threads of the steering shaft bearing adjuster, the housing cover bolts, and the sector adjusting screw with a suitable oil-resistant sealing compound. **Do not apply sealer to female threads, and especially avoid getting any sealer on the steering shaft bearings.**

9. Coat the worm bearings, sector shaft bearing and gear teeth with gear lubricant C3AZ-19578-A.

10. Clamp the housing in a vise, with the sector shaft axis horizontal, and position the steering shaft lower bearing cup and the bearing in place.

11. Position the steering shaft and ball nut assembly in the housing.

12. Position the steering shaft upper bearing on the top of the worm, and install the steering shaft bearing adjuster and cup. Install the lock nut with the flat side against the bearing adjuster and the letter outward. Leave the nut loose.

13. After installing the steering wheel nut on the steering shaft, adjust the worm bearing preload, using an inch-pound torque wrench to check for specified preload.

14. Position the sector adjusting screw and the adjuster shim, and check the end clearance which should not exceed 0.002 inch between the screw head and the end of the sector shaft. If clearance is greater than 0.002 inch, replace the shim.

15. Thread the sector shaft adjusting screw into the housing cover.

16. Install a new gasket on the housing cover.

17. Rotate the steering shaft until the ball nut teeth are in position to mesh with the sector gear, tilting the housing so that the ball nut will tip toward the housing cover opening.

18. Apply enough gear lubricant C3AZ-19578-A to fill the pocket in the housing between the sector shaft bearings 30% full.

19. Push the housing cover with the sector shaft into place.

20. Turn the cover to one side and fill the housing with ½ lb. of gear lubricant C3AZ-19578-A.

21. Install but do not tighten the housing cover attaching bolts. Do not tighten the cover bolts until it is certain that there is some lash between the ball nut and the sector gear teeth.

22. After loosely installing the sector shaft adjusting screw lock nut, adjust the sector shaft mesh to the specified mesh load, then tighten the adjusting screw lock nut. Remove the steering wheel nut.

---

5 **STEERING LINKAGE REPAIR**

The manual steering linkage (Figs. 13, 14, and 15) consists of the Pitman arm, the steering arm-to-idler arm rod, the steering idler arm, and the spindle connecting rods (tie rods). **Do not attempt to straighten bent linkage; use new parts.**

HOISTING INSTRUCTIONS

Damage to suspension and/or steering linkage components may occur if care is not exercised when positioning the hoist adapters of 2 post hoists prior to lifting the car.

If a 2 post hoist is used to lift the car, place the adapters under the front suspension lower arms. **Do not allow the adapters to contact the steering linkage.**

SPINDLE CONNECTING ROD END REPLACEMENT

The spindle connecting rod ends, which are threaded into the outer

ends of the rod sleeves, have non-adjustable, spring-loaded ball studs. A rod end should be replaced when excessive looseness at the ball stud is noticed.

1. Remove the cotter pin and nut from the worn rod end ball stud.

2. Disconnect the end from the spindle, connecting arm, Pitman arm, or idler arm as shown in Fig. 16.

3. Loosen the connecting rod sleeve clamp bolts, and count the number of turns needed to remove the rod end from the sleeve. Discard all rod end parts that were removed from the sleeve. **All new parts should be used when a spindle connecting rod end is replaced.**

4. Thread a new rod end into the sleeve, but do not tighten the sleeve clamp bolts at this time.

5. Insert the stud in the part from which the old one was removed, and install the stud nut. Torque the nut

to specification and install the cotter pin.

6. Check and, if necessary, adjust toe-in (Part 3-1). **After toe-in is checked and adjusted, torque the old sleeve clamp bolts to specification. Add four pounds torque if new bolts are used. The tie rod sleeve clamps must be installed as shown in Fig. 13, Part 3-1, to prevent interference with the side rail.**

SPINDLE SLEEVE REPLACEMENT

A spindle sleeve should be replaced if it becomes worn or damaged (Figs. 13, 14, and 15). **Do not attempt to straighten the sleeve if threaded portion is damaged.**

1. Remove the spindle connecting rod ends as described in the previous sub-section.

2. Screw the spindle rod ends into the new sleeve the same number of turns as the ends that were removed.

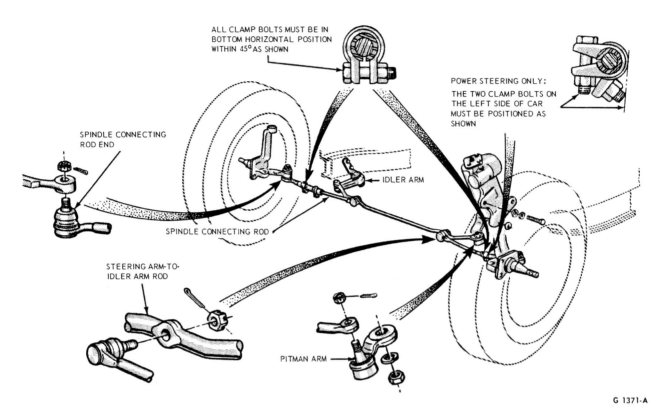

ALL CLAMP BOLTS MUST BE IN BOTTOM HORIZONTAL POSITION WITHIN 45° AS SHOWN

POWER STEERING ONLY: THE TWO CLAMP BOLTS ON THE LEFT SIDE OF CAR MUST BE POSITIONED AS SHOWN

SPINDLE CONNECTING ROD END

IDLER ARM

SPINDLE CONNECTING ROD

STEERING ARM-TO-IDLER ARM ROD

PITMAN ARM

G 1371-A

FIG. 13—Typical Steering Linkage—Comet, Falcon, and Fairlane

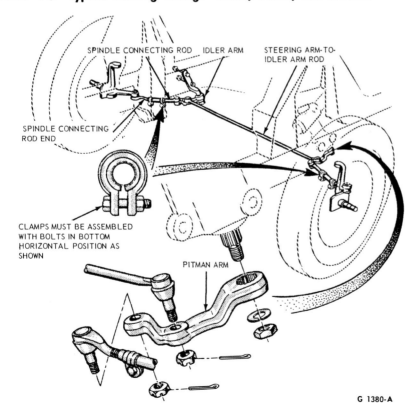

SPINDLE CONNECTING ROD   IDLER ARM   STEERING ARM-TO-IDLER ARM ROD

SPINDLE CONNECTING ROD END

CLAMPS MUST BE ASSEMBLED WITH BOLTS IN BOTTOM HORIZONTAL POSITION AS SHOWN

PITMAN ARM

G 1380-A

FIG. 14—6-Cylinder Manual Steering Linkage—Mustang

Do not tighten the clamp bolts at this time.

3. Position the sleeve assembly on the Pitman arm (or the idler arm)

and the spindle arm. Install the attaching nut, torque it to specification, and install the cotter pin.

4. Check and, if necessary, adjust toe-in (Part 3-1). After toe-in is checked and adjusted, torque the sleeve clamp bolts to specification. The sleeve clamp must be installed with the bolt down to prevent interference with the side rail.

STEERING ARM-TO-IDLER ARM ROD REPLACEMENT

The rod connecting the Pitman arm and the idler arm is non-adjustable and is provided with tapered holes to accommodate the ball studs (Figs. 13, 14, and 15). The rod should be replaced when damaged or when worn at the ball studs.

MUSTANG—6-CYLINDER

1. Remove the cotter pins and nuts from the ball studs at the sector shaft arm and the idler arm, and remove the steering arm-to-idler arm rod (Fig. 16).

2. Position the new steering arm-to-idler arm rod on the idler arm and the steering arm.

3. Install the ball stud retaining nuts and torque to specification.

4. Install cotter pins, lubricate the

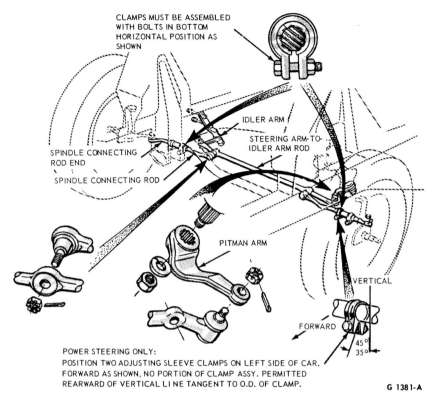

CLAMPS MUST BE ASSEMBLED WITH BOLTS IN BOTTOM HORIZONTAL POSITION AS SHOWN

IDLER ARM

STEERING ARM-TO-IDLER ARM ROD

SPINDLE CONNECTING ROD END

SPINDLE CONNECTING ROD

PITMAN ARM

VERTICAL

FORWARD

45°
35°

POWER STEERING ONLY:
POSITION TWO ADJUSTING SLEEVE CLAMPS ON LEFT SIDE OF CAR. FORWARD AS SHOWN, NO PORTION OF CLAMP ASSY. PERMITTED REARWARD OF VERTICAL LINE TANGENT TO O.D. OF CLAMP.

G 1381-A

FIG. 15—8-Cylinder Manual Steering Linkage—Power Typical—Mustang

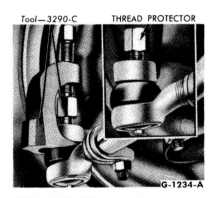

Tool—3290-C   THREAD PROTECTOR

G-1234-A

FIG. 16—Disconnecting Steering Linkage Ball Stud—Typical

power steering ball stud socket, if necessary.

5. Check and, if necessary, adjust toe-in (Part 3-1).

COMET, FALCON, FAIRLANE, AND 8 CYLINDER MUSTANG

Removal

1. Raise the car on a hoist and position safety stands.

2. Remove the 2 cotter pins and nuts retaining both spindle connecting rod ends to the steering arm-to-idler arm rod (Fig. 13).

3. Disconnect the spindle connecting rod ends from the steering arm-to-idler arm rod with Tool-3290-C (Fig. 16).

4. Remove 1 cotter pin and nut retaining the idler arm to the steering arm-to-idler arm rod and disconnect the idler arm from the rod with Tool-3290-C.

5. Remove 1 cotter pin and nut retaining the Pitman arm to the steering arm-to-idler arm rod. Disconnect

the Pitman arm from the rod with Tool-3290-C and remove the rod.

Installation

1. Replace the rubber seals on the spindle connecting rod ends, if required.

2. Position the steering arm-to-idler arm rod to the Pitman arm and idler arm and install the retaining nuts. Torque the nuts to the low end of the specification. Continue to tighten each nut until the slots in the nut align with the hole in the stud. Then install the cotter pin.

3. Position the spindle connecting rod ends to the steering arm-to-idler arm rod and install the retaining nuts. Torque the nuts to the low end of the specification. Continue to tighten each nut until the slots in the nut align with the hole in the stud. Then, install the cotter pin.

4. Remove the safety stands, lower the car, check and adjust toe-in to specification (Part 3-1).

STEERING IDLER ARM AND/OR BUSHING

1. Raise the car and remove the cotter pin and nut retaining the idler arm to the steering arm-to-idler arm rod (Figs. 13, 14, and 15).

2. Remove the cotter pin and nut retaining the idler arm to the bracket and remove the idler arm.

3. Place the idler arm in a vise and replace the bushings as shown in Fig. 17.

4. Position the idler arm to the bracket and steering arm-to-idler arm rod and install the retaining nuts and cotter pins.

5. Lower the car and check caster, camber and toe-in and adjust if required.

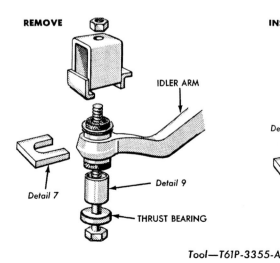

REMOVE

IDLER ARM

Detail 7

Detail 9

THRUST BEARING

Tool—T61P-3355-A

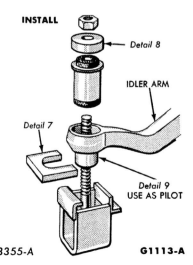

INSTALL

Detail 8

IDLER ARM

Detail 7

Detail 9
USE AS PILOT

G1113-A

FIG. 17—Replacing Idler Arm Bushings—Typical

PART 3-4
POWER STEERING

Section	Page
1 Description and Operation	3-34
Description	3-34
Operation	3-34
Power Steering Pump	3-36
Flow Control Valve	3-36
Pressure Relief Valve	3-37
2 In-Car Adjustments and Repairs	3-37
Power Steering Pump Belt Tension Adjustment	3-37
Control Valve Centering Spring Adjustment	3-37
Control Valve to Power Steering Cylinder Hose	3-37
Power Steering Pump to Control Valve Hose	3-37
3 Removal and Installation	3-38
Steering Gear	3-38

Section	Page
Power Steering Pump	3-38
6 Cylinder	3-38
8 Cylinder	3-38
Power Steering Pump Pulley	3-38
Power Steering Control Valve	3-39
Mustang—6 Cylinder	3-39
Comet, Falcon, and Fairlane	3-39
Power Cylinder	3-40
4 Major Repair Operations	3-40
Control Valve	3-40
Disassembly	3-40
Tube Seat Replacement	3-41
Assembly	3-41
Power Cylinder Seal	3-42
Power Steering Pump Reservoir Replacement	3-42

1 DESCRIPTION AND OPERATION

DESCRIPTION

The Power Steering System (Fig. 1) is a hydraulically controlled linkage-type steering system which includes an integral pump and fluid reservoir, a control valve, a power cylinder, the connecting fluid lines, and the steering linkage. The hydraulic pump, belt-driven from the engine crankshaft, draws fluid from the reservoir and provides fluid pressure for the system. Within the pump itself is a pressure-relief valve which governs the pressures within the steering system according to the varying conditions of operation. After fluid has passed from the pump to the control valve and the power cylinder, it returns to the reservoir.

The power steering pump is a belt driven slipper type pump which is integral with the reservoir. It is constructed so that the reservoir is attached to the rear side of the pump housing front plate and the pump body is incased within the reservoir.

OPERATION

The control valve, operated by steering wheel movement, directs the pressure developed by the pump. When the front wheels are in the straight-ahead position, the control valve spool is held in the center (neutral) position by its centering spring. Fluid then flows around the valve lands and returns to the reservoir (Fig. 2). Within the control valve body there is a reaction limiting valve which reduces parking effort.

When force of about 4 pounds is exerted for a left turn, the valve spool overcomes the pressure of the centering spring and moves toward the right end of the valve. As a result, pressure is exerted on the right side of the power cylinder piston, and fluid in the left end of the cylinder returns to the reservoir (Fig. 2).

If the direction of the force on the steering wheel is reversed, the front wheels will turn to the straight forward position. Or as force on the

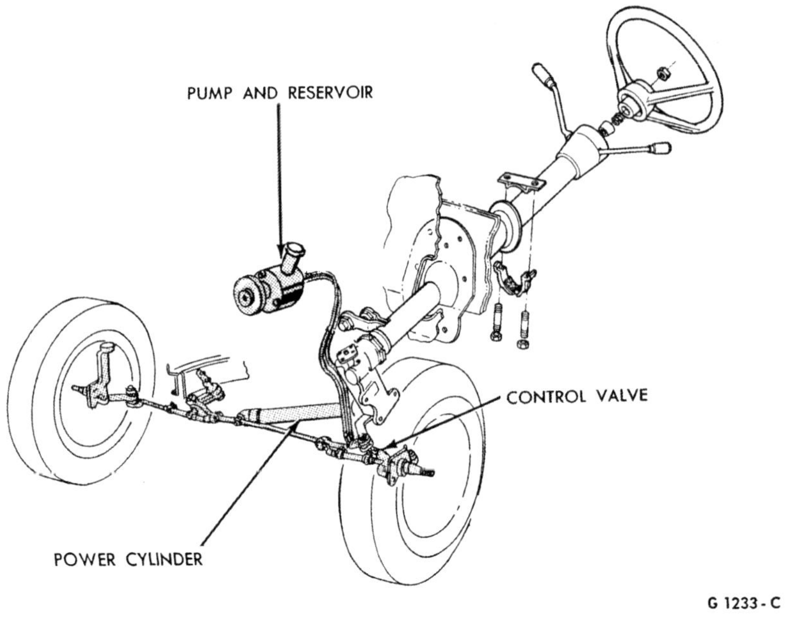

FIG. 1—Power Steering System

G 1233-C

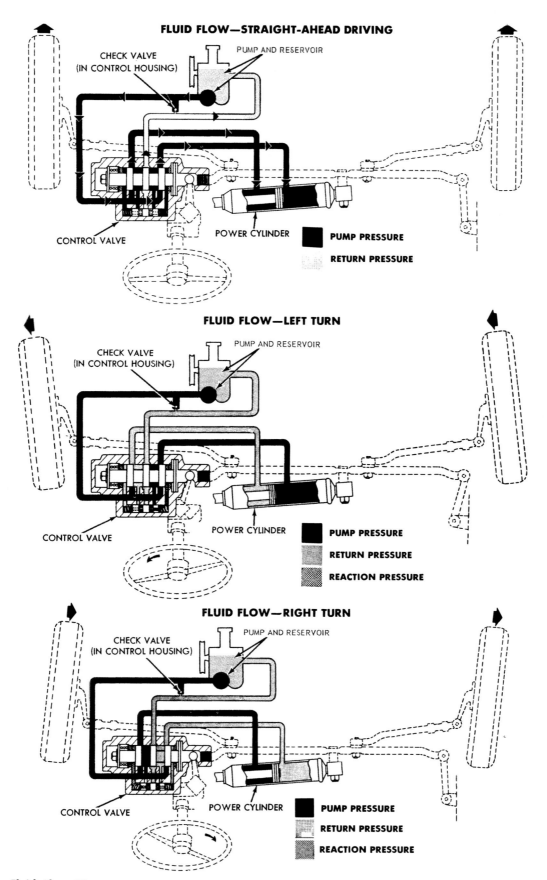

FIG. 2—Fluid Flow Diagram

steering wheel falls below approximately 4 pounds the valve spool centering spring forces the spool back to the center position and there the pressure on both sides of the power cylinder piston is equal. With normal forward driving movement of the car and in the absence of operative pressure within the power cylinder, the front wheels will seek to return to the straight ahead position. This is a normal effect of the front wheel alignment.

For a right turn, the directional forces explained above are reversed (Fig. 2).

If, for any reason, the pump fails to deliver fluid pressure, the car may be steered without pump pressure.

POWER STEERING PUMP

The pump rotor has 8 slippers and springs which rotate inside a cam insert containing two lobes 180° from each other. The cam insert and the pump port plates provide a sealed chamber within which the rotor and slippers rotate between the two lobes for pump operation.

As the rotor turns, the slippers are forced outward against the inner surface of the cam insert by a combination of centrifugal force, slipper spring force and fluid pressure acting on the under side of the slipper. A pair of adjacent slippers, along with the surfaces of the rotor, cam and pressure plates, form a sealed chamber within the crescent-shaped void. As this sealed chamber moves through the crescent shaped void its volume changes, resulting in a pumping action.

As the rotor rotates 90° (Fig. 3), the slipper slides outward in its slot, riding on the cam and the volume of the sealed chamber increases. This creates a vacuum and sets up a suction area. With the inlet port placed in this area, the chamber will fill with fluid. As the rotor rotates from 90° to 180°, the volume of the sealed chamber decreases, thus creating a pressure area. The pressure or outlet port is located in this area. While this pumping action is going on between 0° and 180°, the same condition is occurring between 180° and 360°. This combination creates what is known as a balanced rotor pump. The two pressure and suction quadrants are diametrically opposite each other.

FLOW CONTROL VALVE

Since the pump is a constant displacement pump, the internal flow

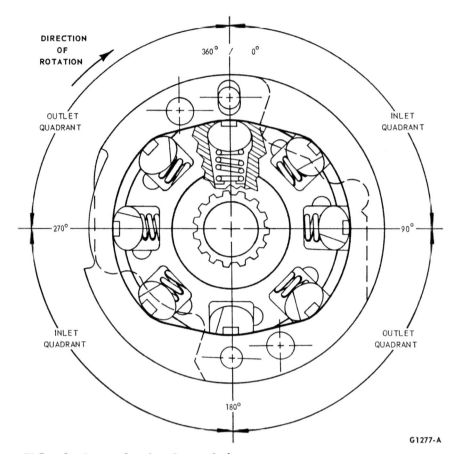

FIG. 3—Power Steering Pump Cycle

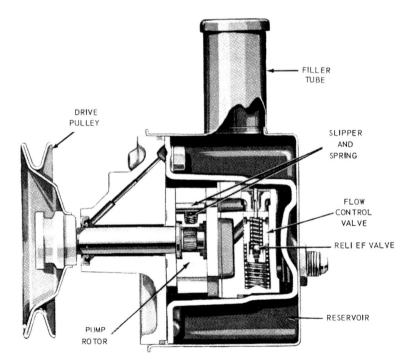

FIG. 4—Power Steering Pump—Sectional View

will vary directly with the pump speed. However, a power steering

gear requires a relatively high constant rate of flow in the parking zone and up to approximately 2800 RPM and thereafter a lower rate of flow. This is accomplished by means of a variable orifice mechanism shown in Fig. 4.

All of the internal pump flow is ported from the pumping mechanism (rotor, slippers, and cam insert), through passage A into the flow control zone. All of flow goes through the orifice and out into the line until the bypass port is cracked open. This is the regulation point. The oil drops in pressure in moving through the orifice. The lower pressure is then sensed through a hole drilled in the cover communicating to the rear of

the spool valve. The differential in pressure thus created on the spool valve increases steadily and proportionally with increasing RPM and this moves the valve progressively back into its bore, thus increasing the opening of the bypass port.

The metering pin (Fig. 4) travels with the spool valve decreasing the net area of the orifice at higher speeds. This action reduces flow to the steering gear.

PRESSURE RELIEF VALVE

When the steering wheel is turned completely to the stop position in the right or left turn direction, or in the

case of a road load of sufficient magnitude, the steering gear will not accept any flow from the pump, except for a very limited volume of oil due to leakage past valve seals. Because of this resistance, excessive hydraulic pressure would be developed, if it were not limited by the pressure relief valve.

When relief pressure is reached, the pressure relief ball is forced off its seat, allowing oil to pass through the spool valve and dump into the bypass port (Fig. 4). The relief valve will continue to limit oil pressure to the relief setting for the duration of the overload condition.

---

2   IN-CAR ADJUSTMENTS AND REPAIRS

HOISTING INSTRUCTIONS

Damage to suspension and/or steering linkage components may occur if care is not exercised when positioning the hoist adapters of 2 post hoists prior to lifting the car.

If a 2 post hoist is used to lift the car, place the adapters under the front suspension lower arms. **Do not allow the adapters to contact the steering linkage.**

PUMP BELT TENSION ADJUSTMENT

Pump drive belt tension cannot be checked accurately using the thumb pressure or belt deflection methods. Correct belt adjustment is assured only with the use of a belt tension gauge.

1. Check the belt tension with a belt tension gauge (T63L-8620-A). With a new belt, or one that has been run for less than 15 minutes, the tension should be within 120-150 lbs. With a belt that has been run for more than 15 minutes, the tension should be within 90-120 lbs.

2. To adjust the belt, loosen the mounting bolts incorporated on the front face of the pump cover plate (hub side) and one nut at the rear. Place a $9/16$ inch open end wrench on the projecting $\frac{1}{2}$ inch boss on the front face of the pump cover plate and pry upward to adjust belt tension. **When adjusting the power steering pump belt tension, do not pry against the pump or reservoir to obtain the proper belt tension. The reservoir will be deformed when pried on or pressed against and a leak will result.**

3. Recheck the belt tension. When the tension has been correctly adjusted, torque the bolts and the nut to specification.

CONTROL VALVE CENTERING SPRING ADJUSTMENT

COMET, FALCON, AND FAIRLANE

1. Raise the car and remove 2 spring cap retaining screws and lock washers and remove the spring cap.

2. Tighten the adjusting nut snug; then, loosen the nut $\frac{1}{4}$ turn. Do not tighten the adjusting nut too tight.

3. Position the spring cap to the valve housing and install the 2 retaining screws and washers.

4. Lower the car.

5. Start the engine and check the turning effort with a spring scale. With the spring scale attached to the rim of the steering wheel, the effort to turn the wheel in both directions should not exceed 12 pounds.

CONTROL VALVE TO POWER STEERING CYLINDER HOSE

COMET, FALCON, AND FAIRLANE

1. Raise the car on a hoist and place a drain pan under the power cylinder.

2. Disconnect the hose from the power cylinder and allow the fluid to drain from the hose. Then, disconnect the hose from the control valve.

3. Connect the hose to the control valve and power cylinder.

4. Remove the drain pan and lower the car.

5. Fill the power steering pump reservoir with fluid to the proper level (Part 3-1).

6. Start the engine and turn the steering wheel to each end of its travel several times to cycle the system. Then, check for leaks.

7. Stop the engine and again check the power steering fluid level. Add fluid as required.

POWER STEERING PUMP TO CONTROL VALVE HOSE

COMET, FALCON, AND FAIRLANE

Removal

1. Remove the fluid from the pump reservoir with a suction gun.

2. Raise the car on a hoist.

3. Remove the clamp retaining the hose tubes to the control valve.

4. Disconnect the fluid return and pressure hoses from the control valve and allow the fluid to drain into a pan.

5. Lower the car and disconnect the fluid return hose from the reservoir.

6. Disconnect the fluid pressure hose from the pump outlet fitting.

7. Remove 1 bolt attaching the hoses, insulator, and the retainer to the frame side rail and remove the hoses, and the insulator and retainer as an assembly from the car.

8. Remove the pressure and return hoses from the retainer and insulator.

Installation

1. Install the pressure and return hoses in the insulator and retainer.

Position the assembly to the frame side rail and install the attaching bolt.

2. Place a hose clamp on the fluid return hose and install the hose on the power steering pump reservoir return fitting.

3. Torque the pump outlet fitting to specification (Part 3-6). Then, connect the pressure hose to the out-let fitting and torque the fitting to specification.

4. Raise the car and connect the pressure and return lines to the control valve.

5. Install the clamp to retain the hose tubes to the control valve.

6. Lower the car and fill the power steering pump reservoir with fluid, C1AZ-19582-A, to the proper level (Part 3-1).

7. Start the engine and turn the steering wheel to each end of its travel several times to cycle the system. Then, check for fluid leaks.

8. Stop the engine and again check the power steering fluid level (Part 3-1). Add fluid as required.

---

3 REMOVAL AND INSTALLATION

HOISTING INSTRUCTIONS

Damage to suspension and/or steering linkage components may occur if care is not exercised when positioning the hoist adapters of 2 post hoists prior to lifting the car.

If a 2 post hoist is used to lift the car, place the adapters under the front suspension lower arms. **Do not allow the adapters to contact the steering linkage.**

STEERING GEAR

Refer to Group 3-3, Section 3 for detailed instructions.

POWER STEERING PUMP

6-CYLINDER

Removal

1. Remove the fill cap from the reservoir and remove the fluid with a suction gun.

2. Disconnect the fluid return hose from the reservoir.

3. Disconnect the oil pressure hose from the pump.

4. Loosen the adjusting bolts and remove the drive belt from the pulley.

5. Drain the coolant from the radiator and remove 3 bolts and spacers attaching the pump bracket to the engine. Remove one bolt attaching the support to the lower edge of the bracket and remove the pump and bracket from the car.

6. Place the bracket in a vise and install a ⅜-16 capscrew in the end of the pump shaft.

7. Install tool T63L-10300-B on the pulley and remove the pulley from the pump shaft. Refer to Fig. 5 for tool installation.

8. Remove 3 bolts retaining the pump to the bracket and remove the pump from the bracket.

Installation

1. Position the pump to the bracket and install the 3 retaining bolts. Torque to specification.

2. Position the pulley to the pump shaft and install tool T65P-3A733A. Press the pulley on the shaft. (Refer to Fig. 4 for tool installation.) Then, remove the tool.

3. Position the pump and bracket to the engine and install the attaching bolts and spacers.

4. Install one bolt to attach the brace to the bottom of the bracket. Torque the bracket attaching bolts to specification (Part 3-6).

5. Position the belt on the pulley and adjust the belt tension to specification with Tool T63L-8620-A (Section 2).

6. Torque the outlet fitting hex nut to specification. Then, connect the pressure hose to the fitting and torque the hose nut to specification.

7. Connect the return hose to the reservoir and tighten the clamp.

8. Fill the radiator with coolant.

9. Fill the pump reservoir to the correct level with transmission fluid (C1AZ-19582-A). Start the engine and turn the steering wheel to each end of its travel several times to cycle the system and check for leaks. Check the fluid level (Section 1, Part 3-1) and fill as required and install the fill cap.

8-CYLINDER

Removal

1. Remove the fill cap from the reservoir and remove the fluid with a suction gun.

2. Disconnect the fluid return hose from the reservoir.

3. Disconnect the oil pressure hose from the pump.

4. Loosen the belt adjusting bolts and nut and remove the drive belt from the pump pulley.

5. Remove 3 bolts and 1 nut retaining the pump to the bracket and remove the pump from the car.

Installation

1. Position the pump to the bracket and loosely install the 2 pivot bolts and 2 adjusting bolts.

2. Position the drive belt on the pulley and adjust the belt tension to specification with tool T63L-8620-A (Section 2). Tighten the adjusting bolts and pivot bolts to specification.

3. Torque the outlet fitting hex nut to specification (Part 3-6). Then, connect the pressure hose to the fitting and torque the hose nut to specification.

4. Connect the return hose to the reservoir and tighten the clamp.

5. Fill the pump reservoir to the correct level with transmission fluid C1AZ-19582-A. Start the engine and turn the steering wheel to each end of its travel several times to cycle the system and check for leaks. Check the fluid level, fill as required, and install the fill cap.

POWER STEERING PUMP PULLEY

REMOVAL

Other than pulley removal and reservoir or seal replacement, the pump should not be disassembled but replaced as a unit.

1. Drain as much of the fluid as possible from the pump through the fill pipe.

2. Install a ⅜-16 capscrew in the end of the pump shaft to prevent damage to the shaft end by the tool screw.

3. Install the pulley remover tool, T63L-10300-B on the pulley hub, and place the tool and pump in a vise as shown in Fig. 5.

4. Hold the pump and rotate the tool nut counterclockwise to remove the pulley (Fig. 5).

INSTALLATION

1. Position the pulley to the pump shaft and install Tool T65P-3A733-A as shown in Fig. 6.

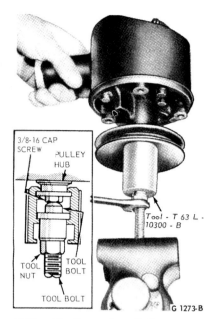

FIG. 5—Removing Pulley From Pump

2. Hold the pump and rotate the tool nut clockwise to install the pulley on the shaft. The pulley face will be flush with the end of the pump shaft. **Install the pulley without in and out pressure on the shaft to prevent damage to internal thrust areas.**

3. Remove the tool.

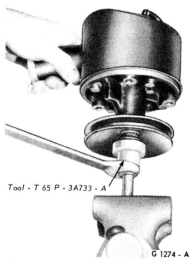

FIG. 6—Pulley Installation

POWER STEERING CONTROL VALVE

MUSTANG—6 CYLINDER

Removal

1. Disconnect the pressure lines leading from the power cylinder to the control valve, at the valve. Allow the lines to drain into a container.

2. Disconnect the lines leading from the power steering pump to the control valve at the valve. Allow the lines to drain into a container. Remove the clamp that secures the lines to the valve.

3. Remove the two bolts that secure the control valve to the steering arm-to-idler arm rod.

4. Remove the cotter pin and the castellated nut that secures the control valve to the Pitman arm.

5. Disconnect the control valve from the Pitman arm as shown in Fig. 7.

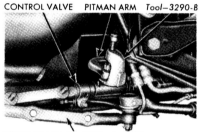

FIG. 7—Disconnecting Control Valve from Pitman Arm— Typical

6. Inspect the tube fittings and the seats in the valve for nicks, burrs or damage. Replace the seats in the valve or the tubes as required.

Installation

1. Place the stud in a straight vertical position. Measure from the center of the stud parallel to the bolt mounting surface (Fig. 8) to the

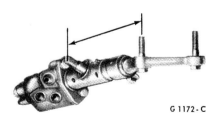

FIG. 8—Control Valve Length Adjustment—Mustang 6-Cylinder

center of the first bolt hole. The distance should be from $4\frac{1}{8}$ -$4^3/_{16}$ inches (6 cyl. models only). If not within these limits adjust the length as required.

2. Secure the control valve stud to

the Pitman arm with the castellated nut and a cotter pin.

3. Secure the end of the control valve to the steering arm-to-idler arm rod with two bolts, lock washers and nuts.

4. Connect the pressure line and the oil return line to their respective fittings on the valve. Install the line retaining clamp around the valve.

5. Connect the two lines from the power cylinder to their respective fittings on the valve.

6. Fill the reservoir to the correct level.

7. Start the engine and turn the steering wheel to each end of its travel several times to cycle the system. Stop the engine.

8. Check the fluid level and fill as necessary. Install the fill cap.

9. Start the engine and check for leaks.

COMET, FALCON, AND FAIRLANE

Removal

1. Disconnect the 4 fluid line fittings at the control valve, and drain the fluid from the lines. Turn the front wheels to the left and right several times to force all the fluid from the system.

2. Loosen the clamping nut and bolt at the right-hand end of the sleeve.

3. Remove the roll pin from the steering arm to idler arm rod through the slot in the sleeve.

4. Remove the control valve ball stud nut.

5. Using the tool shown in Fig. 9, remove the ball stud from the sector shaft arm.

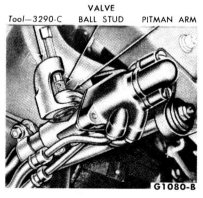

FIG. 9—Control Valve Ball Stud Removal

6. After turning the front wheels fully to the left, unthread the control valve from the steering arm to idler arm rod.

Installation

1. Thread the valve onto the steering arm to idler arm rod until about four threads are still visible on the rod.

2. Position the ball stud in the sector shaft arm.

3. Measure the distance between the center of the grease plug in the sleeve and the center of the stud at the inner end of the left-hand spindle connecting rod (Fig. 10). The distance should be 5⅝ inches. If the distance is not correct, disconnect the ball stud from the sector shaft arm and turn the valve on the steering arm to idler arm rod to increase or decrease the distance.

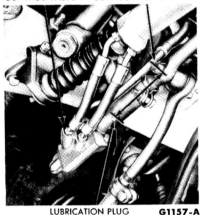

CONTROL VALVE   CONNECTING ROD STUD

LUBRICATION PLUG   G1157-A

FIG. 10—Control Valve Installation Measurement—Typical—Comet, Falcon, and Fairlane

4. When the correct distance is obtained and the ball stud is positioned in the sector shaft arm, align the hole in the steering arm to idler arm rod with the slot near the end of the valve sleeve. Install the roll pin in the rod hole to lock the valve in position on the rod.

5. Torque the valve sleeve clamp bolt to specification.

6. *Install the nut on the ball stud,* and torque the nut to specification.

Install a new cotter pin.

7. Connect the fluid lines to the control valve, and tighten all fittings securely. **Do not over-tighten.**

8. Fill the fluid reservoir with the specified fluid to the F mark on the dip stick.

9. Start the engine and run it at idle speed for about two minutes to warm the fluid in the power steering system.

10. Turn the steering wheel all the way to the left and right several times, and check the system for fluid leaks.

11. Increase the engine speed to about 1000 rpm, and turn the steering wheel all the way to the left and right several times.

12. Stop the engine, and check the control valve and hose connections for fluid leaks. Correct the cause of any leaks.

13. Check the fluid level, and refill the reservoir if necessary.

14. With the engine running check the position of the steering wheel when the front wheels are in the straight-ahead position. **Do not make any adjustments until toe-in is checked.**

15. Keep the engine running, and check toe-in. If either toe-in or steering wheel position is not correct make all necessary adjustments (Part 3-1) at the spindle connecting rod sleeves.

16. Check the effort to turn the wheels in both directions. The effort should be about equal in both directions.

POWER CYLINDER

REMOVAL

1. Disconnect the two fluid lines from the power cylinder and allow them to drain into a container.

2. Remove the pal nut, attaching nut, washer and the insulator from the end of the power cylinder rod.

3. Remove the cotter pin and castellated nut that secures the power cylinder stud to the steering arm-to-idler arm rod.

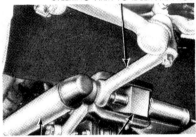

STEERING ARM-TO-IDLER ARM ROD

POWER CYLINDER *Tool*— T64P-3590-F   G 1173-B

FIG. 11—Disconnecting Power Cylinder Stud

4. Disconnect the power cylinder stud from the steering arm-to-idler arm rod as shown in Fig. 11.

5. Remove the insulator sleeve and washer from the end of the power cylinder rod.

6. Inspect the tube fittings and the seats in the power cylinder for nicks, burrs or damage. Replace the seats in the cylinder or the tubes as required.

INSTALLATION

1. Install the washer, sleeve and the insulator on the end of the power cylinder rod.

2. Extend the rod as far as possible. Insert the rod in the bracket on the frame and compress the rod as necessary to insert the stud in the steering arm-to-idler arm rod. Secure the stud with a castellated nut and a cotter pin.

3. Secure the power cylinder rod with an insulator, washer, nut and a pal nut.

4. Connect each of the two fluid lines to their respective part in the cylinder.

5. Fill the reservoir to the correct level.

6. Start the engine and turn the steering wheel to each end of its travel several times to cycle the system. Stop the engine.

7. Check the fluid level and fill as necessary. Install the fill cap.

8. Start the engine and check for leaks.

4 MAJOR REPAIR OPERATIONS

CONTROL VALVE

DISASSEMBLY

1. Wipe all fluid and loose dirt from the outside of the control valve.

2. Remove the centering spring

cap from the valve housing (Fig. 12).

When holding the control valve for disassembly, use a softjawed vise, and clamp the valve only around the sleeve flange to prevent damage to the housing, spool, or sleeve.

3. Remove the nut from the end of the valve spool bolt. Remove the *washers, spacer,* centering spring, adapter, and bushing from the bolt and the valve housing.

4. Remove the two bolts that hold

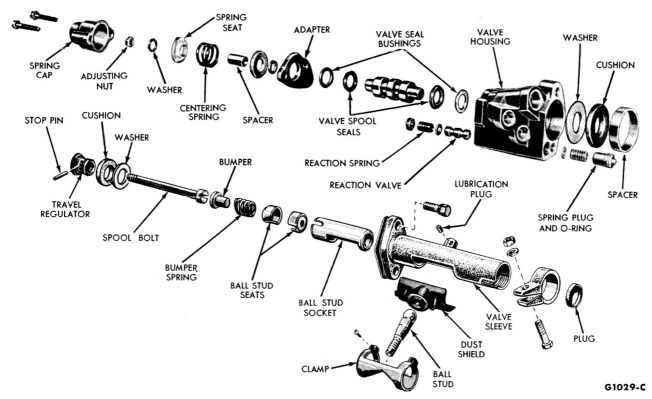

FIG. 12—Control Valve Disassembled—Typical

the valve housing and the sleeve to-gether, and separate the housing from the sleeve.

5. Remove the plug from the valve sleeve.

6. Push the valve spool out of the centering spring end of the valve housing, and remove the seal from the spool.

7. Remove the spacer, bushing, and seal from the sleeve end of the valve housing.

8. Drive the stop pin out of the travel regulator stop with a punch and hammer (Fig. 13). **Pull the head of the valve spool bolt tightly against the travel regulator stop before driving the pin out of the stop.**

9. Turn the travel regulator stop counterclockwise in the valve sleeve to remove the stop from the sleeve.

10. Remove the valve spool bolt, spacer, and rubber washer from the travel regulator stop.

11. Remove the rubber boot and clamp from the valve sleeve.

12. Slide the bumper, spring, and ball stud seat out of the valve sleeve, and remove the ball stud socket from the sleeve.

13. After removing the return port hose seat, remove the return port relief valve.

14. After removing the spring plug

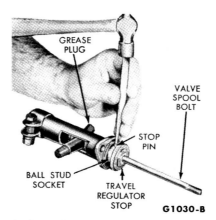

FIG. 13—Removing Stop Pin —Typical

and O-ring, remove the reaction lim-iting valve (Fig. 14).

TUBE SEAT REPLACEMENT

If a hose seat is worn or damaged it should be replaced. It can be re-moved with an Easy-Out tool, or by using a bolt of appropriate size as a puller.

1. Tap the existing hole in the hose seat, using a starting tap of suit-able size. **Be sure to remove all metal chips from the hose seat port after tapping.**

2. Place a nut and large flat wash-er on a bolt of the same size as the

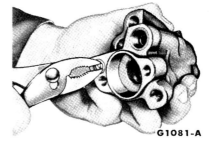

FIG. 14—Removing Reaction Valve Plug

tapped hole. The washer must be large enough to cover the hose seat port.

3. Insert the bolt in the tapped hole, and using the nut as a puller, remove the hose seat.

4. Place a new hose seat in the port, and thread a bolt of suitable size into the port. Tighten the bolt enough to bottom the seat in the port.

ASSEMBLY

Before assembling the control valve, coat all parts except the seals with Automatic Transmission Fluid. Coat the seals with lubricant COAZ-19553-A.

1. Install the reaction limiting valve, the spring, and the plug.

2. Install the return port relief

valve and the hose seat.

3. Insert one of the ball stud seats (flat end first) into the ball stud socket, and insert the threaded end of the ball stud into the socket.

4. Place the socket in the control valve sleeve so that the threaded end of the ball stud can be pulled out through the slot in the sleeve (Fig. 15).

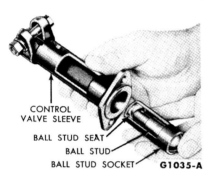

FIG. 15—Installing Ball Socket, Seal and Bracket

5. Place the other ball stud seat, the spring, and the bumper (Fig. 12) in the socket, and install and securely tighten the travel regulator stop.

6. Loosen the stop just enough to align the nearest hole in the stop with slot in the ball stud socket, and install the stop pin in the ball stud socket, travel regulator stop, and valve spool bolt (Fig. 13).

7. Install the rubber boot, clamp, and the plug on the control valve sleeve. **Make sure that the lubrication fitting is turned on tightly and does not bind on the ball stud socket.**

8. Insert the valve spool in the valve housing. **Rotate the spool while inserting it in the housing (Fig. 16).**

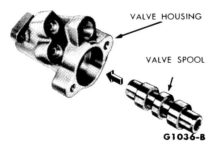

FIG. 16—Inserting Valve Spool

9. Move the spool toward the centering spring end of the housing, and place the small seal bushing, and spacer in the sleeve end of the housing.

10. Press the valve spool against the inner lip of the seal and, at the

same time, guide the lip of the seal over the spool with a small screwdriver. **Do not nick or scratch the seal or the spool during installation.**

11. Place the sleeve end of the housing on a flat surface so that the seal, bushing, and spacer are at the bottom end and push down the valve spool until it stops.

12. Carefully install the spool seal and bushing in the centering spring end of the housing. Press the seal against the end of the spool, guiding the seal over the spool with a small screwdriver. **Do not nick or scratch the seal or the spool during installation.**

13. Pick up the housing, and slide the spool back and forth in the housing to check for free movement.

14. Place the valve sleeve on the housing so that the ball stud is on the same side of the housing as the ports for the two power cylinder lines. Install the two bolts in the sleeve, and torque them to specifications.

15. Place the adapter on the centering spring end of the housing, and install the bushing, washers, spacers, and centering spring on the valve spool bolt.

16. Compress the centering spring, and install the nut on the bolt. Tighten the nut snug, then loosen it not more than ¼ turn (Fig. 17). **Excessive tightening of the nut may break the stop pin at the travel regulator stop.**

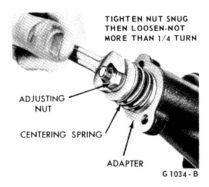

FIG. 17—Adjusting Centering Spring

17. Move the ball stud back and forth in the sleeve slot to check the spool for free movement. See Part 3-6 for the specified travel. Apply COAZ-19553-A (silicone) grease at the sealing areas.

18. Install the centering spring cap on the valve housing, and torque the two cap bolts to specification.

19. Install the nut on the ball stud

so that the valve can be positioned in a vise as shown in Fig 18. Then push forward on the cap end of the valve to check the valve spool for free movement.

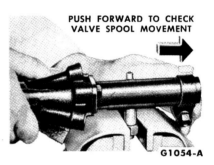

FIG. 18—Inspecting Valve Spool Movement

20. Turn the valve around in the vise, and push forward on the sleeve end to check the spool for free movement.

POWER CYLINDER SEAL

REMOVAL

1. Clamp the power cylinder in a vise, and remove the snap ring from the end of the cylinder. **Be careful not to distort or crack the cylinder in the vise.**

2. Pull the piston rod out all the way to remove the scraper, bushing, and seals. If the seals cannot be removed in this manner, remove them from the cylinder with a sharp pick. Take care, when using a pick, not to damage the shaft or seal seat.

INSTALLATION

When replacing the power cylinder seals, install all of the parts supplied in the repair kit for the cylinder being repaired.

1. Coat the new seals with lubricant COAZ-19553-A and place the parts (Fig. 19) on the piston rod which has been coated with the same grease.

2. Push the rod in all the way, and install the parts in the cylinder with a deep socket slightly smaller than the cylinder opening (Fig. 20).

POWER STEERING PUMP RESERVOIR REPLACEMENT

Reservoir replacement must be done on a clean workbench. Cleanliness of work area and tools is extremely important when repairing any hydraulic unit. Thoroughly clean the exterior of *the pump* with a suitable cleaning solvent. **Do not immerse the shaft oil seal in solvent.**

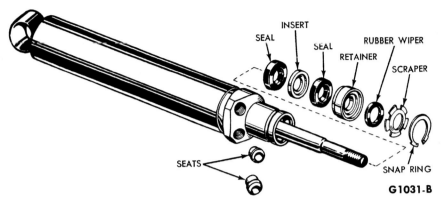

FIG. 19—Power Cylinder

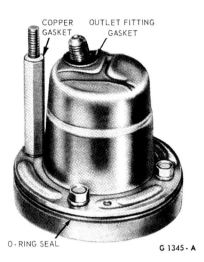

FIG. 22—Gasket Locations

the rear of the reservoir and on the outer edges only.

5. Inspect the assembly to be sure the reservoir is evenly seated on the pump housing plate.

6. Position the service indentification tag on the outlet fitting and install the outlet fitting hex nut. Torque the nut to specification (Part 3-6). **Do not exceed specification.**

7. Install the stud nut and torque to specification.

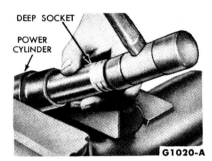

FIG. 20—Installing Power Cylinder Seals

Plug the inlet and outlet openings with plugs or masking tape before cleaning the pump exterior or removing the reservoir.

REMOVAL

1. Position the pump in a bench mounted holding fixture, Tool T57L-500-A.

2. Rotate the pump so the pulley side is facing down and remove the outlet fitting hex nut, stud nuts, and service identification tag.

3. Invert the pump so the pulley side is facing up and remove the reservoir by tapping around the flange with a wood block (Fig. 21).

4. Remove the reservoir O-ring seal, the outlet fitting gasket, and the support stud copper gasket from the pump.

INSTALLATION

1. Install a new gasket on the out-

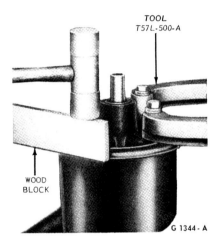

FIG. 21—Removing Pump Reservoir

let fitting, a new copper gasket on the support stud, and a new reservoir O-ring seal on the pump housing plate (Fig 22). **The old gaskets and seal should never be re-used.**

2. Apply vaseline to the reservoir O-ring seal and to the inside edge of the new reservoir flange. **Do not twist the O-ring seal.**

3. Position the reservoir over the pump and align the reservoir with the outlet fitting and the stud hole.

4. Install the reservoir on the pump and O-ring seal with a plastic or rubber hammer and a block of wood as shown in Fig. 23. **Tap at**

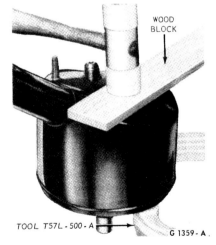

FIG. 23—Installing Reservoir on Pump

PART 3-5
WHEELS AND TIRES

Section	Page
1 Description and Operation	3-44
Front Wheel	3-44
Rear Wheel	3-44
2 In-Car Adjustment and Repairs	3-45
Front Wheel Bearing Adjustment	3-45
3 Removal and Installation	3-45
Wheel and Tire Removal	3-45
Removing Tire From Wheel	3-45
Installing Tire on Wheel	3-45

Section	Page
Wheel and Tire Installation	3-46
4 Major Repair Operations	3-46
Front Wheel Grease Seal and Bearing Replacement and/or Repacking	3-46
Drum Brakes	3-47
Disc Brakes	3-47
Front Hub and Drum Replacement	3-47
Front Hub and Rotor Replacement	3-48

1 DESCRIPTION AND OPERATION

FRONT WHEEL

Each front wheel and tire assembly is bolted to its respective front hub and brake drum or rotor on Mustang with disc brakes (optional on Mustang models). Two opposed tapered roller bearings are installed in each hub. A grease retainer is installed at the inner end of the hub to prevent lubricant from leaking into the drum or on the rotor. The entire assembly is retained to its spindle by the adjusting nut, nut lock and cotter pin (Figs. 1 and 2).

REAR WHEEL

The rear brake drum assembly is retained to studs on the rear axle shaft flange by three speed nuts. The wheel and tire assembly mounts on the same rear axle shaft flange studs and is held against the hub and drum by the wheel nuts. The rear wheel bearing is pressed onto the axle shaft just inside the shaft flange, and the entire assembly is retained to the rear axle housing by the bearing retainer plate which is bolted to the housing flange.

The inner end of each axle shaft is splined to the differential in the rear axle.

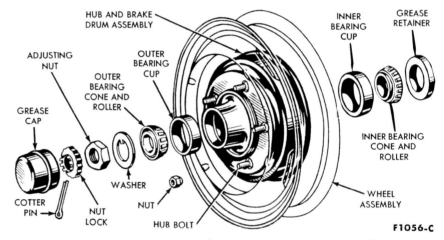

FIG. 1—Front Hub, Bearings and Grease Retainer—Drum Brakes

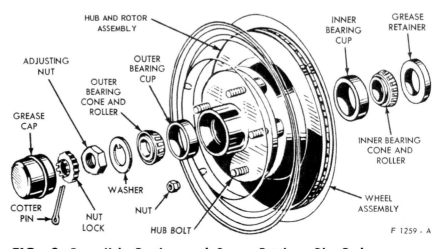

FIG. 2—Front Hub, Bearings and Grease Retainer—Disc Brakes

2 IN-CAR ADJUSTMENTS AND REPAIRS

HOISTING INSTRUCTIONS

Damage to suspension and/or steering linkage components may occur if care is not exercised when positioning the hoist adapters of 2 post hoists prior to lifting the car.

If a 2 post hoist is used to lift the car, place the adapters under the front suspension lower arms. **Do not allow the adapters to contact the steering linkage.**

FRONT WHEEL BEARING ADJUSTMENT

The front wheel bearings should be adjusted if the wheel is too loose on the spindle or if the wheel does not rotate freely. The following procedure will bring the bearing adjustment to specification.

1. Raise the car until the wheel and tire clear the floor.

2. Pry off the hub cap or wheel cover and remove the grease cap from the hub.

3. Wipe the excess grease from the end of the spindle, and remove the cotter pin and nut lock.

4. If equipped with disc brakes, loosen the bearing adjusting nut

three turns. Then, rock the wheel and rotor assembly in and out several times to push the shoe and linings away from the rotor.

5. While rotating the wheel, hub, and drum or rotor assembly, torque the adjusting nut to 17-25 ft-lbs to seat the bearings (Fig 3).

6. Locate the nut lock on the adjusting nut so that the castellations on the lock are aligned with the cotter pin hole in the spindle.

7. Back off both the adjusting nut and the nut lock together until the next castellation on the nut lock aligns with the cotter pin hole in spindle.

8. Install a new cotter pin, and bend the ends of the cotter pin around the castellated flange of the nut lock.

9. Check the front wheel rotation. If the wheel rotates properly, install the grease cap and the hub cap or wheel cover. If the wheel still rotates roughly or noisily, clean or replace the bearings and cups as required (Section 4).

10. Before driving the car (if equipped with disc brakes), pump the brake pedal several times to obtain normal brake lining to rotor clearance and restore normal brake pedal travel.

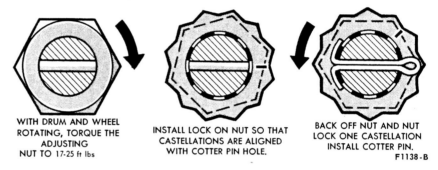

WITH DRUM AND WHEEL ROTATING, TORQUE THE ADJUSTING NUT TO 17-25 ft lbs

INSTALL LOCK ON NUT SO THAT CASTELLATIONS ARE ALIGNED WITH COTTER PIN HOLE.

BACK OFF NUT AND NUT LOCK ONE CASTELLATION INSTALL COTTER PIN.

F1138-B

FIG. 3—Front Wheel Bearing Adjustment

3 REMOVAL AND INSTALLATION

HOISTING INSTRUCTIONS

Damage to suspension and/or steering linkage components may occur if care is not exercised when positioning the hoist adapters of 2 post hoists prior to lifting the car.

If a 2 post hoist is used to lift the car, place the adapters under the front suspension lower arms. **Do not allow the adapters to contact the steering linkage.**

WHEEL AND TIRE REMOVAL

1. Pry off the wheel hub cap or cover. Loosen but do not remove the wheel lug nuts.

2. Raise the car until the wheel and tire clear the floor.

3. Remove the wheel lug nuts from the bolts, and pull the wheel and tire assembly from the hub and drum or rotor.

REMOVING TIRE FROM WHEEL

The tire can be demounted on a

mounting machine. **Be sure that the outer side of the wheel is positioned downward.** If tire irons are used follow the procedure given here.

1. Remove the valve cap and core, and deflate the tire completely.

2. With a bead loosening tool, break loose the tire side walls from the wheel (Fig. 4).

3. **Position the outer side of the**

F1058-A

FIG. 4—Bead Loosening Tool

wheel downward, and insert two tire irons about 8 inches apart between the tire inner bead and the back side of the wheel rim. **Use only tire irons with rounded edges or irons designed for demounting tubeless tires.**

4. Leave one tire iron in position, and pry the rest of the bead over the rim with the other iron. Take small "bites" with the iron around the tire in order to avoid damaging the sealing surface of the tire bead.

5. Stand the wheel and tire upright with the tire outer bead in the drop center well at the bottom of the wheel. Insert the tire iron between the bead and the edge of the wheel rim, and pry the wheel out of the tire.

INSTALLING TIRE ON WHEEL

1. If a used tire is being installed remove all dirt from the tire.

If a tire is being mounted to the original wheel, clean the rim with emery cloth or fine steel wool. Check the rim for dents.

If a new wheel is being installed, coat a new valve with RUGLYDE or similar rubber lubricant and position the valve to the new wheel. Use a rubber hammer or a valve replacing tool to seat the valve firmly against the inside of the rim.

2. Apply RUGLYDE or a similar rubber lubricant to the sealing surface on both tire beads. With the outer side of the wheel down, pry the beads over the wheel rim with two tire irons. **Do not use a hammer or mallet to force the beads over the rim.**

3. Align the balance mark on the tire with the valve on the wheel.

4. Hold the beads against the rim flanges by positioning a tire mounting band over the tire (Fig 5). If a mounting band is not available, tie

F1021-A

FIG. 5—Tubeless Tire Mounting Band

a torniquet of heavy cord around the circumference of the tire. Tighten the cord with a tire iron. Center the tire on the wheel with a rubber mallet.

5. Give the tire a few quick bursts of air to seat the beads properly, then inflate the tire to 40 pounds pressure. Check to see that the bead positioning rings (outer rings near

the side walls) are evenly visible just above the rim flanges all the way around the tire. If the rings are not even, deflate the tire completely and inflate it again.

6. When the rings are properly positioned, deflate the tire to the recommended pressure.

WHEEL AND TIRE INSTALLATION

1. Clean all dirt from the hub and drum or rotor.

2. Position the wheel and tire assembly on the hub and drum or rotor. Install the wheel lug nuts and tighten them alternately in order to draw the wheel evenly against the hub and drum or rotor.

3. Lower the car to the floor, and torque the lug nuts to specification (Part 3-6).

---

4 MAJOR REPAIR OPERATIONS

HOISTING INSTRUCTIONS

Damage to suspension and/or steering linkage components may occur if care is not exercised when positioning the hoist adapters of 2 post hoists prior to lifting the car.

If a 2 post hoist is used to lift the car, place the adapters under the front suspension lower arms. **Do not allow the adapters to contact the steering linkage.**

FRONT WHEEL GREASE SEAL AND BEARING REPLACEMENT AND/OR REPACKING

If bearing adjustment will not eliminate looseness or rough and noisy operation, the hub and bearings should be cleaned, inspected, and repacked. If the bearing cups or the cone and roller assemblies are worn or damaged, they should be replaced.

DRUM BRAKES

1. Raise the car until the wheel and tire clear the floor.

2. Remove the wheel cover or hub cap. Remove the grease cap from the hub. Remove the cotter pin, nut lock, adjusting nut, and flat washer from the spindle. Remove the outer bearing cone and roller assembly (Fig 1).

3. Pull the wheel, hub, and drum assembly off the wheel spindle.

4. Remove the grease retainer and

the inner bearing cone and roller assembly from the hub with a drift.

5. Clean the lubricant off the inner and outer bearing cups with solvent and inspect the cups for scratches, pits, excessive wear, and other damage. If the cups are worn or damaged, remove them with a drift.

6. Soak a new grease retainer in light engine oil at least 30 minutes before installation. Thoroughly clean the inner and outer bearing cones and rollers with solvent, and dry them thoroughly. **Do not spin the bearing with compressed air.**

7. Inspect the cone and roller assemblies for wear or damage, and replace them if necessary. **The cone and roller assemblies and the bearing cups should be replaced as a unit if damage to either is encountered.**

8. Thoroughly clean the spindle and the inside of the hub with solvent to remove all old lubricant. Cover the spindle with a clean cloth, and brush all loose dust and dirt from the brake assembly. **To prevent getting dirt on the spindle, carefully remove the cloth from the spindle.**

9. If the inner and/or outer bearing cups(s) were removed, install the replacement cup(s) in the hub with the tool shown in Figs. 6 or 7. **Be sure to seat the cups properly in the hub.**

10. Pack the inside of the hub with

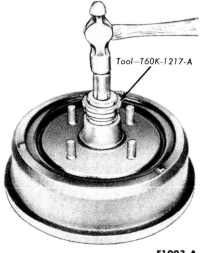

F1093-A

FIG. 6—Installing Front Wheel Bearing Cup—Falcon 6-Cylinder

specified wheel bearing grease. Add lubricant to the hub only until the grease is flush with the inside diameter of both bearing cups (Fig. 8).

11. All old grease should be completely cleaned from the bearings before repacking them with new grease. Pack the bearing cone and roller assemblies with wheel bearing grease. A bearing packer is desirable for this operation. If a packer is not available, work as much lubricant as possible between the rollers

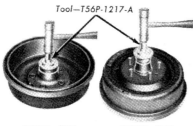

Tool—T56P-1217-A

INNER CUP INSTALLATION   OUTER CUP INSTALLATION

F1057-A

FIG. 7—Installing Front Wheel Bearing Cup—All Fairlane, Comet, and Mustang and 8-Cylinder Falcon

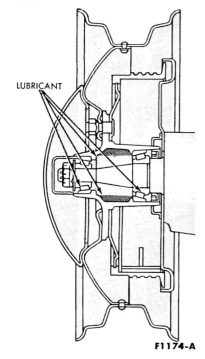

LUBRICANT

F1174-A

FIG. 8—Front Wheel Hub Lubrication

and cages. Lubricate the cone surfaces with grease.

12. Place the inner bearing cone and roller assembly in the inner cup, and install the new grease retainer with the reverse end of the tool shown in Figs. 6 to 7. **Be sure that the retainer is properly seated.**

13. Install the wheel, hub, and drum assembly on the wheel spindle. **Keep the hub centered on the spindle to prevent damage to the grease retainer or the spindle threads.**

14. Install the outer bearing cone and roller assembly and the flat washer on the spindle; then, install the adjusting nut (Fig. 1).

15. Adjust the wheel bearings as outlined in Section 2, and install a

new cotter pin. Bend the ends of the cotter pin around the castellations of the nut lock to prevent interference with the radio static collector in the grease cap. Install the grease cap.

16. Install the hub cap or wheel cover.

DISC BRAKES

1. Raise the car until the wheel and tire clear the floor.

2. Remove the wheel cover or hub cap.

3. Remove the wheel and tire from the hub.

4. Remove 2 bolts attaching the caliper to the caliper bracket. Remove the caliper from the rotor and wire it to the underbody to prevent damage to the brake hose.

5. Remove the grease cap from the hub. Remove the cotter pin, nut lock, adjusting nut, and flat washer from the spindle. Remove the outer bearing cone and roller assembly (Fig. 2).

6. Pull the hub and rotor off the wheel spindle.

7. Remove the grease retainer and the inner bearing cone and roller assembly from the hub.

8. Clean the lubricant off the inner and outer bearing cups with solvent and inspect the cups for scratches, pits, excessive wear, and other damage. If the cups are worn or damaged, remove them with a drift.

9. Soak a new grease retainer in light engine oil at least 30 minutes before installation. Thoroughly clean the inner and outer bearing cones and rollers with solvent, and dry them thoroughly. **Do not spin the bearings with compressed air.**

Inspect the cone and roller assemblies for wear or damage, and replace them if necessary. **The cone and roller assemblies and the bearing cups should be replaced as a unit if damage to either is encountered.**

10. Thoroughly clean the spindle and the inside of the hub with solvent to remove all old lubricant. Cover the spindle with a clean cloth, and brush all loose dust and dirt from the brake assembly. **To prevent getting dirt on the spindle carefully remove the cloth from the spindle.**

11. If the inner and / or outer bearing cup(s) were removed, install the replacement cup(s) in the hub with the tool shown in Figs. 6 or 7.

Be sure to seat the cups properly in the hub.

12. Pack the inside of the hub with specified wheel bearing grease. Add lubricant to the hub only until the grease is flush with the inside diameter of both bearing cups.

13. All old grease should be completely cleaned from the bearings before packing them with new grease. Pack the bearing cone and roller assemblies with wheel bearing grease. A bearing packer is desirable for this operation. If a packer is not available, work as much lubricant as possible between the rollers and cages. Lubricate the cone surfaces with grease.

14. Place the inner bearing cone and roller assembly in the inner cup, and install the new grease retainer with the reverse end of the tool shown in Figs. 6 or 7. **Be sure that the retainer is properly seated.**

15. Install the hub and rotor on the wheel spindle. **Keep the hub centered on the spindle to prevent damage to the grease retainer or the spindle threads.**

16. Install the outer bearing cone and roller assembly and the flat washer on the spindle; then, install the adjusting nut.

17. Position the caliper over the rotor and install the 2 attaching bolts.

18. Install the wheel and tire on the hub.

19. Adjust the wheel bearings as outlined in Section 2, and install a new cotter pin. Bend the ends of the cotter pin around the castellations of the nut lock to prevent interference with the radio static collector in the grease cap. Install the grease cap.

20. Install the hub cap or wheel cover and lower the car.

FRONT HUB AND DRUM REPLACEMENT

When the hub and drum assembly is replaced, new bearings, cups, and grease retainer must be installed in the new assembly. The new grease retainer should be soaked in light engine oil at least 30 minutes before installation.

1. Raise the car until the wheel and tire clears the floor. Pry off the hub cap or wheel cover, and remove the wheel and tire assembly from the hub and drum assembly.

2. Remove the grease cap from the hub. Remove the cotter pin, nut

lock, adjusting nut, and flat washer from the spindle. Remove the outer bearing cone and roller assembly (Fig. 1).

3. Pull the wheel, hub, and drum assembly off the wheel spindle.

4. Remove the protective coating from the new hub and drum with carburetor degreaser. Install new inner and outer bearing cups in the new hub with the tool shown in Figs. 6 or 7. **Be sure to seat the cups properly in the hub.**

5. Pack the inside of the hub with specified wheel bearing grease. Add lubricant to the hub only until the grease is flush with the inside diameter of both bearing cups (Fig. 8).

6. All old grease should be completely cleaned from the bearings before repacking them with new grease. Pack the bearing cone and roller assemblies with wheel bearing grease. A bearing packer is desirable for this operation. If a packer is not available, work as much lubricant as possible between the rollers and cages. Lubricate the cone surfaces with grease.

7. Place the inner bearing cone and roller assembly in the inner cup, and install the new grease retainer with the reverse end of the tool shown in Fig. 6 or 7. **Be sure that the retainer is properly seated.**

8. Install the new hub and drum assembly on the wheel spindle. **Keep the hub centered on the spindle to prevent damage to the grease retainer.**

9. Install the outer bearing cone and roller assembly and the flat washer on the spindle; then, install the adjusting nut (Fig 1).

10. Position the wheel and tire assembly on the new hub and drum assembly. Install the wheel lug nuts and tighten them alternately in order to draw the wheel evenly against the hub and drum. Do not exceed specifications (Part 3-6).

11. Adjust the wheel bearings as outlined in Section 2, and install a new cotter pin. Bend the ends of the cotter pin around the castellations of the nut lock to prevent interference with the radio static collector in the grease cup. Install the grease cup.

12. Install the hub cap or wheel cover.

FRONT HUB AND ROTOR REPLACEMENT

When the hub and rotor assembly is replaced, new bearings, cups, and grease retainer must be installed in the new assembly. The new grease retainer should be soaked in light engine oil at least 30 minutes before installation.

1. Raise the car until the wheel and tire clears the floor. Pry off the hub cap or wheel cover, and remove the wheel and tire assembly from the hub and rotor.

2. Remove 2 bolts attaching the caliper to the caliper bracket. Remove the caliper from the rotor and wire it to the underbody to prevent damage to the brake hose.

3. Remove the grease cap from the hub. Remove the cotter pin, nut lock, adjusting nut, and flat washer from the spindle. Remove the outer bearing cone and roller assembly (Fig 2). Pull the hub and rotor off the wheel spindle.

4. Remove the protective coating from the new hub and rotor with carburetor degreaser. Install new inner and outer bearing cups in the new hub with the tool shown in Figs. 6 or 7. **Be sure to seat the cups properly in the hub.**

5. Pack the inside of the hub with specified wheel bearing grease. Add lubricant to the hub only until the grease is flush with the inside diameter of both bearing cups.

6. All old grease should be completely cleaned from the bearings before repacking them with new grease. Pack the bearing cone and roller assemblies with wheel bearing grease. A bearing packer is desirable for this operation. If a packer is not available, work as much lubricant as possible between the rollers and cages. Lubricate the cone surfaces with grease.

7. Place the inner bearing cone and roller assembly in the inner cup, and install the new grease retainer with the reverse end of the tool shown in Figs. 6 or 7. **Be sure that the retainer is properly seated.**

8. Install the new hub and rotor assembly on the wheel spindle. **Keep the hub centered on the spindle to prevent damage to the grease retainer.**

9. Install the outer bearing cone and roller assembly and the flat washer on the spindle; then, install the adjusting nut (Fig 2).

10. Position the wheel and tire assembly on the new hub and rotor. Install the wheel hub nuts and tighten them alternately in order to draw the wheel evenly against the hub and rotor. Do not exceed specifications (Part 3-6).

11. Adjust the wheel bearings as outlined in Section 2, and install a new cotter pin. Bend the ends of the cotter pin around the castellations of the nut lock to prevent interference with the radio static collector in the grease cap. Install the grease cap.

12. Install the hub cap or wheel cover.

PART 3-6 SPECIFICATIONS

FRONT WHEEL ALIGNMENT

COMET, FALCON AND FAIRLANE	Checking Specifications			Optimum Re-setting Specifications
	Min.	Max.	Maximum Variation Between Wheels	Desired Alignment
Caster	−1°	+1°	½°	0°
Camber	−½°	+1°	½°	+¼°
Toe-in	⅛ in.	⅜ in.	—	¼ in.

MUSTANG				
Caster—6 Cyl.	0°	+2°	½°	+1°
Caster—8 Cyl.	−1°	+1°	½°	0°
Camber—All	−¼°	+1¼°	½°	+½°
Toe-in	⅛ in.	⅜ in.	—	¼ in.

MUSTANG	Optimum Re-Setting Specifications
	Desired Alignment
King Pin Angle	6 Cyl.—7° 8 Cyl.—6⅞°
Turning Angle of Outside Wheel With Inside Wheel Turned 20° 6 Cyl. Std. Steering	18⅞°
6 Cyl. Power Steering	20⅛°
8 Cyl. Std. Steering	19⅛°
8 Cyl. Power Steering	18¾°

COMET, FALCON AND FAIRLANE	Optimum Re-Setting Specifications
	Desired Alignment
King Pin Angle	7½°
Turning Angle of Outside Wheel With Inside Wheel Turned 20°	17¾°

BALL JOINTS

	Radial Play (Inches) Max. Allowable
Upper Ball Joint	0.250
Lower Ball Joint	Replace if Perceptibly Loose

FRONT SUSPENSION TORQUE LIMITS (FIG. 1)

Ref. No.	Description	Torque Ft-Lbs	
		Comet Falcon Fairlane	Mustang
1	Shock Absorber Upper Attachment	20-28	10-15
2	Shock Absorber Upper Bracket to Body	8-13	8-16
3	Front Suspension Compression Bumper to Body	12-17	12-17
4	Brake Backing Plate to Spindle	30-40	25-35
5	Upper Arm and Inner Shaft to Body	75-100	55-75
6	Spring Seat to Upper Arm	17-25	17-25
7	Shock Absorber to Spring Seat	12-17	12-17
8	Wheel Lug Nut 4 Lug Wheel	55-85	—
	5 Lug Wheel	70-115	70-115
9	Wheel Bearing Adjusting Nut	①17-25	①17-25
10	Ball Joint to Spindle (Upper and Lower)	②60-90	②60-90
11	Strut to Lower Arm	55-70	55-70
12	Lower Arm to Underbody	75-100	35-50
13	Stabilizer Bar Mounting Bracket to Underbody	11-16	17-25
14	Strut to Underbody	40-60	40-55
15	Stabilizer Bar to Lower Arm	5-10	5-11

①Torque the adjusting nut to 17-25 ft. lb. Locate nut lock on adjusting nut so castellations are aligned with cotter pin hole in spindle. Then, back off adjusting nut and nut lock so the next castellation aligns with the cotter pin hole.
②Torque to specification; then, tighten the nut to the nearest cotter pin slot and insert the cotter pin.

REAR SUSPENSION TORQUE LIMITS (FIG. 2)

Ref. No.	Description	Torque Ft-Lbs	
		Comet Falcon Fairlane	Mustang
1	Spring Shackle Bars to Body and Spring	15-22	15-22
2	Rear Shock Absorber to Upper Mounting Bracket	15-25	15-25
3	Rear Shock Absorber to Rear Spring Clip Plate	15-25	15-25
4	Rear Spring to Rear Axle U-bolt Nut	30-45	30-45
5	Wheel Lug Nut 4 Lug Wheel	55-85	—
	5 Lug Wheel	70-115	70-115
6	Rear Spring to Rear Spring Front Hangar	45-55	30-50
7	Universal Joint U-bolt Nut	7-10	12-15

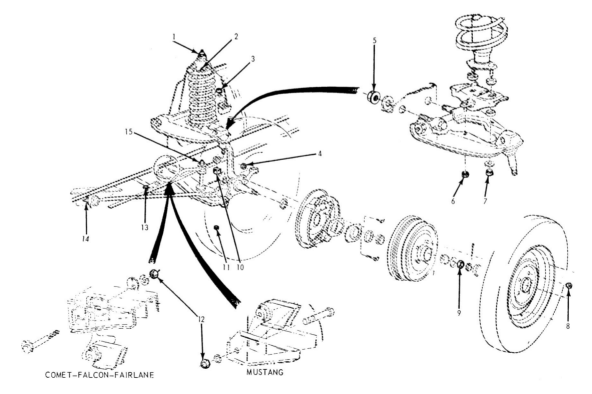

COMET—FALCON—FAIRLANE   MUSTANG

F 1285-A

FIG. 1—Front Suspension Torque Limits

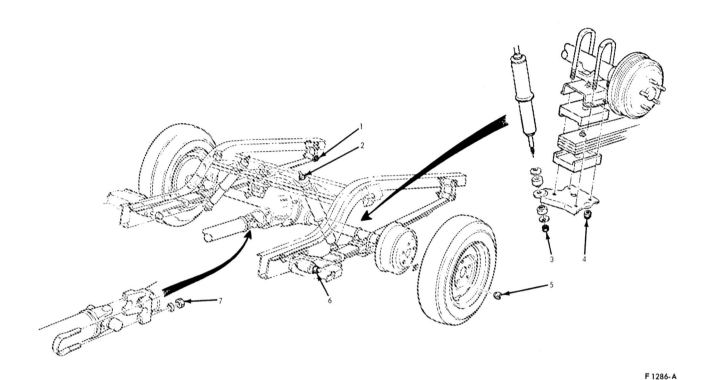

F 1286-A

FIG. 2—Rear Suspension Torque Limits

STEERING GEAR

VEHICLE	COMET FAIRLANE		MUSTANG			FALCON	
Model	HCA-CA	HCA-BZ	HCC-AT	HCC-AX	HCC-AW	HCA-CA	HCA-BY
Gear Type	Manual	Power	Manual	Special Manual	Power	Manual	Power
Gear Ratio	22:1	16:1	19.9:1	16:1	16:1	22:1	16:1
Turns of Steering Wheel (Stop to Stop)③	5	4	4⅝	3¾	3¾	5	4
Worm Bearing Preload⑥ in-lbs	4-5	3-4	4-5	4-5	3-4	4-5	3-4
Total Preload (Worm Bearing plus Sector Mesh)⑤ in-lbs	9-10	④8-9	9-10	9-10	④8-9	9-10	④8-9
Lube Capacity (oz)	11		8			11	
Lube Type	(C3AZ-19578-A)						
Normal Fluid Pressure Against Either Stop (Engine 1000 rpm)					Power	750-900 psi	
Control Valve Spool Travel (from Center)					Power	0.060 in Approx.	
Power Steering Belt Tension Using tool BT-33-73F					Power	New: 120-150 lbs.	
						Used: 90-120 lbs.	

ADJUSTMENTS ALL MODELS:
Adjusting screw clearance at bottom of sector shaft T-slot—.000"-.002".
Sector Shaft end play—steering linkage disconnected—none.
With gear mounted in vehicle or on a suitable fixture and positioned on center, and the sector shaft retained to prevent rotation, apply a 15 lb. in. torque on the steering gear input shaft in both right and left turn directions. The total angular travel of the input shaft cannot exceed 8½ degrees, with 8 lb. in. net mesh load.

NOTES:
③Gear only—not attached to Pitman arm.
④Total (mesh load plus worm bearing preload) must be a minimum of 2 lb. in. greater than worm bearing preload.
⑤Required to rotate input shaft and worm assembly past the center high point.
⑥Torque required to rotate input shaft at approximately 1½ turns either side of center (gear out of vehicle or Pitman arm disconnected)

STEERING GEAR TORQUE LIMITS
COMET, FALCON AND FAIRLANE

Description	Torque	
	Ft-Lbs	In-Lbs
Sector Shaft Cover Bolts	17-25	
Meshload Adjusting Screw Locknut	32-40	
Ball Return Guide Clamp Screw Fairlane (Power)		18-42
Ball Return Guide Clamp Screw (Falcon, Comet, Fairlane—Manual)		42-70
Preload Adjuster Locknut	⑦60-80	

⑦Residual torque must be 40 ft-lbs minimum

MUSTANG

Description	Torque	
	Ft-Lbs	In-Lbs
Sector Shaft Cover Bolts	15-22	
Meshload Adjusting Screw Locknut	32-40	
Ball Return Guide Clamp Screw		18-42
Preload Adjuster Locknut	⑧45-60	

⑧Residual torque must be 35 ft-lbs minimum

STEERING LINKAGE TORQUE LIMITS (Fig. 3)

Ref. No.	Description	Torque Ft-Lbs			
		Comet—Falcon Fairlane		Mustang	
		Standard Steering	Power Steering	Standard Steering	Power Steering
1	Cylinder Mounting Bracket to Under body (Side Hole)	—	28-35	—	28-35
2	Steering Spindle Arm Connecting Rod End to Spindle Arm	⑨30-40		⑨30-40	
3	Idler Arm Mounting Bracket to Underbody	28-35		28-35	
4	Pitman Arm to Steering Arm-to-Idler Arm Rod or to Valve and Link Assembly	⑨35-47		⑨35-47	
5	Steering Spindle Arm Connecting Rod to Steering Arm-to-Idle Arm Rod	⑨30-40		⑨25-30	
6	Cylinder Mounting Bracket to Underbody (Bottom Hole)	—	35-43	—	35-43
7	Power Cylinder to Bracket	—	18-24	—	18-24
8	Power Cylinder to Bracket Lock Nut	—	3-5	—	3-5
9	Steering Gear to Side Rail	40-55		40-65	
10	Pitman Arm to Sector Shaft	150-225		85-110	
11	Power Cylinder to Control Rod	—	⑨35-47	—	⑨35-47
12	Idler Arm to Steering Arm-to-Idler Arm Rod.	⑨60-80		⑨35-47	
13	Steering Spindle Arm Connecting Rod and End Clamp to Adjusting Sleeve	8-14		19-26	

⑨Torque to low limit of specification; then, tighten the nut to the nearest cotter pin slot and insert the cotter pin.

STEERING COLUMN TORQUE LIMITS

Description	Torque Ft-Lbs	
	Mustang	Comet Falcon Fairlane
Steering Wheel Retaining Nut	25-35	25-30
Steering Column to Support Bracket (Instrument Panel)	9-13	12-16
Steering Column Shift Arm to Shift Linkage	—	20-35
Seal Retainer to Dash Panel	—	16-22

POWER STEERING PUMP TORQUE LIMITS (FIG. 4)

Ref. No.	Description	Torque Ft-Lbs
1	Pump Rear Mounting Nut	11-16
2	Reservoir to Support Stud Retaining Nut	11-16
3	Outlet Fitting Hex Nut	43-47
4	Pressure Hose Nut	18-25
5	Pump Attaching Bolts	30-40
6	Bracket to Engine Attaching Bolts (8-Cylinder)	18-25
7	Bracket to Engine Attaching Bolts (6-Cylinder)	7-10
8	Bracket to Cylinder Head (6-Cylinder only)	13-18
9	Rear Support Bracket Retaining Nuts (8-Cylinder Only)	30-40
10	Bracket to Engine Adaptor	17-25
11	Engine Adaptor to Engine	17-25
12	Support Brace to Bracket	30-40

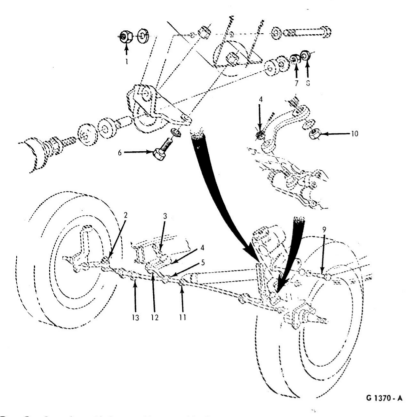

FIG. 3—Steering Linkage Torque Limits

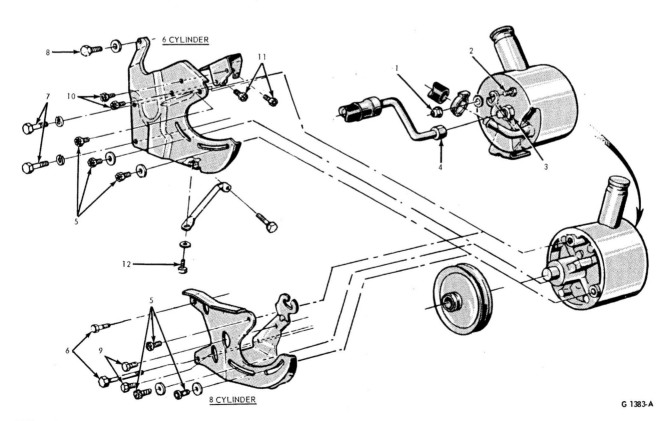

FIG. 4—Power Steering Pump Torque Limits

TIRES

MODELS	TIRE SIZE 6 CYLINDER		TIRE SIZE 8 CYLINDER (289 C.I.D.)		TIRE SIZE 8 CYLINDER (390 C.I.D.)	
	STANDARD	R.P.O.	STANDARD	R.P.O.	STANDARD	R.P.O.
FALCON						
Sedan	6.50 x 13	⑩6.95 x 14	6.95 x 14	—	—	—
Wagon	7.35 x 14	—	7.35 x 14	—	—	—
Ranchero	7.35 x 14	7.75 x 14	7.35 x 14	7.75 x 14	—	—
COMET AND FAIRLANE						
Sedan	6.95 x 14	7.35 x 14	6.95 x 14	7.35 x 14	7.35 x 14	7.75 x 14
Convertible	6.95 x 14	7.35 x 14	6.95 x 14	⑫7.35 x 14	⑭7.35 x 14	⑫7.75 x 14
Hardtop	6.95 x 14	7.35 x 14	6.95 x 14	⑫7.35 x 14	⑭7.35 x 14	⑫7.75 x 14
Wagon	7.75 x 14	7.75 x 14—8 Ply	7.75 x 15	7.75 x 14 — 8 Ply	7.75 x 14	7.75 x 14—8 Ply
MUSTANG						
Convertible	6.95 x 14	⑬6.95 x 14	6.95 x 14	⑬6.95 x 14	—	—
Hardtop	6.95 x 14	⑬6.95 x 14	6.95 x 14	⑬6.95 x 14	—	—
Imp. Handling	—	—	⑪6.95 x 14	—	—	—

⑩—Standard on model 62C
⑪—110 Level 120 mph dual red band nylon
⑫—Standard with air conditioning
⑬—110 Level nylon
⑭—7.75 x 14 standard on Fairlane GT models

SERVICE TOOLS

Ford Tool No.	Description
T57L-500-A	Bench Mounted Holding Fixture
T56P-1217-A	Front Hub Bearing Cup and Grease Seal Replacer
T60K-1217-A	Front Hub Bearing Cup and Grease Seal Replacer
T65P-3000-B or C	Alignment Spacers
T57P-3006-A	Spindle Ball Joint Assembly Remover Press
T60K-3006-A	Spindle Ball Joint Press Adapter Screw
TOOL-3290-C	Tie Rod Ball Ends and Control Valve Ball Stud Remover
T61P-3355-A	Idler Arm Bushing Remover and Replacer
T62F-3576-A	Sector Shaft Bushing Remover and Replacer
T64K-3576-A	Sector Shaft Needle Bearings and Seal Remover and Replacer
T64K-3576-B	Sector Shaft Needle Bearings and Seal Remover and Replacer Adapter
T64P-3590-F	Steering Arm Remover
TOOL-3600-AA	Steering Wheel Remover
T65P-3A733-A	Power Steering Pump Pulley Replacer
T63P-5310-A (TOOL-5310-C)	Front Coil Spring Remover and Replacer
T64K-5310-A	Front Coil Spring Remover and Replacer Adapter (For T63P-5310-A)
T64K-5310-B	Front Coil Spring Remover and Replacer Adapter (For TOOL-5310-C)
T66P-5310-A	Front Coil Spring Remover and Replacer Adapter (For T63 P-5310-A)
T66P-5310-B	Front Coil Spring Remover and Replacer Adapter (For TOOL-5310-C)
T64N-5781-A	Rear Spring Front Bushing Remover and Replacer
T64K-5781-B	Rear Spring Bushing Adapter
T63L-8620-A	Belt Tension Gauge
T63L-10300-B	Pulley Remover
T56L-33610-D	Power Steering Pump Pressure Gauge

REAR AXLE

PART 4-1   **PAGE**
GENERAL AXLE SERVICE 4-1

PART 4-2
REAR AXLES 4-11

PART 4-3   **PAGE**
SPECIFICATIONS 4-31

PART 4-1 GENERAL AXLE SERVICE

Section   **Page**
1 Diagnosis and Testing 4-1
   Diagnosis Guide 4-1
   Rear Axle Noise Diagnosis 4-1
   Limited-Slip Differential 4-2
   Gear Tooth Contact Pattern Check 4-3
   The Ideal Tooth Pattern 4-3
   Hunting Gear Set 4-3
   Non-Hunting Gear Set 4-4
   Partial Non-Hunting Gear Set 4-5
   Shim and Backlash Changes 4-5
2 Common Adjustments and Repairs 4-7
   Pinion and Drive Gear Tooth Contact
     Adjustments 4-7
   Backlash and Differential Bearing Preload
     Adjustments 4-7

Section   **Page**
   Pinion Location 4-8
3 Cleaning and Inspection 4-9
   Inspection Before Disassembly of Carrier 4-9
   Inspection After Disassembly 4-9
   Bearing Cups and Cone and Roller
     Assemblies 4-10
   Differential Bearing Adjusting Nuts 4-10
   Drive Pinion Flange 4-10
   Pinion Retainer 4-10
   Carrier Housing 4-10
   Differential Case 4-10
   Limited-Slip Differential Parts 4-10

Two types of axles are covered in this group. The **integral carrier** type axle is used only in Mustang and Falcon 6-cylinder models. In this type axle, the differential carrier is integral with the axle housing. The **removable carrier** type axle is used in Mustang and Falcon 8-cylinder models, and all Comet and Fairlane models. In this type axle, the differential carrier is bolted to the axle housing and can be removed from the housing for service. A limited-slip differential is available as optional equipment in either type axle.

1 DIAGNOSIS AND TESTING

DIAGNOSIS GUIDE

Certain rear axle and drive line trouble symptoms are also common to the engine, transmission, tires, and other parts of the car. For this reason, be sure that the cause of the trouble is in the rear axle before adjusting, repairing, or replacing any of the axle parts.

REAR AXLE NOISE DIAGNOSIS

Noise characteristics in a rear axle are more difficult to diagnose and repair than mechanical failures. Slight axle noise heard only at a certain speed or under remote conditions must be considered normal. Axle noise tends to peak or be more pronounced at varying speeds and the noise is in no way a sign of trouble in the axle.

Where noise is present in an objectionable form, loud and/or at all speeds, the first efforts should be made to isolate the noise. Rear axle noise is quite often confused with other noises such as tire noise, transmission noise, driveshaft vibration and universal joint noise. Isolation of the noise in any one unit requires skill and experience. An attempt to eliminate a slight noise may baffle even the best diagnostic experts. Axle noises fall into two basic categories: gear noise and/or bearing noise.

Gear Noise

Abnormal gear noise can be rec-ognized since it produces a cycling pitch and will be very pronounced in the speed range at which it occurs, usually under drive, float, cruise or coast conditions. Gear noise tends to peak in a narrow speed range or ranges, while bearing noise will tend to remain constant in pitch.

Bearing Noise

Defective bearings will produce a whine that is constant in pitch and varies with vehicle speed. This fact will help distinguish between bearing and/or gear noise.

1. Pinion bearing noise can be identified as a constant grinding noise. Pinion bearings are rotating at a higher speed than differential side

bearings or axle shaft bearings. The noise is most noticeable at a slight pull between 18 to 25 miles per hour.

2. Wheel bearing noise may be confused with rear axle noise. To differentiate between wheel bearings and rear axle, drive the car on a smooth road at medium low speed. With traffic permitting, turn the car sharply right and left. If noise is caused by wheel bearings, the noise will increase on the defective bearing because of side loading.

3. Side bearings will produce a constant grinding noise of a slower nature than pinion bearing, (side bearing noise cannot be determined by the wheel bearing test), but will be in the same frequency as axle shaft bearings.

Also, certain trouble symptoms are common to both the conventional and locking differential axles, while still other symptoms are found only in the locking differential.

To determine whether the car is equipped with a conventional or a locking differential, check the car warranty plate and the axle ratio tag. Refer to CAR IDENTIFICATION at the front of this manual.

LIMITED-SLIP DIFFERENTIAL

The limited-slip differential can be checked for proper operation without removing the carrier from the axle housing.

Jack up one rear wheel and remove the wheel cover. On a car with a removable carrier type axle, install tool T59L-4204-A on the axle shaft flange studs as shown in Fig. 1. On a car with an integral carrier type axle, use tool T65K-4204-A.

Using a torque wrench of at least 200 ft-lbs capacity, rotate the axle shaft. **Be sure that the transmission is in neutral gear, one rear wheel is on the floor, and the other rear wheel is raised off the floor.** The torque required to continuously rotate the shaft should be a specified in Part 4-3. The initial breakaway torque may be higher than the continuous turning torque, but this is normal. The axle shaft should turn with even pressure throughout the check without slipping or binding.

Tool T59L-4204-A

E1481-A

FIG. 1—Checking Limited-Slip Differential

REAR AXLE TROUBLE SYMPTOMS AND POSSIBLE CAUSES

EXCESSIVE REAR AXLE NOISE (ALL REAR AXLES)	Since gears are in mesh, some rear axle noise is normal. However, excessive noise often indicates the beginning of other troubles in the axle.	Noise caused by a worn or damaged wheel bearing is often loudest when the car is coasting at low speeds, and it usually stops when the brakes are gently applied. To find the noisy bearing, jack up each wheel and check each bearing for roughness while the wheel is rotating, provided that the car is equipped with a conventional differential.

Since gears are in mesh, some rear axle noise is normal. However, excessive noise often indicates the beginning of other troubles in the axle.

A road test can help determine whether the noise is being caused by trouble in the rear axle or in other parts of the car. **Before road-testing the car, make sure that the tire pressures and the rear axle lubricant level are normal. Then drive the car far enough to warm the axle lubricant to its normal operating temperature.**

With the car stopped and the transmission in neutral, run the engine at various speeds. If the noise still exists during this test, it probably comes from the engine or the exhaust system.

To determine if the noise is being caused by the rear axle or the tires, drive the car over several different types of road surfaces. Smooth asphalt or black-top roads minimize tire noises. Tire noises may be eliminated by cross-switching the tires. Snow tires often cause noises not heard with conventional tires.

Noise caused by a worn or damaged wheel bearing is often loudest when the car is coasting at low speeds, and it usually stops when the brakes are gently applied. To find the noisy bearing, jack up each wheel and check each bearing for roughness while the wheel is rotating, provided that the car is equipped with a conventional differential.

If all possible external sources of noise have been checked and eliminated, and the noise still exists, road-test the rear axle under all four driving conditions—drive, cruise, float, and coast. Any noise produced by the sidegears and pinions in the differential case will be most pronounced on turns. A continuous whine under a light load between 20 and 35 miles per hour indicates rough or brinnelled pinion bearings. If the tone of drive, coast and float noise differs with speed and if the noise is very rough and irregular; worn, rough or loose *differential or pinion shaft bearings* are indicated. Remove, disassemble, and inspect the axle.

REAR AXLE TROUBLE SYMPTOMS AND POSSIBLE CAUSES (Continued)

EXCESSIVE REAR AXLE BACKLASH (ALL REAR AXLES)	Excessive backlash in the axle driving parts may be caused by worn axle shaft splines, loose axle shaft flange nuts, loose U-joint flange mountings, excessive backlash be-	tween the drive pinion and ring gear, excessive backlash in the differential gears, or bearings which are worn or out of adjustment.
ONE WHEEL SPINS EXCESSIVELY (LIMITED-SLIP DIFFERENTIAL ONLY)	Use the procedure given under limited-slip differential for checking the locking differential while the unit is in the car. If the torque required to rotate one rear wheel is less than	the specified minimum, the differential is not functioning properly. To repair the unit, remove it from the axle housing.
AXLE HAS A HIGH-PITCHED, CHATTERING NOISE ON TURNS (LIMITED-SLIP DIFFERENTIAL ONLY)	Drive the car in a fairly tight circle, making five circles clockwise and five counterclockwise. This will permit the lubricant to work in between the clutch plates. If the noise does not disappear during this driving test, it is probable that the axle does not have the approved Ford lubricant. The lubricant may be checked by draining two tablespoonfuls from the axle and mixing it with an equal amount of white alcohol, such as rubbing alcohol. Mix the lubricant and alcohol thoroughly and let it	stand for at least two minutes. If the sample now has a blue tint, the lubricant is approved Ford lubricant. If it has a yellow tint, it is not the correct lubricant. Drain and refill the axle with the approved lubricant. It is not necessary to flush the axle housing. After refilling the axle drive the car in fairly tight circles clockwise and counterclockwise. The chattering noise should disappear as soon as the new lubricant works in between the clutch plates.

If the torque reading is less than the specified minimum, check the differential for improper assembly.

A car equipped with a limited-slip differential will always have both wheels driving. If, while the car is being serviced, only one wheel is raised off the floor and the rear axle is driven by the engine, the wheel on the floor will drive the car off the stand or jack.

GEAR TOOTH CONTACT PATTERN CHECK

Paint the gear teeth and roll a pattern as described in Section 3. After diagnosing the tooth pattern as explained here, make the appropriate adjustments as outlined in Section 2.

In making a final gear tooth contact pattern check, it is necessary to recognize the fact that there are three different types of gear set, hunting, non-hunting and partial non-hunting. Each type is determined by the ratio and the number of teeth in the gears. The non-hunting and partial non-hunting types can be identified by the paint timing marks on the pinion and ring gear teeth (Part 4-2, Fig. 30). See Part 4-3 for complete identification specifications.

THE IDEAL TOOTH PATTERN

Figs. 2 and 3 show the ideal tooth pattern. **This pattern is not a rigid standard but merely a general rule.**

In general, desirable tooth patterns should have the following characteristics:

(a) The drive pattern should be fairly well centered on the tooth.

(b) The coast pattern should be centered on the tooth but may be slightly toward the toe.

(c) Some clearance between the pattern and the top of the tooth is desirable.

(d) There should be no hard lines where the pressure is high.

The individual gear set need not conform exactly to the ideal pattern in order to be acceptable. Characteristic differences between the three

types of gear sets as well as differences between individual gear sets of the same type will result in patterns that are acceptable yet different from those shown in Fig. 3.

HUNTING GEAR SET

In a hunting-type gear set, any one pinion gear tooth comes into contact with all drive gear teeth. In this type, several revolutions of the ring gear are required to make all possible gear combinations.

Acceptable Pattern

The drive pattern shown in Fig. 4 was rolled on a hunting-type gear set. Since each pinion tooth came into contact with each ring gear tooth, the pattern is a result of the **com-**

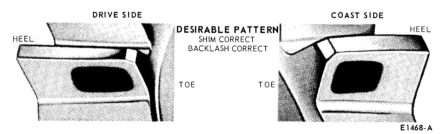

FIG. 2—Ideal Tooth Pattern—Integral Carrier Type Axle

DRIVE SIDE

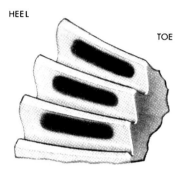

COAST SIDE

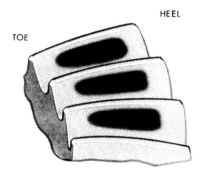

DESIRABLE PATTERN
CORRECT SHIM
CORRECT BACKLASH

E1336-A

FIG. 3—Ideal Tooth Pattern—Removable Carrier Type Axle

E1337-A

FIG. 4—Acceptable Hunting Gear Pattern

bined tooth contacts. Therefore, the pattern is uniform from tooth to tooth.

Unacceptable Pattern

An erratic tooth pattern on a hunting gear set indicates gear runout and possible need for gear replacement.

A pattern that is uniform, but off center indicates a change in shim or backlash (Figs. 9 or 10).

NON-HUNTING GEAR SET

In a non-hunting type gear set, any one pinion gear tooth comes into contact with only a few ring gear teeth. In this type, only one revolution of the ring gear is required to make all possible tooth contact combinations.

Acceptable Patterns

The drive patterns shown in Figs. 5 and 6 were rolled on two different non-hunting type gear sets. The pattern in Fig. 5 runs from the tooth center toward the toe and then back

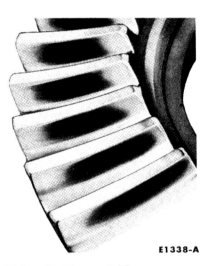

E1338-A

FIG. 5—Unacceptable Non-Hunting Pattern— Center-Toe-Center

to center. The pattern in Fig. 6 runs from the tooth center toward the heel and then back to center. These patterns are not unusual for non-hunting gear sets and are acceptable. The pattern on any one ring gear tooth was formed by only **one** pinion tooth coming into contact with it. Because of this limited tooth contact, the non-hunting pattern can be more erratic than the hunting pattern and still be acceptable. Likewise, the coast pattern on a non-hunting gear set is usually less uniform tooth to tooth than it would be on a hunting gear set (Fig. 7).

Fig. 8 shows a pattern rolled on another gear set. In this case, the pattern is fairly uniform from tooth to tooth.

Unacceptable Patterns

A non-hunting gear set should be checked for runout and possible replacement if the pattern runs from the tooth center toward the toe and

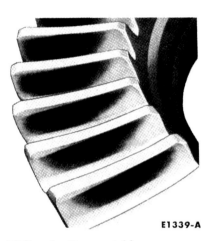

E1339-A

FIG. 6—Unacceptable Non-Hunting Pattern— Center-Heel-Center

E1340-A

FIG. 7—Acceptable Non-Hunting Gear Set—Coast Pattern

back to center on some gear teeth (Fig. 5) while on other teeth of the same gear, the pattern runs from the tooth center toward the heel and back to center (Fig. 6).

A non-hunting gear set requires a

FIG. 8—Acceptable Non-Hunting Pattern—Uniform

change in shimming or backlash when its pattern tends to concentrate toward the heel or toe, top or bottom of **most** teeth (Figs. 9 and 10).

PARTIAL NON-HUNTING GEAR SET

In a partial non-hunting type gear set, any one pinion tooth comes into contact with only part of the ring gear teeth, but more than one revolution of the ring gear is required to make all possible gear tooth combinations.

Tooth to tooth pattern uniformity will usually be in between the hunting and the non-hunting patterns. Partial non-hunting gear set patterns will usually be less uniform than hunting gear set patterns, but more uniform than non-hunting gear set patterns.

SHIM AND BACKLASH CHANGES

The patterns shown in Figs. 9 and 10 are typical of gear sets that have either an incorrect backlash or an incorrect shim adjustment. Since each gear set rolls a characteristic pattern, the patterns in Figs. 9 and 10 should be considered as typical only and should be used as a guide rather than a rigid standard. The drive pattern is rolled on the convex side of the tooth, and the coast pattern is rolled on the concave side.

The movement of tooth contact patterns with changes in backlash and shimming can be summarized as follows:

Integral Carrier Type Axle

1. Thinner shim with the backlash constant moves the pinion farther from the ring gear.

 a. Drive pattern moves toward the top of the tooth (face contact) and toward the heel.

 b. Coast pattern moves toward the top of the tooth and slightly toward the toe.

2. Thicker shim with the backlash constant moves the pinion closer to the ring gear.

 a. Drive pattern moves deeper on the tooth (flank contact) and slightly toward the toe.

 b. Coast pattern moves deeper on the tooth and toward the heel.

3. Decreasing backlash moves the drive gear closer to the pinion:

 a. Drive pattern (convex side of gear) moves slightly lower and toward the toe.

 b. Coast pattern (concave side of gear) moves lower and toward the toe.

4. Increasing backlash moves the ring gear away from the pinion:

 a. Drive pattern moves slightly higher and toward the heel.

 b. Coast pattern moves higher and toward the heel.

If the patterns are not correct, make the changes as indicated. The differential case and drive pinion will have to be removed from the carrier casting to change a shim. When reinstalling the pinion and ring gear of a non-hunting or partial non-hunting gear set, be sure that the marked tooth on the pinion indexes between the marked teeth on the ring gear (Fig. 30, Part 4-2). Refer to Pinion and Ring Gear Tooth Contact Adjustment, Section 2.

Removable Carrier Type Axle

1. Thicker shim with the backlash constant moves the pinion farther from the ring gear:

 a. Drive pattern moves toward the top of the tooth (face contact) and toward the heel.

 b. Coast pattern moves toward the top of the tooth and slightly toward the toe.

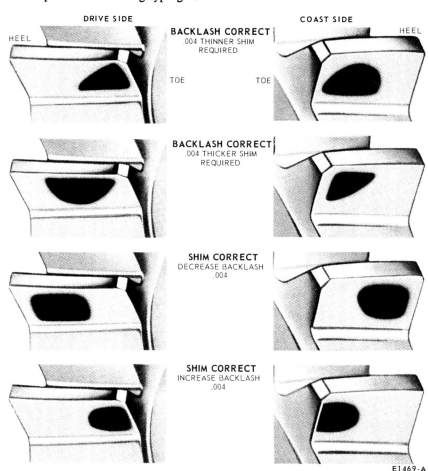

FIG. 9—Typical Gear Tooth Contact Patterns Indicating Shim or Backlash Change—Integral Carrier Type

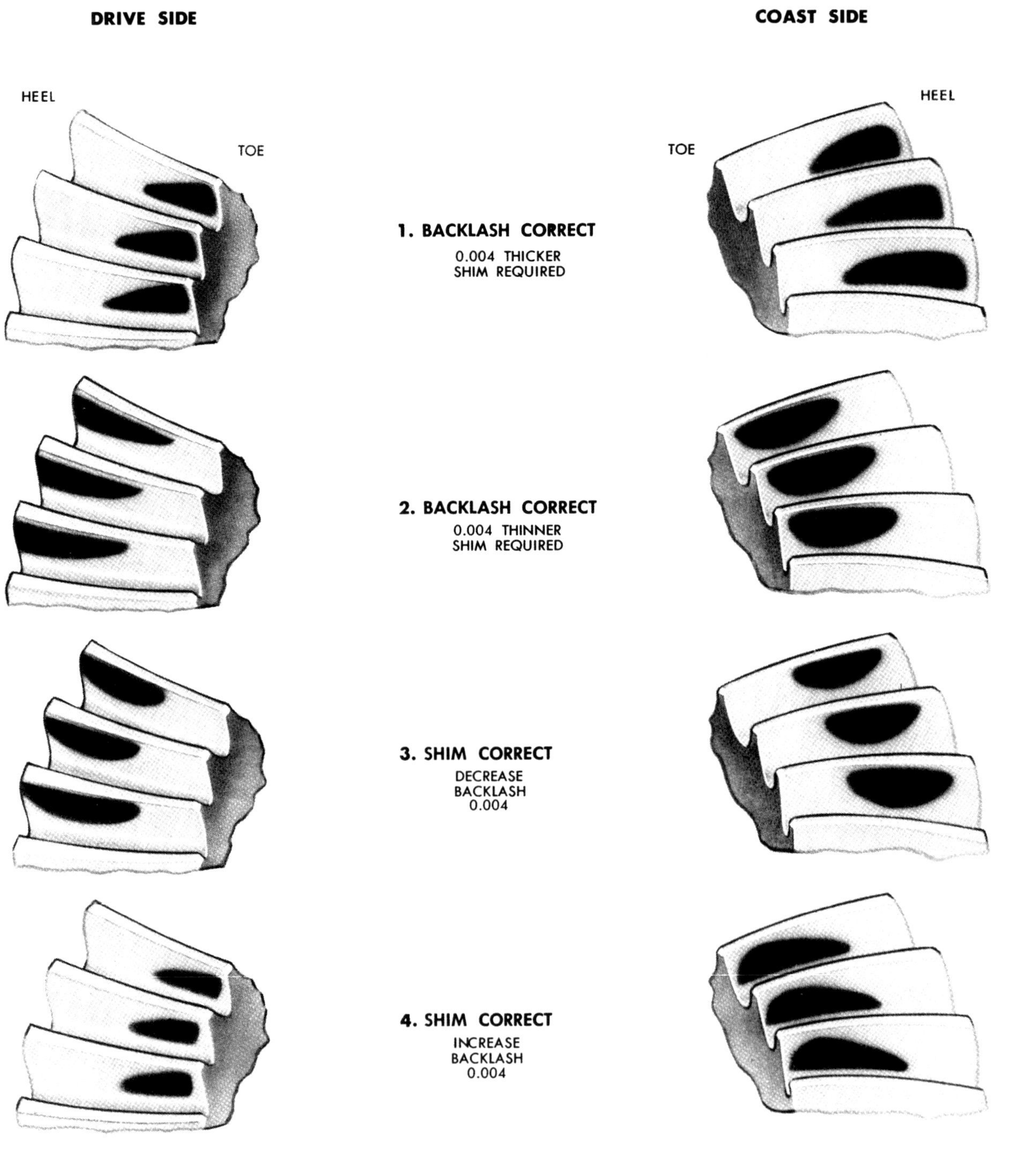

DRIVE SIDE

HEEL

TOE

1. BACKLASH CORRECT

0.004 THICKER
SHIM REQUIRED

2. BACKLASH CORRECT

0.004 THINNER
SHIM REQUIRED

3. SHIM CORRECT

DECREASE
BACKLASH
0.004

4. SHIM CORRECT

INCREASE
BACKLASH
0.004

COAST SIDE

HEEL

TOE

E1342-A

FIG. 10—Typical Gear Tooth Contact Patterns Indicating Shim or Backlash Change—Removable Carrier Type

2. Thinner shim with the backlash constant moves the pinion closer to the ring gear.

a. Drive pattern moves deeper on the tooth (flank contact) and slightly toward the toe.

b. Coast pattern moves deeper on the tooth and toward the heel.

3. Decreasing backlash moves the ring gear closer to the pinion:

a. Drive pattern moves slightly lower and toward the toe.

b. Coast pattern moves lower and toward the toe.

4. Increasing backlash moves the ring gear away from the pinion:

a. Drive pattern moves slightly higher and toward the heel.

b. Coast pattern moves higher and toward the heel.

If the patterns are not correct, make the changes as indicated. The pinion need not be disassembled to change a shim. *All that is required is* to remove the pinion, bearing, and retainer assembly and install a different shim. When reinstalling the pinion and retainer assembly of a non-hunting or partial non-hunting gear

set, be sure that the marked tooth on the pinion indexes between the marked teeth on the ring gear (Fig.

30, Part 4-2). Refer to Pinion and Ring Gear Tooth Contact Adjustment, Section 2.

2 COMMON ADJUSTMENTS AND REPAIRS

PINION AND RING GEAR TOOTH CONTACT ADJUSTMENT

Two separate adjustments affect pinion and ring gear tooth contact. They are pinion location and backlash (Figs. 11 and 12).

Individual differences in matching the differential housing and the gear set require the use of shims to locate the pinion for correct contact with the ring gear. On the integral carrier type axle, the pinion locating shim pack is installed between the pinion rear bearing cone and the pinion gear (Fig. 11), whereas, on the removable carrier type axle, the shims are installed between the pinion retainer and the carrier (Fig. 12). Due to this difference in shim position, it should be noted that adding or removing shims in the integral carrier type (Fig. 11) causes the pinion to move in a direction exactly opposite to the pinion movement caused by adding or removing shims in the removable carrier type (Fig. 12).

When adjusting either type axle,

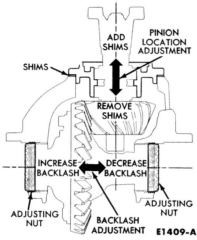

FIG. 12—Pinion and Ring Gear Tooth Contact Adjustment— Removable Carrier Type Axles

shims should be added to or removed from the original shim pack only as indicated by the tooth pattern check described in the foregoing Section 1. When adjusting the integral carrier type axle, **add shims** to move the pinion **toward** the ring gear; **remove** shims to move the pinion **away** from the ring gear (Fig. 11). When adjusting the removable carrier type axle, **remove** shims to move the pinion **toward** the ring gear; add shims to move the pinion **away** from the ring gear (Fig. 12).

The tooth pattern check also indicates whether the ring gear should be adjusted away from or toward the pinion to increase or decrease backlash between the gears.

If the tooth pattern check indicates a change in backlash only, follow the procedure under Backlash and Bearing Preload Adjustments. If the tooth pattern indicates a change in shim thickness, follow the procedure under Pinion Location.

BACKLASH AND DIFFERENTIAL BEARING PRELOAD ADJUSTMENTS

To secure a more uniform control of differential side bearing preload in service repairs, a dial indicator set-up such as shown in Fig. 13 is used.

In both types of axle (Fig. 11 and 12), the ring gear is moved away from or toward the pinion as described in the following procedure.

1. Remove the adjusting nut locks, loosen the differential bearing cap bolts, then torque the bolts to (15 ft-lbs on integral carrier type axles; 20 ft-lbs on removable carrier type axles) before making adjustments.

2. The left adjusting nut is on the ring gear side of the carrier. The right nut is on the pinion side. Loosen the right nut until it is away from the cup. Tighten the left nut until the ring gear is just forced into the pinion with no backlash then rotate the pinion several revolutions to be sure no binding is evident. (Recheck the right nut at this time to be sure that it is still loose.) **Tightening the left nut moves the ring gear into the pinion to decrease backlash, and tightening the right nut moves the ring gear away.**

3. Loosen the left adjusting nut 1 to 1½ notches. Tighten the right nut until it first contacts the bearing cup. Rotate the drive gear several revolutions in each direction while the bearings are loaded, to seat the bearings in their cups to be sure no bind is evident. **This step is important.**

4. Install a dial indicator as shown in Fig. 13.

5. Again loosen the right nut to release the pre-load. If there is any backlash between the gears as shown by the dial indicator, tighten the left nut just enough to remove this backlash. At this time, make sure that one of the slots in the left nut is so located that the lock can be installed without turning the nut. Carefully tighten the right nut until it just contacts the cup. On integral carrier type axles, set a preload of 0.008 inch case spread for new bearings and 0.003 to 0.005 for the original bearings. On removable carrier type axles, the preload is 0.012 inch case spread for new bearings and 0.005 to 0.008 for the original bearings. As preload is applied from the right side, the ring gear is forced away from the pinion and usually results in the correct backlash.

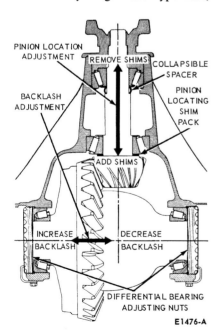

FIG. 11—Pinion and Ring Gear Tooth Contact Adjustment— Integral Carrier Type Axles

E1504-A

FIG. 13—Adjusting Side Bearing Preload

6. Torque the differential cap bolts to specification (15ft-lbs).

7. Measure the backlash on several teeth around the ring gear. If the measurements vary more than (0.002 inch—integral carrier type; 0.003 inch—removable carrier type) there is excessive runout in the gears or their mountings, which must be corrected to obtain a satisfactory unit. If the backlash is out of specification, loosen one adjusting nut and tighten the opposite nut an equal amount, to move the ring gear away from or toward the pinion. **When moving the adjusting nuts, the final movement should always be made in a tightening direction. For example, if the left nut had to be loosened one notch, loosen the nut two notches, then tighten it one. This insures that the nut is contacting the bearing cup, and that the cup cannot shift after being put in service.** After all such adjustments, check to be sure that the case spread remains as specified for the new or original bearings used.

8. Again check the tooth contact pattern. If the pattern is still incorrect, a change in pinion location (shim thickness) is indicated.

PINION LOCATION

Integral Carrier Type Axle

1. Remove the differential case and the drive pinion from the carrier casting, and then remove the pinion bearings as described under Removal of Differential Case and Drive Pinion in Section 4.

2. Measure the original shim thickness with a micrometer. Increase or decrease the shim thickness as indicated by the tooth pattern check described in the foregoing Section 1 and shown in Fig. 9.

3. Install the corrected shim pack and the bearings on the pinion, and then install the pinion and the differential case in the carrier casting as outlined under Installation of Drive Pinion and Differential Case in Section 4 of Part 4-2.

4. Adjust the backlash between the ring gear and pinion as outlined in the foregoing procedure.

5. Make a tooth pattern check. If the pattern is still unsatisfactory, repeat this procedure changing the shim thickness each time until a satisfactory tooth pattern is obtained.

Removable Carrier Type Axle

1. Remove the attaching bolts and the pinion and bearing retainer assembly from the carrier.

2. Measure the original shim thickness with a micrometer. Increase or decrease the shim thickness as indicated by the tooth pattern check described in Section 1.

3. Replace the pinion retainer O-ring (Fig. 47, Part 4-2). Coat the O-ring with axle lubricant before installing. **Do not roll the O-ring into the groove. Snap it into position.**

4. Being careful not to pinch the O-ring, install the pinion and bearing retainer assembly in the carrier with the corrected shim pack.

Before installing the pinion and bearing retainer assembly, determine which type of gear set is being used. The **non-hunting** and **partial non-hunting** types can be identified by the paint timing marks on the gear teeth (Fig. 30, Part 4-2).

If the gear set is of the **non-hunting** or **partial non-hunting** type, clean the teeth on both the pinion and ring gear so that the timing marks are visible. Rotate the differential case and drive gear assembly in the carrier until the marked teeth on the ring gear are opposite the pinion entry hole. Place the pinion retainer assembly in the carrier so that the marked tooth on the pinion indexes between the marked teeth on the ring gear (Fig. 30, Part 4-2).

In almost every case of improper assembly (gear assembled out of time), the noise level and probability of failure will be higher than they would be with properly assembled gears.

When installing the **hunting** type gear set (no timing marks), assemble the pinion and retainer assembly into the carrier without regard to the matching of any particular gear teeth.

5. Install the retainer-to-carrier mounting bolts and torque to specifications.

6. Adjust the backlash between the ring gear and pinion as outlined in the foregoing procedure.

7. Make a tooth pattern check. If the pattern is still unsatisfactory, repeat this procedure changing the shim thickness each time until a satisfactory tooth pattern is obtained.

3 CLEANING AND INSPECTION

INSPECTION BEFORE DISASSEMBLY OF CARRIER

The differential case assembly and the drive pinion should be inspected before they are removed from the housing. These inspections can help to find the cause of the trouble and to determine the correction needed.

On removable carrier type axles, mount the carrier in the holding fixture shown in Fig. 14.

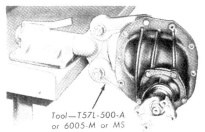

Tool—T57L-500-A
or 6005-M or MS

E1306-B

FIG. 14—Bench Fixture for Carrier Overhaul—Removable Carrier Type Axle

Wipe the lubricant from the internal working parts, and visually inspect the parts for wear or damage.

Rotate the gears to see if there is any roughness which would indicate defective bearings or chipped gears. Check the gear teeth for scoring or signs of abnormal wear.

Check the differential case and the drive pinion for end play.

Set up a dial indicator (Fig. 15 or 16) and check the backlash at several points around the ring gear. Backlash should be within specifications as outlined in the Specifications Section, Part 4-3.

To check the gear tooth contact, paint the gear teeth with the special compound furnished with each service ring gear and pinion. Wrap a cloth around the drive pinion flange to act as a brake. Rotate the ring gear back and forth (use a box wrench on the ring gear attaching bolts for a lever) until a clear tooth contact pattern is obtained.

Certain types of gear tooth contact patterns on the ring gear indicate incorrect adjustment. Noise caused by incorrect adjustment can often be corrected by readjusting the gears. Typical patterns and the necessary corrections are explained under Gear Tooth Contact Pattern Check in Section 1.

Gear tooth runout can sometimes

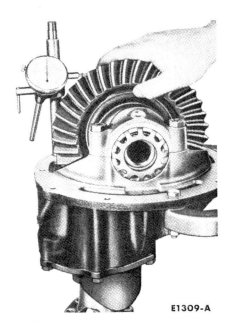

E1309-A

FIG. 15—Checking Backlash —Removable Carrier Type Axle

be detected by an erratic pattern on the teeth. However, a dial indicator should be used to measure the runout of the back face of the ring gear, as shown in Fig. 16 or 17. Refer to Specifications Section for maximum allowable runout.

Loosen the differential bearing cap bolts, and then torque to specification. Remove the adjusting nut locks. Carefully loosen one of the adjusting nuts to determine if any differential bearing preload remains. If at least one notch of preload remains, the differential bearings may be re-used, provided they are not pitted or damaged.

INSPECTION AFTER DISASSEMBLY

Thoroughly clean all parts. Al-

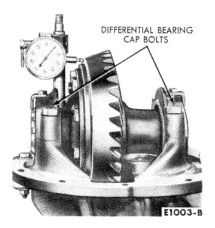

DIFFERENTIAL BEARING CAP BOLTS

E1003-B

FIG. 17—Checking Drive Gear Runout—Removable Carrier Type Axle

ways use new solvent when cleaning bearings. Do not spin bearings with compressed air. Oil the bearings immediately to prevent rusting. Inspect the parts for any major defects. Clean the inside of the housing before rebuilding and installing the parts.

When a scored gear set is replaced, the axle housing should be washed thoroughly and steam cleaned. This can only be done effectively if the axle shafts and shaft seals are removed from the housing. Inspect individual parts as outlined below.

GEARS

Examine the pinion and ring gear teeth for scoring or excessive wear. **Extreme care must be taken not to damage the pilot bearing surface of the pinion.**

The pattern taken during disassembly should be helpful in judging if gears can be re-used. Worn gears cannot be rebuilt to correct a noisy

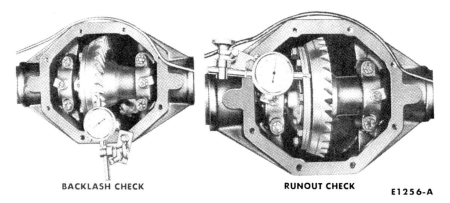

BACKLASH CHECK   RUNOUT CHECK   E1256-A

FIG. 16—Checking Backlash and Runout—Integral Carrier Type Axle

condition. Gear scoring is the result of excessive shock loading or the use of an incorrect lubricant. Scored gears cannot be re-used.

Examine the teeth and thrust surfaces of the differential gears. Wear on the hub of the differential side gear can cause a chucking noise known as chuckle when the car is driven at low speeds. Wear on splines, thrust surfaces, or thrust washers can contribute to excessive drive line backlash.

BEARING CUPS

Check bearing cups for rings, scores, galling, or erratic wear patterns. Pinion bearing cups must be solidly seated. Check by attempting to insert a 0.0015-inch feeler between these cups and the bottoms of their bores.

CONE AND ROLLER ASSEMBLIES

When operated in the cups, bearing rollers must turn without roughness. Examine the roller ends for wear. Step-wear on the roller ends indicates that the bearings were not preloaded properly or that the rollers were slightly misaligned.

If inspection reveals either a defective cup or a defective cone and roller assembly, **both parts should be replaced to avoid early failure.**

DIFFERENTIAL BEARING ADJUSTING NUTS

Temporarily install the bearing caps and test the fit of the adjusting nuts in their threads.

The nuts should turn easily when the caps are tightened to 15 ft-lbs (integral carrier type) or 20 ft-lbs

(removable carrier type). The faces of the nuts that contact the bearing cups must be smooth and square. Polish these with a fine abrasive on a flat surface. Replace the nuts or examine the threads in the carrier, if their fit is not proper. Be sure that the bearing caps and adjusting nuts are on the side which they were machined to fit by observing the punch marks and scribe marks made during disassembly operations.

DRIVE PINION FLANGE

Be sure that the ears of the flange have not been damaged in removing the drive shaft or in removing the flange from the pinion. The end of the flange that contacts the bearing cone (integral carrier type) or the oil slinger (removable carrier type) as well as the flat surface of the pinion nut counterbore must be smooth. Polish these surfaces if necessary. Roughness aggravates backlash noises, and causes wear of the flange with a resultant loss in pinion bearing preload.

PINION RETAINER— REMOVABLE CARRIER TYPE AXLE ONLY

Be sure that the pinion bearing cups are seated. Remove any chips or burrs from the mounting flange. Clean the groove for the O-ring seal and all lubricant passages. If the cups were removed, examine the bores carefully. Any nicks or burrs in these bores must be removed to permit proper seating of the cups.

CARRIER HOUSING

Make sure that the differential bearing bores are smooth and the

threads are not damaged.

Remove any nicks or burrs from the mounting surfaces of the carrier housing.

DIFFERENTIAL CASE

Make sure that the hubs where the bearings mount are smooth. Carefully examine the differential case bearing shoulders, which may have been damaged when the bearings were removed. The bearing assemblies will fail if they do not seat firmly against the shoulders. Check the fit (free rotation) of the differential side gears in their counterbores. Be sure that the mating surfaces of the two parts of the case are smooth and free from nicks or burrs.

LIMITED-SLIP DIFFERENTIAL PARTS

Inspect the clutch plates for uneven or extreme wear. The dog-eared clutch plates must be free from burrs, nicks, or scratches which could cause excessive or erratic wear to the bonding material of the internally splined clutch plates. The internally splined clutch plates should be inspected for condition of the bond, bonding material, and wear. Replace the bonded plates if their thickness is less than 0.085 inch or if the bonded material is scored or badly worn. Inspect the bonded plate internal teeth for wear. Replace them, if excessive wear is evident. Bonded plates should be replaced as a set only.

Examine all thrust surfaces and hubs for wear. Abnormal wear on these surfaces can contribute to a noisy axle.

Inspect the Belleville spring for proper free height of ¼ inch.

PART 4-2 REAR AXLES

Section	Page
1 Description and Operation	4-11
Conventional Axles—Description	4-11
Operation	4-12
Limited-Slip Differential Axle—Description	4-12
Operation	4-12
2 In-Car Adjustments and Repairs	4-13
Rear Axle Shaft, Wheel Bearing and Oil Seal Replacement	4-13
Drive Pinion Oil Seal Replacement	4-14
Universal Joint Flange Replacement	4-16
3 Removal and Installation	4-17
Rear Axle Housing—Integral Carrier Type	4-17
Differential Carrier—Removable Carrier Type	4-18
Rear Axle Housing—Removable Carrier Type	4-18
4 Major Repair Operations—Integral Carrier Type Axle	4-19
Disassembly	4-19
Removal of Differential Case and Drive Pinion	4-19
Disassembly of Conventional Differential Case	4-19
Disassembly of Limited-Slip Differential Case	4-19
Parts Repair or Replacement	4-19

Section	Page
Pinion Bearing Cups	4-19
Differential Case, Bearings and Drive Gear	4-22
Assembly	4-22
Installation of Drive Pinion and Differential Case	4-23
5 Major Repair Operations—Removable Carrier Type Axles	4-24
Disassembly	4-24
Removal and Disassembly of Conventional Differential Case	4-24
Removal and Disassembly of Limited-Slip Differential Case	4-25
Removal and Disassembly of Drive Pinion and Bearing Retainer	4-25
Parts Repair or Replacement	4-26
Pilot Bearing	4-26
Pinion Bearing Cups	4-26
Drive Pinion and Gear Set	4-27
Assembly and Installation of Drive Pinion and Bearing Retainer	4-27
Assembly and Installation of Conventional Differential Case	4-29
Assembly and Installation of Limited-Slip Differential Case	4-30

1 DESCRIPTION AND OPERATION

IDENTIFICATION

A metal tag stamped with the model designation and gear ratio is secured to all Ford-produced axles under one of the rear cover-to-housing bolts (integral carrier type) or the carrier-to-housing bolts (removable carrier type). The first five spaces on the top line are reserved for the model designation letters such as WCY-E, WDJ-C, or WEA-B. These letters indicate a specific combination of the following factors: conventional or limited-slip axle; diameter of ring gear; small or large wheel bearings; and the gear ratio. It is important, therefore, to use the model designation for obtaining the correct replacement parts.

CONVENTIONAL AXLES

DESCRIPTION

Integral Carrier Type Axle

The rear axle assembly is an integral-type housing, hypoid design, with the centerline of the pinion set below the centerline of the ring gear (Fig. 1).

The semi-floating axle shafts are retained in the housing by ball bearings and a bearing retainer at the axle housing outer ends.

The differential assembly is mounted on two opposed tapered roller bearings. The bearings are retained in the housing by removable caps. Differential bearing preload and drive gear backlash is adjusted by nuts located behind each differential bearing cup.

The drive pinion assembly is mounted on two opposed tapered roller bearings. Pinion bearing preload is adjusted by a collapsible spacer on the pinion shaft. Pinion and ring gear tooth contact is adjusted by shims between the rear bearing cone and pinion gear.

A cover on the rear of the differential housing provides access for inspection and the removal and installation of the differential assembly and drive pinion.

Removable Carrier Type Axle

The rear axle is of the banjo-housing, hypoid gear type, in which the centerline of the pinion is mounted

below the centerline of the ring gear (Fig. 2).

The integral pinion gear and shaft and the pinion bearings are assembled in a pinion retainer, which is bolted to the carrier. In this axle, the pinion is straddle mounted; that is, the pinion is supported by bearings both in front of and to the rear of the pinion gear. Two opposed tapered roller bearings support the pinion shaft in front of the pinion gear. A straight roller (pilot) bearing supports the pinion shaft at the rear of the pinion gear. Pinion and ring gear tooth contact is adjusted by shims between the pinion retainer and the carrier housing.

The differential assembly is mounted on two opposed tapered roller bearings, which are retained in the carrier by removable caps. The entire carrier assembly is bolted to the axle housing.

Ball bearing assemblies (rear wheel bearings) are pressed onto the outer ends of the axle shafts and set in the outer ends of the axle housing. These bearings support the semi-float-

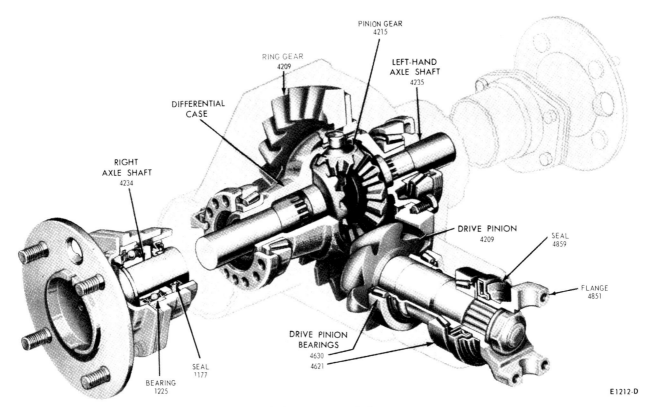

FIG. 1—Typical Rear Axle Assembly—Integral Carrier Type Axle

ing axle shafts at the outer ends. The inner ends of the shafts spline to the differential side gears. Bearing retainer plates hold the shafts in the housing. The left and right axle shafts are not interchangeable, because the left axle shaft is shorter than the right.

OPERATION

The rear axle drive pinion receives its power from the engine through the transmission and drive shaft. The pinion gear rotates the differential case through engagement with the ring gear, which is bolted to the case outer flange. Inside the case, there are two differential pinion gears mounted on the differential pinion shaft which is pinned to the case. These pinion gears are engaged with the side gears, to which the axle shafts are splined. Therefore, as the differential case turns, it rotates the axle shafts and rear wheels. When it is necessary for one wheel and axle shaft to rotate faster than the other, the faster turning side gear causes the pinions to roll on the slower turning

side gear to allow differential action between the two axle shafts.

LIMITED-SLIP DIFFERENTIAL AXLE

The locking differential is provided as optional equipment in both the integral and the removable carrier type axle.

DESCRIPTION

The axle assembly, except for the differential case and its internal components, is identical to the conventional axle.

A constant-friction locking differential, which employs automatic transmission-type clutch plates to control differential action, is available as optional equipment (Fig. 3).

Four steel clutch plates are locked into the differential cover. Three bronze, bonded clutch plates are splined to the left-hand axle shaft. A Belleville spring washer maintains a constant pressure between the steel and bonded clutch plates so that the clutch is always engaged.

OPERATION

The pressure between clutch plates opposes differential action at all times. When the car turns a corner the clutch slips allowing normal dif-

ferential action to take place. Under adverse weather conditions, where one or both wheels may be on a low-traction surface such as snow, ice or mud, the friction between the clutch plates will transfer a portion of the usable torque to the wheel with the most traction. Thus, the wheel that is on ice or snow will not spin, but will have a tendency to operate with the opposite wheel in a combined driving effort.

When performing the following procedures, refer to Part 4-1, Section 3 for cleaning and inspection procedures.

CARE OF AXLE

The lubricant level should be checked every 6000 miles, with vehicle in normal curb attitude. The lubricant level should be at the lower edge of the filler plug hole. It is unnecessary to periodically drain the axle lubricant. The factory fill should remain in the housing for the life of the vehicle, except when repairs are made. *The specified lubricant should be installed when the axle is overhauled.*

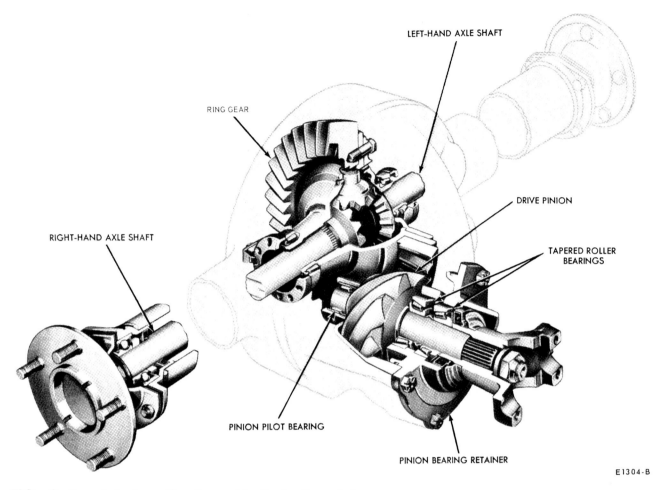

FIG. 2—Rear Axle Assembly—Removable Carrier Type Axle

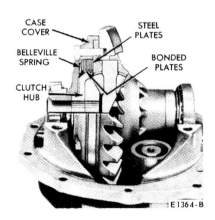

FIG. 3—Typical Limited-Slip Differential

2 IN-CAR ADJUSTMENT AND REPAIR

REAR AXLE SHAFT, WHEEL BEARING AND OIL SEAL REPLACEMENT

The rear axle shafts, wheel bearings, and oil seal can be replaced without removing the differential as-

sembly from the axle housing.

1. Remove the wheel and tire from the brake drum.

2. Remove the Tinnerman nuts that secure the brake drum to the axle housing flange, and then remove

the drum from the flange.

3. Working through the hole provided in each axle shaft flange, remove the nuts that secure the wheel bearing retainer plate. Then pull the axle shaft assembly out of the axle

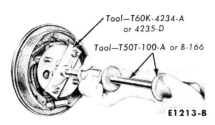

FIG. 4—Removing Axle Shaft—Integral Carrier Type Axle

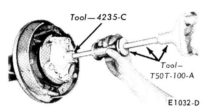

FIG. 5—Removing Axle Shaft —Removable Carrier Type Axle

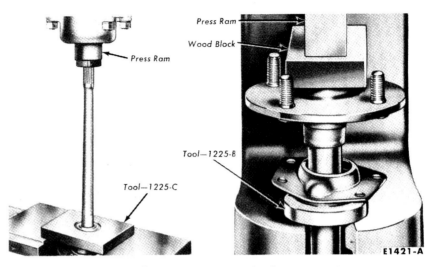

FIG. 7—Removing and Installing Rear Wheel Bearing—Comet

housing (Fig. 4 or 5). **The brake carrier plate must not be dislodged. Install one nut to hold the plate in place after the axle shaft is removed.**

4. If the rear wheel bearing is to be replaced, loosen the inner retainer nick by nicking it deeply with a cold chisel in several places (Fig. 6). It will then slide off easily.

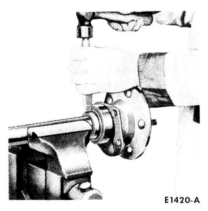

FIG. 6—Removing Rear Wheel Bearing Retainer Ring

5. Remove the bearing from the axle shaft with the tool shown in Fig. 7 or 8. If the push-puller operation shown in Fig. 8 is used, be sure that the puller arms contact **the flat surface** of the axle shaft flange rather than the bolt heads. Also with this method, be careful not to damage or burr the oil seal journal as the bearing breaks loose.

6. **Whenever a rear axle shaft is**

removed, the oil seal must be replaced.** Remove the seal with the tools shown in Fig. 9. Soak new oil seals in SAE 10 oil for ½ hour before installing.

7. Inspect the machined surface of the axle shaft and the axle housing for rough spots or other irregularities which would affect the sealing action of the oil seal. Check the axle shaft splines for burrs, wear or damage. Carefully remove any burrs or rough spots. Replace worn or damaged parts.

8. Lightly coat wheel bearing bores with ball joint grease (C3VY-19586-B).

9. Place the retainer plate on the axle shaft, and press the new wheel bearing on the shaft with the tool shown in Fig. 7 or 8. **The bearing should seat firmly against the shaft shoulder. Do not attempt to press on both the bearing and the inner retainer ring at the same time.**

10. Using the bearing installation tool, press the bearing inner retainer ring on the shaft until the retainer seats firmly against the bearing.

11. Wipe all lubricant from the inside of the axle housing in the area of the oil seal before installing the new seal.

12. Wipe a small amount of oil resistant sealer on the outer edge of the seal before it is installed. **Do not put sealer on the sealing lip.**

13. Install the new oil seal with the tools shown in Fig. 9. **Installation without use of the proper tool will distort the seal and cause leakage. Be sure the new seal has been soaked in SAE 10 oil for ½ hour.**

14. Place a new gasket on each

side of the brake carrier plate, and then carefully slide the axle shaft into the housing so that the rough forging of the shaft will not damage the oil seal. Start the axle splines into the side gear, and push the shaft in until the bearing bottoms in the housing.

15. Install the bearing retainer plate on the mounting bolts at the axle housing, and install the attaching nuts. Torque the nuts to specifications.

16. Install the brake drum and the drum attaching nuts.

17. Install the wheel and tire on the drum.

REMOVAL AND REPLACEMENT OF DRIVE PINION OIL SEAL

Replacement of the pinion oil seal on either type axle involves removal and installation of only the pinion shaft nut and the universal joint flange. However, this operation disturbs the pinion bearing preload, and this preload must be carefully reset when assembling.

1. Raise the car and install safety stands. Remove the rear wheels and brake drums.

2. Make scribe marks on the drive shaft end yoke and the axle U-joint flange to insure proper position of the drive shaft at assembly (Fig. 14). Disconnect the drive shaft from the axle U-joint flange. **Be careful to avoid dropping the loose universal joint bearing cups.** Hold the cups on the spider with tape. Mark the cups so that they will be in their original position in relation to the flange when they are assembled. Remove the drive shaft from the transmission extension housing. Install an oil seal re-

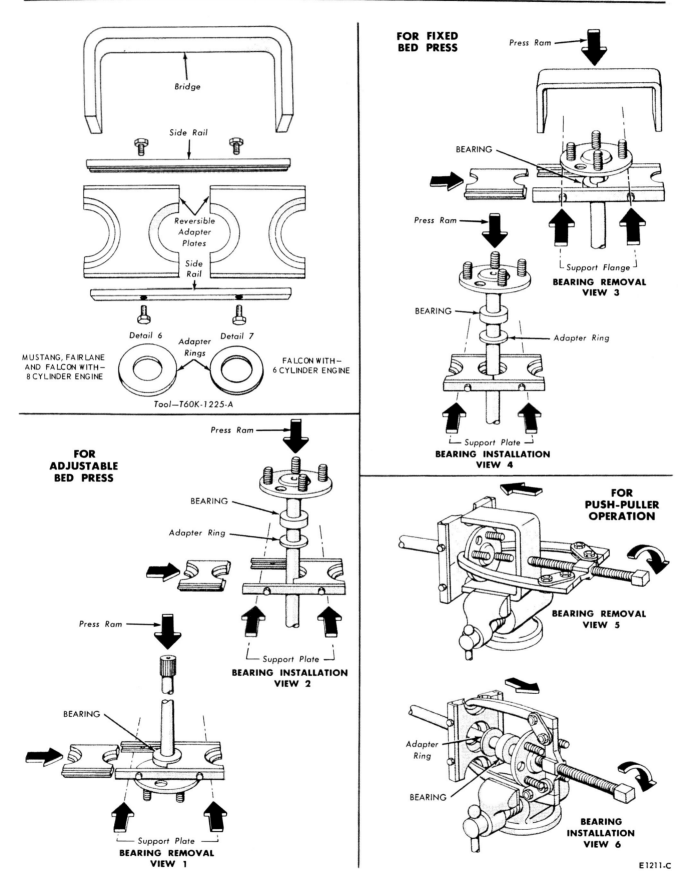

FIG. 8—Removing and Installing Rear Wheel Bearing—Falcon, Mustang and Fairlane

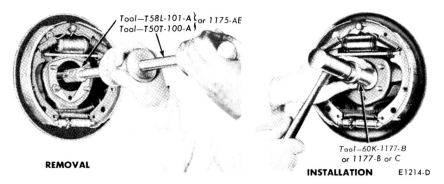

REMOVAL   INSTALLATION

FIG. 9—Removing and Installing Axle Shaft Seal

placer tool in the transmission extension housing to prevent transmission leakage. Refer to the transmission group for the appropriate tool.

3. Install an in-lb torque wrench on the pinion nut. Record the torque required to maintain rotation of the pinion shaft through several revolutions.

4. While holding the flange with the tool shown in Fig. 10, remove the integral pinion nut and washer.

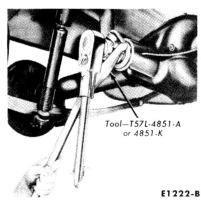

FIG. 10—Typical Drive Pinion Shaft Nut Removal

5. Clean the pinion bearing retainer around the oil seal. Place a drain pan under the seal, or raise the front of the car higher than the rear.

6. Using the tool shown in Fig. 11, remove the pinion U-joint flange.

7. Using the tool shown in Fig. 37, remove the drive pinion oil seal.

8. Clean the oil seal seat.

9. Coat the outer edge of the new seal with a small amount of oil resistant sealer. **Do not put any of the sealer on the sealing lip.** Install the seal in the retainer, using the tool shown in Fig. 12 on integral carrier type axles. With removable carrier type axles, use tool T62F-4676-A or 4676-H on all except cars equipped with high performance engines. On cars equipped with high perform-

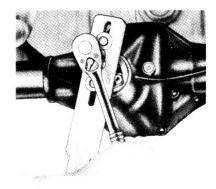

FIG. 11—Typical Drive Pinion Flange Removal

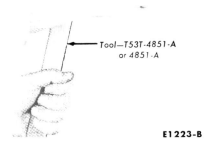

FIG. 12—Typical Drive Pinion Flange Seal Installation

ance engines, use tool 58L-4676-A or 4676-F.

10. Check splines on the pinion

shaft to be sure they are free of burrs. If burrs are evident, remove them by using a fine crocus cloth, working in a rotational motion. Wipe the pinion shaft clean.

11. Apply a small amount of lubricant to the U-joint splines.

12. Align the punch mark on the U-joint flange with the mark on the end of the pinion shaft, and install the flange. With removable carrier type axles, it will be necessary to use the tool shown in Fig. 50 to install the flange.

13. Install a new integral nut and washer on the pinion shaft. (Apply a small amount of lubricant on the washer side of the nut.)

14. Hold the flange with the tool shown in Fig. 36 while tightening the nut.

15. Tighten the pinion shaft nut, rotating the pinion occasionally to insure proper bearing seating, and take frequent preload readings until the preload is at the original recorded reading established in step 3.

16. After original preload has been reached, tighten the pinion nut slowly, until an additional preload has been placed on the bearings, as shown below:

Removable Carrier: 8 to 14 in-lbs.
Integral Carrier: 6 to 12 in-lbs.

The preload should not exceed the amount indicated above, or bearing failure may result. Under no circumstances should the pinion nut be backed-off to lessen preload. If this is done, a new pinion bearing spacer must be installed. In addition, the U-joint flange must never be hammered on, or power tools used.

17. Remove the oil seal replacer tool from the transmission extension housing. Install the front end of the drive shaft on the transmission output shaft.

18. Connect the rear end of the drive shaft to the axle U-joint flange, aligning the punch marks made on the drive shaft end yoke and the axle U-joint flange (Fig. 14).

19. Check the lubricant level. Make sure the axle is in running position. Add whatever amount of specified lubricant is required to reach the lower edge of the filler plug hole.

INSTALLATION OF A NEW UNIVERSAL JOINT FLANGE

1. Raise the car and install safety stands. Remove both rear wheels and brake drums.

2. Disconnect the *drive* shaft from the axle U-joint flange. **Be careful to avoid dropping the loose**

universal joint bearing cups. Hold the cups on the spider with tape. Mark the cups so that they will be in their original position in relation to the flange when they are assembled. Remove the drive shaft from the transmission extension housing. Install an oil seal replacer tool in the transmission extension housing to prevent transmission fluid leakage. Refer to the transmission group for the appropriate tool.

3. Install an in-lb torque wrench on the pinion nut. Record the torque required to maintain rotation of the pinion shaft through several revolutions.

4. While holding the flange with the tool shown in Fig. 36, remove the integral pinion nut and washer.

5. Clean the pinion bearing retainer around the oil seal. Place a drain pan under the seal, or raise the front of the car higher than the rear.

6. Using the tool shown in Fig. 36, remove the U-joint flange.

7. Check splines on the pinion shaft to be sure they are free of burrs. If burrs are evident, remove them by using a fine crocus cloth, working in rotational motion, then wipe clean.

Apply a small amount of lubricant to U-joint splines.

8. Install the U-joint flange using the tool shown in Fig. 50.

9. Install a new integral nut and washer on the pinion shaft. (Apply a small amount of lubricant on the washer side of the nut.)

10. Hold the flange with the tool shown in Fig. 35 while the nut is being tightened.

11. Tighten the pinion shaft nut, rotating the pinion occasionally to insure proper bearing seating, and take frequent preload readings until the preload is at the original recorded reading established in step 3.

12. After original preload has been reached, tighten the pinion nut slowly, until an additional preload of 8 to 14 in-lb over the original reading

is reached. (The preload should not exceed 8 to 14 in-lb over the original reading, or bearing failure may result.)

Under no circumstances should the pinion nut be backed off to lessen preload. If this is done, a new pinion bearing spacer must be installed. (In addition, the U-joint flange must never be hammered on, or pneumatic tools used.)

13. Remove the oil seal replacer tool from the transmission extension housing. Install the front end of the drive shaft on the transmission output shaft.

14. Connect the rear end of the drive shaft to the axle U-joint flange, aligning the scribe marks made on the drive shaft end yoke and the axle U-joint flange (Fig. 14).

14. Check the lubricant level. **Make sure the axle is in running position.** Add whatever amount of specified lubricant is required to reach the lower edge of the filler plug hole.

3 REMOVAL AND INSTALLATION

REAR AXLE HOUSING— INTEGRAL CARRIER TYPE AXLE

REMOVAL

1. Raise the car and support it with safety stands under the rear frame member.

2. Drain the lubricant from the axle.

3. Disconnect the drive shaft at the drive pinion flange.

4. Disconnect the lower end of the shock absorbers.

5. Remove the wheels, brake drums and both axle shafts as outlined in the foregoing Section 2.

6. Remove vent hose front vent tube (Corbin clamp) and remove vent tube from brake tube junction and axle housing.

7. Remove the hydraulic brake T-fitting from the axle housing. **Do not open the hydraulic brake system lines.** Remove the hydraulic brake line from its retaining clip on the axle housing.

8. Remove both axle shaft oil seals with the tools shown in Fig. 9.

9. Remove both brake carrier plates from the axle housing and suspend them above the housing with mechanic's wire. The hydraulic brake lines and the parking brake cables are still attached to the brake carrier plates.

10. Support the rear axle housing on a jack, and then remove the spring clip nuts. Remove the spring clip plates (Fig. 13).

11. Lower the axle housing and remove it from under the car.

12. If the axle housing is being replaced, transfer all the differential and pinion parts to the new housing. See Section 4, Major Repair Operations.

INSTALLATION

1. Raise the axle housing into position so that the spring clip plates

can be installed. On a Comet or Fairlane position the spring upper insulators and retainers between the axle housing and springs and install the lower insulators. Torque the spring clip nuts to specification.

2. Place the brake carrier plates in their normal position on the axle housing. Use new gaskets on each side of the brake carrier plates.

3. Install new axle shaft oil seals with the tool shown in Fig. 9. Soak the new seals in light weight engine oil (SAE 10) for ½ hour before installing them. **Installation without use**

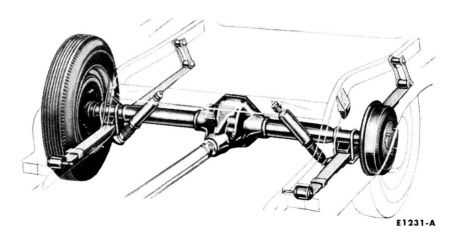

FIG. 13—Rear Axle Installation—Integral Carrier Type

of the proper tool will distort the seal and cause leakage. Coat the outside edges of the new oil seal with a hardening type of sealer such as Permatex No. 2 or its equivalent.

4. Install the axle shafts, brake drums and wheels as outlined in the foregoing Section 2.

5. Attach the hydraulic brake line T fitting to the axle housing, and secure the hydraulic brake line in its retainer on the axle housing.

6. Install vent tube to brake tube junction and install vent hose to vent tube.

7. Raise the axle housing and connect the shock absorbers.

8. Connect the drive shaft at the drive pinion shaft.

9. Fill the axle with the proper grade and amount of lubricant.

10. Road test the car.

DIFFERENTIAL CARRIER— REMOVABLE CARRIER TYPE AXLE

REMOVAL

1. Raise the car on a hoist and remove the two rear wheel and tire assemblies.

2. Remove the two brake drums (3 Tinnerman nuts at each drum) from the axle shaft flange studs. If difficulty is experienced in removing the drums, back off the brake shoes as explained in Part 2-2.

3. Working through the hole provided in each axle shaft flange, remove the nuts that secure the rear wheel bearing retainer plate. Pull each axle shaft assembly out of the axle housing (Fig. 5). Install a nut on one of the brake carrier plate retaining bolts to hold the plate to the axle housing after the shaft has been removed. **Whenever a rear axle shaft is removed, the wheel bearing oil seal must be replaced.** Remove both seals with the tools shown in Fig. 9.

4. Make scribe marks on the drive shaft end yoke and the axle U-joint flange to insure proper position at assembly. Disconnect the drive shaft at the rear axle U-joint, remove the drive shaft from the transmission extension housing. Install an oil seal replacer tool in the housing to prevent transmission leakage. Refer to the transmission group for the appropriate tool.

5. Place a drain pan under the carrier and housing, remove the carrier retaining nuts, and drain the

axle. Remove the carrier assembly from the axle housing.

INSTALLATION

1. Clean the axle housing and shafts using kerosene and swabs. To avoid contamination of the grease in the sealed ball bearings, do not allow any quantity of solvent directly on the wheel bearings. Clean the mating surfaces of the axle housing and carrier.

2. Position the differential carrier on the studs in the axle housing using a new gasket between carrier and housing. Install the copper washers and the carrier-to-housing retaining nuts, and torque to specifications.

3. Remove the oil seal replacer tool from the transmission extension housing. Position the drive shaft so that the front U-joint slip yoke splines to the transmission output shaft.

4. Connect the drive shaft to the axle U-joint flange, aligning the scribe marks made on the drive shaft end yoke and the axle U-joint flange during the removal procedure (Fig. 14). Install the U-bolts and nuts and torque to specifications.

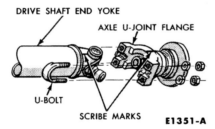

DRIVE SHAFT END YOKE
AXLE U-JOINT FLANGE
U-BOLT
SCRIBE MARKS   E1351-A

FIG. 14—Drive Shaft-to-Axle U-Joint Connection

5. Soak two new rear wheel bearing oil seals in SAE 10 oil for ½ hour before installation. Wipe a small amount of an oil resistant sealer on the outer edge of each seal before it is installed. **Do not put any of the sealer on the sealing lip.** Install the oil seals in the ends of the rear axle housing with the tool shown in Fig. 9.

6. Install the two axle shaft assemblies in the axle housing. The shorter shaft goes into the left side of the housing.

When installing an axle shaft, place a new gasket on each side of the brake carrier plate and carefully slide the axle shaft into the housing so that the rough forging of the shaft will not damage the oil seal. Start the axle splines into the differential side gear, and push the shaft in until the bearing bottoms in the housing.

7. Install the bearing retainers on the attaching bolts on the axle housing flanges. Install the nuts on the bolts and torque to specifications.

8. Install the two rear brake drums and the drum retaining (Tinnerman) nuts.

9. Install the rear wheel and tire assemblies.

10. If the rear brake shoes were backed off, adjust the brakes as outlined in Part 2-1.

11. Fill the rear axle with specified lubricant.

AXLE HOUSING—REMOVABLE CARRIER TYPE AXLE

REMOVAL

1. Remove the carrier assembly from the axle housing as outlined in the foregoing procedure.

2. Position safety stands under the rear frame members.

3. Disengage the brake line from the clips that retain the line to the axle housing.

4. Disconnect the vent tube from the rear axle housing.

5. Remove the brake carrier plate assemblies from the axle housing, and support them with wire. Do not disconnect the brake line.

6. Disconnect each rear shock absorber from the spring clip plate and position out of the way.

7. Lower the rear axle slightly to reduce some of the spring tension. At each rear spring, remove the spring clip (U-bolt) nuts, spring clips, and spring clip plate. Remove the spring lower insulator and retainer. See Part 3-2.

8. Remove the rear axle housing from under the car.

INSTALLATION

1. Position the rear axle housing on the rear springs. On a Comet or Fairlane, position the spring upper insulators and retainers between the axle housing and springs, and install the lower insulators.

2. Install the spring clips (U-bolts), spring clip plate, and nuts. **Torque the spring clip nuts evenly to specifications.**

3. If a new axle housing is being installed, remove the bolts that retain the carrier plate and bearing retainer from the old housing flanges. Position the bolts in the new housing flanges to hold the brake carrier plates in position. Install the carrier plates with new gaskets to the axle housing flanges.

4. Connect the vent tube to the axle housing.

5. Position the brake line to the axle housing, and secure with the retaining clips.

6. Raise the rear axle housing and springs enough to allow connecting the rear shock absorbers to the spring clip plates. Connect the lower stud of each shock absorber to its spring clip plate, and install the bushing, washer, and nut on the stud. **Be sure the spring clip plate is free of burrs. Tighten the nut to specified torque.**

7. Install the carrier assembly and the two axle shaft assemblies in the axle housing as outlined in the Installation procedure under Differential Carrier—Removable Carrier Type Axle.

---

4 MAJOR REPAIR OPERATIONS—INTEGRAL CARRIER TYPE AXLE

DISASSEMBLY

All service operations on the differential case assembly and the drive pinion assembly can be performed with the housing in the car.

REMOVAL OF DIFFERENTIAL CASE AND DRIVE PINION

1. Raise the car and support it on the underbody, so that the rear axle drops down as far as the springs and shock absorbers permit.

2. Remove the cover from the carrier casting rear face, and drain the lubricant. On a Mustang, the muffler assembly must be removed to provide clearance for removing the cover.

3. Perform the Inspection Before Disassembly of Carrier in Part 4-1, Section 3.

4. Remove both rear wheels.

5. Remove the brake drums.

6. Working through the hole provided in the axle shaft flange, remove the nuts that attach the wheel bearing retainers to the axle housing.

7. Pull the axle shafts with the tool shown in Fig. 4. Install a nut on one of the brake carrier plate attaching bolts to hold the plate to the axle housing after the shaft has been removed. **Whenever a rear axle shaft is removed the wheel bearing oil seal must be replaced.** Remove both seals with the tool shown in Fig. 9.

8. Make scribe marks on the drive shaft end yoke and the axle U-joint flange to insure proper position of the drive shaft at assembly (Fig. 14). Disconnect the drive shaft from the axle U-joint flange. **Be careful to avoid dropping the loose universal joint bearing cups.** Hold the cups on the spider with tape. Mark the cups so that they will be in their original position in relation to the flange when they are assembled. Remove the drive shaft from the transmission extension housing. Install an oil seal replacer tool in the transmission extension housing to prevent transmission leakage. Refer to the transmission group for the appropriate tool.

9. Remove the differential bearing adjusting nut locks (Fig. 15).

10. Mark one differential bearing cap and the case (Fig. 16) to help position the parts properly during assembly.

11. Remove the differential bearing cap bolts and bearing caps. **Hold the differential case assembly in the housing after the caps are removed.**

12. Remove the differential case and bearing cups (Fig. 17).

13. Hold the drive pinion flange and remove the pinion nut (Fig. 10).

14. Remove the pinion flange (Fig. 11).

15. With a soft-faced hammer, drive the pinion out of the front bearing cone and remove it through the rear of the carrier casting.

16. Drive against the pinion front bearing cone, and drive the pinion flange seal and the bearing cone out of the front of the carrier casting.

17. To remove and install the pinion rear bearing cone use the tools in Fig. 18.

18. Measure the shim which is found under the bearing cone with a micrometer. Record the thickness of the shim.

DISASSEMBLY OF CONVENTIONAL DIFFERENTIAL CASE

1. If the differential bearings are to be removed, use the tools shown in Fig. 19.

2. Remove the bolts that attach the ring gear to the differential case. Press the ring gear from the case or tap it off with a soft-faced hammer.

3. With a drift, drive out the differential pinion shaft lock pin (Fig. 20).

4. Drive out the pinion shaft with a brass drift. Remove the gears and thrust washers.

DISASSEMBLY OF LIMITED-SLIP DIFFERENTIAL CASE

1. Place the differential case in a hydraulic press, and apply about one ton pressure across the case bearing hubs while removing the drive gear attaching bolts. This procedure will contain the spring pressure between the differential case and cover until after the bolts are removed, and thereby prevent stripping of the threads.

2. Release the hydraulic press ram, and remove the differential case cover.

3. Remove the Belleville spring (Fig. 21).

4. Remove the steel and the bonded clutch plates.

5. Remove the differential clutch hub, outer side gear, and thrust washer.

6. Remove the ring gear from the differential case.

7. Drive out the differential pinion shaft lock pin.

8. With a brass drift, drive out the differential pinion shaft. Then remove the pinion gears, inner side gear and thrust washers.

PARTS REPAIR OR REPLACEMENT

Clean and inspect all the parts as outlined in Part 4-1, Section 3. Before assembling the carrier, repair or replace all parts as indicated by the inspection.

The principal replacement operations are covered in the following procedures. All other repair or replacement operations are performed during Cleaning and Inspection Part 4-1, Section 3, or during the Assembly in this section.

PINION BEARING CUPS

Do not remove the pinion bearing cups from the carrier casting unless the cups are worn or damaged.

If the pinion bearing cups are to be replaced, drive them out of the carrier casting with a drift. Install the new cups with the tool shown in Fig. 22. Make sure the cups are properly seated in their bores. If a 0.0015-inch feeler gauge can be inserted between a cup and the bottom of its bore at any point around the

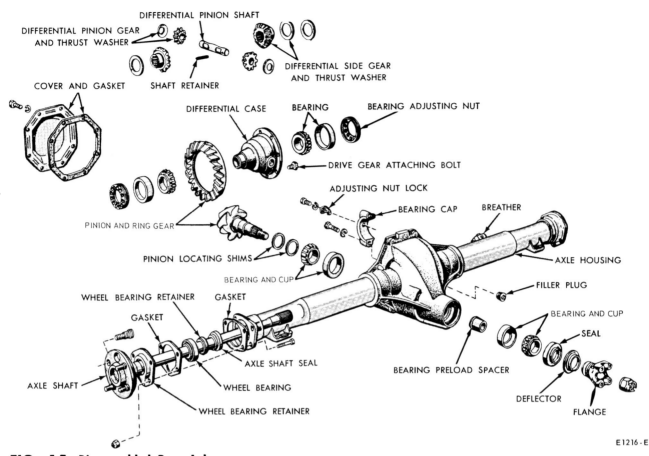

FIG. 15—Disassembled Rear Axle

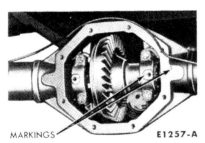

FIG. 16—Typical Differential Bearing Cap Marking

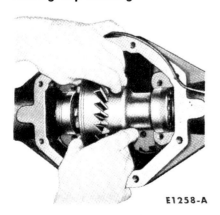

FIG. 17—Differential Case Removal or Installation

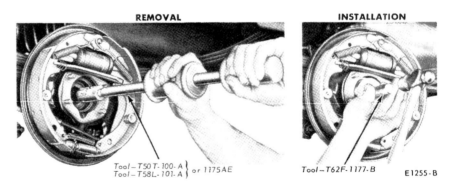

FIG. 18—Pinion Rear Bearing Cone Removal and Installation

cup, the cup is not properly seated.

Whenever the cups are replaced, the cone and roller assemblies should also be replaced.

DRIVE PINION AND GEAR SET

Individual differences in machining the carrier casting and the gear set require a shim between the pinion rear bearing cone and the pinion gear to locate the pinion for correct tooth contact with the ring gear. In order to adjust the shim pack to the correct thickness for a given gear

set, each pinion gear is marked with an adjustment number such as the +2 marking in Fig. 23.

When replacing a ring gear and pinion it should be noted that the **original** factory installed shim is of the correct thickness to adjust for individual variations in **both** the carrier casting dimension and in the original gear set dimension; therefore, *to select* the correct shim thickness for the new gear set to be installed, follow these steps:

1. Measure the thickness of the

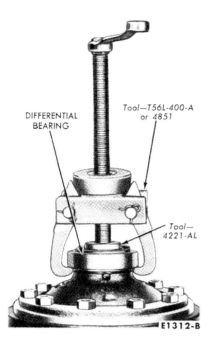

FIG. 19—Differential Bearing Removal

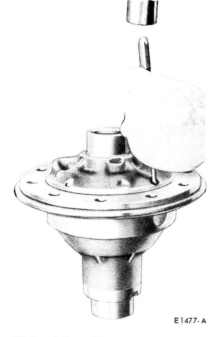

FIG. 20—Differential Pinion Shaft Lock Pin Removal

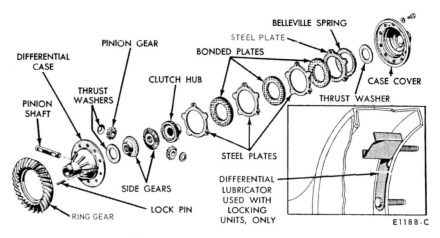

FIG. 21—Locking Differential Assembly

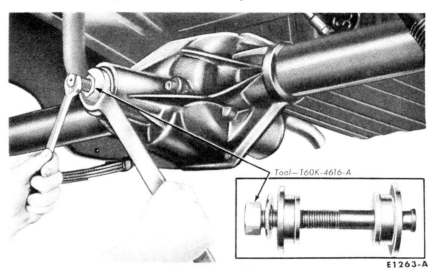

FIG. 22—Pinion Bearing Cup Removal or Installation

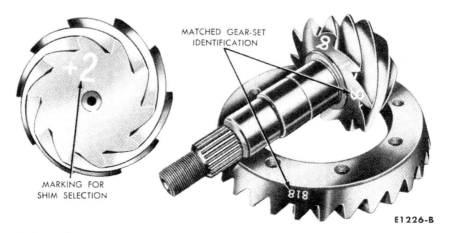

FIG. 23—Gear Set Markings

original shim with a micrometer.

2. Note the shim adjustment number on both the old pinion and the new pinion.

3. Refer to Table 1 to determine the correct amount of shim thickness change. The amount shown in Table 1 under the old pinion shim adjustment number and in line with the new pinion number is the amount of **change** that should be made to the original shim thickness.

If the old pinion is marked +4, for example, and the new pinion is marked −2, the table indicates that 0.006 inch of shim stock should be added to the **original** shim pack.

TABLE 1—Drive Pinion Adjusting Shim Thickness Changes (Inch)

Old Pinion Marking	New Pinion Marking								
	−4	−3	−2	−1	0	+1	+2	+3	+4
+4	+0.008	+0.007	+0.006	+0.005	+0.004	+0.003	+0.002	+0.001	0
+3	+0.007	+0.006	+0.005	+0.004	+0.003	+0.002	+0.001	0	−0.001
+2	+0.006	+0.005	+0.004	+0.003	+0.002	+0.001	0	−0.001	−0.002
+1	+0.005	+0.004	+0.003	+0.002	+0.001	0	−0.001	−0.002	−0.003
0	+0.004	+0.003	+0.002	+0.001	0	−0.001	−0.002	−0.003	−0.004
−1	+0.003	+0.002	+0.001	0	−0.001	−0.002	−0.003	−0.004	−0.005
−2	+0.002	+0.001	0	−0.001	−0.002	−0.003	−0.004	−0.005	−0.006
−3	+0.001	0	−0.001	−0.002	−0.003	−0.004	−0.005	−0.006	−0.007
−4	0	−0.001	−0.002	−0.003	−0.004	−0.005	−0.006	−0.007	−0.008

If the **original** shim pack was lost or if a new carrier casting is being installed, substitute a **nominal** 0.018 inch shim for the **original**, and follow the foregoing procedure for a trial build-up. If any further shim change is necessary, it will be indicated in the tooth pattern check.

A new ring gear and pinion should always be installed in an axle as a matched set (never separately). **Be sure that the same matching number appears on both the drive pinion and the ring gear.** Note the number 818 in Fig. 23.

4. After determining the correct shim thickness as explained in the foregoing steps, install the new pinion and ring gear as outlined under Assembly.

DIFFERENTIAL CASE, BEARINGS, AND DRIVE GEAR

If the ring gear runout check (before disassembly) exceeded specifications, the condition may be caused by a warped gear, a defective case, or excessively worn differential bearings.

To determine the cause of excessive runout proceed as follows:

1. Assemble the two halves of the differential case together **without** the ring gear, and press the two differential side bearings on the case hubs.

2. Place the cups on the bearings and set the differential case in the carrier.

3. Install the bearing caps and adjusting nuts as outlined in steps 11 thru 14 under Installation of Drive Pinion and Differential Case in this section.

4. Tighten the right nut two notches beyond the position where it first contacts the bearing cup. Rotate the differential case several revolutions in each direction while the bearings are loaded to seat the bearings in their cups. **This step is important.**

5. Again loosen the right nut to release the preload. Check to see that the left nut contacts the bearing cup. Using the dial indicator set-up shown in Fig. 13, Part 4-1, adjust the preload to 0.012 case spread for new bearings or 0.005 to 0.008 for the original bearings, if re-used.

6. Check the runout of the differential case flange with a dial indicator. If the runout does **not now** exceed specifications, install a new ring gear. If the runout still exceeds specifications, the ring gear is true and the trouble is due to either a defective case or worn bearings.

7. Remove the differential case from the carrier and remove the side bearings from the case.

8. Install **new** bearings on the case hubs, and again install the differential assembly in the carrier **without** the ring gear.

9. Check the case runout again with the new bearings. If the runout is **now** within limits, the old bearings were excessively worn. Use the new bearings for assembly. If the runout is still excessive, the case is defective and should be replaced.

ASSEMBLY

Refer to Part 4-1 for Cleaning and Inspection before starting assembly operations.

ASSEMBLY OF CONVENTIONAL DIFFERENTIAL CASE

1. Lubricate all the differential parts with axle lubricant, before they are installed in the case.

2. Place the side gears and thrust washers in the case.

3. Place the two pinion gears and thrust washers exactly opposite each other in the case openings and in mesh with the side gears.

4. Turn the pinions and thrust washers until the holes in the pinion

gears align with the pinion shaft holes in the case.

5. Start the pinion shaft into the differential case. Carefully align the shaft lock pin hole with the pin hole in the case. Drive the shaft into place and install the lock pin (Fig. 20).

6. Place the ring gear on the differential case and install the bolts. Torque the bolts to specification.

7. If the differential bearings have been removed, press them on as shown in Fig. 24.

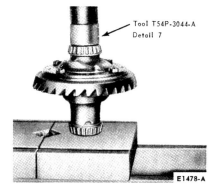

FIG. 24—Differential Bearing Installation

ASSEMBLY OF LIMITED-SLIP DIFFERENTIAL CASE

1. Place the side gear and thrust washer in the differential case (Fig. 24). **Lubricate all parts liberally with axle lubricant during assembly.**

2. With a soft-faced hammer, drive the pinion shaft into the case only far enough to retain a pinion thrust washer and pinion gear.

3. Place the second pinion and thrust washer in position, and drive *the pinion shaft into place.* **Carefully line up the pinion shaft lock pin holes.**

4. Install the pinion shaft lock

pin. **The lock pin must not extend beyond the surface of the case.**

5. Insert two 2-inch $^7/_{16}$ (N. F.) bolts through the differential case flange, and thread them three or four turns into the ring gear as a guide in aligning the ring gear bolt holes. Press or tap the drive gear into position.

6. Clamp the differential case in a soft-jawed vise. Install the other differential side gear on the differential pinion gears. Place the clutch hub on the side gear. Place the thrust washer on the hub (Fig. 25).

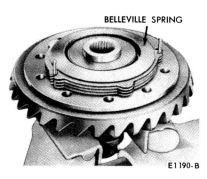

FIG. 26—Belleville Spring Installation

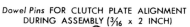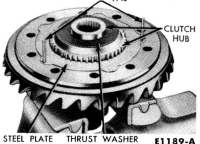

FIG. 25—Clutch Plate Installation

7. To align the clutch plates during assembly, insert two $^3/_{16}$ x 2 dowel pins into the differential case. Place a steel plate on the differential case so that the slots in the ears straddle the dowel pin (Fig. 25). **Lubricate all the limited-slip differential parts with axle lubricant so that an accurate torque check can be made.**

8. Place a bonded plate on the steel plate. Make sure the bonded plate inner spline teeth properly engage the hub spline. Assemble the remaining plates: a steel plate, a bonded plate, a steel plate, a bonded plate, and lastly a steel plate.

9. Place the Belleville spring on the top steel plate. The Belleville spring is assembled with the concave side down (Fig. 26). Carefully center the Belleville spring so that it will fit into the cover.

10. Place the differential case cover on the case (Fig. 27). Start the ring gear bolts.

11. Tighten the bolts evenly and alternately across the diameter of the drive gear. As the bolts are tightened the Belleville spring is compressed and the differential case and cover are pulled together.

12. Remove the dowel pins.

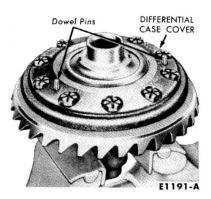

FIG. 27—Differential Cover Installation

13. Torque the case to ring gear bolts to specifications.

14. Check the torque required to rotate one side gear while the other side gear is held (Fig. 28). Ignore the torque required to start the side gear turning. The torque required to keep it moving steadily should be between 100 and 125 ft-lbs, if new clutch plates were installed. The torque should be at least 50 ft-lbs, if the original clutch plates were installed. If the required torque is not within these limits, check for improper assembly.

15. If the differential bearings have been removed press them on as shown in Fig. 24.

INSTALLATION OF DRIVE PINION AND DIFFERENTIAL CASE

1. Place the shim and pinion rear bearing cone on the pinion shaft. Press the bearing and shim firmly against the pinion shaft shoulder (Fig. 18).

2. Place a **new** pinion bearing preload spacer on the pinion shaft.

3. Lubricate the pinion rear bearing with axle lubricant.

4. Lubricate the pinion front bearing cone and place it in the housing.

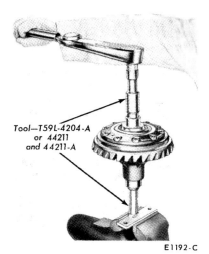

FIG. 28—Differential Torque Check

5. Coat the outside edge of a new oil seal with an oil resistant sealer and install it in the carrier casting (Fig. 12).

6. Insert the drive pinion shaft flange into the seal and hold it firmly against the pinion front bearing cone. From the rear of the carrier casting, insert the pinion shaft into the flange.

7. Place the flat washer on the pinion shaft and start the nut. Use a new nut. Hold the flange with the tool shown in Fig. 10 and tighten the pinion shaft nut. As the pinion shaft nut is tightened, the pinion shaft is pulled into the front bearing cone and into the flange.

As the pinion shaft is pulled into the front bearing cone, pinion shaft end play is reduced. While there is still end play in the pinion shaft, the flange and cone will be felt to bottom. This indicates that the bearing cone and flange have bottomed on the collapsible spacer.

From this point, a much greater torque must be applied to turn the pinion shaft nut, since the spacer must be collapsed. From this point, also, the nut should be tightened very slowly and the pinion shaft end play checked often, so that the pinion bearing preload does not exceed the limits.

If the pinion shaft nut is tightened to the point that pinion bearing preload exceeds the limits, the pinion shaft must be removed and a new collapsible spacer installed. **Do not decrease the preload by loosening the pinion shaft nut.** This will remove the compression between the pinion front and rear bearing cones and the collapsible spacer and may permit the front bearing cone to turn on the pinion shaft.

8. As soon as there is preload on the bearings, **turn the pinion shaft in both directions several times to set the bearing rollers.**

9. Adjust the bearing preload to specification. Measure the preload with the tool shown in Fig. 29.

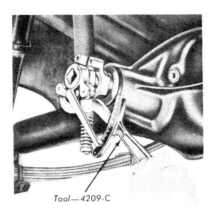

Tool—4209-C

E1228-B

FIG. 29—Checking Pinion Bearing Pre-load

10. Wipe a thin coating of lubricant on the bearing bores so that the differential bearing cups will move easily.

11. Place the cups on the bearings and set the differential case assembly in the carrier casting (Fig. 17).

If the gear set is of the **non-hunting** or **partial non-hunting** type, assemble the differential case and ring gear assembly in the carrier so that the marked tooth on the pinion indexes between the marked teeth on the ring gear as shown in Fig. 30.

In almost every case of improper assembly (gears assembled out of time), the noise level and probability of failure will be higher than they would be with properly assembled gears.

When installing the **hunting** type

PAINT MARKING INDICATES POSITION IN WHICH GEARS WERE LAPPED   E1335-A

FIG. 30—Typical Gear Set Timing Marks

gear set (no timing marks), assemble the differential case and ring gear assembly in the carrier without regard to the matching of any particular gear teeth.

12. Slide the case assembly along the bores until a slight amount of backlash is felt between the gear teeth. Hold the differential case in place.

13. Set the adjusting nuts in the bores so that they just contact the bearing cups.

14. Carefully position the bearing caps on the carrier casting. Match the marks made when the caps were removed.

15. Install the bearing cap bolts and lockwashers. As the bolts are tightened, turn the adjusting nut with the tool shown in Fig. 31.

16. If the adjusting nuts do not turn freely as the cap bolts are tightened, remove the bearing caps and again inspect for damaged

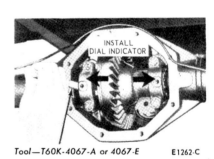

INSTALL DIAL INDICATOR

Tool—T60K-4067-A or 4067-E   E1262-C

FIG. 31—Backlash and Bearing Pre-load Adjustment

threads or incorrectly positioned caps. Tightening the bolts to the specified torque is done to be sure that the cups and adjusting nuts are seated. Loosen the cap bolts, and torque them to only 5 ft-lbs before making adjustments. Refer to part 4-1 for backlash and bearing pre-load adjustment procedures.

---

5 MAJOR REPAIR OPERATIONS—REMOVABLE CARRIER TYPE AXLES

DISASSEMBLY

After removing the carrier from the axle housing as described in section 3, mount the carrier in a holding fixture and perform the Inspection Before Diassembly of Carrier as explained in Part 4-1, Section 3. Then disassemble the carrier as outlined in the following procedures.

REMOVAL AND DISASSEMBLY OF CONVENTIONAL DIFFERENTIAL CASE

1. Mark one differential bearing cap and the mating bearing support with punch marks to help position the parts properly during assembly of the carrier. Also, mark one of the bearing adjusting nuts and the carrier with scribe marks for proper

location during assembly (Fig. 45).

2. Remove the adjusting nut locks, bearing caps, and adjusting nuts. Then lift the differential assembly out of the carrier.

3. If the differential bearings are to be removed, use the tool shown in Fig. 19. On cars equipped with high performance engines, use tool T57L-4220-A.

4. Mark the differential case, cover, and ring gear for assembly in the original position.

5. Remove the bolts that attach the ring gear to the differential case. Press the gear from the case or tap it off with a soft-faced hammer.

6. With a drift, drive out the differential pinion shaft lock pin (Fig. 32) and separate the 2-piece differential case.

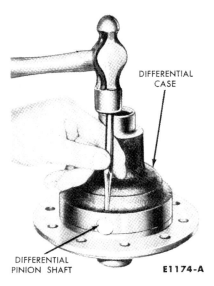

FIG. 32—Removing Differential Pinion Shaft Lock Pin

7. Drive out the pinion shaft with a brass drift (Fig. 33).

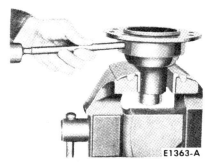

FIG. 33—Driving Out Differential Pinion Shaft

8. Remove the gears and thrust washers. (Fig. 34).

REMOVAL AND DISASSEMBLY OF LIMITED-SLIP DIFFERENTIAL CASE

1. Remove the differential case from the carrier and remove the

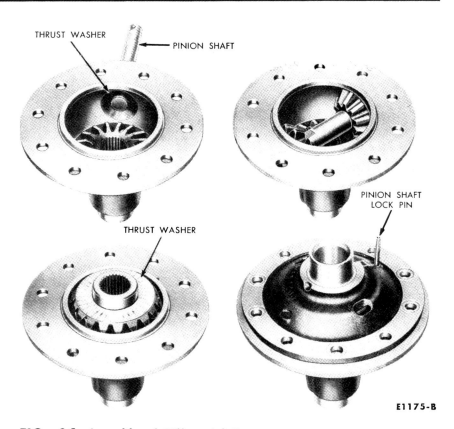

FIG. 34—Assembly of Differential Case

bearings from the differential as outlined in steps 1 through 4 in the foregoing procedure.

2. Place the differential case in a hydraulic press, and apply about one ton pressure across the case bearing hubs while removing the ring gear attaching bolts. This procedure will contain the spring pressure between the differential case and cover until after the bolts are moved, and thereby prevent stripping of the threads. Loosen **alternate** bolts an **equal** amount so that the spring pressure will release evenly.

3. Release the hydraulic press ram, and remove the differential case cover.

4. Remove the Belleville spring (Fig. 21).

5. Remove the steel and the bonded clutch plates.

6. Remove the differential clutch hub, outer side gear, and thrust washer.

7. Remove the ring gear from the differential case.

8. Drive out the differential pinion shaft lock pin.

9. With a brass drift, drive out the differential pinion shaft. Then remove the pinion gears, inner side gear, and thrust washers.

REMOVAL AND DISASSEMBLY OF DRIVE PINION AND BEARING RETAINER

1. Turn the carrier case upright, and remove the pinion shaft nut (Fig. 35). Then remove the U-joint flange (Fig. 36).

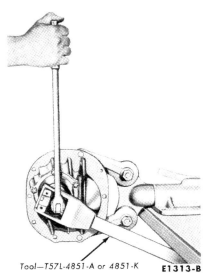

Tool—T57L-4851-A or 4851-K   E1313-B

FIG. 35—Removing Pinion Shaft Nut

2. Remove the seal (Fig. 37) and the slinger.

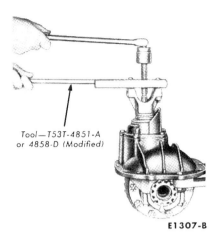

Tool—T53T-4851-A
or 4858-D (Modified)

E1307-B

FIG. 36—Removing U-Joint Flange

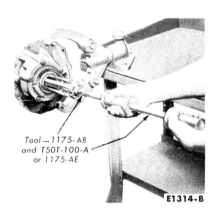

Tool—1175-AB
and T50T-100-A
or 1175-AE

E1314-B

FIG. 37—Removing Pinion Seal

3. Remove the pinion, bearing, and retainer assembly from the carrier housing (Fig. 48). Measure the shim thickness with a micrometer. Record this original shim thickness. If a new gear set is installed during assembly, a new shim will have to be installed. The original shim thickness is one of the factors necessary in calculating the new shim thickness. **Extreme care must be taken not to damage the mounting surfaces of the retainer and carrier.**

4. Place a protective sleeve (hose) on the pinion pilot bearing surface. Press the pinion shaft out of the pinion front bearing cone (Fig. 38).

5. *Press the pinion shaft out of the pinion rear bearing cone (Fig. 39).*

PARTS REPAIR OR REPLACEMENT

Clean and inspect all the parts as outlined in Part 4-1, Section 3. Before assembling the carrier, repair or replace all parts as indicated by the inspection.

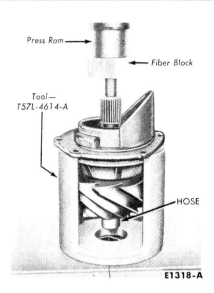

Press Ram
Fiber Block
Tool—T57L-4614-A
HOSE

E1318-A

FIG. 38—Removing Pinion Front Bearing Cone

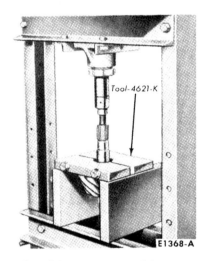

Tool-4621-K

E1368-A

FIG. 39—Removing Pinion Rear Bearing Cone

The principal replacement operations are covered in the following procedures. All other repair or replacement operations are performed during Cleaning and Inspection Part 4-1, Section 3, or during the Assembly in this section.

PILOT BEARING

1. Remove the pilot bearing as shown in Fig. 40. Drive out the pilot bearing and the bearing retainer together. On cars with high performance engines, use handle adapter T53L-200A with tool 757L-4625-A or 4625-K.

2. Drive the new bearing in until it bottoms as shown in Fig. 41. On cars with high performance engines,

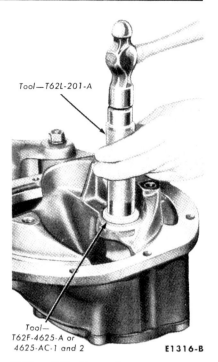

Tool—T62L-201-A

Tool—
T62F-4625-A or
4625-AC-1 and 2

E1316-B

FIG. 40—Removing Pilot Bearing

Tool—T62F-4625-A
or 4625-AC-1 and 2

Tool—
T62L-201-A

E1315-B

FIG. 41—Installing Pilot Bearing

use handle adapter 753L-200-A with tool 757L-4625-A, or 4625-K, or 4625-KA.

3. Using the same tool, install a **new** pilot bearing retainer with the concave side up.

PINION BEARING CUPS

Do not remove the pinion bearing cups from the retainer unless the cups are worn or damaged. The flange and pilot of the retainer are machined during manufacture by locating on these cups after they are *installed in their bores. If the* cups are worn or damaged, they should be removed and replaced as shown in Fig. 42. On cars equipped with high performance engines, use the following tools: T57L-4614-A with T57L-4616-A for front cup removal except Comet; tool 4615-D for Comet front cup removal; T57L-4614-A with T57L-4616-A2 for front cup installation and T57L-4614-A with T55P-4616-A2 for rear cup installation.

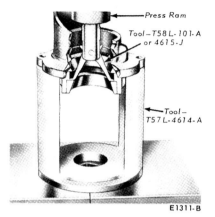

FIG. 42—Removing Pinion Bearing Cup

After the new cups are installed, make sure they are seated in the retainer by trying to insert a 0.0015-inch feeler gauge between the cup and the bottom of the bore.

Whenever the cups are replaced, the cone and roller assemblies should also be replaced.

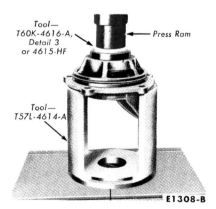

FIG. 43—Installing Pinion Bearing Cup

DRIVE PINION AND GEAR SET

When replacing a ring gear and pinion, note that the original factory installed shim is of the correct thickness to adjust for individual variations in both the carrier housing dimension and in the original gear set dimension. Therefore, to select

the correct shim thickness for the new gear set to be installed, follow these steps:

1. Measure the thickness of the **original shim** with a micrometer.

2. Note the shim adjustment number on both the old pinion and the new pinion. Each pinion gear is marked with an adjustment number such as the +1 marking in Fig. 44.

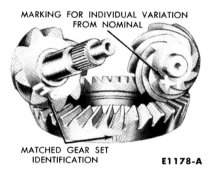

MARKING FOR INDIVIDUAL VARIATION FROM NOMINAL

MATCHED GEAR SET IDENTIFICATION   E1178-A

FIG. 44—Pinion and Ring Gear Markings

3. Refer to Table 2 to determine the correct amount of shim thickness change. The amount shown in the table under the old pinion shim adjustment number and in line with the new pinion number is the amount of **change** that should be made to the **original** shim thickness.

If the old pinion is marked +4, for example, and the new pinion is marked −2, the table indicates that 0.006 inch of shim stock should be removed from the **original** shim pack.

If the **original** shim pack was lost or if a new carrier housing is being installed, substitute a **nominal** 0.020-inch shim for the **original**, and follow the foregoing procedure for a trial build-up. If any further shim change is necessary, it will be indicated in the tooth pattern check.

A new ring gear and pinion should always be installed in an axle as a matched set (never separately). **Be sure that the same matching number appears on both the drive pinion and the ring gear.** Note the number 170 in Fig. 44.

4. After determining the correct shim thickness as explained in the foregoing steps, install the new pinion and ring gear as outlined under Assembly.

DIFFERENTIAL CASE, BEARINGS AND RING GEAR

If the ring gear runout check (before disassembly) exceeded specifications, the condition may be caused

by a warped gear, a defective case, or excessively worn differential bearings.

To determine the cause of excessive runout proceed as follows:

1. Assemble the two halves of the differential case together **without** the ring gear, and press the two differential side bearings on the case hubs.

2. Place the cups on the bearings and set the differential case in the carrier.

3. Install the bearing caps and adjusting nuts as outlined in step 11 thru 14 under Assembly and Installation of Conventional Differential Case in this section.

4. Tighten the right nut two notches beyond the position where it first contacts the bearing cup. Rotate the differential case several revolutions in each direction while the bearings are loaded to seat the bearings in their cups. **This step is important.**

5. Again loosen the right nut to release the preload. Check to see that the left nut contacts the bearing cup. Using the dial indicator set-up shown in Fig. 13, Part 4-1, adjust the preload to 0.012 case spread for new bearings or 0.005 to 0.008 for the original bearings, if re-used.

6. Check the runout of the differential case flange with a dial indicator. If the runout does **not now** exceed specifications, install a new drive gear. If the runout still exceeds specifications, the ring gear is true and the trouble is due to either a defective case or worn bearings.

7. Remove the differential case from the carrier and remove the side bearings from the case.

8. Install **new** bearings on the case hubs, and again install the differential assembly in the carrier **without** the ring gear.

9. Check the case runout again with the new bearings. If the runout is **now** within limits, the old bearings were excessively worn. Use the new bearings for assembly. If the runout is still excessive, the case is defective and should be replaced.

ASSEMBLY

Refer to Part 4-1 for Cleaning and Inspection before starting assembly operations. Fig. 45 shows the disassembled parts.

ASSEMBLY AND INSTALLATION OF DRIVE PINION AND BEARING RETAINER

1. Install the drive pinion rear

TABLE 2 — DRIVE PINION ADJUSTING SHIM THICKNESS CHANGES (Inches)

New Pinion Marking	Old Pinion Marking								
	−4	−3	−2	−1	0	+1	+2	+3	+4
+4	+0.008	+0.007	+0.006	+0.005	+0.004	+0.003	+0.002	+0.001	0
+3	+0.007	+0.006	+0.005	+0.004	+0.003	+0.002	+0.001	0	−0.001
+2	+0.006	+0.005	+0.004	+0.003	+0.002	+0.001	0	−0.001	−0.002
+1	+0.005	+0.004	+0.003	+0.002	+0.001	0	−0.001	−0.002	−0.003
0	+0.004	+0.003	+0.002	+0.001	0	−0.001	−0.002	−0.003	−0.004
−1	+0.003	+0.002	+0.001	0	−0.001	−0.002	−0.003	−0.004	−0.005
−2	+0.002	+0.001	0	−0.001	−0.002	−0.003	−0.004	−0.005	−0.006
−3	+0.001	0	−0.001	−0.002	−0.003	−0.004	−0.005	−0.006	−0.007
−4	0	−0.001	−0.002	−0.003	−0.004	−0.005	−0.006	−0.007	−0.008

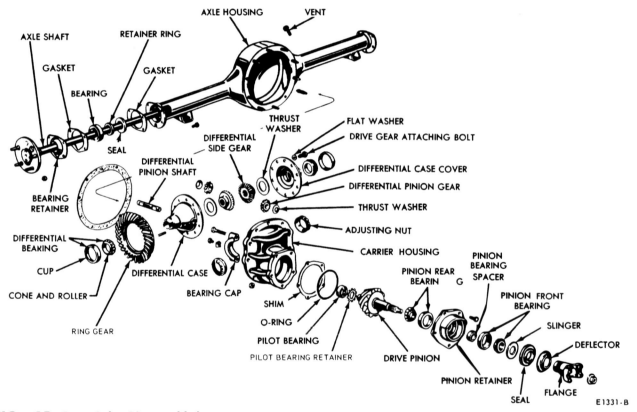

FIG. 45—Rear Axle—Disassembled

bearing cone and roller on the pinion shaft (Fig. 46). On cars equipped with high performance engines use tool T57L-4621-B along with tool 757L-4614-A as shown in Fig. 46. Place a new spacer on the pinion shaft (Fig. 47).

2. Place the bearing retainer on the pinion shaft, and install the front bearing cone and roller in the retainer. Press the front bearing cone and roller into position with the same tools as used in Fig. 46 for front bearing installation. On cars with high performance engines, use

T57L-4621-B along with tool T57L-4614-A.

3. Lubricate the O-ring with axle lubricant and install it in its groove in the pinion retainer. Be careful not to twist it. Snap the O-ring into position.

4. Place the proper shim on the carrier housing and install the pinion and retainer assembly being careful not to pinch the O-ring (Fig. 48).

5. Install the pinion retainer bolts. Torque bolts to specifications.

6. Place the slinger on the pinion shaft.

7. Coat the outside edge of a new oil seal with a small amount of a new oil resistant sealer. **Do not put any of the sealer on the sealing lip.** Install the seal in the bearing retainer (Fig. 49). On cars with high performance engines, use tool T58L-4676-A or tool 4676-F.

New seals should be soaked in SAE 10 oil for ½ hour before use.

8. Install the U-joint flange (Fig. 50).

9. *Start a new integral nut and washer on the pinion shaft.*

10. Hold the flange (Fig. 35) and

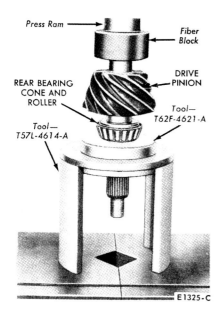

FIG. 46—Installing Pinion Rear Bearing Cone

pound torque wrench is not available tool 4209-C may be used in combination with tool 4209-C12. Correct preload will be obtained when the torque required to rotate the pinion in the retainer is as specified in Part 4-3. If the torque required to rotate the pinion is less then specified, tighten the pinion shaft nut a little at a time until the proper preload is established. **Do not overtighten the nut.** If excessive preload is obtained as a result of overtightening, replace the collapsible bearing spacer.

Do not back off the pinion shaft nut to establish pinion bearing preload. If the torque on the pinion shaft nut is less than 175 ft-lbs. after bearing preload is established, a new collapsible spacer must be used.

ASSEMBLY AND INSTALLATION OF CONVENTIONAL DIFFERENTIAL CASE

1. Place a side gear and thrust

line up the pinion shaft lock pin holes.

4. Place the second side gear and thrust washer in position (Fig. 34), and install the cover on the differential case. Install the pinion shaft lock pin. A pinion or axle shaft spline can be inserted in the side gear spline to check for free rotation of the differential gears.

5. Insert two $7/16$ (N. F.) bolts two inches long through the differential case flange, and thread them three or four turns into the ring gear as a guide in aligning the ring gear bolt holes. Press or tap the ring gear into position.

6. Install and tighten the ring gear bolts and washers evenly, and torque them alternately across the gear to specification.

7. If the differential bearings have been removed, press them on as shown in Fig. 52.

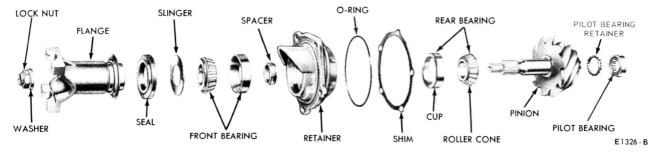

FIG. 47—Pinion and Bearing Retainer

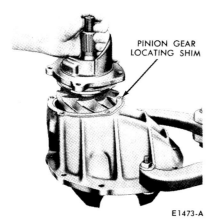

FIG. 48—Installing Pinion and Retainer

tighten the pinion shaft nut to 175 ft-lbs. Do not exceed 175 ft-lbs at this time. As the pinion shaft nut is tightened, rotate the pinion shaft frequently to allow the bearing to seat.

11. Check the pinion bearing preload as shown in Fig. 51. If an inch-

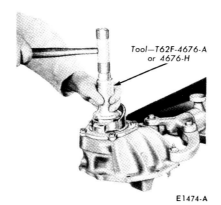

FIG. 49—Installing Oil Seal

washer in the differential case bore Fig. 34). **Lubricate all differential parts liberally with axle lubricant during assembly.**

2. With a soft-faced hammer, drive the pinion shaft into the case only far enough to retain a pinion thrust washer and pinion gear.

3. Place the second pinion and thrust washer in position, and drive the pinion shaft into place. **Carefully**

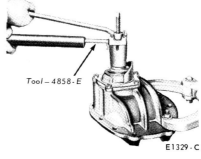

FIG. 50—Installing U-Joint Flange

8. Wipe a thin coating of lubricant on the bearing bores so that the differential bearing cups will move easily.

9. Place the cups on the bearings. If the gear set is of the **non-hunting** or **partial non-hunting** type, assemble the differential case and ring gear assembly in the carrier so that the marked tooth on the pinion indexes between the marked teeth on the ring gear as shown in Fig. 30.

In almost every case of improper

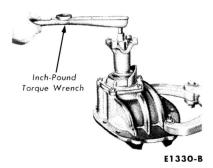

FIG. 51—Checking Pinion Bearing Pre-load

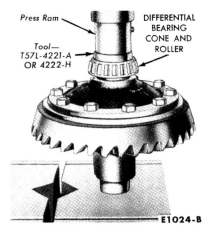

FIG. 52—Installing Differential Bearing

assembly (gears assembled out of time), the noise level and probability of failure will be higher than they would be with properly assembled gears.

When installing the **hunting** type gear set (no timing marks) assemble the differential case and ring gear assembly in the carrier without regard to the matching of any particular gear teeth.

10. Slide the assembly along the bores until a slight amount of backlash is felt between the gear teeth.

11. Set the adjusting nuts in the bores so that they just contact the bearing cups. The nuts should be

engaged about the same number of threads on each side.

12. Carefully position the bearing caps on the carrier. Match the marks made when the caps were removed.

13. Install the bearing cap bolts and alternately torque them to 70-80 ft-lbs.

14. If the adjusting nuts do not turn freely as the cap bolts are tightened, remove the bearing caps and again inspect for damaged threads or incorrectly positioned caps. Tightening the bolts to the specified torque is done to be sure that the cups and adjusting nuts are seated. Loosen the cap bolts, and torque them to only 25 ft-lbs. before making adjustments.

15. Adjust the backlash between the ring gear and pinion as outlined in Part 4-1, Section 2.

16. Be sure to make a final tooth pattern check before installing the carrier assembly in the axle housing.

ASSEMBLY AND INSTALLATION OF LIMITED-SLIP DIFFERENTIAL CASE

1. Place the side gear and thrust washer in the differential case (Fig. 21). **Lubricate all parts liberally with axle lubricant during assembly.**

2. With a soft-faced hammer, drive the pinion shaft into the case only far enough to retain a pinion thrust washer and pinion gear.

3. Place the second pinion and thrust washer in position, and drive the pinion shaft into place. **Carefully line up the pinion shaft lock pin holes.**

4. Install the pinion shaft lock pin. **The lock pin must not extend beyond the surface of the case.**

5. Insert two 2-inch $^7/_{16}$ (N. F.) bolts through the differential case flange, and thread them three or four turns into the ring gear as a guide in aligning the ring gear bolt holes. Press or tap the ring gear into position.

6. Clamp the differential case in a soft-jawed vise. Install the other differential side gear on the differential

pinion gears. Place the clutch hub on the side gear. Place the thrust washer on the hub (Fig. 25).

7. To align the clutch plates during assembly, insert two $^3/_{16}$ x 2 dowel pins into the differential case. Place a steel plate on the differential case so that the slots in the ears straddle the dowel pin (Fig. 25). **Lubricate all the locking differential parts with axle lubricant so that an accurate torque check can be made.**

8. Place a bonded plate on the steel plate. Make sure the bonded plate inner spline teeth properly engage the hub spline. Assemble the remaining plates: a steel plate, a bonded plate, a steel plate, a bonded plate, and lastly a steel plate.

9. Place the Belleville spring on the top steel plate. The Belleville spring is assembled with the concave side down (Fig. 26). Carefully center the Belleville spring so that it will fit into the cover.

10. Place the differential case cover on the case (Fig. 27). Start the ring gear bolts.

11. Tighten the bolts evenly and alternately across the diameter of the ring gear. As the bolts are tightened the Belleville spring is compressed and the differential case and cover are pulled together.

12. Remove the dowel pins.

13. Torque the case to ring gear bolts to specifications.

14. Check the torque required to rotate one side gear while the other side gear is held (Fig. 28). Ignore the torque required to start the side gear turning. The torque required to keep it moving steadily should be between 155 and 195 ft-lbs, if new clutch plates were installed. The torque should be a least 75 ft-lbs, if the original clutch plates were installed. If the required torque is not within these limits, check for improper assembly.

15. Install the side bearings on the differential case, and install the case in the carrier as described in steps 7 through 16 under Assembly and Installation of Conventional Differential Case.

PART 4-3 SPECIFICATIONS

REAR AXLE LUBRICATION

Axle Type	Ford Specification	Ford Part No.	Capacity
Integral Carrier	M2C28-B	C2AZ-19590-A	2½ Pints (Approximate)
Removable Carrier (Except with 289-4V Engine)	M-2C50-B	C1AZ-19580-E or F	4½ Pints (Approximate)
Removable Carrier (With 289-4V Engine)	M2C57-A	C2AZ-19580-D	5 Pints (Approximate)
All Axles Equipped With Locking Differential	Use M-2C50-B, plus 4 ounces of M-2C58-A (C1AA-19B546-A) additive per refill of M-2C50-B		

For temperatures above —25°F use SAE 90 Grade lubricant.
For temperatures below —25°F use SAE 80 Grade lubricant.

REAR AXLE—INTEGRAL CARRIER TYPE

DRIVE PINION ADJUSTING SHIM THICKNESS CHANGES—INCH

Old Pinion Marking	New Pinion Marking								
	—4	—3	—2	—1	0	+1	+2	+3	+4
+4	+0.008	+0.007	+0.006	+0.005	+0.004	+0.003	+0.002	+0.001	0
+3	+0.007	+0.006	+0.005	+0.004	+0.003	+0.002	+0.001	0	—0.001
+2	+0.006	+0.005	+0.004	+0.003	+0.002	+0.001	0	—0.001	—0.002
+1	+0.005	+0.004	+0.003	+0.002	+0.001	0	—0.001	—0.002	—0.003
0	+0.004	+0.003	+0.002	+0.001	0	—0.001	—0.002	—0.003	—0.004
—1	+0.003	+0.002	+0.001	0	—0.001	—0.002	—0.003	—0.004	—0.005
—2	+0.002	+0.001	0	—0.001	—0.002	—0.003	—0.004	—0.005	—0.006
—3	+0.001	0	—0.001	—0.002	—0.003	—0.004	—0.005	—0.006	—0.007
—4	0	—0.001	—0.002	—0.003	—0.004	—0.005	—0.006	—0.007	—0.008

REAR AXLE RATIOS, GEAR AND CODE IDENTIFICATION

Identification Tag	Ring Gear Diameter (Inches)	Type of Differential	Axle Ratio
WCY-R	7¼	Conventional	2.88:1
WCY-AA	7¼	Limited-Slip	
WCY-E	7¼	Conventional	3.20:1
WCY-AJ	7¼	Conventional	
WCY-L	7¼	Limited-Slip	

CONTINUED ON NEXT PAGE

REAR AXLE—INTEGRAL CARRIER TYPE (Continued)

ADJUSTMENTS

	Inch
Backlash Between Ring Gear and Pinion	0.008-0.012
Backlash Variation Between Teeth	Max. 0.003
Runout of Backface of Ring Gear as Assembled	Max. 0.003
Thickness: Differential Side Gear Thrust Washers Differential Pinion Gear Thrust Washers	0.030-0.032 0.030-0.032
Ring Bearing Cone to Pinion Gear Nominal Shim	0.017
Shims Available:	0.008-0.024

TORQUE LIMITS

	Ft-lbs
Rear Cover Bolts	10-17
Differential Bearing Cap Screws	40-55
Differential Bearing Adusting Nut Lock Bolts	12-25
Rear Shock Absorbers to Rear Spring Clip Plate Assembly Nuts	15-25
Universal Joint Bolt Nuts	7-10
Ring Gear Attaching Bolts	40-55
Rear Axle Shaft Bearing Retaining Nuts	30-40
Spring Clip Nuts (Rear Springs to Axle Housing)	13-20
Minimum Torque Required to Tighten Pinion Flange Lock Nut to Obtain Correct Pinion Bearing Preload	140
Pinion Bearing Preload New Bearings Used Bearings	17-27① 6-12①
Differential Bearing Preload (Case Spread-Thousandths) New Bearings Used Bearings	0.008 0.003-0.005

①Inch-pounds

REAR AXLE—REMOVABLE CARRIER TYPE

REAR AXLE RATIOS, GEAR AND CODE IDENTIFICATION

Identification Tag	Ring Gear Diameter (Inches)	Type of Differential	Axle Ratio	Identification Tag	Ring Gear Diameter (Inches)	Type of Differential	Axle Ratio
WCZ-E	7¾	Conventional	2.80:1	WDE-B	9	Conventional	3.00:1
WDJ-B	7¾	Limited-Slip	2.80:1	WEB-C	9	Conventional	3.25:1
WCZ-F	8	Conventional	3.00:1	WED-C	9	Limited-Slip	3.00:1
WDJ-C	8	Limited-Slip	3.00:1	WED-A	9	Limited-Slip	3.25:1
WCZ-S	8¾	Conventional	3.50:1	WDY-B	8	Conventional	3.25:1
WCZ-R	8¾	Conventional	3.89:1	WDY-C	8	Conventional	3.50:1
WDZ-A	7¾	Limited-Slip	2.80:1	WEA-B	8	Limited-Slip	3.50:1
WDW-C	8	Conventional	3.25:1	WDY-A	8	Conventional	3.00:1
WDW-E	7¾	Conventional	2.80:1	WEA-F	8	Limited-Slip	3.25:1
WDW-A	7¾	Conventional	2.80:1	WEA-A	8	Limited-Slip	3.00:1
WDW-D	8	Conventional	3.50:1	WEC-A	9	Conventional	3.00:1
WDZ-C	8	Limited-Slip	3.25:1	WEC-B	9	Conventional	3.25:1
WDW-B	8	Conventional	3.00:1	WEE-A	9	Limited-Slip	3.25:1
WDC-B	8	Limited-Slip	3.00:1	WEE-C	9	Limited-Slip	3.00:1

ADJUSTMENTS

	Inch
Backlash Between Ring Gear and Pinion	0.008-0.012
Maximum Backlash Variation Between Teeth	0.003
Maximum Runout of Backface of Ring Gear as Assembled	0.003

ADJUSTMENTS (Continued)

	Inch
Thickness Differential Side Gear Thrust Washers Differential Pinion Gear Thrust Washers	0.030-0.032 0.030-0.032
Nominal Pinion Locating Shim (By Ring-Gear Size) 7¾" and 8" 8¾" and 9"	0.022 0.015
Available Shims (In steps of 0.001 inch)	0.010-0.029

CONTINUED ON NEXT PAGE

REAR AXLE—REMOVABLE CARRIER TYPE (Continued)

TORQUE LIMITS

Description	7¾"-8" Ring Gear Ft-lbs	8¾"-9" Ring Gear Ft-lbs
Differential Bearing Cap Screws	55-70	70-85
Differential Bearing Adjusting Nut Lock Bolts	12-25	12-25
Carrier to Housing Stud Nuts	30-40	30-40
Pinion Retainer to Carrier Cap Screws	30-45	30-45
Ring Gear Attaching Bolts	65-80	65-80
Rear Axle Shaft Bearing Retainer Bolts	30-40	30-40
Rear Shock Absorber to Rear Spring Clip Plate Assembly Nuts	15-22	15-22
Pinion Flange U-Bolt Nuts	12-15	15-20
Spring Clip Nuts (Rear Spring to Axle Housing)	30-45	30-45
Minimum Torque Required to Tighten Pinion Nut to Obtain Correct Pinion Bearing Preload	175①	175①

Pinion Bearing Preload	New Bearings and New Seal	17-32 inch-pounds	22-32 inch-pounds
	Used Bearings and New Seal	8-14 inch-pounds	8-14

Differential Bearing Preload (Case Spread-Thousandths) New Bearings Original Bearings	0.012 0.005-0.008

①If this torque can not be obtained with a used spacer, install a new spacer.

REAR AXLES WITH LOCKING DIFFERENTIAL

Torque Check		Integral Carrier Type Axles	Removable Carrier Type Axles
Minimum torque required to turn axle shaft and side gear with one wheel on the ground		50 ft-lbs	75 ft-lbs
Bench Check After Assembly	With New Clutch Plates	100-125 ft-lbs	155-195 ft-lbs
	With Original Clutch Plates	50 ft-lbs Minimum	75 ft-lbs Minimum

SPECIAL TOOLS

Ford Tool No.	Former No.	Description
T50T-100-A	B-166	Impact Hammer
T58L-101-A		Puller Attachment
T62L-201-A	—	Handle Adapter
T56L-400-A	4851-A	Puller
T57L-500-A	—	Bench Mounted Holding Fixture
TOOL-1175-AB	1175-AB	Grease Seal Remover (Head Only)
T50T-100-A and TOOL-1175-AB	1175-AE	Seal Remover
T60K-1177-B	1177-B	Rear Wheel Bearing Oil Seal
T60K-1225-A or TOOL-1225-C		Axle Shaft Bearing Remover and Replacer. Axle Shaft Bearing Remover
TOOL-1225-B		Axle Shaft Bearing Replacer
T60K-4067-A	4067-E	Differential Bearing Adjuster Nut Wrench
TOOL-4209-C	4209-C	Pinion Tension Scale with TOOL-4209-C12 Socket
TOOL-4221-AL	4221-AL	Differential Bearing Cone Remover Pilot (Use with TOOL-4221-C or TOOL-4851-A)
T57L-4221-A	4222-K	Differential Bearing Cone Replacer
TOOL-4222-H	4222-H	Differential Bearing Cone Replacer
T60K-4234-A	4235-D	Rear Axle Shaft Assembly Remover Adapter
T57L-4614-A	4614	Drive Pinion and Drive Pinion Retainer Assembly Support
TOOL-4615-J	4615-J	Drive Pinion Front Bearing Cup Remover
T60K-4616-A	4615-HF 4625-HR	Pinion Bearing Cup Replacer
T57L-4616-A	4615-D	Pinion Front Bearing Cup Remover
T57L-4616-A2		Pinion Front Bearing Cup Replacer
T55P-4616-A2		Pinion Rear Bearing Cup Replacer
TOOL-4621-K	4621-K	Drive Pinion Rear Bearing Cone Remover
T62F-4621-A		Pinion Bearing Cone Replacer
T62F-4625-A	4625-AC-1 & 2	Drive Pinion Pilot Bearing Remover and Replacer
T55P-4676-A	4676-G	Drive Pinion Oil Seal Replacer
T62F-4676-A	4676-H	Drive Pinion Oil Seal Replacer
T53T-4851-A	4851-A 4858-D	Flange (Universal Joint) Axle End Remover
T57L-4851-A	4851-K	Universal Joint Flange Holder
TOOL-4858-E	4858-E	Companion Flange and Pinion Bearing Replacer
T59L-4204-A	44211 and 44211-A	Locking Differential Torque Check
T65K-4204-A		Locking Differential Torque Check Adapter

DRIVE PINION ADJUSTING SHIM THICKNESS CHANGES (inch)

New Pinion Marking	Old Pinion Marking								
	−4	−3	−2	−1	0	+1	+2	+3	+4
+4	+0.008	+0.007	+0.006	+0.005	+0.004	+0.003	+0.002	+.001	0
+3	+0.007	+0.006	+0.005	+0.004	+0.003	+0.002	+0.001	0	−0.001
+2	+0.006	+0.005	+0.004	+0.003	+0.002	+0.001	0	−0.001	−0.002
+1	+0.005	+0.004	+0.003	+0.002	+0.001	0	−0.001	−0.002	−0.003
0	+0.004	+0.003	+0.002	+0.001	0	−0.001	−0.002	−0.003	−0.004
−1	+0.003	+0.002	+0.001	0	−0.001	−0.002	−0.003	−0.004	−0.005
−2	+0.002	+0.001	0	−0.001	−0.002	−0.003	−0.004	−0.005	−0.006
−3	+0.001	0	−0.001	−0.002	−0.003	−0.004	−0.005	−0.006	−0.007
−4	0	−0.001	−0.002	−0.003	−0.004	−0.005	−0.006	−0.007	−0.008

DRIVE SHAFT AND CLUTCH

GROUP 5

PART 5-1   **PAGE**
DRIVE SHAFT .5-1

PART 5-2
GENERAL CLUTCH SERVICE **5-4**

PART 5-3   **PAGE**
CLUTCH **5-9**

PART 5-4
SPECIFICATIONS **5-14**

PART 5-1   DRIVE SHAFT

Section	Page
1 Trouble Diagnosis	5-1
2 Description and Operation	5-1
3 Replacement	5-2

Section	Page
Removal	5-2
Installation	5-2

1 TROUBLE DIAGNOSIS

DRIVE SHAFT TROUBLE DIAGNOSIS AND POSSIBLE CAUSES

DRIVE SHAFT VIBRATION	Undercoating or other foreign material on shaft. Universal joint U-bolts loose. Universal joints worn, or lack of lubricant. Drive shaft mis-aligned (drive line angle).	Drive shaft and universal joints 180° out of phase. Broken rear spring center bolt. Broken rear spring. Rear springs not matched (Sagged to one side). Drive shaft damaged (bent) or out of balance (missing balance weights).
U-JOINT NOISE	Universal joint U-bolts loose. Lack of lubrication.	Worn U-joints. Worn needle bearings

2 DESCRIPTION AND OPERATION

The drive shaft is the means of transferring power from the engine, through the transmission, to the differential in the rear axle, and then to the rear wheels. The drive shaft incorporates two universal joints and a slip yoke. The universal joints (Fig. 1) are provided with a threaded plug which can be removed for lubrication when necessary. The splines in the yoke and on the transmission output shaft permit the drive shaft to move forward and rearward as the axle moves up and down.

All drive shafts are balanced. If the car is to be undercoated, cover the drive shaft and universal joints to prevent application of the undercoating material.

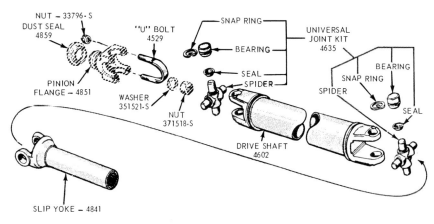

FIG. 1—Drive Shaft and Universal Joints Disassembled

E1432-C

3 REPLACEMENT

REMOVAL

1. To maintain drive shaft balance, mark the relationship of the rear drive shaft yoke and the drive pinion flange of the axle (if the yellow alignment marks are not visible) with the shaft so that they may be installed in their original positions.

2. Disconnect the rear U-joint from the axle drive pinion flange. Wrap tape around the loose bearing caps to prevent them from falling off the spider. Pull the drive shaft toward the rear of the car until the slip yoke clears the transmission expansion housing and the seal. Install the appropriate Extension Housing Seal Installation tool into the extension housing to prevent lubricant leakage.

3. Place the drive shaft in a vise being careful not to damage it.

4. Remove the snap rings that retain the bearings in the slip yoke and in the drive shaft.

5. Position the tool shown in Fig. 2 on the shaft and press the bear-

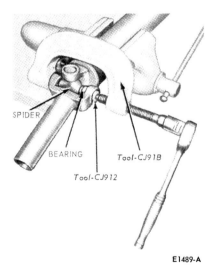

E1489-A

FIG. 2—Removing Universal Joint Bearing

ing out of the slip yoke. If the bearing cannot be pressed all the way out of the yoke, remove it with vise grip or channel lock pliers.

6. Reposition the tool to press on the spider to remove the bearing from the opposite side of the yoke.

7. Remove the yoke from the spider.

8. Remove the bearings and spider

from the drive shaft in the same manner.

9. Clean all foreign matter from the yoke area at each end of the drive shaft.

INSTALLATION

1. Start a new bearing into the yoke at the rear of the drive shaft.

2. Position the spider in the rear yoke and press the bearing ¼ inch below the surface (Fig. 3).

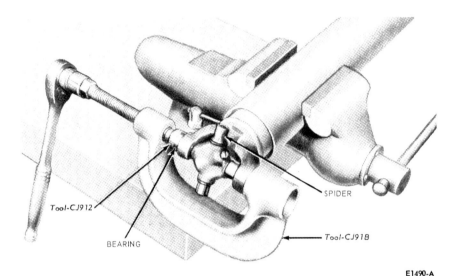

E1490-A

FIG. 3—Installing Universal Joint Bearing

3. Remove the tool and install a new snap ring.

4. Start a new bearing into the opposite side of the yoke.

5. Install the tool and press on the bearing until the opposite bearing contacts the snap ring.

Remove the tool and install a new snap ring. It may be necessary to grind the surface of the snap ring to permit easier entry.

6. Reposition the drive shaft and install the new spider and two new bearings in the same manner as the rear yoke.

7. Position the slip yoke on the spider and install two new bearings and snap rings.

8. Check the joint for freedom of movement. If a bind has resulted from misalignment during the foregoing procedures, a sharp rap on the yokes with a brass hammer will seat the bearing needles and usually provide freedom of movement. Care must be taken to support the shaft end during this operation, as well as

preventing blows to the bearings themselves. Do not install the drive shaft unless the universal joints are free of bind.

10. If either the rubber seal on the output shaft or the seal and integral boot in the end of the transmission extension housing is damaged in any manner, replace the seal or seals as required. Also, if the lugs on the axle pinion flange are shaved or distorted so that the bearings

slide, replace the flange.

11. Lubricate the yoke spline with B8A-19589-A lubricant. This spline is sealed so that the transmission fluid does not "wash" away the spline lubricant (Fig. 4). Remove the tool from the extension housing. Install the yoke on the transmission output shaft.

Install the driveshaft so that the index marks or the yellow mark (if visible) on the yoke is in line with the yellow mark on the axle pinion flange. This prevents vibration which occurs when the balance of the shaft and balance of the axle pinion flange become additive instead of neutralizing. If a vibration exists, the driveshaft should be disconnected from the axle, rotated 180° and reinstalled.

12. Install the U-bolts and nuts that attach the U-joint to the drive pinion flange. Torque the U-bolt nuts to *12-15 ft.-lbs. (7-10 ft-lbs.* on a Falcon and Mustang equipped with a 6-cylinder engine and standard transmission).

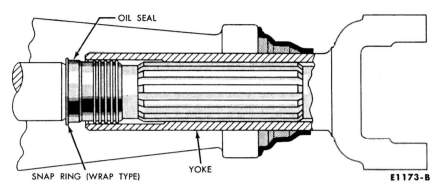

FIG. 4—Output Shaft Spline Seal

PART 5-2 GENERAL CLUTCH SERVICE

Section	Page
1 Diagnosis and Testing	5-4
2 Flywheel Housing Alignment	5-5
Inspection	5-5
Correction	5-5
Engine In Car	5-5
Engine Out of Car	5-7

Section	Page
3 Cleaning and Inspection	5-7
Release Bearing	5-7
Pressure Plate and Cover	5-8
Clutch Disc	5-8
Pilot Bushing	5-8

1 DIAGNOSIS AND TESTING

DIAGNOSIS GUIDE—CLUTCH

TROUBLE SYMPTOMS	POSSIBLE CAUSES	CORRECTION
LOSS OF OR EXCESSIVE CLUTCH PEDAL FREE PLAY AND/OR INADEQUATE RESERVE	1. Clutch linkage out of adjustment. 2. Worn clutch disc. 3. Bent or cracked equalizer bar.	1. Adjust clutch linkage. 2-3. Replace worn or defective parts.
CLUTCH PEDAL HANG UP OR EXCESSIVE CLUTCH PEDAL EFFORT	**CLUTCH** 1. Assist spring not positioned properly. 2. Binding at pedal support bracket, or equalizer rod at firewall. **RELEASE BEARING** 1. Lack of lube on transmission input shaft bearing retainer.	1. Install correctly. 2. Lubricate with engine oil or replace support bracket bushing if defective. 1. Clean and lubricate retainer with thin coat of Lithium base grease (no Polyethylene).
CLUTCH NOISY WHEN PEDAL FREE TRAVEL IS TAKEN OUT, ENGINE RUNNING	1. Release bearing failure due to: A. improper travel adjustment. B. bearing cocked on hub. C. release lever out of plane. D. flywheel housing misalignment. E. excessive crankshaft end play.	1. A. Adjust travel to specification. B. Install correctly. C. Check fulcrum plate and return spring. Install correctly. D. Align to specification. E. Repair to specifications.
CLUTCH NOISY WITH ENGINE OFF	1. Insufficient lubricant on assist spring seats. 2. Clutch assist spring clunking. 3. Binding at pedal support bracket or equalizer rod at fire wall.	1. Lubricate linkage and/or spring seats. 2. Lubricate spring ends. 3. Lubricate with engine oil or replace support bracket bushing if defective.
CLUTCH SLIPS OR CHATTERS	1. Incorrect pedal free travel. 2. Worn or contaminated clutch lining. 3. Grease or oil on clutch facings from: A. release bearing B. engine C. release lever D. pilot bearing E. transmission	1. Adjust travel to specification. 2-3. Replace defective parts. (If grease or oil is causing the clutch to slip, replace the disc. Remove the grease or oil from the pressure plate and re-use if it is not burned or scored).

DIAGNOSIS GUIDE—CLUTCH (Continued)

TROUBLE SYMPTOMS	POSSIBLE CAUSES	CORRECTION
THUD	1. Excessive engine crankshaft end play.	1. Repair to specification.
CLUTCH PEDAL SCRUBBING —ENGINE OFF	1. Pedal push rod rubbing on firewall felt and insulator. 2. Pedal shaft binding at support bracket. 3. Lack of lube on transmission input shaft bearing retainer.	1. Lubricate and check clearance. 2. Lubricate with engine oil or replace support bracket bushing if defective. 3. Clean and lubricate retainer with a thin coat of Lithium base grease (no Polyethylene).

2 FLYWHEEL HOUSING ALIGNMENT

Alignment of the flywheel housing bore and rear face with the engine should be checked as a possible cause of any of the following troubles: excessive transmission gear wear, transmission jumping out of gear, especially third gear, drive line vibration, excessive pilot bushing wear, noisy release bearing, or excessive clutch spin time.

INSPECTION

1. With the clutch release bearing removed, install the indicator pilot tool shown in Fig. 1.

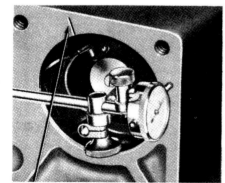 

MAXIMUM FACE RUN OUT +0.009 INCH   MAXIMUM NEGATIVE BORE RUN OUT 0.015 INCH **C1017-C**

FIG. 1—Flywheel Housing Alignment Check

2. Clean the faces of the flywheel housing bolt bosses, and remove all burrs, nicks, and paint from the mounting face of the housing

3. Install the dial indicator on the pilot and adjust the holder so the button will contact a circumference just inside of the transmission mounting holes (Fig. 1).

4. Push the flywheel forward to remove crankshaft end play. Set the dial indicator face to read zero.

5. Remove the spark plugs to alleviate compression.

6. While forcing the flywheel forward, rotate the crankshaft through one revolution and note the point of maximum runout. Mark runout on the face of housing as detailed in Steps 1 and 2 of the Dia-L-Igner instructions (Fig. 2).

7. Position the dial indicator to check bore alignment (Fig. 1). The bore must be clean and free of burrs, nicks and paint.

8. Pull the crankshaft through one revolution. Note the indicator reading and mark the maximum point of runout on the face of the housing as detailed in Steps 3 and 4 of the Dia-L-Igner instructions (Fig. 2).

9. Remove the dial indicator from the crankshaft and the housing.

10. Select the Dia-L-Igner pilot (Fig. 3) which will fit snugly in the bore of the flywheel housing.

11. Press the pilot into place on the locator on the back of the dial.

12. Position the Dia-L-Igner on the face of the housing (Fig. 4) with the pilot in the bore.

13. Rotate the face runout arrow to the positive face runout mark on the housing.

14. Without moving the face runout arrow, route arrow A until it is at the negative bore reading.

15. Slide arrow A to register the amount of bore runout on the—.010 —line of the white scale. Use the scale No. to coincide with the pilot being used.

16. Rotate arrow B until it points in the direction of the face runout arrow and its centerline is parallel to the centerline of the face runout arrow.

17. Determine the amount of the face runout on the B arrow scale.

18. The value of the circular line beneath the amount of face runout will be the desired reading. If the reading is in excess of 0.014 inch the housing alignment is unacceptable.

19. Remove the Dia-L-Igner gauge from the flywheel housing.

20. Install the spark plugs and connect the wires.

CORRECTION

ENGINE IN CAR

Since any change in face alignment will change bore alignment, it

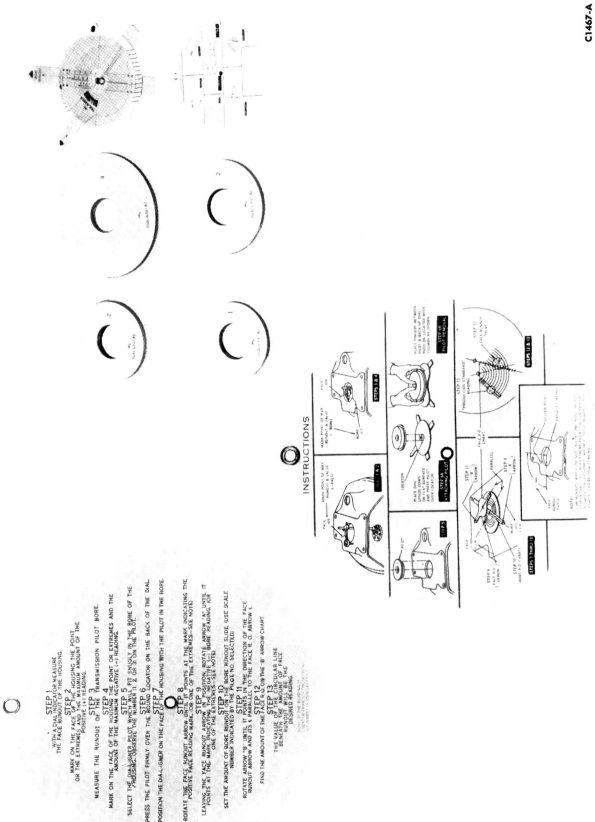

FIG. 2—Dia-L-Igner Gauge

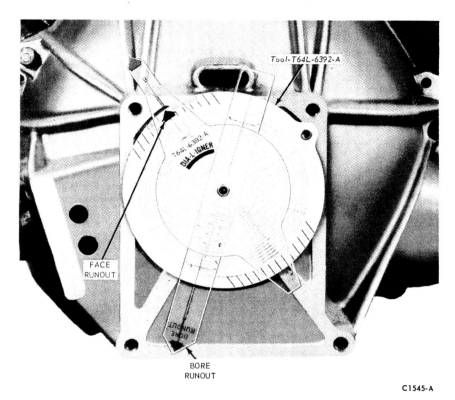

FIG. 3—Dia-L-Igner Gauge Installed

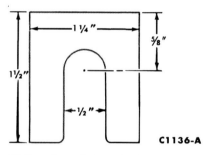

FIG. 4—Fabricated Flywheel Housing Shim

may be possible to correct bore alignment by changing face alignment. Face alignment can be changed by shimming between the flywheel housing and engine. Fig. 4 shows the type of shim which can be fabricated. **Not more than 0.010 inch thickness shims may be used between the**

flywheel housing and engine. If a 0.010-inch shim will not bring face and bore alignment within limits, replace the flywheel housing.

The shim required is one half the maximum (−) indicator reading, and should be located at the point of maximum minus (−) indicator reading.

If both the bore and face alignment are out of limits, shim between the flywheel housing and engine to bring face alignment within limits. Check the bore alignment.

If the bore alignment is out of limits and the face alignment is within limits, shim the flywheel housing to the limit of face misalignment and check the bore alignment. If it is not within limits, replace the housing.

ENGINE OUT OF CAR

The same procedure to correct

alignment may be used with the engine out of the car or in the car, up to the point of replacing the flywheel housing. If the bore alignment cannot be brought within limits by shimming, follow this procedure:

1. Remove the flywheel housing from the engine and remove the dowel pins. Install the flywheel housing and tighten the attaching bolts.

2. Install the dial indicator (Fig. 1). Check the face alignment, and shim as required to bring face alignment within limits.

3. Position the indicator to check the bore alignment. If the bore alignment is not within limits, reduce the tension on the flywheel housing attaching bolts so that the housing can be moved by striking it with a lead hammer or a block of wood and a steel hammer.

4. The lateral alignment should be brought within limits so that an indicator reading is within limits between the 9 o'clock and 3 o'clock positions on the bore circle. When the lateral alignment is within limits, the housing usually can be moved straight up or down without disturbing the lateral alignment. When alignment is within limits, torque the housing bolts and recheck bore alignment.

5. If the flywheel housing cannot be moved enough to bring the alignment within limits, mark the holes restricting movement, and then remove the housing and drill the marked bolt holes 1/32 inch larger.

6. When the flywheel housing bore alignment is within limits and the attaching bolts are at normal torque, hand ream the dowel pin holes 1/32 inch larger. Use a straight reamer and ream from the flywheel housing side. Oversize dowel pins can be made from drill rod stock.

7. Remove the flywheel housing and then install the oversize dowel pins in the cylinder block. Complete the assembly in the usual way.

8. Recheck the flywheel housing with the Dia-L-Igner gauge to make sure that the housing is within the specified limits.

---

3 **CLEANING AND INSPECTION**

RELEASE BEARING

Wipe all oil and dirt off the release bearing. **The bearing is prelubricated and should not be cleaned with solvent.**

Inspect the bearing retainer for

loose spring clips and rivets.

Inspect the release bearing assembly for burrs which may cause the assembly to drag on the transmission bearing retainer. Any such burrs should be cleaned up with fine crocus

cloth. If burrs are found, inspect the transmission input shaft bearing retainer for evidence of scoring. Any scoring should be polished out with crocus cloth. Coat bearing retainer with a thin film of lithium-base grease

C3VY-19586-A. Prior to release bearing installation, apply a light film of Lubriplate on both sides of the release lever fork where it contacts the release bearing hub and retaining springs. Apply a light film of grease (C3VY-19586-A) to the release bearing surface that contacts the pressure plate fingers. Care must be exercised when applying lubricants to the release bearing, release bearing hub and the release lever fork to avoid excessive grease from contaminating the clutch disc.

Hold the bearing inner race and rotate the outer race while applying pressure to it. If the bearing rotation is rough or noisy, replace the bearing.

Most release bearing failures are caused by improper clutch pedal adjustments. If the clutch linkage does not have enough free travel, the release bearing will constantly touch the release fingers and will spin whenever the engine is running.

When installing a release bearing, use the tool shown in Fig. 5.

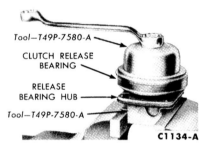

Tool—T49P-7580-A

CLUTCH RELEASE BEARING

RELEASE BEARING HUB

Tool—T49P-7580-A

C1134-A

FIG. 5—Installing Clutch Release Bearing on Hub

Release bearing failure can be caused by the release lever contact points being out of plane. Check the wear on the release bearing assembly where the release lever contacts it.

If one side of the assembly shows more wear than the other, the release lever is bent out of plane, or is not centering on the bracket on the flywheel housing.

Misalignment between the engine and transmission can cause release bearing failure. Other symptoms of misalignment are: transmission jumping out of gear, especially third gear, drive line vibration; excessive wear in the pilot bushing, excessive clutch disc spin time resulting in gear clash, and excessive transmission gear wear.

PRESSURE PLATE AND COVER

Inspect the surface of the pressure plate for burn marks, scores, or ridges. Generally, pressure plate resurfacing is not recommended. However, minor burn marks, scores, or ridges may be removed. During the resurfacing process, the flatness of the pressure plate must be maintained. If the pressure plate is badly heat-checked or deeply scored, replace the pressure plate and cover assembly. Clean the pressure plate and flywheel surfaces with a suitable solvent to be sure the surfaces are free from any oil film. **Do not use cleaners with petroleum base, and do not immerse the pressure plate in the solvent.**

Place the plate on the floor, being careful not to score or scratch the surface. Force each individual finger down, then release it quickly. If the finger does not return quickly, a binding condition is indicated, and the pressure plate should be replaced.

The pressure plate should be lubricated with a lithium-base grease between the driving lugs and the edges of the pressure plate. Depress the pressure plate fingers fully, apply the lubricant, and then move the fingers up and down until the lubricant is worked in. **Do not apply excessive lubricant.**

CLUTCH DISC

Inspect the clutch disc facings for oil or grease. **Eliminate the source of any oil or grease before replacing the disc.** An excessive amount of grease in the pilot housing or release bearing hub will find its way to the disc facings. Too much lubricant in the transmission or a plugged transmission vent will force the transmission lubricant out the input shaft and onto the disc facings.

Inspect the clutch disc for worn or loose facings. Check the disc for distortion and for loose rivets at the hub. Check for broken springs. **Springs loose enough to rattle will not cause noise when the car is operating.** Replace the disc assembly if any of these defects are present. **Be especially careful when installing a new disc to avoid dropping it or contaminating it with oil or grease.**

PILOT BUSHING

Check the fit of the clutch pilot bushing in the bore of the crankshaft.

The bushing is pressed into the crankshaft and should not be loose. Inspect the inner surface of the bushing for wear or a bell-mouthed condition. If the bushing is worn or damaged, replace the bushing with a new service bearing. Refer to the applicable engine for the replacement procedure.

PART 5-3   CLUTCH

Section	Page
1 Description and Operation	5-9
2 In-Car Adjustments and Repairs	5-10
Clutch Pedal Adjustment	5-10
Clutch Pedal and/or Bushing Replacement	5-10

Section	Page
Equalizer Bar and/or Bushing Replacement	5-11
3 Clutch Removal and Installation	5-12

1 DESCRIPTION AND OPERATION

DESCRIPTION

The clutch is of the centrifugal single dry disc type and consists of the clutch disc, pressure plate and the clutch release bearing (Fig. 1).

OPERATION

The clutch is actuated by a clutch pedal and a series of mechanical linkage.

When the clutch pedal is in the engaged position, the clutch disc facings are clamped between the friction surface of the engine flywheel and the face of the clutch pressure plate, thereby connecting engine power to the transmission. Depressing the clutch pedal actuates the clutch release shaft fork which moves the clutch release bearing against the clutch fingers. This, in turn, moves the pressure plate away from the clutch disc. Since the disc is splined to the transmission input shaft, the clutch disc and transmission input shaft will stop when the clutch is disengaged, thereby disconnecting engine power from the transmission.

C1161-B

FIG. 1—Clutch Assembly—Typical

2 IN-CAR ADJUSTMENTS AND REPAIRS

CLUTCH PEDAL ADJUSTMENT

Adjust the clutch pedal free travel whenever the clutch does not disengage properly, or when new clutch parts are installed. **Improper adjustment of the clutch pedal free travel is one of the most frequent causes of clutch failure and can be a contributing factor in some transmission failures.**

FREE TRAVEL

1. Disconnect the clutch return spring from the release lever.
2. Loosen the release lever rod lock nut (Figs. 2 and 3).
3. Move the clutch release lever rearward until the release bearing lightly contacts the clutch pressure plate release fingers.
4. Adjust the adapter length until the adapter seats in the release lever pocket.
5. Insert a feeler gauge (0.128 thick for 8 cyl.; 0.178 thick for 6 cyl.) against the back face of the rod adapter. Then, tighten the lock nut (finger tight) against the gauge.
6. Remove the feeler gauge. Hold the lock nut in position and tighten the adapter against the nut. Torque the adapter to 10-15 ft-lbs.

7. Install the clutch return spring.
8. Check the free travel at the pedal for conformance to specification. Readjust if necessary.
9. As a final check, measure the pedal free travel with the transmission in neutral and the engine running at about 3000 rpm. If the free travel at this speed is not a minimum of ½ inch, readjust the clutch pedal free travel. Otherwise, the release fingers may contact the release bearing continuously, resulting in premature bearing and clutch failure. **Free travel must be exactly to specification.**

CLUTCH PEDAL AND/OR BUSHING REPLACEMENT

REMOVAL (COMET, FALCON, FAIRLANE)

1. Remove the retaining clip (Fig. 2) that secures the equalizer rod to the clutch pedal. Disconnect the rod from the pedal.
2. Remove the lower bolt retaining the assist spring bracket to the pedal support. Then, loosen the upper bracket retaining bolt (approximately 4 turns) and disconnect the spring from the clutch pedal and bracket. Do not lose the spring inserts.

3. Disconnect the brake pedal push rod from the brake pedal.
4. Remove the bolt that secures the left air vent control cable bracket to the instrument panel. Position the control cable to one side.
5. Remove the retaining clip and flat washer from the clutch pedal shaft. Then, remove the shaft, bushing, clutch pedal and brake pedal from the support.
6. Remove the bushings from the pedal shaft, and transfer the pedal pad.

INSTALLATION (COMET, FALCON, FAIRLANE)

1. Lubricate the clutch pedal shaft bushings and position them on the shaft. Then, position the brake pedal and clutch pedal in the pedal support.
2. Install the flat washer and retaining clip on the pedal shaft.
3. Position the assist spring to the pedal and bracket. Pry the bracket forward and install the lower bolt. Torque the bolts to specifications.
4. Position the master cylinder push rod, bushing, and washers on the brake pedal and secure with a retaining clip.

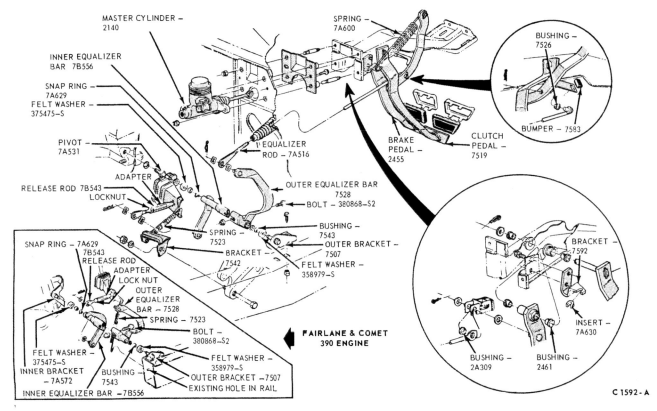

FIG. 2—Clutch and Linkage Disassembled

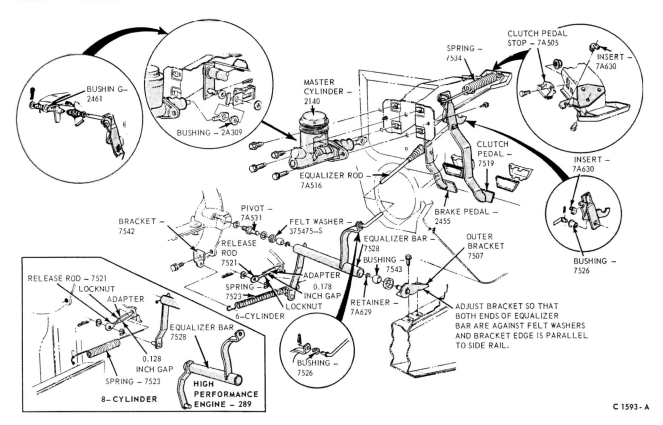

FIG. 3—Mustang Clutch and Linkage Disassembled

5. Connect the equalizer rod to the clutch pedal and secure it in place with a retaining clip.

6. Position the air vent control cable bracket to the instrument panel and secure with the attaching bolt.

7. Adjust the clutch pedal free travel.

REMOVAL (MUSTANG)

1. Remove the retaining clip (Fig. 3) that secures the equalizer rod to the clutch pedal.

2. Remove the attaching nut from the clutch pedal stop, then remove the stop.

3. Pull the clutch pedal upward as far as possible, then disconnect the spring from the pedal and the bracket. Do not lose the two inserts.

4. Remove the retaining clip that secures the master cylinder push rod to the brake pedal. Lift the rod and bushings off the brake pedal.

5. Working from the engine compartment, remove the two nuts and flat washers that secure the parking brake mounting bracket to the cowl panel.

6. Remove the two bolts that secure the handbrake and the air vent control cable bracket to the instrument panel. Position these controls to one side.

7. Remove the three bolts that secure the left air vent to the plenum chamber. Remove the air vent and control cable.

8. Remove the retaining clip and flat washer from the right end of the clutch pedal shaft.

9. While supporting the brake pedal, slide the clutch pedal from the mounting bracket.

10. Remove the delrin bushings from the pedals.

INSTALLATION (MUSTANG)

1. Lubricate the delrin bushings and position them in place.

2. Hold the brake pedal in place, then slide the clutch pedal shaft through the support and the brake pedal. Secure the clutch pedal with a flat washer and the retaining clip.

3. Position the master cylinder push rod and delrin bushings on the brake pedal and secure them with a retaining clip.

4. Pull the clutch pedal all the way up, then install the delrin insulators and the spring.

5. Install the clutch pedal stop.

6. Connect the equalizer rod to the clutch pedal and secure it in place with a retaining clip.

7. Hold the air vent duct in place on the plenum chamber and secure

it with the three attaching bolts.

8. Hold the hand brake control and the air vent control cable bracket in place on the lower end of the instrument panel and secure them with the two attaching bolts.

9. Working from the engine compartment, secure the parking brake mounting bracket to the cowl panel with two flat washers and nuts.

10. Check, and if necessary, position the clutch pedal release rod in the clutch release lever.

11. Adjust the clutch pedal free travel as required.

EQUALIZER BAR AND/OR BUSHING REPLACEMENT

COMET, FALCON, FAIRLANE (EXCEPT COMET AND FAIRLANE WITH 390 V-8)

1. Disconnect the clutch pedal equalizer rod at the equalizer bar (Fig. 2).

2. Raise the car and disconnect the return spring at the release lever. Disconnect the release lever rod from the equalizer lever.

3. Remove the equalizer bar center bolt.

4. Separate the equalizer bar and remove both sections from the car.

5. Remove the equalizer bar outer bracket and bushing assembly.

6. Remove the snap ring, bushing, felt washer, and flat washer from the outer bracket and inner pivot.

7. Position a flat washer, felt washer, and bushing on each pivot and secure with the snap ring.

8. Install the outer bracket and bushing assembly to the frame (Fig. 2). Torque the bracket attaching bolts to specifications.

9. Position the outer section of the equalizer bar on the outer bracket pivot.

10. Connect both sections of the equalizer bar and position it on the inner pivot.

11. Install the equalizer bar center bolt and torque to specifications. Make sure that both ends of the equalizer bar are against the felt washers.

12. Connect the release rod and the release lever return spring.

13. Adjust the clutch pedal free travel.

14. Lower the car. Connect the clutch pedal equalizer rod to the equalizer bar and secure with the retaining clip.

15. Check the free travel at the pedal for conformance to specification. Readjust if necessary.

**COMET AND FAIRLANE—
390 V-8**

1. Disconnect the clutch pedal equalizer rod at the equalizer bar (Fig. 2).

2. Raise the car and disconnect the

return spring at the release lever. Disconnect the release lever rod from the equalizer lever.

3. Remove the equalizer bar center bolt.

4. Remove the bolts retaining the equalizer bar inner bracket to the flywheel housing and remove the bracket and bushing assembly.

5. Separate the equalizer bar and remove both sections from the car.

6. Remove the equalizer bar outer bracket and bushing assembly.

7. Remove the snap ring, bushing, and felt washer from each bracket assembly.

8. Position a felt washer, and bushing on each bracket assembly and secure with the snap ring.

9. Install the outer bracket and bushing assembly to the frame (Fig. 2.) Torque the bracket attaching bolts to specifications.

10. Position the outer section of the equalizer bar on the outer bracket pivot.

11. Connect the two sections of the equalizer bar. Insert the inner bracket pivot into the equalizer bar and install the assembly to the flywheel housing. Torque the attaching bolts to specifications.

12. Install the equalizer bar center bolt and torque to specifications. Make sure that both ends of the equalizer bar are against the felt washers.

13. Connect the release rod and the release lever return spring.

14. Adjust the clutch pedal free travel.

15. Lower the car. Connect the clutch pedal equalizer rod to the equalizer bar and secure with the retaining clip.

16. Check the free travel at the pedal for conformance to specifications. Readjust if necessary.

MUSTANG

1. Disconnect the clutch pedal equalizer rod at the equalizer bar (Fig. 3).

2. Raise the car and disconnect the release lever return spring at the lever.

3. Remove the equalizer bar outer bracket and bushing assembly.

4. Remove the release rod from the equalizer bar, and then remove the equalizer bar. Remove the bushing and washers from the inner mounting stud.

5. Position the equalizer bar, washers, inner bushing, and retainer on the inner stud.

6. After positioning the outer bushing, install the outer bracket (with the equalizer bar in place).

7. Connect the release rod and the release lever return spring.

8. Lower the car. Connect the clutch pedal equalizer rod to the equalizer bar and secure with the retaining pin.

9. Adjust the clutch pedal free travel as required.

---

3 CLUTCH REMOVAL AND INSTALLATION

REMOVAL

1. Raise the car on a hoist.

2. Disconnect the drive shaft from the rear U-joint flange. Then slide the drive shaft off the transmission output shaft. Insert appropriate Extension Housing Seal Installation tool over the output shaft and into the extension housing oil seal.

3. Disconnect the speedometer cable from the extension housing.

4. Remove the back-up lamp switch (if so equipped) from the shift linkage control bracket.

5. Disconnect the gear shift rods from the transmission levers. If the car is equipped with a 4-speed transmission, remove the bolts that secure the shift control bracket to the extension housing.

6. Support the engine with a transmission jack and remove the two nuts

securing the transmission rear support to the crossmember.

7. Raise the rear of the engine with the transmission jack. Remove the two nuts, washers, and bolts securing the crossmember to the frame supports. Remove the crossmember.

8. Remove the bolts that attach the transmission to the flywheel housing.

9. Move the transmission rearward until the input shaft clears the flywheel housing, then remove the transmission.

10. Disconnect the clutch release lever return spring from the release lever.

11. Remove the starter cable. Remove the starter motor from the flywheel housing.

12. Remove the bolts that secure the engine rear plate to the front

lower part of the flywheel housing.

13. Remove the bolts that attach the flywheel housing to the cylinder block and remove the housing and the release lever as a unit.

14. Loosen the six pressure plate cover attaching bolts evenly to release the spring tension. **If the same pressure plate and cover is to be installed after the clutch is overhauled, mark the cover and flywheel so that the pressure plate can be installed in the same position, to maintain a balanced assembly.**

15. Remove the six attaching bolts while holding the pressure plate cover then, remove the pressure plate and clutch disc.

INSTALLATION

1. Hold the clutch disc, and pressure plate and cover assembly in position on the flywheel. Start the cover attaching bolts to hold the pieces in place but do not tighten them. **Avoid dropping the parts or contaminating them with oil or grease.**

2. Align the clutch disc with a clutch arbor as shown in Fig. 4 and

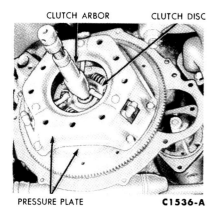

CLUTCH ARBOR   CLUTCH DISC

PRESSURE PLATE   C1536-A

FIG. 4—Installing Clutch Disc

torque the six pressure plate cover attaching bolts evenly to specification. Then remove the tool.

3. Make certain that the release bearing and hub is properly installed on the release lever. Coat the bearing retainer inside diameter with a light film of lithium soap-type grease. **Do not lubricate the bearing hub.**

4. Make certain that the flywheel housing and the cylinder block mounting surfaces are clean. Position the flywheel housing on the cylinder block and install the attaching bolts. Torque the bolts to specifications.

5. Seat the clutch release rod in the release lever socket and install the release lever return spring.

6. Secure the engine rear plate to the front of the flywheel housing with the attaching bolts.

7. Install the starting motor and connect the cable.

8. The mounting surfaces of the transmission and the flywheel housing must be free of dirt, paint, and burrs. Install two guide pins in the flywheel housing lower mounting bolt holes. Move the transmission forward on the guide pins until it is positioned against the flywheel housing.

9. Install the two upper mounting bolts. Then, remove the guide pins and install the two lower mounting

bolts. Torque all bolts to specifications.

10. Raise the rear of the engine high enough to provide clearance for installing the crossmember. Install the two crossmember-to-frame support attaching bolts, washers, and nuts. Do not tighten at this time.

11. Align the bolts in the transmission rear support with the bolt holes in the crossmember, then lower the engine and remove the jack. Install the two transmission rear support-to-crossmember washers and nuts and torque to specifications. Tighten the crossmember-to-frame support nuts.

12. Connect the gear shift rods to the transmission levers. If the car is equipped with a 4-speed transmission, connect the shift control bracket to the extension housing. Adjust the shift linkage.

13. Install the back-up lamp switch (if so equipped) on the shift linkage control bracket.

14. Remove the tool from the transmission output shaft, and install the drive shaft.

15. Adjust the clutch pedal total travel and free play.

PART 5-4 SPECIFICATIONS

CLUTCH SPECIFICATION

CAR LINE	ENGINE	TRANSMISSION	PRESSURE PLATE				DISC		
			DIAMETER (INCHES)	NO. OF SPRINGS	COLOR IDENTIFICATION (PAINT DAUB)		DIAMETER (INCHES)	NO. OF SPRINGS	SPRING COLOR
Fairlane Falcon Mustang Comet	200-1V	Standard	9	6	Pressure Plate—Blue Cover—Orange Springs—Aluminum Stripe		9	6	Blue
Falcon	170	Standard	8.5	6	Pressure Plate—Blue Optional Green Cover—Blue Springs—No Color		8.5	3 3	Dark Green No Color
Mustang	200	4-Speed	8.5	9	Pressure Plate—Aluminum Optional Bronze Cover—Orange Springs—Green		8.5	4 2	Yellow Stripe Aluminum
Fairlane Comet	200	Standard Heavy Duty	10.4	9	Pressure Plate—White Cover—Black Springs—Bronze		10.4	4 6	Orange—Small Orange—Large
Fairlane Comet	289 2V, 4V	Standard	10	9	Pressure Plate—Green Cover—Grey Springs—Bronze		10	6	Orange—Small
Falcon Mustang	289 2V, 4V	Standard 4-Speed						6	Orange—Large
Fairlane Comet	289 2V	4-Speed	10.4	9	Pressure Plate—White Cover—Pink Springs—Bronze		10.4	6 6	Orange—Small Orange—Large
Mustang	289 Hi Performance	4-Speed	10.4	9	Pressure Plate—Bronze Cover—Bronze Springs—Green		10.4	8	Grey
Fairlane Comet	390 2V, 4V	Standard 4-Speed	11	9	Pressure Plate—Purple Cover—White Springs—White Stripe		11	8	Aluminum

CLUTCH ADJUSTMENTS

Description	Inches
Clutch Pedal Free Travel (Engine Running)	7/8"-1 1/8"
Release Lever Rod Lock Nut-to-Rod Adapter end (to obtain free travel adjustment)	6-Cyl. 0.178 8-Cyl. 0.128
Clutch Housing Alignment If Dia-L-Igner reading is greater than that indicated, the clutch housing alignment is unacceptable	0.014
Maximum Shim to Correct Alignment	0.010

SPECIAL TOOLS

Tool Number	Description
T60K-7657-A or B 7657-C	Transmission Extension Housing Oil Seal Replacer
CJ-91-B	Universal Joint Bearing Replace Tool
T64-L 6392-A	Dia-L-Igner Gauge
T49-P 7580-A	Transmission Clutch Release Bearing Replacer

LUBRICATION

Description	Lubricant	Part No.
Clutch Release Bearing	Lithium Base Grease	C3VY-19586-A
Clutch Linkage Assist Spring		
Pressure Plate Lugs	Lithium Base Grease	C4AZ-19590-A
Pressure Plate Fingers		
Release Fork Tips—Both Sides	Lubriplate	COAZ-19584-A
Interlock Linkage (Overdrive Transmissions)		
Equalizer Bar, Pivot, Bracket and Bushings Clutch Pedal Shaft and Support Bracket	SAE-10W— Engine Oil	—

TORQUE SPECIFICATIONS

DESCRIPTION	FT-LBS
Clutch Pressure Plate	23-28
Clutch Pedal Free Travel Adjustment Nut	10-15
Flywheel Housing to Block Bolts—6 Cyl.	23-33
—8 Cyl.	40-50

MANUAL SHIFT TRANSMISSIONS

GROUP 6

PART 6-1   **PAGE**
GENERAL TRANSMISSION SERVICE 6-1

PART 6-2
MODEL 2.77 THREE-SPEED
TRANSMISSION 6-10

PART 6-3
MODEL 3.03 THREE-SPEED
TRANSMISSION 6-16

PART 6-4
DAGENHAM FOUR-SPEED
TRANSMISSION 6-25

PART 6-5   **PAGE**
FORD DESIGN FOUR-SPEED
TRANSMISSION 6-35

PART 6-6
OVERDRIVE TRANSMISSION 6-45

PART 6-7
SPECIFICATIONS 6-56

PART 6-1 GENERAL TRANSMISSION SERVICE

Section	Page
1 Diagnosis and Testing	6-1
2 Common Adjustments and Repairs	6-8
Rear Seal Replacement	6-8
Rear Bushing and Seal Replacement	6-8

Section	Page
Lubrication	6-8
3 Cleaning and Inspection	6-8
Cleaning	6-8
Inspection	6-9

1 DIAGNOSIS AND TESTING

The problems related to the transmission usually are: excessive amount of noise, hard shifting efforts, transmission jumps out of gear, gears clash when transmission is shifted from one gear ratio to another, and lubricant leakage.

The car should be road tested, if possible, to determine or confirm complaint. Under normal operating conditions, a large percentage of transmission complaints are due to maladjusted or faulty components outside of the transmission, such as, clutch, clutch linkage, steering columns and shift linkage. Before and during the road test, make sure that the clutch is functioning properly, the shift linkage is properly adjusted, the steering column is properly aligned and, that the transmission is filled to the proper level with lubricant.

The following diagnosis procedure is compiled as a guide in correcting problems related to manual transmissions. Trouble symptoms, possible causes and corrective measures are listed in the order they should be checked to eliminate all possibility of maladjustment or faulty components outside of the transmission prior to any transmission removal and disassembly. If the transmission was removed, repaired and reinstalled, make certain the clutch and all the gear shift linkage is adjusted to specifications. Road test the vehicle to be sure that the problem has been completely corrected.

DIAGNOSIS GUIDE—TRANSMISSIONS

To eliminate all possibility of maladjustments or faulty components in the clutch and/or clutch linkage, refer to Clutch Diagnosis and Testing, Group 5 (Driveshaft and Clutch), of the shop manual.

TROUBLE SYMPTOMS	POSSIBLE CAUSES	CORRECTION
RATTLE OR BUZZ IN FLOOR SHIFT LEVER	Some floor shift transmissions are subject to shift lever buzz or rattle.	

CONTINUED ON NEXT PAGE

DIAGNOSIS GUIDE—TRANSMISSIONS (Continued)

TROUBLE SYMPTOMS	POSSIBLE CAUSES	CORRECTION
RATTLE OR BUZZ IN FLOOR SHIFT LEVER (Continued)	No transmission overhaul should be attempted to correct this problem as it is often mistaken for a grating noise in the transmission. **1.** Loose nuts at transmission levers and shift rods. If the nuts are loose, check for bell-mouthing of slots. **2.** Bent transmission shift rods or linkage interference. **3.** Lack of lubrication of shift linkage, trunnions and external shift mechanism (floor shift). **4.** Improperly located console and excessive boot compression. (floor shift) **5.** Grommets damaged allowing hold down bolts and/or hold down washers to ground out against lever (floor shift).	**1.** Adjust levers and shift rods to proper crossover, torque nuts to specification. Replace bell-mouthed rods or levers. **2.** Replace bent rods or levers. **3.** Clean and lubricate with Lithium base grease (no Polethylene). **4.** Install correctly. **5.** Replace defective parts. Install correctly.
GEAR CLASH	**CLUTCH LINKAGE** **1.** Lack of clutch pedal reserve, free play and total travel. **2.** Bottoming of clutch release arm in window of clutch housing. **3.** Bent or cracked equalizer bar.	**1.** Adjust to specification. **2.** Grind opening in clutch housing or release arm to provide clearance. **3.** Replace defective parts.
	SHIFT LINKAGE **1.** Improper crossover. **2.** Loose nuts at transmission levers and shift rods. If the nuts are loose, check for bell-mouthing of slots. **3.** Bent transmission shift rods or linkage interference. **4.** Lack of lubrication of shift linkage, trunnions and external shift mechanism (floor shift).	**1-2.** Adjust levers and shift rods to proper crossover, torque nuts to specification. Replace bell-mouthed rods or levers. **3.** Replace bent rods. **4.** Clean and lubricate with Lithium base grease (no Polyethylene).

	CLUTCH
	1. Excessive engine idle speed.
	2. Inadequate clutch pedal reserve resulting in excessive spin time.
	3. Incorrect pedal free travel.
	4. Disc binding on transmission input shaft.
	5. Excessive disc runout.
	6. Flywheel housing misalignment.
	7. Oil or grease on clutch facings from:
	   A. Release bearing
	   B. engine
	   C. release lever
	   D. pilot bearing
	   E. transmission
		1. Adjust engine idle rpm.
		2. Adjust clutch linkage to specification. Check for damaged input shaft pilot bearing or excessive clutch disc runout—replace defective parts.
		3. Adjust to specification.
		4. Check for burrs on splines, replace if necessary.
		5-7-8. Replace clutch disc.
		6. Align to specification.

CONTINUED ON NEXT PAGE

DIAGNOSIS GUIDE—TRANSMISSIONS (Continued)

TROUBLE SYMPTOMS	POSSIBLE CAUSES	CORRECTION
GEAR CLASH (Continued)	**8.** Damaged or contaminated clutch lining.	

	TRANSMISSION
	  1. Forward Gear Clash
	    A. Weak or broken insert springs in the synchronizer assembly.
	    B. Worn blocking rings and/or cone surfaces.
	    C. Broken blocking rings.
	    D. Excessive output shaft end play.
	    E. Shifter fork loose on shift rails.
	    F. Binding input shaft pilot bearing (non-synchronized low gear transmission only).
	    G. Worn shifter forks or sleeves.
	  2. Reverse Gear Clash (Allow approximately three-four seconds after the clutch pedal has been depressed before shifting into reverse gear).
	    A. If gear clash continues after allowing proper time for the clutch plate to stop, check the clutch adjustments to make sure that they are within specifications.
	    B. Excessive engine idle speed.
	    C. Binding input shaft pilot bearing.
	    D. Worn or damaged clutch disc.
		1. A-B-C-D-F-G Replace worn or defective parts.
		
		E. Torque shifter fork set screws to specification.
		
		2. A. Adjust clutch to specification—See possible causes under Clutch for gear clash trouble symtoms.
		
		B. Adjust engine idler rpm.
		C-D. Replace defective parts.

HARD SHIFTING	**SHIFT LINKAGE**
	  1. Improper crossover.
	  2. Loose nuts at transmission levers and shift rods. If the nuts are loose, check for bell-mouthing of slots.
	  3. Bent transmission shift rods or linkage interference.
	  4. Lack of lubrication of shift linkage, trunnions and external shift mechanism (floor shift).
	  5. Improperly located console and excessive boot compression (floor shift).
		1-2. Adjust levers and rods to proper crossover, torque nuts to specification. Replace bell-mouthed rods or levers.
		
		3. Replace bent rods or levers.
		
		4. Clean and lubricate with Lithium base grease (no Polyethylene).
		
		5. Install correctly.

	STEERING COLUMNS
	  1. Improper column alignment, looseness, binding and worn surfaces. Make certain the toe plate at the base of the column is fastened securely to the firewall.
	  2. Worn shift key or broken weld securing shift key to top or bottom of shift tube.
	  3. Loose shift lever pin in die cast selector lever hub.
	  4. Keyway in die cast selector lever hub pounded out.
		1. Align column properly, replace defective column parts and fasten toe plate to firewall securely.
		
		2-3-4. Replace defective parts.

CONTINUED ON NEXT PAGE

DIAGNOSIS GUIDE—TRANSMISSIONS (Continued)

TROUBLE SYMPTOMS	POSSIBLE CAUSES	CORRECTION
HARD SHIFTING (Continued)	**5.** Alignment of column to steering gear pilot bushing. **6.** Loose screws securing die casting to bottom of tube. Excessive radial movement in the column linkage. (If the vehicle has high mileage or is subjected to hard use, even though the crossover has been properly set, the column may have deteriorated to a point where proper crossover engagement will not occur due to excessive radial movement in the column linkage (lost motion). **7.** Lack of lubrication at column lower plate.	**5.** Align properly. **6.** Replace defective parts. Tighten screws securely. **7.** Clean and lubricate with Lithium base grease (no Polyethylene).
	CLUTCH LINKAGE **1.** Loss of clutch pedal reserve, free play and total travel.	**1.** Adjust to specification.
	TRANSMISSION **1.** Excessive shift effort **A.** Shift side cover loose or damaged (Dagenham, Warner Gear four speed overdrive transmission only). **B.** Shift levers, shafts or forks worn or bent. **C.** Synchronizer worn or broken. **D.** Shift rail components not functioning properly. **E.** Worn shifter forks or sleeves. **2.** Sticking in Gear **A.** Low lubricant level. **B.** Corroded transmission levers (shaft). **C.** Defective (tight) input shaft pilot bearing. **D.** Stuck detent plug. **E.** Burred or battered teeth on synchronizer sleeve and/or input shaft. **F.** Shifter fork loose on shift rails.	**1. A.** Torque screws to specification. Replace damaged cover. **B-C-E.** Replace worn or defective parts. **D.** Install correctly, replace defective parts, if necessary. **2. A.** Fill to bottom of filler plug hole. **B-D.** Free-up and clean parts, replace if necessary. **C-E.** Replace defective parts. **F.** Torque shifter fork set screw to specification.
GEAR JUMPOUT	**SHIFT LINKAGE** **1.** Improper crossover. **2.** Loose nuts at transmission levers and shift rods. If the nuts are loose, check for bell-mouthing of slots. **3.** Bent transmission shift rods or linkage interference. **4.** Lack of lubrication of shift linkage, trunnions and external shift mechanism (floor shift). **5.** Improperly located console and excessive boot compression (floor shift).	**1-2** Adjust levers and rods to proper crossover. Torque nuts to specification. Replace bell-mouthed rods or levers. **3.** Replace bent rods or levers. **4.** Clean and lubricate with Lithium base grease (no Polyethylene). **5.** Install correctly.

CONTINUED ON NEXT PAGE

DIAGNOSIS GUIDE—TRANSMISSIONS (Continued)

TROUBLE SYMPTOMS	POSSIBLE CAUSES	CORRECTION
GEAR JUMPOUT (Continued)	**STEERING COLUMNS** **1.** Improper column alignment looseness, binding and worn surfaces. Make certain the toe plate at the base of the column is fastened securely to the firewall. **2.** Alignment of column to steering gear pilot bushing. **3.** Worn shift key or broken weld securing shift key to top or bottom of shift tube. **4.** Keyway in die cast selector lever hub pounded out. **5.** Loose screws securing die casting to bottom of tube. Excessive radial movement in the column linkage. (If the vehicle has high mileage or is subjected to hard use, even though the crossover has been properly set, the column may have deteriorated to a point where proper crossover engagement will not occur due to excessive radial movement in the column linkage (lost motion).	**1.** Align column properly, replace defective column parts and fasten toe plate to firewall securely. **2.** Align properly. **3-4.** Replace defective parts. **5.** Replace defective parts. Tighten screws securely.
	TRANSMISSION **1.** Transmission misaligned or loose. **2.** Bent or worn shift fork, lever and/or shaft. **3.** Worn input shaft pilot bearing. **4.** End play in input shaft (bearing retainer loose or broken, loose or worn bearings on input and output shafts). **5.** Detent springs broken. **6.** Detent notches worn. **7.** Worn clutch teeth on the respective gear and/or worn clutch teeth on synchronizer sleeve. **8.** Shift side cover loose or damaged (Dagenham and Warner Gear four speed and overdrive transmission only). **9.** Shifter forks loose on shift rails.	**1.** Align to specification. Torque transmission-to-flywheel housing bolts and flywheel housing-to-engine bolts to specifications. **2-3-5-6-7.** Replace worn or defective parts. **4.** Torque retainer bolts to specification. Replace worn or defective parts. **8.** Torque screws to specification. Replace damaged cover. **9.** Torque shifter fork set screw to specification.
LOCKED IN GEAR When a complaint of momentary locknut is encountered in transmissions with non-synchronized low - gear, determine whether or not a normal "blockout" condition exists. If a "blockout" condition does exist, the customer should be informed that the transmission	**SHIFT LINKAGE** **1.** Improper crossover. **2.** Loose nuts at transmission levers and shift rods. If the nuts are loose, check for bell-mouthing of slots. **3.** Bent transmission shift rods or linkage interference.	**1-2.** Adjust levers and rods to proper crossover. Torque nuts to specification. Replace bell-mouthed rods and levers. **3.** Replace bent rods or levers.

DIAGNOSIS GUIDE—TRANSMISSIONS (Continued)

TROUBLE SYMPTOMS	POSSIBLE CAUSES	CORRECTION
LOCKED IN GEAR (Continued) gears cannot be pulled into mesh because of gear tooth to tooth abutment which can be eliminated by releasing and depressing the clutch pedal again (thus spinning the clutch disc). This will re-index the drive and driven gear teeth and allow the gears to mesh.	**STEERING COLUMN** 1. Tricking of shift linkage. Make certain that when slowly shifting out of low gear, the low gear shift lever at the transmission is completely out of low gear detent prior to the column shift lever dropping through neutral crossover. If the transmission shift lever is not completely out of low gear detent, the shift interlock in the transmission will prevent engagement of second gear and a lockup condition occurs. 2. Improper column alignment, looseness, binding and worn surfaces. Make certain the toe plate at the base of the column is fastened securely to the firewall. 3. Alignment of column to steering gear pilot bushing. 4. Worn shift key or broken weld securing shift key to top or bottom of shift tube. 5. Loose shift lever pin in die cast selector lever hub. 6. Keyway in die cast selector lever hub pounded out. 7. Loose screws securing die casting to bottom of tube. Excessive radial movement in the column linkage. (If the vehicle has high mileage or is subjected to hard use even though the crossover has been properly set, the column may have deteriorated to a point where proper crossover engagement will not occur due to excessive radial movement in the column linkage (lost motion). Lack of lubrication at column lower plate.	**CORRECTION** 1-2. Adjust column properly, replace defective parts and fasten toe plate to firewall securely. 3. Align properly. 4-5-6. Replace defective parts. 7. Replace defective parts. Tighten screws securely. Clean and lubricate with Lithium base grease (no Polyethylene).
	TRANSMISSION 1. Shift rail components not functioning properly. 2. Gear seizure. 3. Synchronizer inserts out of position.	1-3. Install correctly, replace defective parts. 2. Replace defective parts.
NOISY IN FORWARD SPEEDS	1. Low lubricant level. 2. Transmission misaligned or loose. 3. Input shaft bearings worn or damaged. 4. Output shaft bearing worn or damaged.	1. Fill to bottom of filler plug hole. 2. Align to specification. Torque transmission-to-flywheel housing bolts and flywheel housing-to-engine bolts to specifications. 3-4-5-6-7. Replace worn or defective parts.

CONTINUED ON NEXT PAGE

DIAGNOSIS GUIDE—TRANSMISSIONS (Continued)

TROUBLE SYMPTOMS	POSSIBLE CAUSES	CORRECTION
NOISY IN FORWARD SPEEDS (Continued)	**5.** Mainshaft gears worn or damaged. (In any case of scored or broken gears, the mating gears should be checked). **6.** Countershaft gear or bearings worn or damaged. **7.** Failure of the operator to fully engage the gears on every shift before engaging the clutch and applying engine power. Gear roll-over noise, inherent in manual transmissions, is caused by the constant mesh gears turning at engine idle speed, while the clutch is engaged and the transmission in neutral; and throwout bearing rub are sometimes mistaken for **mainshaft bearing noise.** Gear roll-over noise will disappear when the clutch is disengaged or when the transmission is engaged in gear. Throwout bearing rub will disappear when the clutch is engaged. In the event that a bearing is defective, the noise is more pronounced while engaged in gear under load or coast than in neutral. When complaints of this nature are encountered, it will be necessary to road test the vehicle to determine if bearing noise exists. **Under no circumstances should any transmission rework be attempted to eliminate gear roll-over noise, or throwout bearing rub.**	
NOISY IN REVERSE	**1.** Reverse idler gear or shaft, worn or damaged. **2.** Reverse sliding gear worn or broken.	**1-2.** Replace worn or defective parts.
LUBRICANT LEAKS	**1.** Excessive lubricant. **2.** Vent plugged. **3.** Input shaft bearing retainer loose or cracked, seal or gasket damaged. **4.** Worn or damaged extension housing seal. **5.** Worn shifter shaft seals. **6.** Shift side c o v e r bolts not sealed. (Dagenham and W a r n e r Gear four speed and overdrive transmission only). **7.** Shift side cover loose or gasket damaged. (Dagenham and Warner Gear four speed and overdrive transmission only). **8.** Extension housing b o l t s not sealed.	**1.** Drain to bottom of filler plug hole. **2.** Free up. **3.** Add sealer and torque retainer bolts to specifications. Replace defective parts. **4-5-9.** Replace defective parts. **5-6-7-8-10.** Add sealer to bolts, and torque to specifications. Replace defective parts.

CONTINUED ON NEXT PAGE

DIAGNOSIS GUIDE—TRANSMISSIONS (Continued)

TROUBLE SYMPTOMS	POSSIBLE CAUSES	CORRECTION
LUBRICANT LEAKS (Continued)	**9.** Expansion plug at front of case not seated properly. **10.** Access cover loose or gasket damaged.	

2 COMMON ADJUSTMENTS AND REPAIRS

REAR SEAL REPLACEMENT

1. Remove the driveshaft.
2. Remove the seal from the extension housing with the tool shown in Fig. 1.

3. Install the new seal in the extension housing with the tool shown in Fig. 2.

4. Install the driveshaft.

REAR BUSHING AND SEAL REPLACEMENT

1. Remove the driveshaft from the car.
2. Insert the tool shown in Fig. 3 into the extension housing until it grips the front side of the bushing.
3. Turn the screw clockwise until the seal and the bushing are free of the housing.
4. Drive a new bushing into the extension housing with the tool shown in Fig. 4.

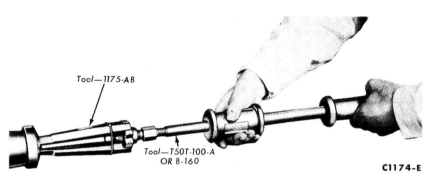

Tool—1175-AB

Tool—T50T-100-A OR B-160

C1174-E

FIG. 1—Removing Extension Housing Seal

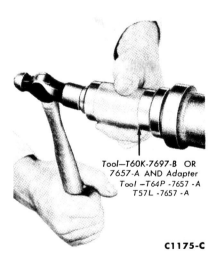

Tool—T60K-7697-B OR 7657-A AND Adapter Tool—T64P-7657-A T57L-7657-A

C1175-C

FIG. 2—Installing Extension Housing Seal

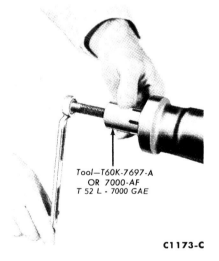

Tool—T60K-7697-A OR 7000-AF T52L-7000 GAE

C1173-C

FIG. 3—Removing Extension Housing Bushing and Seal

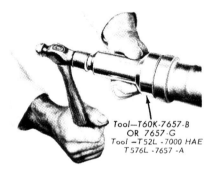

Tool—T60K-7657-B OR 7657-G Tool—T52L-7000 HAE T576L-7657-A

C1176-D

FIG. 4—Installing Extension Housing Bushing

5. Install a new seal in the housing as shown in Fig. 2.
6. Install the driveshaft.

LUBRICATION

Lubrication level should be in line with the bottom of filler hole right side of transmission case.

3 CLEANING AND INSPECTION

CLEANING

1. Wash all parts, except the ball bearings, in a suitable cleaning solvent. Brush or scrape all foreign matter from the parts. Be careful not

to damage any parts with the scraper. Dry all parts with compressed air.

2. Rotate the ball bearings in a cleaning solvent until all lubricant is

removed. Hold the bearing assembly to prevent it from rotating and dry it with compressed air.

3. Lubricate the bearings with approved transmission lubricant and

wrap them in a clean, lint-free cloth or paper until ready for use.

INSPECTION

1. Inspect the transmission case for being cracked, worn or damaged bearing bores, damaged threads or any other damage which could affect the operation of the transmission.

2. Inspect the front face of the case for small nicks or burrs that could cause misalignment of the transmission with the flywheel housing. Remove all small nicks or burrs with a fine stone.

3. Replace a cover that is bent or distorted. Make sure that the vent hole in the cover is open.

4. Check the condition of the shift levers, forks, shift rails and the lever and shafts.

5. Examine the ball bearing races for being cracked, worn or rough. Inspect the balls for looseness, wear, end play or other damage. Check the bearings for looseness in the bores.

If any of these conditions exist, replace the bearings.

6. Replace roller bearings that are broken, worn or rough.

7. Replace the countershaft (cluster) gear if the teeth are chipped, broken or worn. Replace the countershaft if it is bent, scored or worn.

8. Replace the reverse idler gear or sliding gear if the teeth are chipped, worn or broken. Replace the idler gear shaft if bent, worn or scored.

9. Replace the input shaft and gear if the splines are damaged or if the teeth are chipped, worn or broken. If the roller bearing surface in the bore of the gear is worn or rough, or if the cone surface is damaged, replace the gear and the gear rollers.

10. Replace all other gears that are chipped, broken or worn.

11. Check the synchronizer sleeves for free movement on their hubs. Make sure that the alignment marks (etched marks) are properly indexed.

12. Inspect the synchronizer blocking rings for widened index slots, rounded clutch teeth and smooth internal surfaces (must have machined grooves). With the blocker ring on the cone, the distance between the face of the blocker ring and the clutch teeth on the gear must not be less than 0.010 inches.

13. Replace the speedometer drive gear if the teeth are stripped or damaged. Make certain to install the correct size replacement gear.

14. Replace the output shaft if there is any evidence of wear or if any of the splines are damaged.

15. Inspect the bushing and the seal in the extension housing. Replace them if they are worn or damaged. The bushing and/or seal should be replaced after the extension housing has been installed on the transmission.

16. Replace the seal in the input shaft bearing retainer.

17. Replace the seals on the cam and shafts.

PART 6-2
MODEL 2.77 THREE-SPEED TRANSMISSION

Section	Page
1 Description and Operation	6-10
Description	6-10
Operation	6-10
2 In-Car Adjustments and Repairs	6-11
Gear Shift Linkage Adjustment—Comet, Falcon, and Fairlane (6 and 8 cylinder)	6-11
Gear Shift Linkage Adjustment—Mustang	6-11
3 Removal and Installation	6-12
Removal	6-12
Installation	6-12

Section	Page
4 Major Repair Operations	6-12
Disassembly	6-12
Parts Repair or Replacement	6-12
Gear Shift Lever	6-12
Cam and Shaft and Oil Seals	6-13
Input Shaft Bearing	6-14
Output Shaft Bearing	6-14
Synchronizer	6-14
Countershaft Gear Bearings	6-15
Front Bearing Retainer Seal	6-15
Assembly	6-15

1 DESCRIPTION AND OPERATION

DESCRIPTION

The 2.77 C.D. three-speed transmission is used in all models with a 170 or 200 C.I.D. engine. The designation 2.77 C.D. is the actual distance between the centerline of the countershaft and the centerline of the input shaft.

An identification plate (Fig. 1) is attached to the upper right extension housing attaching bolt.

A synchronizer is provided for shifting to second and third speeds. Shifts to first and reverse speeds are accomplished with a sliding gear.

Ball bearings support the input shaft and gear and the center of the output shaft. Needle bearings in the input shaft bore support the front of the output shaft. The countershaft gear (cluster gear) also runs on 2 rows of needle bearings. A bronze bushing is used in the reverse idler gear.

A bushing located at the rear of the extension housing supports the rear of the output shaft. The synchronizer and the blocking rings are the conventional tapered ring and straight clutch gear type.

OPERATION

When first gear is selected, the shift lever moves the first and reverse sliding gear into mesh with the low gear on the countershaft (cluster) gear. Power flow is now from the input gear, through the countershaft gear to the first and reverse sliding gear and out through the output shaft.

When second gear is selected, the shift lever moves the second and third speed synchronizer sleeve rearward to force the blocking ring conical surface against the matching cone on the constant mesh intermediate gear located on the output shaft. When the vehicle is moving, as when shifting from low to a higher gear ratio, the internal teeth of the synchronizer sleeve and those on the blocking ring will not index until the intermediate gear is brought up or down to the speed of the synchronizer sleeve which is rotating at output shaft speed.

The synchronizer sleeve with further movement will slide over the blocking ring and engage the clutch teeth on the constant mesh intermediate gear. Since the intermediate gear is now locked to the output shaft by means of the synchronizer sleeve, power flow is from the input shaft through the countershaft gear to the constant mesh intermediate gear to the ouput shaft.

Engagement of third speed is the same as second except for ratio. In third gear, the clutch teeth on the input shaft are locked directly to the output shaft by the second and third speed synchronizer to provide a ratio of 1:1.

Reverse gear is accomplished by moving the first and reverse sliding gear rearward to engage the reverse idler gear. The drive is then from the input gear, through the countershaft gear, to and through the reverse idler gear to the first and reverse *sliding gear which is splined to* the output shaft. The gears in this

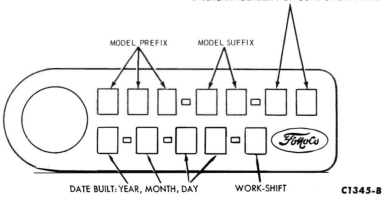

CHANGE WITHIN TRANSMISSION AFFECTING INTERCHANGEABILITY OF COMPONENT PARTS

MODEL PREFIX   MODEL SUFFIX

DATE BUILT: YEAR, MONTH, DAY   WORK-SHIFT   C1345-B

FIG. 1—Transmission Identification Tag

position will rotate the output shaft in a reverse direction.

An interlock pin prevents selection of more than one gear at a time. De-

tent balls are provided to hold the selected gear in the desired position.

2 IN-CAR ADJUSTMENTS AND REPAIRS

GEAR SHIFT LINKAGE ADJUSTMENT—COMET, FALCON, FAIRLANE (6 AND 8 CYLINDER)

1. Place the gearshift lever in the neutral position.

2. Loosen the two gearshift rod adjustment nuts.

3. Insert a dealer fabricated special tool in the slot provided in the lower steering column. (See Fig. 2.) It may be necessary to align the levers to insert the tool.

4. Tighten the two gearshift rod adjustment nuts.

5. Remove the tool from the slot in the steering column.

6. Start the engine and shift the selector lever to each position to make sure it operates freely.

GEAR SHIFT LINKAGE ADJUSTMENT—MUSTANG

1. Loosen the three shift linkage adjustment nuts. Install a ¼ inch diameter alignment pin through the control bracket and levers as shown in Fig. 3.

2. Tighten the three linkage adjustment nuts and then remove the alignment pin.

3. Check the gear shift lever for a smooth crossover.

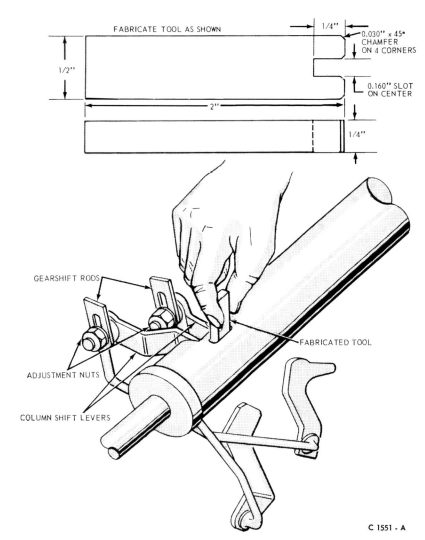

FABRICATE TOOL AS SHOWN

1/4"

0.030" x 45° CHAMFER ON 4 CORNERS

1/2"

0.160" SLOT ON CENTER

2"

1/4"

GEARSHIFT RODS

FABRICATED TOOL

ADJUSTMENT NUTS

COLUMN SHIFT LEVERS

C 1551 - A

FIG. 2—Comet, Falcon and Fairlane Gearshift Linkage Adjustment

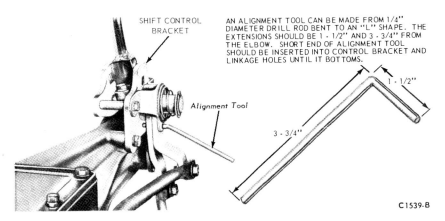

SHIFT CONTROL BRACKET

AN ALIGNMENT TOOL CAN BE MADE FROM 1/4" DIAMETER DRILL ROD BENT TO AN "L" SHAPE. THE EXTENSIONS SHOULD BE 1 - 1/2" AND 3 - 3/4" FROM THE ELBOW. SHORT END OF ALIGNMENT TOOL SHOULD BE INSERTED INTO CONTROL BRACKET AND LINKAGE HOLES UNTIL IT BOTTOMS.

Alignment Tool

1 - 1/2"

3 - 3/4"

C1539-B

FIG. 3—Gearshift Linkage Adjustment—Mustang

3 REMOVAL AND INSTALLATION

REMOVAL

1. Raise the car on a hoist.
2. Remove the driveshaft. Insert the extension housing seal installation tool, Fig. 2, Part 6-1, into the opening of the extension housing to prevent the lubricant from leaking out.
3. Disconnect the speedometer cable from the extension housing, and disconnect the gear shift rods from the transmission shift levers.

On a Mustang, remove the three bolts that attach the shift selector assembly to the extension housing and allow the assembly to hang by the shift lever.

4. Remove the two nuts retaining the transmission rear support to the crossmember.
5. Place a transmission jack under the flywheel housing and raise the rear of the engine slightly.
6. Remove the two cotter pins, nuts, and bolts that attach the crossmember to the frame supports.
7. Disconnect the brake cable from the equalizer lever. Separate the lever from the crossmember.
8. Remove the crossmember from

the frame supports and allow it to hang by the brake cable.

9. Move the jack under the transmission. Remove the four transmission to flywheel housing mounting bolts.
10. Move the transmission back just far enough to clear the input shaft and remove it from under the car.

INSTALLATION

1. Install two guide pins in the flywheel housing lower mounting holes. Start the input shaft through the release bearing. Align the output shaft splines with the splines in the clutch disc. Move the transmission forward on to the guide pins. If the transmission front bearing retainer hangs-up on the release bearing hub, move the clutch release lever to free it.
2. Move the transmission forward until the input shaft is through the clutch hub and enters the pilot bearing.
3. Install the two upper transmission to flywheel housing attaching bolts and lockwashers.

4. Remove the two guide pins and install the two lower attaching bolts. Torque all attaching bolts to specifications.
5. Position the crossmember to the frame supports. Install the equalizer lever and brake cable.
6. Secure the transmission rear support to the crossmember. Secure the crossmember to the frame supports and remove the transmission jack.
7. Connect the gear shift rods and the speedometer cable.

On a Mustang, position the shift selector assembly to the extension housing and install the attaching bolts.

8. Remove the tool (Fig. 2, Part 6-1) from the rear of the extension housing. Install the driveshaft, and torque rear U-bolt nuts to specification.
9. Fill the transmission with approved lubricant. Check the shifting action of the transmission.
10. Adjust the clutch pedal total travel, free travel and shift linkage as required.

4 MAJOR REPAIR OPERATIONS

DISASSEMBLY

1. Mount the transmission in a holding fixture and drain the lubricant.
2. Remove the transmission cover and gasket.
3. Remove the extension housing attaching bolts and remove the extension housing and gasket. To prevent the output shaft from following the housing (with the resultant loss of needle bearings), tap the end of the output shaft with a soft-faced hammer while withdrawing the extension housing. See disassembly (Fig. 4).
4. Remove the speedometer drive gear snap ring, the gear, and drive ball from the output shaft.
5. Remove the retainer for the reverse idler shaft and countershaft (Fig. 4).
6. Hold the countershaft gear with a hook and using the tool (dummy shaft) shown in Fig. 5, drive the countershaft rearward out of the countershaft gear and the transmission case. Then, carefully lower the

countershaft gear and dummy shaft to the bottom of the case.

7. After removing the input shaft bearing retainer and gasket, remove the input shaft assembly and front synchronizer blocking ring from the transmission case (Fig. 6).
8. Remove the synchronizer retaining snap ring from the output shaft. Then, while holding the synchronizer assembly together, pull the output shaft out of the transmission case. The intermediate gear and the low and reverse gear will slide off the output shaft as it is withdrawn from the case. Lift the synchronizer assembly, intermediate, low and reverse sliding gears out of the case and remove the two shift forks. **For reference in assembly, notice which synchronizer hub end faces forward.**
9. Using a soft drift, drive the reverse idler shaft out of the transmission case. Lift the reverse idler gear and the countershaft gear out of the case.
10. Remove the shift levers.

PARTS REPAIR OR REPLACEMENT

GEAR SHIFT LEVER

1. Remove the snap ring from the end of the selector shaft with pointed snap ring pliers (Fig. 7).
2. Remove the flat washer and spring.
3. After removing two bolts, pull the retainer, selector levers, and spacer from the shaft.
4. Drive the short selector lever pin from the shaft with a large pin punch.
5. Drive the long trunnion pin from the shaft and remove the trunnion and shaft.
6. If necessary to remove the studs from the selector levers, remove the cotter pins, flat washers, wave washers and studs.
7. Lubricate all mating friction surfaces with Lubriplate before assembly.
8. Install the shaft in the bracket. Position the trunnion and drive the long straight pin through the trun-

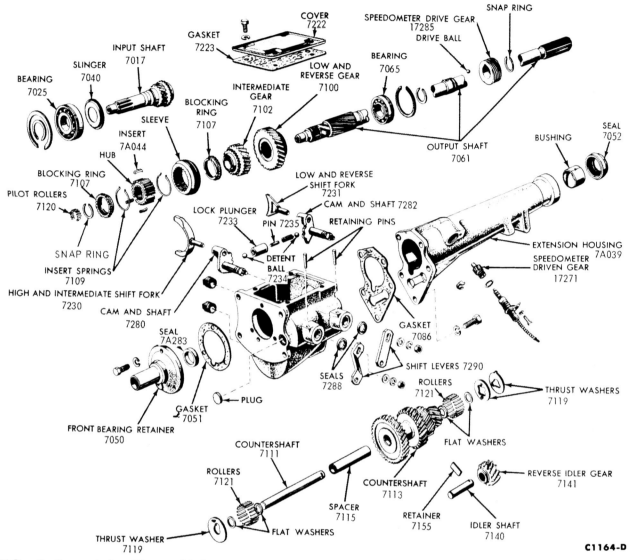

FIG. 4—Transmission Disassembled

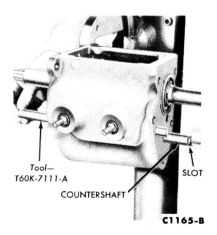

Tool—
T60K-7111-A

SLOT

COUNTERSHAFT

C1165-B

FIG. 5—Removing or Installing Countershaft

nion and into the shaft until an equal

length of the pin is exposed on both sides of the shaft.

9. Drive the short pin into the shaft until the pin is centered in the shaft.

10. Install the levers and spacer on the shaft as shown in Fig. 7.

11. Position the retainer and start the bolts. Before tightening the bolts be sure that the retainer is not interfering with free movement of the shaft. Tighten the bolts.

12. Install the spring, flat washer and snap ring.

13. Install the lever studs if they were removed.

CAM AND SHAFTS AND OIL SEALS

1. From the underside of the case, use a punch to drive out the tapered

pins that hold the cam and shaft assemblies in the case (Fig. 8). **Use hard, firm blows.** Using a plastic hammer, drive the intermediate and high cam and shaft toward the inside of the case and separate the detent balls and spring from the plunger. Push out the cam and shaft assemblies, and remove the plunger.

2. If required, the cam and shaft oil seals in the case may be removed with the tools shown in Fig. 9.

3. Install new seals in the case.

4. Install the reverse and low shift cam and shaft through the case opening. Assemble the spacer and spring in the plunger. Apply grease to each ball and position them in each end of the plunger. Hold the plunger assembly in position and install the intermediate and high cam and shaft in

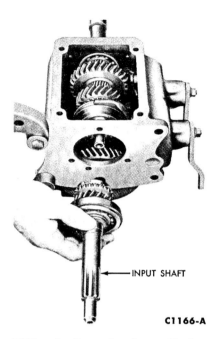

FIG. 6—Removing Input Shaft

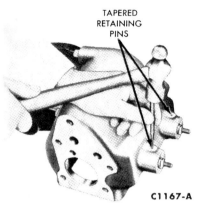

FIG. 8—Removing Cam and Shaft Retaining Pins

INPUT SHAFT BEARING

1. Remove the snap ring securing the input shaft bearing, and press the input shaft out of the bearing and oil slinger.

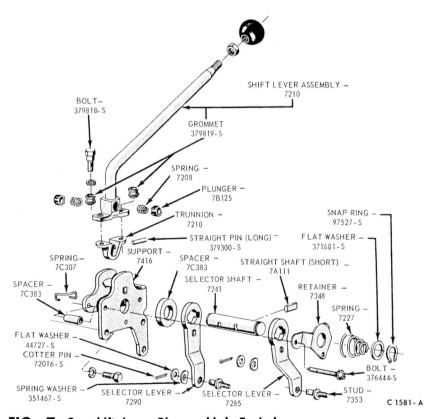

FIG. 7—Gearshift Lever Disassembled—Typical

the case opening, allowing the balls to register in the cam detents.

5. Align the cam and shaft grooves with the openings in the shaft bosses in the case, and install the retaining pins. Check the cam action. Bent pins may restrict movement.

2. Press the input shaft bearing and oil slinger onto the input shaft with the tool shown in Fig. 10, and install the snap ring on the shaft.

OUTPUT SHAFT BEARING

1. Remove the snap ring securing

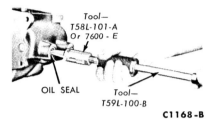

FIG. 9—Removing Cam and Shaft Oil Seals

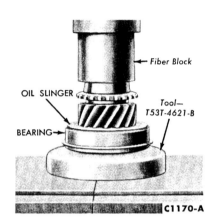

FIG. 10—Installing Input Shaft Bearing

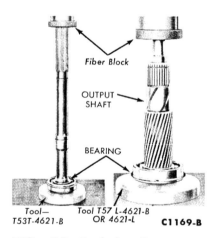

FIG. 11—Replacing Output Shaft Bearing

the output shaft bearing. Remove the bearing as shown in Fig. 11.

2. Press the output shaft bearing onto the shaft as shown in Fig. 11, and install the snap ring on the shaft.

SYNCHRONIZER

1. Remove the synchronizer sleeve, blocking rings, inserts, and retainers from the synchronizer hub.

2. Hold the three inserts in place in the synchronizer hub (Fig. 4).

3. Align the etch mark on the hub with the etch mark on the sleeve. Slip the hub and inserts into the sleeve making sure that the etch marks are aligned.

4. Secure the hub and inserts in the sleeve with the two insert springs.

COUNTERSHAFT GEAR BEARINGS

1. Remove the flat washers, dummy shaft, spacer, and roller bearings from the countershaft gear.

2. Insert the spacer and dummy shaft into the countershaft gear. Position one flat washer at each end of the spacer (Fig. 4). Coat the bore in each end of the countershaft with grease and install twenty roller bearings in each end of the gear. Apply a coating of grease to the other two flat washers and the thrust washers and assemble at each end of the countershaft gear. **Note the position of the tangs on the thrust washers.**

3. Place the case in a vertical position. Align the gear bore and thrust washers with the bores in the case and install the countershaft.

4. Place the case in a horizontal position and check the countershaft gear end play with a feeler gauge. The end play should be 0.004-0.018 inch. If not within these limits, replace the thrust washers.

5. After establishing the correct end play, install the dummy shaft in the countershaft gear and allow the gear to remain at the bottom of the case until the output and input shafts have been installed.

FRONT BEARING RETAINER SEAL

1. Remove the input shaft seal from the front bearing retainer as shown in Fig. 12.

2. Install a new input shaft seal as shown in Fig. 13.

ASSEMBLY

1. If the countershaft gear is not already positioned in the bottom of the case, do it at this time.

2. Position the reverse idler gear, and insert the shaft (from the rear) through the case just far enough to hold the gear.

3. Using a light coat of grease,

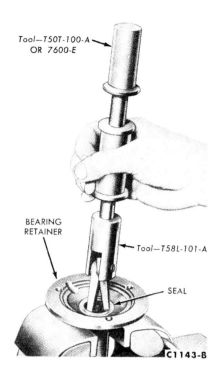

FIG. 12—Removing Input Shaft Seal

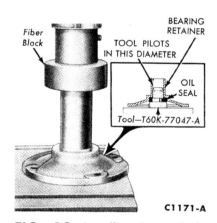

FIG. 13—Installing Input Shaft Seal

assemble the needle bearings in the input shaft. **A thick film of grease could plug the lubricant holes and prevent lubrication to the bearings.** Install the front synchronizer blocking ring on the input shaft.

4. Install the shift forks on the cam and shaft assemblies, with the large fork on the intermediate and high cam and shaft. The web of the

low and reverse fork must be to the rear of the shaft center.

5. Start the output shaft through the rear opening of the transmission case. Place the low and reverse sliding gear on the shaft, followed by the intermediate gear. Tilt the output shaft enough to allow the rear shift fork to engage the sliding gear groove.

6. With the longer hub end forward slide the synchronizer assembly on to the output shaft and engage the synchronizer sleeve in the intermediate and high shift fork.

7. Install the synchronizer hub snap ring.

8. Position the input shaft and synchronizer front blocking ring in the front of the case seating the output shaft pilot in the roller bearings of the input gear.

9. Place a new gasket on the input shaft bearing retainer. Install the input shaft bearing retainer, using sealer on the bolts. Line up the drain groove in the retainer with the oil hole in the case.

10. Raise the countershaft gear to align the dummy shaft with the countershaft holes in the case. Start the countershaft into the case from the rear, and carefully drive the shaft into position.

11. Install the reverse idler gear shaft and the reverse idler shaft and countershaft retainer.

12. Install the speedometer drive gear and drive ball. Then secure the gear with the snap ring.

13. Install a new gasket, and the extension housing, using sealer on the bolts. Torque the bolts to specification.

14. Install the shift levers.

15. If the extension housing bushing and/or seal is to be replaced, refer to Part 6-1, Section 2, for the detailed instructions.

16. Pour lubricant over the entire gear train while rotating the input or output shaft. Install the transmission case cover and gasket. Use sealer on the bolts. **The gasket vent holes must be toward the rear, and the cover vent hole must be toward the front.**

17. Check transmission operation through all shift positions.

PART 6-3
MODEL 3.03 THREE-SPEED TRANSMISSION

Section	Page
1 Description and Operation	6-16
Description	6-16
Operation	6-16
2 In-Car Adjustment and Repairs	6-17
Gear Shift Linkage Adjustment—	
Comet, Falcon and Fairlane	6-17
Gear Shift Linkage Adjustment—	
Mustang	6-17
3 Removal and Installation	6-18
Removal	6-18

Section	Page
Installation	6-19
4 Major Repair Operations	6-19
Disassembly	6-19
Parts Repair or Replacement	6-21
Gear Shift Lever	6-21
Shift Levers and Seals	6-21
Input Shaft Bearing	6-22
Synchronizers	6-22
Countershaft Gear Bearings	6-22
Assembly	6-23

1 DESCRIPTION AND OPERATION

DESCRIPTION

The 3.03 HEF Model three-speed transmission (Fig. 1) is used on all cars having a 200 H.D. or 289 C.I.D. engine. A 3.03 HEG Model transmission is used on all cars equipped with a 390 C.I.D. engine. The desig-

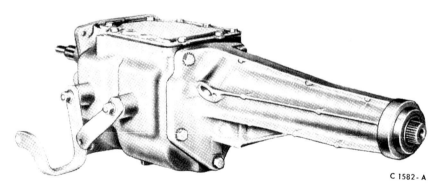

FIG. 1—3-Speed Transmission

C 1582-A

tween the centerline of the countershaft and the centerline of the input shaft.

A transmission service identification tag is located on the right side of the case at the front. The first line on the tag will show the transmission model and service identification code when required. The second nation 3.03 is the actual distance be-line will show the transmission serial number.

This transmission is of the fully synchronized type, with all gears except the reverse gear and sleeve being in constant mesh. All forward-speed changes are accomplished with synchronizer sleeves (Fig. 2) instead of sliding gears. The synchro-nizers enable quicker shifts, greatly reduce gear clash and permit down-shifting, high to intermediate between 40-20 mph and from intermediate to low below 20 mph.

The forward-speed gears are heli-cal-cut and are in constant mesh (Fig. 2). Gears used in the reverse gear train are spur-cut and are not synchronized.

Ball bearings support the input

shaft and gear and the center of the output shaft (Figs. 12 and 16). Roller bearings in the input shaft bore and 19).

support the front of the output shaft. The countershaft gear (cluster gear) runs on two rows of roller bearings. Two bronze bushings are used in the reverse idler gear (Fig. 11). A bushing located at the rear of the extension housing supports the rear of the output shaft.

Synchronizers and blocking rings are the conventional tapered ring and straight clutch gear type (Figs. 17

The shift forks, shift rails, detent mechanism, and related parts are provided in the transmission case (Fig. 9).

OPERATION

When the first-speed gear is se-lected, the shift lever moves the reverse gear and sleeve forward and forces the synchronizer blocking ring conical surface against the matching cone on the constant mesh first gear located on the output shaft. If the

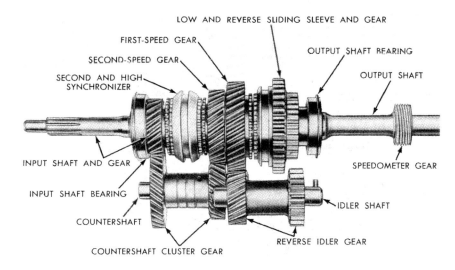

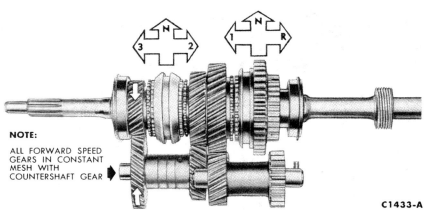

NOTE:

ALL FORWARD SPEED GEARS IN CONSTANT MESH WITH COUNTERSHAFT GEAR

C1433-A

FIG. 2—Power Flow—3-Speed Transmission

car is moving, the internal teeth of the reverse gear and sleeve and blocking ring will not index until the constant mesh first gear is brought up or down to the speed of the reverse gear and sleeve which is rotating at output shaft speed.

The reverse gear and sleeve has internal splines that, with further movement, will slide over the blocking ring and engage external clutch teeth on the constant mesh first gear. Since first gear is now locked to the output shaft and is always meshed

with the countershaft (cluster) gear, the power flow is from the input gear, through the countershaft gear, to the constant mesh first gear, through the reverse gear and sleeve to the output shaft, and out the rear of the transmission.

Engagement of second and third gears is the same as first except for ratio. In third gear, the input gear and shaft is locked directly to the output shaft by the second and third speed synchronizer to provide a ratio of 1:1.

Spur teeth are cut on the outside of the reverse gear and sleeve. The reverse gear and sleeve like the hub are always locked to the output shaft. Reverse gear is engaged by sliding the reverse gear and sleeve into mesh with the spur gear at the rear of the idler gear. The drive is then from the input gear, through the countershaft gear, to and through the reverse idler gear to the output shaft reverse gear and sleeve. The gears in this position will rotate the output shaft in a reverse direction.

A system of interlocks and detents in the transmission case prevents the selection of more than one gear at a time and helps to hold any gear in the selected position.

2 IN-CAR ADJUSTMENTS AND REPAIRS

GEAR SHIFT LINKAGE ADJUSTMENT—COMET, FALCON, FAIRLANE

1. Place the gear shift lever in the neutral position.

2. Loosen the two gearshift rod adjustment nuts.

3. Insert a dealer fabricated special tool in the slot provided in

the lower steering column. (See Fig. 3).

It may be necessary to align the levers to insert the tool.

4. Tighten the two gearshift rod adjustment nuts.

5. Remove the tool from the slot in the steering column.

6. Start the engine and shift the selector lever to each position to make sure it operates freely.

GEAR SHIFT LINKAGE ADJUSTMENT—MUSTANG

1. Loosen the three shift linkage adjustment nuts. Install a ¼ inch diameter alignment pin through the control bracket and levers as shown in Fig. 4.

2. Tighten the three linkage adjustment nuts and then remove the alignment pin.

3. Check the gear shift lever for a smooth crossover.

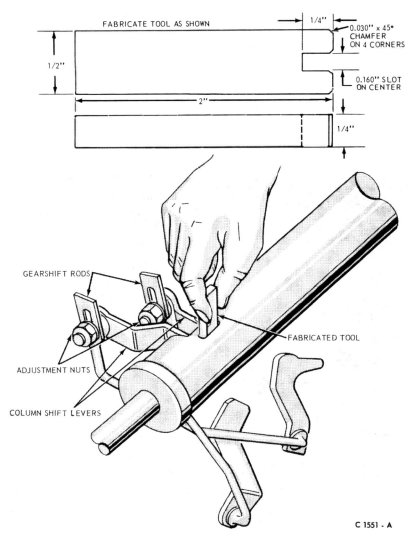

FIG. 3—Comet, Falcon and Fairlane Gearshift Linkage Adjustment

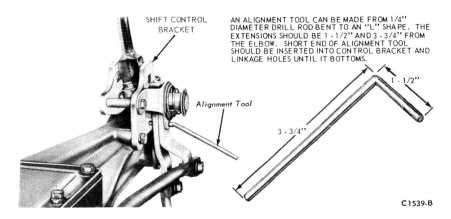

AN ALIGNMENT TOOL CAN BE MADE FROM 1/4"
DIAMETER DRILL ROD BENT TO AN "L" SHAPE. THE
EXTENSIONS SHOULD BE 1-1/2" AND 3-3/4" FROM
THE ELBOW. SHORT END OF ALIGNMENT TOOL
SHOULD BE INSERTED INTO CONTROL BRACKET AND
LINKAGE HOLES UNTIL IT BOTTOMS.

FIG. 4—Three-Speed Shift Linkage Adjustment

3 REMOVAL AND INSTALLATION

REMOVAL

1. Raise the car on a hoist.
2. Disconnect the driveshaft from the rear U-joint flange.

3. Slide the front of the driveshaft out of the extension housing and off the output shaft. Insert the tool shown in Fig. 2, Part 6-1, to

prevent the lubricant from leaking out.

4. Remove the cap screw and lock washer that secures the speedometer

cable retainer to the extension housing. Pull the speedometer cable out of the extension housing.

5. Remove the cotter pin, flat washer, and spring washer that secure the shift rods to the shift levers on the transmission.

6. On a car equipped with a floor mounted gear shift selector lever, remove the three bolts that attach the shift selector assembly to the extension housing and allow the assembly to hang by the shift lever.

7. Remove the two nuts securing the transmission rear support to the crossmember.

8. Raise the rear of the engine enough to remove the weight from the crossmember. Remove the two nuts, washers and bolts securing the crossmember to the frame supports. Remove the crossmember.

9. Support the transmission with a transmission jack and remove the four flywheel housing-to-transmission case attaching bolts and lock washers.

10. Move the transmission and jack rearward until the input shaft is clear of the flywheel housing.

11. Remove the transmission from under the car. **Do not depress the clutch pedal while the transmission is removed.**

INSTALLATION

1. Make certain that the machined surfaces of the transmission case and the flywheel housing are free of dirt, paint and burrs.

2. Install a guide pin in each lower mounting bolt hole.

3. Start the input shaft through the release bearing. Align the splines on the input shaft with the splines in the clutch disc. Move the transmission forward on the guide pins until the input shaft pilot enters the bearing or bushing in the crankshaft. If the transmission front bearing retainer binds up on the clutch release bearing hub, work the release bearing lever until the hub slides onto the retainer. Install the two transmission-to-flywheel housing upper mounting bolts and lock washers. Remove the two guide pins and install the lower mounting bolts and lock washers. Torque the four mounting bolts to specifications.

4. Raise the rear of the engine high enough to provide clearance for installing the crossmember. Install the two crossmember-to-frame support attaching bolts, washers, and nuts. Do not tighten at this time.

5. Align the bolts in the transmission rear support with the bolt holes in the crossmember, then lower the engine and remove the jack. Install the two transmission rear support-to-crossmember washers and nuts and torque to specifications. Tighten the crossmember-to-frame support nuts.

6. On a car equipped with a floor mounted gear shift selector lever, position the shift selector assembly to the extension housing and install the attaching bolts.

7. Connect each shift rod to its respective lever on the transmission with a spring washer, flat washer, and cotter pin.

8. Insert the speedometer cable and driven gear in the extension housing and secure with a cap screw and lock washer.

9. Remove the tool shown in Fig. 2. Part 6-1, from the extension housing. Slide the front universal joint yoke onto the output shaft and into the extension housing. Connect the rear universal joint to the axle pinion flange and torque the nuts to specifications.

10. Fill the transmission to the proper level with the approved lubricant and lower the car.

11. Adjust the clutch pedal free travel and the shift linkage as required.

4 MAJOR REPAIR OPERATIONS

DISASSEMBLY

1. Mount the transmission in a holding fixture and drain the lubricant.

2. Remove the nine cap screws that attach the cover to the case. Remove the cover and the gasket (Fig. 5) from the case.

3. Remove the five cap screws and lock washers that attach the extension housing to the case. Remove the extension and gasket from the case.

4. Remove the four cap screws and lock wahers that attach the front bearing retainer to the case.

Remove the retainer and gasket from the case.

5. Remove the lubricant filler plug from the right side of the case. Working through the plug opening, drive the roll pin out of the case and countershaft with a ¼-inch punch (Fig. 6).

6. Hold the countershaft gear with

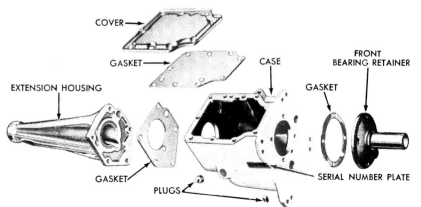

FIG. 5—Transmission Case and Related Parts—Typical

C 1583-A

C 1561-A

FIG. 6—Removing Countershaft Roll Pin

a hook and with the tool (dummy shaft) shown in Fig. 7, push the countershaft out the rear of the case.

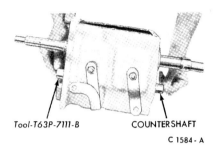

Tool-T63P-7111-B   COUNTERSHAFT

C 1584 - A

FIG. 7—Removing Countershaft

The countershaft (cluster) gear and thrust washers (Fig. 11) can be lowered to the bottom of the case. Remove the countershaft from the rear of the case.

7. Remove the snap ring that secures the speedometer drive gear on the shaft. Slide the speedometer drive gear off the output shaft. Remove the speedometer drive gear lock ball from the shaft.

8. Remove the snap ring that retains the output shaft bearing on the shaft. Remove the bearing from the case and shaft as shown in Fig. 8.

9. Place both shift levers in the neutral (center) position.

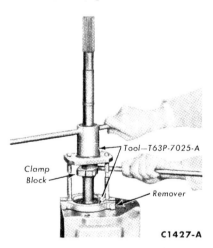

Tool—T63P-7025-A

Clamp Block

Remover

C1427-A

FIG. 8—Removing Output Shaft Bearing

10. Remove the set screw (Fig. 9) that retains the detent springs and plugs in the case. Remove the detent spring and plug from the case.

11. Remove the set screw that secures the first and reverse shift fork to the shift rail. Slide the first and reverse shift rail out through the rear of the case.

12. Slide the first and reverse synchronizer forward as far as pos-

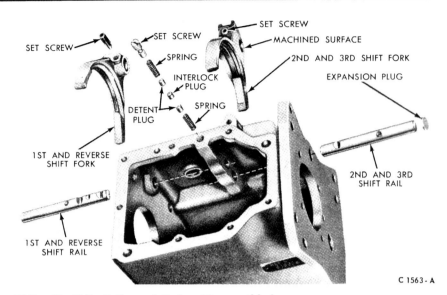

SET SCREW — SET SCREW — SET SCREW — MACHINED SURFACE

SET SCREW — SPRING — 2ND AND 3RD SHIFT FORK

INTERLOCK PLUG — EXPANSION PLUG

DETENT PLUG — SPRING

1ST AND REVERSE SHIFT FORK

2ND AND 3RD SHIFT RAIL

1ST AND REVERSE SHIFT RAIL

C 1563 - A

FIG. 9—Shift Rails and Forks—Disassembled

sible, then rotate the first and reverse shift fork upward, then lift it from the case.

13. Move the second and third-speed shift fork to the second speed position to gain access to the set screw. Remove the set screw from the fork. Rotate the shift rail 90° as shown in Fig. 10.

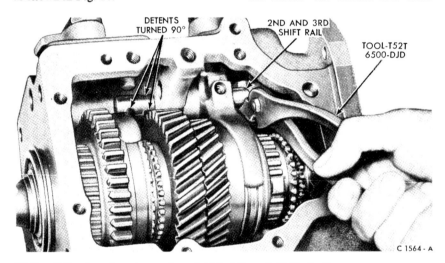

DETENTS TURNED 90°

2ND AND 3RD SHIFT RAIL

TOOL-T52T 6500-DJD

C 1564 - A

FIG. 10—Rotating Second and Third-Speed Shift Rail

14. Lift the interlock plug (Fig. 9) from the case with a magnet.

15. Tap on the inner end of the second and third shift rail to remove the expansion plug (Fig. 9) from the front of the case. Remove the shift rail.

16. Remove the second and third detent plug and spring from the detent bore.

17. Pull the input gear and shaft forward until the gear contacts the case, and then remove the large snap ring. It is necessary to move the gear forward to provide clearance when removing the output shaft assembly in HEG models. On HEF models, the input shaft and gear is removed from the front of the case at this time.

18. Rotate the second and third shift fork upward, and lift it from the case.

19. Carefully lift the output shaft assembly out through the top of the case.

On HEG models, work the input shaft bearings and gear back through the bore in the case and out the top.

20. Driving from the front of the case, remove the reverse idler gear shaft from the case and *then lift the* reverse idler gear and two thrust washers (Fig. 11) from the case.

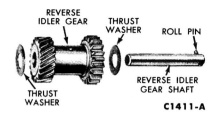

FIG. 11—Reverse Idler Shaft and Gear—Disassembled

21. Remove the snap ring from the front of the output shaft, then slide the synchronizers and the second speed gear (Fig. 12) off the shaft.

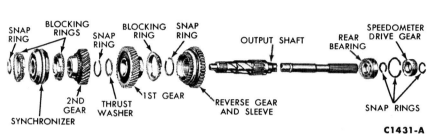

FIG. 12—Output Shaft—Disassembled

22. Remove the next snap ring and tabbed thrust washer from the output shaft, and then slide the first gear and blocking ring off the shaft.

23. Remove the next snap ring from the output shaft, and slide the reverse gear and sleeve off the shaft.

PARTS REPAIR OR REPLACEMENT

GEAR SHIFT LEVER

1. Remove the snap ring from the end of the selector shaft with pointed snap ring pliers (Fig. 13).

2. Remove the flat washer and spring.

3. After removing two bolts, pull the retainer, selector levers, and spacer from the shaft.

4. Drive the short selector lever pin from the shaft with a large pin punch.

5. Drive the long trunnion pin from the shaft and remove the trunnion and shaft.

6. If necessary to remove the studs from the selector levers, remove the cotter pins, flat washers, wave washers and studs.

7. Lubricate all mating friction surfaces with Lubriplate before assembly.

8. Install the shaft in the bracket. Position the trunnion and drive the long straight pin through the trunnion and into the shaft until an

equal length of the pin is exposed on both sides of the shaft.

9. Drive the short pin into the shaft until the pin is centered in the shaft.

10. Install the levers and spacer on the shaft as shown in Fig. 13.

11. Position the retainer and start the bolts. Before tightening the bolts be sure that the retainer is not interfering with free movement of the shaft. Tighten the bolts.

12. Install the spring, flat washer and snap ring.

13. Install the lever studs if they were removed.

SHIFT LEVERS AND SEALS

1. Remove the nut, lock washer and flat washer that secures each shift lever (Fig. 14) to the lever and shaft in the transmission case. Lift

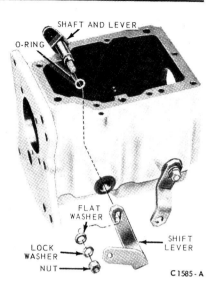

FIG. 14—Shift Lever and Shaft—Disassembled

the levers off the shafts. Slide each lever and shaft out of the case. Discard the "O" ring from each shaft.

2. Lubricate the new seals with transmission lubricant and install them on the shafts.

3. Install the lever and shafts in the case.

4. Position a shift lever on each shaft and secure them with a flat washer, lock washer and nut.

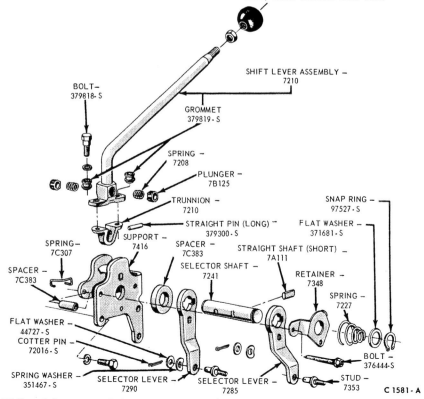

FIG. 13—Gear Shift Lever Disassembled—Typical

INPUT SHAFT BEARING

1. Remove the snap ring securing the input shaft bearing (Fig. 15), and press the input shaft out of the bearing.

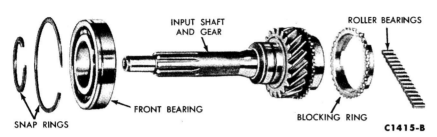

FIG. 15—Input Shaft Gear—Disassembled

2. Press the input shaft bearing onto the input shaft with the tool shown in Fig. 16 and install the snap ring on the shaft.

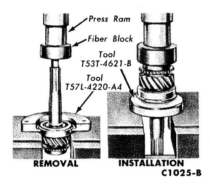

FIG. 16—Replacing Input Shaft Bearing

SYNCHRONIZERS

1. Push the synchronizer hub from each synchronizer sleeve.

2. Separate the inserts and insert springs from the hubs. Do not mix the parts from the second and third speed synchronizer with the first and reverse synchronizer (Figs. 17 and 19).

3. Install the rear insert spring (Fig. 20) in the groove of the first and reverse synchronizer hub. Make sure that the spring covers all insert grooves. Start the hub in the sleeve making sure that the alignment marks are properly indexed. Position the three inserts in the hub making sure that the small end is over the spring and that the shoulder is on the inside of the hub. Slide the sleeve and reverse gear onto the hub until the detent is engaged. Install the front insert spring in the hub to hold the inserts against the hub.

4. Install one insert spring (Fig. 19) into a groove of the second and third speed synchronizer hub, mak-

ing sure that all three insert slots are fully covered. With the alignment marks on the hub and sleeve aligned, start the hub into the sleeve. Place the three inserts on top of the re-

taining spring and push the assembly together. Install the remaining insert spring, so that the spring ends cover the same slots as does the other spring. Do not stagger the springs. Place a synchronizer blocking ring on each end of the synchronizer sleeve.

COUNTERSHAFT GEAR BEARINGS

1. Remove the dummy shaft, 50 roller bearings, and the two bearing retainer washers from the countershaft gear (Fig. 18).

2. Coat the bore in each end of the countershaft gear with grease.

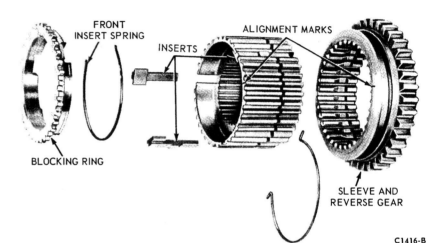

FIG. 17—First and Reverse Synchronizer—Disassembled

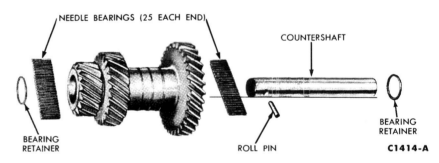

FIG. 18—Countershaft Gear—Disassembled

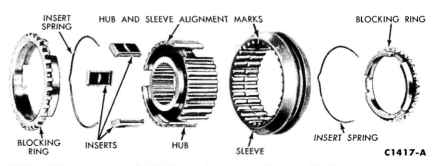

FIG. 19—Second and Third Synchronizer—Disassembled

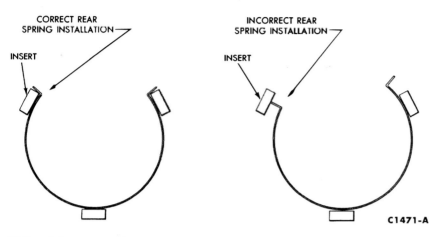

FIG. 20—First and Reverse Speed Synchronizer Insert Spring Installation

3. Hold the dummy shaft in the gear and install the 25 roller bearings and a retainer washer in each end of the gear.

4. Position the countershaft gear, dummy shaft, and roller bearings in the case.

5. Place the case in a vertical position. Align the gear bore and the thrust washers with the bores in the case and install the countershaft.

6. Place the case in a horizontal position and check the countershaft gear end play with a feeler gauge. The end play should be 0.004-0.018 inch. If not within these limits, replace the thrust washers.

7. After establishing the correct end play, install the dummy shaft in the countershaft gear and allow the gear to remain at the bottom of the case.

ASSEMBLY

1. Place countershaft gear in proper position at bottom of case. The countershaft gear will remain in the bottom of the case until the output and the input shafts have been installed.

2. Coat the reverse idler gear thrust surfaces in the case with a thin film of lubricant and position the two thrust washers (Fig. 11) in place.

3. Position the reverse idler gear and dummy shaft in place. Align the gear bore and thrust washers with the case bores and install the reverse idler shaft.

4. Measure the reverse idler gear end play with a feeler gauge. End play should be 0.004-0.018 inch. If the end play is not within limits, replace the thrust washers. If the end

play is within limits, leave the reverse idler gear installed.

5. Lubricate the output shaft splines and machined surfaces with transmission lubricant.

6. Slide the first and reverse gear and sleeve (Fig. 12) onto the output shaft with the teeth end of the gear facing toward the rear of the shaft. Secure it in place with the snap ring.

7. Place the blocking ring on the tapered machined surface of the first gear.

8. Rotate the gear as necessary to engage the three notches in the blocking ring with the synchronizer inserts. Secure the first gear with the thrust washer and snap ring.

9. Slide the blocking ring onto the tapered machined surface of the second gear. Slide the second gear with blocking ring and the second and third gear synchronizer onto the mainshaft. The tapered machined surface of the second gear must be toward the front of the shaft. Make sure that the notches in the blocking ring engage the synchronizer inserts. Secure the synchronizer with a snap ring.

10. Coat the bore of the input shaft and gear with a thin film of grease. **A thick film of grease will plug the lubricant holes and prevent lubrication to the bearings.** Install the bearings (Fig. 15) in the bore.

If working on an HEG model transmission, install the input gear and bearing through the top of the case and through the bore in the front of the case. On HEF models, the input shaft is installed through the front of the case. Install the snap ring in the bearing groove.

11. Position the output shaft assembly in the case. Position the second and third shift fork on the second and third speed synchronizer.

12. Place a detent plug spring and a plug in the case (Fig. 9). Place the second and third speed synchronizer in the second speed position (toward rear of transmission). Align the fork and install the second and third speed shift rail. It will be necessary to depress the detent plug to enter the rail in the bore. Move the rail inward until the detent plug engages the forward notch (second speed position).

13. Secure the fork to the shaft with the set screw. Move the synchronizer to the neutral position.

14. Install the interlock plug in the case. If the second and third shift rail is in the neutral position, the top of the interlock will be slightly lower than the surface of the first and reverse shift rail bore.

15. Move the first and reverse synchronizer forward to the first speed position. Place the first and reverse shift fork in the groove of the first and reverse synchronizer. Rotate the fork into position and install the first and reverse shift rail. Move the rail inward until the center notch (neutral) is aligned with the detent bore. Secure the fork to the shaft with the set screw. Install the remaining detent plug and spring. Secure the detent spring with the slotted head set screw. Turn the set screw in until the head is flush to 0.020 inch below the top of the case.

16. Install a new expansion plug in the case.

17. Hold the input shaft and blocking ring in position, and then move the output shaft forward to seat the pilot in the roller bearings of the input gear.

18. Tap the input gear bearing into place in the case while holding the output shaft to prevent the roller bearings from dropping. Install the front bearing retainer and new gasket, making sure that the oil return slot is at the bottom of the case. Install and torque the four attaching screws to 30-36 ft-lbs.

19. Install the large snap ring on the rear bearing. Place the bearing on the output shaft with the snap ring end toward the rear of the shaft. Press the bearing into place with the tool shown in Fig. 21. Secure the bearing to the shaft with a snap ring.

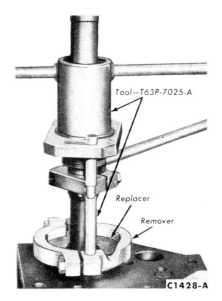

FIG. 21—Installing Output Shaft Rear Bearing

20. Hold the speedometer drive gear lock ball in the detent and slide the speedometer drive gear into place. Secure the gear with a snap ring.

21. Place the transmission in the vertical position. Working through the drain hole in the bottom of the case, align the bore of the countershaft gear and the thrust washers with the bore of the case with a screwdriver.

22. Working from the rear of the case, push the dummy shaft out of the countershaft gear with the countershaft. Before the countershaft is completely inserted in the bore, make sure that the hole that accommodates the roll pin is in alignment with the hole in the case. Push the countershaft into place and install the roll pin.

23. Coat a new extension housing gasket with sealer and position it on the case.

24. Install lock washers on the five attaching screws. Dip the threads of the cap screws in sealer. Secure the housing to the case and torque the cap screws to 42-50 ft-lbs.

25. Install the filler and drain plugs in the case. Make sure that the magnetic plug is installed in the bottom of the case.

26. Place the transmission in gear. Pour lubricant over the entire gear train while rotating the input or output shaft.

27. Coat a new cover gasket (Fig. 5) with sealer. Secure the cover with nine cap screws. Torque the screws to 14-19 ft-lbs.

28. Check the operation of the transmission in all of the gear positions.

PART 6-4
DAGENHAM FOUR-SPEED TRANSMISSION

Section	Page
1 Description and Operation	6-25
Description	6-25
Operation	6-25
2 In-Car Adjustment and Repairs	6-26
Gear Shift Linkage Adjustments	6-26
3 Removal and Installation	6-26
Removal	6-26
Installation	6-27
4 Major Repair Operations	6-27

Section	Page
Disassembly	6-27
Parts Repair or Replacement	6-28
Gear Shift Lever	6-28
Shift Cover	6-28
Synchronizers	6-29
Input Shaft Bearing	6-29
Countershaft Gear Bearings	6-29
Assembly	6-30

1 DESCRIPTION AND OPERATION

DESCRIPTION

1. The Dagenham four-speed transmission (Fig. 1) is of the fully synchronized type, with all gears except the reverse sliding gear being in constant mesh. All forward speed changes are accomplished with synchronizer sleeves (Fig. 2) instead of sliding gears. The synchronizers will enable quicker shifts, greatly reduce gear clash and permit down-shifting in all forward speeds.

The shift linkage is mounted directly on the transmission extension housing (Fig. 1) and enters the driver's compartment through an opening in the floor pan. A flexible rubber boot is provided to seal the driver's compartment from the exterior.

The shift pattern is shown on the top of the gear shift lever knob. A finger-operated release lever is provided on the shift lever (Fig. 3) to prevent the transmission from being accidentally shifted into reverse gear.

The forward speed gears are helical-cut and are in constant mesh (Fig. 2). Gears used in the reverse gear train are spur-cut and are not synchronized.

Ball bearing assemblies support the input gear and the center of the output shaft (Figs. 8 and 9). Roller bearings in the input gear bore support the front of the output shaft. The countershaft gear (cluster) also runs on two rows of roller bearings. A bronze bushing is used in the reverse idler gear (Fig. 17). The rear of the output shaft is supported by the driveshaft front yoke which in turn runs on a steel-backed bushing that is pressed into the extension housing.

Synchronizers and blocking rings are the conventional tapered ring and straight clutch gear-type (Fig. 16).

A removable shift cover contains the shift cams, forks, shafts, detents and interlocks (Figs. 13 and 14).

A service identification tag is located under the upper right hand extension to case attaching bolt. The tag will show the transmission model and service identification code when required.

OPERATION

When first gear is selected, the shift lever and linkage move the first and second shift fork and synchro-

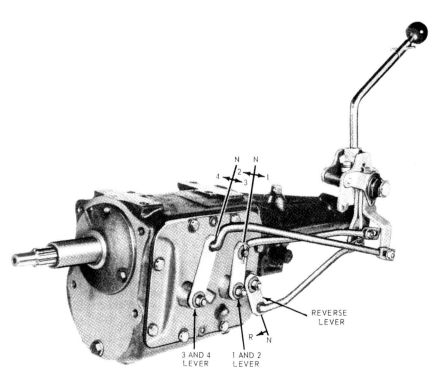

N N
4 2 1
3

REVERSE LEVER

3 AND 4 LEVER   1 AND 2 LEVER

R   N

C 1586 - A

FIG. 1—4-Speed Floor Shift Transmission

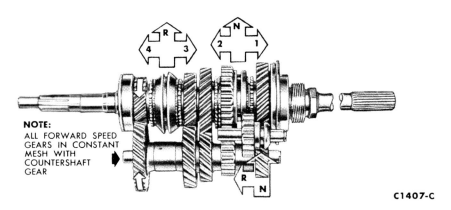

FIG. 2—Power Flow—4-Speed Transmission

nizer sleeve toward the rear and force the synchronizer blocking ring conical surface against the matching cone on the output shaft first gear. If the car is moving, the synchronizer sleeve, blocking ring and first gear clutch teeth will not index until first gear is brought up or down to the speed of the synchronizer and the output shaft. The synchronizer sleeve has internal splines that, with

further movement, will slide over the blocking ring and engage external clutch teeth on the first gear. Since first gear is now locked to the output shaft and is always meshed with the countershaft (cluster) gear, the power flow is from the input gear, through the countershaft gear, to the first gear on the output shaft, through the synchronizer sleeve and hub to the output shaft and out the

rear of the transmission.

Engagement of second and third gears is the same as first except for ratio.

Fourth gear operation is accomplished in the same manner as first, second, and third, but the input gear is locked directly to the output shaft and the ratio is 1:1.

Spur teeth are cut on the outside of the first and second gear synchronizer sleeve. The sleeve and hub are always locked to the output shaft. Reverse gear is engaged by sliding an idler gear into mesh with the teeth on the first and second synchronizer sleeve and the spur teeth on the countershaft gear. The drive is then from the input gear, through the countershaft gear, through the idler gear, to the output shaft reverse gear (synchronizer sleeve) and the output shaft, which is rotated in a reverse direction.

A system of interlocks and detents in the shift cover prevents the selection of more than one gear speed at a time and helps to hold any gear in the selected position.

2 **IN-CAR ADJUSTMENT AND REPAIRS**

GEAR SHIFT LINKAGE ADJUSTMENT

To adjust the linkage, place the shift lever in the neutral position and raise the car on a hoist. Insert a ¼-inch fabricated alignment tool into the alignment hole as shown in Fig. 3. If the rod will not enter, check for bellied or bent shift rods. If the shift rods are the correct shape, check for loose lever lock nuts at the rod ends. Reset the linkage by loosening the three rod-retaining lock nuts and moving the levers until the alignment tool will enter the alignment holes. Make sure the transmission shift levers are in neutral and the reverse shift lever is in the neutral detent (Fig. 1). Install the shift rods and torque the lock nuts to 15-20 ft-lbs. Remove the alignment tool. Operate the shift levers to make sure that the detents are engaging. Lower the car and check for smooth cross-over operation.

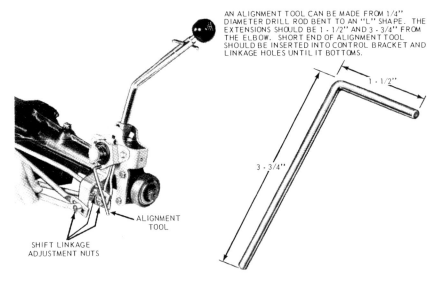

FIG. 3—Gear Floor Shift Linkage Adjustment—Typical

3 **REMOVAL AND INSTALLATION**

REMOVAL

1. Raise the car on a hoist.

2. Remove the starter cable from the starter and remove the starter.

3. Disconnect the driveshaft at the pinion flange and tape the

U-joint bearing races in place if the joint does not have a strap spot welded to it. Pull the driveshaft off the transmission and insert the tool shown in Fig. 2, Part 6-1 into the seal and extension housing to prevent lubricant leakage.

4. Remove the back-up lamp switch (if so equipped) from the shift linkage control bracket.

5. Remove the clip from the equalizer bar at the clutch release rod and remove the rod. Remove the linkage return spring from the release lever.

6. Disconnect the parking brake front cable from the equalizer bar. Disconnect the speedometer cable from the extension housing.

7. Loosen the shift linkage adjusting nuts shown in Fig. 3.

8. Remove the retaining clip, flat washer and spring washer that secures the shift rods to the shift levers.

9. Remove the bolts that attach the shift linkage control bracket to the extension housing and allow the assembly to hang by the shift lever.

10. Support the engine with a transmission jack and remove the extension housing-to-engine rear support attaching nuts.

11. Raise the rear of the engine and remove the transmission support crossmember from the underbody.

12. Support the transmission and remove the flywheel housing-to-engine and engine rear plate-to-housing attaching bolts.

13. Move the transmission and flywheel housing assembly toward the rear until the transmission input shaft splines are clear of the clutch assembly. Lower the transmission. **Do not depress the clutch pedal while the transmission is removed.**

INSTALLATION

1. Raise the transmission and align the input shaft splines with those in the clutch hub. Move the transmission forward until the flywheel housing is against the engine.

2. Install the flywheel housing-to-engine and engine rear plate-to-housing attaching bolts. Torque the bolts to specifications.

3. Position the transmission support crossmember to the underbody and install the attaching bolts.

4. Lower the engine and transmission and install the extension housing-to-engine rear support attaching nuts. Torque the nuts to specifications.

5. Position the shift linkage control bracket to the extension housing and install the attaching bolts.

6. Secure each shift rod to its respective lever with the spring washer, flat washer and retaining pin.

7. Connect the parking brake front cable to the equalizer bar and the speedometer cable to the extension housing.

8. Connect the clutch release rod to the clutch equalizer shaft and to the clutch release lever. Attach the retaining clip and lever return spring.

9. Remove the tool from the extension housing and slide the driveshaft yoke onto the transmission output shaft, being careful not to damage the seal.

10. Be sure the pinion flange locating slots are clean, and then position the U-joint. Install the bolts and torque them to specifications.

11. Install the back-up lamp switch (if so equipped) on the shift linkage control bracket.

12. Install the starter and cable.

13. Place both forward gear shift levers and the reverse shift lever in the neutral position and insert a ¼ inch diameter alignment tool in the shift linkage alignment hole (Fig. 3). Adjust the linkage and tighten the adjusting nuts. Remove the alignment tool. Adjust the clutch pedal free travel as required.

14. Fill the transmission to the proper level with specified lubricant.

15. Lower the car. Check the shift crossover motion for full shift engagement and smooth crossover operation.

4 MAJOR REPAIR OPERATIONS

DISASSEMBLY

1. Mount the transmission in a holding fixture and drain the lubricant.

2. Insert a reworked screwdriver (Fig. 4) through the clutch release lever and unhook the retainer that secures the clutch release lever to the retainer bracket.

3. Remove the four attaching bolts and the flywheel housing from the transmission.

4. Remove the eight attaching bolts and the shift cover from the transmission.

5. Remove the three bolts and the input gear bearing retainer from the front of the transmission.

6. Remove the four bolts that secure the extension housing and output shaft bearing adapter to the transmission case. In the event that two long and two shorter bolts are used, the two longer bolts must be installed in the upper right and lower left holes (viewed from the rear). Remove the extension housing.

7. Working from the front of the case, drive the countershaft, with a drift, until it is just clear of the front wall of the case. Hold the countershaft gear with a hook and using the tool shown in Fig. 5, push the countershaft out of the countershaft (cluster) gear and transmission case. Carefully lower the countershaft gear to the bottom of the case.

8. Remove the output shaft assembly from the rear of the case (Fig. 6).

9. Remove the input gear and bearing (Fig. 7) from the front of the case.

10. Lift the countershaft gear assembly out through the cover opening of the case. Note the smallest diameter thrust washer is positioned between the rear of the countershaft gear and the case and that the larger diameter steel and bronze washers are at the front (Fig. 17).

11. Thread a $5/16$-24 bolt into the rear of the reverse idler gear shaft and pull the shaft using tools T50T-7140-B (adapter) and T59L-1000-A (puller). Remove the idler gear.

12. Remove the lock washer and nut which retains the speedometer drive gear and spacer from the rear of the output shaft.

13. Remove the speedometer gear and drive ball. Remove the speedometer gear spacer (Fig. 8).

14. Place the output shaft assembly in an arbor press as shown in Fig. 9 and press the bearing, adapter, first gear, first and second speed synchronizer assembly, and second gear off the shaft. Do not lose the

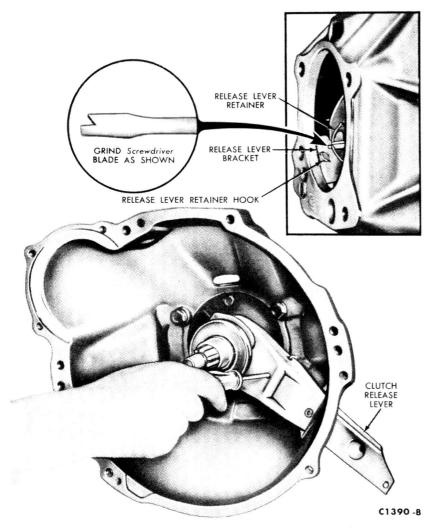

FIG. 4—Removing or Installing Clutch Release Lever Retainer

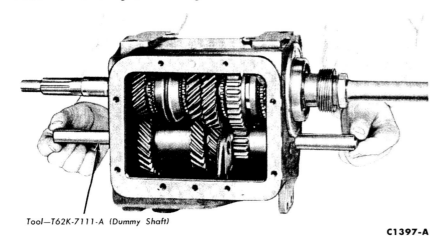

Tool—T62K-7111-A (Dummy Shaft)

C1397-A

FIG. 5—Removing or Installing Countershaft

first speed gear sleeve retainer ball.

15. With snap ring pliers, remove the snap ring from in front of the third and fourth-speed synchronizer on the output shaft. Press the third gear and the synchronizer off the

shaft as shown in Fig. 10.

PARTS REPAIR OR REPLACEMENT

GEAR SHIFT LEVER

1. Remove the snap ring from the

end of the selector shaft with pointed snap ring pliers (Fig. 11).

2. Remove the flat washer and spring.

3. After removing two bolts, pull the retainer, selector levers, and bracket from the shaft.

4. Drive the short selector lever pin from the shaft with a large pin punch.

5. Drive the long trunnion pin from the shaft and remove the trunnion and shaft.

6. If necessary to remove the studs from the selector levers, remove the cotter pins, flat washers, wave washers and studs.

7. Lubricate all mating friction surfaces with Lubriplate before assembly.

8. Install the shaft in the bracket. Position the trunnion and drive the long straight pin through the trunnion and into the shaft until an equal length of the pin is exposed on both sides of the shaft.

9. Drive the short pin into the shaft until the pin is centered in the shaft.

10. Install the levers and the neutral index bracket on the shaft as shown in Fig. 11.

11. Position the retainer and start the bolts. Before tightening the bolts be sure that the retainer is not interfering with free movement of the shaft. Tighten the bolts.

12. Install the spring, flat washer and snap ring.

13. Install the lever studs if they were removed.

SHIFT COVER

1. Remove the levers from the cam and shafts (Fig. 12).

2. Remove the roll pin from the upper fork and shaft and remove the shaft and forks.

3. Remove the reverse cam and shaft.

4. Rotate the reverse fork and shaft to disengage the detent ball and remove the fork and shaft (Fig. 13). Hold a cloth over the shaft cover boss nearest to the fork to catch the detent ball and spring when the shaft clears the boss hole.

5. Remove the 1-2 and 3-4 shift cam assemblies. Hold a cloth over the interlock and cam assemblies to catch the detent balls.

6. Push the interlock sleeve, spring and remaining ball out of the cover.

7. Remove the 1-2 and 3-4-to-reverse interlock pins from the reverse

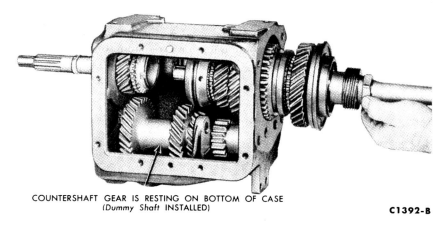

COUNTERSHAFT GEAR IS RESTING ON BOTTOM OF CASE
(Dummy Shaft INSTALLED)

C1392-B

FIG. 6—Removing or Installing Output Shaft

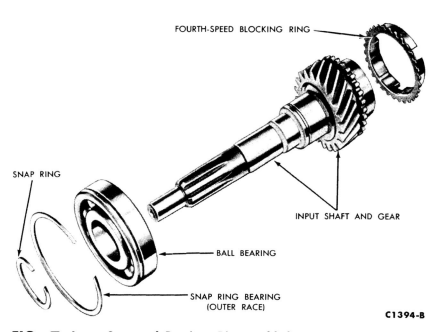

FOURTH-SPEED BLOCKING RING

INPUT SHAFT AND GEAR

SNAP RING

BALL BEARING

SNAP RING BEARING
(OUTER RACE)

C1394-B

FIG. 7—Input Gear and Bearing—Disassembled

fork and shaft bosses in the cover.

8. If the seals need replacing, remove them with a screwdriver and install them as shown in Fig. 14.

9. Place the 1-2 and 3-4-to-reverse interlock pins in the holes in the reverse fork and shaft bosses (Figs. 12 and 13).

10. Install the 3-4 shift cam in the cover.

11. Install the parts of the 1-2 and 3-4 cam interlock, sleeve, ball, spring and another ball, in that order.

12. Hold the 3-4 cam in neutral position and the 1-2 ball depressed while the 1-2 cam is installed in the cover.

13. Install the 1-2 and the 3-4 levers, washers and nuts.

14. Check the clearance between the interlock, detent sleeve and the

1-2 and 3-4 shift cams in, and between, all shift positions. The sleeve to cam clearance must be a minimum of 0.0005 inch and a maximum of 0.010 inch. Service sleeves are available in the following lengths ±0.010 inch: 1.2875, 1.2905, 1.2935, 1.2965, 1.2995, and 1.3025.

15. With the 1-2 and 3-4 shift cams in neutral and the 1-2 and 3-4-to-reverse interlock pin resting on the cams, install the reverse shaft detent spring and ball and the reverse fork and shaft.

16. Install the reverse shift cam through the cover and into the aligned fork and shaft. Install the reverse cam operating lever (washer and nut loose).

17. Position the 1-2 and 3-4 forks onto the shift cams and install the fork shaft. Align the shaft hole with

the one in the cover and install the lock pin.

18. Check all shift positions for freedom of movement, detent and interlock action.

SYNCHRONIZERS

1. Before disassembling the synchronizers, scribe an alignment mark across the hub and sleeve if they do not have alignment marks. The alignment marks will permit the sleeves and hubs to be assembled in their original positions.

2. Remove the front and rear insert springs from both synchronizer assemblies (Fig. 15).

3. Slide the sleeves off the hubs. Remove the hub inserts (detents).

4. Place the long inserts (detents) into the slots in the 1-2 synchronizer hub and slide the combination sleeve and reverse gear over it making sure that the etch or scribe marks on the hub and sleeve are aligned (Fig. 15). Snap the insert springs into place. The tab on each spring must set into the underside of an insert.

5. Position the short inserts (detents) into the slots in the 3-4 synchronizer hub and slide the clutch sleeve over it making sure that the etch or scribe marks are aligned. Install the insert springs in the same manner as with the 1-2 synchronizer.

INPUT SHAFT BEARING

1. If the input shaft and gear bearing needs replacing, remove it as shown in Fig. 16.

2. Press the bearing onto the input shaft with the outer race snap ring groove toward the front (Fig. 16).

3. Install the snap rings on the bearing outer race and on the gear shaft with snap ring pliers.

COUNTERSHAFT GEAR BEARINGS

1. Remove the thrust washers from each end of the countershaft gear (Fig. 17).

2. Remove the dummy shaft from the gear.

3. Remove the two washers and 22 roller bearings from each end of the gear. Coat the bore in each end of the countershaft with grease.

4. Place the tool (dummy shaft) shown in Fig. 5 in the countershaft (cluster) gear. Starting on either end, drop a steel washer (Fig. 17) over the tool and into the gear. Install 22 roller bearings into the gear. Lay another steel washer on the ends

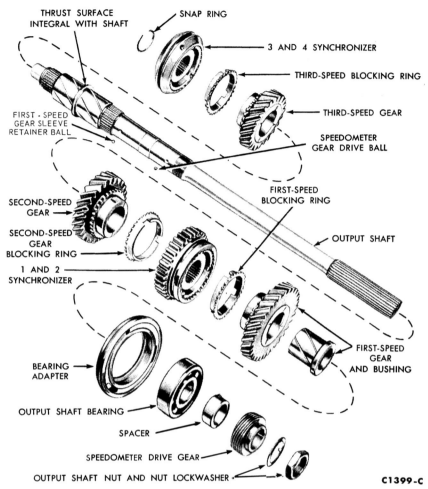

FIG. 8—Output Shaft Disassembled

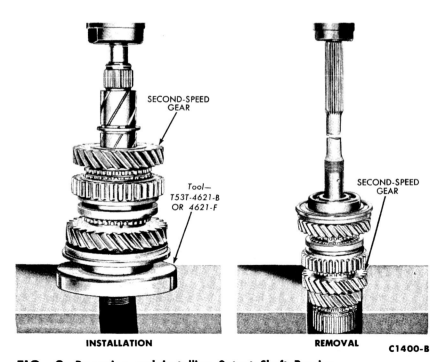

INSTALLATION   REMOVAL   C1400-B

FIG. 9—Removing and Installing Output Shaft Bearing

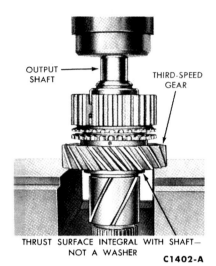

THRUST SURFACE INTEGRAL WITH SHAFT—NOT A WASHER   C1402-A

FIG. 10—Removing Third Gear and Third and Fourth Synchronizer Hub

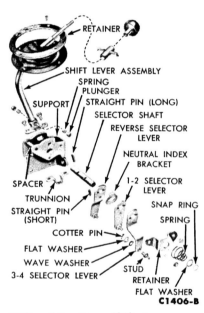

FIG. 11—Gear Shift Lever Disassembled

of the bearings and the thrust washers that were previously selected.

5. Repeat the above operation for the other end of the gear. Do not lose the bearings and washers in the initially assembled end when inverting the gear to assemble the opposite end.

ASSEMBLY

1. Place the second gear on the rear of the output shaft with the clutch teeth and tapered synchronizer end toward the rear. Install a blocking ring with the clutch teeth toward the front (Fig. 8).

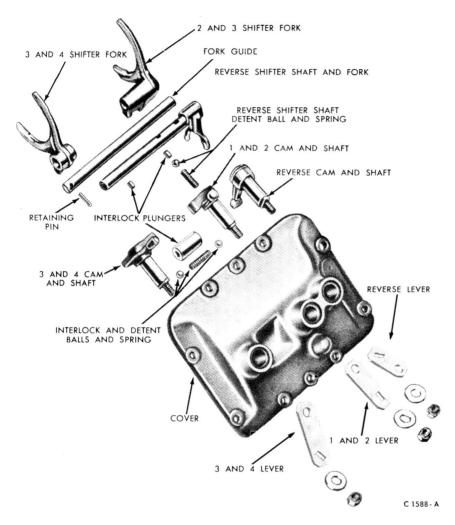

FIG. 12—Gear Shift Cover Disassembled

2. Install the first and second synchronizer and reverse gear assembly on the rear of the output shaft with the shift fork groove toward the rear. Be sure the second-speed blocking ring is not cocked on the gear and that the three index slots align with the synchronizer inserts (detents).

3. Install the first-speed blocking ring with the clutch teeth to the rear and the slots engaging the synchronizer inserts (detents). Pack grease into the ball pocket on output shaft then insert the first-speed gear sleeve retainer ball. See (Fig. 8).

4. With taper and clutch teeth to front, and the sleeve (bushing) shoulder to the rear, slide the first gear and sleeve onto the output shaft and align the slot on the I.D. of the first-speed gear sleeve over the ball.

5. Assemble the output shaft ball bearing into the recess in the bearing adapter. Position the adapter and bearing on the rear of the output shaft with the adapter forward. Hold the first gear and sleeve (bushing) forward and place the assembly in a press with the tool resting against the rear of the bearing inner race. Press the bearing until it is seated firmly against the first gear sleeve (bushing).

6. Place the spacer, speedometer gear drive ball, speedometer gear (shoulder to rear), lock washer (tab into speedometer gear), and nut on the output shaft (Fig. 8). **Torque the nut to 80 ft-lbs to insure axial location of the synchronizer hub, first speed gear sleeve, rear mainshaft bearing, spacer and speedometer drive gear on the output shaft. Loosen the locknut and retorque to 25 ft.-lbs. Bend the washer over a flat on the nut.**

7. Set the third-speed gear on the front of the output shaft with the clutch teeth toward the front. Place the blocking ring on the gear.

8. Install the 3-4 synchronizer

with the wide thrust surface of the hub toward the rear. Align the blocking ring slots with the synchronizer inserts (detents). The hub to shaft spline fit may require a slight press to assemble.

9. Using snap ring pliers, install the snap ring in its groove on the front of the output shaft.

10. Position the countershaft gear, dummy shaft, and roller bearings in the case.

11. Place the case in a vertical position. Align the gear bore and the thrust washers with the bores in the case and install the countershaft.

12. Place the case in a horizontal position and check the countershaft gear end play with a feeler gauge. The end play should be 0.004-0.018 inch. If not within these limits, replace the thrust washers.

13. After establishing the correct end play, install the dummy shaft in the countershaft gear and allow the gear to remain at the bottom of the case until the output and input shafts have been installed.

14. Using a light film of grease, install roller bearings in the bore of the input shaft and gear. **A thick film of grease could plug the lubricant holes and restrict lubrication to the bearings.**

15. Install the input shaft and gear in the case front bore. Place the fourth gear blocking ring on the rear of the input gear with the clutch teeth forward.

16. Enter the output shaft assembly through the rear of the case and guide the output shaft front pilot into the input gear bore and bearings (Fig. 7). Be sure the fourth gear synchronizer blocking ring slots index with the inserts (detents) on the 3-4 synchronizer.

17. Raise the countershaft (cluster) gear and thrust washers until the countershaft can be inserted from the rear of the case into the gear and bearings. The shaft should push through, easily displacing the tool. Push on the shaft until it contacts the front of the case (Fig. 5). Position the flat on the rear of the countershaft in a horizontal plane so it will align with the slot in the extension housing. Tap the shaft into place.

18. Install the reverse idler gear with the fork groove toward the rear and the idler shaft flat horizontal and parallel with the countershaft flat.

19. Position a new extension housing gasket on the rear of the case, using a non-drying sealer.

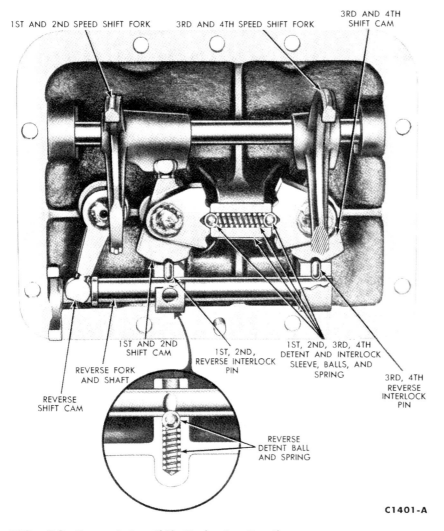

FIG. 13—Transmission Shift Mechanism Details

case, bearing and adapter before torquing the bolts. If two long and two short bolts are used, install the two long bolts in the upper right and lower left holes.

21. If the input gear bearing retainer seal needs replacing, refer to Fig. 19. Install the new bearing retainer gasket, using sealer. Install the bearing retainer with the drain slot facing downward. Apply sealer to the bolts and torque to specifications.

22. Place the 1-2 and 3-4 synchronizer in neutral and the reverse idler gear in reverse (forward) position. Set the reverse shift lever in the reverse position. Install a new shift cover gasket on the case, using sealer. Install the shift cover. Use sealer on the bolts and torque them to specifications.

23. Install the flywheel housing. Use sealer on the retaining bolts and torque them to specifications.

24. Install the clutch release bearing on the clutch release lever. Position the release lever through the housing from inside the housing and clip the lever retainer onto its hook as shown in Fig. 4.

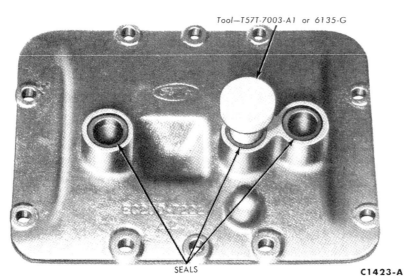

FIG. 14—Installing Cam and Shaft Seals

20. Install the extension housing. Align the dowel in the housing with the hole in the rear bearing adapter

(Fig. 18). Using sealer, install the extension housing bolts. Be sure the housing is seated squarely on the

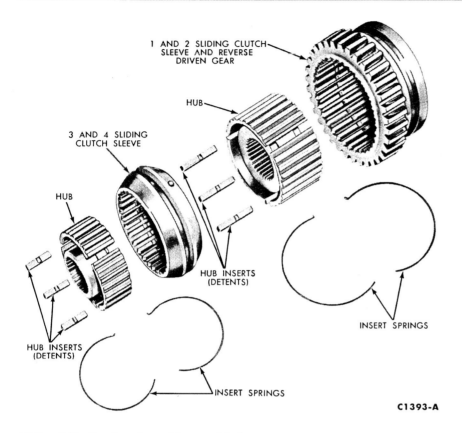

1 AND 2 SLIDING CLUTCH SLEEVE AND REVERSE DRIVEN GEAR

HUB

3 AND 4 SLIDING CLUTCH SLEEVE

HUB

HUB INSERTS (DETENTS)

INSERT SPRINGS

HUB INSERTS (DETENTS)

INSERT SPRINGS

C1393-A

FIG. 15—Synchronizers Disassembled

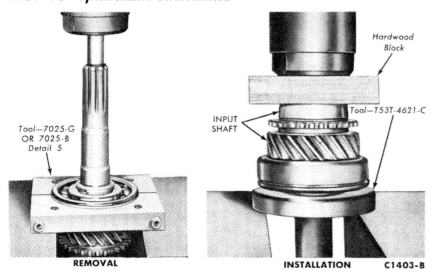

Tool—7025-G OR 7025-B Detail 5

REMOVAL

Hardwood Block

INPUT SHAFT

Tool—T53T-4621-C

INSTALLATION   C1403-B

FIG. 16—Removing and Installing Input Gear Bearing

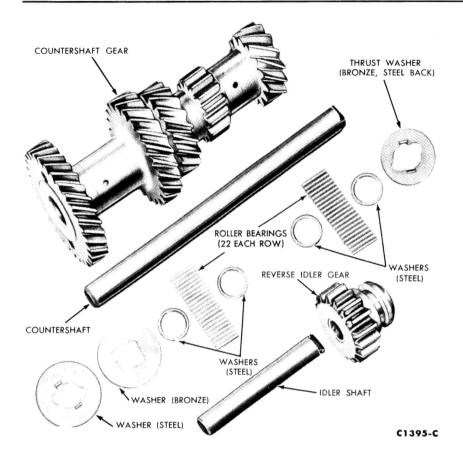

COUNTERSHAFT GEAR

THRUST WASHER
(BRONZE, STEEL BACK)

ROLLER BEARINGS
(22 EACH ROW)

WASHERS
(STEEL)

REVERSE IDLER GEAR

COUNTERSHAFT

WASHERS
(STEEL)

WASHER (BRONZE)

WASHER (STEEL)

IDLER SHAFT

C1395-C

FIG. 17—Countershaft and Idler Gear Disassembled

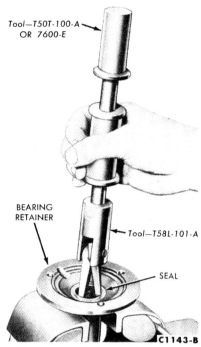

Tool—T50T-100-A
OR 7600-E

BEARING
RETAINER

Tool—T58L-101-A

SEAL

C1143-B

FIG. 19—Removing Input
Shaft Bearing Retainer Seal—
Typical

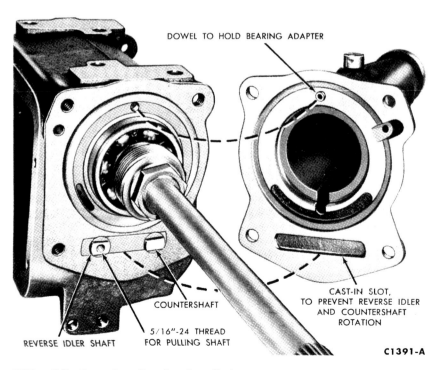

DOWEL TO HOLD BEARING ADAPTER

COUNTERSHAFT

REVERSE IDLER SHAFT

5/16"-24 THREAD
FOR PULLING SHAFT

CAST-IN SLOT,
TO PREVENT REVERSE IDLER
AND COUNTERSHAFT
ROTATION

C1391-A

FIG. 18—Extension Housing Installation

PART 6-5
FORD DESIGN FOUR-SPEED TRANSMISSION

Section	Page
1 Description and Operation	6-35
Description	6-35
Operation	6-35
2 In-Car Adjustment and Repairs	6-36
Shift Linkage Adjustment	6-36
3 Removal and Installation	6-37
Removal	6-37
Installation	6-37
4 Major Repair Operations	6-38
Disassembly	6-38

Section	Page
Parts Repair or Replacement	6-39
Gear Shift Lever	6-39
Cam and Shaft Seals	6-40
Input Shaft Bearing	6-40
Synchronizers	6-41
Countershaft Gear Bearings	6-41
Reverse Idler Gear Bearings	6-41
Input Shaft Seal	6-41
Assembly	6-41

1 DESCRIPTION AND OPERATION

DESCRIPTION

The Ford designed 4-speed transmission (Fig. 1) is of the fully synchronized type with all gears except the reverse sliding gear being in constant mesh. All forward-speed changes are accomplished with synchronizer sleeves. The synchronizers will enable quicker shifts, greatly reduce gear clash, and permit downshifting into any forward-speed gear while the car is moving.

The shift linkage is mounted directly on the transmission extension housing (Fig. 1) and enters the driver's compartment through an opening in the floor pan. A flexible rubber dust boot (Fig. 3) is provided to seal the driver's compartment from the exterior.

The shift pattern is shown on the top of the gear shift lever knob. A finger-operated release lever is provided on the shift lever to prevent the transmission from being accidentally shifted into reverse gear. All forward-speed gears in the transmission are helical-type, however, the reverse sliding gear and the exterior of the first- and second-speed synchronizer sleeve are spur-type gears. The specifications of this section Part 6-6 lists the transmission model numbers and vehicles in which they are used.

A transmission service identification tag is located on the right side of the case at the front. The first line on the tag will show the transmission model and service identification code when required. The second line will show the transmission serial number.

The four-speed transmission will be designated by the numeral 5 on the vehicle warranty plate.

OPERATION

In first-speed (Figure 2), the first- and second-speed synchronizer sleeve is moved rearward by the shift fork. The sleeve engages the first-speed blocking ring, which acts as a cone clutch applied to the free-wheeling first-speed gear. This action speeds up or slows down the first-speed gear to match the speed of the output shaft. Further movement of the sleeve locks the first-and-second-speed synchronizer hub to the first-speed gear by means of internal splines. On engagement of the clutch, power flows through the input shaft and gear to the meshed countershaft gear and thence to the first-speed gear. This gear transmits the power through the locked synchronizer hub to the transmission output shaft. All the other forward-speed gears are in idler motion, as they are all driven

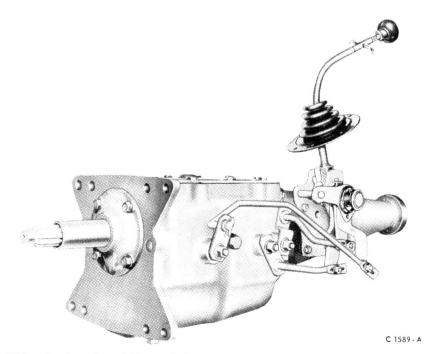

C 1589 - A

FIG. 1—Four-Speed Transmission

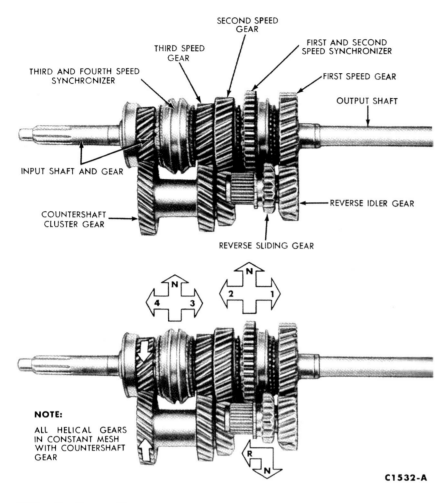

FIG. 2—Power Flow

by the countershaft (cluster) gear, but they do not transmit power because they are not locked to the output shaft. All the forward-speed shifts are made in the same manner as the first-speed shift, due to the constant-mesh features.

Reverse gear is engaged by moving the reverse sliding gear forward on the reverse idler gear until it meshes with the external teeth (spur-type) of the first- and second-speed synchronizer sleeve. Movement of the sliding gear is accomplished by the center shaft lever. With all forward-speed synchronizer sleeves in neutral, power flow in reverse is through the input shaft to the constant-mesh countershaft (cluster) gear, thence to the constant mesh reverse idler. Splines then carry the power through the reverse sliding gear to the first-and-second speed synchronizer sleeve which is locked to the output shaft. As the reverse sliding gear is meshed with the synchronizer sleeve, power is transmitted to the output shaft, rotating it in a reverse direction.

2 IN-CAR ADJUSTMENTS AND REPAIRS

SHIFT LINKAGE ADJUSTMENT

1. Loosen the three shift linkage adjustment nuts. Install a ¼ inch diameter alignment tool through the control bracket and levers as shown in Fig. 3.

An alignment tool can be made from ¼″ diameter drill rod bent to an "L" shape. The extensions should be 1½″ and 3¾″ from the elbow. Short end of alignment pin should be inserted into control bracket and

linkage holes until it bottoms.

2. Tighten the three linkage adjustment nuts and then remove the alignment pin.

3. Check the gear shift lever for a smooth crossover.

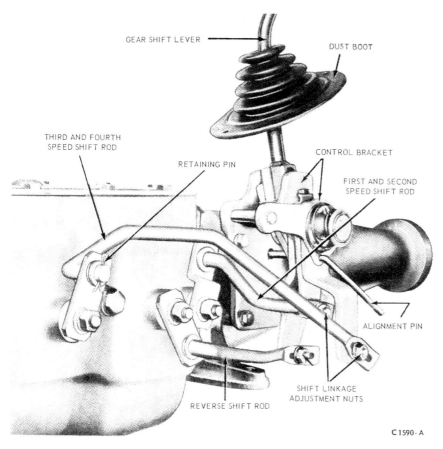

GEAR SHIFT LEVER

DUST BOOT

THIRD AND FOURTH
SPEED SHIFT ROD

RETAINING PIN

CONTROL BRACKET

FIRST AND SECOND
SPEED SHIFT ROD

ALIGNMENT PIN

REVERSE SHIFT ROD

SHIFT LINKAGE
ADJUSTMENT NUTS

C 1590 - A

FIG. 3—Adjusting Shift Linkage

3 REMOVAL AND INSTALLATION

REMOVAL

1. Raise the car on a hoist.

2. Disconnect the drive shaft from the rear U-joint flange. Slide the drive shaft off the transmission output shaft and install the extension housing seal installation tool into the extension housing to prevent lubricant leakage.

3. Disconnect the speedometer cable from the extension housing.

4. Remove the retaining clip, flat washer and spring washer that secures the shift rods to the shift levers.

5. Remove the bolts that attach the shift linkage control bracket to the extension housing and allow the assembly to hang by the shift lever.

6. Support the engine with a transmission jack and remove the two nuts securing the transmission rear support to the crossmember.

7. Raise the rear of the engine with the transmission jack. Remove the two nuts, washers and bolts se-

curing the crossmember to the frame supports. Remove the crossmember.

8. Support the transmission on a jack and remove the bolts that attach the transmission to the flywheel housing.

9. Move the transmission and jack rearward until the transmission input shaft clears the flywheel housing. If necessary, lower the engine enough to obtain clearance for transmission removal.

Do not depress the clutch pedal while the transmission is removed.

INSTALLATION

1. Make sure that the mounting surfaces of the transmission and the flywheel housing are free of dirt, paint, and burrs. Install two guide pins in the flywheel housing lower mounting bolt holes. Move the transmission forward on the guide pins until the input shaft splines enter the clutch hub splines and the case is positioned against the flywheel housing.

2. Install the two upper transmission to flywheel housing mounting bolts snug and then remove the two guide pins. Install the two lower mounting bolts. Torque all mounting bolts to specifications.

3. Raise the rear of the engine high enough to provide clearance for installing the crossmember. Install the two crossmember-to-frame support attaching bolts, washers, and nuts. Do not tighten at this time.

4. Align the bolts in the transmission rear support with the bolt holes in the crossmember, then lower the engine and remove the jack. Install the two transmission rear support-to-crossmember washers and nuts and torque to specifications. Tighten the crossmember-to-frame support nuts.

5. Position the shift linkage control bracket to the extension housing and install the attaching bolts.

6. Secure each shift rod to its respective lever with the spring wash-

er, flat washer, and retaining pin.

7. Connect the speedometer cable to the extension housing.

8. Remove the extension housing installation tool and slide the forward end of the drive shaft over the transmission output shaft. Connect the drive shaft to the rear U-joint flange.

9. Place both forward gear shift levers and the reverse shift lever in the neutral position and insert a ¼ inch diameter alignment tool in the shift linkage alignment hole (Fig. 3). Adjust the linkage and tighten the adjusting nuts. Remove the alignment tool. Adjust the clutch pedal free travel as required.

10. Fill the transmission to the proper level with the specified lubricant.

11. Lower the car. Check the shift crossover motion for full shift engagement and smooth crossover operation.

4 MAJOR REPAIR OPERATIONS

DISASSEMBLY

1. Mount the transmission in a holding fixture and drain the lubricant.

2. Remove the cover attaching screws from the case. Lift the cover and gasket from the case.

3. Remove the extension housing attaching screws and lock washers. Remove the housing and the gasket.

4. Remove the input shaft bearing retainer attaching screws. Slide the retainer off the input shaft.

5. Support the countershaft gear with a wire hook. Working from the front of the case, push the countershaft out the rear of the case as shown in Fig. 4. Lower the countershaft to the bottom of the case with the wire hook. Remove the hook.

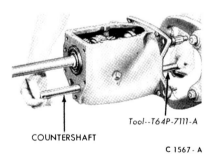

COUNTERSHAFT

Tool--T64P-7111-A

C 1567 - A

FIG. 4—Removing Countershaft from Case

6. Place the first-and-second-speed gear shift lever and the reverse shift lever in the neutral position. Place the third- and fourth-speed gear shift lever in the third-speed position.

7. Remove the bolt that retains the third- and fourth-speed shift rail detent spring and the plug in the left side of the case as shown in Fig. 5. Remove the spring and the plug with a magnet.

8. Remove the detent mechanism set screw from the top of the case. Remove the detent spring and plug with a small magnet.

9. Remove the attaching screw

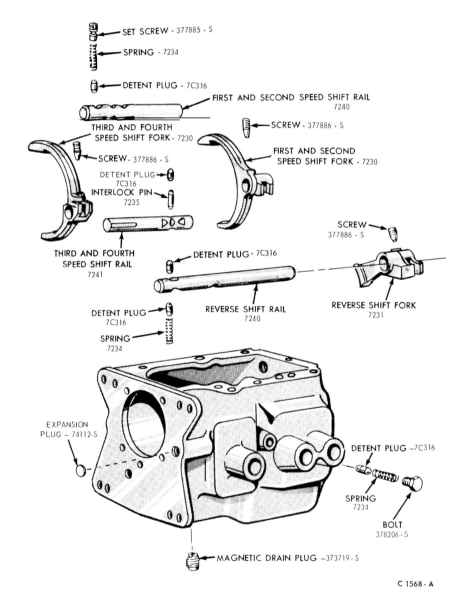

C 1568 - A

FIG. 5—Shift Rails and Forks Disassembled

from the third- and fourth-speed shift fork. Tap on the inner end of the shift rail to unseal the expansion plug from the front of the case. Then withdraw the third- and fourth-speed shift rail from the front of the case.

Do not lose the interlock pin from the shift rail.

10. Remove the set screw from the first- and second-speed shift fork. Slide the first- and second-speed shift rail out the rear of the case.

11. Remove the interlock plug and the detent plug from the top of the case (Fig. 5) with a magnet.

12. Remove the snap ring that secures the speedometer drive gear to the output shaft. Slide the gear off the shaft, then remove the speedometer gear drive ball.

13. Remove the snap ring that secures the output shaft bearing to the shaft.

14. Remove the output shaft bearing as shown in Fig. 6.

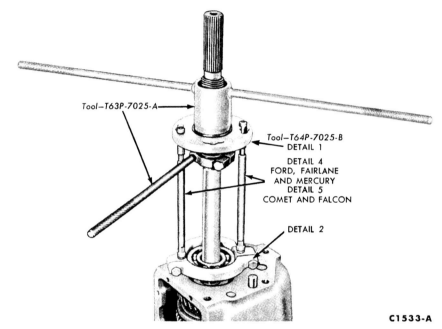

FIG. 6—Removing Output Shaft Bearing

15. Remove the input shaft and bearing and the blocking ring from the front of the case.

16. Move the output shaft to the right side of the case to provide clearance for the shift forks. Rotate the forks as shown in Fig. 7, then lift them from the case.

17. Support the thrust washer and first-speed gear to prevent them from sliding off the shaft, then lift the output shaft assembly from the case as shown in Fig. 8.

18. Remove the reverse gear shift fork set screw. Rotate the reverse shift rail 90° as shown in Fig. 9. Slide the shift rail out the rear of the case. Lift the reverse shift fork from the case.

19. Remove the reverse detent plug and spring from the case with a magnet.

20. Remove the reverse idler gear shaft from the case as shown in Fig. 10.

21. Lift the reverse idler gear and the thrust washers from the case. Be careful not to drop the bearings and the dummy shaft from the gear.

22. Lift the countershaft gear and the thrust washers from the case. Be careful not to drop the bearings or the dummy shaft from the countershaft gear.

23. Remove the snap ring from the front of the output shaft. Slide the third- and fourth-speed synchronizer (Fig. 11) blocking ring and the

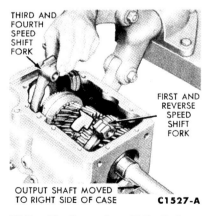

FIG. 7—Removing Shift Forks from Case

third-speed gear off the shaft.

24. Remove the next snap ring and the second-speed gear thrust washer from the shaft. Slide the second-speed gear and the blocking ring off the shaft.

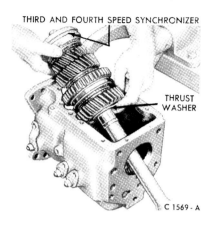

FIG. 8—Removing Output Shaft Assembly

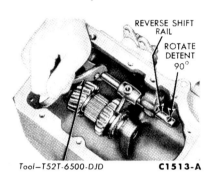

FIG. 9—Rotating Reverse Shift Rail

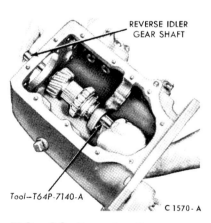

FIG. 10—Removing Reverse Idler Gear Shaft

25. Remove the next snap ring, then slide the first- and second-speed synchronizer, blocking ring and the first-speed gear off the shaft.

26. Remove the thrust washer from the rear of the shaft.

PARTS REPAIR OR REPLACEMENT

GEAR SHIFT LEVER

1. Remove the snap ring from the

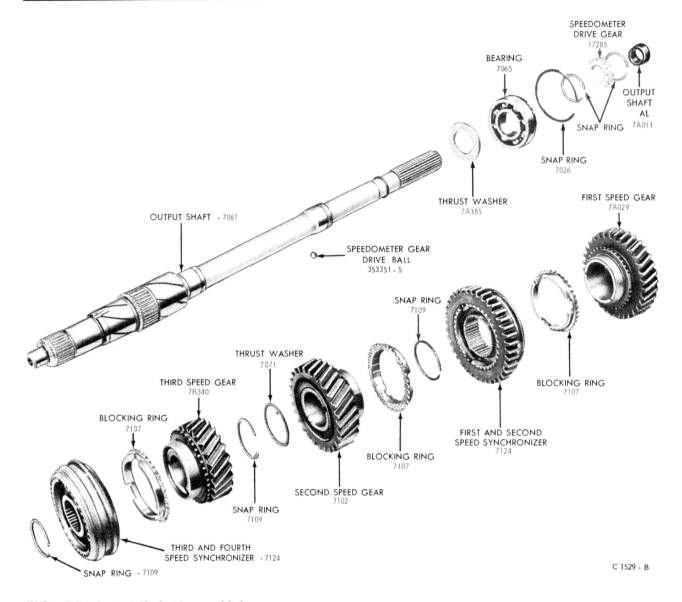

FIG. 11—Output Shaft Disassembled

end of the selector shaft with pointed snap ring pliers (Fig. 12).

2. Remove the flat washer and spring.

3. After removing two bolts, pull the retainer, selector levers, and bracket from the shaft.

4. Drive the short selector lever pin from the shaft with a large pin punch.

5. Drive the long trunnion pin from the shaft and remove the trunnion and shaft.

6. If necessary to remove the studs from the selector levers, remove the cotter pins, flat washers, wave washers and studs.

7. Lubricate all mating friction surfaces with Lubriplate before assembly.

8. Install the shaft in the bracket.

Position the trunnion and drive the long straight pin through the trunnion and into the shaft until an equal length of the pin is exposed on both sides of the shaft.

9. Drive the short pin into the shaft until the pin is centered in the shaft.

10. Install the levers and the neutral index bracket on the shaft as shown in Fig. 12.

11. Position the retainer and start the bolts. Before tightening the bolts be sure that the retainer is not interfering with free movement of the shaft. Tighten the bolts.

12. Install the spring, flat washer and snap ring.

13. Install the lever studs if they were removed.

CAM AND SHAFT SEALS

1. Remove the attaching nut, lock washer and the flat washer from each shift lever and remove the three levers.

2. Remove the three cam and shafts from inside the case.

3. Remove the O-ring from each cam and shaft (Fig. 13) and discard the O-rings.

4. Dip the new O-rings in gear lubricant and install them on the cam and shafts.

5. Slide each cam and shaft into its respective bore in the transmission case.

6. Position a shift lever on each cam and shaft and secure with a flat washer, lock washer and nut.

INPUT SHAFT BEARING

1. Remove the snap ring that se-

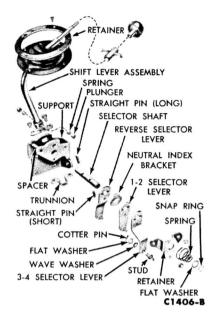

FIG. 12—**Gear Shift Lever Disassembled—Typical**

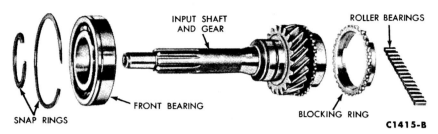

FIG. 14—**Input Shaft Gear Disassembled**

2. Press the input shaft gear out of the bearing as shown in Fig. 15.

3. Press a new bearing onto the input shaft with the tool shown in Fig. 15.

4. Secure the bearing with a snap ring.

SYNCHRONIZERS

1. Push the synchronizer hub from each synchronizer sleeve (Fig. 16).

2. Separate the inserts and insert springs from the hubs. Do not mix the parts of the first- and second-

3. Position the hub in the sleeve, making sure that the alignment marks are properly indexed.

4. Place the three inserts into place on the hub. Install the insert springs making sure that the irregular surface (hump) is seated in one of the inserts. Do not stagger the springs.

COUNTERSHAFT GEAR BEARINGS

1. Remove the dummy shaft, two bearing retainer washers, and the 21 roller bearings (Fig. 17) from each end of the countershaft gear.

2. Coat the bore in each end of the countershaft gear with grease.

3. Hold the dummy shaft in the gear and install the 21 roller bearings and the retainer washer in each end of the gear.

REVERSE IDLER GEAR BEARINGS

1. Slip the reverse idler sliding gear off of the reverse idler gear (Fig. 18).

2. Remove the dummy shaft, two bearing retainer washers and the 44 roller bearings from the reverse idler gear.

3. Coat the bore in each end of the reverse idler gear with grease.

4. Hold the dummy shaft in the gear and install the 22 roller bearings and the retainer washer in each end of the gear.

5. Install the reverse idler sliding gear on the reverse idler gear making sure that the shift fork groove is toward the front (Fig. 18).

INPUT SHAFT SEAL

1. Remove the seal from the input shaft bearing retainer as shown in Fig. 19.

2. Coat the sealing surface with lubricant.

3. Install the seal as shown in Fig. 20.

ASSEMBLY

1. Coat the countershaft gears

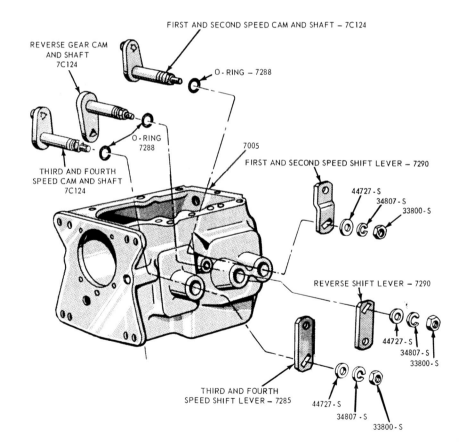

FIG. 13—**Cam and Shafts and Shift Levers Disassembled**

cures the bearing to the shaft (Fig. 14).

speed synchronizer with the third- and fourth-speed synchronizer.

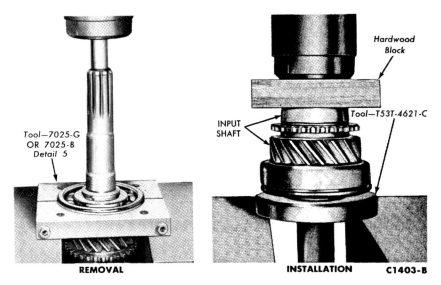

FIG. 15—Replacing Input Shaft Bearing

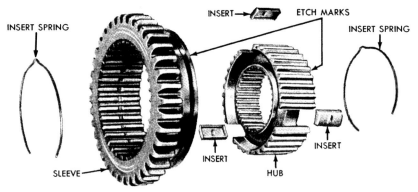

FIRST AND SECOND SPEED SYNCHRONIZER

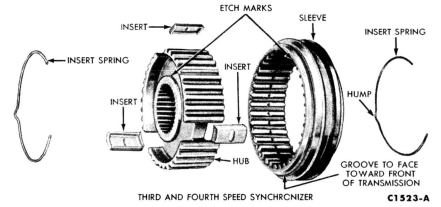

THIRD AND FOURTH SPEED SYNCHRONIZER   C1523-A

FIG. 16—Synchronizers Disassembled

thrust surfaces in the case with a thin film of lubricant and position a thrust washer (Fig. 17) at each end of the case.

2. Position the countershaft gear, dummy shaft, and roller bearings in the case.

3. Place the case in a vertical position. Align the gear bore and the

thrust washers with the bores in the case and install the countershaft.

4. Place the case in a horizontal position and check the countershaft gear end play with a feeler gauge. The end play should be 0.004-0.018 inch. If not within these limits, replace the thrust washers.

5. After establishing the correct

end play, install the dummy shaft in the countershaft gear and allow the gear to remain at the bottom of the case.

6. Coat the reverse idler gear thrust surfaces in the case with a thin film of lubricant and position the two thrust washers (Fig. 18) in place.

7. Position the reverse idler gear, sliding gear, dummy shaft and the roller bearings in place making sure that the shift fork groove in the sliding gear is toward the front of the case.

8. Align the gear bore and thrust washers with the case bores and install the reverse idler shaft.

9. Measure the reverse idler gear end play with a feeler gauge. End play should be 0.004-0.018 inch. If the end play is not within limits, replace the thrust washers. If the end play is within limits, leave the reverse idler gear installed.

10. Position the reverse gear shift rail detent spring and detent plug in the case. Hold the reverse shift fork in place on the reverse idler sliding gear and install the shift rail from the rear of the case. Secure the fork to the rail with the Allen head set screw.

11. Install the first- and second speed synchronizer onto the front of the output shaft (Fig. 11) making sure that the shift fork groove is toward the rear of the shaft.

12. Position the blocking ring on the second-speed gear.

13. Slide the second-speed gear onto the front of the shaft, make sure that the inserts in the synchronizer engage the notches in the blocker ring.

14. Install the second-speed gear thrust washer and snap ring.

15. Slide the third-speed gear onto the shaft with the synchronizer coned surface toward the front.

16. Place a blocking ring on the third-speed gear.

17. Slide the third- and fourth-speed gear synchronizer onto the shaft making sure that the inserts in the synchronizer engage the notches in the blocking ring.

18. Install the snap ring on the front of the output shaft.

19. Position the blocking ring on the first-speed gear.

20. Slide the first-speed gear onto the rear of the output shaft making sure that the notches in the blocking ring engage the synchronizer inserts.

21. Install the heavy thrust washer on the rear of the output shaft.

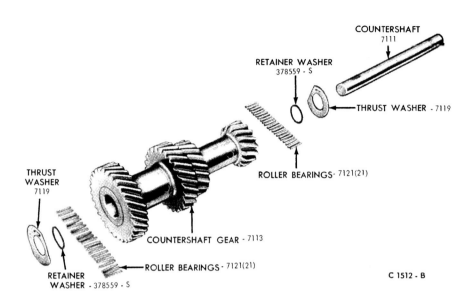

FIG. 17—Countershaft Gear Disassembled

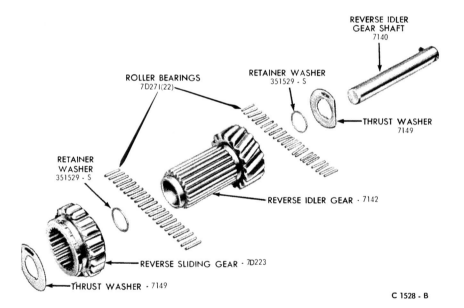

FIG. 18—Reverse Idler Gear Disassembled

22. Support the thrust washer and first-speed gear to prevent them from sliding off the shaft. Carefully lower the output shaft assembly into the case as shown in Fig. 8.

23. Position the first- and second-speed shift fork and the third- and fourth-speed shift fork in place on their respective gears and rotate them into place.

24. Place a detent plug (Fig. 5) in the detent bore. Place the reverse shift rail into neutral position.

25. Coat the third- and fourth speed shift rail interlock pin with grease and position it in the shift rail.

26. Align the third- and fourth-speed shift fork with the shift rail bores and slide the shift rail into place making sure that the three detents are facing toward the outside of the case. Place the front synchronizer into third-speed position and install the set-screw in the third- and fourth-speed shift fork. Move the synchronizer to the neutral position. Install the third- and fourth-speed shift rail detent plug, spring and bolt in the left side of the transmission case (Fig. 5). Place the interlock plug (tapered ends) in the detent bore.

27. Align the first- and second-speed shift fork with the case bores and slide the shift rail into place. Secure the fork with the set screw. Install a detent plug and spring in the detent bore. Thread the set screw into the case until the head is flush to 0.020 inch below the surface of the case.

28. Coat the input gear bore with a thin film of grease, then install the 15 roller bearings in the bore. **A thick film of grease could plug the lubricant holes and restrict lubrication to the bearings.**

29. Position the front blocking ring in the third- and fourth-speed synchronizer. Place the input shaft gear in the transmission case making sure that the output shaft pilot enters the roller bearings in the input gear.

30. Place a new gasket on the input shaft bearing retainer. Dip the attaching bolts in sealer and install and tighten them to specifications.

31. Install the output shaft bearing as shown in Fig. 21. Install the snap ring to retain the bearing.

32. Position the speedometer gear drive ball in the output shaft and slide the gear into place. Secure the gear with the snap ring.

33. Place the transmission in a vertical position as shown in Fig. 22. Align the countershaft gear bore and thrust washers with the bore in the case. Install the countershaft.

34. Use a new gasket and secure the extension housing to the case with the attaching screws. Use a sealer on the extension housing attaching screws. Torque the screws to specifications.

35. Install the filler and drain plugs in the case if they were removed. Make sure that the magnetic plug is installed in the bottom of the case.

36. Pour the specified lubricant over the entire gear train while rotating the input shaft.

37. Place each shift fork in all positions to make sure that they operate properly.

38. Use a new cover gasket and install the cover. Coat the cover attaching screws with sealer and install and tighten them to specifications.

39. Coat the third- and fourth-speed shift rail plug bore with a sealer and install a new expansion plug.

40. If the extension housing bushing and seal are to be replaced, refer to Section 4.

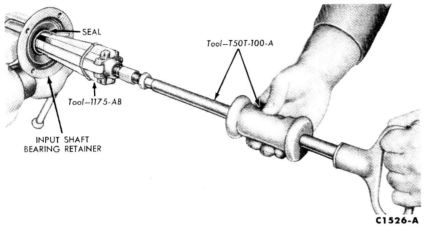

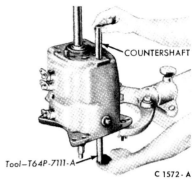

FIG. 22—Installing Countershaft

FIG. 19—Removing Input Shaft Seal

FIG. 20—Installing Input Shaft Seal

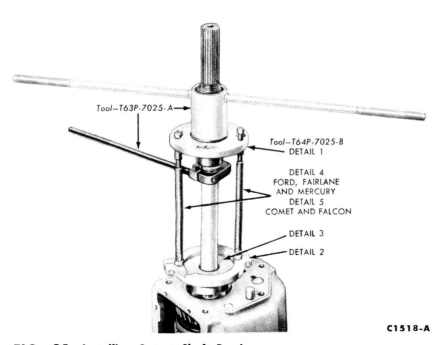

FIG. 21—Installing Output Shaft Bearing

PART 6-6
OVERDRIVE TRANSMISSION

Section	Page
1 Diagnosis and Testing	6-45
Mechanical Checks	6-45
Overdrive Control Handle Clearance Check	6-45
Overdrive Control Lever Position Check	6-45
Pawl Engagement Check	6-45
Electrical Checks	6-45
Governor Circuit Check	6-45
Solenoid Circuit Check	6-46
Interrupter Circuit Check	6-46
2 Cleaning and Inspection	6-47
Cleaning	6-47
Inspection	6-47
3 Description and Operation	6-47
Description	6-47
Operation	6-47

Section	Page
Mechanical Operation	6-47
Electrical System Operation	6-48
4 In-Car Adjustments and Repairs	6-49
Overdrive Control Cable Adjustment	6-49
5 Transmission Removal and Installation	6-50
Removal	6-50
Installation	6-50
6 Major Repair Operations	6-50
Disassembly	6-50
Parts Repair or Replacement	6-52
Input Shaft	6-52
Synchronizer	6-52
Output Shaft Bearing	6-52
Cam and Shaft Seals	6-52
Countershaft Rollers	6-53
Assembly	6-53

1 DIAGNOSIS AND TESTING

When trouble occurs in the overdrive unit, check the mechanical operation of the unit before checking the operation of the overdrive electrical control system.

MECHANICAL CHECKS

OVERDRIVE CONTROL HANDLE CLEARANCE CHECK

Check the specified clearance between the overdrive control handle shank and the bezel on the instrument panel.

OVERDRIVE CONTROL LEVER POSITION CHECK

Raise the car and check the position of the overdrive control lever at the overdrive unit housing. The lever should rest firmly against its stop at the rear. If the lever is not all the way back the overdrive shift rail may be locking the pawl and preventing it from engaging the balk ring gear.

With the engine stopped and the clutch engaged, shift the transmission to third or second gear and shift the overdrive control lever to the automatic (rearward) position. The drive shaft should then turn freely in a clockwise direction (when viewed from the front), but should lock up when turned counterclockwise.

With the transmission remaining in third or second gear, shift the overdrive control lever to the locked-out (forward) position. The drive shaft should lock up when turned either clockwise or counterclockwise.

PAWL ENGAGEMENT CHECK

Check the mechanical engagement of the pawl with the balk ring gear, using the following procedure:

1. Turn the ignition switch to the ON position and raise the car.

2. Shift the overdrive control lever to the locked-out (forward) position, and shift the transmission to neutral.

3. Turn the drive shaft clockwise and, at the same time ground the governor white wire with a jumper. The solenoid will click, indicating that it is energized.

4. Keep the solenoid energized, and shift the transmission to third or second gear to lock the transmission output shaft against rotation. Shift the overdrive control lever to the automatic (rearward) position.

5. Turn the drive shaft clockwise. At less than ¼ turn of the driveshaft, the pawl will engage the balk ring gear and lock the drive shaft against rotation in both directions.

If the pawl does not engage the balk ring gear, replace the solenoid and repeat the test. If the pawl still

does not engage, remove the overdrive unit from the car for inspection and repair.

ELECTRICAL CHECKS

GOVERNOR CIRCUIT CHECK

1. Turn the ignition switch ON and OFF, and listen for the relay or solenoid to click. If either clicks as soon as the ignition switch is turned ON, the governor circuit (Fig. 1) is grounded or the relay is defective.

2. To determine which condition is present, remove the wire from the TH-SW terminal on the relay and turn the ignition switch ON. If the relay clicks, the relay is defective. If it does not click, the governor circuit is grounded.

3. To check the governor operation when the relay does not click as the ignition switch is turned On, disconnect the wire at the TH-SW terminal.

4. Raise the rear wheels off the floor.

5. Connect a test lamp between the battery and the wire removed from the TH-SW terminal.

6. Start the engine and, with the transmission in third-speed, bring the speedometer reading up through 28 mph. The lamp should light at or about this speed.

7. Throttle the engine down

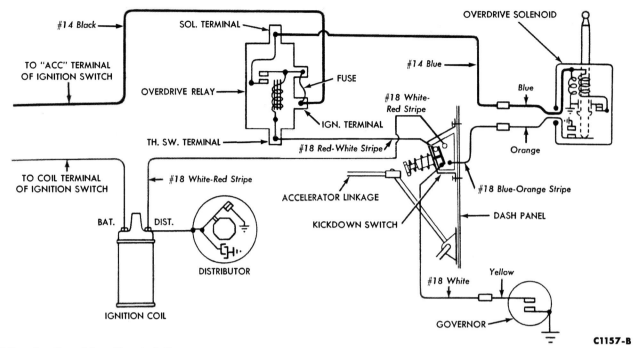

FIG. 1—Overdrive Electrical System

through 22 mph and at or about this speed the lamp should go out. If the lamp lights, and goes out at or about these speeds, the governor and governor circuit are working properly.

8. Turn the ignition switch ON and raise the car. Disconnect the yellow wire from the white wire at the governor connector.

9. Ground the white wire on the transmission case. If the relay and solenoid click, the governor circuit is working properly from the TH-SW terminal to the connector (Fig. 1), and the trouble is in the yellow wire or the governor. If the relay and solenoid do not click when the white wire is grounded, the trouble is between the TH-SW terminal and the connector (Fig. 1).

SOLENOID CIRCUIT CHECK

1. With the engine stopped and the ignition switch ON, ground the TH-SW terminal on the relay. If the relay and solenoid click as the ground is made and broken, the solenoid circuit is working properly. If the relay does not click as the TH-SW terminal is grounded, check the relay IGN terminal with a test lamp.

2. With the ignition switch ON, the test lamp should light when it is connected between the IGN terminal on the relay and at a ground. If it does not, the trouble is between the ignition switch and the IGN terminal.

3. Connect the test lamp at the other end of the fuse and at a ground. If the lamp lit at the IGN end and not at the other, replace the fuse. **Sometimes the fuse will "open" under the fuse end caps where the "open" cannot be seen.**

4. With current at both ends of the fuse, connect the test lamp between the solenoid terminal and at a ground. Ground the TH-SW terminal. The lamp should light. If it does not, replace the relay.

5. With the relay working properly, the solenoid should click when the TH-SW terminal is grounded. If it does not, connect a jumper from the SOLENOID relay terminal to the short blue wire separated from its connector near the solenoid. If the solenoid does not click when the relay closes with the jumper wire connected, replace the solenoid. If it does click, replace the wire from the SOLENOID relay terminal to the connector.

INTERRUPTER CIRCUIT CHECK

If the interrupter circuit does not ground the engine ignition momentarily when the driver depresses the accelerator pedal to the floor, the overdrive unit cannot shift from overdrive to direct.

1. The first check of the ignition interrupter circuit is at the ignition coil. The black wire which runs from the ignition coil to the kickdown switch must be connected to the DIST terminal on the coil. Sometimes this wire is improperly

connected to the BAT terminal during ignition work.

2. Disconnect the blue wire with an orange band (Fig. 1) from its connector near the solenoid, and ground it to the transmission case with a jumper.

3. With the engine running at fast idle, push the kickdown switch stem in until it bottoms (Fig. 2). When the stem bottoms, the engine should stop.

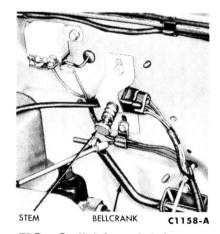

STEM   BELLCRANK   C1158-A

FIG. 2—Kickdown Switch Installation

If it does not stop, the circuit is open between the DIST terminal and the connector.

4. To check the ignition grounding contacts *inside the solenoid*, disconnect the jumper and remove the solenoid from the overdrive unit.

5. Attach the solenoid to an adapter so that the stem can extend fully when the solenoid is energized. Make sure the solenoid is grounded.

6. Connect both solenoid wires at their connectors.

7. Ground the governor wire with a jumper.

8. With the engine running at fast idle, press in on the kickdown switch stem until it bottoms. The engine should stop. If it does not, replace the solenoid.

2 CLEANING AND INSPECTION

CLEANING

Clean and inspect the transmission unit parts in the same manner as for the conventional transmission. Clean all overdrive parts thoroughly.

INSPECTION

Check the balk ring tension, as shown in Fig. 3 for a pull of 3½-5½ pounds. Read the spring scale while the balk ring is turning, because the initial effort required to start the ring turning may be considerably higher than the specified pull. Replace the assembly if the tension is not within specifications.

Check the inner surface of the free-wheel clutch outer race. If the surface is worn or "chattered," the overdrive output shaft must be replaced.

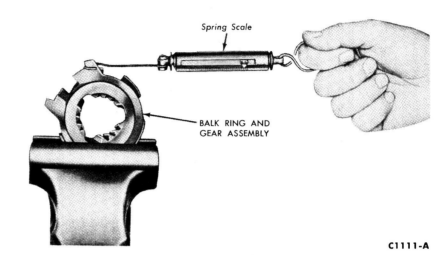

C1111-A

FIG. 3—Checking Balk Ring Tension

Check the clutch rollers for cracks and wear. Replace the complete set of 12 rollers if any are cracked or worn.

3 DESCRIPTION AND OPERATION

DESCRIPTION

The overdrive transmission is used on Fairlane cars having 289 C.I.D. engines. A transmission service identification tag is located under the upper right extension to case attaching bolt. The tag will show the transmission model and service identification code when required.

The overdrive unit is basically an automatic planetary transmission attached to the rear of a conventional three-speed transmission (Fig. 4) to provide four forward speeds instead of three. The overdrive can be mechanically locked out by a control cable located on the instrument panel.

The electrical system which controls the operation of the overdrive when the control cable is pushed in, consists of a relay, a manual kickdown switch, solenoid, governor, and the circuit wiring.

OPERATION

MECHANICAL OPERATION

Direct, Free-Wheeling Drive

When the control handle is pushed

in, the drive through the overdrive unit from start to approximately 28 mph is direct (1.00:1) and free-wheeling.

The power flow is from the transmission output shaft, through the overrunning clutch (free-wheel unit), to the overdrive main shaft (Fig. 5).

This drive is said to be free-wheeling because the overrunning clutch permits the transmission output shaft to drive the overdrive main shaft, but it does not permit the drive to reverse. **In a free-wheeling drive, the engine can drive the rear wheels, but the rear wheels cannot drive the engine.**

In direct, free-wheeling drive, the planetary gearing is in neutral, because the sun gear can run free. It can rotate clockwise (from the front), counterclockwise, or stand still, depending on the relative speeds of the planet carrier (transmission output shaft), and the internal ring gear (overdrive main shaft). At a 0.70:1 ratio, the sun gear will stand still. At a higher ratio, the sun gear will turn clockwise (from the

front). At a lower ratio than 0.70:1, it will turn counterclockwise.

Overdrive

To shift the overdrive unit from the direct (1.00:1) to overdrive (0.70:1) the sun gear is held against rotation (Fig. 5).

This is accomplished by engaging a pawl in the balk ring gear which is splined to the sun gear.

In overdrive, the power flow is from the transmission output shaft to the planet carrier splined to it, through the planet gears and then to the sun gear. With the sun gear held against rotation, the planet gears are forced to "walk around" the sun gear and drive the internal ring gear. The transmission output shaft will then drive the overdrive main shaft at a ratio of 0.70:1.

In overdrive, the overrunning clutch is uncoupled because the outer race (overdrive main shaft) is turning faster than the clutch cam (transmission output shaft). Overdrive is a two-way drive; the engine can drive the rear wheels and the rear wheels

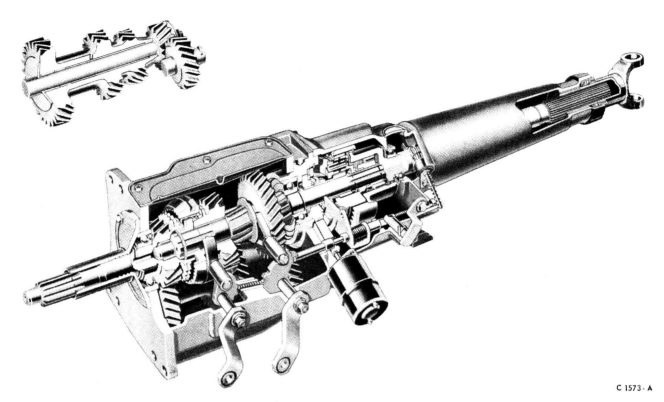

C 1573 - A

FIG. 4—Overdrive Transmission

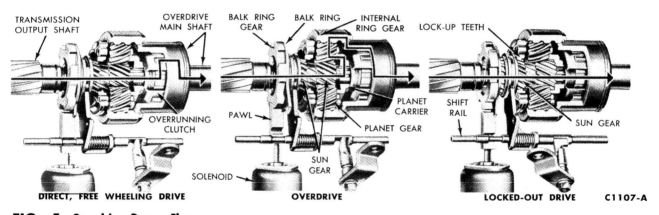

C1107-A

FIG. 5—Overdrive Power Flow

can drive the engine.

To shift from overdrive back to direct, the pawl is disengaged from the balk ring gear, permitting the sun gear to run free. The overdrive gearing is now in neutral. As soon as the speed of the transmission output shaft comes up to the speed of the overdrive main shaft, the overrunning clutch automatically locks up and direct drive is restored.

Locked-Out Drive

When the control handle is pulled out, the overdrive unit cannot function at any car speed. This lockout is accomplished by the shift rail moving the sun gear into engagement with

the lock-up teeth on the planet carrier (Fig. 5).

When the sun gear is locked to the planet carrier, the planetary gearing is locked as one mechanical unit and the transmission output shaft is locked to the overdrive main shaft. This lock-up is necessary in reverse, because the transmission output shaft reverses its rotation and therefore cannot drive the overdrive main shaft through the overrunning (one-way) clutch. The lock-up in reverse is accomplished by the low and reverse position. This locked-up drive is also necessary when the car is pushed to start the engine, since the overrunning clutch will not transmit

power from the overdrive main shaft to the transmission output shaft.

ELECTRICAL SYSTEM

The overdrive electrical system, which engages and disengages the pawl, consists of a relay, a manual kick-down switch, a solenoid, a centrifugal governor and the circuit wiring.

There are three separate circuits (Section 1, Fig. 1) in the electrical system: a governor circuit which opens and closes the relay, a solenoid circuit which supplies current through the relay to energize the solenoid, and an ignition interrupter circuit, which momentarily grounds the engine ignition for full-throttle downshift (kickdown).

Pawl Engagement

The electrical system does not operate until car speed reaches approximately 28 mph. At this speed, the governor contacts close, permitting current to flow from the battery through the relay to the solenoid.

There are two coils in the solenoid, usually referred to as the "pull-in" and "hold-in" coils. The pull-in coil is energized only while the solenoid plunger is being pulled in. As soon as the plunger is in, a set of points inside the solenoid opens the pull-in circuit.

As the plunger is pulled in, an engaging spring and a return spring are engaged.

Under pressure from the pawl engaging spring, the pawl is pushed in until it strikes the balk ring.

The usual position of the balk ring when the solenoid engaging spring pushes the pawl against it is shown in the left view of Fig. 6. When the transmission output shaft is driving the overdrive main shaft through the overrunning clutch, all elements of the planetary gearing are revolving as a unit, and in a counterclockwise (from the rear) direction. This rotates the balk ring against the pawl.

When the driver releases the throttle, the overdrive main shaft overruns the transmission output shaft. When this overrun exceeds the ratio of 0.70:1, the sun gear and balk ring reverse, releasing the pawl to engage the balk ring gear.

The position of the balk ring, should the solenoid be energized when the car is coasting (engine idling) up through 28 mph, is shown in the right view of Fig. 6. Under this condition the sun gear will be rotating clockwise (from the rear) and the pawl will be blocked.

The pawl engages when the engine speeds up, and brings the transmission output shaft up through the 0.70:1 ratio with the overdrive main shaft. This action will cause the sun gear to reverse its clockwise (from the rear) rotation and release the pawl to engage the bulk ring gear.

Pawl Disengagement

The pawl disengages under two conditions. First, when the car speed drops below approximately 22 mph, the governor opens the circuit through the relay and de-energizes the solenoid, permitting the return spring to pull out the pawl. Second, the driver may shift the overdrive back to direct drive at any road speed, by pressing the accelerator pedal to the floor so that it depresses the kickdown switch stem.

When this happens, the kickdown switch opens the governor circuit through the relay, and de-energizes the solenoid, permitting the return spring to try to pull out the pawl.

Also, it closes the interrupter circuit and grounds the ignition long enough for the return spring to pull out the pawl.

Normal ignition is restored as soon as the pawl comes out, and the solenoid stem opens the ignition grounding contacts. The actual time of ignition interruption is equal to that required for one revolution of the crankshaft.

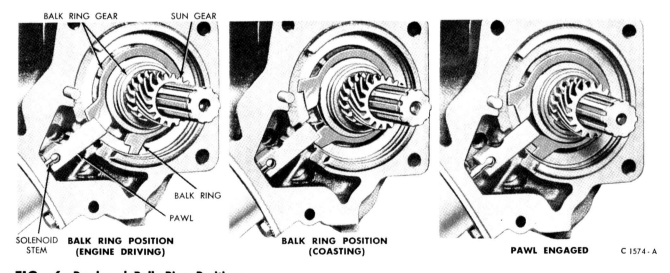

BALK RING GEAR   SUN GEAR

BALK RING

PAWL

SOLENOID STEM   **BALK RING POSITION (ENGINE DRIVING)**   **BALK RING POSITION (COASTING)**   **PAWL ENGAGED**   C 1574 - A

FIG. 6—Pawl and Balk Ring Positions

4 IN-CAR ADJUSTMENTS AND REPAIRS

OVERDRIVE CONTROL CABLE ADJUSTMENT

1. Loosen the overdrive cable lock nut at the overdrive control lever.

2. Position the overdrive cable until there is ¼ inch clearance between the cable control handle and bezel.

3. Move the overdrive control lever to the rear against the stop. When moving the lever, be careful not to move the cable out of position.

4. Tighten the control cable lock nut on the overdrive.

5 TRANSMISSION REMOVAL AND INSTALLATION

REMOVAL

The overdrive unit cannot be removed from the car as a separate assembly. Remove the transmission and overdrive unit together, following the steps detailed below:

1. Disconnect the solenoid and governor wires from the connectors near the solenoid.

2. Remove the overdrive wiring harness from its clip on the transmission.

3. Disconnect the overdrive control cable from the lever on the side of the overdrive unit and from the clamp at the solenoid.

4. Remove the overdrive transmission from the car, following the procedure given in Part 6-2 for removing the 3-speed Conventional Drive transmission.

Do not depress the clutch pedal while the transmission is removed.

INSTALLATION

The overdrive unit must be assembled and installed on the transmission before the transmission is installed in the car.

1. Install the overdrive transmission in the car, following the procedure given in Part 6-2 for installing the 3-speed Conventional Drive transmission.

2. Connect the overdrive control cable to the lever on the side of the overdrive unit. With the cable connected, there must be ¼ inch clearance between the control handle shank and the bezel when the lever at the overdrive housing is against its rear stops.

3. Connect the solenoid and governor to the connectors near the solenoid.

4. Install the overdrive wiring harness in its clip on the transmission.

6 MAJOR REPAIR OPERATIONS

DISASSEMBLY

1. Mount the transmission in a holding fixture. Then, drain the transmission and the overdrive unit.

2. Remove the solenoid retaining screw, and then rotate the solenoid about ¼ turn to remove it.

3. Remove the governor.

4. Remove the transmission cover and gasket.

5. With a sharp punch, pierce the snap ring hole cover in the overdrive housing (Fig. 7), and remove the cover.

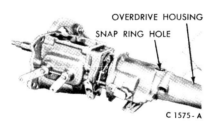

OVERDRIVE HOUSING

SNAP RING HOLE

C 1575-A

FIG. 7—Removing Overdrive Housing

6. Remove the four overdrive housing to transmission case bolts, and the overdrive control shaft pin.

7. Pull the overdrive control lever and shaft out as far as possible. Spread the snap ring that retains the overdrive output shaft bearing and then remove the overdrive housing (Fig. 7).

It may be necessary to tap the overdrive output shaft with a soft-faced hammer to free the output shaft bearing from the housing.

8. Remove the overdrive output shaft from the assembly. Catch any

of the free-wheel unit rollers that drop out. Remove the rest of the rollers.

9. Remove the speedometer gear retaining snap ring. Remove the gear and drive ball.

10. If the overdrive output shaft bearing is to be replaced use the tools shown in Fig. 8.

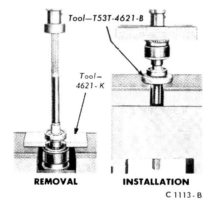

Tool—T53T-4621-B

Tool—4621-K

REMOVAL   INSTALLATION

C 1113-B

FIG. 8—Replacing Output Shaft Bearing

11. Remove the free-wheel unit retainers (Fig. 9). Then remove the clutch, planet carrier, sun gear, and shift rail.

12. Remove the snap ring from the adapter, and then remove the plate and trough, balk ring gear and pawl.

13. Remove the input shaft bearing retainer and gasket (Fig. 10).

Replace the input shaft seal with the same tools that are used on the conventional 3-speed transmission.

14. Rotate the overdrive adapter

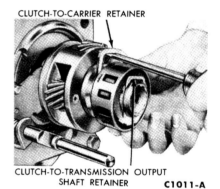

CLUTCH-TO-CARRIER RETAINER

CLUTCH-TO-TRANSMISSION OUTPUT SHAFT RETAINER   C1011-A

FIG. 9—Removing Free Wheel Unit Retainer

to expose the countershaft lock, and remove the lock.

15. With a drift, drive the countershaft toward the rear until it just clears the hole at the front of the case, support the countershaft gear with a hook then push the countershaft out of the rear with the tool shown in Fig. 11.

16. Lower the countershaft gear to the bottom of the case to provide clearance for removal of the input shaft and bearing. Tap the input shaft and bearing out of the front of the case.

17. Remove the shift lever shaft retaining pins (Fig. 12).

18. Pull the low and reverse shift lever out as far as it will go; then remove the low and reverse fork.

19. Remove the overdrive adapter and *transmission* output shaft as an assembly (Fig. 13).

20. Remove the snap ring at the front of the transmission output

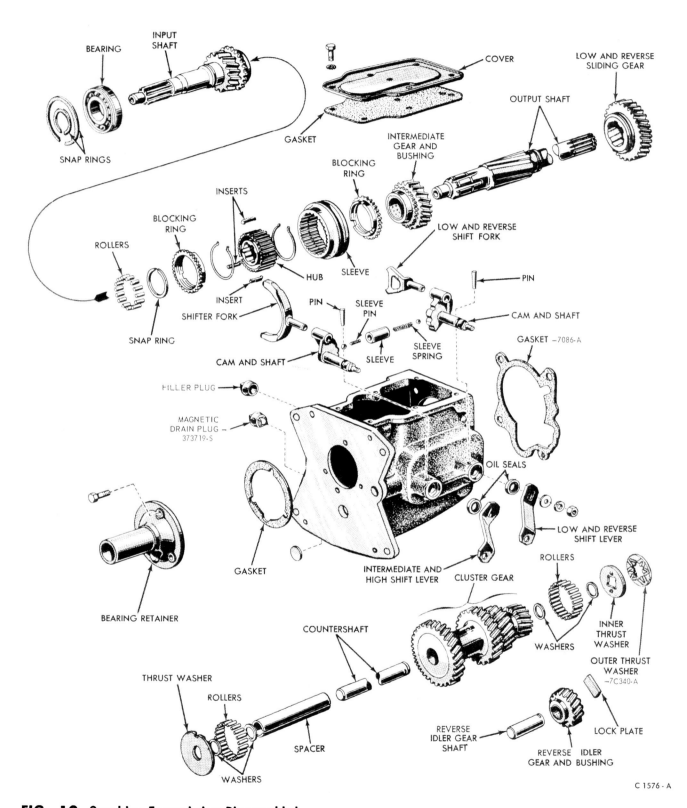

FIG. 10—Overdrive Transmission Disassembled

shaft, and then slide the synchronizer intermediate gear, and the sliding low and reverse gear off the shaft.

21. Lift the countershaft gear, thrust washers and dummy shaft from the case.

22. Drive the reverse idler gear shaft out of the rear of the case with a brass drift and a hammer, and re-

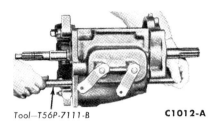

FIG. 11—Removing Countershaft

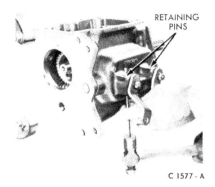

FIG. 12—Removing Shift Lever Shaft Retaining Pin

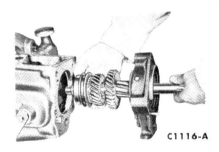

FIG. 13—Removing Output Shaft and Adapter

move the idler gear from the case.

23. Remove the lock plunger, spring, pin, and detent balls from the case (Fig. 14).

PARTS REPAIR OR REPLACEMENT

INPUT SHAFT BEARING

1. If the input shaft bearing is to be replaced, remove the snap ring that retains the bearing, and press the bearing and baffle off the shaft (Fig. 15).

2. Press a new bearing into place on the gear and shaft.

SYNCHRONIZER

1. Disassemble the synchronizer

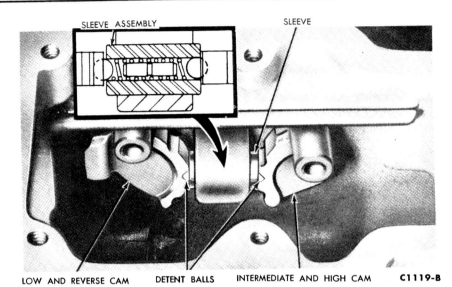

FIG. 14—Cams and Detent Balls Installed

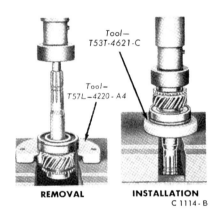

FIG. 15—Replacing Input Shaft Bearing

unit (Fig. 10) by sliding the intermediate and high sleeve off the hub. Remove the three inserts and two springs from the hub.

2. Assemble the synchronizer unit by installing the two springs on the hub and placing the three inserts in the hub. Hook one spring end in an insert as shown in Fig. 16.

3. After lining up the etched marks on the sleeve and hub splines, slide the sleeve into place on the hub.

OUTPUT SHAFT BEARING

1. Remove the snap ring which retains the output shaft in the adapter (Fig. 17), and tap the bearing out of the adapter. Remove the baffle from the adapter.

2. Remove the snap ring and press the old bearing off and the new bearing on with the tools shown in Fig. 18.

Install the snap ring to retain the bearing.

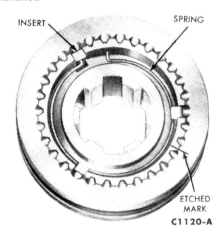

FIG. 16—Synchronizer

3. Position the baffle in the adapter (Fig. 17). Tap the bearing and shaft into place in the adapter.

4. Install the snap ring to retain the bearing.

CAM AND SHAFT SEALS

1. Remove the nuts and lock

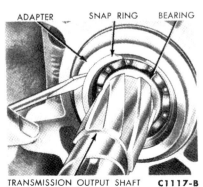

FIG. 17—Removing Output Shaft Bearing Snap Ring

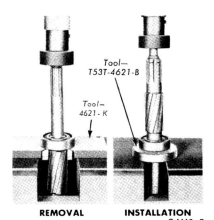

REMOVAL   INSTALLATION
C 1118 - B

FIG. 18—Replacing Output Shaft Bearing

washers that secure the levers on the cam and shaft units, and remove the levers from the shafts and cams.

2. Remove the cams and shafts, detent balls, pin, spring, and sleeve (Fig. 10) from the case.

3. Remove the seals with a suitable puller and discard.

4. Install the new seals with a suitable driver.

5. Install the intermediate and high cam and shaft assembly in the case.

6. Insert a detent ball, sleeve, spring and pin in the bore of the case. Move the cam and shaft so that the detent ball seats in the neutral (center) notch.

7. Install the low and reverse cam and shaft assembly, and then install the levers on the shafts with nuts and lock washers.

8. Install a detent ball in the sleeve at the low and reverse end. Then push the low and reverse cam toward the detent ball far enough to hold the ball in place in the neutral notch. The ball must seat in the notch of the cam.

9. Install the shift lever shaft retaining pins (Fig. 12).

10. In order to assure positive shifting, and eliminate the possibility of engaging more than one set of gears at the same time, the clearance between the ramp of one cam and the sleeve must be checked.

COUNTERSHAFT ROLLERS

1. Remove the thrust washers from each end of the countershaft.

2. Remove the dummy shaft, retainer washers, rollers, and spacer from the countershaft gear.

3. Position the spacer and the dummy shaft in the countershaft.

4. Place a retainer washer in each end of the countershaft gear.

5. Apply grease to all of the rollers and place them in each end of the countershaft gear.

6. Apply grease to the two remaining retainer washers and to the contact surface of the thrust washers. Install the retainer washers and the thrust washers on each end of the gear.

ASSEMBLY

Always use new gaskets and gasket sealer during assembly. To provide initial lubrication, apply a thin coating of lubricant on all parts before installation.

1. Position the countershaft gear, dummy shaft, and roller bearings in the case.

2. Place the case in a vertical position. Align the gear bore and the thrust washers with the bores in the case and install the countershaft.

3. Place the case in a horizontal position and check the countershaft gear end play with a feeler gauge. The end play should be 0.004-0.018 inch. If not within these limits, replace the thrust washers.

4. After establishing the correct end play, install the dummy shaft in the countershaft gear and allow the gear to remain at the bottom of the case.

5. Install the reverse idler gear in the case, with the chamfered gear teeth ends toward the front.

6. Drive the reverse idler shaft into the case, with the locking notch aligned with the countershaft hole.

7. Install the low and reverse sliding gear on the output shaft, with the shifter fork groove toward the front.

8. Install the intermediate gear on the output shaft, with the clutch teeth toward the front.

9. Place a blocking ring on the intermediate gear, and install the synchronizer assembly on the transmission output shaft, with the hub thrust surface toward the rear (Fig. 16). Install the snap ring that retains the synchronizer.

10. Install the shift forks in the cams inside the transmission case. **The offset in the low and reverse fork goes toward the front.**

11. Install a new solenoid seal in the overdrive adapter.

12. Place a new gasket on the overdrive adapter and hold it in place with gasket sealer.

13. Install the overdrive adapter

and transmission output shaft assembly in the transmission.

14. Engage the shift forks with the high and intermediate sleeve, and with the low and reverse sliding gear.

15. Seat the overdrive adapter squarely against the transmission case, and secure with a cap screw.

16. Coat the bore of the input shaft with a thin film of grease and install the pilot roller bearings.

17. Place the blocking ring on the input shaft gear and hold them in position. Move the input shaft forward to seat the output shaft pilot in the roller bearings of the input shaft.

18. Tap the input shaft and bearing into the case with a soft hammer, and at the same time line up the slots in the blocking ring with the synchronizer inserts.

19. Place a new gasket on the input shaft bearing retainer, and hold it in place with gasket sealer.

20. Install the input shaft bearing retainer to the transmission case.

21. Swing the transmission to an inverted position in the fixture.

22. Remove the cap screw holding the adapter in place. Pull the adapter outward approximately ¼ inch, and rotate it to expose the countershaft hole.

23. Work the countershaft gear into normal position by rotating the input and output shafts.

24. Push the countershaft into the case from the rear.

25. Align the slots in the countershaft with the slot in the reverse idler shaft and install the lock plate.

26. Rotate the adapter to its normal position and set it squarely against the transmission case. Check the blocking rings to make sure the slots are aligned with the synchronizer inserts.

27. Swing the transmission so that the input shaft is pointing down.

28. Place the balk ring gear assembly and pawl in the adapter (Fig. 19).

29. Place the plate and trough assembly in the adapter and install its snap ring.

30. Install the sun gear and shift rail (Fig. 20).

31. Install the planet carrier and the clutch cam. Install the retainers.

32. Install the 12 clutch rollers and hold them in position with a strong rubber band.

33. Rotate the roller cage counterclockwise (from the rear) until the rollers are off the cam surfaces.

PAWL BALK RING GEAR

INSTALL WITH MACHINED
RECESS IN THIS POSITION   C1013-A

FIG. 19—Plate and Trough Installed

The rubber band will hold them there.

34. Slide the overdrive output shaft carefully over the clutch rollers. The rubber band will not affect operation of the overdrive.

35. Align the shift rail spring with the holes in the overdrive housing.

36. Place a new gasket on the overdrive adapter, and hold it in place with gasket sealer (Fig. 21).

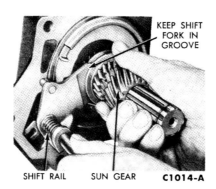

KEEP SHIFT FORK IN GROOVE

SHIFT RAIL   SUN GEAR   C1014-A

FIG. 20—Sun Gear and Shift Rail Installation

37. Install the overdrive housing over the overdrive output shaft and shift rail.

38. If the overdrive output shaft bearing snap ring does not drop into its groove when the housing is seated squarely on the adapter, pry the overdrive output shaft bearing toward the rear, working through the snap ring hole. Install the overdrive housing attaching bolts.

39. Engage the overdrive shaft lever by pushing it inward. The lever is correctly engaged when a spring load is apparent as the lever is pushed forward.

40. Install the retaining pin in the overdrive housing to hold the control shaft in place.

41. If the overdrive housing bushing and seal are to be replaced, use the same tools which are used on conventional transmissions.

42. Thread the governor into the overdrive housing.

43. Position the solenoid in the adapter. Rotate the solenoid ¼ turn from normal position so that the half ball on the solenoid stem can engage the pawl.

If the solenoid stem is properly engaged, the solenoid cannot be removed from the overdrive in its normal position. Any attempt to pull it out will merely compress the engaging spring in the solenoid. Install the two solenoid attaching screws.

44. Install the drain plugs in the transmission case and in the overdrive housing. Make sure the magnetic plugs are installed in the bottom of the case.

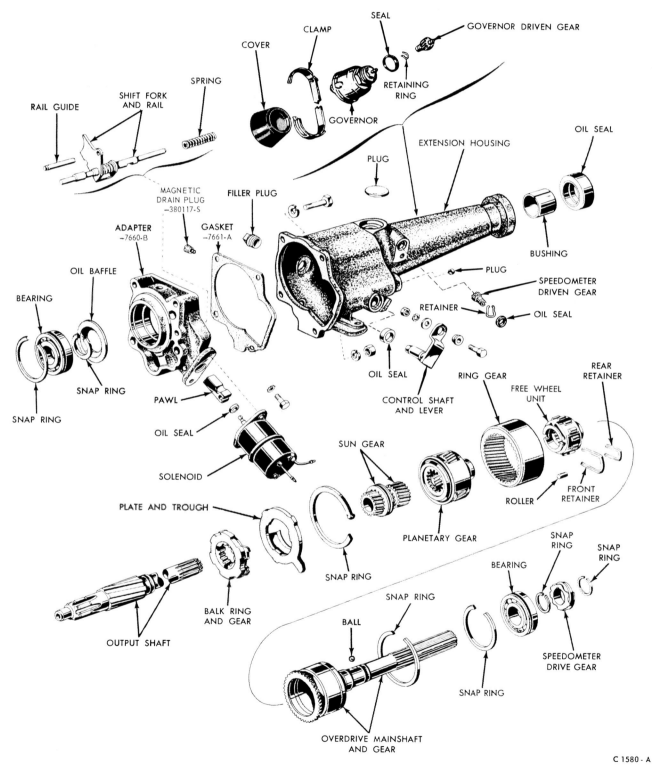

FIG. 21—Overdrive Unit Disassembled

PART 6-7
SPECIFICATIONS

THREE-SPEED TRANSMISSION—2.77

GEAR RATIOS

Car Usage	Transmission Model	Engine C.I.D.	Gear			
			First Speed	Second Speed	Third Speed	Reverse
Falcon	HED-BH	170-1V	3.29	1.83	1.00:1	4.46
Falcon Ranchero	HED-BJ	170-1V	3.29	1.83	1.00:1	4.46
Mustang	HED-BG	200-1V	2.76	1.69	1.00:1	3.74
Falcon, Comet, Fairlane	HED-BF	200-1V	2.76	1.69	1.00:1	3.74

CLEARANCES

Description	Inches
Cam Ramp to Interlock Shift Sleeve—Clearance	0.001-0.013
(5) Interlock Shift Sleeve Available—Length	1.286-1.288
Countershaft Gear End Play	0.004-0.018

TORQUE LIMITS

Description	Ft-Lbs
Extension Housing Bolts—$^7/_{16}$—14 —⅜—16	42-50
Input Shaft Bearing Retainer to Transmission Case Bolts	30-36
Transmission to Flywheel Housing Bolts	37-42
Transmission Cover to Transmission Case Bolts	14-19
Engine Rear Support to Extension Housing Bolt	18-24
Engine Rear Support to Extension Housing Bracket Nut	18-24
Gear Shift Levers to Cam and Shaft Assembly Lock Nuts	14-19
Filler Plug to Case	10-15
Drain Plug to Case	20-30

LUBRICANT REFILL CAPACITIES

Application	Pints (Approximate)
All Models	2

LUBRICANTS & SEALERS

Application	Material
Transmission	Mild EP Gear Oil C3RZ 19547-B
Main Shaft Roller Bearing Countershaft Gear Roller Bearing	Lube Grease M-4659
Bolts and Gaskets	Sealer M-4G91-B
Steering Column Lower Plate	Lithium Base Grease (No Polyethylene) C3VY-19586-A

THREE-SPEED TRANSMISSION—3.03

GEAR RATIOS

Car Usage	Transmission Model	Engine C.I.D.	Ratio			
			First Speed	Second Speed	Third Speed	Reverse
Fairlane	HEF-CX	200-1V H.D. 289-2V-4V	2.99	1.75	1.00:1	3.17
Fairlane and Comet	HEG-W HEG-X	390-2V-4V	2.42	1.61	1.00:1	2.33
Falcon and Comet	HEF-CX	289-2V-4V	2.99	1.75	1.00:1	3.17
Mustang	HEF-CW	289-2V-4V	2.99	1.75	1.00:1	3.17

THREE-SPEED TRANSMISSION—3.03 (Continued)
CLEARANCES

Description	Inches
Countershaft Gear End Play	0.004-0.018
Reverse Idler Gear End Play	0.004-0.018

LUBRICANTS & SEALERS

Application	Material
Transmission	Mild EP Gear Oil C3RZ 19547-B
Main Shaft Roller Bearing / Countershaft Gear Roller Bearing	Lube Grease M-4659
Bolts and Gaskets	Sealer M-4G91-B
Steering Column Lower Plate	Lithium Base Grease (No Polyethylene) C3VY-19586-A

LUBRICANT REFILL CAPACITIES

Application	Pints (Approximate)
All Models	3.5

TORQUE LIMITS

Description	Ft-Lbs.
Input Shaft Bearing Retainer to Transmission Case	30-36
Extension Housing to Transmission Case	42-50
Access Cover to Transmission Case	14-19
Gear Shift Control Levers to Cam and Shaft	18-23
Shift Fork to Shift Rail	10-18
Filler Plug to Case	10-15
Drain Plug to Case	20-30
Transmission to Flywheel Housing	37-42
Detent Set Screw (Special)	*

*Flush to 0.020 inches below top of case.

DAGENHAM FOUR-SPEED TRANSMISSION

GEAR RATIOS

Transmission Model	Vehicle Usage	Engine C.I.D.	1st	2nd	3rd	4th	Rev.
HEJ-E	Mustang	200-IV	3.16	2.21	1.41	1.1	3.34

CLEARANCES

Description	Inches
Countershaft Gear End Play	0.008-0.022

TORQUES

Description	Ft.-Lbs.
Extension Housing to Case Bolts	40-45
Flywheel Housing to Case Bolts	40-45
Flywheel Housing to Engine Bolts	23-28
Input Shaft Bearing Retainer Bolts	12-15
Output Shaft Bearing Nut	20-25
Shift Housing Retaining Bolts	12-15
Shift Lever to Linkage Cap Screws	15-20
Shift Rod Lock Nuts	15-20

FORD FOUR-SPEED TRANSMISSION

GEAR RATIOS

Trans. Model	Vehicle Usage	Engine Displacement	1st	2nd	3rd	4th	Rev.
HEH-BV	Falcon, Comet, Fairlane	289-2V 289-2V & 4V	2.78	1.93	1.36	Direct	2.78
HEH-AR	Fairlane Comet	390-2V & 4V	2.32	1.69	1.29	Direct	2.32
HEH-BW	Mustang	289-4V	2.78	1.93	1.36	Direct	2.78
HEH-BX	Mustang	289-4V H.P.	2.32	1.69	1.29	Direct	2.32

FORD FOUR-SPEED TRANSMISSION (Continued)
TORQUES

Description	Part Name	Ft-Lbs.
Input Shaft Bearing Retainer to Transmission Case	Bolt— 5/16-18 x ¾ Hex Head	19-25
Extension Housing to Transmission Case	Bolt—7/16-14 x 1¼ Hex Head	42-50
Access Cover to Transmission Case	Screw—15/16-18 x ⅝ Hex Head Screw—5/16-18 x 1 Hex Head	14-19
Gear Shift Lever to Cam and Shaft	Nut—⅜-24 Hex	18-23
Shift Fork to Shift Rail	Screw—5/16-24 x .92 Set Locking	10-18
Filler Plug to Case	Plug—½-14	10-20
Drain Plug to Case	Plug—½-14 (Magnetic)	20-30
Detent Set Screw (Special)	Screw—⅜-16 x .88 Set	Flush to 0.020" below surface
Third and Fourth Shift Rail Detent Bolt	Bolt—⅜-16 x .38 Hex Head	10-18
Transmission to Flywheel Housing Bolts	Bolt—7/16-14	37-42

LUBRICANT REFILL CAPACITIES

Application	Pints (Approximate)
All Models	4

LUBRICANTS & SEALERS

Application	Material
Transmission	Mild EP Gear Oil C3RZ 19547-B
Main Shaft Roller Bearing Countershaft Gear Roller Bearing	Lube Grease M-4659
Bolts and Gaskets	Sealer M-4G91-B
Shift Linkage, Trunnions and External Shift Mechanism Steering Column Lower Plate	Lithium Base Grease (No Polyethylene) C3VY-19586-A

CLEARANCES

Description	Inches
Countershaft Gear End Play	0.004-0.018
Reverse Idler Gear End Play	0.004-0.018

OVERDRIVE

GEAR RATIOS

Trans. Model	Trans. Assy. Part Number	Vehicle Usage	Engine Displacement	Ratios				
				1st	2nd	3rd	Rev.	O.D.
HEK-X	C50R-7003-N	Fairlane	289-2V	2.80	1.69	Direct	3.80	.70

TORQUE SPECIFICATIONS

Description	Ft-Lbs.
Input Shaft Bearing Retainer to Transmission Case Bolt	12-15
Transmission to Flywheel Housing Bolts	37-42
Gearshift Housing to Transmission Case Bolts	12-15
Transmission Extension Housing to Case Bolts or Nuts	42-50
Gearshift Control Levers to Cam and Shaft Assembly Nuts	12-15
Overdrive Assembly to Transmission Case Nuts	37-42
Engine Rear Support to Extension Housing Bolts	35-40
Filler Plug to Case	10-20
Drain Plug to Case (Magnetic)	20-30

LUBRICANTS & SEALERS

Application	Material
Transmission	Mild EP Gear Oil C3RZ-19547-B
Main Shaft Roller Bearing Countershaft Gear Roller Bearing	Lube Grease M-4659
Bolts and Gaskets	Sealer M-4G91-B
Steering Column Lower Plate	Lithium Base Grease (No Polyethylene) C3VY 19586-A

TRANSMISSION COMPONENT END PLAY

Component	End Play
Countershaft Gear to Case	0.004-0.018
Cam Ramp to Interlock Shift Sleeve—Clearance	0.001-0.007

LUBRICANT REFILL CAPACITIES

Application	Pints (Approximate)
Fairlane	3.7

SERVICE TOOLS

Tool Numbers	Description
T50T-100A	Impact Hammer—Long
T59L-100B	Impact Hammer—Short
T58L-101A	Puller Attachment
1175AB	Grease Seal Remover
T57L-4220-A	Differential Bearing Assembly Remover
T53T-4621-B or (4621-F)	Drive Pinion Bearing Cone Replacer Front & Rear
T53T-4621-C	Drive Pinion Bearing Cone Replacer
T-4621-K	Drive Pinion Bearing Cone Replacer
T53T-4242-F11	Differential Side Bearing Cone Replacer or Input Shaft Bearing Remover
6135-G	Piston Pin Remover & Replacer
T52T-6500 DJD (6500-D)	Solid Tappet Remover or Reverse Shift Rail Pliers
T52L-7000 GAE	Extension Housing Bushing and Seal Remover
	Extension Housing Bushing Installer
T57T-7003-A	Transmatic Drive Bushing Replacer
T63P-7025-A	Output Shaft Bearing Remover & Replacer
T64P-7025-B	Output Shaft Bearing Remover & Replacer

SERVICE TOOLS (Continued)

Tool Numbers	Description
T-7025B	Rear Main Shaft Bearing Remover
T-7025G	Main Shaft Bearing Remover & Replacer
T57L-7111-A	Cluster Gear Roller Retainer Shaft
T60K-7111-A	Cluster Gear Roller Retainer Shaft
T62K-7111-A	Cluster Gear Roller Retainer Shaft
T64P-7111-A	Cluster Gear Roller Retainer Shaft
T56P-7111-B	Cluster Gear Roller Retainer Shaft
T63P-7111-B	Cluster Gear Roller Retainer Shaft
T64P-7140-A	Reverse Idler Shaft Remover
T57L-7657-A	Transmission Extension Housing Oil Seal Replacer
T64P-7657-A	Transmission Extension Housing Oil Seal Replacer
760K-7657-B (7657-G)	Transmission Extension Housing Oil Seal Replacer
T7688	Lockout Lever Oil Seal Replacer
T60K-7697-A	Transmission Extension Housing Bushing Remover
T57P-77047-A	Transmission Input Shaft Oil Seal Replacer —Standard Transmission
T60K-77047-A	Transmission Input Shaft Oil Seal Replacer— Standard Transmission

AUTOMATIC TRANSMISSION

GROUP 7

PART 7-1   PAGE
GENERAL TRANSMISSION SERVICE ..**7- 1**

PART 7-2
C4 AUTOMATIC DUAL RANGE
TRANSMISSION **7-15**

PART 7-3   PAGE
C6 AUTOMATIC DUAL RANGE
TRANSMISSION **7-53**

PART 7-4
SPECIFICATIONS **7-82**

PART 7-1

GENERAL TRANSMISSION SERVICE

Section   **Page**

1 Diagnosis and Testing........................7- 1
   Transmission Fluid Level Check..............7- 1
   Fluid Aeration Check........................7- 1
   Transmission Fluid Leakage Checks...........7- 1
   Fluid Leakage Converter Area................7- 2
   Converter Leakage Check....................7- 3
   Engine Idle Speed Check....................7- 3
   Anti-Stall Dashpot Clearance Check..........7- 3
   Manual Linkage Checks......................7- 4
   Control pressure and Vacuum Diaphragm Unit
     Check....................................7- 4
   Stall Test.................................7- 7
   Initial Engagement Checks..................7- 7

Section   **Page**

   Shift Point Checks.........................7- 7
   Air Pressure Checks........................7- 7
   Diagnosis Guide
     C4 Automatic Dual Range Diagnosis Guide..7- 9
     C6 Automatic Dual Range Diagnosis Guide..7-10

2 Common Adjustments and Repairs
   Transmission Fluid Drain and Refill..........7- 8
   Oil Cooler Flushing Procedure...............7-11
   Oil Cooler Tube Replacement................7-11

3 Cleaning and Inspection
   Cleaning..................................7-11
   Inspection................................7-12

1   DIAGNOSIS AND TESTING

When diagnosing transmission problems, first refer to the diagnosis guide for detailed information on the items that could be causing the problem. The following preliminary checks should be made in the order given:

1. Check the fluid level. Check the fluid for a burnt clutch plate odor.
2. Check the engine idle speed and dashpot adjustments.
3. Check the manual linkage adjustment.
4. Check the accelerator pedal height and downshift linkage.
5. Check the throttle linkage to assure wide open throttle operation.
6. Check the engine for proper operation.

TRANSMISSION FLUID LEVEL CHECK

1. Make sure that the vehicle is standing level. Then firmly apply the parking brake.

2. Run the engine at normal idle speed. If the transmission fluid is cold, run the engine at fast idle speed (about 1200 rpm) until the fluid reaches its normal operating temperature. When the fluid is warm, slow the engine down to normal idle speed.

3. Shift the selector lever through all positions, and place the lever at P. Do not turn off the engine during the fluid level checks.

4. Clean all dirt from the transmission fluid dipstick cap before removing the dipstick from the filler tube.

5. Pull the dipstick out of the tube, wipe it clean, and push it all the way back into the tube.

6. Pull the dipstick out of the tube again, and check the fluid level. If necessary, add enough fluid to the transmission through the filler tube to raise the fluid level to the F (full) mark on the dipstick. **Do not overfill the transmission.**

FLUID AERATION CHECK

A fluid level that is too high will cause the fluid to become aerated. Aerated fluid will cause low control pressure, and the aerated fluid may be forced out the vent.

Check the transmission fluid level. Low fluid level can affect the operation of the transmission, and may indicate fluid leaks that could cause transmission damage.

TRANSMISSION FLUID LEAKAGE CHECKS

Check the speedometer cable connection at the transmission. Leakage at the oil pan gasket often can be stopped by tightening the attaching bolts to the proper torque. If necessary, replace the gasket. Check the fluid filler tube connection at the transmission. If the filler tube O-ring seal is leaking, replace the seal.

The transmission fluid is water cooled; check the fluid lines and fittings between the transmission and the cooler in the radiator tank for looseness, wear, or damage. If leakage cannot be stopped by tightening a fitting, replace the defective parts.

Check the engine coolant in the radiator. If transmission fluid is present in the coolant, the cooler in the radiator tank is probably leaking.

The cooler can be further checked for leaks by disconnecting the lines at the cooler fittings and applying 5 psi air pressure to the fittings. The radiator cap must be removed when making this check to relieve the pressure on the exterior side of the cooler. If the cooler is leaking and will not hold this pressure, the radiator must be replaced. **The cooler cannot be replaced separately.**

If leakage is found at either the throttle lever shaft or the manual lever shaft, replace either or both seals.

Inspect the pipe plug in the case. If the plug shows leakage, torque the plug to specification. If tightening does not stop the leaks, replace the plug.

On a C6 transmission the TV pressure port plug on the right rear side of the case must also be inspected.

When converter drain plugs leak, remove the two drain plugs with a six-point wrench. Coat the threads with FoMoCo Perfect Sealing Compound or its equivalent, and install the plugs. Torque the drain plugs to specification. **Fluid leakage from the converter housing may be caused by engine oil leaking past the rear main bearing or from oil gallery plugs. Be sure to determine the exact cause of the leak.**

Oil-soluble aniline or fluorescent dyes premixed at the ratio of ½ teaspoon of dye powder to ½ pint of transmission fluid have proved helpful in locating the source of the fluid leakage. Such dyes may be used to determine whether an engine oil or transmission fluid leak is present, or if the fluid in the oil cooler leaks into the engine coolant system. A black light, however, must be used with the fluorescent dye solution.

FLUID LEAKAGE CONVERTER AREA

In diagnosing and correcting fluid leaks in the front pump and converter area, use the following procedures to facilitate locating the exact cause of the leakage. Leakage at the front of the transmission, as evidenced by fluid around the converter housing, may have several sources. By careful observation, it is possible, in many instances, to pinpoint the source of the leak before removing the transmission from the car. The paths which the fluid takes to reach the bottom of the converter housing are shown in Fig. 1.

1. Fluid leaking by the front pump seal lip will tend to move along the drive hub and onto the back of the impeller housing. Except in the case of a total seal failure, fluid leakage by the lip of the seal will be deposited on the inside of the converter housing only, near the outside diameter of the housing.

2. Fluid leakage by the outside diameter of the seal and front pump body will follow the same path as leaks by the front pump seal or may run down the face of the front pump.

3. Fluid that leaks by a front pump and converter housing to case bolts will be deposited on the inside of the converter housing only. Fluid will not be deposited on the back of the converter.

4. Leakage by the front pump to case and O-ring seal may cause fluid

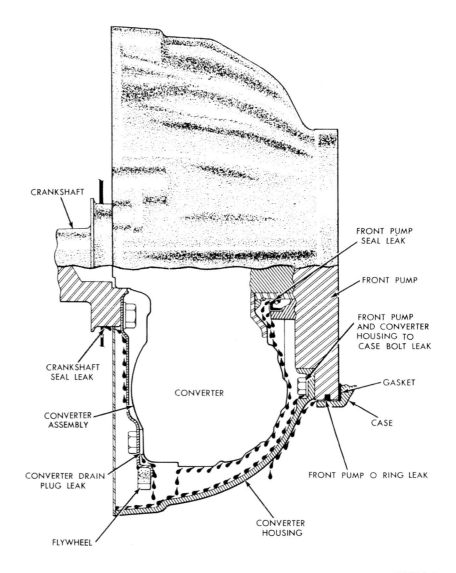

FIG. 1—**Typical Converter Area Leakage Checks**

D1513-A

to be deposited on the outside lower part of the converter housing as shown in Fig. 1.

5. Fluid leakage from the converter drain plugs will appear at the outside diameter of the converter.

Engine oil leaks are sometimes improperly diagnosed as front pump seal leaks. The following areas of possible leakage should also be checked to determine if engine oil leakage is causing the problem:

(a) Leakage at the rocker arm cover (valley cover) may allow oil to flow over the converter housing or seep down between the converter housing and cylinder block causing oil to be present in or at the bottom of the converter housing.

(b) Oil gallery plug leaks will allow oil to flow down the rear face of the block to the bottom of the converter housing.

(c) Leakage by the crankshaft seal will work back to the flywheel, and then into the converter housing.

Fluid leakage from other areas, forward of the transmission could cause fluid to be present around the converter housing due to blow-back or road draft.

The following procedure should be used to determine the cause of leakage before any repairs are made:

(a) Remove the transmission dipstick and note the color of the fluid. Original factory fill fluid is dyed red to aid in determining if leakage is

from the engine or transmission. Unless a considerable amount of make-up fluid has been added or the fluid has been changed, the red color should assist in pinpointing the leak.

Since road draft may cause leaking valley cover oil to be present on the transmission, this leakage, if present, should be eliminated before performing work on the transmission.

(b) Remove the converter lower housing cover. Clean off any fluid from the top and bottom of the converter housing, front of the transmission case, and rear face of the engine and engine oil pan. Clean the converter area by washing with suitable non-flammable solvent, and blow dry with compressed air.

(c) Wash out the converter housing, the front of the flywheel, and the converter drain plugs. The converter housing may be washed out using cleaning solvent and a squirt-type oil can. Blow all washed areas dry with compressed air.

(d) Start and run the engine until the transmission reaches its normal operating temperature. Observe the back of the block and top of the converter housing for evidence of fluid leakage. Raise the car on a hoist and run the engine at fast idle, then at engine idle, occasionally shifting to the drive and reverse ranges to increase pressures within the transmission. Observe the front

of the flywheel, back of the block (in as far as possible), and inside the converter housing (Fig. 1). Run the engine until fluid leakage is evident and the probable source of leakage can be determined.

CONVERTER LEAKAGE CHECK

During the above fluid leakage checks, if there are indications that the welds on the torque converter are leaking, the converter will have to be removed and the following check made before the unit is replaced:

A leak checking tool (Fig. 2), can be made from standard parts.

1. Install the plug in the converter (Fig. 3) and expand it by tightening the wing nut. Attach the safety chains.

2. Install the air valve in one of the drain plug holes.

3. Introduce air pressure into the converter housing. Check the pressure with a tire gauge and adjust it to 20 psi.

4. Place the converter in a tank of water. Observe the weld areas for bubbles. If no bubbles are observed, it may be assumed that the welds are not leaking.

ENGINE IDLE SPEED CHECK

Check and, if necessary, adjust the engine idle speed, using the procedure given in Group 10.

If the idle speed is too low, the engine will run roughly. An idle speed that is too high will cause the car to creep when the transmission is shifted into gear and will cause rough transmission engagement.

ANTI-STALL DASHPOT CLEARANCE CHECK

After the engine idle speed has been properly adjusted, check the

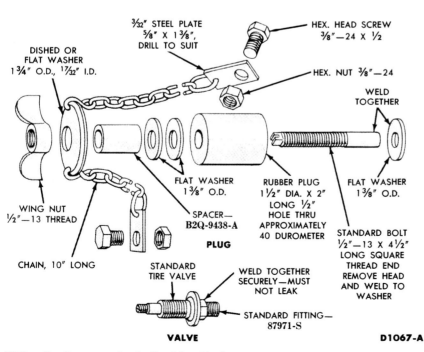

FIG. 2—Converter Leak Checking Tool

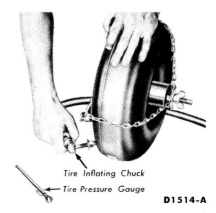

Tire Inflating Chuck
Tire Pressure Gauge

D1514-A

FIG. 3—Typical Converter Leak Checking Tool

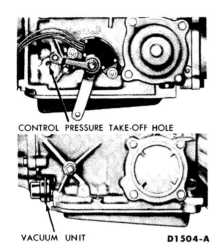

CONTROL PRESSURE TAKE-OFF HOLE

VACUUM UNIT　　　　　D1504-A

FIG. 4—Vacuum Diaphragm and Control Pressure Connecting Point—C4 Transmission

anti-stall dashpot clearance. Follow the procedure given in Group 10 for checking and adjusting this clearance.

MANUAL LINKAGE CHECKS

Correct manual linkage adjustment is necessary to position the manual valve for proper fluid pressure direction to the different transmission components. Improperly adjusted manual linkage may cause cross-leakage and subsequent transmission failure. Refer to Linkage Adjustments for detailed manual linkage adjustment procedures.

CONTROL PRESSURE AND VACUUM DIAPHRAGM UNIT CHECK

When the vacuum diaphragm unit (Fig. 4) is operating properly and

the downshift linkage is adjusted properly, all the transmission shifts (automatic and kickdown) should occur within the road speed limits specified in the Specification Section.

If the automatic shifts do not occur within limits or the transmission slips during shift points, the following procedure is suggested to separate engine, transmission, linkage, and diaphragm unit or valve body problems.

1. Attach a tachometer to the engine and a vacuum gauge to the transmission vacuum line at the vacuum unit (Fig. 6).
2. Attach a pressure gauge to the control pressure outlet at the transmission (Fig. 5).
3. Firmly apply the parking brake and start the engine.
4. Adjust the engine idle speed to the specified rpm. If the engine idle speed cannot be brought within limits by adjustment at the carburetor idle adjustment screw, check the throttle and downshift linkage for a binding condition. If the linkage is satisfactory, check for vacuum leaks in the transmission diaphragm unit (Fig. 7), and its connecting tubes and hoses. Check all other vacuum operated units for vacuum leaks.

VACUUM UNIT CHECK

To check the vacuum unit for diaphragm leakage, remove the unit from the transmission. Use a distributor tester equipped with a vacuum pump (Fig. 7). Set the regulator knob so that the vacuum gauge reads 18 inches with the end of the vacuum hose blocked off.

Then connect the vacuum hose to

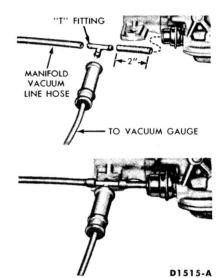

"T" FITTING
MANIFOLD VACUUM LINE HOSE
2"
TO VACUUM GAUGE
D1515-A

FIG. 6—Typical Vacuum Test Line Connections

the transmission vacuum unit. If the gauge still reads 18 inches, the vacuum unit diaphragm **is not leaking.** As the hose is removed from the transmission vacuum unit, hold a finger over the end of the control rod. When the hose is removed, the internal spring of the vacuum unit should push the control rod outward.

CONTROL PRESSURE TESTS

The test results of the following checks should agree with the specifications given in Tables 1 and 2. When performing control pressure tests, make certain that the service brake pedal is held in the applied position.

TEST NUMBER 1—CONTROL PRESSURE CHECK AT ENGINE IDLE

1. With the transmission in neu-

Tool – T57L-77820-A

TV PRESSURE PORT
VACUUM DIAPHRAGM

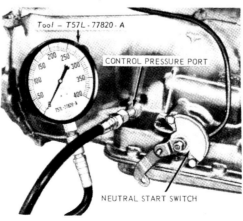

Tool – T57L-77820-A
CONTROL PRESSURE PORT
NEUTRAL START SWITCH
D1643-A

FIG. 5—Vacuum Diaphragm and Control and TV Pressure Connecting Points—C6 Transmission

D1302-A

FIG. 7—Testing Transmission Vacuum Unit for Leakage

TABLE 1—C4 Transmission
CONTROL PRESSURE AT ZERO OUTPUT SHAFT SPEED

Test No.	Engine Speed or Manifold Vacuum	Throttle Position	Shift Selector Lever Position	[1]Control (Line) Pressure (psi)
1	Idle—Above 18 Inches of Vacuum	Closed	P, N, D1, D2, L	55-62
			R	55-100
2	17.0 Approximate Inches of Vacuum	As Required	D1, D2, L	Line Pressure Increase
3	10 Inches of Vacuum	As Required	D1, D2, L	96-105
4	3 Inches of Vacuum	As Required	D1, D2, L	138-148
			R	215-227

[1]Transmission oil at normal operating temperature.

TABLE 2—C6 Transmission
CONTROL PRESSURE AT ZERO OUTPUT SHAFT SPEED

Test No.	Engine Speed or Manifold Vacuum	Throttle Position	Shift Selector Lever Position	[1]Control (Line) Pressure (psi)
1	Idle—Above 17 Inches of Vacuum	Closed	P, N, D1, D2, L	51-66
			R	72-108
2	15 Approximate inches of Vacuum	As Required	D1, D2, L	Line Pressure Increase
3	10 Inches of Vacuum	As Required	D1, D2, L	90-109
4	1 Inch or Less of Vacuum	To & Thru Detent	D1, D2, L	152-167
			R	225-247

[1]Transmission fluid at normal operating temperature.

tral, and at the correct engine idle, the vacuum gauge should show a minimum of 18 inches at sea level for the C4 transmission or 17 inches for the C6 transmission. If the vacuum reading is lower than 18 inches, an engine problem is indicated or there is leakage in the vacuum line. Make necessary repairs to obtain a minimum vacuum reading of 18 inches for the C4 transmission or 17 inches for the C6 transmission.

At engine idle, check the transmission control pressure gauge at all selector lever positions. Transmission control pressures should agree with the specifications in Tables 1 and 2.

At altitudes above sea level, it may not be possible to obtain 18 inches vacuum at engine idle. At these altitudes with idle vacuum of less than 18 inches, refer to the following specifications to determine idle speed control pressure in forward driving ranges.

C4 TRANSMISSION

Engine Vacuum (At Idle)	Control Pressure (psi)
17 Inches	55-62
16 Inches	55-68
15 Inches	55-74
14 Inches	55-80
13 Inches	55-87
12 Inches	55-93
11 Inches	55-99

C6 TRANSMISSION

Engine Vacuum (At Idle)	Control Pressure (psi)
17 inches	51-66
16 inches	51-72
15 inches	51-78
14 inches	51-84
13 inches	51-90
12 inches	51-97
11 inches	51-103

2. At engine idle, depress and release the accelerator pedal quickly and observe the vacuum gauge. The amount of vacuum should decrease and increase with the changes in throttle openings. If the vacuum response to changes in throttle opening is too slow the vacuum line to the diaphragm unit could be restricted. **Make the necessary repairs before completing the test.**

TEST NUMBER 2—CONTROL PRESSURE INCREASE CHECK —C4 TRANSMISSION

The control pressure increase should be checked in all ranges except Park and Neutral. Shift the transmission into D1, D2, L, and R, and check control pressure increase in each range. With the correct control pressure at engine idle, advance the throttle until the engine vacuum reading is approximately 17.0 inches. As the vacuum gauge reading decreases into these specifications, **the control pressure should start to increase.**

Control pressure increase may be noted immediately when the throttle is opened due to the increased pump output, resulting from increased engine rpm. When this happens, the pressure increase point can be checked by using a distributor vacuum tester. Install the distributor tester vacuum line on the diaphragm assembly. Adjust the tester to provide over 18 inches of vacuum. Increase the engine to 600-700 rpm. Replace the tester vacuum reading to approximately 17.0 inches and observe the transmission pressure gauge for the pressure increase.

TEST NUMBER 2—CONTROL PRESSURE INCREASE CHECK —C6 TRANSMISSION

A control pressure check should be made at 15 inches of vacuum in D1, D2 and L. Advance the throttle until the engine vacuum reading is 15 inches, then check the control pressure regulation. Control pressure should be as shown in Table 2.

TEST NUMBER 3—CONTROL PRESSURE CHECK AT 10 INCHES OF VACUUM

A control pressure check should be made at 10 inches of vacuum in D1, D2, and L. Advance the throttle until the engine vacuum reading is 10 inches and check the control pressure regulation. Control pressure should be as shown in Tables 1 and 2.

TEST NUMBER 4—CONTROL PRESSURE CHECK AT THREE INCHES OF VACUUM—C4 AND C6 TRANSMISSION

Check control pressure at three inches of vacuum in D1, D2, and L. The control pressure should be as shown in Tables 1 and 2. Then move the selector lever to R. With the vacuum at three inches the control pressure should be as shown in Tables 1 and 2.

While making this pressure test, do not hold the throttle open for more than five seconds in each detent position. Between each test move the selector lever to neutral and run the engine at 1000 rpm for fifteen seconds to cool the converter.

If the vacuum and pressure gauge readings are within specifications, the diaphragm unit and transmission control pressure regulating system are operating properly.

If the transmission control pressure is too low, too high, fails to rise with throttle opening, or is extremely erratic, use the procedure given under the following appropriate heading to resolve the problem.

CONTROL PRESSURE TEST RESULTS

TEST NUMBER 1—CONTROL PRESSURE IS LOW AT ENGINE IDLE

If control pressure at engine idle is low in all selector lever positions, trouble other than the diaphragm unit is indicated.

When control pressure at engine idle is low in all ranges, check for excessive leakage in the front oil pump, case, and control valve body, or a sticking control pressure regulator valve.

TEST NUMBER 1—CONTROL PRESSURE IS HIGH AT ENGINE IDLE

If transmission control pressure at engine *idle is too high* in all ranges, the trouble may be in the diaphragm unit or its connecting vacuum tubes and hoses, throttle valve, or control rod.

With the engine idling, disconnect the hose from the diaphragm unit and check the engine manifold vacuum. Hold a thumb over the end of the hose and check for vacuum. If the engine speeds up when the hose is disconnected and slows down as the thumb is held against the end of

the hose, the vacuum source is satisfactory.

Stop the engine, and remove the diaphragm unit and the diaphragm unit control rod. Inspect the control rod for a bent condition and for corrosion. Check the diaphragm unit for leakage with the distributor tester.

TEST NUMBER 2—CONTROL PRESSURE DOES NOT INCREASE WITH VACUUM AT APPROXIMATELY 17.0 INCHES —C4 TRANSMISSION

When the control pressure is within specifications at engine idle, but does not increase as the vacuum is decreased to the specified limits, first check the control rod between the vacuum unit and throttle valve for proper engagement. If the control rod is not assembled into the end of the throttle valve or vacuum unit, the valve cannot regulate throttle pressure to increase control pressure. Next check for a stuck primary throttle valve, pressure booster valve, or a stuck control pressure regulator valve.

If control pressure increases before or after vacuum is decreased to approximately 17.0 inches, check for a leaking diaphragm assembly, bent diaphragm can, or worn or bent control rod.

TEST NUMBER 2—CONTROL PRESSURE NOT WITHIN LIMITS AT 15 INCHES OF VACUUM—C6 TRANSMISSION

If the control pressure is within specification at engine idle, but has not risen to the specified range at 15 inches of vacuum, make the checks outlined in test number 2 to isolate and correct the cause.

TESTS NUMBER 3 AND 4— CONTROL PRESSURE NOT WITHIN LIMITS AT 10 OR 3 INCHES OF VACUUM—(C4) OR AT 1.0 INCH OR LESS (C6)

If idle pressure and pressure point increase are within specifications but pressures at 10 or 3 inches of vacuum on the C4 transmission or 1.0 inch or less on the C6 transmission are not within specification in all ranges, excessive leakage, low pump capacity, or a restricted oil pan screen is indicated.

If pressures are not within specifications for specific selector lever positions only, this indicates excessive leakage in the clutch or servo circuits used in those ranges.

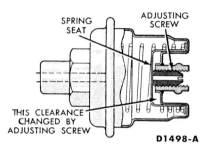

FIG. 8—Adjustable Vacuum Unit

When the control pressure is within specifications at engine idle, **but not within specifications** at the pressure rise point of approximately 17.0 inches of vacuum, at 10 inches of vacuum, or at 3 inches of vacuum on the C4 transmission, or 1.0 or less on the C6 transmission, the vacuum diaphragm unit may need adjustment.

The vacuum diaphragm assembly used on the C4 or C6 Automatic Dual Range transmission has an adjusting screw in the vacuum hose connecting tube (Fig. 8). The inner end of the screw bears against a plate which in turn bears against the vacuum diaphragm spring.

All readings slightly high or all readings slightly low may indicate the vacuum unit needs adjustment to correct a particular shift condition.

For example, on a C4 transmission, if the pressure at 10 inches of vacuum was 120 psi and the pressure at 3 inches of vacuum was *170* psi, and upshifts and downshifts were harsh, a diaphragm adjustment to reduce the diaphragm assembly spring force would be required.

If pressure readings are low, and line pressure does not start to build up until vacuum drops to 15 inches, an adjustment to increase diaphragm spring force is required.

To increase control pressure, turn the adjusting screw in clockwise. To reduce control pressure, back the adjusting screw out by turning it counterclockwise.

One complete turn of the adjusting screw (360°) will change idle line control pressure approximately 2-3 psi. After adjustment is made, install the vacuum line and recheck the pressures, particularly the pressure at 10 inches of vacuum.

The diaphragm should not be adjusted to provide pressures below the ranges previously specified in order to change shift feel. To do so could result in soft or slipping

shifts and damage to the transmission.

STALL TEST

Start the engine to allow it to reach its normal temperature. Apply both the parking and service brakes while making tests.

The stall test is made in D2, D1, L, or R, at full throttle to check engine performance, converter clutch operation or installation, and the holding ability of the forward clutch, reverse-high clutch and low-reverse band and the gear train one-way clutch. **While making this test, do not hold the throttle open for more than five seconds at a time.** Then move the selector lever to Neutral and run engine at 1000 rpm for about 15 seconds to cool the converter before making the next test. If the engine speed recorded by the tachometer exceeds the maximum limits specified in Table 3, release the accelerator immediately because clutch or band slippage is indicated.

TABLE 3—Stall Speed Limits

Engine Model CID	Engine Speed (rpm)	Transmission Type
170-1V	1450-1650	C4
200-1V	1600-1800	C4
289-2V	1750-1950	C4
289-4V	1800-2000	C4
390-2V	1750-1950	C6
390-4V	1800-2000	C6

STALL SPEED TOO HIGH

If stall speed exceeds specifications, band or clutch slippage is indicated, depending on transmission selector lever position. Excessive engine rpm only in D1, D2 and L indicates forward clutch slippage. Excessive engine rpm only in R indicates either reverse-high clutch or low-reverse band slippage in the C4 transmission, and either reverse-high or low-reverse slippage in the C6 transmission. Excessive engine rpm only in D1 indicates gear train one-way clutch slippage.

STALL SPEED TOO LOW

When the stall test speeds are low and the engine is properly tuned, converter stator clutch problems are indicated. A road test must be per-

formed to determine the exact cause of the trouble.

If the stall test speeds are 300 to 400 rpm below the specifications shown in Table 3, and the car cruises properly but has very poor acceleration, the converter stator clutch is slipping.

If the stall test speeds are 300 to 400 rpm below the specified values, and the car drags at cruising speeds and acceleration is poor, the stator clutch could be installed backwards.

Remove the converter and check the stator clutch as described in Cleaning and Inspection.

When the stall test shows normal speeds, the acceleration is good, but the car drags at cruising speeds, the difficulty is due to a seized stator assembly. If the stator is defective, replace the converter.

INITIAL ENGAGEMENT CHECKS

Initial engagement checks are made to determine if initial band and clutch engagements are smooth.

Run the engine until its normal operating temperature is reached. With the engine at the correct idle speed, shift the selector lever from N to D2, D1, L, and R. Observe the initial band and clutch engagements. Band and clutch engagements should be smooth in all positions. Rough initial engagements in D1, D2, L, or R are caused by high engine idle speed or high control pressures.

SHIFT POINT CHECKS

Check the light throttle upshifts in D1. The transmission should start in first gear, shift to second, and then shift to third within the shift points specified in the specifications section.

While the transmission is in third gear, depress the accelerator pedal through the detent (to the floor). The transmission should shift from third to second or third to first, depending on the car speed.

Check the closed throttle downshift from third to first by coasting down from about 30 mph in third gear. The shift should occur within the limits specified in the specifications section.

When the selector lever is at D2, the transmission can operate only in second and third gears. Shift points for second to third and third to second are the same in both D2 and D1.

With the transmission in third gear

and road speed over 30 mph, the transmission should shift to second gear when the selector lever is moved from D2 or D1 to L. The transmission will downshift from second or third to first gear when this same manual shift is made below approximately 20 mph with a C4 transmission or approximately 10 mph with a C6 transmission. **This check will determine if the governor pressure and shift control valves are functioning properly.**

During the shift check operation, if the transmission does not shift within specifications or certain gear ranges cannot be obtained, refer to the Diagnosis Guide to resolve the problem.

AIR PRESSURE CHECKS

A NO DRIVE condition can exist, even with correct transmission fluid pressure, because of inoperative clutches, bands. The inoperative units can be located through a series of checks by substituting air pressure for the fluid pressure to determine the location of the malfunction.

When the selector lever is at D2, a NO DRIVE condition may be caused by an inoperative forward clutch. A NO DRIVE condition at D1 may be caused by an inoperative forward clutch or one-way clutch. When there is no drive in L, the difficulty could be caused by improper functioning of the forward clutch or low-reverse band and the one-way clutch in a C4, or the forward clutch or low-reverse and one-way clutches in the C6 transmission. The low-reverse band in the C4 transmission and low-reverse in the C6 transmission cannot be checked in L. If the low-reverse band or clutch fails, the one-way clutch will hold the gear train and operation will be normal except that there will be no engine braking. Failure to drive in reverse range could be caused by a malfunction of the reverse-high clutch or low-reverse band in the C4 transmission, or the low-reverse clutch or the reverse-high clutch in the C6 transmission. Erratic shifts could be caused by a stuck governor valve.

To make the air pressure checks, drain the transmission fluid, and then remove the oil pan and the control valve body assembly. The inoperative units can be located by introducing air pressure into the transmission case passages leading to the clutches, servos, and governor.

FORWARD CLUTCH

Apply air pressure to the transmission case forward clutch passage (Fig. 9). A dull thud can be heard when the clutch piston is applied. If no noise is heard, place the finger tips on the input shell and again apply air pressure to the forward clutch passage. Movement of the piston can be felt as the clutch is applied.

GOVERNOR

Apply air pressure to the control pressure to governor passage and listen for a sharp clicking or whistling noise. The noise indicates secondary governor valve movement.

REVERSE-HIGH CLUTCH

Apply air pressure to the reverse-high clutch passage (Fig. 9). A dull thud indicates that the reverse-high clutch piston has moved to the applied position. If no noise is heard, place the finger tips on the clutch drum and again apply air pressure to detect movement of the piston.

INTERMEDIATE SERVO

Hold the air nozzle in the intermediate servo apply passage (Fig. 9). Operation of the servo is indicated by a tightening of the intermediate band around the drum. Continue to apply air pressure into the intermediate servo apply passage, and introduce air pressure into the intermediate servo release passage. The intermediate servo should release the band against the apply pressure.

LOW-REVERSE CLUTCH— C6 TRANSMISSION

Apply air pressure to the low-reverse clutch apply pressure passage. A dull thud indicates that the piston has moved to the apply position. If no thud is heard, apply air pressure again while holding the palm of the hand on the exterior at the rear of the case to detect clutch apply movement.

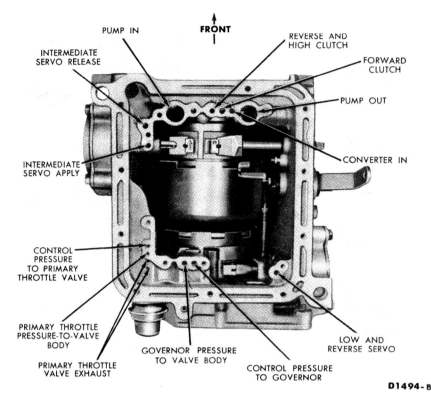

FIG. 9—Oil Pressure Passage Holes

LOW-REVERSE SERVO— C4 TRANSMISSION

Apply air pressure to the low-reverse apply passage (Fig. 8). The low-reverse band should tighten around the drum if the servo is operating properly.

If the servos do not operate, disassemble, clean and inspect them to locate the source of the trouble.

If air pressure applied to any clutch passage fails to operate the clutch or operates more than one clutch at once, remove and, with air pressure, check the fluid passages in the case and front pump to detect obstructions.

If the passages are clear, remove the clutch assemblies, and clean and inspect the malfunctioning clutch to locate the trouble.

DIAGNOSIS GUIDE

The Transmission Diagnosis Guide lists the most common trouble symptoms that may be found in the transmission, and gives the items that should be checked to find the cause of the trouble.

The items to check for each trouble symptom are arranged in a logical sequence which should be followed for quickest results. The letter symbols for each item are explained in the Key to the Diagnosis Guide.

If items A, B, C, D, E, and the stall test have already been checked during the preliminary checks and adjustments, they need not be repeated when following the Diagnosis Guide.

---

2 COMMON ADJUSTMENTS AND REPAIRS

TRANSMISSION FLUID DRAIN AND REFILL

Normal maintenance and lubrication requirements do not necessitate periodic automatic transmission fluid changes.

If a major failure, such as a clutch,

band, bearing, etc., has occurred within the transmission, it will have to be removed for service. At this time the converter must be thoroughly flushed to remove all dirt.

When filling a dry transmission and converter, install 5 quarts of

fluid. Start the engine, shift the selector lever as in Step 5 below, and check and add fluid as necessary.

Following is the procedure for *partial drain and refill due to minor repairs.*

1. Place a drain pan under the

C4 AUTOMATIC DUAL RANGE DIAGNOSIS GUIDE

Trouble Symptom	Items to Check	
	Transmission in Vehicle	Transmission Out of Vehicle
Rough Initial Engagement in D1 or D2	K B W F E	
Rough Initial Engagement D2 Only	G J	
1-2 or 2-3 Shift Points Incorrect	A L B C D W E	
Rough 2-3 Shift	B F E	
Engine Overspeeds on 2-3 Shift	B G W E F	r
No Shift Points	B C D E J	
No 2-3 Shift	C R D E	b r
No 3-1 Shift in D1	B E	
No Forced Downshifts	L W E	
Runaway Engine on Forced Downshift	G F E J B	c
Rough 3-2 or 3-1 Shift at Closed Throttle	K B E	
Shifts 1-3 in D1 and D2	G J	
No Engine Braking In First Gear—Manual Low Range	H I	
Creeps Excessively in D1 or D2	K	
Slips or Chatters in First Gear, D1	A B W F E	a c i
Slips or Chatters in Second Gear	A B G W F E J	a c
Slips or Chatters in R	A H W F E I	b c
No Drive in D1 only	C E	i
No Drive in D2 only	C	
No Drive in R only	C H I E R	b c
No Drive in D1, D2, or L	D W R	a
No Drive in Any Selector Lever Position	A C W F E R	c h
Lockup in D2 only	H I	i
Lockup in R only		a g
Parking Lock Binds or Does Not Hold	C	g
Transmission Overheats	A O F	n
Maximum Speed Too Low, Poor Acceleration		n
Transmission Noisy in N	F	d
Transmission Noisy in First, Second, and Reverse Gear	F	h d
Transmission Noisy in P	F	d
Fluid Leak	M N O P Q S U X	j m p

KEY TO DIAGNOSIS GUIDE

TRANSMISSION IN VEHICLE	
A	Fluid Level
B	Vacuum Diaphragm Unit or Tubes
C	Manual Linkage
D	Governor
E	Valve Body
F	Control Pressure Regulator Valve
G	Intermediate Band
H	Low-Reverse Band
I	Low-Reverse Servo
J	Intermediate Servo
K	Engine Idle Speed
L	Downshift Linkage
M	Convertor Drain Plugs
N	Oil Pan Gasket, or Filler Tube
O	Oil Cooler and Connections
P	Manual or Downshift Lever Shaft Seal
Q	1/8-inch Pipe Plug in Side of Case
R	Perform Air-Pressure Check
S	Extension Housing to Case Gaskets and Lockwashers
U	Extension Housing Rear Oil Seal
W	Perform Control Pressure Check
X	Speedometer Driven Gear Adapter Seal

TRANSMISSION OUT OF VEHICLE	
a	Forward Clutch
b	Reverse-High Clutch
c	Leakage in Hydraulic System
d	Front Pump
g	Parking Linkage
h	Planetary Assembly
i	Planetary One-Way Clutch
j	Engine Rear Oil Seal
m	Front Pump Oil Seal
n	Converter One-Way Clutch
p	Front Pump to Case Gasket or Seal
r	Reverse-High Clutch Piston Air Bleed Valve

C6 AUTOMATIC TRANSMISSION DIAGNOSIS GUIDE

Trouble Symptom	Items to Check	
	Transmission in Car	Transmission Out of Car
No Drive in D1, D2 and L	C W E R	a c
Rough Initial Engagement in D1 or D2	K B W E	a
1-2 or 2-3 Shift Points Incorrect or Erratic	A B L C D W E R	
Rough 1-2 Upshifts	B J G W E	
Rough 2-3 Shifts	B J W G E R	b r
Dragged Out 1-2 Shift	A B J W G E R	c
Engine Overspeeds on 2-3 Shift	C A B J W E G	b r
No 1-2 or 2-3 Shift	C L B D W E G J	b c
No 3-1 Shift in D1 or 3-2 Shift in D2	D E	
No Forced Downshifts	L W E	
Runaway Engine on Forced 3-2 Downshift	W J G E B	c
Rough 3-2 or 3-1 Shift at Closed Throttle	K B J W E	
Shifts 1-3 in D1 and D2	G J E D R	
No Engine Braking in First Gear—Manual Lo Range	C H E D R	c
Creeps Excessively	K	
Slips or Chatters in First Gear, D1	A B W E	a c i
Slips or Chatters in Second Gear	A B J G W E R	a c
Slips or Chatters in R	A B C H W E R	b c r
No Drive in D1 Only	C W E	i
No Drive in D2 Only	A C W J E R	c
No Drive in L Only	A W E R	c
No Drive in R Only	A C H W E R	b c r
No Drive in Any Selector Lever Position	A C W E R	c d
Lockup in D1 Only	E	g c
Lockup in D2 Only	H E	b g c i
Lockup in L Only	E	g c
Lockup in R Only	E	a g c
Parking Lock Binds or Does Not Hold	C	g
Transmission Overheats	O E B W	n s
Maximum Speed Too Low, Poor Acceleration	Y Z	n
Transmission Noisy in N and P	A E	d
Transmission Noisy in First, Second, Third or Reverse Gear	A E	h a d i
Fluid Leak	A M N O P Q S U X B J	i m p
Car moves Forward in N	C	a

PROBABLE TROUBLE SOURCES

A Fluid Level	W Perform Control Pressure Check
B Vacuum Diaphragm Unit or Tubes Restricted—Leaking—Adjustment	X Speedometer Driven Gear Adapter Seal
C Manual Linkage	Y Engine Performance
D Governor	Z Car Brakes
E Valve Body	a Forward Clutch
G Intermediate Band	b Reverse-High Clutch
H Low-Reverse Clutch	c Leakage in Hydraulic System
J Intermediate Servo	d Front Pump
K Engine Idle Speed	g Parking Linkage
L Downshift Linkage—Including Inner Lever Position	h Planetary Assembly
M Converter Drain Plugs	i Planetary One-Way Clutch
N Oil Pan Gasket, Filler Tube or Seal	j Engine Rear Oil Seal
O Oil Cooler and Connections	m Front Pump Oil Seal
P Manual or Downshift Lever Shaft Seal	n Converter One-Way Clutch
Q 1/8 Inch Pipe Plugs in Case	p Front Pump to Case Gasket or Seal
R Perform Air Pressure Check	r Reverse-High Clutch Piston Air Bleed Valve
S Extension Housing to Case Gasket	s Converter Pressure Check Valves
U Extension Housing Rear Oil Seal	

transmission. Loosen and remove all but two of the oil pan bolts, from the front of the case and drop the rear edge of the oil pan to drain the fluid. Remove and thoroughly clean the oil pan and screen. Discard the oil pan gasket.

2. Place a new gasket on the oil pan, and install the screen and pan on the transmission.

3. Add three quarts of fluid to the transmission through the filler tube.

4. Run the engine at idle speed for about two minutes. Check the fluid level, and add fluid if necessary. Run the engine at fast idle speed (about 1200 rpm) until it reaches its normal operating temperature. **Do not race the engine.**

5. Shift the selector lever through all the positions, place it at P, and check the fluid level. If necessary, add enough fluid to the transmission to raise the level to the F (Full) mark on the dipstick. **Do not overfill the transmission.**

OIL COOLER FLUSHING PROCEDURE

When a clutch or band failure or other internal trouble has occurred in the transmission, any metal particles or clutch plate or band material that may have been carried into the cooler should be removed from the system by flushing the cooler and lines before the transmission is put back into service. In no case should an automatic transmission having a clutch or band failure or other internal trouble resulting in fluid contamination, be put back into service without first flushing the transmission oil cooler.

1. After installing a new or rebuilt automatic transmission and converter assembly in the car, **Do Not Connect the Cooler Return Line to the Transmission.** Place the transmission selector lever in the P (park) position and connect the cooler inlet (converter out) line to the transmission. Place a pan under the end of the cooler return line that will hold transmission fluid. **Do Not Start the Engine.**

2. Install 5 quarts of automatic transmission fluid meeting Ford Specification.

3. Start the engine and allow it to run at normal idle speed for 3 minutes with the selector lever in P (park) position. Stop the engine and add additional transmission fluid required to complete total fill. Start the engine and allow it to run at normal idle speed.

4. Allow approximately two quarts of transmission fluid to drain into the pan placed under the end of the cooler return line.

5. If the fluid does not run clean after draining two quarts of it through the cooler, shut off the engine and add **two additional quarts** of transmission fluid.

6. Repeat steps 3 through 5 until the transmission fluid flowing out of the cooler return line is clean.

7. If there is no fluid flow or the fluid does not flow freely, shut off the engine and disconnect both cooler lines from the transmission and cooler.

8. Use an air hose with not more than 100 psi air pressure to reverse flush the cooler lines and the cooler. After reverse flushing, connect both

lines at the cooler and the cooler inlet line (converter out) to the transmission.

9. Start the engine and check the fluid flow. If the transmission fluid flows freely, proceed with steps 3 through 6. If there is no fluid flow, check for pinched cooler lines. If the flow is restricted, replace cooler lines and/or the radiator.

10. Shut off the engine, and connect the cooler return line to the transmission. Check the transmission fluid level as indicated under heading Transmission Fluid Level Check. Add or remove transmission fluid as required until the proper fluid level is obtained on the dipstick. DO NOT OVERFILL THE TRANSMISSION.

11. **Do not attempt to correct cooler or cooler line leaks by closing off the lines.**

OIL COOLER TUBE REPLACEMENT

When fluid leakage is found at the oil cooler, the entire radiator must be replaced. **The oil cooler cannot be removed from the radiator for replacement.**

When one or more of the fluid cooler steel tubes must be replaced, each replacement tube must be fabricated from the same size steel tubing as the original line.

Using the old tube as a guide, bend the new tube as required. Add the necessary fittings, and install the tube.

After the fittings have been tightened, add fluid as needed, and check for fluid leaks.

3 CLEANING AND INSPECTION

CLEANING

TRANSMISSION

Clean all parts with suitable solvent and use moisture-free air to dry off all parts and clean out the various fluid passages.

The composition clutch plates and bands should not be cleaned in a vapor degreaser or with any type of detergent solution. To clean these parts, wipe them off with a lint-free cloth. New clutch plates and bands should be soaked in transmission fluid for fifteen minutes before they are assembled.

CONVERTER

If there is reason to believe that the converter has an excessive amount of foreign material in it, a commercial converter cleaning machine or the following cleaning procedure should be used.

1. With the converter on the bench, remove both drain plugs and tilt the converter in all directions to drain as much fluid as possible.

2. Install the drain plugs and fill the converter through the pump drive hub with a light-body oil such as kerosene, or a cleaning solvent suitable for transmission cleaning.

3. Install the tool shown in Fig. 10 in the converter. Expand the bushing in the turbine spline. Rotate the tool to circulate the fluid in the converter.

4. Remove both drain plugs and thoroughly drain the converter.

5. Repeat the procedure given in steps 2, 3, and 4, as required, to remove all foreign material.

6. Install the drain plugs.

The torque converter is permanently enclosed in a welded steel housing and cannot be disassembled for servicing.

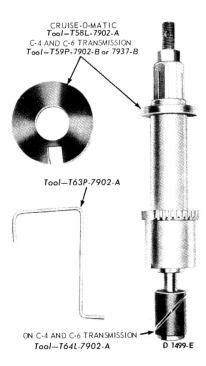

CRUISE-O-MATIC
Tool—T58L-7902-A
C-4 AND C-6 TRANSMISSION
Tool—T59P-7902-B or 7937-B

Tool—T63P-7902-A

ON C-4 AND C-6 TRANSMISSION
Tool—T64L-7902-A

D 1499-E

FIG. 10—Converter Checking Tool

INSPECTION

A special tool (Fig. 13) must be used to check the condition of the converter. This special tool is used to check the turbine and stator end play and the operation of the one-way stator clutch.

INSPECTION

TURBINE AND STATOR END PLAY CHECK

1. Insert the tool into the converter pump drive hub until it bottoms.

2. Install the guide over the converter pump drive hub.

3. Expand the split fiber bushing in the turbine spline by tightening the adjusting nut. Tighten the adjusting nut until the tool is securely locked to the turbine spline.

4. Attach a dial indicator to the tool (Fig. 13). *Position the indicator button on a converter pump drive hub, and set the dial face at 0 (zero).*

5. Lift the tool upward as far as it will go and note the indicator reading. The indicator reading is the total end play which the turbine and stator share. If the total end play exceeds specifications, replace the converter.

6. Loosen the adjusting nut to free the split bushing, and then remove the tool from the converter.

STATOR ONE-WAY CLUTCH CHECK

1. Install the stator outer race holding tool in one of the holes provided in the stator.

2. Insert the tool in the converter pump drive hub.

3. As the tool enters the converter, the spline on the tool (Fig. 13) will engage the stator clutch inner race spline.

4. Place a torque wrench on the tool (Fig. 13). The tool (and stator inner race) should turn freely clockwise (from the pump drive hub side of the converter). It should lock up and hold a 10 ft-lb pull when the wrench is turned counterclockwise. Try the clutch for lockup and hold in at least five different locations around the converter. If the clutch fails to lock up and hold a 10 ft-lb torque, replace the converter unit.

The metal ring, which is a part of this tool, will have to be held by hand, to hold the lock pin during this check.

5. Remove the tools from the converter.

STATOR TO IMPELLER INTERFERENCE CHECK

1. Position a stator support shaft on the bench with the spline end of the stator shaft pointing up (Fig. 11).

2. Place the front pump rotor over the stator shaft with the flat side of the rotor down.

3. Place the converter over the stator support shaft so that the front pump flats are in normal (running) engagement with the pump rotor. The converter pump driving hub will bottom the rotor.

4. While holding the stator shaft stationary, try to rotate the converter counterclockwise. The converter should rotate freely without

D1364-A

FIG. 11—Checking Stator to Impeller Interference

any signs of interference or scraping within the converter assembly.

5. If there is an indication of scraping, the trailing edges of the stator blades may be interfering with the leading edges of the impeller blades. In such cases, replace the converter.

STATOR TO TURBINE INTERFERENCE CHECK

1. Position the converter, front side down, on the bench.

2. Install the front pump assembly (complete) to engage the mating splines of the stator support and stator, and pump drive gear flats.

3. Install the input shaft, engaging the splines with the turbine hub (Fig. 12).

4. While holding the pump stationary, attempt to rotate the turbine with the input shaft. The turbine should rotate freely in both directions without any signs of interference or scraping noise.

5. If interference exists, the stator front thrust washer may be worn, allowing the stator to hit the turbine. In such cases, the converter must be replaced.

FRONT PUMP AND STATOR SUPPORT

1. Inspect the clutch drum journal for wear and roughness.

2. Check the side clearances between the clutch apply pressure seal rings and their grooves in the stator support. These clearances should be between 0.0035 and 0.0045 inch.

3. Remove the clutch apply rings

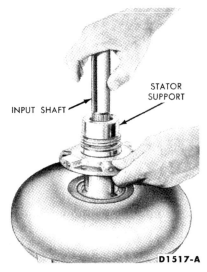

INPUT SHAFT

STATOR SUPPORT

D1517-A

FIG. 12—Checking Stator to Turbine Interference

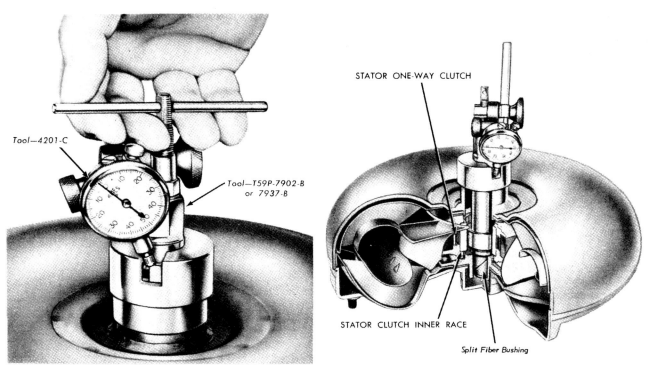

Tool—4201-C

Tool—T59P-7902-B or 7937-B

STATOR ONE-WAY CLUTCH

STATOR CLUTCH INNER RACE

Split Fiber Bushing

END PLAY CHECK

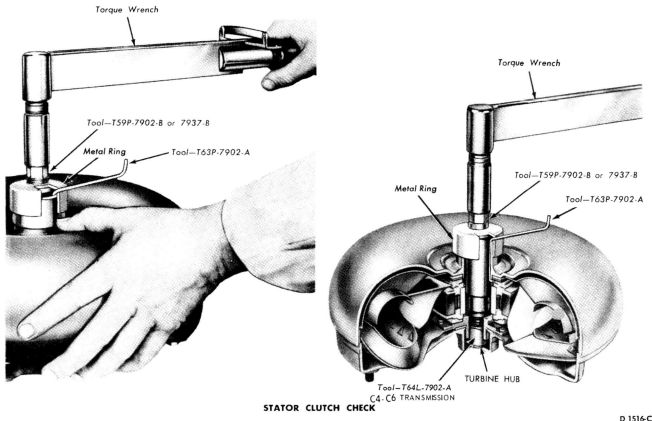

Torque Wrench

Tool—T59P-7902-B or 7937-B

Metal Ring

Tool—T63P-7902-A

Torque Wrench

Metal Ring

Tool—T59P-7902-B or 7937-B

Tool—T63P-7902-A

Tool—T64L-7902-A
C4-C6 TRANSMISSION

TURBINE HUB

STATOR CLUTCH CHECK

D 1516-C

FIG. 13—Converter Tool Installation—Typical

and install them in their normal running position in the clutch drum. Then check the ring gaps. This ring gap clearance should be between 0.002 and 0.009 inch.

4. Inspect the input shaft bushings in the stator support shaft for wear.

Check the oil ring grooves in the stator support for nicks, burrs or damaged edges. Check the gasket mating surface of the pump body for damaged surface.

5. Inspect the converter pump drive hub bushing in the front pump housing. Inspect the pump seal in the pump housing for defects that would cause fluid leakage.

GOVERNOR

1. Inspect the governor valves and housing for wear. **Crocus cloth may be used to polish the valves if care is taken to avoid rounding the sharp edges.**

2. Install the governor valves in the governor housing and check them for free movement. Each valve should fall of its own weight when dry.

CLUTCH ASSEMBLY

1. Inspect the composition clutch plates for damage. These plates should be flat. If the plates are not flat, they must be replaced. If the old plates are to be re-used, they must **not** be cleaned in a vapor degreaser or cleaned with any type of detergent solution. Wipe them clean with lint-free towels.

If new composition plates are to be installed, soak them in automatic transmission fluid for at least 15 minutes before assembling them in the clutch drum. This soaking prevents damage to the plates during the transmission fluid fill period and initial running-in.

2. Inspect the steel clutch plates. These clutch plates should also be flat. If they are not flat, they should be replaced.

3. Inspect the clutch release springs for being broken or distorted.

4. Inspect the clutch piston ball check valve for free movement and proper seating. Make sure the orifice in the clutch piston is open.

5. Inspect the clutch drum bushing for wear.

CONTROL VALVE BODY

1. Inspect all valve and plug bores for scores. Check all fluid passages for obstruction. Inspect the check valves for free movement. Inspect all mating surfaces for burrs or distortion. Inspect all plugs and valves for burrs and scores. **Crocus cloth can be used to polish valves and plugs if care is taken to avoid rounding the sharp edges of the valves and plugs.**

2. Inspect all springs for distortion. Check all valves and plugs for free movement in their respective bores. Valves and plugs, when dry, must fall from their own weight in their respective bores.

PINION CARRIERS

1. The pins and shafts in the planet assemblies should be checked for loose fit and/or complete disengagement. Replacement, using a new planet assembly, should be made if either condition is found to exist.

2. Inspect the pinion gears for damaged or excessively worn areas.

3. Check for free rotation of the pinion gears.

4. Inspect the C4 transmission front planet thrust surface for excessive wear.

SERVO-ASSEMBLIES

1. Inspect the servo piston and seals for defects that would cause hydraulic leakage.

2. Inspect the cover seal and gasket cover sealing surface for defects.

CASE

1. Inspect the case for cracks.

2. With an air hose, check all fluid passages for obstruction or cross leakage.

3. Check all case linkage parts for free travel and proper engagement.

4. Check the vent passage for obstructions with an air hose.

ONE-WAY CLUTCH

1. Inspect the outer and inner races for scores or damaged surface area where the rollers contact the races.

2. Inspect the rollers and springs for excessive wear or damage.

3. Inspect the spring and roller cage for bent or damaged spring retainers.

PART 7-2

C4 AUTOMATIC DUAL RANGE TRANSMISSION

Section	Page
1 Description and Operation	
Description	7-15
Operation	7-15
2 In-Car Adjustments and Repairs	
Control Linkage Adjustments	7-24
Throttle and Downshift Linkage Adjustments	7-24
Manual Linkage Adjustment	7-28
Neutral Start Switch Adjustment	7-30
Neutral Start Switch Replacement	7-31
Band Adjustments	7-31
Oil Pan and Control Valve Body Replacement	7-31
Intermediate Servo Repair	7-31

Section	Page
Low-Reverse Servo Piston Replacement	7-32
Extension Housing Bushing and Rear Seal Replacement	7-32
Extension Housing and Governor Replacement	7-32
3 Removal and Installation	
Removal	7-33
Installation	7-33
4 Major Repair Operations	
Disassembly of Transmission	7-34
Parts Repair or Replacement	7-38
Assembly of Transmission	7-47

1 DESCRIPTION AND OPERATION

DESCRIPTION

Figure 1 shows the location of the converter, front pump, clutches, gear train and most of the internal parts used in the C4 transmission. The identification tag (Fig. 2) attached by the low-reverse servo cover bolt, includes the model prefix and suffix, as well as a service identification number and date code. The service identification number indi-

cates changes to service details which affect interchangeability **when the transmission model is not changed.** For interpretation of this number, see the Master Parts Catalog.

Table 1 shows the engine and transmission model applications.

OPERATION
TORQUE CONVERTER

The hydraulic torque converter

(Fig. 3) consists of an impeller (pump), a turbine, and a stator. All these parts are enclosed and operate in a fluid-filled housing.

When the engine is running, the fluid in the torque converter flows from the impeller to the turbine and back to the impeller through the stator. This flow produces a maximum torque increase of about 2 to 1 when the turbine is stalled. When

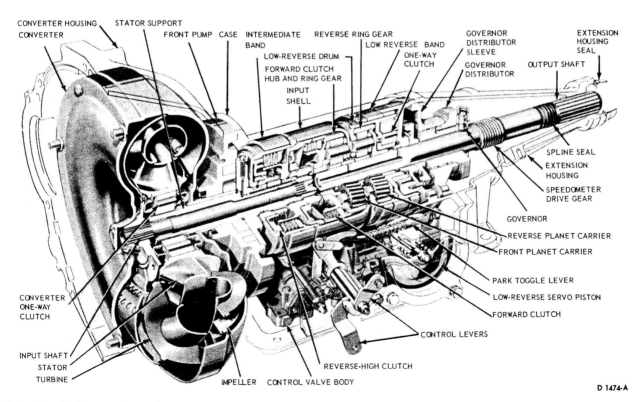

FIG. 1—C4 Automatic Dual Range Transmission

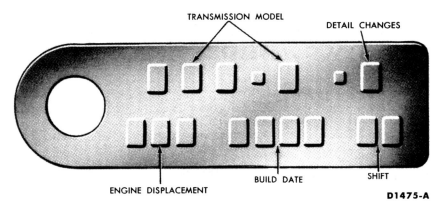

FIG. 2—Identification Tag

enough torque is developed by the impeller, the turbine begins to rotate, turning the turbine shaft (input shaft).

The converter torque multiplication gradually tapers off as turbine

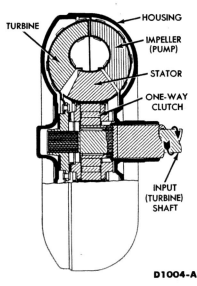

FIG. 3—Sectional View of Torque Converter—Typical

speed approaches impeller speed, and it becomes 1 to 1 when the turbine is being driven at $9/10$ impeller speed. This is known as the coupling point.

When the turbine is rotating at less than $9/10$ impeller speed, the converter is multiplying torque. The fluid leaving the turbine blades strikes the front face of the stator blades. These blades are held stationary by the action of a one-way clutch (Fig. 3) as long as the fluid is directed against the front face of the blades.

When the turbine rotates faster than $9/10$ impeller speed the converter no longer multiplies torque. The fluid is directed against the back face of the stator blades. As the one-way clutch permits the stator to rotate only in the direction of impeller rotation, the stator begins to turn with the impeller and turbine. The converter operates as an efficient fluid coupling as long as the turbine speed remains greater than $9/10$ impeller speed.

A constant flow of fluid into and out of the converter is maintained. The fluid coming out of the con-

verter is forced through a cooler located in the radiator tank.

PLANETARY GEAR TRAIN, CLUTCHES, BANDS, AND SERVOS

Planetary Gear Train. The gear train consists of an input shaft that is splined to the turbine of the converter and the forward clutch cylinder (Fig. 4). The forward clutch cylinder rotates the steel internal clutch plates of the forward clutch and the composition clutch plates of the reverse-high clutch. When the reverse-high clutch is applied, the external area of the clutch hub is splined to and drives the input shell to rotate the sun gear. When the forward clutch is applied, the composition clutch plates drive the forward clutch hub and ring gear. The ring gear rotates the forward planet gears.

When applied, the intermediate band holds the reverse-high clutch drum, input shell and sun gear from rotating.

The sun gear, which is driven by the input shell, is meshed with the forward and reverse planet gears. The reverse planet carrier and low reverse drum are locked together with external splines. The low-reverse drum can be held from rotating by the low-reverse band. In D1 the low-reverse drum is also held from rotating by a roller type one-way clutch.

The forward planet carrier, reverse ring gear hub, park gear and governor oil collector are all splined to the output shaft.

Forward Clutch. The input shaft is splined to and drives the forward clutch cylinder (Fig. 4). Rotation of the cylinder drives the steel clutch plates in the forward clutch and the composition clutch plates of the reverse-high clutch.

When the forward clutch piston is applied by hydraulic pressure, the movement of the piston against the disc spring locks the steel and composition clutch plates together to drive the forward clutch hub and ring gear.

When hydraulic pressure is released from the piston, the disc spring moves the piston to the released position. As the disc spring moves, the steel and composition clutch plates are released. This stops the rotation of the forward clutch hub and ring gear (Fig. 4). The forward clutch is applied in all forward drive gear ratios.

TABLE 1—Engine and Transmission Application

CAR MODEL	TRANSMISSION MODEL	ENGINE MODEL
Falcon	PCS-V	170-1V
Mustang	PCS-Y	200-1V
Comet-Falcon-Fairlane (Column Shift)	PCS-W	200-1V
Comet-Fairlane (Floor Shift)	PCS-AA	200-1V
Comet-Falcon-Fairlane (Column Shift)	PCW-AN	289-2V-4V
Mustang	PCW-AS	289-2V-4V
Comet-Fairlane (Floor Shift)	PCW-AR	289-2V
Fairlane—Police	PCW-AY	200-1V
Taxi	PCW-AZ	289-2V

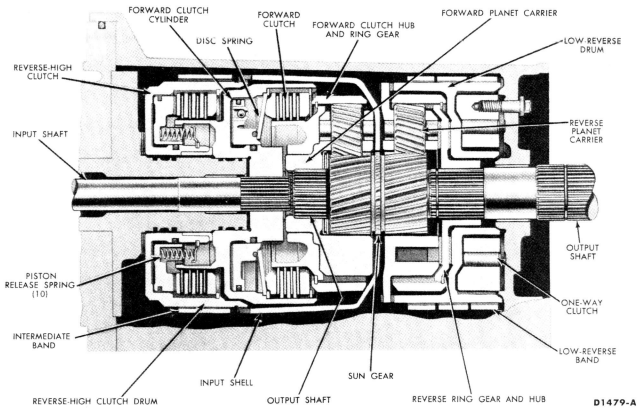

FIG. 4—Gear Train, Clutches and Bands

Reverse-High Clutch. When hydraulic pressure is directed to the clutch piston, the piston moves against the release springs (Fig. 4). The piston movement locks the steel and rotating composition clutch plates together. The steel clutch plates drive the reverse-high clutch drum which is splined to the input shell. Rotation of the input shell drives the sun gear which is splined to the input shell.

To release the reverse-high clutch, hydraulic pressure is exhausted from the apply side of the piston. The return springs move the piston to the released position. The steel and composition clutch plates are now released to stop rotation of the reverse-high clutch drum, input shell and sun gear.

Intermediate Servo and Band. The intermediate servo is machined into the transmission case and the band has an **external** adjustment screw (Fig. 5). To apply the servo, hydraulic pressure is directed from the control valve body, through a hole in the case to the hole in the servo piston stem. The pressure passes through the center of the piston stem and then to the apply side of the piston. The piston moves against the return spring to tighten the intermediate band around the reverse-high clutch drum.

To release the servo piston, hydraulic pressure is directed to the release side of the piston. The release pressure is assisted by the compressed return spring to move the servo piston and intermediate band to the OFF position. The intermediate servo and band are applied only during the intermediate gear operation.

Low-Reverse Servo and Band. The low-reverse servo is machined into the transmission case and the band has an **external** adjustment screw (Fig. 6). To apply the servo, hydraulic pressure is directed from the control valve body through a hole in the case to a hole in the piston stem. The pressure then passes through the center of the piston stem to the apply area of the servo piston. The apply pressure force moves the piston against the piston return spring to tighten the low-reverse band around the low-reverse drum.

To release the servo piston and band, the hydraulic pressure is exhausted from the apply side of the piston. The compressed return spring

expands to release the piston and the low-reverse band.

POWER FLOW

All Gear Rotations are viewed from the front of transmission. Table 2 shows the gear ratios obtained in the different selector lever positions.

Power Flow Neutral. In neutral (Fig. 7) the clutches or bands are not applied, therefore, no power is transmitted to the output shaft.

Power Flow First Gear. In low gear (Fig. 7), the forward clutch is applied, and the planet one-way clutch or low-reverse band is holding the low-reverse drum and reverse planet carrier from rotating. The power flow is through the input shaft and into the forward clutch. The input shaft is splined to and drives the forward clutch cylinder. Rotation of the forward clutch drives the forward clutch hub and ring gear. The ring gear rotates the forward planet gears clockwise to cause the sun gear to rotate counterclockwise.

Counterclockwise rotation of the sun gear turns the reverse planet gear clockwise. The reverse planet carrier being splined to the low-reverse drum is held from rotating

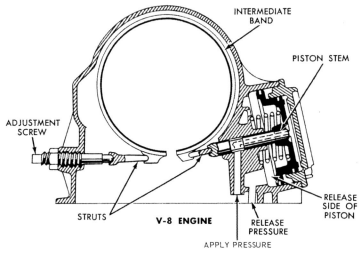

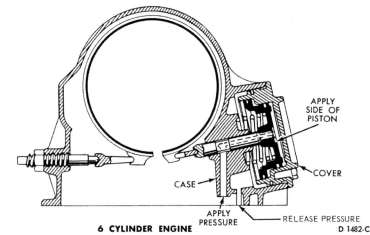

FIG. 5—Intermediate Servo and Band

shaft and rotates the output shaft clockwise.

The output shaft rotation is at a reduced speed, compared to the input shaft rotation, but at an increased torque.

The output shaft rotation at a reduced speed is caused by the fact that the forward planet carrier rotates at the same speed of the output shaft and in the same direction since the carrier is splined to the output shaft. The forward ring gear and planet assembly are rotating in the same direction, but the planet carrier is rotating at a slower speed than the ring gear. Therefore, the low gear ratio (torque multiplication) is a combination of the ratios provided by the forward and reverse planet assemblies.

Power Flow Intermediate Gear. In intermediate gear (Fig. 7), the forward clutch is applied and the intermediate band is holding the reverse high clutch drum, input shell and sun gear from turning.

The power flow is through the input shaft into the forward clutch and forward front planet assembly ring gear. The sun gear is held from rotating by the intermediate band. This causes the forward planet pinions to rotate (walk) around the sun gear, carrying the forward planet carrier with them. The forward planet carrier, being splined to the output shaft, causes clockwise rotation of the output shaft at a reduction in speed compared to the speed of the input shaft, and at an increase in torque.

Clockwise rotation of the output shaft causes clockwise rotation of the output shaft ring gear, causing the reverse planet pinions to also rotate (walk) around the sun gear in a clockwise direction. The reverse planet carrier will also rotate clockwise and the one-way clutch inner race being splined to the reverse planet carrier, will overrun.

Power Flow High Gear. In high gear (Fig. 7), the forward and reverse-high clutches are applied. The power flow is through the input shaft into the forward clutch cylinder. (The forward clutch cylinder rotates the steel clutch plates of the forward clutch and the composition clutch plates of the reverse-high clutch). The forward clutch directs the power flow through the forward clutch hub and ring gear to the forward planet carrier.

The reverse-high clutch directs

by the one-way clutch or low-reverse band.

With the reverse planet carrier held stationary, the clockwise rotation of the reverse planet gears rotates the reverse ring gear and hub clockwise. The hub of the reverse ring gear is splined to the output

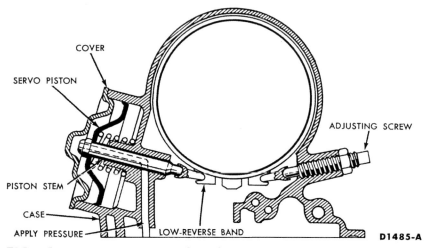

FIG. 6—Low-Reverse Servo and Band

TABLE 2—Gear Ratios

Transmission Selector Position	Gear	Gear Ratios	Forward Clutch	Reverse High Clutch	Intermediate Band	Low Reverse Band	One-Way Clutch
N or P	Neutral	——	Off	Off	Off	Off	Off
L	Low	2.46:1	On	Off	Off	On	Holding
D1	Low	2.46:1	On	Off	Off	Off	Holding
D1 or D2	Intermediate	1.46:1	On	Off	On	Off	Over-Running
D1 or D2	High	1.00:1	On	On	Off	Off	Over-Running
R	Reverse	2.20:1	Off	On	Off	On	Not Affected

the power flow through the input shell to the sun gear. With the sun gear and the forward clutch hub ring gear driven at the same speed the forward planet assembly (that is splined to the output shaft) is forced to rotate the output shaft at the same speed and direction to provide high gear.

Power Flow Reverse. In reverse (Fig. 7), the reverse-high clutch and low-reverse band are applied. The power flow is through the input shaft, reverse-high clutch, input shell and to the sun gear. Clockwise rotation of the sun gear causes counterclockwise rotation of the reverse planet gears.

The low-reverse band, holding the low-reverse drum and reverse planet carrier from turning, causes the reverse planet gears to rotate counterclockwise.

This rotates the reverse ring gear and hub counterclockwise. The hub splined to the output shaft rotates the output shaft counterclockwise at a reduction in speed and at an increase in torque for reverse gear.

HYDRAULIC CONTROL SYSTEM

The hydraulic system described below (Fig. 8) includes all models.

Front Pump. Fluid for operation of the hydraulic control system is supplied by one gear type pump mounted on the front of the transmission case. Pump intake is through a screen which is part of the main control assembly, into the case casting and pump. Discharge is through the case into the main control assembly. Fluid from the front pump is directed to the following valves in the main control assembly:

Main Oil Pressure Regulator
Valve
Throttle Booster Valve
Manual Valve

In addition, fluid is also directed to the primary throttle valve, which is located in the rear of the case. Fluid delivered to these valves is at a pressure controlled by the main oil pressure regulator valve.

Main Oil Pressure Regulator Valve. The main regulator valve assembly consists of the main oil pressure regulator valve and spring, retainer, main oil pressure booster valve, spring and sleeve, located in one bore in the main control assembly (Fig. 8).

Fluid is delivered to three valleys of the main regulator valve, from the front pump. The difference in diameter between the end land and the second land provides an area differential for regulation. Fluid pressure in this area tends to move the valve against spring force. Spring force is such that at approximately 60 psi front pump pressure, the main valve will move so that the third land uncovers the converter feed port, allowing additional pump volume to be used to charge the converter. If volume supplied by the front pump is greater than that required to maintain 60 psi line pressure, and converter and lube requirements, the valve will move further allowing the fourth land to uncover the port which allows excess pump volume to be discharged into the sump.

Pressures over 60 psi which are required under various operating conditions are obtained by delivering fluid under pressure to the pressure booster valve, where it will cause the pressure booster valve to assist the main regulator valve spring in increasing regulated line pressure.

Source of these pressures which cause variations in control pressure are discussed later.

Manual Valve. Two passages deliver control pressure to the manual valve. The valve is positioned by the

manual linkage according to mode of operation desired, to direct fluid out of two or more of the line passages which lead from the manual valve. The five passages (Fig. 8) leading from the manual valve (from left to right) are:

1. D2
2. D1
3. D
4. L-R
5. R

The D2 passage is charged in D2 range only.

The D1 passage is charged in D2 and D1 ranges.

The D passage is charged in all forward ranges, (including manual low).

The L-R passage is charged in L and R ranges.

The R passage is charged in reverse range only.

In Park and Neutral the valve blocks the flow of control pressure and exhausts the five passages leading from the manual valve.

The D passage supplies fluid pressure to the governor secondary valve, D2 valve and forward clutch.

The D2 passage supplies fluid to the adjoining ends of the D2 and 1-2 shift valves.

The D1 passage supplies fluid to the 2-3 shift valve.

The L and R passage supplies fluid to the lower end of the intermediate band accumulator valve, end of the manual low valve, through the downshift valve, to and through the throttle modulator valve bore, under the 2-3 shift valve and to the underside of the first land of the 1-2 shift valve.

In addition, fluid is supplied to the D2 valve and through the valve when it is in the closed (up) position, to the Low and Reverse Servo, applying the low and reverse band. The same fluid is also directed to the

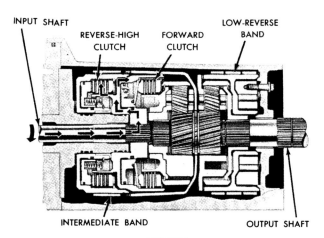

INPUT SHAFT
REVERSE-HIGH CLUTCH
FORWARD CLUTCH
LOW-REVERSE BAND
INTERMEDIATE BAND
OUTPUT SHAFT

NEUTRAL

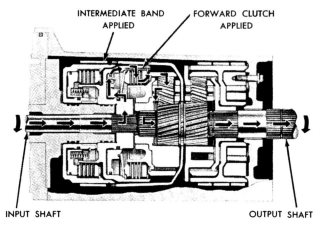

INTERMEDIATE BAND APPLIED
FORWARD CLUTCH APPLIED
INPUT SHAFT
OUTPUT SHAFT

SECOND GEAR

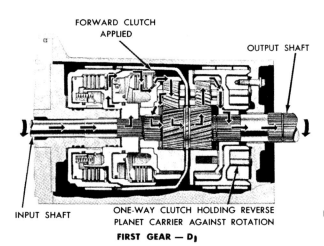

FORWARD CLUTCH APPLIED
OUTPUT SHAFT
INPUT SHAFT
ONE-WAY CLUTCH HOLDING REVERSE PLANET CARRIER AGAINST ROTATION

FIRST GEAR — D₁

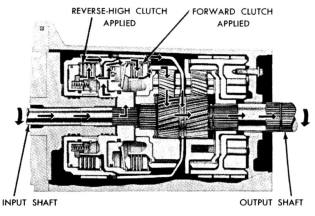

REVERSE-HIGH CLUTCH APPLIED
FORWARD CLUTCH APPLIED
INPUT SHAFT
OUTPUT SHAFT

HIGH GEAR

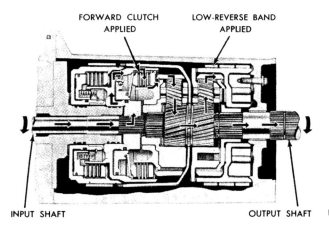

FORWARD CLUTCH APPLIED
LOW-REVERSE BAND APPLIED
INPUT SHAFT
OUTPUT SHAFT

FIRST GEAR — MANUAL LOW

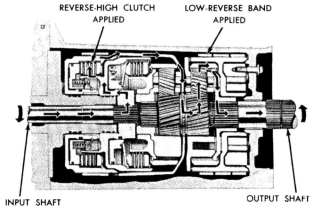

REVERSE-HIGH CLUTCH APPLIED
LOW-REVERSE BAND APPLIED
INPUT SHAFT
OUTPUT SHAFT

REVERSE

D1476-A

FIG. 7—Power Flow

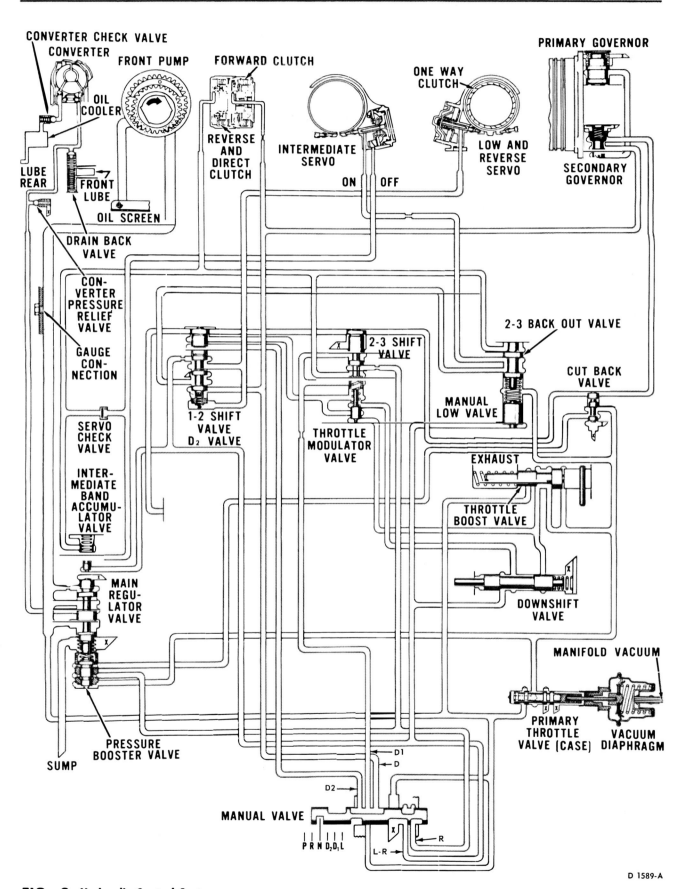

FIG. 8—Hydraulic Control System

spring end (opposite governor) of the D2 valve.

The R passage supplies fluid to the middle valley of the pressure booster valve, through the 2-3 shift valve to the reverse and direct clutch, applying it, and to the release side of the intermediate servo. Fluid is also supplied to the end of the 2-3 back-out valve, and to the intermediate band accumulator valve.

Primary Throttle Valve. The primary throttle valve is actuated by changes in manifold vacuum. Primary throttle pressure starts at 20″ (nominal) of mercury vacuum. Primary throttle pressure is delivered to the:

1. End of the pressure booster valve.

2. Upper valley of pressure booster valve (through cutback valve).

3. Downshift valve and throttle modulator valve (through throttle booster valve).

4. End of the throttle booster valve.

5. Spring end of the 2-3 back-out valve and manual low valve. Figure 9 shows how primary throttle pressure varies with engine vacuum.

Pressure Booster Valve. T.V. pressure is delivered to the upper valley of the pressure booster valve and to the end of the pressure booster valve. When force created on the booster valve by T.V. pressures in these two areas exceeds pressure booster valve spring force, the force will be added to the main regulator valve spring force transmitted to the main regulator valve. This will provide increased control pressures required to compensate for increased throttle openings and engine torque output. Figure 9 shows how control pressure varies with engine vacuum at O output shaft rpm.

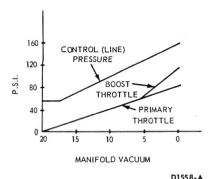

FIG. 9—Throttle Pressure Regulation

Governor

AT REST (0 MPH). Control pressure (line) is fed to the secondary governor valve through the center passage in the valve body. Because of the differential in area of the inner and outer lands of the valve, the valve will be forced inward, shutting off line pressure feed to the governor passage and allowing this passage to be opened to exhaust, at the inner end of the valve. At the same time, line pressure will pass by two flats on the outer end of the valve, pressurizing the line leakage passage leading to the primary governor valve. At rest, the spring on the outer end of the primary governor valve holds the primary governor valve inward, blocking further flow of the fluid in the line leakage passage. This causes pressure in the line leakage passage to build to the same value as line pressure. As a consequence, the secondary governor valve is held in and there is no pressure in the governor circuit.

ABOVE 10 MPH. When vehicle speed reaches approximately 10 mph, centrifugal force on the primary governor valve overcomes spring force, and the valve moves outward, opening the line leakage passage to exhaust. This action reduces the pressure on the end of the secondary governor valve to zero (0), allowing the secondary valve to also move outward, due to spring force and centrifugal force. When the secondary valve moves outward, it closes the governor exhaust passage, and allows line pressure to enter the governor passage. As pressure builds in the governor passage it will create a force on the secondary governor valve due to the differential in areas of the inner and outer lands of the valve. This force tends to move the valve inward. When the force on the valve created by pressure in the governor passage exceeds the centrifugal force plus spring force, the valve will move inward, allowing governor pressure to exhaust, and close the passage between line pressure and governor pressure. When governor pressure is reduced, the secondary valve will again move outward, closing the governor exhaust port and opening the line pressure to governor passage. Above 10 mph, governor pressure is regulated in this manner, and will vary with vehicle speeds.

If vehicle speed drops below 10 mph, the primary valve spring will

move the primary governor valve in, closing the line leakage exhaust port at the primary valve. Pressure in the line leakage passage will become equal to line pressure, forcing the secondary governor valve in. This action shuts off line pressure feed to the governor passage and exhausts the governor circuit.

When the secondary governor valve is regulating, governor pressure will be delivered to the cut-back valve, end of the 2-3 shift valve and the 1-2 shift valve. Figure 10 shows the relationship between governor pressure and output shaft RPM.

Throttle Booster Valve. Throttle plate openings above 50° provide very little change in engine vacuum as compared to throttle plate openings below 50°. The throttle booster valve is provided to boost throttle pressure and provide the necessary shift delay for engine throttle plate openings above 50°.

Below approximately 60 PSI primary TV pressure, TV pressure flows to and through the throttle boost valve unaffected, working on the end of the boost valve and on the area differential on the spring side of the boost valve. As a consequence, TV pressure passes through the throttle boost valve unaffected.

When TV pressure increases above 60 psi, the force created by TV pressure acting on the end of the throttle boost valve, minus the force of TV pressure acting on the area differential on the spring side, will exceed the force of the spring. This causes the valve to move against the spring, closing off primary TV pressure to the area differential on the spring side and permitting this area to be fed from line pressure, causing a boost in the pressure used for shift delay only. Because the area of the

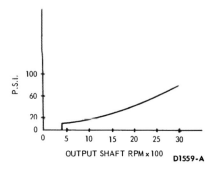

FIG. 10—Governor Pressure Regulator

end of the throttle boost valve exceeds the area differential on the spring side by 2½ to 1, throttle boost pressure above 60 psi primary TV pressure will increase 2.5 psi, per 1 psi primary TV.

TV pressure from the throttle booster valve is delivered to the downshift valve and throttle modulator valve.

Figure 9 shows the relationship between primary TV pressure and boosted throttle pressure.

Throttle Modulator Valve. The throttle modulator valve, located in the end of the 2-3 shift valve bore reduces throttle pressure which acts on the ends of the 2-3 shift valve and on the area differential of the 1-2 shift valve. Modulated throttle pressure in these areas provides shift delay in relation to throttle opening.

Cut Back Valve. Increased line pressure is required to prevent clutch and band slippage under stall conditions. Dependent upon car speed, the requirements for increased line pressure are considerably reduced. When governor pressure acting on the end of the cutback valve exceeds the force of TV pressure acting on its area opposing governor, the cutback valve will move cutting off primary TV pressure being fed to the upper valley of the pressure booster valve. This action reduces the assist that the pressure booster valve provides to the main regulator valve spring. The cutback valve movement will therefore vary with engine throttle opening and car speed.

1-2 Shift Valve Train. The 1-2 shift valve train is composed of the 1-2 shift valve, the D2 valve, and the 1-2 shift valve spring.

D-1 RANGE. In D1 range the 1-2 shift valve is held closed (up) by modulated throttle pressure acting on the differential area between the two lands of the 1-2 shift valve, by D fluid pressure acting on the differential in area between the two lands at the spring end of the D2 valve, and by the 1-2 shift valve spring. Governor pressure tends to move the 1-2 shift valve train against these forces. When force created by governor pressure exceeds the forces holding the 1-2 shift valve train closed, the 1-2 shift valve and D2 valve will be opened (moved downward), closing the exhaust port and allowing D fluid to pass through the D2 valve to accomplish the 1-2 shift. When

the D2 valve is moved downward D fluid is exhausted from the differential in areas provided by the lower two lands of the D2 valve. This action eliminates the force created by D fluid which tends to hold the 1-2 shift valve train closed.

If governor pressure is reduced to the point where spring force and modulated throttle pressure force exceeds governor pressure force, the 1-2 shift valve train will move up (close) cutting off the flow of D fluid through the valve and opening the exhaust port allowing a downshift to low gear.

If the throttle is open to the point where modulated throttle pressure acting on the 1-2 shift valve plus the 1-2 shift valve spring force creates a force greater than that provided by governor pressure, the 1-2 shift valve train will be closed, providing a torque demand downshift to low.

If the throttle is open through detent, the downshift valve moves to allow boosted throttle pressure to enter the modulated throttle pressure passage at the 1-2 shift valve to provide a forced 2-1 downshift.

L RANGE. In L range L-R fluid enters the modulated throttle pressure passage to provide a manual low downshift to first gear. Once the transmission is in low gear L-R fluid, which is directed to the D2 valve, passes through the D2 valve and is delivered to the spring end of the D2 valve preventing an upshift. L-R fluid which passes through the D2 valve also applies the reverse and low servo.

D2 RANGE. In D2 range, D2 fluid is introduced between the 1-2 shift and D2 valves. This action opens the D2 valve and holds it open, providing a second gear start and preventing a 2-1 downshift.

2-3 Shift Valve. The 2-3 shift valve is held closed by throttle modulator valve spring force, modulated throttle pressure force, and by D1 fluid pressure force acting on the differential in area of the lands of the valve to which it is delivered.

Governor pressure tends to open the 2-3 shift valve. When force created by governor pressure exceeds the forces holding the valve closed, the valve will move downward (open) closing the exhaust passage (through the manual valve) and opening the D1 passage to allow D1 fluid to apply the reverse-high clutch and release the intermediate servo.

With the shift valve open (down)

the throttle modulator valve is held down cutting off modulated throttle pressure to the 2-3 shift valve and 1-2 shift valve. In addition, the port which delivered D1 fluid to the differential in area of the shift valve lands, is closed.

The shift valve will be reopened (moved up) causing a downshift under one or more of the following conditions:

GOVERNOR PRESSURE REDUCED. If governor pressure is reduced to the point where it can no longer hold the shift valve down against spring force and TV pressure force, the valve will move up causing a downshift. Under closed throttle conditions, the 2-3 shift valve will close at approximately 10 mph (speed at which governor pressure is cut off). Since governor pressure is cut off at this speed the 1-2 shift valve train also closes at the same time. This will provide a 3-1 downshift when coasting in D1 range.

THROTTLE PRESSURE INCREASE. If throttle pressure is increased sufficiently, it will move the throttle modulator valve and consequently the 2-3 shift valve up, causing a 3-2 torque demand downshift.

THROTTLE PRESSURE INTRODUCED BELOW 2-3 SHIFT VALVE. If the downshift valve is moved through detent, boosted throttle pressure is directed to the undersize of the 2-3 shift valve, forcing the valve up and causing a forced 3-2 downshift. Maximum 3-2 forced downshift speed is controlled by governor pressure.

EXHAUSTING D1 FLUID FEED TO THE 2-3 SHIFT VALVE. If manual valve is moved to L range, the D1 passage which feeds oil to the 2-3 shift valve will be opened to exhaust allowing direct clutch apply-intermediate servo release fluid to exhaust, permitting the intermediate band to apply, causing a 3-2 downshift.

2-3 Back-Out Valve. The purpose of the 2-3 back-out valve is to provide smooth upshifts, when the throttle is suddenly closed while accelerating in second gear. Operation is as follows:

NORMAL THROTTLE-ON 2-3 UPSHIFTS. When the 2-3 shift valve moves to cause a 2-3 upshift, D1 fluid passes through the valve to apply the direct clutch and release the intermediate servo. This same fluid is also directed to the end of the 2-3 back-out valve. However, with throttle open, primary throttle pressure on the opposite end of the 2-3 back-out valve, assists spring force in holding the valve up, so that there will be no valve movement until after the 2-3 shift has been completed.

BACK-OUT 2-3 UPSHIFTS. When the throttle is closed during a 2-3 upshift, and before the shift is completed, there may be enough pressure in the direct clutch cylinder to apply the clutch at the reduced engine torque input, but not enough pressure to release the intermediate servo. This condition could cause a harsh 2-3 shift. However, if the throttle is closed during a 2-3 shift, primary throttle pressure will be reduced to zero (0), and reverse and direct clutch apply pressure on the end of the 2-3 back-out valve will move the valve down against spring force. This action immediately connects the clutch apply circuit to the intermediate servo apply circuit, reducing the pressure on apply side of the servo to the same value as in the direct clutch (and also on the release side of the intermediate servo). When this happens, the intermediate band is released, to provide a smooth 2-3 shift.

Manual Low Valve. The manual low valve insures that the 2-3 back-out valve will be moved up the instant that pressure drops in the direct clutch apply-intermediate servo release circuit, when a shift to manual low range is made or a forced downshift is made, from high gear. This is accomplished by directing control pressure to the end of the manual low valve, when L range is selected or, by directing TV pressure to the end of the manual low valve, when the downshift valve is moved to the downshift position.

Intermediate Band Accumulator Valve. The intermediate band accumulator valve train is composed of the intermediate band accumulator valve and spring. The intermediate band accumulator valve train in conjunction with the intermediate servo check valve controls intermediate servo apply force on all applications of the intermediate band, under all operating conditions, in D1 and D2 ranges. In low range the intermediate servo accumulator valve provides no control on the application of the intermediate band on 3-2 downshifts.

Operation is as follows:

(D1 AND D2 RANGES) (1-2 UPSHIFTS AND 3-2 DOWNSHIFTS). Fluid pressure from the D2 valve acting on the apply side of the intermediate servo piston tending to apply the servo, causes the fluid which is trapped in the intermediate servo release passage to be pressurized. This pressure acting on the area differential of the intermediate servo accumulator valve will cause the accumulator valve to move against its spring to exhaust, to maintain a certain level of pressure on the release side of the intermediate servo until it has completely stroked, applying the band. Force created by this pressure on the release side of the servo, plus spring force, is subtracted from the force of control pressure acting on the apply side of the servo, thereby controlling the servo apply force during any condition requiring the intermediate band to be on in D1 or D2 ranges.

(LOW RANGE) (3-2 DOWNSHIFT). Low and reverse pressure acting on the end of the intermediate servo accumulator valve will move the valve against the accumulator valve spring to insure that the fluid in the release side of the intermediate servo can exhaust freely.

(D1 AND D2 RANGES) (2-3 UPSHIFTS). During a 2-3 upshift, D1 fluid from the 2-3 shift valve will unseat the intermediate servo check valve, bypassing the intermediate servo accumulator valve, allowing the release side of intermediate servo to be pressurized at the same pressure level as the direct clutch.

---

2 IN-CAR ADJUSTMENTS AND REPAIRS

CONTROL LINKAGE ADJUSTMENTS

The transmission control linkage adjustments should be performed in the order in which they appear in this section of the manual.

THROTTLE AND DOWNSHIFT LINKAGE ADJUSTMENTS

1. Apply the parking brake, and place the selector lever at N.
2. Run *the engine at normal idle* speed. If the engine is cold, run the engine at fast idle speed (about 1200 rpm) until it reaches normal operating temperature. When the engine is warm, slow it down to normal idle speed.
3. Connect a tachometer to the engine.
4. Adjust engine idle speed to the specified rpm with the transmission selector lever at D1 or D2, the drive positions.

5. The carburetor throttle lever must be against the hot idle speed adjusting screw at the specified idle speed in D1 (large dot) or D2 (small dot). To make sure that the carburetor throttle lever is against the idle adjusting screw, refer to Group 10 for the carburetor adjusting procedures.

COMET, FALCON AND FAIRLANE LINKAGE—6 CYLINDER AND 289 CID ENGINES

1. With the engine off, check the accelerator pedal for a height of 4½ inches measured from the top of the pedal at the pivot point (Fig. 11 and 12) to the floor pan. To obtain the correct pedal height, adjust the accelerator connecting link at point A.
2. With the engine OFF, disconnect the downshift control cable at point B from the accelerator shaft lever.
3. With the carburetor choke in the **off** position, depress the accelerator pedal to the floor. Block the pedal to hold it in the wide open position.
4. Rotate the downshift lever C counter clockwise to place it against the internal stop.
5. With the lever held in this position, and all slack removed from the cable, adjust the trunnion so that it will slide into the accelerator shaft lever. Turn it one additional turn clockwise, then secure it to the lever with the retaining clip.
6. Remove the block to release the accelerator linkage.

COMET AND FAIRLANE LINKAGE—289 CID ENGINE

1. Disconnect the bellcrank to carburetor rod at *point C and the* accelerator connecting link from the throttle shaft at point B (Fig. 13).

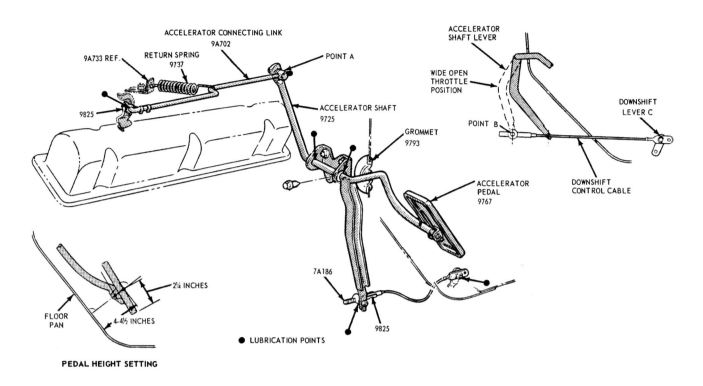

FIG. 11—Throttle Linkage with 289 CID Engine

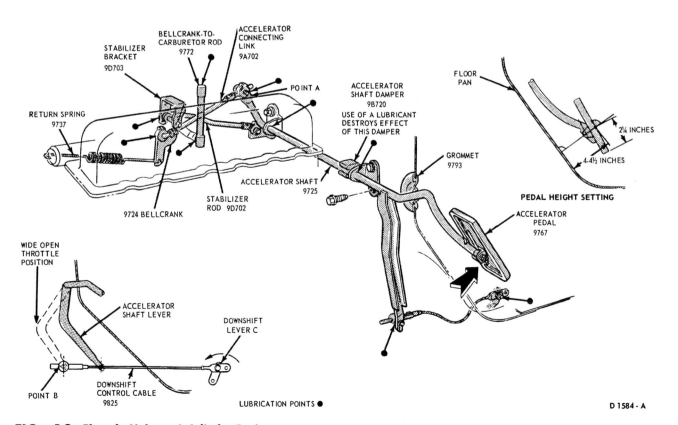

FIG. 12—Throttle Linkage 6 Cylinder Engine

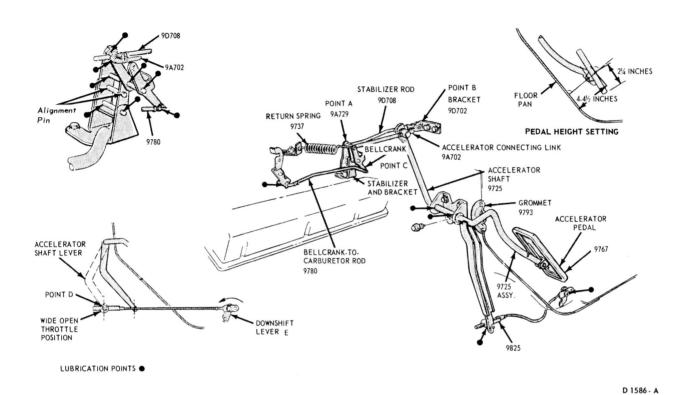

FIG. 13—Throttle Linkage with 289 CID Engine-Comet-Fairlane

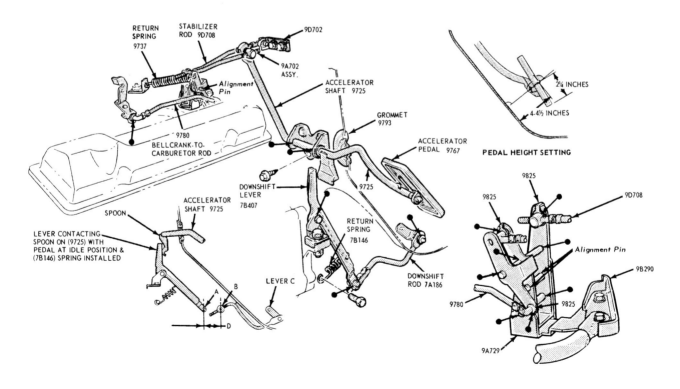

FIG. 14—Throttle Linkage—Comet and Fairlane with 390-CID Engine

2. Disconnect the stablizer rod from the stablizer at point A.

3. Insert a ¼ inch diameter pin through the stabilizer and the bracket (Fig. 13).

4. Adjust the length of the stabilizer rod so that the trunnion enters the stabilizer freely. Secure the stabilizer rod with the retaining clip.

5. Secure the carburetor-to-bellcrank rod to the bellcrank with the attaching clip at point C.

6. Adjust the length of the accelerator rod connecting link to obtain an accelerator pedal height of 4-4½ inches measured at the pedal as shown in Fig. 13. Connect the accelerator connecting link to the accelerator shaft with the retaining clip after the proper accelerator pedal height has been established.

7. With the engine **off**, disconnect the downshaft control cable at point D from the accelerator shaft lever.

8. Rotate the downshift lever E counter clockwise to place it against the internal stop.

9. With the lever held in this position, and all slack removed from the cable, adjust the trunnion so that it will slide into the downshift lever. Turn it one additional turn clockwise, then secure it to the accelerator shaft lever with the retaining clip.

10. Remove the block to release the accelerator linkage.

COMET AND FAIRLANE LINKAGE—390-CID ENGINE

1. Disconnect the bellcrank-to-carburetor rod at point C and the accelerator rod from the throttle shaft at point B (Fig. 14).

2. Disconnect the stabilizer rod from the stabilizer at point A.

3. Insert a ¼ inch diameter pin through the stabilizer and the bracket (Fig. 14).

4. Adjust the length of the stabilizer rod so that the trunnion enters the stabilizer freely. Secure the stabilizer rod with the retaining clip.

5. Secure the carburetor-to-bellcrank rod to the bellcrank with the attaching clip at point C.

6. Adjust the length of the accelerator rod to obtain an accelerator pedal height of 4-4½ inches measured at the pedal as shown in Fig. 14. Connect tthe accelerator rod to the accelerator shaft with the retaining clip after the proper accelerator pedal height has been established.

7. With the engine off, disconnect

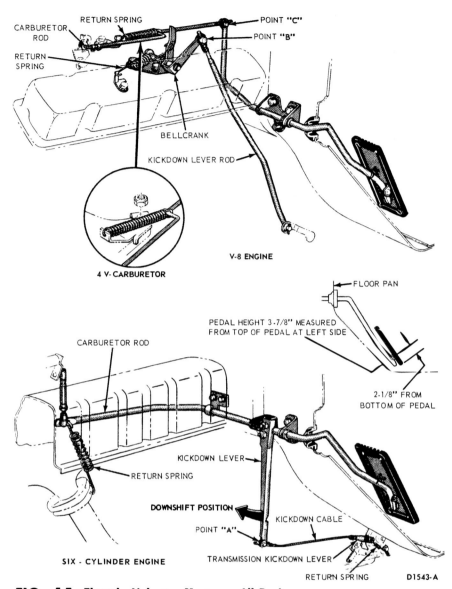

V-8 ENGINE

4 V- CARBURETOR

SIX - CYLINDER ENGINE

FIG. 15—Throttle Linkage—Mustang—All Engines

the downshift rod from the lever at point D (Fig. 14).

8. With the carburetor choke in the **off** position, depress the accelerator pedal to the floor. Block the pedal to hold it in the wide open position.

9. Rotate the downshift lever on the transmission in a counter clockwise direction to place it against the internal stop.

10. Adjust the trunnion at point D so that it enters the downshift lever freely.

11. Turn it one additional turn counter clockwise to lengthen the rod. Secure it to the lever with the retaining clip.

12. Remove the block from the accelerator pedal.

MUSTANG LINKAGE—ALL ENGINES

1. With the engine stopped and the accelerator pedal in normal idle position, check the pedal for a height of 3⅞ inches (Fig. 15). **Be sure the fast idle cam is not contacting the fast idle adjusting screw of the carburetor.**

2. To check for free pedal travel, depress the accelerator pedal to the full-throttle position (carburetor throttle lever against full-throttle stop). Release the pedal and re-check the pedal height.

3. If necessary, adjust the accelerator pedal height as follows:

On six-cylinder engines, disconnect the carburetor return spring and carburetor rod. Adjust the length of the rod to bring the pedal height within specifications. Connect the carburetor rod and tighten the jam nut. Install the return spring.

On V-8 engines, disconnect the carburetor return spring and the carburetor rod at point C (Fig. 15). Adjust the length of the rod to bring the pedal height within specifications. Connect the carburetor rod and return spring.

4. If necessary, adjust the transmission kickdown linkage as follows:

On six-cylinder engines, disconnect the kickdown cable return spring at the transmission. Disconnect the carburetor return spring at the manifold. Disconnect the kickdown cable at Point A (Fig. 15).

Position the kickdown lever in the downshift position (carburetor-wide open position). Hold the kickdown lever on the transmission against the stop, in a counterclockwise direction (kickdown position).

Adjust the trunnion at point A on the kickdown cable so it aligns with the hole in the kickdown lever and install the attaching clip. Install the return springs.

On eight-cylinder engines, disconnect the kickdown return spring at the bellcrank. Disconnect the carburetor return spring (Fig. 15).

Disconnect the kickdown lever rod at point B. Hold the carburetor rod in the wide open throttle position. The step in the rod should place the bellcrank in the downshift position. Hold the kickdown lever rod in the downward position. This positions the transmission lever in the downshift position.

Adjust the kickdown lever trunnion at point B so it aligns with the hole in the bellcrank. Install the trunnion and retaining clip. Release the levers and install the carburetor rod and bellcrank return springs.

MANUAL LINKAGE ADJUSTMENT

COMET, FALCON, FAIRLANE

Column Shift Transmission.

1. With the engine stopped, loosen the clamp at the shift lever at point A so that the shift rod is free to slide in the clamp (Fig. 16).

2. Position the transmission selector lever into the D1 (large dot) position making sure that the selector lever is against the D, stop on the selector plate.

3. Shift the manual lever at the

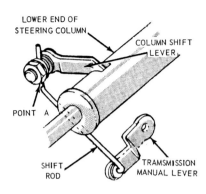

FIG. 16—Manual Linkage— Typical

transmission into the D1 detent position, second from the rear.

4. Tighten the clamp on the shift rod at point A.

5. Check the pointer alignment and transmission operation for all selector lever detent positions.

Console Shift Transmission. Before adjusting the manual linkage, check the starter neutral switch operation. If the switch needs adjusting the adjustment can be made at the time the manual linkage is adjusted. The handle must be tight on the selector lever.

1. Move the selector lever to the D1 detent position against the stop.

2. Raise the car and loosen the manual linkage rod attaching nut (Fig. 17). Move the transmission manual lever to the D1 position, second from the rear. The last detent position is low position.

3. With the selector lever and the transmission manual lever in the D1 position, tighten the rod attaching nut to specifications.

Selector Lever Removal, Adjustment and Installation.

1. Raise the car on a hoist or jack stands.

2. Remove the retainer that secures the manual linkage rod to the lower end of the manual lever (Fig. 17).

3. Remove the flat washer and two insulator washers and disconnect the rod from the arm.

4. Working from inside of the car, remove the selector lever handle attaching screw. Lift the handle off the selector lever.

5. Remove the console trim panel from the top of the console.

6. Disconnect the quadrant lamp wires from the harness.

7. Remove the four bolts that secure the selector lever control housing to the console. Lift the selector lever housing from the console.

8. It is necessary to disassemble the quadrant to adjust the selector lever. To disassemble the quadrant, remove the two retainers from the underside of the dial and the two attaching screws from the opposite side. Separate the dial, insulators, retainer, pointer and the plate from the housing.

9. Install the selector lever handle.

10. Position the selector lever as shown in Figure 19. With a feeler gauge, check the clearance between the detent pawl and plate. The clearance should be 0.005 to 0.010 inch. If necessary adjust the height of the detent pawl as shown in Figure 19.

11. Remove the handle from the selector lever.

12. Position the plate, pointer, retainer, insulators and the dial on the control housing. Secure these items with two screws and two retainers.

13. Position the selector lever housing in the console. Install the four attaching bolts (Fig. 17).

14. Connect the quadrant lamp wires to their connectors.

15. Position the console plate and secure it with the attaching screws.

16. Install the handle and the button on the selector lever. Secure the handle with the lock screw.

17. Secure the manual linkage rod to the arm with two insulating washers, a flat washer and a retainer (Fig. 17).

18. Adjust the linkage as required. Lower the car.

MUSTANG

Linkage Adjustment.

1. Position the transmission selector lever in D1 (large dot) position (Fig. 18).

2. Raise the car and loosen the manual lever control rod retaining nut. Move the transmission manual lever to the D1 position, second detent position from the back of the transmission. The last detent position is manual low.

3. With the transmission selector lever against the stop and manual lever in the D1 positions, torque the attaching nut 20 to 25 ft-lbs.

4. *Check the operation of the transmission in each selector lever position.*

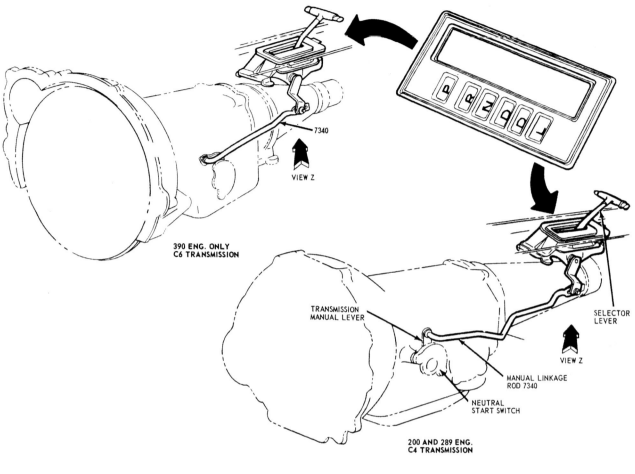

390 ENG. ONLY
C6 TRANSMISSION

VIEW Z

TRANSMISSION
MANUAL LEVER

SELECTOR
LEVER

VIEW Z

MANUAL LINKAGE
ROD 7340

NEUTRAL
START SWITCH

200 AND 289 ENG.
C4 TRANSMISSION

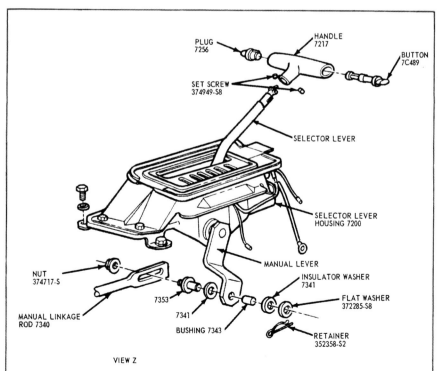

PLUG
7256

HANDLE
7217

BUTTON
7C489

SET SCREW
374949-S8

SELECTOR LEVER

SELECTOR LEVER
HOUSING 7200

MANUAL LEVER

NUT
374717-S

INSULATOR WASHER
7341

FLAT WASHER
372285-S8

7353

7341

BUSHING 7343

RETAINER
352358-S2

MANUAL LINKAGE
ROD 7340

VIEW Z

D-1626-A

FIG. 17—Manual Linkage Adjustment Console—Comet and Fairlane

Selector Lever Removal Adjustment and Installation.

1. Raise the car and remove the manual lever control rod attaching nut (Fig. 18).

2. Lower the car, remove the selector lever handle attaching screw.

3. Remove the dial housing attaching screws and the housing.

4. Remove the selector lever plate attaching screws and the plate.

5. Disconnect the dial indicator light (Fig. 19).

6. Remove the selector housing and lever assembly attaching bolts. Remove the selector lever and housing.

7. Remove the selector lever to housing attaching nut (Fig. 19). Remove the lever from the housing.

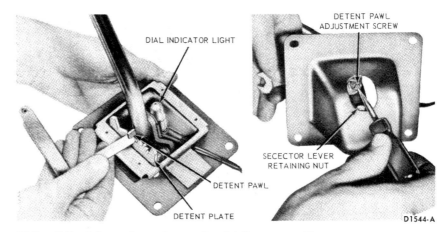

FIG. 19—Selector Lever Detent Pawl Adjustment—Mustang

8. Install the selector lever in the housing and install the attaching nut. Torque the nut to 20 to 25 ft-lbs.

9. Install the dial indicator light.

10. Install the selector lever handle.

11. Position the selector lever as shown in Figure 19. With a feeler gauge check the clearance between the detent pawl and plate. The clearance should be 0.005 to 0.010 inch. If necessary adjust the height of the detent pawl as shown in Figure 19.

12. Remove the handle from the selector lever.

13. Install the selector housing and lever assembly as shown in Figure 18. Torque the attaching bolts 8-12 ft-lbs.

14. Connect the dial indicator light wires.

15. Install the selector lever plate and tighten the attaching screws.

16. Install the dial housing and tighten the attaching screws.

17. Install the selector lever handle and tighten the attaching screw.

18. Position the selector lever in the D1 (large dot) position.

19. Raise the car. Install the transmission manual lever rod to the selector lever. Adjust the manual linkage.

20. Lower the car and check the transmission operation in each selector lever detent position.

NEUTRAL START SWITCH ADJUSTMENT

1. **With the manual lever properly adjusted,** loosen the two switch attaching bolts (Fig. 20).

2. With the transmission manual lever in neutral, rotate the switch and *insert the gauge pin* (No. 43 drill shank end) into the gauge pin holes of the switch. **The gauge pin**

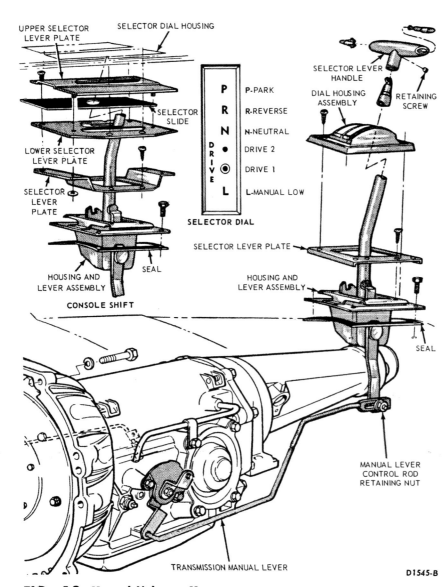

FIG. 18—Manual Linkage—Mustang

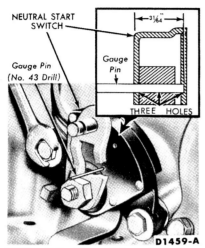

FIG. 20—Neutral Start Switch

has to be inserted to a full $3\frac{1}{64}$ inch into the three holes of the switch (Fig. 20).

3. Torque the two switch attaching bolts to specification. Remove the gauge pin from the switch.

4. Check the operation of the switch. The engine should start only with the transmission selector lever in Neutral and Park.

NEUTRAL START SWITCH REPLACEMENT

1. Remove the downshift linkage rod from the transmission downshift lever.

2. Apply penetrating oil to the downshift lever shaft and nut. Remove the transmission downshift outer lever retaining nut and lever (Fig. 20).

3. Remove the two neutral start switch attaching bolts.

4. Disconnect the two multiple wire connectors. Remove the neutral switch from the transmission.

5. Install the neutral start switch on the transmission. Install the two attaching bolts.

6. With the transmission manual lever in neutral, rotate the switch and install gauge pin (No. 43 drill) into the gauge pin hole (Fig. 20).

7. Tighten the switch attaching bolts to specification and remove the gauge pin.

8. Install the outer downshift lever and attaching nut, and torque the nut to specification. Install the downshift linkage rod to the downshift lever.

9. Install the switch wires. Connect the wire multiple connectors, red to red and blue to blue. Check the operation of the switch in each detent position. The engine should

start only with the transmission selector lever in N (neutral) and P (park).

BAND ADJUSTMENTS
INTERMEDIATE BAND

1. Clean all the dirt from the band adjusting screw area. Loosen the lock nut several turns.

2. With the tool shown in Fig. 21, tighten the adjusting screw until the tool handle clicks. The tool is a preset torque wrench which clicks and overruns when the torque on the adjusting screw reaches 10 ft-lbs.

Tool—T59P-77370-B or 7345

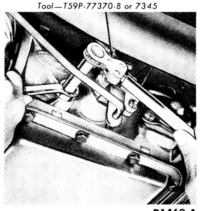

FIG. 21—Intermediate Band Adjustment

3. **Back off the adjusting screw exactly 1¾ turns.**

4. Hold the adjusting screw from turning and torque the locknut to specification.

LOW-REVERSE BAND

1. Clean all the dirt from the band adjusting screw area. Loosen the lock nut several turns.

2. With the tools shown in Fig. 22, tighten the adjusting screw until the

Tool—T59P-77370-B or 7345

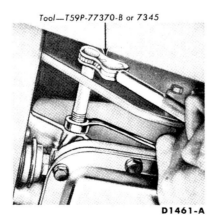

FIG. 22—Low-Reverse Band Adjustment

tool handle clicks. The tool is a preset torque wrench which clicks and overruns when the torque on the adjusting screw reaches 10 ft-lbs.

3. **Back off the adjusting screw exactly 3 full turns.**

4. Hold the adjusting screw from turning and torque the lock nut to specification.

OIL PAN AND CONTROL VALVE BODY REPLACEMENT

1. Raise the car so the transmission oil pan is accessible.

2. Loosen the oil pan retaining bolts and lower one edge of the oil pan to drain the transmission oil. **If the same fluid is to be used again, filter the fluid through a 100 mesh screen. Re-use the fluid only if it is in good condition.**

3. Remove the transmission oil pan attaching bolts, oil pan and gasket.

4. Remove the valve body to case attaching bolts (Fig. 33). Remove the valve body from the case and the transmission inner control levers.

5. Refer to the Major Repair Operation for control valve body repair operation.

6. Thoroughly clean and remove all the gasket material from the oil pan and the oil pan mounting face of the case. Install the valve body to the case, engaging the transmission inner control levers with the valve body manual and downshift valves.

7. Install the valve body to case attaching bolts. Torque the bolts to specification. **Operate the external manual and downshift levers to check for proper travel of the valve body manual and downshift valves.**

8. Place a new gasket on the oil pan. Install the oil pan and attaching bolts. Torque the bolts to specification.

9. Lower the car and fill the transmission with fluid. Check the transmission oil pan area for fluid leakage.

INTERMEDIATE SERVO REPAIR

1. Raise the car and remove the four servo cover to case attaching bolts.

2. Remove the servo cover, gasket, piston, and piston return spring. Remove the piston from the cover (Fig. 53).

3. Remove the piston seals and cover gasket.

4. Install new piston seals on the piston. Lubricate the piston seals with clean transmission fluid. Install

the servo piston in the cover.

5. Install the piston return spring in the case. Place a new gasket on the cover. Install the piston and cover into the transmission case making sure that the slotted end of the piston is in a horizontal position so that it will engage the strut. Use two $5/16$–18x1¼ bolts, 180° apart to position the cover against the case.

6. Install the two servo cover attaching bolts. Remove the two 1¼ -inch bolts and install two attaching bolts. Torque the bolts to specification.

7. Adjust the intermediate band. Lower the car and check the transmission fluid level.

8. If the band cannot be adjusted properly, the struts are not in position. Remove the oil pan and valve body. Install the struts, valve body, oil pan, and adjust the band. Refill the transmission with fluid.

LOW-REVERSE SERVO PISTON REPLACEMENT

1. Raise the car on a hoist.

2. Loosen the reverse band adjusting screw lock nut. Tighten the reverse band adjusting screw to 10 ft-lbs torque. (Tightening the screw will insure that the band strut will be held against the case by the band, preventing it from falling down when the reverse servo piston assembly is removed).

3. Remove the four servo cover to case attaching bolts. Remove the identification tag and vent tube retaining clip. Remove the servo cover and seal from the case.

4. Remove the reverse servo piston and stem from the case as an assembly.

5. Insert a small screwdriver in the hole of the piston stem (Fig. 52). Remove the piston attaching nut.

6. Remove the servo piston from the stem. The piston seal cannot be replaced without replacing the piston. The seal is bonded to the piston.

7. Install a new piston on the stem. Install the attaching nut. Torque the nut to specification.

8. Install the reverse servo piston assembly in the case. Make sure that the release spring is in position.

9. Install the reverse servo cover and a new seal, positioning the breather tube clip and service identification tag under the proper cover-to-case bolts. Torque the bolts to specification.

10. Adjust the reverse band.

11. Lower the car and check the transmission fluid level.

EXTENSION HOUSING BUSHING AND REAR SEAL REPLACEMENT

1. Disconnect the drive shaft from the transmission.

2. When only the rear seal needs replacing, carefully remove it with a tapered chisel or the tools shown in Fig. 23. Remove the bushing as shown in Fig. 24. **Use the bushing remover carefully so that the spline seal is not damaged.**

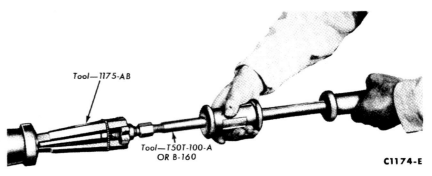

Tool—1175-AB

Tool—T50T-100-A
OR B-160

C1174-E

FIG. 23—Removing Extension Housing Seal

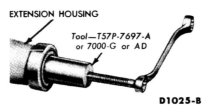

EXTENSION HOUSING

Tool—T57P-7697-A or 7000-G or AD

D1025-B

FIG. 24—Removing Extension Housing Bushing

3. When installing a new bushing use the special tool shown in Fig. 25.

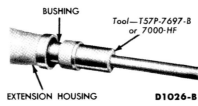

BUSHING

Tool—T57P-7697-B or 7000-HF

EXTENSION HOUSING   D1026-B

FIG. 25—Installing Extension Housing Bushing

4. Before installing a new seal, inspect the sealing surface of the universal joint yoke for scores. If scores are found, replace the yoke.

5. Inspect the counterbore of the housing for burrs and remove with crocus cloth.

6. Install the seal into the housing with the tool shown in Fig. 26. The

seal should be firmly seated in the bore. Coat the inside diameter of the fiber portion of the seal with B8A-19589-A lubricant.

7. Coat the front universal joint spline with B8A-19589-A lubricant and install the drive shaft.

EXTENSION HOUSING AND GOVERNOR REPLACEMENT

1. Raise the car on the hoist.

2. Remove the drive shaft. Position the transmission jack to support the transmission.

3. Remove the speedometer cable from the extension housing.

4. Remove the extension housing to crossmember mount attaching bolts. Raise the transmission and remove the mounting pad between the extension housing and the crossmember.

5. Loosen the extension housing attaching bolts to drain the transmission fluid. Disconnect the exhaust inlet pipes at the manifold and lower the inlet pipes.

6. Remove the six extension housing-to-case attaching bolts and remove the extension housing.

7. Remove the governor housing-to-governor distributor attaching bolts (Fig. 27). Remove the governor housing from the distributor.

8. Refer to Major Repair Operations for governor repair operations.

9. Install the governor housing on the governor distributor (Fig. 27). Install the attaching bolts and torque the bolts to specification.

10. Install a new extension housing gasket on the case. Install the extension housing and six attaching bolts. Torque the bolts to specification.

11. Install the transmission mounting pad to the crossmember. Lower the transmission and install the extension housing-to-crossmember attaching bolts. Torque the attaching bolts to specification. Remove the

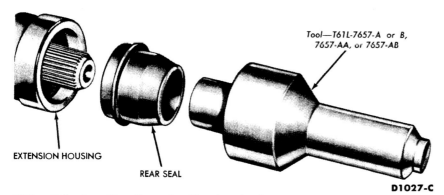

EXTENSION HOUSING

REAR SEAL

Tool—T61L-7657-A or B,
7657-AA, or 7657-AB

D1027-C

FIG. 26—Installing Extension Housing Seal

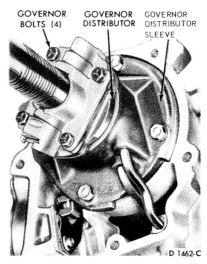

GOVERNOR BOLTS (4)   GOVERNOR DISTRIBUTOR   GOVERNOR DISTRIBUTOR SLEEVE

D 1462-C

FIG. 27—Governor Installed

transmission jack.

12. Connect the speedometer cable to the extension housing. Install the drive shaft.

13. Install the inlet pipes on the manifold.

14. Lower the car and fill the transmission with fluid.

15. Check the extension housing area for fluid leakage.

3 REMOVAL AND INSTALLATION

REMOVAL

1. Raise the car and remove the two converter cover attaching bolts at the lower front side of the converter housing. Remove the cover.

2. Remove the two converter drain plugs (Fig. 28). Drain the fluid from the converter. Install the two converter drain plugs.

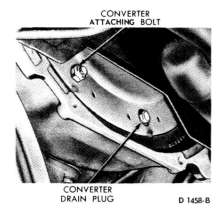

CONVERTER ATTACHING BOLT

CONVERTER DRAIN PLUG   D 1458-B

FIG. 28—Converter Drain Plug Location

3. Remove the drive shaft and install the extension housing seal replacer tool in the extension housing.

4. Disconnect the vacuum hose from the transmission vacuum unit. Disconnect the vacuum line from the retaining clip.

5. Remove the two extension housing to crossmember bolts.

6. Disconnect the speedometer cable from the extension housing.

7. Disconnect the exhaust pipe flange from the manifolds.

8. Remove the parking brake cable from the equalizer lever.

9. Loosen the transmission oil pan bolts and drain the fluid at one corner of the oil pan. Tighten the attaching bolts after the fluid has drained.

10. Disconnect the fluid cooler lines from the transmission case. Remove the fluid tube from the case.

11. Remove the manual and kickdown linkage rods from the transmission control levers.

12. Disconnect the neutral start switch wires from the retaining clamps and connectors.

13. Remove the starter cable. Remove the starter attaching bolts and remove the starter from the converter housing.

14. Remove the four converter-to-flywheel attaching nuts.

15. Position the transmission jack to support the transmission and secure the transmission to the jack with a safety chain.

16. Remove the four crossmember and mounting pad attaching bolts and lower the crossmember.

17. Remove the five converter housing-to-engine attaching bolts. Lower the transmission (Fig. 29), and remove it from under the car.

INSTALLATION

1. With the converter properly installed, place the transmission on the jack (Fig. 29). Secure the trans-

D1505-A

FIG. 29—Transmission Mounted on Jack

mission to the jack with the safety chain.

2. Raise the transmission into position and install the five converter housing-to-engine attaching bolts. Torque the bolts to specification. Remove the safety chain from the transmission.

3. Position the crossmember and mounting pad into position and install the four attaching bolts. Torque the bolts to specifications.

4. Lower the transmission and install the extension housing and cross member attaching bolts. Torque the bolts to specification.

5. Install the four flywheel-to-converter attaching nuts. Torque the nuts to specification.

6. Remove the transmission jack.

Connect the vacuum hose to the transmission vacuum unit. Install the vacuum line retaining clip.

7. Install the transmission fluid filler tube. Connect the fluid cooling lines to the transmission case.

8. Connect the neutral start switch wires to their respective connectors and secure the harness in the retaining clamps.

9. Connect the linkage rods to the transmission downshift and manual control levers.

10. Connect the speedometer cable to the extension housing.

11. Connect the exhaust inlet pipes to the manifolds.

12. Install and adjust the parking brake cable at the equalizer lever.

13. Install the converter housing cover and torque the attaching bolts to specification.

14. Install the starter and torque the bolts to specification. Connect the starter cable.

15. Install the drive shaft. Torque the companion flange U-bolt nuts to specification.

16. Lower the car and fill the transmission with fluid. Adjust the manual and kickdown linkage.

---

4 MAJOR REPAIR OPERATIONS

Before removing any of the subassemblies, thoroughly clean the outside of the transmission to prevent dirt from entering the mechanical parts. During the repair operations, refer to Part 7-1 for common adjustments and repairs or cleaning and inspection procedures.

During the transmission disassembly or assembly operations, ten thrust washers located between the sub-assemblies must be removed and installed. It is important that each thrust washer be in the correct position during the assembly operation.

To properly locate and identify the thrust washers, the various positions of the thrust washers are shown in the illustrations and are numbered 1 through 10. Number 1 is the first thrust washer located at the front pump. The last thrust washer, No. 10, is located at the parking gear.

DISASSEMBLY OF TRANSMISSION

1. Remove the converter from the transmission front pump and converter housing.

2. Remove the transmission vacuum unit with the tool shown in Fig. 30. Remove the vacuum unit gasket and control rod.

3. From the vacuum unit hole in the case, remove the primary throttle valve (Fig. 31).

4. Remove the two extension housing-to-case attaching bolts and mount the transmission in the holding fixture as shown in Fig. 32.

5. Remove the oil pan attaching bolts, and the oil pan and gasket.

6. Remove the eight control valve body attaching bolts (Fig. 33). Remove the control valve body from the case.

7. Loosen the intermediate band adjusting screw (Fig. 34) and remove

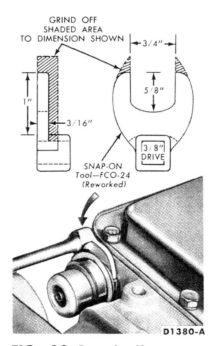

FIG. 30—Removing Vacuum Unit

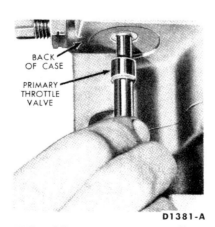

FIG. 31—Removing or Installing Primary Throttle Valve

FIG. 32—Transmission Mounted in Holding Fixture

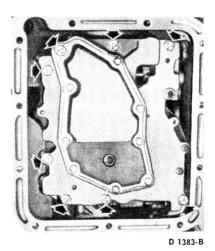

FIG. 33—Control Valve Attaching Bolts

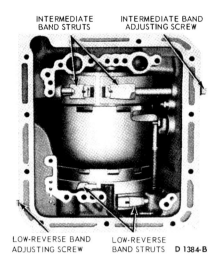

FIG. 34—Band Adjusting Studs and Struts

the intermediate band struts from the case. Loosen the low-reverse band adjusting screw and remove the low-reverse band struts (Fig. 34).

TRANSMISSION END PLAY CHECK

1. To keep the output shaft in alignment during the end play check, install the extension housing oil seal replacer tool or a front universal joint yoke in the extension housing.

2. Remove one of the front pump-to-case attaching bolts and mount the dial indicator as shown in Fig. 35.

3. The input shaft is a loose part and has to be properly engaged with the spline of the forward clutch hub during the end play checking procedure. Move the input shaft and

gear train toward the back of the transmission case.

4. With the dial indicator contacting the end of the input shaft, set the indicator at zero (Fig. 35).

5. Insert a screwdriver behind the input shell (Fig. 35). Move the input shell and the front part of the gear train forward.

6. Record the dial indicator reading. The end play should be 0.008 to 0.042 inch. If the end play is not within specifications, **the selective thrust washer (Fig. 31) must be replaced.**

When it is necessary to change a thrust washer, use the selective thickness of thrust washer No. 2 to obtain the proper end play. Fig. 36 shows the selectivity that is available to obtain the correct selective thrust washers.

REMOVAL OF CASE AND EXTENSION HOUSING PARTS

1. Rotate the holding fixture to put the transmission in a vertical position with the converter housing up.

2. Remove the six converter housing and front pump to case retaining bolts. Remove the converter housing from the front pump.

3. Remove the front pump by inserting a screwdriver behind the input shell (Fig. 38). Move the input shell forward until the front pump seal is above the edge of the case. Remove the front pump and gasket from the case. If the selective thrust washer No. 1 did not come out with the front pump, remove it from the top of the reverse-high clutch.

4. Remove the intermediate and

SELECTIVE THRUST WASHERS *

WASHER NO. 1 (FIBER)		WASHER NO. 2 (STEEL-BACK BRONZE)	
THICKNESS (INCHES)	IDENTIFICATION (DYE-COLOR)	THICKNESS (INCHES)	IDENTIFICATION (STAMPED NO.)
0.038-.042	GREEN	0.041-.043	1
0.053-.057	TAN	0.053-.056	2
0.070-.074	BLACK	0.073-.075	3
0.087-.091	YELLOW	0.090-.092	4
0.104-.108	BLUE	0.107-.109	5
0.121-0.125	RED		
0.138-0.142	PURPLE		

* SELECTION IN PAIRS NOT APPLICABLE

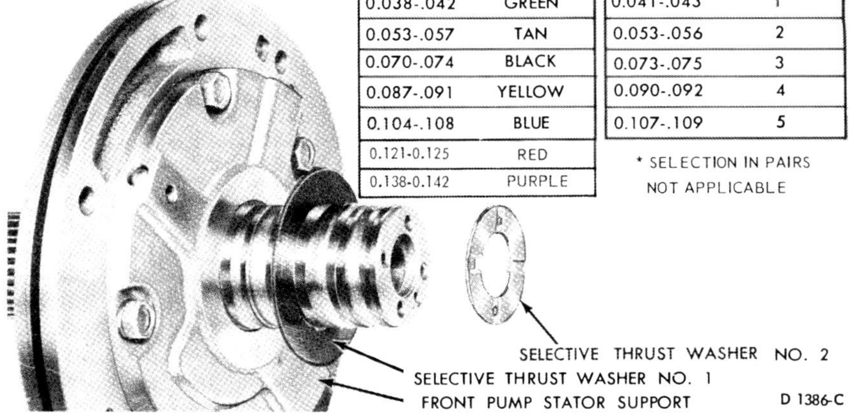

SELECTIVE THRUST WASHER NO. 2
SELECTIVE THRUST WASHER NO. 1
FRONT PUMP STATOR SUPPORT   D 1386-C

FIG. 36—Selective Thrust Washer Locations

Tool—4201-C   D1385-B

FIG. 35—Checking End Play

7. Remove the dial indicator and remove the input shaft from the front pump stator support (Fig. 37).

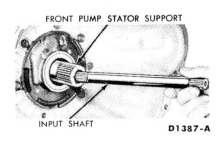

FRONT PUMP STATOR SUPPORT

INPUT SHAFT   D1387-A

FIG. 37—Removing or Installing Input Shaft

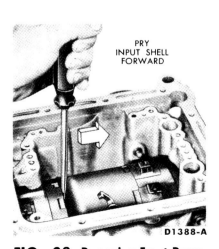

PRY INPUT SHELL FORWARD

D1388-A

FIG. 38—Removing Front Pump

INTERMEDIATE BAND CLEARANCE
HOLE IN CASE　　　**D1389-A**

FIG. 39—Removing or Installing Intermediate Band

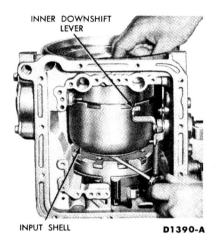

INNER DOWNSHIFT LEVER

INPUT SHELL　　　**D1390-A**

FIG. 40—Lifting Input Shell and Gear Train

low-reverse band adjusting screws from the case. Rotate the intermediate band to align the band with the clearance hole in the case (Fig. 39). Remove the intermediate band from the case. If the intermediate band is to be re-used, do not clean it in a vapor degreaser, or with a detergent

solution. Clean the band with a lint free cloth.

5. Using a screwdriver between the input shell and rear planet carrier (Fig. 40) lift the input shell upward and remove the forward part of the gear train as an assembly (Fig. 41).

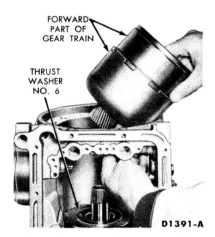

FORWARD PART OF GEAR TRAIN

THRUST WASHER NO. 6

D1391-A

FIG. 41—Removing or Installing Forward Part of Gear Train

6. Place the forward part of the gear train in the holding fixture shown in Fig. 42.

7. From the gear train in the holding fixture, remove the reverse-high clutch and drum from the forward clutch (Fig. 43).

8. If thrust washer No. 2 (Fig. 31) did not come out with the front pump, remove the thrust washer from the forward clutch cylinder. Remove the forward clutch from the

forward clutch hub and ring gear (Fig. 43).

9. If thrust washer No. 3 (Fig. 42) did not come out with the forward clutch, remove the thrust washer from the forward clutch hub.

10. Remove the forward clutch hub and ring gear from the front planet carrier (Fig. 43).

11. Remove thrust washer No. 4 and the front planet carrier from the input shell.

12. Remove the input shell, sun gear and thrust washer No. 5 from the holding fixture (Fig. 43).

13. From inside the transmission case, remove thrust washer No. 6

FORWARD GEAR TRAIN ASSEMBLY

Holding Fixture Tool—77530-A　　**D1392-A**

FIG. 42—Forward Part of Gear Train Positioned in Holding Fixture

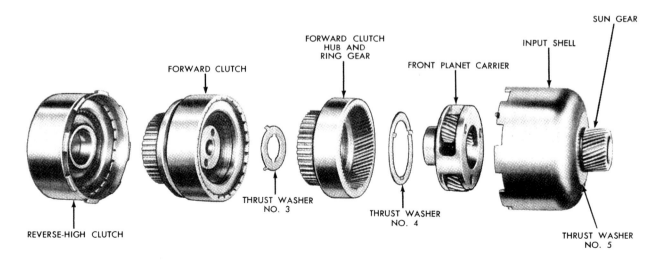

FORWARD CLUTCH

FORWARD CLUTCH HUB AND RING GEAR

FRONT PLANET CARRIER

INPUT SHELL

SUN GEAR

THRUST WASHER NO. 3

THRUST WASHER NO. 4

THRUST WASHER NO. 5

REVERSE-HIGH CLUTCH

D1393-A

FIG. 43—Forward Part of Gear Train Disassembled

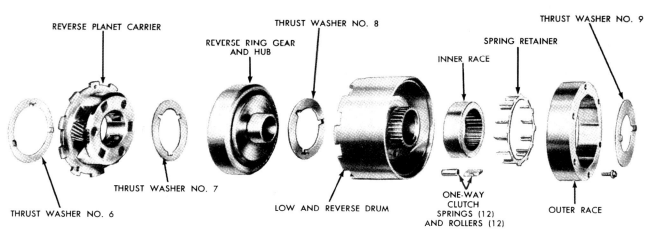

FIG. 44—Lower Part of Gear Train Disassembled

(Fig. 44) from the top of the reverse planet carrier.

14. Remove the reverse planet carrier and thrust washer No. 7 from the reverse ring gear and hub (Fig. 44).

15. Move the output shaft forward and with the tool shown in Fig. 45 remove the reverse ring gear hub to output shaft retaining ring.

FIG. 45—Removing or Installing Reverse Ring Gear Hub Retaining Ring

16. Remove the reverse ring gear and hub from the output shaft. Remove thrust washer No. 8 from the low and reverse drum.

17. Remove the low-reverse band from the case (Fig. 46).

18. Remove the low-reverse drum from the one-way clutch inner race (Fig. 44).

19. Remove the one-way clutch inner race by rotating the race clockwise as it is removed.

20. Remove the 12 one-way clutch rollers, springs and the spring

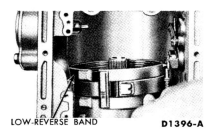

FIG. 46—Removing or Installing Low-Reverse Band

FIG. 47—Removing or Installing Output Shaft and Governor Distributor

retainer from the outer race (Fig. 44). **Do not lose or damage any of the 12 springs or rollers. The outer race of the one-way clutch cannot be removed from the case until the extension housing, output shaft and governor distributor sleeve are removed.**

21. Remove the transmission from the holding fixture. Position the transmission on the bench in a vertical position with the extension housing up. Remove the four extension housing-to-case attaching bolts. Remove the extension housing and gasket from the case.

22. Pull outward on the output shaft and remove the output shaft and governor distributor assembly from the governor distributor sleeve (Fig. 47).

23. Remove the governor distributor lock ring from the output shaft (Fig. 48). Remove the governor distributor from the output shaft.

24. Remove the four distributor sleeve-to-case attaching bolts. Remove the distributor sleeve from the case. **Do not bend or distort the oil tubes as the tubes are removed**

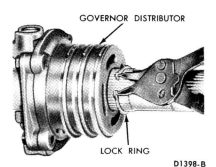

FIG. 48—Removing or Installing Governor Distributor Lock Ring

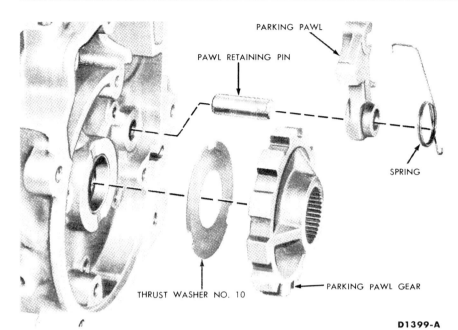

FIG. 49—Parking Pawl Mechanism

from the case with the distributor sleeve.

25. Remove the parking pawl return spring, pawl and retaining pin from the case (Fig. 49).

26. Remove the parking gear and thrust washer No. 10 from the case.

27. Remove the six one-way clutch outer race to case attaching bolts with the tool shown in Fig. 50. As the bolts are removed, hold the outer race located inside the case in position. Remove the outer race and thrust washer No. 9 from the case (Fig. 44).

PARTS REPAIR OR REPLACEMENT

During the repair of the sub-assemblies, certain general instruc-

tions which apply to all units of the transmissions must be followed. These instructions are given here to avoid unnecessary repetition.

Handle all transmission parts carefully to avoid nicking or burring the bearing or mating surfaces.

Lubricate all internal parts of the transmission before assembly with clean automatic transmission fluid. **Do not use any other lubricants except on gaskets and thrust washers which may be coated with vaseline to facilitate assembly.** Always install new gaskets when assembling the transmission.

Tighten all bolts and screws to the recommended torque outlined in the Specification Section.

TRANSMISSION CASE AND LINKAGE REPAIR

Low-Reverse Servo.

1. Remove the four servo cover to case attaching bolts. Remove the transmission identification tag, vent tube and retaining clip from the case.

2. Remove the servo cover, cover seal, servo piston and piston return spring from the case (Fig. 51).

3. The servo piston seal is bonded to the piston. If the seal has to be replaced, replace the piston assembly which includes the seal. Disassemble the servo piston from the piston rod by inserting a small screwdriver in the hole of the piston rod and removing the piston attaching nut (Fig. 52). Install the new servo piston and torque the piston attaching nut to specification.

4. Place the piston return spring in the servo bore of the case. Lubricate the piston seal with clean transmission fluid and install the servo piston (Fig. 51).

5. Place a new cover seal on the cover and install the servo cover. Install the identification tag and the vent tube and retaining clip. Install

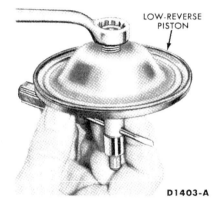

FIG. 52—Removing or Installing Low-Reverse Servo Piston

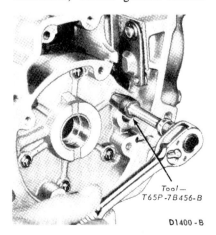

FIG. 50—Removing One-Way Clutch Outer Race Attaching Bolts

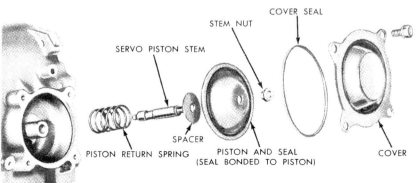

FIG. 51—Low-Reverse Servo Disassembled

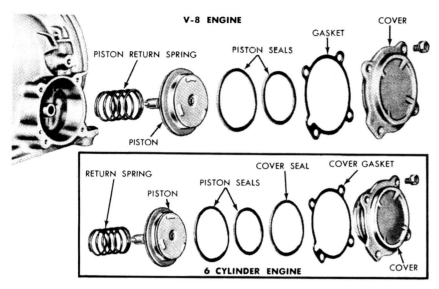

FIG. 53—Intermediate Servo Disassembled

the four cover attaching bolts. Torque the cover to case retaining bolts to specification.

Intermediate Servo Repair

1. Remove the four servo cover-to-case attaching bolts.
2. Remove the servo cover, gasket, servo piston, and piston return spring from the case (Fig. 53).
3. On a transmission used with six cylinder engines, remove the intermediate servo piston from the cover by inserting air pressure into the pressure hole in the cover (Fig 54).

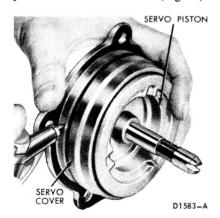

FIG. 54—Removing Intermediate Servo Piston—6 Cylinder Engine

4. Remove the seal rings from the servo piston and cover.
5. Install a new seal on the cover and servo piston. Figure 55 shows the correct servo piston and cover for each transmission model. Lubri-

cate the seals with clean transmission oil. Install the piston into the cover. Be careful not to damage the piston seal.
6. Install the piston return spring in the servo bore of the case.
7. Place a new gasket on the servo cover. Position the servo piston and cover assembly into the case

making sure that the slot is in a horizontal position to engage the strut. Use two 5/16-18 bolts, 1¼ inch long, 180° apart, to position the cover against the case. Install two cover attaching bolts. Remove the two 1¼ inch bolts and install the other two cover attaching bolts. Torque the attaching bolts to specification.

Downshift and Manual Linkage

1. Remove the downshift outer lever attaching nut. Remove the downshift outer and inner levers. Remove the neutral start switch by placing a screwdriver behind the switch and carefully prying the switch off of the lever. From inside the transmission case, remove the upper retaining ring and flat washer from the manual lever link (Fig. 56). Remove the upper end of the lever link from the case retaining pin.
2. From the back of the transmission case, remove the upper retaining ring and flat washer from the parking pawl link (Fig. 57). Remove the pawl link from the case retaining pin.
3. From the back of the transmission case, remove the parking pawl link, toggle rod, and manual lever link as an assembly (Fig. 58).

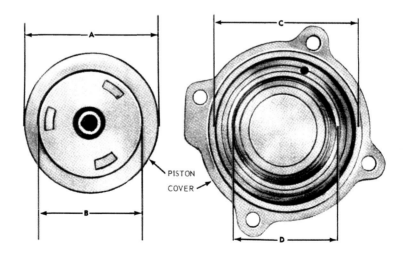

CAR	ENGINE	TRANS. MODEL	SERVO PISTON		SERVO COVER	
			DIA. A	DIA. B	INSIDE DIA. C	INSIDE DIA. D
FALCON	170-IV	PCS-V	3.3265	2.3765	3.340	2.390
CFFM	200-IV	PCS-Y, W & AA	3.3265	2.4865	3.340	2.500
CFFM	289-2V, 4V	PCW-AN, AS & AR	3.7875	2.8265	NONE	2.840
FAIRLANE	289-4V H.P.	PCW-AY & AZ	3.7875	3.1175	NONE	3.131

D 1492-F

FIG. 55—Intermediate Servo Piston and Cover Identification

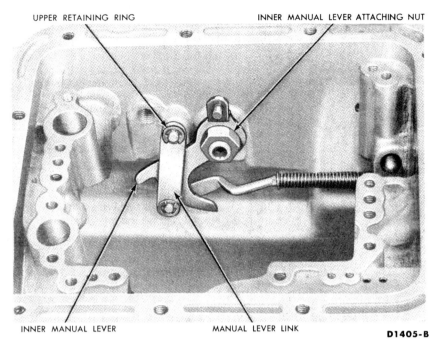

UPPER RETAINING RING　　　INNER MANUAL LEVER ATTACHING NUT

INNER MANUAL LEVER　　　MANUAL LEVER LINK

D1405-B

FIG. 56–Case Internal Linkage

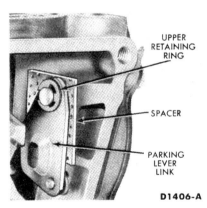

UPPER RETAINING RING

SPACER

PARKING LEVER LINK

D1406-A

FIG. 57–Parking Pawl Link Installed

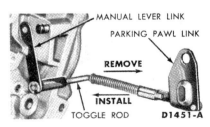

MANUAL LEVER LINK

PARKING PAWL LINK

REMOVE

INSTALL

TOGGLE ROD　D1451-A

FIG. 58–Removing or Installing Parking Pawl Toggle Rod

4. Remove the rear parking pawl link lower retaining ring, flat washer and link from the toggle rod (Fig. 59).

5. Remove the manual lever link lower retaining ring, flat washer and link from the toggle rod.

6. Remove the inner manual

attaching nut and lever. Remove the outer manual lever from the case.

7. To remove the manual lever seal, use the tools shown in Fig. 60. To install the new seal, use the tool shown in Fig. 61.

8. Install the outer manual lever in the case. Install the inner manual lever and attaching nut (Fig. 56). Torque the nut to specification.

9. From the back of the transmission case, install the parking toggle rod and link assembly into the case (Fig. 58).

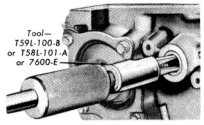

Tool— T59L-100-B or T58L-101-A or 7600-E

D1408-A

FIG. 60–Removing Manual Lever Seal

Tool—77288

D1409-A

FIG. 61–Installing Manual Lever Seal

10. Install the parking pawl link on the case retaining pin. Install the flat washer and link retaining ring (Fig. 57).

11. Position the inner manual lever behind the manual lever link, with the cam of the lever contacting the lower link pin (Fig. 62).

12. Install the upper end of the manual lever link on the case re-

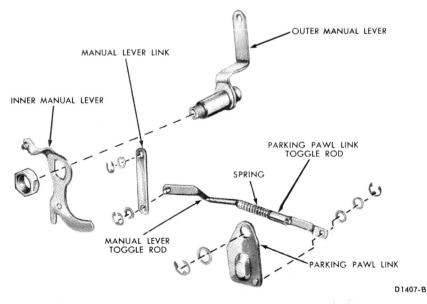

MANUAL LEVER LINK

OUTER MANUAL LEVER

INNER MANUAL LEVER

PARKING PAWL LINK TOGGLE ROD

SPRING

MANUAL LEVER TOGGLE ROD

PARKING PAWL LINK

D1407-B

FIG. 59–Case Linkage

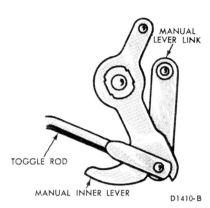

FIG. 62—Inner Manual Lever Location

taining pin. Install the flat washer and retaining ring.

13. Operate the manual lever and check for correct linkage operation.

14. Install the neutral start switch.

15. Install the inner and outer downshift levers. Torque the attaching nut to specifications.

Thread Repair—Case. Thread service kits may be purchased from local jobbers or the Heli-Coil Corporation. To repair a damaged thread, the following procedures should be carefully followed.

1. Drill out the damaged threads, **using the same drill size as the thread OD.** For example, use a $\frac{5}{16}$-inch drill for a $\frac{5}{16}$-18 thread.

2. Select the proper **special** tap and tap the drilled hole. The tap is marked for the size of the thread being repaired. Thus, the special tap marked $\frac{5}{16}$-18 will not cut the same thread as a standard $\frac{5}{16}$-18 tap. It does cut a thread large enough to accommodate the insert, and after the insert is installed the original thread size ($\frac{5}{16}$-18) is restored.

3. Select the proper coil inserting tool. These tools are marked with the thread size being repaired. Place the insert on the tool and adjust the sleeve to the length of the insert being used.

Press the insert against the face of the tapped hole. Turn the tool clockwise and wind the insert into the hole until the insert is ½ turn below the face.

4. Working through the insert, bend the insert tang straight up and down until it breaks off at the notch.

5. If the inserts are not properly installed, they can be removed with the extractor tool. Place the extractor tool in the insert so that the blade rests against the top coil ¼ to ½ turn away from the end of the

coil. Tap the tool sharply with a hammer so that the blade cuts into the insert. Exert downward pressure on the tool and turn it counterclockwise until the insert is removed.

CONTROL VALVE

Disassembly

1. Remove the screws that attach the oil screen to the body and remove the screen (Fig. 63).

2. Remove the lower valve body attaching screws and separate the lower valve body, separator plate, gasket and hold-down plates (Fig. 64) from the upper valve body.

3. Depress the manual valve detent spring with the tool shown in Fig. 65. Remove the spring retaining pin (roll pin) from the upper valve

body. Remove the spring and detent plunger.

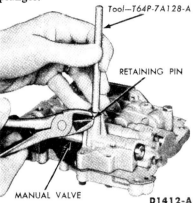

FIG. 65—Removing Manual Valve

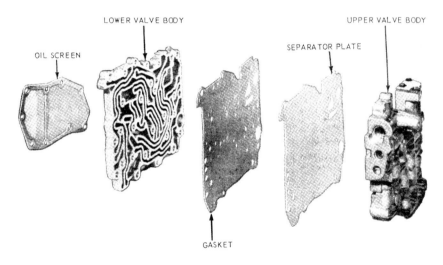

FIG. 63—Upper and Lower Valve Bodies Disassembled

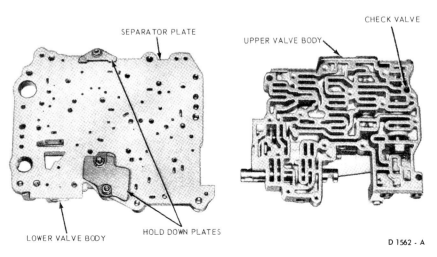

FIG. 64—Separating Upper and Lower Valve Bodies

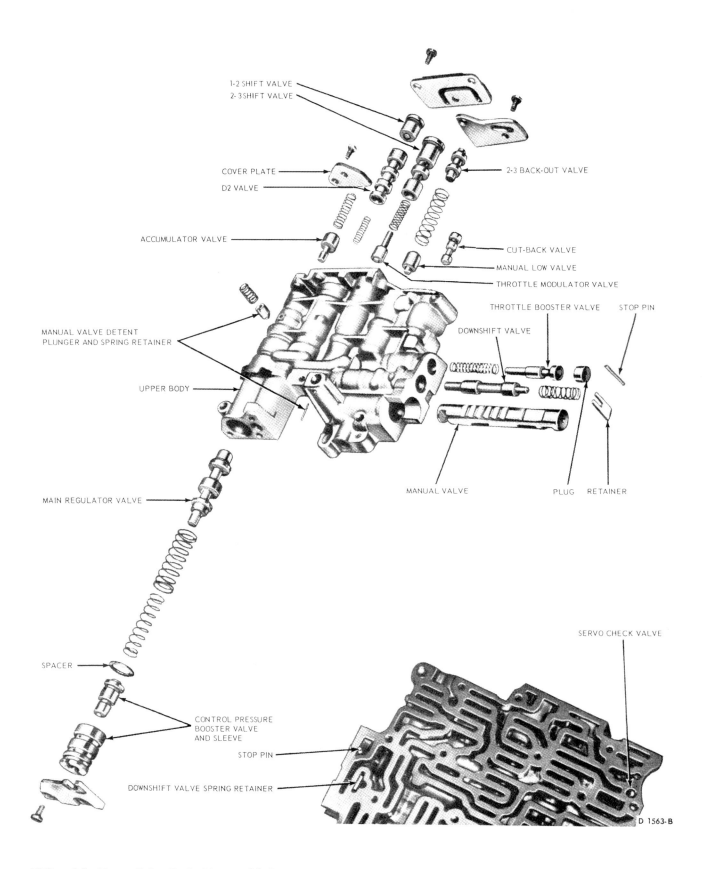

FIG. 66—Upper Valve Body Disassembled

4. Slide the manual valve out of the body.

5. Remove the cut-back and the back-out valve cover plate from the valve body (Fig. 66).

6. Remove the cut-back valve from the body.

7. Remove the 2-3 back-out valve, spring and the manual low valve from the body.

8. Remove the 1-2 shift valve and the 2-3 shift valve cover plate from the valve body.

9. Remove the 2-3 shift valve and the throttle modulator valve from the body.

10. Remove the 1-2 shift valve, D2 valve and the spring from the body.

11. Remove the intermediate band accumulator valve cover plate from the valve body.

12. Remove the spring and the intermediate band accumulator valve.

13. Remove the pressure booster valve cover plate (Fig. 66).

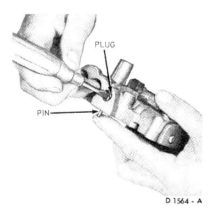

FIG. 67—Removing Throttle Booster Valve

14. Remove the pressure booster valve, washer, springs and the main regulator valve.

15. Carefully pry the downshift valve retainer from the body, then remove the spring and valve.

16. Hold the upper valve body as shown in Fig. 67 and depress the throttle booster valve plug to release the retaining pin. Remove the plug, valve and the spring.

17. Remove the two hold-down plates and the separator plate from the lower valve body.

Assembly

1. Position the separator plate and the two hold-down plates on the lower valve body and install the four attaching screws and torque them to specification.

2. Place the throttle booster valve spring, valve (long end into spring) and the plug (Fig. 66). Depress the plug and install the retaining pin.

3. Insert the downshift valve into the body with the large diameter facing inward. Install the downshift valve spring and the retainer (Fig. 66).

4. Place the main regulator valve in the body with the large diameter facing inward. Install the two springs and the spacer, pressure booster valve and sleeve.

5. Hold the pressure booster valve cover plate in place and install the three attaching screws and torque them to specification.

6. Position the intermediate band accumulator valve and spring in the body. Secure the cover to the body with the attaching screw. Torque the screw to specifications.

7. Position the spring, D2 valve and the 1-2 shift valve in the body.

8. Place the throttle modulator valve, spring, and 2-3 shift valve in the body.

9. Secure the 1-2 shift valve and the 2-3 valve cover plate to the body and torque the screws to specifications.

10. Place the manual low valve, spring, and the 2-3 back-out valve in the body.

11. Place the cut-back valve in the body.

12. Secure the cut-back and the back-out cover plate to the body with two screws. Torque the screws to specifications.

13. Slide the manual valve into the body making sure that the notch for the manual lever is toward the inside and that the detent notches are facing upward.

14. Place the detent plunger and spring in the body. Depress the spring and install a new roll pin.

15. Position a new rubber check valve in the upper valve body (Fig. 64).

16. Place a new gasket, separator plate and the lower valve body in place on the upper valve body and secure them with the attaching screws. Torque the screws to specifications.

17. Secure the oil screen to the body with the attaching screws. Torque the screws to specifications.

FRONT PUMP

1. Remove the four seal rings from the stator support and the O-ring seal from the pump housing.

2. Remove the five bolts that attach the stator support to the front pump housing. Remove the stator support from the pump housing (Fig. 68).

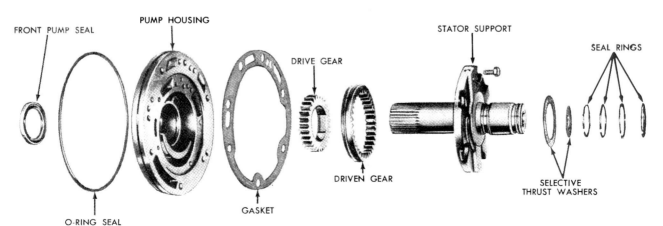

FIG. 68—Front Pump and Stator Support Disassembled

3. Remove the drive and driven gears from the front pump housing.

4. Install the drive and driven gears in the pump housing. Each

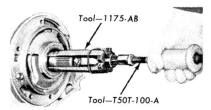

FIG. 69—Removing Front Pump Seal

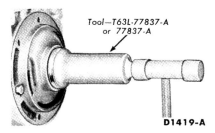

FIG. 70—Installing Front Pump Seal

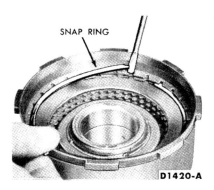

FIG. 71—Removing Reverse-High Clutch Snap Ring

gear has an identification mark on the side of the gear teeth that are chamfered. **The chamfered side with the identification mark has to be positioned downward against the face of the pump housing.**

5. Place the stator support in the pump housing and install the five attaching bolts. Torque the bolts to specifications.

6. Install the four seal rings on the stator support. Two large rings are assembled first in the ring grooves toward the front of the stator support. Install the O-ring seal on the pump housing (Fig. 68).

7. Check the pump gears for free rotation by placing the pump on the converter drive hub in its normal running position and turning the pump housing.

8. If the front pump seal must be replaced, mount the pump in the transmission case and remove the seal with the tool shown in Fig. 69. To install the new seal use the tool shown in Fig. 70.

REVERSE-HIGH CLUTCH

1. Remove the pressure clutch plate retaining snap ring (Fig. 71).

2. Remove the pressure plate, and the drive and driven clutch plates. (Fig. 72). If the composition clutch plates are to be reused, do not clean the plates in a vapor degreaser or with a detergent solution. Wipe the plates clean with lint-free cloth.

3. To remove the piston spring retainer snap ring, place the clutch hub in the arbor press. With the tools shown in Fig. 73, compress the piston return springs and remove the snap ring. When the arbor press ram is released, guide the spring retainer to clear the snap ring groove of the drum.

4. Remove the spring retainer and ten piston return springs.

5. Remove the piston by inserting air pressure in the piston apply hole of the clutch hub (Fig. 74).

6. Remove the piston outer seal from the piston and the piston inner seal from the clutch drum.

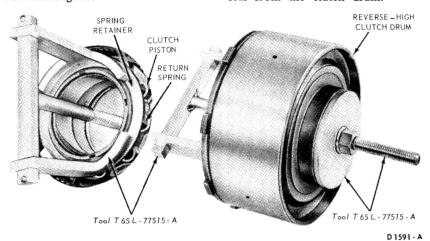

FIG. 73—Removing or Installing Clutch Piston Spring Retainer Snap Ring

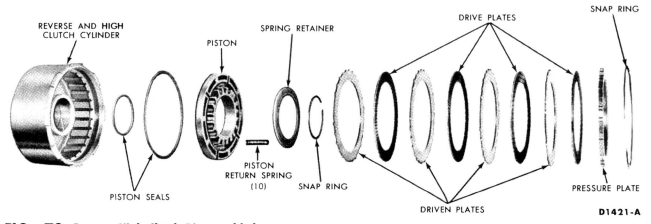

FIG. 72—Reverse-High Clutch Disassembled

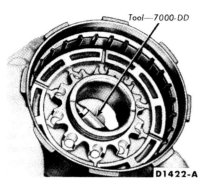

FIG. 74—Removing Reverse-High Clutch Piston

FIG. 75—Checking Reverse-High Clutch Snap Ring Clearance

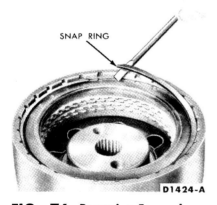

FIG. 76—Removing Forward Clutch Pressure Plate Snap Ring

7. Install a new inner seal in the clutch drum and a new outer seal on the clutch piston (Fig. 71). Lubricate the seals with clean transmission fluid and install the piston into the clutch drum.

8. Place the ten clutch piston springs into position on the clutch piston. Place the spring retainer on top of the springs. To install the snap ring, use the tools shown in Fig. 73. As the press ram is moved downward, make sure the spring retainer is centered to clear the drum. Install the snap ring. **Before the press ram is released make sure the snap ring is positioned inside of the four snap ring guides on the spring retainer.**

9. When new composition clutch plates are used, soak the plates in transmission oil for fifteen minutes before the plates are assembled. Install the clutch plates alternately by starting first with a steel plate then a non-metallic plate (Fig. 72). The last plate installed is the pressure plate. For the correct number of clutch plates required for each transmission model, refer to Part 7-4.

10. Install the pressure plate retaining snap ring (Fig. 71). Make sure the snap ring is fully seated in the snap ring groove of the clutch hub.

11. With a feeler gauge, check the clearance between the snap ring and the pressure plate (Fig. 75).

12. The pressure plate should be held downward as the clearance is checked. The clearance should be 0.050-0.060 inch. If the clearance is not within specifications, selective thickness snap rings are available in these thicknesses, 0.102-0.106, 0.088-0.092, 0.074-0.078, 0.060-0.064 and 0.102-0.106 inch. Install

the correct size snap ring and recheck the clearance.

FORWARD CLUTCH

1. Remove the clutch pressure plate retaining snap ring (Fig. 76).

2. Remove the pressure plate, and the drive and driven clutch plates from the clutch hub (Fig. 77).

3. Remove the disc spring retaining snap ring (Fig. 78).

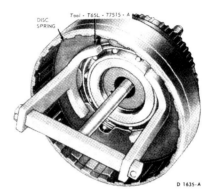

FIG. 78—Removing or Installing Disc Spring Snap Ring

FIG. 79—Removing Forward Clutch Piston

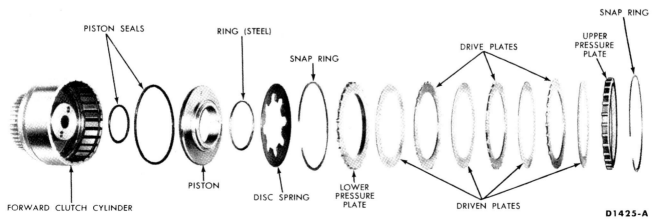

FIG. 77—Forward Clutch Disassembled

4. Apply air pressure at the clutch piston pressure hole (Fig. 79), to remove the piston from the clutch hub.

5. Remove the clutch piston outer seal and the inner seal from the clutch hub (Fig. 77).

6. Install new clutch piston seals on the clutch piston and drum. Lubricate the seals with clean transmission fluid.

7. Install the clutch piston into the clutch hub. Install the steel ring on the piston. Install the disc spring and retaining snap ring (Fig. 78).

8. Install the lower pressure plate with the flat side up and radius side downward.

Install one non-metallic clutch plate and alternately install the drive and driven plates. The last plate installed will be the top pressure plate. (Fig. 77). Refer to Specification Section for the correct number of clutch plates for the applicable model transmission.

9. Install the pressure plate retaining snap ring (Fig. 76). Make sure the snap ring is fully seated in the ring groove of the clutch hub.

10. With a feeler gauge, check the clearance between the snap ring and the pressure plate (Fig. 80). Downward pressure on the plate should be used when making this check. The clearance should be 0.020-0.036 inch for transmissions having four internal splined clutch plates and 0.026-0.042 inch for transmissions having five internal splined clutch plates.

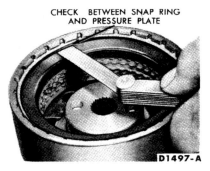

CHECK BETWEEN SNAP RING AND PRESSURE PLATE

D1497-A

FIG. 80—Checking Forward Clutch Snap Ring Clearance

11. If the clearance is not within specifications, selective snap rings are available in these thicknesses, 0.102-0.106, 0.088-0.092, 0.074-0.078 and 0.060-0.064 inch. Insert the correct size snap ring and recheck the clearance.

FORWARD CLUTCH HUB AND RING GEAR

1. Remove the forward clutch hub retaining snap ring (Fig. 81).

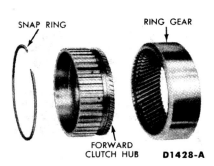

SNAP RING　　　　RING GEAR

FORWARD CLUTCH HUB　D1428-A

FIG. 81—Forward Clutch Hub and Ring Gear Disassembled

2. Remove the forward clutch hub from the ring gear.

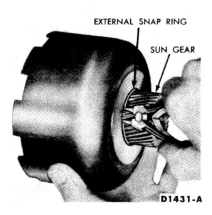

EXTERNAL SNAP RING

SUN GEAR

D1431-A

FIG. 82—Removing or Installing Sun Gear External Snap Ring

3. Install the forward clutch hub in the ring gear. Make sure the hub is bottomed in the groove of the ring gear.

4. Install the front clutch hub retaining snap ring. Make sure the snap ring is fully seated in the snap ring groove of the ring gear.

INPUT SHELL AND SUN GEAR

1. Remove the external snap ring from the sun gear (Fig. 82).

2. Remove thrust washer No. 5 from the input shell and sun gear (Fig. 83).

3. From inside the input shell, remove the sun gear. Remove the internal snap ring from the sun gear.

4. Install the internal snap ring on the sun gear. Install the sun gear in the input shell.

5. Install thrust washer No. 5 on the sun gear and input shell (Fig. 83).

6. Install the external snap ring on the sun gear (Fig. 82).

REVERSE RING GEAR AND HUB

1. Remove the hub retaining snap ring from the reverse ring gear.

2. Remove the hub from the reverse ring gear (Fig. 84).

3. Install the hub in the reverse ring gear. Make sure the hub is fully seated in the groove of the ring gear.

4. Install the snap ring in the reverse ring gear. Make sure the snap ring is fully seated in the snap ring groove of the ring gear.

GOVERNOR AND OIL DISTRIBUTOR

1. Remove the rings from the governor oil distributor (Fig. 85).

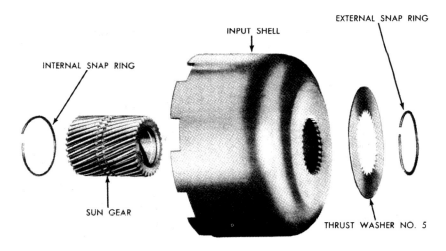

INTERNAL SNAP RING

INPUT SHELL

EXTERNAL SNAP RING

SUN GEAR

THRUST WASHER NO. 5

D1432-A

FIG. 83—Input Shell and Sun Gear Disassembled

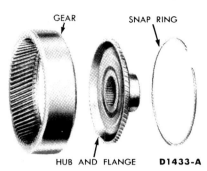

FIG. 84—Reverse Ring Gear and Hub Disassembled

2. Remove the governor housing to distributor attaching bolts. Remove the governor from the oil distributor.

3. Remove the primary governor valve retaining ring (Fig. 86). Remove the washer, spring, and primary governor valve from the housing.

4. Remove the secondary governor valve spring retaining clip, spring, and governor valve from the housing.

5. Install the secondary governor valve in the housing. Install the spring and retaining clip. **Make sure the clip is installed with the small concaved area facing downward, to hold the spring in the correct position.**

6. Install the primary governor valve in the housing. Install the spring, washer and retaining ring. **Make sure the washer is centered in the housing on top of the spring and the retaining ring is fully seated in the ring groove of the housing.**

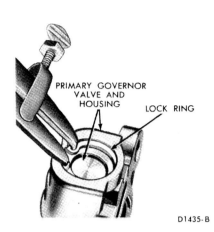

FIG. 86—Removing or Installing Retaining Ring

7. Install the governor assembly on the oil distributor and torque the attaching bolts to specification.

8. Install the rings on the distributor. Check the rings for free rotation in the ring grooves of the oil distributor.

ASSEMBLY OF TRANSMISSION

When assembling the transmission sub-assemblies (Fig. 87), make sure that the correct thrust washer is used beween certain sub-assemblies. Vaseline should be used to hold the thrust washers in their proper location. Lubricate thrust washers, bushings and journal with automatic transmission fluid. If the end play is not within specifications,

after the transmission is assembled, either the wrong selective thrust washers were used, or a thrust washer came out of position during the transmission assembly operation.

1. Install thrust washer No. 9 inside the transmission case (Fig. 88).

2. Place the one-way clutch outer race inside the case. From the back of the case install the six outer race to case attaching bolts. **Torque the bolts to specification with the tools shown in Fig. 89.**

3. Place the transmission case in a vertical position with the back face of the case upward. Install the parking pawl retaining pin in the case (Fig. 90).

4. Install the parking pawl on the case retaining pin. Install the parking pawl return spring as shown in Fig. 90.

5. Install thrust washer No. 10 on the parking pawl gear (Fig. 91). Place the gear and thrust washer on the back face of the case (Fig. 90).

6. Place the two fluid distributor tubes in the governor distributor sleeve. Install the distributor sleeve on the case. As the distributor sleeve is installed, the tubes have to be inserted in the two holes in the case and the parking pawl retaining pin has to be inserted in the alignment hole in the distributor sleeve.

7. Install the four governor distributor sleeve-to-case attaching bolts and torque the bolts to specification.

8. Install the governor distributor assembly on the output shaft. Install the distributor retaining snap ring. Fig. 92 shows the correct snap ring that is to be used.

9. Check the rings in the governor distributor, making sure that they are fully inserted in the grooves and will rotate freely. Install the output shaft and governor distributor assembly in the distributor sleeve (Fig. 47).

10. Place a new extension housing gasket on the case. Install the extension housing, vacuum tube clip, and the extension housing-to-case attaching bolts. Torque the bolts to specification.

11. Place the transmission in the holding fixture with the front pump mounting face of the case up. **Make sure thrust washer No. 9 is still located at the bottom of the transmission case (Fig. 88).**

12. Install the one-way clutch spring retainer into the outer race (Fig. 93).

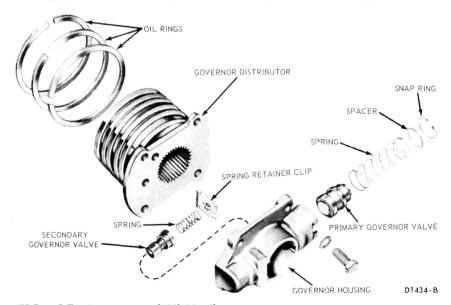

FIG. 85—Governor and Oil Distributor

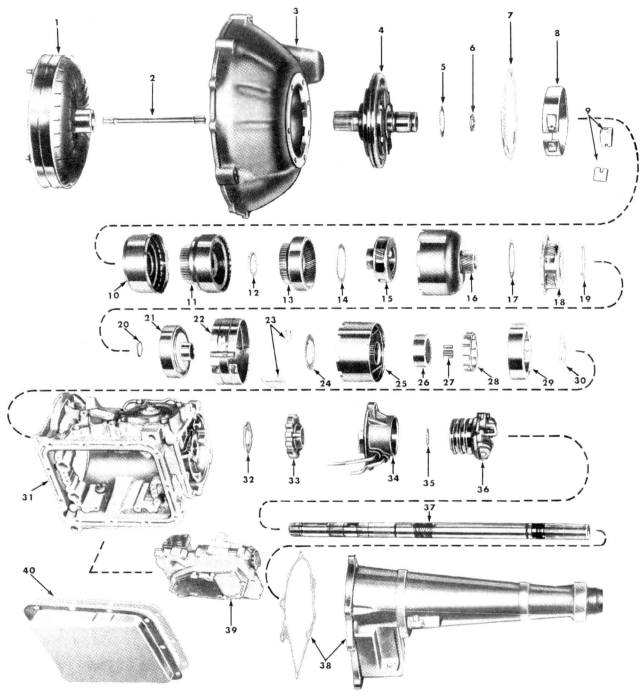

1. CONVERTER	12. THRUST WASHER NO. 3	21. REVERSE RING GEAR	30. THRUST WASHER NO. 9
2. *INPUT SHAFT*	13. FORWARD CLUTCH HUB	AND HUB	31. CASE
3. CONVERTER HOUSING	AND RING GEAR	22. LOW AND REVERSE BAND	32. THRUST WASHER NO. 10
4. FRONT PUMP	14. THRUST WASHER NO. 4	23. BAND STRUTS	33. PARKING GEAR
5. THRUST WASHER NO. 1	15. FRONT PLANET CARRIER	24. THRUST WASHER NO. 8	34. GOVERNOR DISTRIBUTOR
6. THRUST WASHER NO. 2	16. INPUT SHELL, SUN GEAR	25. LOW AND REVERSE DRUM	SLEEVE
7. FRONT PUMP GASKET	AND THRUST WASHER NO. 5	26. ONE-WAY CLUTCH	35. SNAP RING
8. INTERMEDIATE BAND	17. THRUST WASHER NO. 6	INNER RACE	36. GOVERNOR VALVES &
9. BAND STRUTS	18. REVERSE PLANET CARRIER	27. ROLLER (12) AND SPRING (12)	DISTRIBUTOR
10. REVERSE AND HIGH	19. THRUST WASHER NO. 7	28. SPRING AND ROLLER CAGE	37. OUTPUT SHAFT
CLUTCH DRUM	20. SNAP RING	29. ONE-WAY CLUTCH OUTER	38. EXTENSION HOUSING AND GASKET
11. FORWARD CLUTCH AND		RACE	39. CONTROL VALVE BODY
CYLINDER			40. OIL PAN AND GASKET

D 1378-B

FIG. 87—Transmission Sub-Assemblies

FIG. 88—Number 9 Thrust Washer Location

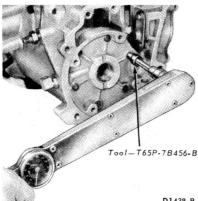

FIG. 89—Installing One-Way Clutch Outer Race Attaching Bolt

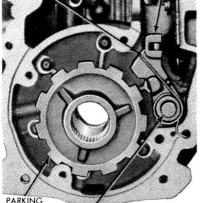

FIG. 90—Parking Pawl and Gear

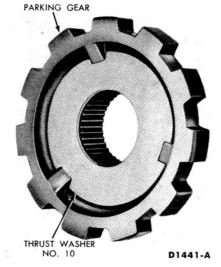

FIG. 91—Number 10 Thrust Washer Location

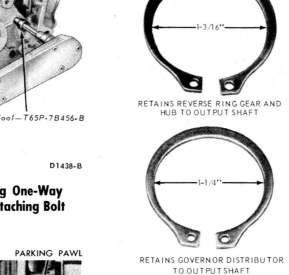

FIG. 92—Governor and Reverse Ring Gear and Hub Snap Ring Identification

13. Install the inner race inside of the spring retainer.

14. Install the individual springs between the inner and outer race as shown in Fig. 93.

15. Starting at the back of the transmission case, install the one-way clutch rollers by slightly compressing each spring and positioning the roller between the spring and the spring retainer.

16. After the one-way clutch has been assembled rotate the inner race clockwise to center the rollers and springs. Install the low and reverse drum (Fig. 87). The splines of the drum have to engage with the splines of the one-way clutch inner race. Check the one-way clutch operation by rotating the low and reverse drum. The drum should rotate clockwise but should not rotate counterclockwise.

17. Install thrust washer No. 8 on top of the low and reverse drum (Fig. 94). Install the low-reverse band in the case, with the end of the band for the small strut toward the low-reverse servo (Fig. 39).

18. Install the reverse ring gear and hub on the output shaft.

19. Move the output shaft forward and install the reverse ring gear hub to output shaft retaining ring (Fig. 43).

20. Place thrust washers Nos. 6 and 7 on the reverse planet carrier (Fig. 95).

21. Install the planet carrier in the reverse ring gear and engage the tabs of the carrier with the slots in the low-reverse drum.

22. On the bench, install the forward clutch in the reverse-high clutch by rotating the units to mesh the reverse-high clutch plates with the splines of the forward clutch (Fig. 96).

23. Using the end play check reading that was obtained during the transmission disassembly to determine which No. 2 steel backed thrust washer is required, proceed as follows:

a. Position the stator support vertically on the work bench and install the correct No. 2 thrustwasher to bring the end play within specifications.

b. Install the reverse-high clutch and the forward clutch on the stator support.

c. Invert the complete unit making sure that the intermediate brake drum bushing is seated on the forward clutch mating surface.

d. Select the thickest fiber washer (No. 1) that can be inserted between the stator support and the intermediate brake drum thrust surfaces and still maintain a slight clearance. Do not select a washer that must be forced between the stator support and intermediate brake drum.

e. Remove the intermediate brake drum and forward clutch unit from the stator support.

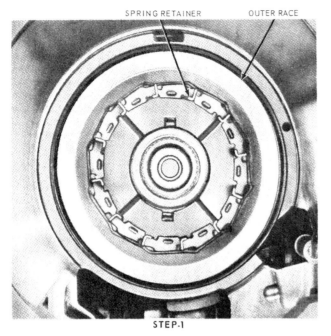

SPRING RETAINER　　OUTER RACE

STEP-1

INSTALL SPRING RETAINER INTO OUTER RACE

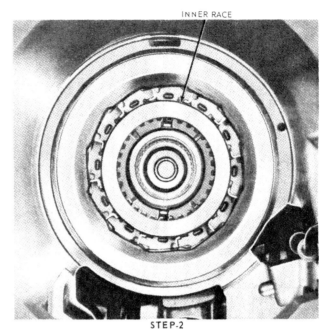

INNER RACE

STEP-2

INSTALL INNER RACE

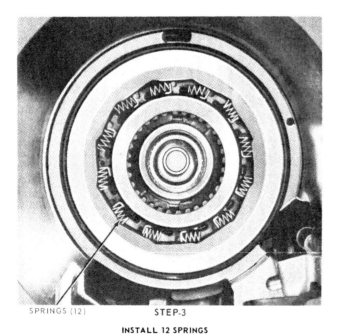

SPRINGS (12)　　STEP-3

INSTALL 12 SPRINGS

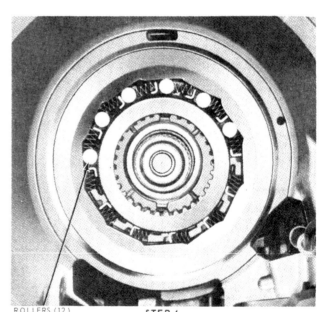

ROLLERS (12)　　STEP-4

INSTALL 12 ROLLERS　　D1551-A

FIG. 93—One-Way Clutch Installation

f. Install the selected Nos. 1 and 2 thrustwashers on the front pump stator support (Fig. 34) using enough vaseline to hold the thrust washers in position during the front pump installation.

24. Install thrust washer No. 3 on the forward clutch (Fig. 97).

25. Install the forward clutch hub and ring in the forward clutch by rotating the units to mesh the forward clutch plates with the splines on the forward clutch hub (Fig. 98).

26. Install thrust washer No. 4 on the front planet carrier (Fig. 99). Install the front planet carrier into the forward clutch hub and ring gear. **Check the forward thrust bearing race inside the planet carrier for proper location against the thrust bearing. Make sure the race is centered for alignment with the sun gear on the input shell (Fig. 100).**

27. Install the input shell and sun gear on the gear train (Fig. 101). Rotate the input shell to engage the drive lugs of the reverse-high clutch. If the drive lugs will not engage, the outer race inside the forward planet carrier is not centered to engage the end of the sun gear inside the input shell. Center the thrust bearing race and install the input shell.

28. Hold the gear train together and install the forward part of the

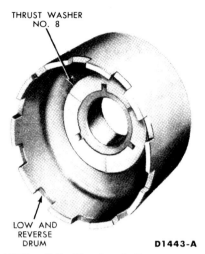

FIG. 94—Number 8 Thrust Washer Location

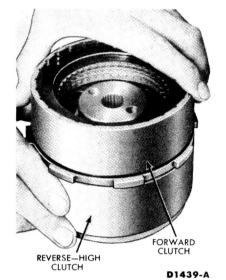

FIG. 96—Installing Clutch Units

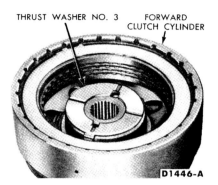

FIG. 97—Number 3 Thrust Washer Location

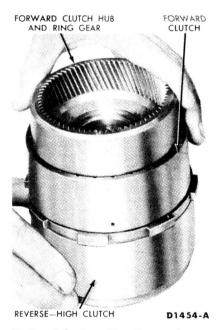

FIG. 98—Installing Forward Clutch Hub and Ring Gear

gear train assembly in the case (Fig. 39).

The input shell sun gear must mesh with the reverse pinion gears. The front planet carrier internal splines must mesh with the splines on the output shaft.

29. A new band should be soaked in transmission fluid for fifteen minutes before it is installed. Install the intermediate band through the front of the case (Fig. 37) so that the arrow on the band end forging, points toward the front of the transmission.

30. Install a new front pump gasket on the case. Line up the bolt holes in the gasket with the holes in the case.

31. Lubricate a new front pump O-ring seal with transmission fluid and install it on the pump. Install the front pump stator support into the reverse-high clutch. Align the pump-to-case attaching bolt holes.

32. Position the converter housing on the front pump and case. Install all but one front pump-to-case attaching bolts and torque them to specification.

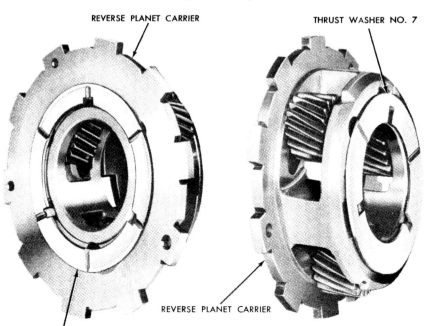

FIG. 95—Numbers 6 and 7 Thrust Washer Location

FIG. 99—Number 4 Thrust Washer Location

FIG. 100—Installing Front
Planet Carrier

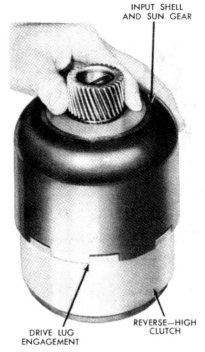

FIG. 101—Installing Input Shell

33. Install the input shaft (Fig. 35).

Rotate the holding fixture to place the transmission in a horizontal position. Check the transmission end play as shown in Fig. 33. If the end play is not within specification, either the wrong selective thrust washers (Fig. 34) were used, or one of the 10 thrust washers (Fig. 84) is not properly positioned.

34. Remove the dial indicator used for checking the end play and install the one converter housing-to-case attaching bolt. Torque the bolt to specification.

35. Install the intermediate and low-reverse band adjusting screws in the case. Install the struts for each band (Fig. 34).

36. Adjust the intermediate and low-reverse band. Refer to In-Car Adjustments and Repair for band adjusting procedures.

37. Install a universal joint yoke on the output shaft. Rotate the input and output shafts in both directions to check for free rotation of the gear train.

38. Install the control valve body (Fig. 33). As the valve body is installed engage the manual and downshift valves with the inner control levers. Torque the eight control valve body-to-case attaching bolts to specification.

39. Place a new oil pan gasket on the case and install the oil pan and oil pan-to-case attaching bolts. Torque the bolts to specification.

40. Remove the transmission from the holding fixture. Install the two extension housing-to-case attaching bolts. Torque the bolts to specification.

41. Install the primary throttle valve in the transmission case (Fig. 31).

42. Install the vacuum unit, gasket, and control rod in the case. Using the tools shown in Fig. 102, torque the vacuum unit to 15-23 ft-lbs.

43. Make sure the input shaft is properly installed in the front pump stator support and gear train. Install the converter in the front pump and the converter housing.

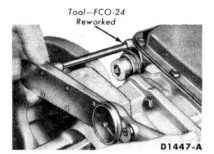

FIG. 102—Installing Vacuum Unit

PART 7-3
C6 AUTOMATIC DUAL RANGE TRANSMISSION

Section	Page
1 Description and Operation	
Description	7-53
Operation	7-53
2 In-Car Adjustment and Repairs	
Control Linkage Adjustments	7-62
Throttle and Downshift Linkage Adjustments	7-62
Manual Linkage Adjustment	7-63
Selector Lever Removal, Adjustment and Installation	7-65
Neutral Start Switch Adjustment	7-65
Neutral Start Switch Replacement	7-65
Band Adjustment	7-65

Section	Page
Oil Pan and Control Valve Body Replacement	7-66
Intermediate Servo Repair	7-66
Extension Housing and Governor Replacement	7-66
Extension Housing Bushing and Rear Seal Replacement	7-67
3 Removal and Installation	
Removal	7-68
Installation	7-68
4 Major Repair Operations	
Disassembly of Transmission	7-69
Parts Repair or Replacement	7-71
Assembly of Transmission	7-80

1 DESCRIPTION AND OPERATION

DESCRIPTION

Figure 1 shows the location of the converter, front pump, clutches, gear train and most of the internal parts used in the C6 transmission. The identification tag (Fig. 2) attached by the servo cover bolt, includes the model prefix and suffix, as well as a service identification number and serial number. The service identification number indicates changes to service details which affect interchangeability **when the transmission model is not changed.** For interpretation of this number, see the Master Parts Catalog.

Table 1 shows the engine and transmission model applications.

The C6 transmission is a three speed dual range unit capable of transmitting the higher torque output of the new improved engines. The converter housing and the fixed splines which engage the splined OD of the low-reverse clutch steel plates, are both cast integrally into the case.

Only one (intermediate) band is used in the C6 transmission. This along with the forward clutch is used to obtain intermediate gear.

The only adjustments on the transmission proper, are for the intermediate band and the neutral safety switch.

The fluid is drained from the transmission by loosening the pan bolts and allowing it to drain. Then by finally removing all bolts except two from the front. This will allow the pan to drain more thoroughly.

OPERATION
TORQUE CONVERTER

The hydraulic torque converter (Fig. 3) consists of an impeller (pump), a turbine, and a stator. All these parts are enclosed and operate in a fluid-filled housing.

When the engine is running, the fluid in the torque converter flows from the impeller to the turbine and back to the impeller through the stator. This flow produces a maximum torque increase of about 2 to 1 when the turbine is stalled. When enough torque is developed by the impeller, the turbine begins to rotate, turning the turbine shaft (input shaft).

The converter torque multiplication gradually tapers off as turbine speed approaches impeller speed, and it becomes 1 to 1 when the turbine is being driven at $9/10$ impeller speed. This is known as the "coupling point."

When the turbine is rotating at less than $9/10$ impeller speed, the converter is multiplying torque. The fluid leaving the turbine blades strikes the front face of the stator blades. These blades are held stationary by the action of the one-way clutch (Fig. 3) as long as the fluid is directed against the front face of the blades.

When the turbine rotates faster than $9/10$ impeller speed the converter no longer multiplies torque. The fluid is directed against the back face of the stator blades. As the one-way clutch permits the stator to rotate only in the direction of impeller rotation, the stator begins to turn with the impeller and turbine. The converter operates as an efficient fluid coupling as long as the turbine speed remains greater than $9/10$ impeller speed.

A constant flow of fluid into and

TABLE 1—Engine and Transmission Application

Car Model	Transmission Model	Engine Model
Comet-Fairlane (Col. Shift)	PDD-J	390-2V
Comet-Fairlane (Fl. Shift)	PDD-P	390-2V
Comet-Fairlane (Col. Shift)	PDD-E	390-4V
Comet-Fairlane (Fl. Shift)	PDD-R	390-4V

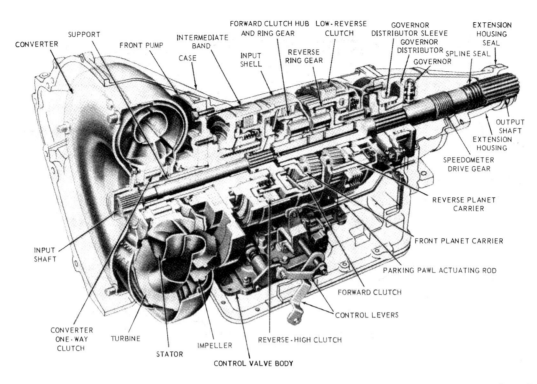

D 1593 - A

FIG. 1—C6 Automatic Transmission—Sectional

out of the converter is maintained. The fluid coming out of the converter is forced through a cooler located in the radiator tank.

PLANETARY GEAR TRAIN, CLUTCHES, BAND, AND SERVO

Planetary Gear Train. The gear train consists of an input shaft that is splined to the turbine of the converter and the forward clutch cylinder (Fig. 4). The forward clutch cylinder rotates the steel internal clutch plates of the forward clutch and the composition clutch plates of the reverse-high clutch. When the reverse

high clutch is applied, the external area of the clutch hub is splined to and drives the input shell to rotate the sun gear. When the forward clutch is applied, the composition clutch plates drive the forward clutch hub and ring gear. The ring gear rotates the forward planet gears.

When applied, the intermediate band holds the reverse-high clutch drum, input shell and sun gear from rotating.

The sun gear, which is driven by the input shell, is meshed with the forward and reverse planet gears. The reverse planet carrier and low reverse clutch hub are locked to-

gether. The low-reverse clutch hub can be held from rotating by the reverse clutch. In D1 the low-reverse clutch hub is also held from rotating by a roller type one-way clutch.

The forward planet carrier, reverse ring gear hub, park gear and

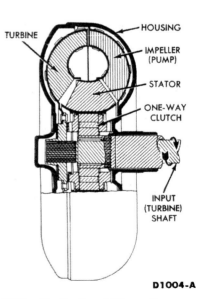

D1004-A

FIG. 3—Sectional View of Torque Converter—Typical

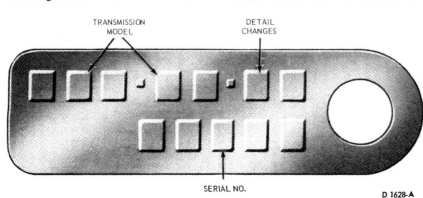

D 1628-A

FIG. 2—Identification Tag

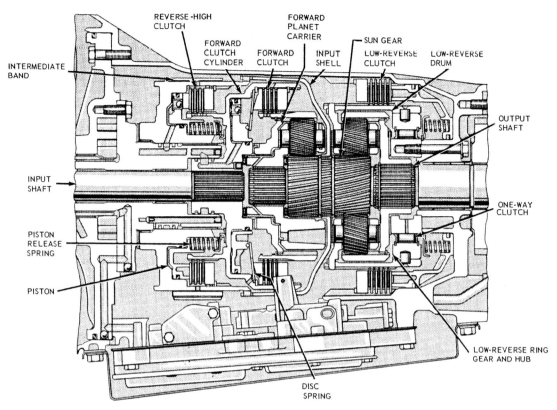

FIG. 4—Gear Train, Clutches and Band

governor distributor are all splined to the output shaft.

Forward Clutch. The input shaft is splined to and drives the forward clutch cylinder (Fig. 4). Rotation of the cylinder drives the steel clutch plates in the forward clutch and the composition clutch plates of the reverse-high clutch.

When the forward clutch piston is applied by hydraulic pressure, the movement of the piston against the disc spring locks the steel and composition clutch plates together to drive the forward clutch hub and ring gear.

When hydraulic pressure is released from the piston, the disc spring moves the piston to the released position. As the disc spring moves, the steel and composition clutch plates are released. This stops the rotation of the forward clutch hub and ring gear (Fig. 4). The forward clutch is applied in all forward drive gear ratios.

Reverse-High Clutch. When hydraulic pressure is directed to the clutch piston, the piston moves against the release springs (Fig. 4). The piston movement locks the steel and rotating composition clutch plates together. The steel clutch plates drive the reverse high clutch

drum which is splined to the input shell. Rotation of the input shell drives the sun gear which is splined to the input shell.

To release the reverse-high clutch, hydraulic pressure is exhausted from the apply side of the piston. The return springs move the piston to the released position. The steel and composition clutch plates are now released to stop rotation of the reverse-high clutch drum, input shell and sun gear.

Intermediate Servo and Band. The intermediate servo is machined into the transmission case and the band has an **external** adjustment screw (Fig. 5). To apply the servo, hydraulic pressure is directed from the control valve body, through a hole in the case to the hole in the servo piston stem. The pressure passes through the center of the piston stem and then to the apply side of the piston. The piston moves against the return spring to tighten the in-

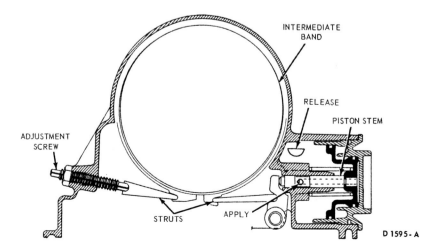

FIG. 5—Intermediate Servo and Band

termediate band around the reverse-high clutch drum.

To release the servo piston, hydraulic pressure is directed to the release side of the piston. The release pressure is assisted by the compressed return spring to move the servo piston and intermediate band to the OFF position. The intermediate servo and band are applied only during the intermediate gear operation.

POWER FLOW

All Gear Rotations are viewed from the front of transmission. Table 2 shows the gear ratios obtained in the different selector lever positions.

Power Flow Neutral. In neutral (Fig. 6) the clutches or bands are not applied, therefore, no power is transmitted to the output shaft.

Power Flow First Gear. In low gear (Fig 6), the forward clutch is applied, and the planet one-way clutch or reverse clutch is holding the reverse planet carrier from rotating. The power flow is through the input shaft and into the forward clutch. The input shaft is splined to and drives the forward clutch cylinder. Rotation of the forward clutch drives the forward clutch hub and ring gear. The ring gear rotates the forward planet gears clockwise to cause the sun gear to rotate counter-clockwise.

Counterclockwise rotation of the sun gear turns the reverse planet gear clockwise. The reverse planet carrier being splined to the low-reverse clutch hub is held from rotating by the one-way clutch or reverse clutch.

With the reverse planet carrier held stationary, the clockwise rotation of the reverse planet gears rotates the reverse ring gear. The hub of the reverse ring gear is splined to the output shaft and rotates the output shaft clockwise.

The output shaft rotation is at a reduced speed, compared to the input shaft rotation, but at an increased torque.

The output shaft rotation at a reduced speed is caused by the fact that the forward planet carrier rotates at the same speed of the output shaft and in the same direction since the carrier is splined to the output shaft. The forward ring gear and planet assembly are rotating in the same direction, but the planet carrier is rotating at a slower speed than the ring gear. Therefore, the low

gear ratio (torque multiplication) is a combination of the ratios provided by the forward and reverse planet assemblies.

Power Flow Intermediate Gear. In intermediate gear (Fig. 6), the forward clutch is applied and the intermediate band is holding the reverse-high clutch drum, input shell and sun gear from turning.

The power flow is through the input shaft into the forward clutch and forward planet assembly ring gear. The sun gear is held from rotating by the intermediate band. This causes the forward planet pinions to rotate (walk) around the sun gear, carrying the forward planet carrier with them. The forward planet carrier, being splined to the output shaft, causes clockwise rotation of the output shaft at a reduction in speed compared to the speed of the input shaft, and at an increase in torque.

Clockwise rotation of the output shaft causes clockwise rotation of the output shaft ring gear, causing the reverse planet pinions to also rotate (walk) around the sun gear in a clockwise direction. The reverse planet carrier will also rotate clockwise and the one-way clutch inner race, being splined to the reverse planet carrier, will overrun.

Power Flow High Gear. In high gear (Fig. 6), the forward and reverse-high clutches are applied. The power flow is through the input shaft into the forward clutch cylinder. (The forward clutch cylinder rotates the steel clutch plates of the forward clutch and the composition clutch plates of the reverse-high clutch). The forward clutch directs the power flow through the forward clutch hub and ring gear to the forward planet carrier.

The reverse-high clutch directs the power flow through the input shell to the sun gear. With the sun gear and the forward clutch hub ring gear driven at the same speed the forward planet assembly (that is splined to the output shaft) is forced to rotate the output shaft at the same speed and direction to provide high gear.

Power Flow Reverse. In reverse (Fig. 6), the reverse-high clutch and reverse clutch are applied. The power flow is through the input shaft, reverse-high clutch, input shell and to the sun gear. Clockwise rotation of the sun gear causes counterclockwise rotation of the reverse planet

gears.

The reverse-clutch, holding the reverse planet carrier from turning, causes the reverse planet gears to rotate counterclockwise.

This rotates the reverse ring gear and hub counterclockwise. The hub splined to the output shaft rotates the output shaft counterclockwise at a reduction in speed and at an increase in torque for reverse gear.

HYDRAULIC CONTROL SYSTEM

Front Pump. Fluid for operation of the hydraulic control system (Fig. 7) is supplied by a gear type pump mounted on the front of the transmission case. Pump intake is through a screen which is part of the main control assembly, into the case casting and pump. Discharge is through the case into the main control assembly. Fluid from the front pump is directed to the main oil pressure regulator valve, throttle booster valve, manual valve, 1-2 accumulator valve.

In addition, fluid is also directed to the primary throttle valve, which is located in the rear of the case. Fluid delivered to these valves is at a pressure controlled by the main oil pressure regulator valve.

Main Oil Pressure Regulator Valve. The main regulator valve assembly consists of the main oil pressure regulator valve and spring, main oil pressure booster valve, spring and sleeve. This assembly is located in one bore of the main control assembly.

Fluid is delivered to two valleys of the main regulator valve from the front pump. The difference in diameter between the end land and the second land provides an area differential for regulation. Fluid pressure in this area tends to move the valve against spring force. Spring force is such that at approximately 60 psi front pump pressure, the main valve will move so that the fourth land uncovers the converter feed port, allowing additional pump volume to be used to charge the converter and provide fluid for cooling and lubrication. If volume supplied by the front pump is greater than that required to maintain 60 psi line pressure and converter and lube requirements, the valve will move further allowing the third land to uncover the port which allows excess pump volume to be discharged into the sump.

Pressures over 60 psi which are

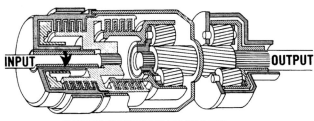

CLUTCHES AND THE BAND ARE RELEASED

NEUTRAL

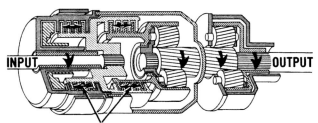

BOTH THE FORWARD AND THE REVERSE AND HIGH CLUTCH ARE APPLIED. ALL PLANETARY GEAR MEMBERS ARE LOCKED TO EACH OTHER AND ARE LOCKED TO THE OUTPUT SHAFT.

HIGH GEAR

THE FORWARD CLUTCH IS APPLIED. THE FRONT PLANETARY UNIT RING GEAR IS LOCKED TO THE INPUT SHAFT.

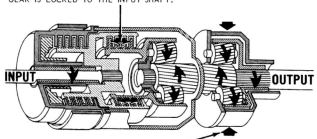

THE LOW AND REVERSE CLUTCH (LOW RANGE) OR THE ONE-WAY CLUTCH (D1 RANGE) IS HOLDING THE REVERSE UNIT PLANET CARRIER STATIONARY.

FIRST GEAR

THE REVERSE AND HIGH CLUTCH IS APPLIED. THE INPUT SHAFT IS LOCKED TO THE REVERSE AND HIGH CLUTCH DRUM, THE INPUT SHELL AND THE SUN GEAR

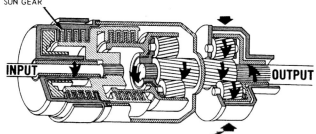

THE LOW AND REVERSE CLUTCH IS APPLIED. THE REVERSE UNIT PLANET CARRIER IS HELD STATIONARY.

REVERSE

THE INTERMEDIATE BAND IS APPLIED. THE REVERSE AND HIGH CLUTCH DRUM, THE INPUT SHELL AND THE SUN GEAR ARE HELD STATIONARY.

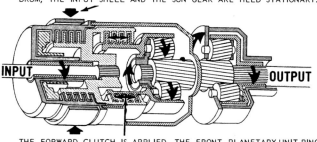

THE FORWARD CLUTCH IS APPLIED. THE FRONT PLANETARY UNIT RING GEAR IS LOCKED TO THE INPUT SHAFT.

SECOND GEAR

GEAR RATIOS			
FIRST 2.46:1			
	SECOND 1.46:1		
		HIGH 1.00:1	
			REVERSE 2.17:1

D1596-A

FIG. 6—Power Flow C6 Trans.

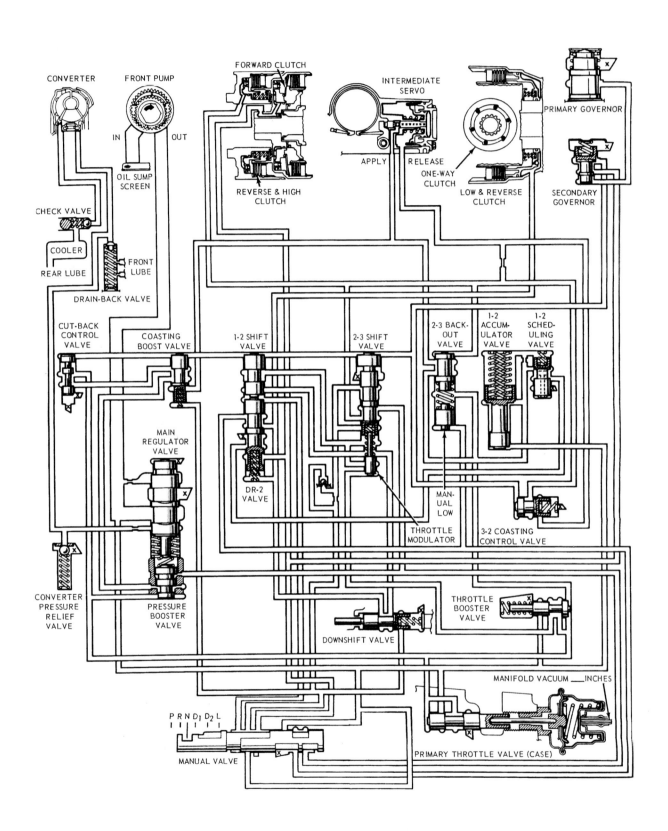

D 1624 - A

FIG. 7—Hydraulic Control System

required under various operating conditions are obtained by delivering fluid under pressure to the pressure booster valve, where it will cause the pressure booster valve to assist the main regulator valve spring in increasing regulated line pressure.

Source of these pressures which cause variations in control pressure are discussed later.

Manual Valve. Two passages deliver control pressure to the manual valve. The valve is positioned by the manual linkage according to mode of operation desired, to direct fluid out of two or more of the line passages which lead from the manual valve. The five passages leading from the manual valve (from left to right) are:

1. D2
2. D1
3. D
4. L–R
5. R

The D2 passage is charged in D2 range only.

The D1 passage is charged in D2 and D1 ranges.

The D passage is charged in all forward ranges, (including manual low).

The L–R passage is charged in L and R ranges.

The R passage is charged in reverse range only.

In Park and Neutral, the valve blocks the flow of control pressure and exhausts the five passages leading from the manual valve.

The D passage supplies fluid pressure to the governor secondary valve, D2 valve and forward clutch.

The D2 passage supplies fluid to the adjoining ends of the D2 and 1-2 shift valves.

The D1 passage supplies fluid to the 2-3 shift valve, downshift valve and coasting boost valve.

The L and R passage supplies fluid to the end of the manual low valve and to the D2 valve. When the D2 valve is in the closed (up) position, fluid passes through the valve and to the following places:

1. Spring end of the D2 valve.
2. Reverse clutch.
3. Through the downshift valve to the throttle modulator valve bore, under the 2-3 shift valve and to the underside of the first land of the 1-2 shift valve.

The R passage supplies fluid to the upper valley of the pressure booster valve, through the 2-3 shift valve to the reverse-high clutch, to

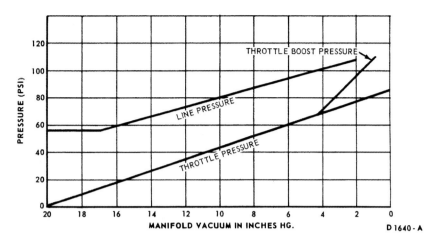

FIG. 8—Primary Throttle Pressure, Throttle Boost Pressure and Control Pressure Versus Engine Manifold Vacuum

apply it and to the release side of the intermediate servo. Fluid is also supplied to the end of the 2-3 back-out valve, and to the 3-2 coasting control valve.

Primary Throttle Valve. The primary throttle valve is actuated by changes in manifold vacuum. Primary throttle pressure starts at 20 inches (nominal) of mercury vacuum. Primary throttle pressure is delivered to the:

1. End of the pressure booster valve.
2. Lower valley of pressure booster valve (through cutback valve and coasting boost valves).
3. Throttle modulator valve (through throttle booster valve).
4. End of the throttle booster valve.
5. Spring end of the 2-3 backout valve and manual low valve.

Fig. 8 shows how primary throttle pressure varies with engine vacuum.

Altitude-Compensating Diaphragm Assembly. To compensate for change in shift feel which might result from operation at higher alti-

tudes, an altitude-compensating throttle diaphragm assembly will be available for service.

The operating principle of the altitude-compensating device is dependent upon the collapsing force obtained from an evacuated bellows located within the diaphragm assembly. The force created by the bellows increases or decreases the force on the throttle valve actuating rod. At higher altitudes the force that the bellows transmits to the actuating rod is decreased, resulting in a decrease in primary TV pressure, which tends to make shift feel comparable with that obtained at lower altitudes. Fig. 9 shows the construction of the altitude-compensating diaphragm assembly.

Pressure specifications for a car equipped with the altitude-compensating diaphragm will not be the same at altitude, as at sea level. Refer to Section 7-1 Table 3 for differences.

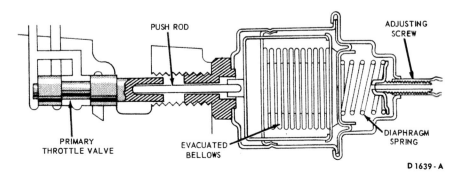

FIG. 9—Altitude-Compensating Vacuum Diaphragm

Pressure Booster Valve

FORWARD DRIVING
RANGES (D1, D2, L)

TV pressure is delivered to the lower valley of the pressure booster valve and to the end of the pressure booster valve. When force created on the booster valve by TV pressures in these two areas exceeds pressure booster valve spring force, the force will be added to the main regulator valve spring force transmitted to the main regulator valve. This will provide increased control pressures required to compensate for increased throttle openings and engine torque output. Fig. 10 shows how control pressure varies with engine vacuum at zero output shaft rpm.

REVERSE (R). Additional fluid pressure is required in reverse to prevent clutch and/or band slippage under stall or partial stall conditions. This additional pressure is provided by directing line pressure to the upper valley of the pressure booster valve when reverse range is selected. The differential in area between the lands of this valve provides a force which is added to the TV pressure forces present in the lower valley and on the end of the valve, to boost line pressure to a higher value than is available in the forward driving ranges.

Governor

AT REST (0 MPH). Control pressure (line) is fed to the secondary governor valve through the center passage in the valve body. Because of the differential in area of the inner and outer lands of the valve, the valve will be forced inward, shutting

off line pressure feed to the governor passage and allowing this passage to be opened to exhaust, at the inner end of the valve. At the same time, line pressure will pass by two flats on the outer end of the valve, pressurizing the line leakage passage leading to the primary governor valve. At rest, the spring on the outer end of the primary governor valve holds the primary governor valve inward, blocking further flow of the fluid in the line leakage passage. This causes pressure in the line leakage passage to build to the same value as line pressure. As a consequence, the secondary governor valve is held in and there is no pressure in the governor circuit.

ABOVE 10 MPH. When speed reaches approximately 10 mph, centrifugal force on the primary governor valve overcome spring force, and the valve moves outward, opening the line leakage passage to exhaust. This action reduces the pressure on the end of the secondary governor valve to zero (0), allowing the secondary valve to also move outward, due to spring force and centrifugal force. When the secondary valve moves outward, it closes the governor exhaust passage, and allows line pressure to enter the governor passage. As pressure builds in the governor passage, it will create a force on the secondary governor valve due to the differential in areas of the inner and outer lands of the valve. This force tends to move the valve inward. When the force on the valve created by pressure in the governor passage exceed the centrifugal force plus spring force, the

valve will move inward, allowing governor pressure to exhaust, and close the passage between line pressure and governor pressure. When governor pressure is reduced, the secondary valve will again move outward, closing the governor exhaust port and opening the line pressure to governor passage. Above 10 mph, governor pressure is regulated in this manner, and will vary with the car speeds.

If the car speed drops below 10 mph, the primary valve spring will move the primary governor valve in, closing the line leakage exhaust port at the primary valve. Pressure in the line leakage passage will become equal to line pressure, forcing the secondary governor valve in. This action shuts off line pressure feed to the governor passage and exhausts the governor circuit.

When the secondary governor valve is regulating, governor pressure will be delivered to the cutback valve, end of the 2-3 shift valve, 1-2 shift valve and end of the line pressure coasting boost valve and 3-2 coasting control valve. Fig. 10 shows the relationship between governor pressure and output shaft rpm.

Throttle Booster Valve. Throttle plate openings above 50° provide very little change in engine vacuum as compared to throttle plate openings below 50°. The throttle booster valve is used to boost throttle pressure and provide the necessary shift delay for engine throttle plate openings above 50°.

Below approximately 65 psi primary TV pressure, TV pressure flows to and through the throttle boost valve unaffected, working on the end of the boost valve and on the area differential in the first valley.

When TV pressure increases above 65 psi, the force created by TV pressure acting on the end of the throttle boost valve, minus the force of TV pressure acting on the area differential in the first valley will exceed the force of the spring. This causes the valve to move against the spring, closing off primary TV pressure to the area differential and permitting this area to be fed from line pressure, causing a boost in the pressure used for shift delay only. Because the area of the end of the throttle boost valve exceeds the area differential in the first valley by 3 to 1, throttle boost pressure above 65 psi primary TV pressure will increase 3 psi for each 1 psi increase

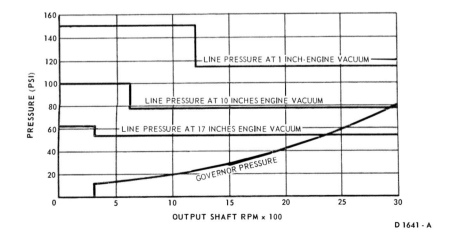

FIG. 10—Control Line Pressure and Governor Pressure Versus Output Shaft rpm

in primary TV.

Figure 8 shows the relationship between primary TV pressure and boosted throttle pressure.

Throttle Modulator Valve. The throttle modulator valve, located in the end of the 2-3 shift valve bore reduces throttle pressure which acts on the end of the 2-3 shift valve and on the area differential of the 1-2 shift valve. Modulated throttle pressure in these areas provides shift delay in relation to throttle opening.

Cutback Valve. Increased line pressure is required to prevent clutch and band slippage under stall conditions. Dependent upon car speed, the requirements for increased line pressure are considerably reduced. When governor pressure acting on the end of the cutback valve exceeds the force of TV pressure acting on its area opposing governor, the cutback valve will move cutting off primary TV pressure being fed to the lower valley of the pressure booster valve, thru the coasting boost valve. This action reduces the assist that the pressure booster valve provides to the main regulator valve spring. The cutback valve movement will therefore vary with engine throttle opening and car speed. Figure 10 shows how line pressure varies with output shaft rpm (car speed) at constant vacuum values.

Coasting Boost Valve. When using manual low to force a 3-2 coasting (throttle closed) downshift in order to use the engine as a brake, additional pressure may be required to insure positive band applications. With the throttle closed there will be no TV pressure present at the pressure booster valve.

At speeds above approximately 55 mph, additional pressure is obtained thru the use of the coasting boost valve. When the manual valve is shifted to manual low (L), line pressure is exhausted from the end of the coasting boost valve, allowing governor pressure to move the valve downward. This action blocks the TV pressure passage from the cut-back control valve and allows intermediate servo apply pressure to pass thru the coasting boost valve to the lower valley of the pressure booster valve, increasing main line pressure.

1-2 Shift Valve Train. The 1-2 shift valve train is composed of the 1-2 shift valve, the D2 valve, and the 1-2 shift valve spring.

D1 RANGE. In D1 range the 1-2 shift valve is held closed (up) by modulated throttle pressure acting on the differential area between the two lands of the 1-2 shift valve, by D fluid pressure acting on the differential in area between the two lands at the spring end of the D2 valve, and by the 1-2 shift valve spring. Governor pressure tends to move the 1-2 shift valve train against these forces. When force created by governor pressure exceeds the forces holding the 1-2 shift valve train closed, the 1-2 shift valve and D2 valve will be opened (move downward), closing the exhaust port and allowing D fluid to pass through the D2 valve to accomplish the 1-2 shift. When the D2 valve is moved downward, D fluid is exhausted from the differential in areas provided by the lower two lands of the D2 valve and modulated throttle pressure from area differential on 1-2 valve. This action eliminates the force created by D fluid which tends to hold the 1-2 shift valve train closed.

If governor pressure is reduced to the point where spring force exceeds governor pressure force, the 1-2 shift valve train will move up (close) cutting off the flow of D fluid through the valve and opening the exhaust port allowing a downshift to low gear.

If the throttle is opened through detent, the downshift valve moves to allow line pressure to enter the modulated throttle pressure passage at the 1-2 shift valve to provide a forced 2-1 downshift.

L-RANGE. Once the transmission is in low gear L-R fluid, which is directed to the D2 valve, passes through the D2 valve and is delivered to the spring end of the D2 valve, preventing an upshift. L-R fluid which passes through the D2 valve also applies the reverse clutch. Coasting downshifts to first gear are not possible above approximately 10 mph in low range.

D2 RANGE. In D2 range, D2 fluid is introduced between the 1-2 shift and D2 valves. This action opens the D2 valve and holds it open, providing a second gear start and preventing a 2-1 downshift.

1-2 Scheduling Valve and 1-2 Accumulator Valve. The 1-2 scheduling and 1-2 accumulator valves are used to control the rate of band application during a 1-2 shift.

During operation in first gear prior to the 1-2 shift, control pressure is present on the end of the 1-2 accumulator valve and holds the valve up in its bore against spring pressure.

When the 1-2 shift valve train moves to make a 1-2 shift, line pressure passes thru the D-2 valve and goes to the 1-2 scheduling valve. This pressure passes thru the scheduling valve bore, goes to the differential in area between the two lands of the 1-2 accumulator valve and thru the 2-3 backout valve to apply the intermediate servo. This same fluid also passes thru a hole in the center of the 1-2 scheduling valve to the end of the valve, and also thru an orifice which feeds the fluid to the spring ends of the 1-2 accumulator and 1-2 scheduling valves.

The fluid which passes thru the center of the 1-2 scheduling valve tends to move the valve upward against spring force. However, the spring effort and fluid pressure created by the fluid which has passed thru the orifice to the spring end of the valve will hold the valve down.

As fluid flows thru the orifice to the spring ends of the 1-2 accumulator and scheduling valves, and pressure increases on the spring ends of the valves, the 1-2 accumulator valve starts to move downward. This movement of the 1-2 accumulator valve causes a flow of fluid thru the orifice, resulting in a lower pressure existing on the spring sides of the valves.

As a consequence, the fluid pressure on the end of the 1-2 scheduling valve opposite the spring will be higher than the pressure on the spring end of the valve, causing the valve to move upward. This action cuts off fluid supply to the intermediate servo (and thru the orifice) and opens an exhaust port at the end of the 1-2 scheduling valve. When the exhaust port opens, the pressure on the end of the 1-2 scheduling valve opposite the spring is reduced, allowing the valve to again move downward and opening the line to the intermediate servo apply.

In this manner, the 1-2 scheduling valve regulates to control the intermediate servo apply during a 1-2 shift, until the 1-2 accumulator valve has fully bottomed in its bore and there is no more fluid flow thru the orifice.

2-3 Shift Valve. The 2-3 shift valve is held closed by throttle modulator valve spring force, modulated throttle pressure force, and by D1 fluid pressure force acting on the differential in area of the lands of the valve to which it is delivered.

Governor pressure tends to open the 2-3 shift valve. When force created by governor pressure exceeds the forces holding the valve closed, the valve will move downward (open) closing the exhaust passage (through the manual valve) and opening the D1 passage to allow D1 fluid to apply the reverse-high clutch and release the intermediate servo.

With the shift valve open (down) the throttle modulator valve is held down cutting off modulated throttle pressure to the 2-3 shift valve and 1-2 shift valve. In addition, the port which delivered D1 fluid to the differential in area of the shift valve lands, is closed.

The shift valve will be reopened (moved up) causing a downshift under one or more of the following conditions:

GOVERNOR PRESSURE REDUCED. If governor pressure is reduced to the point where it can no longer hold the shift valve down against spring force, the valve will move up causing a downshift. Under closed throttle conditions, the 2-3 shift valve will close at approximately 10 mph, (speed at which governor pressure is cut off). Since governor pressure is cut off at this speed, the 1-2 shift valve train also closes at the same time. This will provide a 3-1 downshift when coasting in D1 range.

THROTTLE PRESSURE INCREASED. If throttle pressure is increased sufficiently, it will move the throttle modulator valve and consequently the 2-3 shift valve up, causing a 3-2 torque demand downshift.

LINE PRESSURE INTRODUCED BELOW 2-3 SHIFT VALVE. If the downshift valve is moved through detent, line pressure is directed to the underside of the

2-3 shift valve, forcing the valve up and causing a forced 3-2 downshift. Maximum 3-2 forced downshift speed is controlled by governor pressure.

In addition to the above, a 3-2 downshift will occur when the manual valve is moved to L range. The D1 passage which feeds fluid to the 2-3 shift valve will then be opened to exhaust, allowing reverse-high clutch apply-intermediated servo release fluid to exhaust and causing a 3-2 downshift.

2-3 Backout Valve. The purpose of the 2-3 back-out valve it to provide smooth upshifts, when the throttle is suddenly closed while accelerating in second gear. Operation is as follows:

NORMAL THROTTLE ON 2-3 UPSHIFTS. When the 2-3 shift valve moves to cause a 2-3 upshift, D1 fluid passes through the valve to apply the direct clutch and release the intermediate servo. This same fluid is also directed to the end of the 2-3 back-out valve. However, with throttle open, primary throttle pressure on the opposite end of the 2-3 back-out valve, assists spring force in holding the valve up, so that there will be no valve movement until after the 2-3 shift has been completed.

BACK-OUT 2-3 UPSHIFTS. When the throttle is closed during a 2-3 upshift, and before the shift is completed, there may be enough pressure in the reverse-high clutch cylinder to apply the clutch at the reduced engine torque input, but not enough pressure to release the intermediate servo. This condition could cause a harsh 2-3 shift. However, if the throttle is closed during a 2-3 shift, primary throttle pressure will be reduced to zero (0), and reverse-high clutch apply pressure on the end of the 2-3 back-out valve will move the valve down against spring

force. This action immediately connects the clutch apply circuit to the intermediate servo apply circuit, reducing the pressure on apply side of the servo to the same valve as in the reverse-high clutch (and also on the release side of the intermediate servo). When this happens, the intermediate band is released, to provide a smooth 2-3 shift.

3-2 Coasting Control Valve. The 3-2 coasting control valve controls the intermediate servo apply force to provide acceptable 3-2 downshifts under both coasting and throttle-on conditions.

THROTTLE-ON 3-2 SHIFT. During a 3-2 throttle-on downshift, car speed will be such that governor pressure will hold the 3-2 coasting control valve bottomed in its bore against its spring. In this position, intermediate servo release fluid exhausts through the coasting control valve and 2-3 shift valve during a 3-2 downshift, allowing a rapid apply of the intermediate band.

COASTING 3-2 SHIFT (D2 RANGE). At the 3-2 coasting downshift speed, governor pressure is reduced to zero and the 3-2 coasting control valve will be moved by spring force to the bottom of its bore. This blocks the direct passage of intermediate servo release fluid to exhaust and requires that this fluid be exhausted through a controlling orifice. Therefore, the band application is cushioned during a 3-2 coasting downshift, resulting in a smooth shift.

Manual Low Valve. The manual low valve insures that the 2-3 back-out valve will be moved up the instant that pressure drops in the reverse-high clutch apply—intermediate servo release circuit, when a shift to manual low range is made. This is accomplished by directing control pressure to the end of the manual low valve, when L range is selected.

2 IN-CAR ADJUSTMENTS AND REPAIRS

CONTROL LINKAGE ADJUSTMENTS

The transmission control linkage adjustments should be performed in the order in which they appear in this section of the manual.

THROTTLE AND DOWNSHIFT LINKAGE ADJUSTMENTS

1. Apply the parking brake and

place the selector lever at N.

2. Run the engine at normal idle speed. If the engine is cold, run the engine at fast idle speed (about 1200 rpm) until it reaches normal operating temperature. When the engine is warm, slow it down to normal idle speed.

3. Connect a tachometer to the engine.

4. Adjust engine idle speed to the specified rpm with the transmission selector lever at D1 or D2, the drive positions.

5. **The carburetor throttle lever must be against the hot idle speed adjusting screw at the specified idle speed in D1 (large dot) or D2 (small dot).** To make sure that the carburetor throttle lever is against the idle

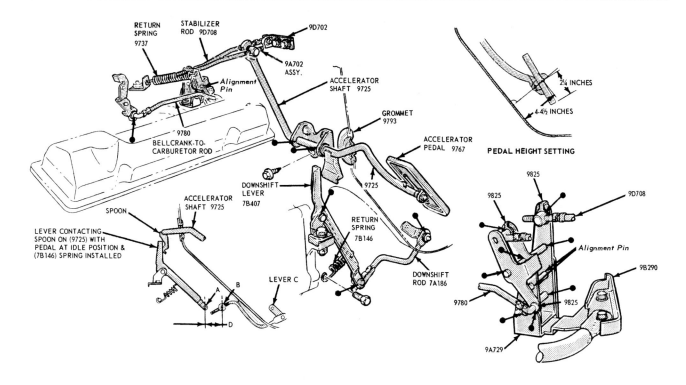

● LUBRICATION POINTS   D 1625-A

FIG. 11—Throttle Linkage—Comet and Fairlane with 390 CID

adjusting screw, refer to Group 10 for the carburetor adjusting procedures.

COMET AND FAIRLANE LINKAGE—390-CID ENGINE

1. Disconnect the bellcrank-to-carburetor rod at point C and the accelerator rod from the throttle shaft at point B (Fig. 11).

2. Disconnect the stabilizer rod from the stabilizer at point A.

3. Insert a ¼ inch diameter pin through the stabilizer and the bracket (Fig. 11).

4. Adjust the length of the stabilizer rod so that the trunnion enters the stabilizer freely. Secure the stabilizer rod with the retaining clip.

5. Secure the carburetor-to-bellcrank rod to the bellcrank with the attaching clip at point C.

6. Adjust the length of the accelerator rod to obtain an accelerator pedal height of 4-4½ inches measured at the pedal as shown in Fig. 11. Connect the accelerator rod to the accelerator shaft with the retaining clip after the proper accelerator pedal height has been established.

7. With the engine off, disconnect the downshift rod from the lever at point D (Fig. 11).

8. With the carburetor choke in the **off** position, depress the accelerator pedal to the floor. Block the pedal to

hold it in the wide open position.

9. Rotate the downshift lever on the transmission in a counterclockwise direction to place it against the internal stop.

10. Adjust the trunnion at point D so that it enters the downshift lever freely.

11. Turn it one additional turn counter clockwise to lengthen the rod. Secure it to the lever with the retaining clip.

12. Remove the block from the accelerator pedal.

MANUAL LINKAGE ADJUSTMENT

Column Shift Transmission.

1. With the engine stopped, loosen the clamp at the shift lever at point A so that the shift rod is free to slide in the clamp (Fig. 12).

2. Position the transmission selecter lever into the D1 (large dot) position making sure that the selecter lever is against the D, stop on the selecter plate.

3. Shift the manual lever at the transmission into the D1 detent position, second from the rear.

4. Tighten the clamp on the shift rod at point A.

5. Check the pointer alignment and transmission operation for all selector lever detent positions.

Console Shift Transmission. Be-

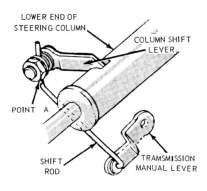

D1568 -B

FIG. 12—Manual Linkage—Typical

fore adjusting the manual linkage, check the starter neutral switch operation. If the switch needs adjusting the adjustment can be made at the time the manual linkage is adjusted. The selector lever handle (Fig. 13), must be tight on the selector lever.

1. Move the shift lever to the D1 detent position against the stop.

2. Raise the car and loosen the manual linkage rod attaching nut (Fig. 13). Move the transmission manual lever to the D1 position, second from the rear. The last detent position is low position.

3. With the selector lever and the

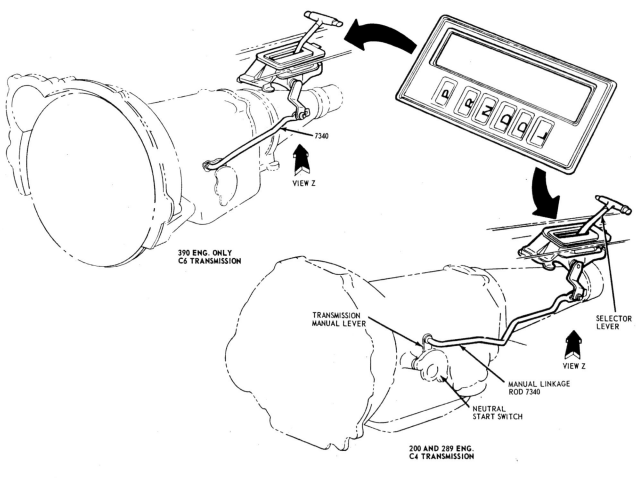

390 ENG. ONLY
C6 TRANSMISSION

VIEW Z

7340

TRANSMISSION
MANUAL LEVER

SELECTOR
LEVER

VIEW Z

MANUAL LINKAGE
ROD 7340

NEUTRAL
START SWITCH

200 AND 289 ENG.
C4 TRANSMISSION

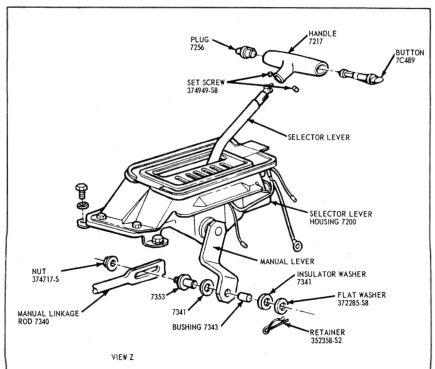

PLUG
7256

HANDLE
7217

BUTTON
7C489

SET SCREW
374949-S8

SELECTOR LEVER

SELECTOR LEVER
HOUSING 7200

MANUAL LEVER

NUT
374717-S

INSULATOR WASHER
7341

MANUAL LINKAGE
ROD 7340

7353

7341

BUSHING 7343

FLAT WASHER
372285-S8

RETAINER
352358-S2

VIEW Z

D-1626-A

FIG. 13—Manual Linkage Adjustment—Console

transmission manual lever in the D1 position, tighten the rod attaching nut to specifications (Fig. 13).

Selector Lever Removal, Adjustment and Installation.

1. Raise the car on a hoist or jack stands.

2. Remove the retainer that secures the manual linkage rod to the lower end of the manual lever (Fig. 13).

3. Remove the flat washer and two insulator washers and disconnect the rod from the arm.

4. Working from inside of the car, remove the selector lever handle attaching screw. Lift the handle off the selector lever.

5. Remove the console trim panel from the top of the console.

6. Disconnect the quadrant lamp wires from the harness.

7. Remove the four bolts that secure the selector lever control housing to the console. Lift the selector lever housing from the console.

8. It is necessary to disassemble the quadrant to adjust the selector lever. To disassemble the quadrant, remove the two retainers from the underside of the dial and the two attaching screws from the opposite side. Separate the dial, insulators, retainer, pointer and the plate from the housing.

9. Install the selector lever handle.

10. Position the selector lever as shown in Figure 14. With a feeler gauge, check the clearance between the detent pawl and plate. The clearance should be 0.005 to 0.010 inch. If necessary adjust the height of the detent pawl as shown in Figure 14.

11. Remove the handle from the selector lever.

12. Position the plate, pointer,

retainer, insulators and the dial on the control housing. Secure these items with two screws and two retainers.

13. Position the selector lever housing in the console. Install the four attaching bolts (Fig. 13).

14. Connect the quadrant lamp wires to their connectors.

15. Position the console plate and secure it with the attaching screws.

16. Install the handle and the button on the selector lever. Secure the handle with the lock screw.

17. Secure the manual linkage rod to the arm with two insulating washers, a flat washer and a retainer (Fig. 13).

18. Adjust the linkage as required. Lower the car.

NEUTRAL START SWITCH ADJUSTMENT

1. **With the manual lever properly adjusted,** loosen the two switch attaching bolts (Fig. 15).

2. With the transmission manual lever in neutral, rotate the switch and insert the gauge pin (No. 43 drill shank end) into the gauge pin holes of the switch. **The gauge pin has to be inserted to a full 31/64 inch into the three holes of the switch (Fig. 15).**

3. Torque the two switch attaching bolts to specification. Remove the gauge pin from the switch.

4. Check the operation of the switch. The engine should start only with the transmission selector lever in Neutral and Park.

NEUTRAL START SWITCH REPLACEMENT

1. Remove the downshift linkage

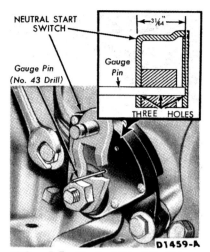

FIG. 15—Neutral Start Switch

rod from the transmission downshift lever.

2. Apply penetrating oil to the outer downshift lever attaching nut. Remove the transmission downshift outer lever attaching nut and lever (Fig. 15).

3. Remove the two neutral start switch attaching bolts.

4. Disconnect the two multiple wire connectors. Remove the neutral switch from the transmission.

5. Install the neutral start switch on the transmission. Install the two attaching bolts.

6. With the transmission manual lever in neutral, rotate the switch and install gauge pin (No. 43 drill) into the gauge pin hole (Fig. 15).

7. Tighten the switch attaching bolts to specification and remove the gauge pin.

8. Install the outer downshift lever and attaching nut, and torque the nut to specification. Install the downshift linkage rod to the downshift lever.

9. Install the switch wires. Connect the wire multiple connectors, red to red and blue to blue. Check the operation of the switch in each detent position. The engine should start only with the transmission selector lever in N (neutral) and P (park).

BAND ADJUSTMENT

1. Raise the car on a hoist or jack stands.

2. Clean the threads of the intermediate band adjustment screw.

3. Loosen the adjustment screw lock nut.

4. Tighten the band adjustment screw as shown in Fig. 16 until the wrench overruns, then back it off 1⅛ turns. Tighten the adjustment screw lock nut to specification being

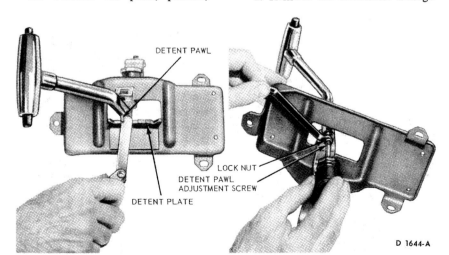

FIG. 14—Selector Lever Detent Pawl Adjustment

DETENT PAWL

LOCK NUT
DETENT PAWL
ADJUSTMENT SCREW

DETENT PLATE

D 1644-A

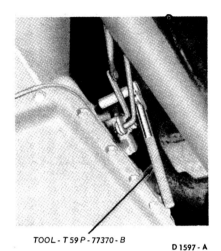

TOOL - T 59 P - 77370 - B   D 1597 - A

FIG. 16—Adjusting Intermediate Band

careful not to disturb the adjustment screw setting.

5. Lower the car.

OIL PAN AND CONTROL VALVE BODY REPLACEMENT
REMOVAL

1. Raise car on a hoist or jack stands.

2. Place a drain pan under the transmission. Loosen and remove all but two of the oil pan bolts from the front of the case and drop the rear edge of the oil pan to drain the fluid. Remove and thoroughly clean the oil pan and screen. Discard the oil pan gasket.

3. Remove the valve body attaching bolts and remove the valve body from the case.

4. Position the valve body to case making sure that the selector and downshift levers are engaged, then install and torque the attaching bolts to specification.

5. Clean the oil pan and gasket surfaces thoroughly.

6. Using a new pan gasket, secure the pan to the transmission case and torque the attaching bolts to specification.

7. Lower the car and fill the transmission to the correct level with the specified fluid.

INTERMEDIATE SERVO REPAIR
REMOVAL

1. Raise the car on a hoist or stands.

2. Remove the engine rear support-to-extension housing attaching bolts.

3. Raise the transmission high enough to remove the weight from the engine rear support.

4. Remove the bolt that secures the engine rear support to the crossmember. Remove the support.

5. Lower the transmission and remove the jack.

6. Place a drain pan beneath the servo. Remove the bolts that attach the servo cover to the transmission case. Loosen the band adjusting screw lock nut.

7. Remove the cover, piston, spring and gasket from the case, screwing the band adjusting screw inwards as the piston is removed. This insures that there will be enough tension on the band to keep the struts properly engaged in the band end notches while the piston is removed.

SEAL REPLACEMENT

1. Apply air pressure to the port in the servo cover to remove the

piston and stem.

2. Remove the seals from the piston (Fig. 17).

3. Remove the seal from the cover.

4. Dip the new seals in transmission fluid.

5. Install the new seals on the piston.

6. Install the new seal on the cover.

7. Dip the piston in transmission fluid and install it in the cover.

INSTALLATION

1. Position a new gasket on the servo cover.

2. Position the servo spring on the piston stem.

3. Insert the servo piston stem in the case. Secure the cover with the attaching bolts, taking care to back off the band adjusting screw while tightening the cover bolts. Make sure that the vent tube retaining clip is in place.

4. Raise the transmission high enough to install the engine rear support. Secure the support to the extension housing with the attaching bolts. Lower the transmission as required to install the support to crossmember attaching bolt. Torque the attaching bolts to specification.

5. Remove the jack.

6. Adjust the band as detailed in Section 2.

7. Lower the car and replenish the fluid as required.

EXTENSION HOUSING AND GOVERNOR REPLACEMENT
REMOVAL

1. Raise the car on a hoist or jack stands.

2. Place a large drain pan under the transmission. Loosen the drain pan attaching bolts and allow the fluid to drain. Starting at the rear of the pan, gradually remove all bolts but two and allow the fluid to drain further. After the fluid has drained, install two bolts loosely in the rear side of the pan.

3. Disconnect the parking brake cable from the equalizer.

4. Remove the torque plate attaching bolts and remove the plate.

5. Disconnect the driveshaft from the rear axle flange and remove it from the transmission.

6. Disconnect the speedometer cable from the extension housing.

7. Remove the two nuts that secure the engine rear mount to the crossmember.

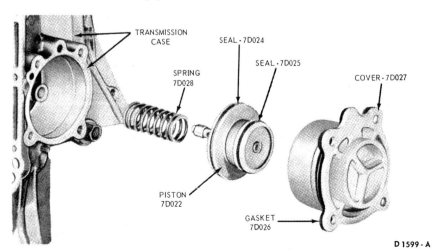

TRANSMISSION CASE

SEAL - 7D024

SEAL - 7D025

COVER - 7D027

SPRING 7D028

PISTON 7D022

GASKET 7D026

D 1599 - A

FIG. 17—Servo Disassembled

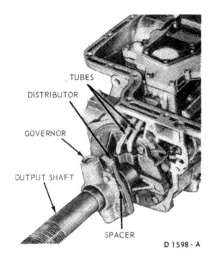

FIG. 18—Governor Installed

8. Place a jack under the transmission and raise it just enough to remove the weight from the crossmember.

9. Remove the cotter pins and nuts that attach the crossmember to the frame side supports. Remove the crossmember.

10. Remove the engine rear support-to-extension housing attaching bolts and remove the support.

11. Lower the transmission to permit access to the extension housing attaching bolts.

12. Remove the extension housing attaching bolts and slide the housing off the output shaft.

13. Remove the four bolts that attach the governor to the distributor (Fig. 18). Slide the governor off the output shaft.

14. Secure the governor (Fig. 18) to the distributor flange with the attaching bolts. Torque the bolts to specification.

15. Clean the mounting surface on the transmission and on the extension housing. Position a new gasket on the transmission.

16. Hold the extension housing in place and secure it with the attaching bolts.

17. Raise the transmission high enough to position the engine rear support and the crossmember.

18. Secure the engine rear support to the crossmember with the attaching bolts. Torque the nuts to specification.

19. Position the crossmember on the frame side supports. Install the attaching nuts and torque them to specification. Secure the nuts with cotter pins.

20. Lower the transmission and

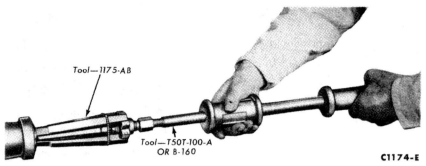

FIG. 19—Removing Extension Housing Seal

remove the jack. Install and torque the engine rear support-to-extension housing attaching bolts to specification.

21. Secure the speedometer cable to the extension housing with the attaching bolt.

22. Connect the parking brake to the equalizer.

23. Install the drive shaft.

24. Secure the torque plate to the floor pan with the attaching bolts. Torque them to specification.

25. Fill the transmission to the correct level with the specified fluid.

EXTENSION HOUSING BUSHING AND REAR SEAL REPLACEMENT

1. Disconnect the drive shaft from the transmission.

2. When only the rear seal needs replacing, carefully remove it with a tapered chisel or the tools shown in Fig. 19. Remove the bushing as shown in Fig. 20. **Use the bushing remover carefully so that the spline seal is not damaged.**

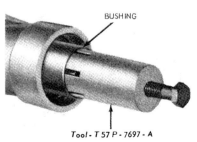

FIG. 20—Removing Extension Housing Bushing

3. When installing a new bushing use the special tool shown in Fig. 21.

4. Before installing a new seal, inspect the sealing surface of the universal joint yoke for scores. If scores are found, replace the yoke.

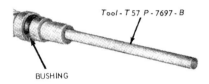

FIG. 21—Installing Extension Housing Bushing

5. Inspect the counterbore of the housing for burrs with crocus cloth.

6. Install the seal into the housing with the tool shown in Fig. 22. The seal should be firmly seated in the bore. Coat the inside diameter of the fiber portion of the seal with B8A-19589-A lubricant.

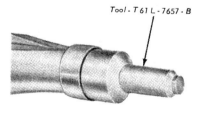

FIG. 22—Installing Extension Housing Seal

7. Coat the front universal joint spline with B8A-19589-A lubricant and install the drive shaft.

3 REMOVAL AND INSTALLATION

REMOVAL

1. Working from inside the engine compartment, disconnect the neutral switch wires from the harness connector and the retaining clip on the dash.

2. Remove the bolt that secures the filler tube to the rear of the right cylinder head.

3. Raise the car on a hoist or jack stands.

4. Remove the converter drain plug access cover from the lower end of the converter housing.

5. Place a drain pan under the converter housing and remove the two converter drain plugs. Install the plugs after the fluid has drained.

6. Place the drain pan under the transmission oil pan. Starting at the rear of the pan and working toward the front, loosen the attaching bolts and allow the fluid to drain. Finally remove all of the pan attaching bolts except two at the front, to allow the oil to further drain. After the oil has drained, install two bolts on the rear side of the pan to temporarily hold it in place.

7. Disconnect the drive shaft from the rear axle flange and remove it from the transmission. Install tool T61L-7657-A in the rear of the extension housing to prevent the fluid from leaking.

8. Disconnect the downshift rod from the transmission downshift lever.

9. Disconnect the shift rod from the manual lever.

10. Disconnect the speedometer cable from the extension housing.

11. Disconnect the rubber hose from the vacuum diaphragm at the rear of the transmission. Remove the vacuum tube from the retaining clip at the transmission.

12. Disconnect the starter cable from the terminal on the starter. Remove *the starter attaching* bolts and remove it from the housing.

13. Lift the fluid filler tube from the transmission case.

14. Remove the four converter-to-flywheel attaching nuts.

15. Remove the two nuts that attach the engine rear support to the crossmember.

16. Raise the transmission with a jack just enough to remove the weight from the crossmember.

17. Remove the cotter pins from the crossmember-to-frame side support attaching nuts and remove the nuts. Lift the crossmember from the frame side supports.

18. Remove the bolts that attach the engine rear support to the extension housing and remove the support.

19. Lower the transmission, then disconnect the fluid cooler lines from the transmission case.

20. Secure the transmission to the jack with a chain.

21. Remove the six bolts that attach the converter housing to the cylinder block.

22. Move the jack rearward until the transmission clears the engine, then tip it forward to provide clearance. Lower the transmission and remove it from under the car.

23. Remove the converter from the transmission. Mount the transmission in a holding fixture if repairs are necessary.

INSTALLATION

1. Mount the transmission in a transmission jack and secure it with a safety chain.

2. Install the converter on the front pump.

3. Rotate the flywheel so that the drain plug holes are in a vertical position. Rotate the converter so that the drain plugs are in the same relative position as the drain plug holes in the flywheel.

4. Roll the transmission into position under the car and raise it to alignment with the engine. Move it forward until the converter housing contacts the cylinder block. Install and torque the converter-to-cylinder block attaching bolts.

5. Remove the jack safety chain from the transmission.

6. Connect the two fluid cooler lines to the fittings in the transmission case.

7. Secure the engine rear support to the extension housing with the attaching bolts. Torque the bolts to specification.

8. Position the crossmember on the frame side supports and install and tighten the attaching nuts to specification. Install cotter pins to retain the nuts.

9. Remove the transmission jack from under the car. Install and torque the engine rear support-to-crossmember attaching nuts.

10. Install the converter-to-flywheel attaching nuts and torque them to specifications. Tighten the drain plugs to specification.

11. Secure the converter drain plug access cover to the lower end of the converter housing with the attaching bolts.

12. Install a new O-ring on the lower end of the fluid filler tube. Dip the O-ring in clean automatic transmission fluid and insert the filler tube in the transmission case.

13. Secure the starter to the converter housing. Connect the cable to the terminal on the starter.

14. Connect the speedometer cable to the extension housing.

15. Connect the shift rod to the manual lever at the transmission.

16. Connect the downshift rod to the lever on the transmission. Adjust the rod. Part 7-2 if required.

17. Remove the tool from the extension housing and install the drive shaft.

18. Lower the car.

19. Working from the engine compartment, secure the fluid filler tube to the rear of the right cylinder head with the attaching bolt.

20. Connect the neutral switch wires to the harness. Secure the wires to the dash with the retaining clip.

21. Fill the transmission with the specified lubricant as detailed in Part 7-1.

4 MAJOR REPAIR OPERATIONS

DISASSEMBLY OF TRANSMISSION

1. Mount the transmission in holding fixture T59P-7000-A (Fig. 23).

2. Remove the oil pan attaching bolts. Remove the pan and gasket.

3. Remove the valve body attaching bolts (Fig. 24). Lift the valve body from the transmission case.

4. Attach a dial indicator to the front pump as shown in Fig. 25. Install tool T61L-7657-B in the extension housing to center the shaft.

5. Pry the gear train to the rear of the case and at the same time, press the input shaft inward until it bottoms (Fig. 25). Set the dial indicator to read zero.

6. Pry the gear train forward (Fig. 25) and note the amount of gear train end play, on the dial indicator. Record the end play to facilitate assembling the transmission. Remove the dial indicator from the pump and the tool from the extension housing.

7. Remove the vacuum diaphragm, rod and the primary throttle valve from the case.

8. Slip the input shaft out of the front pump.

9. Remove the front pump attaching bolts. Pry the gear train forward as shown in Fig. 26 to remove the pump.

10. Loosen the band adjustment screw and remove the two struts.

11. Rotate the band 90° counterclockwise to align the ends with the slot in the case (Fig. 27). Slide the band off the direct drive clutch drum.

12. Remove the forward part of the gear train as an assembly as shown in Fig. 28.

13. Remove the large snap ring that secures the reverse planet carrier in the low-reverse clutch hub. Lift the planet carrier from the drum.

14. Remove the snap ring (Fig. 29) that secures the reverse ring gear and hub on the output shaft. Slide the ring gear and hub off the shaft.

15. Rotate the low-reverse clutch hub in a clockwise direction and at the same time, withdraw it from the case.

16. Remove the reverse clutch snap ring from the case, then remove the clutch discs, plates and pressure plate from the case.

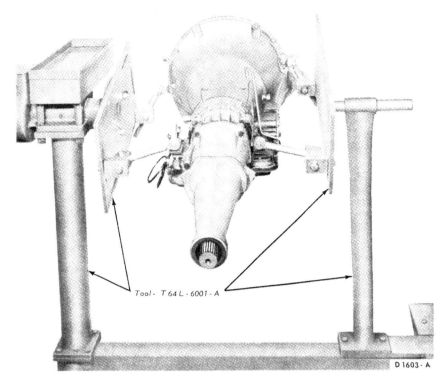

Tool - T 64 L - 6001 - A

D 1603 - A

FIG. 23—Transmission Mounted in Holding Fixture

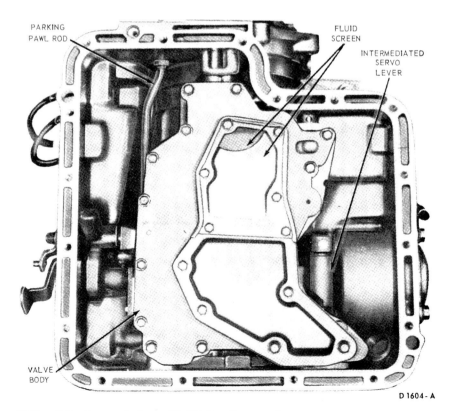

PARKING PAWL ROD

FLUID SCREEN

INTERMEDIATED SERVO LEVER

VALVE BODY

D 1604 - A

FIG. 24—Transmission with Oil Pan Removed

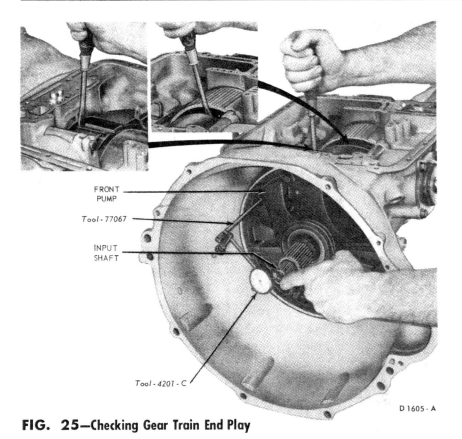

FIG. 25—Checking Gear Train End Play

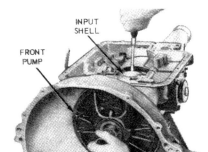

FIG. 26—Removing Front Pump

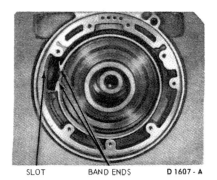

FIG. 27—Removing or Installing Band

17. Remove the extension housing attaching bolts. Remove the extension housing and gasket.

18. Slide the output shaft assembly from the transmission case.

19. Remove the distributor sleeve attaching bolts and remove the sleeve, parking pawl gear and the thrust washer.

20. Compress the reverse clutch piston release spring with tool T65P-77515-A (Fig. 30). Remove the snap ring. Remove the tool and the spring

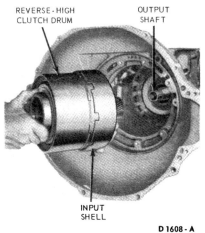

FIG. 28—Removing or Installing Forward Part of Gear Train

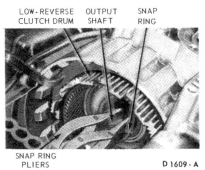

FIG. 29—Removing or Installing Reverse Ring Gear Hub Retaining Ring

retainer.

21. Remove the one-way clutch inner race attaching bolts from the rear of the case. Remove the inner race from inside of the case.

22. Remove the low-reverse clutch

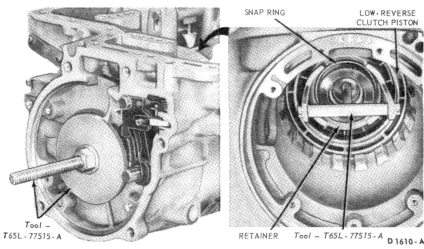

FIG. 30—Compressing Low-Reverse Clutch Springs

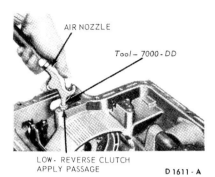

FIG. 31—Removing Low-Reverse Clutch Piston

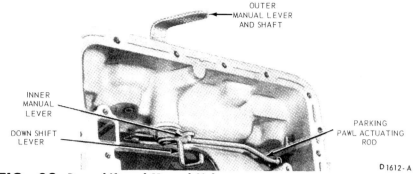

FIG. 32—Downshift and Manual Linkage

piston from the case as shown in Fig. 31.

PARTS REPAIR OR REPLACEMENT

During the repair of the subassemblies, certain general instructions which apply to all units of the transmission must be followed. Following these instructions will avoid unnecessary repetition.

All transmission parts must be handled carefully to avoid nicking or burring the bearing or mating surfaces.

Lubricate all internal parts of the transmission with clean automatic transmission fluid before assembling them.

Do not use any other lubricants except on gaskets and thrust washers. These may be coated with vaseline to facilitate assembly. Always use new gaskets and seals when assembling a transmission.

Tighten all bolts and screws to the recommended torque as outlined in the Specification Section.

TRANSMISSION CASE AND LINKAGE

Downshift and Manual Linkage

1. Remove the nut and lock washer that secures the outer downshift

lever to the transmission and remove the lever.

2. Remove the two bolts that secure the neutral safety switch to the case. Insert a screwdriver between the switch and case as close as possible to the shaft. Gently pry the switch from the case.

3. Slide the downshift lever out from the inside of the case (Fig. 32). Remove the seal from the recess in the manual lever shift.

4. Remove the C-ring that secures the parking pawl actuating rod to the manual lever. Remove the rod from the case.

5. Remove the nut that secures the inner manual lever to the shaft. Remove the inner lever from the

shaft. Slide the outer lever and shaft from the case.

6. Remove the seal from the case with Tools T59L-100-B and T58L-101-A or 7600-E.

7. Dip the new seal in transmission fluid and install it in the case as shown in Fig. 33.

8. Slide the outer manual lever and shaft in the transmission case.

9. Position the inner lever on the shaft and install the attaching nut. Tighten the nut to specification. Install the parking pawl actuating rod and secure it to the inner manual lever with a C-washer.

10. Install a new downshift lever seal in the recess of the outer lever shaft. Slide the downshift lever and

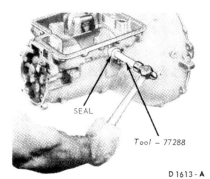

FIG. 33—Installing Manual Lever Seal

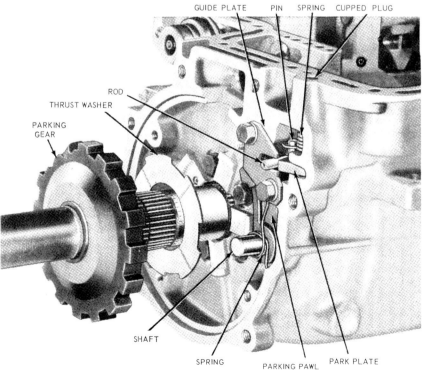

FIG. 34—Parking Pawl Mechanism

shaft into position.

11. Position the neutral safety switch on the manual lever and secure it with the two attaching bolts. Leave the attaching bolts loose to adjust the switch after installing the control valve.

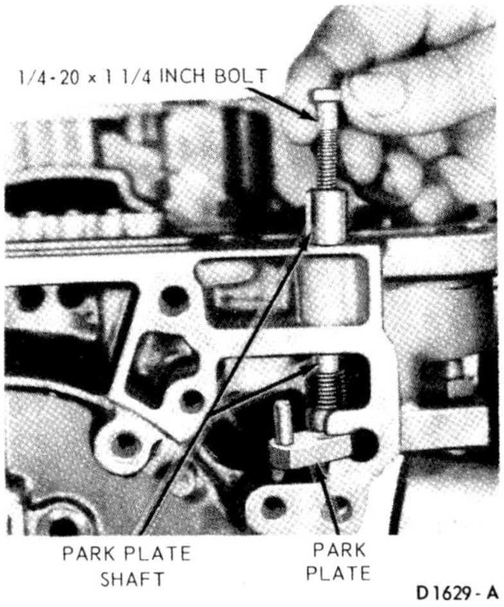

FIG. 35—Removing Park Plate Shaft

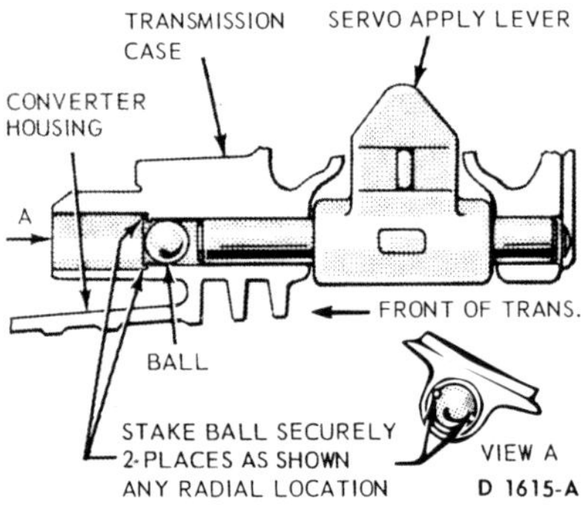

FIG. 36—Servo Apply Lever Installation

12. Place the outer downshift lever on the shaft and secure it with a lock washer and nut.

Parking Pawl Linkage

1. Remove the bolts that secure the parking pawl guide plate to the case (Fig. 34). Remove the plate.

2. Remove the spring, parking pawl and shaft from the case.

3. Working from the pan mounting surface, drill a ⅛ inch diameter hole through the center of the cupped plug. Pull the plug from the case with a wire hook.

4. Lift the end of the spring off the park plate pin to relieve the tension.

5. Thread a ¼-20 inch screw (Fig. 35) into the park plate shaft. Pull the shaft from the case with the screw.

6. Position the spring and park plate in the case and install the shaft.

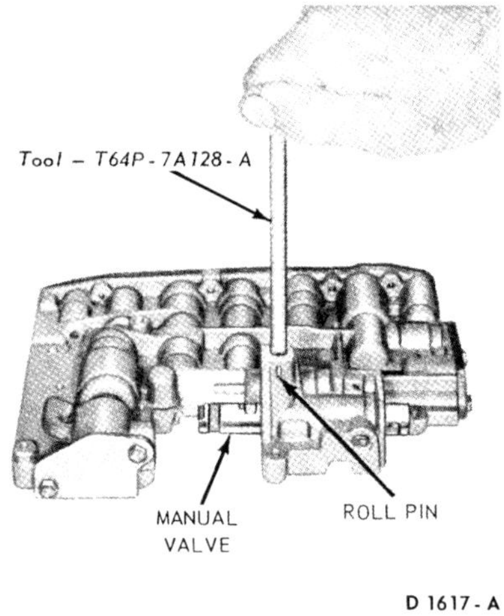

FIG. 38—Removing Manual Valve

Hook the end of the spring over the pin on the park plate.

7. Install a new cupped washer (Fig. 34) to retain the shaft.

8. Install the parking pawl shaft in the case. Slip the parking pawl and spring into place on the shaft.

9. Position the guide plate on the case making sure that the actuating rod is seated in the slot of the plate. Secure the plate with two bolts and lock washers.

Servo Apply Lever

1. Working from inside of the transmission case, carefully drive on the servo apply lever shaft to remove the ball. The shaft (Fig. 36) can be withdrawn from the case by hand.

2. Hold the servo apply lever in position and install the new shaft.

3. Press the ball into position and stake it in two places as shown in Fig. 36.

Thread Repair Case. Thread service kits may be purchased from local jobbers or the Heli-Coil Corporation. To repair a damaged thread, the following procedures should be carefully followed.

1. Drill out the damaged threads **using the same size threads as the thread OD.** For example, use a $\frac{5}{16}$-inch drill when repairing a $\frac{5}{16}$-18 inch thread.

2. Select the proper **special** tap and tap the drilled hole. The tap is marked for the size of the thread being repaired. Thus, the special tap supplied with the repair kit marked $\frac{5}{16}$-18 will not cut the same thread as a standard $\frac{5}{16}$-inch tap. It will cut a thread large enough to accommodate the insert, and after the insert is installed, the original thread size ($\frac{5}{16}$-16 inch) is restored.

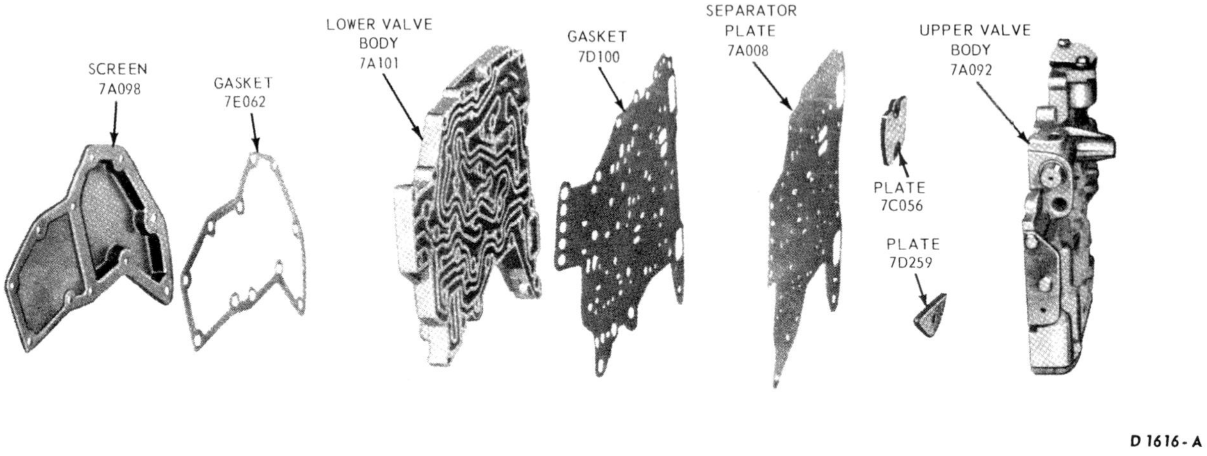

FIG. 37—Upper and Lower Valve Bodies Disassembled

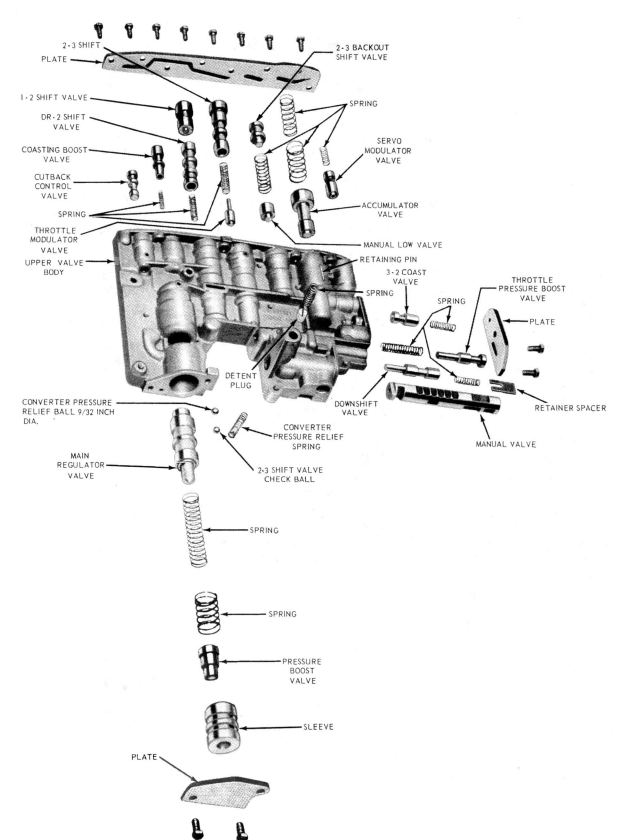

FIG. 39—Upper Valve Body Disassembled

3. Select the proper coil inserting tool. These tools are marked with the thread size being repaired. Place the insert on the tool and adjust the sleeve to the length of the insert being used.

Press the insert against the face of the tapped hole. Turn the tool clockwise and wind the insert into the hole until the insert is one half turn below the face.

4. Working through the insert, bend the insert tang straight up and down until it breaks off at the notch.

5. If the inserts are not properly installed, they can be removed with the extractor tool. Place the extractor tool in the insert so that the blade rests against the top coil ¼ - ½ turn away from the end of the coil. Tap the tool sharply with a hammer so that the blade cuts into the insert. Exert downward pressure on the tool and turn it counterclockwise until the insert is removed.

CONTROL VALVE

Disassembly

1. Remove the nine screws that attach the screen to the lower valve body (Fig. 37) and remove the screen.

2. Remove the twelve screws and the two plates that attach the two valve bodies.

3. Separate the bodies and remove the separator plate and gasket.

4. Depress the manual valve detent spring with the tool shown in Fig. 38. Remove the retaining pin from the upper valve body. Remove the spring and detent plunger.

5. Slide the manual valve (Fig. 39) out of the valve body.

6. Cover the downshift valve port with a finger, then working from the underside of the body remove the downshift valve retainer. Remove the spring and downshift valve.

7. Apply pressure on the pressure booster valve retaining plate and remove the two attaching screws. Slowly release the pressure and remove the plate, sleeve and the pressure booster valve. Remove the two springs and the main regulator valve from the same bore.

8. Apply pressure on the throttle booster valve retaining plate and remove the two attaching screws. Slowly release the pressure and remove the plate, throttle booster valve and spring, and the 3-2 coasting control valve spring from the body.

9. Apply pressure on the remaining valve retaining plate and remove

the eight attaching screws.

10. Hold the valve body so that the plate is facing upward. Slowly release the pressure and remove the plate.

11. When removing the various valves from the control valve body, keep all ports covered with your fingers except the bore the valve is being removed from. Remove the 1-2 shift capacity scheduling and accumulator valves and springs (Fig. 39) from the valve body.

12. Remove the 2-3 back-out valve, spring and the manual low valve.

13. Remove the 2-3 shift valve, spring and the throttle modulator valve.

14. Remove the 1-2 shift valve, D2 shift valve and the spring from the valve body.

15. Remove the coasting boost valve and the spring from the body.

16. Remove the cut back control valve to complete the disassembly of the control valve.

Assembly

1. Place the cut back control valve (Fig. 39) in the valve body.

2. Place the spring and the coasting boost valve in the body.

3. Place the spring, D2 shift valve and the 1-2 shift valve in the body.

4. Place the throttle modulator valve and spring and the 2-3 shift valve in the valve body.

5. Place the manual low valve and spring and the 2-3 back out valve in the valve body.

6. Place the 1-2 shift accumulator valve and springs and the 1-2 shift scheduling valve and spring in the valve body.

7. Carefully place the valve retaining plate on the body and secure it with the eight attaching screws. Tighten the screws to specification.

8. Place the throttle booster valve and spring in the valve body. Place the 3-2 coasting control valve and spring in the valve body and install the retaining plate. Torque the attaching screws to specification.

9. Place the main regulator, two springs, pressure booster valve and the sleeve in the valve body.

10. Install the pressure booster plate and torque the two attaching screws to specification.

11. Place the downshift valve and spring in the valve body. Compress the spring and install the retainer from the underside of the body.

12. Place the manual valve in the

valve body and install the detent plug, spring and the retaining pin in the body.

13. Place the valve body on a clean surface with the passage side facing up. Place the converter relief valve spring in its bore (Fig. 40).

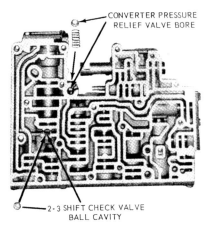

CONVERTER PRESSURE RELIEF VALVE BORE

2-3 SHIFT CHECK VALVE BALL CAVITY

D 1630 - A

FIG. 40—Converter Pressure Relief Valve and 2-3 Shift Check Valve Location

Coat the converter relief valve check ball with vaseline and place it on top of the spring. Place the 2-3 shift check valve ball in its cavity.

14. Carefully position the separator plate, new gasket and the lower valve body on the upper valve body and install and torque the attaching bolts to specification.

15. Secure the screen to the lower valve body with the attaching bolts and torque them to specification.

16. Position the two reinforcing

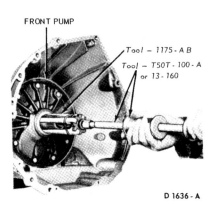

FRONT PUMP

Tool – 1175 - A B
Tool – T50T - 100 - A or 13 - 160

D 1636 - A

FIG. 41—Removing Front Pump Seal

plates on the separator plate and torque the screws to specification.

FRONT PUMP

The front seal can be replaced (Figs. 41 and 42) after the pump has been installed on the transmission.

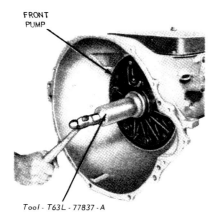

FRONT
PUMP

Tool - T63L - 77837 - A

D 1637 - A

FIG. 42—Installing Front Pump Seal

Disassembly

1. Remove the two seal rings and the selective thrust washer (Fig. 43).
2. Remove the O-ring seal from the pump housing.
3. Remove the five bolts that secure the pump support to the pump housing. Lift the support from the housing.
4. Remove the drive and the driven gear from the housing.

Assembly

1. Install the drive and driven gears in the pump housing. Each gear has an identification mark on one face. **The identification mark on each gear must be toward the front of the pump housing.**
2. Position the pump support in the pump housing and install and torque the five attaching bolts to specification.
3. Carefully install two new seal rings on the pump support. Make sure that the ends of the rings are engaged to lock them in place.
4. Install the selective thrust washer. Make sure that the correct thickness selective washer is being used to obtain the specified end play.
5. Place the pump on converter making sure that the drive gear engages the converter hub. Rotate the pump to make sure that the gears rotate freely.

REVERSE-HIGH CLUTCH

Disassembly

1. Separate the drive train as shown in Fig. 44. Remove the pressure plate retaining snap ring from the reverse-high clutch as shown in Fig. 45.
2. Remove the pressure plate and the drive and driven clutch plates (Fig. 46).
3. Install Tool T65L-77515-A (Fig. 47) on the reverse-high clutch drum. Make sure that the legs clear the snap ring enough to permit expanding it enough for removing it. Remove the snap ring and remove the tool.
4. Remove the spring retainer and the piston return springs.
5. Apply air pressure to the piston apply hole in the clutch hub (Fig. 48) and remove the piston.
6. Remove the piston outer seal

from the piston and the inner seal from the clutch drum (Fig. 46).

Assembly

1. Dip the new seals in transmission fluid and install one on the drum and one on the piston.
2. Install the piston in the clutch drum.
3. Position the piston return springs in the piston sockets. Place the spring retainer on the springs.
4. Install Tool T65L-77515-A (Fig. 47) and compress the springs. Make certain that the spring retainer is centered while compressing the springs. Install the snap ring. Before releasing the pressure on the tool, make certain that the snap ring is positioned inside of the four snap ring guides on the spring retainer.
5. Dip the clutch plates in clean transmission fluid. Install the clutch plates alternately starting with a steel drive plate and a composition plate (Fig. 46).
6. After all clutch plates have been installed, position the pressure plate in the clutch drum with the chamfered side facing up. Install the pressure plate snap ring.
7. With a feeler gauge, check the clearance between the pressure plate and snap ring (Fig. 49).
8. The pressure plate should be held downward as the clearance is checked. The clearance should be 0.022-0.036. If the clearance is not within specifications, selective thickness snap rings are available in the following thicknesses: 0.065-0.069, 0.074-0.078, 0.083-0.087. Install the correct size snap ring and recheck the clearance.

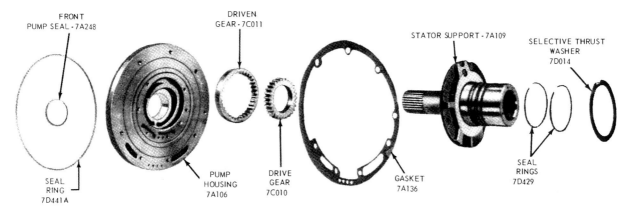

FRONT
PUMP SEAL - 7A248

DRIVEN
GEAR - 7C011

STATOR SUPPORT - 7A109

SELECTIVE THRUST
WASHER
7D014

SEAL
RING
7D441A

PUMP
HOUSING
7A106

DRIVE
GEAR
7C010

GASKET
7A136

SEAL
RINGS
7D429

D 1619 - A

FIG. 43—Front Pump Disassembled

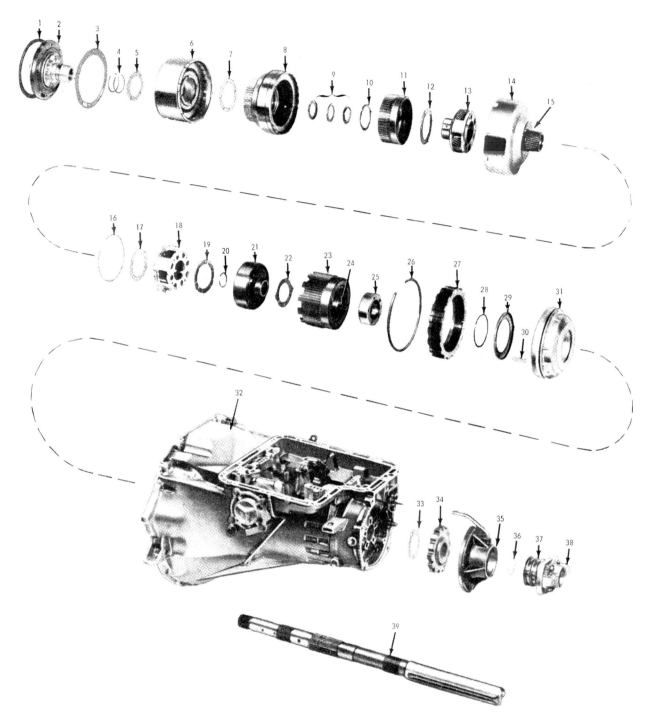

1. FRONT PUMP SEAL RING	11. FORWARD CLUTCH HUB	20. REVERSE RING GEAR AND
2. FRONT PUMP	ASSEMBLY	HUB RETAINING RING
3. GASKET	12. NUMBER 5 THRUST WASHER	21. REVERSE RING GEAR AND HUB
4. SEAL	13. FORWARD PLANET ASSEMBLY	22. NUMBER 9 THRUST WASHER
5. NUMBER 1 THRUST WASHER	14. INPUT SHELL AND SUN	23. LOW – REVERSE CLUTCH HUB
(SELECTIVE)	GEAR ASSEMBLY	24. ONE – WAY CLUTCH
6. REVERSE – HIGH CLUTCH	15. NUMBER 6 THRUST WASHER	25. ONE – WAY CLUTCH INNER RACE
ASSEMBLY	16. SNAP RING	26. SNAP RING
7. NUMBER 2 THRUST WASHER	17. NUMBER 7 THRUST WASHER	27. LOW - REVERSE CLUTCH
8. FORWARD CLUTCH ASSEMBLY	18. REVERSE PLANET ASSEMBLY	28. SNAP RING
9. NUMBER 3 THRUST WASHER	19. NUMBER 8 THRUST WASHER	29. LOW – REVERSE PISTON RETURN
10. NUMBER 4 THRUST WASHER		

	SPRING RETAINER
	30. RETURN SPRING
	31. LOW – REVERSE PISTON
	32. CASE
	33. NUMBER 10 THRUST WASHER
	34. PARKING GEAR
	35. GOVERNOR DISTRIBUTOR SLEEVE
	36. SNAP RING
	37. GOVERNOR DISTRIBUTOR
	38. GOVERNOR
	39. OUTPUT SHAFT

D 1620 - A

FIG. 44—Drive Train Disassembled

FORWARD CLUTCH

Disassembly.

1. Remove the clutch pressure plate retaining snap ring (Fig. 50).

2. Remove the rear pressure plate, the drive and driven plates and the forward pressure plate from the clutch hub (Fig. 51).

3. Remove the snap ring (Fig. 52)

that secures the disc spring in the clutch cylinder. Remove the disc spring.

4. Apply air pressure to the clutch apply passage in the cylinder (Fig. 53) to remove the piston.

5. Remove the seal from the piston and the seal from the clutch hub (Fig. 51).

Assembly

1. Dip two new seals in transmission fluid. Install the smaller seal on the clutch hub and the other seal on the clutch piston.

2. Install the clutch piston in the cylinder.

3. Make sure that the steel pressure ring is in the groove on the piston. Position the disc spring in the cylinder with the convex face downward. Install the spring as shown in

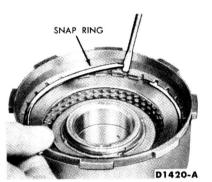

FIG. 45—Removing Reverse-High Pressure Plate Snap Ring

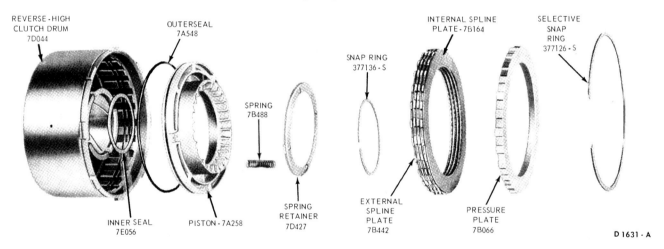

FIG. 46—Reverse-High Clutch Disassembled

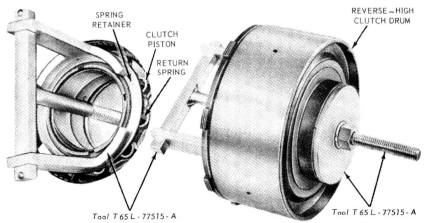

FIG. 47—Removing or Installing Snap Ring

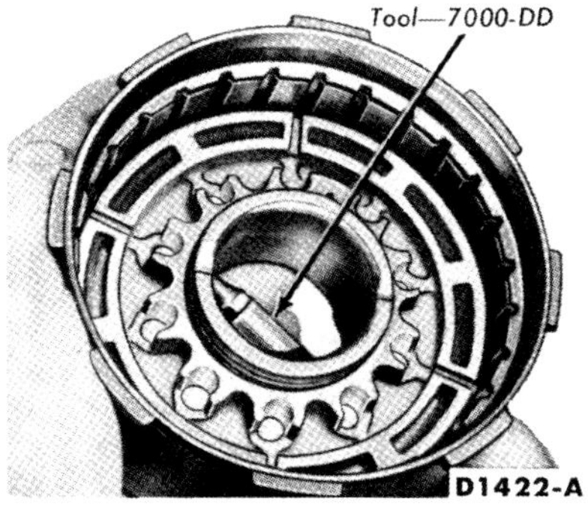

FIG. 48—Removing Reverse-High Clutch Piston

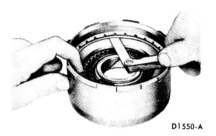

FIG. 49—Checking Reverse-High Clutch Snap Ring Clearance

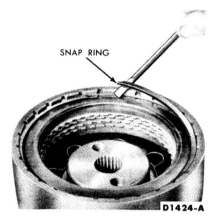

FIG. 50—Removing Forward Clutch Pressure Plate Snap Ring

Fig. 52. Secure the disc with the retaining snap ring.

4. Install the forward pressure plate with the flat side up and the beveled side downward. Install first a composition driven plate and a steel drive plate. Install the remaining plates in this sequence. The last plate installed will be the rear pressure plate with the internal chamfered side facing up (Fig. 51). Install the snap ring and make certain that it seats fully in the groove.

5. With a feeler gauge, check the clearance between the snap ring and the pressure plate (Fig. 54). Downward pressure on the plate should be maintained when making this check. The clearance should be 0.048-0.061 inch.

6. If the clearance is not within specifications, selective snap rings are available in the following thicknesses: 0.065-0.069, 0.074-0.078, and 0.083-0.087 inch. Insert the correct size snap ring and recheck the clearance.

INPUT SHELL AND SUN GEAR

Disassembly

1. Remove the rear snap ring from the sun gear as shown in Fig. 55.

2. Remove the thrust washer from the input shell and sun gear (Fig. 55).

FIG. 52—Removing or Installing Disc Spring

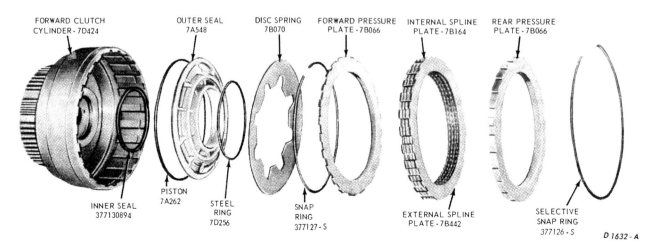

FIG. 51—Forward Clutch Disassembled

FIG. 53—Removing Forward Clutch Piston

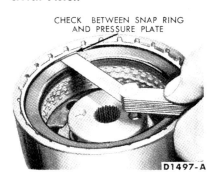

FIG. 54—Checking Forward Clutch Snap Ring Clearance

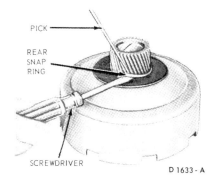

FIG. 55—Removing or Installing Sun Gear Rear Snap Ring

3. Working from inside the input shell remove the sun gear. Remove the forward snap ring from the gear.

Assembly

1. Install the forward snap ring on the forward end (short end) of the sun gear (Fig. 56). Working from inside the input shell, slide the sun gear and snap ring into place making sure that the longer end is at the rear (Fig. 56).

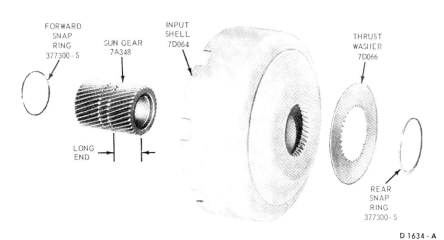

FIG. 56—Input Shell and Sun Gear Disassembled

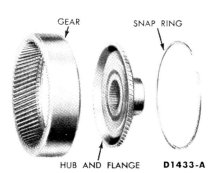

FIG. 57—Output Shaft Hub and Ring Gear

2. Place the No. 6 thrust washer on the sun gear and install the rear snap ring.

OUTPUT SHAFT HUB AND RING GEAR

Disassembly

1. Remove the hub retaining snap ring (Fig. 57) from the ring gear.

2. Lift the hub from the ring gear.

Assembly

1. Position the hub in the ring gear.

2. Secure the hub with the retaining snap ring. Make certain that the snap ring is fully engaged with the groove.

ONE-WAY CLUTCH

Disassembly

1. Remove the snap ring (Fig. 58) from the rear of the low-reverse clutch hub.

2. Lift the one-way clutch from the hub.

3. Remove the remaining snap ring from the hub.

Assembly

1. Install the snap ring in the inner groove of the low-reverse clutch hub.

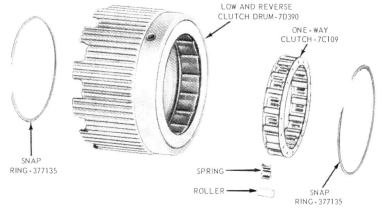

FIG. 58—One-Way Clutch Disassembled

2. Make sure that all of the rollers are in place and that the springs contact them properly.

3. Place the low-reverse clutch hub on the bench with the one-way clutch race facing upward.

4. Place the one-way clutch on the hub so that the springs load the rollers in a counterclockwise direction when looking downward at the unit (Fig. 59).

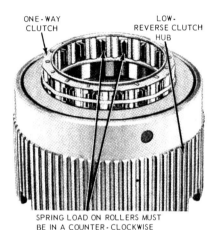

ONE-WAY CLUTCH　　　LOW-REVERSE CLUTCH HUB

SPRING LOAD ON ROLLERS MUST BE IN A COUNTER-CLOCKWISE DIRECTION FOR INSTALLATION　　D 1622-A

FIG. 59—Installing One-Way Clutch

5. Work each roller inward just enough to enter it in the ramp. Do this to each individual roller until the one-way clutch is positioned in the race. Placing a rubber band around the clutch as shown in Fig. 59 helps to contract the rollers to permit installation. After all of the rollers have started, remove the rubber band.

6. Install the snap ring at the rear of the low-reverse clutch hub to secure the one-way clutch.

SERVO

Disassembly

1. Apply air pressure to the port in the servo cover to remove the piston and stem.

2. Remove the seals from the piston.

3. Remove the seal from the cover.

Assembly

1. Dip the new seals in transmission fluid.

2. Install the new seals on the piston.

3. Install the new seal on the cover.

4. Dip the piston in transmission fluid and install it in the cover.

LOW-REVERSE CLUTCH PISTON

Disassembly

1. Remove the inner and the outer seal from the reverse clutch piston.

Assembly

1. Dip the two new seals in clean transmission fluid.

2. Install the seals on the piston.

OUTPUT SHAFT

Disassembly

1. Remove the governor attaching bolts and remove the governor.

2. Remove the snap ring that secures the governor distributor on the output shaft (Fig. 60) and slide it off the front of the shaft.

3. Remove the seal rings from the distributor.

Assembly

1. Carefully install new seal rings on the distributor.

2. Working from the front end of the output shaft, slide the governor distributor into place on the shaft. Install the snap ring to secure it. Make sure that the snap ring is seated in the groove.

3. Position the governor on the distributor (Fig. 60) and secure them with the attaching screws.

ASSEMBLY OF TRANSMISSION

1. Place the transmission case in a holding fixture.

2. Tap the reverse clutch piston into place in the case with a clean rubber hammer.

3. Hold the one-way clutch inner race in position and install and torque the attaching bolts to specification.

4. Install a low-reverse clutch return spring in each pocket in the clutch piston. Press the springs firmly into the piston to prevent them from falling out.

5. Position the spring retainer over the springs and position the retainer snap ring in place on the one-way clutch inner race.

6. Install the compressing tool shown in Fig. 31 and compress the springs just enough to install the low-reverse clutch piston retainer snap ring.

7. Install the snap ring, then remove the compressing tool.

8. Place the transmission case on the bench with the front end facing downward.

9. Position the parking gear thrust washer and the gear on the case (Fig. 34).

10. Position the oil distributor and tubes in place on the rear of the case. Install and torque the attach-

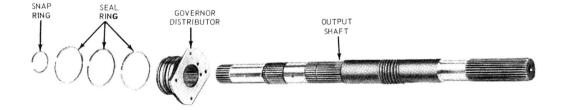

SNAP RING　　SEAL RING　　GOVERNOR DISTRIBUTOR　　OUTPUT SHAFT　　GOVERNOR

D 1623-A

FIG. 60—Output Shaft Disassembled

ing bolts to specification.

11. Install the output shaft and governor as an assembly.

12. Place a new gasket on the rear of the transmission case. Position the extension housing on the case and install the attaching bolts. Torque the attaching bolts to specification.

13. Place the case in the holding fixture.

14. Align the low-reverse clutch hub and one-way clutch with the inner race at the rear of the case. Rotate the low-reverse clutch hub clockwise while applying pressure to seat it on the inner race.

15. Install the low-reverse clutch plates, starting with a steel plate and following with friction and steel plates alternately. If new composition plates are being used, soak them in clean transmission fluid for fifteen minutes before installation. Install the pressure plate and the snap ring. Test the operation of the low-reverse clutch by applying air pressure at the clutch pressure apply hole in the case. The transmission cases are machined to accommodate a five-plate clutch pack.

16. Install the reverse planet ring gear thrust washer and the ring gear and hub assembly. Insert the snap ring in the groove in the output shaft.

17. Assemble the front and rear thrust washers onto the reverse planet assembly. Retain them with vaseline, and insert the assembly into the ring gear. Install the snap ring in the ring gear.

18. Set the reverse-high clutch on the bench, with the front end facing down. Install the thrust washer on the rear end of the reverse-high clutch assembly. Retain the thrust washer with vaseline and insert the splined end of forward clutch into the open end of the reverse-high clutch so that the splines engage the reverse-high friction plates (Fig. 46).

19. Install the thrust washer and retain it with vaseline, on the front end of the forward planet ring gear and hub. Insert the ring gear into the forward clutch.

20. Install the thrust washer on the front end of the forward planet assembly. Retain the washer with vaseline and insert the assembly into the ring gear. Install the input shell and sun gear assembly.

21. Install the reverse-high clutch, forward clutch, forward planet assembly and input shell and sun gear as an assembly into the transmission case.

22. Insert the intermediate band into the case around the direct clutch cylinder with the narrow band end facing toward the servo apply level. Install the struts and tighten the band adjusting screw sufficiently to retain the band.

23. Place a selective thickness bronze thrust washer on the rear shoulder of the stator support and retain it with vaseline. Lay a new gasket on the rear mounting face of the pump and position the pump on the case being careful not to damage the O-ring. Install six of the seven mounting bolts and torque them to specification.

24. Adjust the intermediate band as detailed in Section 2 and install the input shaft.

25. Install tool 4201-C at the seventh pump mounting bolt (Fig 25) and check the transmission end play. Remove the tool.

26. Install the control valve in the case, making sure that the levers engage the valves properly.

27. Install the primary throttle valve, rod, and the vacuum diaphragm in the case.

28. Install a new pan gasket and the oil pan.

29. Install the converter assembly.

30. Install the transmission in the car.

PART 7-4   SPECIFICATIONS

C4 TRANSMISSION

CONTROL PRESSURE AT ZERO OUTPUT SHAFT SPEED—C4 TRANSMISSION

Engine Speed	Throttle	Manifold Vac. Ins. HG.	Selector Lever Position	Control Pressure (PSI)
Idle	Closed	①Above 18	P, N, D1, D2, L	55-62
			R	55-100
As Req'd.	As Req'd.	Approx. 17.0	D1, D2, L	Pressure Starts to Increase
As Req'd.	As Req'd.	10	D1, D2, L	96-105
As Req'd.	As Req'd.	3	D1, D2, L	138-148
			R	215-227

①Cars checked at high altitudes

At altitudes above sea level it may not be possible to obtain 18″ of engine vacuum at idle. For idle vacuums of less than 18″ refer to following table to determine idle speed pressure specification in forward driving ranges (D1, D2 or L).

Engine Vacuum	Control Pressure (PSI)
17	55-62
16	55-68
15	55-74
14	55-80
13	55-87
12	55-93
11	55-99

LUBRICANT REFILL CAPACITY

Models	Capacity
PCS-V, Y, W and AA	7 qts 25 oz
PCW-AN, AR, AS, AY and AZ	8 qts 27 oz

CHECKS AND ADJUSTMENTS

Operation	Specification
Transmission End Play Check	0.008-0.042 inch Selective Thrust Washers Available
Turbine and Stator End Play Check	0.060 inch (maximum)
Intermediate Band Adjustment	Adjust screw to 10 ft-lbs torque, and back off 1¾ turns
Low-Reverse Band Adjustment	Adjust screw to 10 ft-lbs torque, and back off three turns
Forward Clutch Pressure Plate to Snap Ring Clearance	0.022 to 0.042 inch Selective Snap Ring Thicknesses 0.092-0.088 0.078-0.074 0.064-0.060
Reverse-High Clutch Pressure Plate to Snap Ring Clearance	0.060-0.080 inch Selective Snap Ring Thicknesses 0.092-0.088 0.078-0.074 0.064-0.060 0.102-0.106②

②Use with PCW and PCS models.

SELECTIVE THRUST WASHERS— CONTROL TRANSMISSION END PLAY③ (No. 1 and 2)

Thrust Washer No. 1		Thrust Washer No. 2	
Composition Thrust Washer	Color of Washer	No. Stamped on Washer	Metal Thrust Washer
0.108-0.104	Blue	5	0.109-0.107
0.091-0.087	Yellow	4	0.092-0.090
0.074-0.070	Black	3	0.075-0.073
0.057-0.053	Tan	2	0.058-0.056
0.042-0.038	Green	1	0.043-0.041
0.121-0.125	Red		
0.138-0.142	Purple		

③Selection in pairs not applicable.

CONTROL VALVE BODY SPRING IDENTIFICATION

Spring	Total Coils	Free Length	OD	Wire Diameter	Lbs. Load at Length	
Manual Valve Detent	9	0.740	0.295	0.045	7.500	0.601
2-3 Backout Control Valve	10	1.515	0.450	0.026	1.353	0.580
Main Oil Pressure Regulator Valve	9.75	1.860	0.615	0.047	6.200	0.608
Throttle Pressure Modulator	15	1.513	0.292	0.286	3.675	0.620
Control 1-2 Shift Valve	13	0.950	0.230	0.019	1.000	0.450
Throttle Downshift Valve	9	1.042	0.360	0.031	3.000	0.476
Throttle Pressure Booster Valve	15	1.421	0.326	0.036	5.250	0.730
Control Pressure Booster Valve	23.5	0.965	0.290	0.032	1.000	0.715
④Intermediate Band Accumulator Valve	12.5	1.107	0.325	0.025	1.100	0.551

④Not Used on PCW-AY and AZ Models.

SHIFT SPEEDS—ACTUAL M.P.H.
COMET, FALCON, FAIRLANE & MUSTANG WITH 6 CYLINDER ENGINE

	Range	Shift	1	2	3	4	5	6	7	8
Minimum Throttle	D1	1-2	7-9	7-9	8-10	8-10	8-11	9-11	9-11	9-11
	D1	2-3	10-19	11-19	11-20	11-20	12-21	12-22	13-23	13-23
	D2	3-2	9	9	10	10	11	11	11	11
	D1	3-1	9	9	10	10	11	11	11	11
	L	2-1	19	19	20	20	21	22	23	23
Maximum Throttle	D1	1-2	25-34	26-35	27-36	28-37	29-39	30-40	32-42	33-42
	D1, D2	2-3	47-63	43-61	50-66	52-68	54-70	56-73	60-76	60-76
	D1, D2	3-2	62	63	66	68	71	74	77	77
	D1	2-1 or 3-1	29	29	31	32	33	34	36	36

Car	Engine CID	Axle Ratio	Tire Size	Use Column No.
Comet or Falcon	200-1V	3.50:1	6.95 x 14	1
Falcon	170-1V		7.35 x 14 or 7.75 x 14	2
Falcon	170-1V or 200-1V	3.25:1	6.50 x 13	2
			7.35 x 14 or 7.75 x 14	4
			6.95 x 14	3
		3.20:1	6.50 x 13 or 6.95 x 14	3
Falcon	170-1V	2.83:1 or 2.80:1	6.50 x 13	6
Comet or Falcon	200-1V		6.95 x 14 or 7.35 x 14	7

Car	Engine CID	Axle Ratio	Tire Size	Use Column No.
Fairlane	200-1V	3.50:1	6.95 x 14	1
			7.35 x 14 or 7.75 x 14	2
		3.25:1	6.95 x 14	3
			7.35 x 14 or 7.75 x 14	4
		3.00:1	6.95 x 14	5
			7.35 x 14 or 7.75 x 14	6
		2.80:1	6.95 x 14	7
			7.35 x 14	8
Mustang	200-1V	3.20:1	6.95 x 14	3
		3.00:1	6.95 x 14	5
		2.83:1 or 2.80:1	6.95 x 14	7

SHIFT SPEEDS—ACTUAL M.P.H.
COMET, FALCON, FAIRLANE & MUSTANG WITH 289-2V ENGINE

	Range	Shift	1	2	3	4	5	6	7	8
Minimum Throttle	D1	1-2	7-9	7-9	8-10	8-10	8-11	9-11	9-11	9-11
	D1	2-3	10-18	11-19	11-20	11-20	12-21	12-22	13-23	13-23
	D2	3-2	9	9	10	10	11	11	11	11
	D1	3-1	9	9	10	10	11	11	11	11
	L	2-1	18	19	20	20	21	22	23	23
Maximum Throttle	D1	1-2	27-35	28-37	30-38	30-40	32-41	33-43	34-44	35-45
	D1, D2	2-3	50-63	51-66	54-69	55-71	58-74	60-77	63-79	64-80
	D1, D2	3-2	61	63	66	68	71	74	76	77
	D1	2-1 or 3-1	28	29	31	32	33	34	35	36

Car	Engine CID	Axle Ratio	Tire Size	Use Column No.
Comet or Falcon	289-2V	3.25:1	6.95 x 14	3
			7.35 x 14 or 7.75 x 14	4
		3.00:1	6.50 x 13	2
			6.95 x 14	5
			7.35 x 14 or 7.75 x 14	6
		2.80:1	6.50 x 13	6
			6.95 x 14	7
			7.35 x 14	8
Fairlane		3.50:1	6.95 x 14	1
			7.35 x 14	2
		3.25:1	6.95 x 14	3

Car	Engine CID	Axle Ratio	Tire Size	Use Column No.
Fairlane (Cont'd)	289-2V	3.00:1	7.35 x 14 or 7.75 x 14	4
			6.95 x 14	5
		2.80:1	7.35 x 14 or 7.75 x 14	6
			6.95 x 14	7
			7.35 x 14	8
Mustang	289-2V	3.20:1	6.95 x 14	3
		3.00:1	6.95 x 14	5
		2.80:1 or 2.83:1	6.95 x 14	7

SHIFT SPEEDS—ACTUAL M.P.H.
COMET, FALCON, FAIRLANE & MUSTANG WITH 289-4V ENGINE

	Range	Shift	1	2	3	4	5	6	7	8
Minimum Throttle	D1	1-2	7-9	7-9	8-10	8-10	8-10	9-11	9-11	9-11
	D1	2-3	10-18	11-19	11-20	11-21	12-21	12-22	13-23	13-23
	D2	3-2	9	9	10	10	10	11	11	11
	D1	3-1	9	9	10	10	10	11	11	11
	L	2-1	18	19	20	21	11	22	23	23
Maximum Throttle	D1	1-2	29-37	30-39	32-40	32-42	34-43	35-45	36-46	38-47
	D1, D2	2-3	53-66	54-69	56-71	58-74	62-76	63-80	65-82	68-83
	D1, D2	3-2	61	63	65	69	71	74	76	77
	D1	2-1 or 3-1	28	29	30	32	33	34	35	36

Car	Engine CID	Axle Ratio	Tire Size	Use Column No.
Comet or Falcon	289-4V	3.25:1	6.50 x 13 or 6.95 x 14	3
			7.35 x 14 or 7.75 x 14	4
		3.00:1	6.95 x 14	5
			7.35 x 14 or 7.75 x 14	6
		2.80:1	6.50 x 13 or 6.95 x 14	7
			7.35 x 14	8
Fairlane		3.50:1	6.95 x 14	1
			7.35 x 14 or 7.75 x 14	2
		3.25:1	6.95 x 14	3

Car	Engine CID	Axle Ratio	Tire Size	Use Column No.
Fairlane (Cont'd)	289-4V	3.00:1	7.35 x 14 or 7.75 x 14	4
			6.95 x 14	5
		2.80:1	7.35 x 14 or 7.75 x 14	6
			6.95 x 14	7
			7.35 x 14	8
Mustang	289-4V	3.20:1	6.95 x 14	4
		3.00:1	6.95 x 14	5
		2.80:1 or 2.83:1	6.95 x 14	7

STALL SPEED LIMITS

Engine Model	Engine Speed (rpm)
170—6-Cyl.	1450-1650
200—6-Cyl.	1600-1800
289—2V	1750-1950
289—4V	1800-2000

CLUTCH PLATES

Transmission Model	Reverse-High Clutch		Forward Clutch	
	Steel Plates	Composition Plates	Steel Plates	Composition Plates
PCS—170, 200-1V	3	3	3	4
PCW—289-2V 289-4V	4	4	4	5

TORQUE LIMITS

Description	Foot Pounds
Pressure Gauge Tap..	9-15
Conv. Hsg. Lower Cover to Trans............................	10-13
Downshift Lever to Case.....................................	12-16
Oil Pan to Case...	12-16
Cooler Bracket & Oil Pan to Case...........................	12-16
Int. Servo Cover to Case....................................	12-20
Rev. Servo Cover to Case....................................	12-20
Support to Front Pump.......................................	12-20
Distributor Sleeve to Case..................................	12-20
Reverse Servo Piston to Rod................................	12-20
Outer Race to Case...	13-20
Diaphragm Assy. to Case.....................................	15-23
Converter Drain Plug...	20-30
Flywheel to Converter.......................................	20-30
Ext. Hsg. to Case..	28-40
Conv. Housing & Pump to Case..............................	28-40
Front Oil Pump to Case......................................	28-40
Converter Housing to Case..................................	28-40

TORQUE LIMITS (Continued)

Description	Foot Pounds
Manual Lever to Shaft..	30-40
Int. Band Adj. Stop to Case.................................	35-45
Rev. Band Adj. Stop to Case................................	35-45
Transmission to Engine:	
6 Cyl. Falcon, Comet, Fairlane, Mustang...............	23-33
8 Cyl. Falcon, Comet, Fairlane, Mustang...............	40-50

Description	Inch Pounds
End Plate to Control Assy....................................	20-35
Lower to Upper Valve Body..................................	40-55
	80-120
Screen & Lwr. to Upper Valve Body.........................	40-55
Neutral Switch to Case......................................	55-75
Screen & Control Assy. to Case.............................	80-120
Control Assy. to Case..	80-120
Gov. Body to Distributor Body..............................	80-120
Cooler Line Fittings..	80-120

C6 TRANSMISSION

C6 TRANSMISSION SHIFT SPEEDS (Approximate)

	Range	Shift	1	2
Minimum Throttle	D1	1-2	7-13	6-12
	D1	2-3	11-21	11-20
	D2	3-2	7-9	6-8
	D1	3-1	7-9	6-8
	L	2-1	7-9	6-8
Maximum Throttle	D1	1-2	38-45	35-42
	D1, D2	2-3	72-82	66-76
	D1, D2	3-2	64-73	59-68
	D1	2-1 or 3-1	26-34	24-31

Car	Engine Displacement	Axle Ratio	Tire Size	Use Column No.
Comet-Fairlane	390—2V	3.00:1	7.35 x 15	1
	390—4V	3.25:1	7.75 x 15	2

CONVERTER IDENTIFICATION AND STALL SPEEDS

Converter Part Number	Size Inches Diameter	Stall Ratio	Identification No.[1]	Transmission Models	Engine CID	Stall Speed
C6AP-7902-A	12	2.10:1	26	PDD-J, P	390-2V	1750-1950
				PDD-E, R	390-4V	1800-2000

[1]Converter identification is stamped on the converter cover adjacent to the converter drive stud.

CHECKS AND ADJUSTMENTS

Transmission End Play	0.008-0.044 inch Selective Thrust Washers Available
Turbine and Stator End Play	0.060 inch
Intermediate Band Adjustment	Adjust screw to 10 ft-lbs torque, then back off 1⅛ turns and tighten lock nut to specification.
Forward Clutch Pressure Plate-to-Snap Ring Clearance	0.048-0.061 Inch
	Selective Snap Ring Thicknesses 0.065-0.069 Inch 0.083-0.087 Inch 0.074-0.078 Inch
Reverse—High Clutch Pressure Plate-to-Snap Ring Clearance	Transmission Models
	PDD- E, J, P, R
	0.022-0.036 Inch
	Selective Snap Ring Clearances 0.065-0.069 Inch 0.083-0.087 Inch 0.074-0.078 Inch

LUBRICANT REFILL CAPACITY

Approximate Capacity..............Quarts..................13.3

LOW—REVERSE CLUTCH PLATES

Transmission Model	Steel Plates	Composition Plates
PDD-E, J, P, R	5	5

REVERSE—HIGH CLUTCH PLATES

Transmission Model	Steel Plates	Composition Plates
PDD-E, J, P, R	3	3

FORWARD CLUTCH PLATES

Transmission Model	Steel Plates	Composition Plates
PDD-E, J, P, R	3	4

INTERMEDIATE BAND WIDTH (Inches)

Transmission Model	PDD-E, J, P, R 1¹³⁄₁₆

SPECIAL TOOLS

Ford Tool No.	Former No.	Description
TOOL FCO-24	—	Vacuum Diaphragm Wrench
T50T-100-A	—	Impact Slide Hammer
T58L-101-A	—	Puller Attachment
T53L-200-A	—	Handle Adapter
T57L-500-A	—	Bench Mounted Holding Fixture
TOOL-1175-AB	1175-AB	Grease Seal Remover (Head Only)
T50T-100-A and	1175-AE	Seal Remover

SPECIAL TOOLS (Continued)

Ford Tool No.	Former No.	Description
TOOL-1175-AB		
TOOL-3552-H	3552-H	Special Jaws for 7600-E
TOOL-4201-C	4201-C	Differential Backlash and Runout Gauge, with Universal Bracket, Dial Indicator and Bracket
TOOL-7000-DD	7000-DD	Air Nozzle Rubber Tip Assembly
T52L-7000-GAE	7000-G	Transmission Extension Housing Rear Bearing Remover
T52L-7000-HAE	7000-HF	Transmission Extension Housing Rear Bearing Remover
T64L-6001-A		Transmission Holding Fixture
T64P-7A128-A		Manual Valve Detent Spring
T64P-7B456-A and	—	Clutch Race to Case Bolt Socket
T65P-7B456-B		
T58L-101-A and	7600-E	Seal Remover (Head and Hammer)
T59L-100-B		
T61L-7657-A	7657-AA	Transmission Extension Housing Oil Seal Replacer
T61L-7657-B	7657-AB	Transmission Extension Housing Oil Seal Replacer
T57P-7697-A	—	Transmission Extension Housing Bushing Remover
T57P-7697-B	—	Transmission Extension Housing Bushing Replacer
T60-K-7697-A	7000-AF	Transmission Extension Housing Bushing Remover
T59P-7902-B	7937-B	Welded Converter Sprag Driver and Gauge Post
T63P-7902-A	—	Converter Stator Check Adapter
T64L-7902-A	—	Welded Converter Sprag Driver and Gauge Post Adapter Kit for T59P-7902-B
T59P-77067		Dial Indicator Support Fixture
TOOL-77288	77288	Control Shaft Seal Replacer
T59P-77370-B	7345	Front Band Torque Wrench
T65P-77370-A		Rear Band Torque Wrench Mustang Only
T59P-77423-A	7355-B	Rear Band Torque Wrench
T65L-77515-A		Rear Clutch Spring Compressor
T57L-77820-L		400 lb Pressure Gauge
T63L-77837-A	77837-A	Front Pump Seal Replacer

INTERMEDIATE SERVO COVER AND PISTON DIMENSIONS

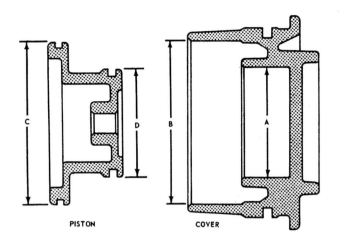

PISTON   COVER

Models	Piston	Cover	Diameter - Inches			
			A	B	C	D
PDD-J, P	C6SP-7D021-A	C6SP-7D027-A	2.040	3.025	3.016	2.031
PDD-E, R	C6AP-7D021-A	C6AP-7D027-A	2.075	2.980	2.971	2.066

D 1642-B

ENGINE

GROUP 8

PART 8-1   PAGE
GENERAL ENGINE SERVICE....... 8-1
PART 8-2
170 AND 200 SIX 8-24
PART 8-3
289 V-8 8-50

PART 8-4   PAGE
390 V-8 8-81
PART 8-5
SPECIFICATIONS 8-109

PART 8-1 GENERAL ENGINE SERVICE

Section	Page
1 Diagnosis and Testing........................	8- 2
Diagnosis Guide...........................	8- 2
Camshaft Lobe Lift........................	8- 8
Compression Test..........................	8- 8
Manifold Vacuum Test.....................	8- 9
Hydraulic Valve Lifter Tests...............	8- 9
Positive Crankcase Ventilation System Test....	8-10
Crankshaft End Play.......................	8-10
Flywheel Face Runout—Manual-Shift Transmissions...	8-10
Flywheel Runout—Automatic Transmission...	8-11
Flywheel Ring Gear Runout................	8-11
Camshaft End Play........................	8-11
Timing Chain Deflection...................	8-12
2 Common Adjustments and Repairs.............	8-12
Valve Clearance—Hydraulic Valve Lifters, 170 and 200 Six...................	8-12
Valve Clearance—Hydraulic Valve Lifters, 289 Regular V-8..................	8-12
Valve Clearance—Hydraulic Valve Lifters, 390 V-8......................	8-13
Valve Lash—Mechanical Tappets, 289 High Performance V-8................	8-14
Valve Rocker Arm and/or Shaft Assembly....	8-14
Push Rods................................	8-14
Cylinder Heads...........................	8-14
Valves...................................	8-16

Section	Page
Camshaft..................................	8-17
Crankshaft................................	8-17
Pistons, Pins and Rings...................	8-17
Cylinder Block............................	8-18
Flywheel Ring Gear—Manual-Shift Transmissions........................	8-18
3 Cleaning and Inspection....................	8-18
Intake Manifold...........................	8-18
Exhaust Manifold..........................	8-18
Valve Rocker Arm and/or Shaft Assembly....	8-18
Push Rods................................	8-19
Cylinder Heads...........................	8-19
Hydraulic Valve Lifters....................	8-20
Mechanical Tappets........................	8-20
Timing Chain and Sprockets...............	8-20
Camshaft..................................	8-20
Crankshaft Vibration Damper and Sleeve.....	8-21
Crankshaft................................	8-21
Flywheel—Manual-Shift Transmissions.......	8-21
Flywheel—Automatic Transmissions........	8-21
Connecting Rods..........................	8-21
Pistons, Pins and Rings...................	8-22
Main and Connecting Rod Bearings.........	8-22
Cylinder Block............................	8-22
Oil Pan..................................	8-23
Oil Pump.................................	8-23
Positive Crankcase Ventilation System.......	8-23

This part covers engine diagnosis, tests and adjustment and repair procedures. In addition, the cleaning and inspection procedures are covered.

On cars equipped with a Thermactor exhaust emission control system, refer to Group 12 for diagnosis, test and repair of the exhaust emission control components.

For engine removal, disassembly, assembly, installation and major re-

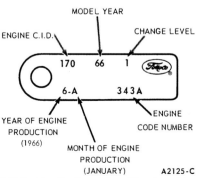

FIG. 1—Engine Identification Tag

pair procedures, refer to the pertinent part of this group.

An engine identification tag is attached to the engine. The symbol code (Fig. 1) identifies each engine for determining parts usage; i.e., engine cubic inch displacement and model year. The change level and engine code number determine if parts are peculiar to a specific engine.

1 DIAGNOSIS AND TESTING

DIAGNOSIS

On engines equipped with a Thermactor exhaust emission control system, disconnect the Thermactor system before performing engine diagnosis procedures. Disconnect the anti-backfire valve vacuum sensing and air supply lines at the intake manifold connections. Plug the manifold connections to preclude leakage.

Engine performance complaints usually fall under one of the basic headings listed in the Diagnosis Guide. When a particular trouble can not be traced to a definite cause by a simple check, the possible items that could be at fault are listed in the order of their probable occurrence. Check the items in the order listed.

For example, under Poor Acceleration, the ignition system is listed as a probable cause of the trouble. All the conventional ignition system items that affect acceleration are listed. Check all these items before proceeding to the next probable cause.

For diagnosis procedures of ignition system malfunctions, refer to Group 9.

DIAGNOSIS GUIDE

ENGINE WILL NOT CRANK	The cause of this trouble is usually in the starting system (Group 14). If the starting system is not at fault, check for a hydrostatic lock or a seized engine as follows: Remove the spark plugs; then attempt to crank the engine with the	starter. If the engine cranks, it indicates that water is leaking into the cylinders. Remove the cylinder head(s) and inspect the gasket(s) and/or head(s) for cracks. Examine the cylinder block for cracks.
ENGINE CRANKS NORMALLY, BUT WILL NOT START	Check the fuel supply. If there is sufficient fuel in the tank and the proper starting procedure is used, the cause of the trouble probably lies in either the ignition or the fuel system. To determine which system is at fault, perform the following test: Disconnect a spark plug wire. Check the spark intensity at the end of the wire by installing a terminal adapter in the end of the wire. Then hold the adapter approximately ³⁄₁₆ inch from the exhaust manifold and crank the engine. **IF THERE IS NO SPARK OR A WEAK SPARK AT THE SPARK PLUGS** The cause of the trouble is in the ignition system. **Disconnect the brown lead (I terminal) and the red and blue lead (s terminal) at the starter relay.** Install an auxiliary starter switch between the battery and s terminals of the starter relay. To determine if the cause of the trouble is in the primary or the secondary circuit, remove the coil high tension lead from the top of the distributor, **and hold it approximately 3/16 inch from the cylinder head.** With the ignition on, crank the engine and check for a spark. If the spark at the coil high tension lead is good, the cause of the trouble is probably in the distributor cap, rotor or spark plug wires. If there is no spark or a weak spark at the coil high tension lead, the cause of the trouble is probably	in the primary circuit, coil to distributor high tension lead, or the coil. **IF THERE IS A GOOD SPARK AT THE SPARK PLUGS** Check the spark plugs. If the spark plugs are not at fault, check the following items: **MANUAL CHOKE** Check the choke linkage for binding or damage. Make certain the choke plate closes when the choke knob on the instrument panel is pulled out and that the plate opens when the knob is pushed in. **AUTOMATIC CHOKE** Check the position of the choke plate. If the engine is hot, the plate should be open. If the plate is not open, the engine will load up due to the excessively rich mixture and will not start. If the engine is cold, the plate should be closed. If the plate is not operating properly, check the following items: The choke plate and linkage for binding. The fast idle cam linkage for binding. Thermostatic spring housing adjustment. **FUEL SUPPLY AT THE CARBURETOR** Work the throttle by hand several times. Each time the throttle is actuated, *fuel should spurt from the accelerating pump discharge port (6-cylinder) or nozzles (V-8).*

CONTINUED ON NEXT PAGE

DIAGNOSIS GUIDE (Continued)

ENGINE CRANKS NORMALLY, BUT WILL NOT START (Continued)	If fuel is discharged by the accelerating pump, the engine is probably flooded, or there is water in the fuel system, or an engine mechanical item is at fault. If fuel is not discharged by the accelerating pump, disconnect the carburetor fuel inlet line at the carburetor. Use a suitable container to catch the fuel. Crank the engine to see if fuel is reaching the carburetor. If fuel is not reaching the carburetor, check: The fuel filter. The fuel pump. The carburetor fuel inlet line for	obstructions. The fuel pump flexible inlet line for a collapsed condition. The fuel tank line for obstructions. For fuel tank vent restriction. If fuel is reaching the carburetor, check: The fuel inlet system including the fuel inlet needle and seat assembly and the float assembly. **ENGINE** Mechanical failure in camshaft drive. Anti-backfire valve stuck open (if equipped with Thermactor exhaust emission control).
ENGINE STARTS, BUT FAILS TO KEEP RUNNING	**FUEL SYSTEM** Idle fuel mixture needle(s) not properly adjusted. Engine idle speed set too low. The choke not operating properly. Float setting incorrect. Fuel inlet system not operating properly. Dirt or water in the fuel lines or in the fuel filter. Carburetor icing. Fuel pump defective.	Check for dirt in the carburetor not allowing fuel to enter or be discharged from the idle system. **IGNITION SYSTEM** Defective spark plugs. Leakage in the high tension wiring. Open circuit in primary resistance wire. Breaker points not properly adjusted.
ENGINE RUNS, BUT MISSES	Determine if the miss is steady or erratic and at what speed the miss occurs by operating the engine at various speeds under load. **MISSES STEADILY AT ALL SPEEDS** Isolate the miss by operating the engine with one cylinder not firing. This is done by operating the engine with the ignition wire removed from one spark plug at a time, until all cylinders have been checked. Ground the spark plug wire removed. If the engine speed changes when a particular cylinder is shorted out, that cylinder was delivering power before being shorted out. If no change in the engine operation is evident, the miss was caused by that cylinder not delivering power before being shorted out. In this case, check the: **IGNITION SYSTEM** If the miss is isolated in a particular cylinder, perform a spark test on the ignition lead of that cylinder.	If a good spark does not occur, the trouble is in the secondary circuit of the system. Check the spark plug wire and the distributor cap. If a good spark occurs, check the spark plug. If the spark plug is not at fault, a mechanical component of the engine is probably at fault. **ENGINE** Intake manifold gasket leak. Perform a manifold vacuum or compression test to determine which mechanical component of the engine is at fault. **MISSES ERRATICALLY AT ALL SPEEDS** **EXHAUST SYSTEM** Exhaust system restricted. **IGNITION SYSTEM** Breaker points not properly adjusted. Defective breaker points, condenser, secondary wiring, coil or spark plugs. High tension leakage across the coil, rotor or distributor cap. Defective ignition switch.

CONTINUED ON NEXT PAGE

DIAGNOSIS GUIDE (Continued)

| **ENGINE RUNS, BUT MISSES (Continued)** | **FUEL SYSTEM**
Float setting incorrect.
Fuel inlet system not operating properly.
Dirt or water in the fuel lines or carburetor.
Restricted fuel filter.
Loose booster venturi (V-8).

COOLING SYSTEM
Check the cooling system for internal leakage and/or for a condition that prevents the engine from reaching normal operating temperature.

ENGINE
Perform a manifold vacuum or compression test to determine which mechanical component of the engine is at fault.
Anti-backfire valve stuck open (if equipped with Thermactor exhaust emission control).

MISSES AT IDLE ONLY
FUEL SYSTEM
Idle fuel mixture needle(s) not properly adjusted.
Restriction in idle fuel system.

IGNITION SYSTEM
Excessive play in the distributor shaft.
Worn distributor cam.
Defective coil, rotor, condenser, | breaker points, ignition wiring or spark plugs.

ENGINE
Valve lash (engines with mechanical valve lifters) or valve clearance (engines with hydraulic valve lifters) set too tight. Worn camshaft lobe(s).
Perform a manifold vacuum or compression test to determine which mechanical component of the engine is at fault.

MISSES AT HIGH SPEED ONLY
FUEL SYSTEM
Power valve or passages clogged or damaged.
Low or erratic fuel pump pressure.
Fuel inlet system not operating properly.
Restricted fuel filter.
Restricted main fuel system.
Positive crankcase ventilation system restricted or not operating properly.

IGNITION SYSTEM
Defective spark plugs.

COOLING SYSTEM
Engine overheating.

ENGINE
Perform a manifold vacuum or compression test to determine which mechanical component of the engine is at fault. |
| **ROUGH ENGINE IDLE** | **FUEL SYSTEM**
Engine idle speed set too low.
Idle fuel mixture needle(s) not properly adjusted.
Float setting incorrect.
Air leaks between the carburetor, spacer and the manifold and/or fittings.
Intake manifold gasket leak (V-8).
Fuel leakage at the carburetor fuel bowl.
Power valve leaking fuel (V-8).
Idle fuel system air bleeds or fuel passages restricted.
Fuel bleeding from the accelerating pump discharge port (6-cylinder) or nozzles (V-8).
Secondary throttle plate(s) not closing (4-barrel carburetor).
Improper secondary throttle plate stop adjustment (4-barrel carburetor).
Leaking fuel pump, lines or fittings. | **IGNITION SYSTEM**
Improperly adjusted or defective breaker points.
Fouled or improperly adjusted spark plugs.
Incorrect ignition timing.
Spark plug misfiring.

ENGINE
Loose engine mounting bolts or worn engine support insulator.
Cylinder head bolts not properly torqued.
Valve clearance set too tight.
Crankcase ventilation regulator valve defective or a restricted vent tube.
Worn camshaft lobes.
Perform a manifold vacuum or compression test to determine which mechanical component is at fault.
Anti-backfire valve stuck open (if equipped with Thermactor exhaust emission control). |

CONTINUED ON NEXT PAGE

DIAGNOSIS GUIDE (Continued)

POOR ACCELERATION	**IGNITION SYSTEM** Incorrect ignition timing. Fouled or improperly adjusted spark plugs. Improperly adjusted or defective breaker points. Distributor not advancing properly. Loose or defective spark control valve (6-cylinder). **FUEL SYSTEM** Accelerating pump malfunction. Float setting incorrect. Throttle linkage not properly adjusted. Accelerating pump stroke not properly adjusted. Leaky power valve, gaskets or accelerating pump diaphragm. Power valve piston stuck in the up position (6-cylinder). Dirt or corrosion in accelerating	system. Distributor vacuum passages in the carburetor blocked. Restricted fuel filter. Defective fuel pump. **BRAKES** Improper adjustment—too tight. **TRANSMISSION** Clutch slippage (manual-shift transmissions). Improper band adjustment (automatic transmissions). Converter One-Way Clutch (automatic transmissions). **ENGINE** Perform a manifold vacuum or compression test to determine which mechanical component of the engine is at fault.
ENGINE DOES NOT DEVELOP FULL POWER, OR HAS POOR HIGH SPEED PERFORMANCE	**FUEL SYSTEM** Restricted air cleaner. Restricted fuel filter. Clogged or undersize main or secondary jets and/or low float setting. Power valve or passages clogged or damaged. Fuel pump pressure incorrect. Distributor vacuum passage in the carburetor blocked. Power valve piston stuck in the up position (6-cylinder). Secondary throttle plates not opening (V-8). Automatic choke malfunctioning or improperly adjusted. **IGNITION SYSTEM** Ignition timing not properly adjusted. Defective coil, condenser or rotor. Distributor not advancing properly. Excessive play in the distributor shaft. Distributor cam worn. Fouled or improperly adjusted spark plugs, or spark plugs of incorrect heat range. Improperly adjusted or defective breaker points.	**EXHAUST SYSTEM** Restriction in system. **COOLING SYSTEM** Thermostat inoperative or of incorrect heat range. Thermostat installed incorrectly. Check the cooling system for internal leakage and/or for a condition that prevents the engine from reaching normal operating temperature. **ENGINE** Perform a manifold vacuum or engine compression test to determine which mechanical component of the engine is at fault. One or more camshaft lobes worn beyond wear limit. Worn valve guides. Positive crankcase ventilation system not operating properly. Anti-backfire valve stuck open (if equipped with Thermactor exhaust emission control). **TRANSMISSION** Improper band adjustment (automatic transmissions).
EXCESSIVE FUEL CONSUMPTION	Determine the actual fuel consumption with test equipment installed in the car. If the test indicates that the fuel consumption is not excessive, demonstrate to the owner how improper driving habits will affect fuel con-	sumption. If the test indicates that the fuel consumption is excessive, make a preliminary check of the following items before proceeding to the fuel and ignition systems.

CONTINUED ON NEXT PAGE

DIAGNOSIS GUIDE (Continued)

EXCESSIVE FUEL CONSUMPTION (Continued)	**PRELIMINARY CHECKS** **CHASSIS ITEMS** Check: Tires for proper pressure. Front wheel alignment. Brake adjustment. **EXHAUST SYSTEM** System restricted. **ODOMETER** Check calibration. **IGNITION SYSTEM** Check: Distributor breaker points. Ignition timing. **ENGINE** Crankcase ventilation regulator valve defective or restricted tubes (Positive Crankcase Ventilation System). Anti-backfire valve stuck open (if equipped with Thermactor exhaust emission control). **FINAL CHECKS** **FUEL SYSTEM** Check: Fuel pump pressure. Engine idle speed. Idle fuel mixture needle(s) for proper adjustment. Automatic choke for proper operation. Fast idle speed screw for proper adjustment.	Accelerating pump stroke adjustment. Anti-stall dashpot for proper adjustment. Air cleaner for restrictions. Float setting or fuel level. Jets for wear and/or damage. Power valve operation. Air bleeds for obstructions. Accelerating pump discharge port (6-cylinder) or nozzles (V-8) for siphoning. Accelerator linkage for binds. Choke adjustment. **IGNITION SYSTEM** Check: Ignition timing. Spark plug condition and adjustment. Distributor spark advance operation. Spark control valve for proper seating (6-cylinder). **ENGINE** Perform a manifold vacuum or engine compression test to determine which mechanical component of the engine is at fault. Check valve clearance (hydraulic lifters) or valve lash (mechanical tappets). **COOLING SYSTEM** Check thermostat operation and heat range. **TRANSMISSION** Check band adjustment (automatic transmissions).
ENGINE OVERHEATS	**TEMPERATURE SENDING UNIT AND GAUGE** Unit or gauge defective (not indicating correct temperatures) or constant voltage regulator defective. **ENGINE** Cylinder head bolts not properly torqued. Incorrect valve lash (engine with mechanical valve lifters) or valve clearance (engines with hydraulic valve lifters). Low oil level or incorrect viscosity oil used. **COOLING SYSTEM** Insufficient coolant.	Cooling system leaks. Drive belt tension incorrect. Radiator fins obstructed. Thermostat defective. Thermostat improperly installed. Cooling system passages blocked. Water pump inoperative. Faulty fan drive. **IGNITION SYSTEM** Incorrect ignition timing. Incorrect distributor advance. **EXHAUST SYSTEM** Restrictions in system. **BRAKES** Improper adjustment—too tight.

CONTINUED ON NEXT PAGE

DIAGNOSIS GUIDE (Continued)

LOSS OF COOLANT	**COOLING SYSTEM** Leaking radiator or water pump. Loose or damaged hose connections. Radiator cap defective. Overheating. **ENGINE** Cylinder head gasket defective.	Intake manifold to cylinder head gasket defective (V-8). Cylinder head or intake manifold bolts (V-8) not properly torqued. Cylinder block core plugs leaking. Temperature sending unit leaking. Cracked cylinder head or block, or warped cylinder head or block gasket surface.
ENGINE FAILS TO REACH NORMAL OPERATING TEMPERATURE	**TEMPERATURE SENDING UNIT AND GAUGE** Unit or gauge defective (not indicating correct temperature) or constant voltage regulator defective.	**COOLING SYSTEM** Thermostat inoperative or of incorrect heat range.
NOISY HYDRAULIC VALVE LIFTER	A noisy hydraulic valve lifter can be located by operating the engine at idle speed and placing a finger on the face of the valve spring retainer. If the lifter is not functioning properly, a shock will be felt when the valve seats. Another method of identifying a noisy lifter is by the use of a piece of hose. With the engine operating at idle speed, place one end of the hose near the end of the valve stem and the other end to the ear and listen for a metallic noise. Repeat this procedure on each intake and exhaust valve until the noisy lifter(s) has been located. The most common causes of hydraulic valve lifter troubles are dirt, gum, varnish, carbon deposits and air bubbles. Dirt in the lifter assembly can prevent the disc valve from seating, or it may become lodged between the plunger and body surfaces. In either case, the lifter becomes inoperative due to failure to "pump-up," or because the internal parts are no longer free to function properly. When dirt is found to be responsible for lifter malfunction, remove the lifter assembly and thoroughly clean it. Recommended engine oil and filter change intervals should be followed to minimize lifter problems caused by dirt (Group 19). Deposits of gum and varnish cause similar conditions to exist which may result in lifter malfunction. If these conditions are found to be present, the lifter should be disassembled and cleaned in solvent to remove all traces of deposits. Air bubbles in the lubricating oil,	caused by an excessively high or low oil level, may likewise cause lifter malfunction. A damaged oil pick-up tube may allow air to be drawn into the lubricating system. Check for engine oil aeration as follows: Check the engine oil level to be sure it is within specification and correct as required. **Be sure the correct engine oil dipstick is being used.** Operate the engine at approximately 1200 rpm until normal operating temperature is reached. Stop the engine and remove the oil pressure sending unit. Install a fitting in this opening with a petcock-type valve that will permit attachment of a ¼ to ⅜-inch-diameter hose of sufficient length to direct the oil discharge into the oil filler pipe. Close the valve. Start the engine and operate it at approximately 500 rpm for a minimum of 5 minutes; then, open the valve slightly to permit a steady discharge of oil. Check the oil flow for air bubbles. Increase the engine speed to approximately 1000 rpm and check for air bubbles in the oil. **To facilitate checking for air bubbles, direct the oil flow over white paper or through a piece of transparent tube. The engine should not be operated at excessive speeds or for extended periods with the oil bleed attached.** If oil aeration is evident, remove the oil pan for further test and/or inspection of the oil pump intake system. Perform corrective action as required to remove air from the lubricating oil.

TESTING

CAMSHAFT LOBE LIFT

Check the lift of each lobe in consecutive order and make a note of the readings.

1. Remove the air cleaner and the valve rocker arm cover(s).

2. On a 170 or 200 six or a 390 V-8, remove the valve rocker arm shaft assemblies and install a solid tappet-type push rod in the push rod bore of the camshaft lobe to be checked or use the adapter for ball-end push rods shown in Fig. 2.

On a 289 V-8, remove the rocker arm stud nut, fulcrum seat and rocker arm. Use the adapter for ball-end push rods (Fig. 3).

3. Make sure the push rod is in the valve lifter socket. Install a dial indicator in such a manner as to have the ball socket adapter of the indicator on the end of the push rod and in the same plane as the push rod movement (Fig. 2 or 3).

On a socket-type push rod, position the actuating point of the indicator in the push rod socket and in the same plane as the push rod movement (Fig. 2).

4. **Disconnect the brown lead (I terminal) and the red and blue lead (S terminal) at the starter relay.** Install an auxiliary starter switch between the battery and S terminals of the starter relay. **Crank the engine with the ignition switch OFF.**

"Bump" the crankshaft over until the tappet or lifter is on the base

circle of the camshaft lobe. **At this point, the push rod will be in its lowest position.**

5. Zero the dial indicator. Continue to rotate the crankshaft slowly until the push rod is in the fully raised position.

6. Compare the total lift recorded on the indicator with specifications.

7. To check the accuracy of the original indicator reading, continue to rotate the crankshaft until the indicator reads zero. **If the lift on any lobe is below specified wear limits, the camshaft and the valve lifters operating on the worn lobe(s) must be replaced.**

8. On a 170 or 200 six or a 390 V-8, install the rocker arm shaft assemblies.

On a 289 V-8, install the rocker arm, fulcrum seat and stud nut. Adjust the valve clearance (Section 2).

On a 289 high performance V-8, install the rocker arm, fulcrum seat and stud nut. Perform a preliminary valve lash adjustment. Install the valve rocker arm cover(s) and **partially tighten the retaining bolts.** Operate the engine until normal operating temperature has been reached. Remove the valve rocker arm cover(s). Check and adjust the valve lash (Section 2).

9. Install the valve rocker arm cover(s) and the air cleaner.

COMPRESSION TEST

Dynamic Compression Test. To perform a dynamic compression check, follow the procedures in Part 9-1, Section 1 under Ignition System Tests—Rotunda Testers.

Compression Gauge Check

1. Be sure the crankcase oil is at

the proper level. Be sure the battery is fully charged. Operate the engine for a minimum of 30 minutes at 1200 rpm or until the engine is at normal operating temperature. Turn the ignition switch off, then remove all the spark plugs.

2. Set the throttle plates (primary throttle plates only on a 4-barrel carburetor) and choke plate in the wide open position.

3. Install a compression gauge in No. 1 cylinder.

4. **Disconnect the brown lead (I terminal) and the red and blue lead (S terminal) at the starter relay.** Install an auxiliary starter switch between the battery and S terminals of the starter relay. **Crank the engine with the ignition switch OFF.** Using an auxiliary starter switch, crank the engine a minimum of five pumping strokes, and record the highest reading.

Note the number of compression strokes required to obtain the highest reading.

5. Repeat the test on each cylinder, cranking the engine the same number of times for each cylinder as was required to obtain the highest reading on the No. 1 cylinder.

Test Conclusions. A variation of 20 psi from specified pressure is satisfactory. However, the compression of all cylinders should be uniform within 20 psi.

A reading of more than the allowable tolerance above normal indicates excessive deposits in the cylinder or wrong cylinder head(s) on the engine.

A reading of more than the allowable tolerance below normal indicates leakage at the cylinder head gasket, piston rings or valves or wrong cylinder head(s) on the engine.

A low, even compression in two adjacent cylinders indicates a cylinder head gasket leak. This should be checked before condemning the rings or valves.

To determine whether the rings or the valves are at fault, squirt the equivalent of a tablespoon of heavy oil into the combustion chamber. Crank the engine to distribute the oil and repeat the compression test. The oil will temporarily seal leakage past the rings. If approximately the same reading is obtained, the rings are satisfactory, but the valves are leaking. If the compression has increased substantially over the original reading, there is leakage past the rings.

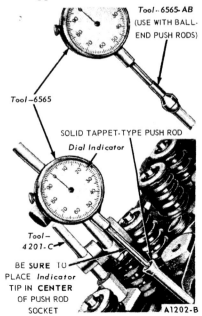

FIG. 2—Camshaft Lobe Lift— 170 and 200 Six

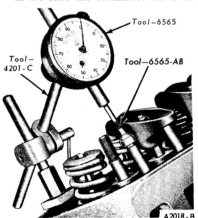

FIG. 3—Camshaft Lobe Life— 289 V-8

During a compression test, if the pressure fails to climb steadily and remains the same during the first two successive strokes, but climbs higher on the succeeding strokes, or fails to climb during the entire test, it indicates a sticking valve.

MANIFOLD VACUUM TEST

A manifold vacuum test aids in determining the condition of an engine and in helping to locate the cause of poor engine performance. To check manifold vacuum:

1. Operate the engine for a minimum of 30 minutes at 1200 rpm or until the engine is at normal operating temperature.

2. On 6-cylinder engines, install an accurate, sensitive vacuum gauge in the intake manifold fitting.

On a V-8 engine, remove the plug or power brake line at the rear of the intake manifold and install an accurate, sensitive vacuum gauge.

3. Operate the engine at recommended idle rpm, with the transmission selector lever in neutral.

4. Check the vacuum reading on the gauge.

Test Conclusions. Manifold vacuum is affected by carburetor adjustment, valve timing, ignition timing, the condition of the valves, cylinder compression, the condition of the positive crankcase ventilation system, and leakage of the manifold, carburetor, carburetor spacer or cylinder head gaskets.

Because abnormal gauge readings may indicate that more than one of the above factors are at fault, exercise caution in analyzing an abnormal reading. For example, if the vacuum is low, the correction of one item may increase the vacuum enough so as to indicate that the trouble has been corrected. It is important, therefore, that each cause of an abnormal reading be investigated and further tests conducted, where necessary, in order to arrive at the correct diagnosis of the trouble.

Table 1 lists various types of readings and their possible causes.

Allowance should be made for the effect of altitude on the gauge reading. The engine vacuum will decrease with an increase in altitude.

HYDRAULIC VALVE LIFTER TESTS

Dirt, deposits of gum and varnish and air bubbles in the lubricating oil can cause hydraulic valve lifter failure or malfunction.

Dirt, gum and varnish can keep

TABLE 1—Manifold Vacuum Gauge Readings

Gauge Reading	Engine Condition
18 inches or over—All engines.	Normal.
Low and steady.	Loss of power in all cylinders possibly caused by late ignition or valve timing, or loss of compression due to leakage around the piston rings.
Very low.	Intake manifold, carburetor, spacer or cylinder head gasket leak.
Needle fluctuates steadily as speed increases.	A partial or complete loss of power in one or more cylinders caused by a leaking valve, cylinder head or intake manifold gasket, a defect in the ignition system, or a weak valve spring.
Gradual drop in reading at engine idle.	Excessive back pressure in the exhaust system.
Intermittent fluctuation.	An occasional loss of power possibly caused by a defect in the ignition system or a sticking valve.
Slow fluctuation or drifting of the needle.	Improper idle mixture adjustment or carburetor, spacer or intake manifold gasket leak or restricted crankcase ventilation system.

a check valve from seating and cause a loss of hydraulic pressure. An open valve disc will cause the plunger to force oil back into the valve lifter reservoir during the time the push rod is being lifted to force the valve from its seat.

Air bubbles in the lubricating system can be caused by too much oil in the system or too low an oil level. Air may also be drawn into the lubricating system through an opening in a damaged oil pick-up tube. **Air in the hydraulic system can cause a loss of hydraulic pressure in the valve lifter.**

Assembled valve lifters can be tested with tool 6500-E to check the leak down rate. The leak down rate specification (Part 8-5) is the time in seconds for the plunger to move the length (Part 8-5) of its travel while under a 50 lb. load. Test the valve lifters as follows:

1. **Disassemble and clean the lifter to remove all traces of engine oil.** Lifters cannot be checked with engine oil in them. Only the testing fluid can be used.

2. Place the valve lifter in the tester, with the plunger facing upward. Pour hydraulic tester fluid into the cup to a level that will cover the valve lifter assembly. **The fluid can be purchased from the**

manufacturer of the tester. **Do not use kerosene, for it will not provide an accurate test.**

3. Place a 5/16-inch steel ball in the plunger cup (Fig. 4).

4. Adjust the length of the ram so that the pointer is 1/16-inch below the starting mark when the

Tool—6500-E

A1894-A

FIG. 4—Placing Steel Ball in Valve Lifter Plunger

ram contacts the valve lifter plunger (Fig. 5) to facilitate timing as the pointer passes the Start Timing Mark.

Use the center mark on the pointer scale as the Stop Timing point instead of the original Stop Timing mark at the top of the scale.

5. Work the valve lifter plunger up and down until the lifter fills

Tool—6500-E   A1895-A

FIG. 5—Adjusting the Ram Length

with fluid and all traces of air bubbles have disappeared.

6. Allow the ram and weight to force the valve lifter plunger downward. Measure the exact time it takes for the pointer to travel from the Start Timing to the Stop Timing marks of the tester.

7. A valve lifter that is satisfactory must have a leak-down rate (time in seconds) within the minimum and maximum limits specified.

8. If the valve lifter is not within specifications, replace it with a new lifter. **Always test a new lifter before installing it in the engine.** It is not necessary to disassemble and clean new valve lifters before testing, because the oil contained in new lifters is test fluid.

9. Remove the fluid from the cup and bleed the fluid from the lifter by depressing the plunger up and down. **This step will aid in depressing the lifter plungers when checking the valve clearance.**

POSITIVE CRANKCASE VENTILATION SYSTEM TEST

A malfunctioning positive crankcase ventilation system may be indicated by loping or rough engine idle. Do not attempt to compensate for this poor idle condition by disconnecting the crankcase ventilation system and/or making carburetor adjustments. The removal of the crankcase ventilation system from the engine will adversely affect the fuel economy and engine ventilation with resultant shortening of engine life.

To determine whether the loping or rough idle condition is caused by a malfunctioning crankcase ventilation system, perform either of the following tests.

Regulator Valve Test. Install a

known good regulator valve in the crankcase ventilation system.

Start the engine and compare the engine idle condition to the prior idle condition.

If the loping or rough idle condition remains when the good regulator valve is installed, the crankcase ventilation regulator valve is not at fault. Check the crankcase ventilation system for restriction at the intake manifold or carburetor spacer. If the system is not restricted, further engine component diagnosis will have to be conducted to find the malfunction.

If the idle condition is found to be satisfactory, replace the regulator valve and clean the hoses, fittings, etc.

Air Intake Test. This test uses the AC positive crankcase ventilation tester (Fig. 6) which is operated by engine vacuum through the oil filler opening. Follow the procedures described below to install the tester and check the crankcase ventilation system for faulty operation.

1. **With the engine at normal operating temperature,** remove the oil filler cap and the dipstick.

2. Connect one end of the hose to the tester body and connect the other end of the hose to the tester adapter.

3. Use the dipstick hole plug to plug the opening in the dipstick tube.

4. Insert the tester adapter in the filler cap opening and turn the selector knob (Fig. 6) to number 2 for the 289 and 390 V-8 or number 4 for the 170 and 200 six.

5. Start the engine and let it idle.

6. With the plugs secure, and the tube free of kinks, hold the tester body upright and note the color in the tester windows. Fig. 7 lists the various colors and the probable cause or related condition of the crankcase ventilation system.

7. Clean or replace the malfunctioning or defective components, and repeat the test to ensure that the crankcase ventilation system is operating satisfactorily.

CRANKSHAFT END PLAY

1. Force the crankshaft toward the rear of the engine.

2. Install a dial indicator so that the contact point rests against the crankshaft flange and the indicator axis is parallel to the crankshaft axis (Fig. 8).

3. Zero the dial indicator. Push the crankshaft forward and note the reading on the dial.

4. If the end play exceeds the wear limit, replace the thrust bearing. If the end play is less than the minimum limit, inspect the thrust bearing faces for scratches, burrs, nicks or dirt. If the thrust faces are not defective or dirty, they probably were not aligned properly. Install the thrust bearing and align the faces following the procedure recommended under Main Bearing Replacement in the pertinent engine section. Check the crankshaft end play.

FLYWHEEL FACE RUNOUT— MANUAL-SHIFT TRANSMISSIONS

Install a dial indicator so that the

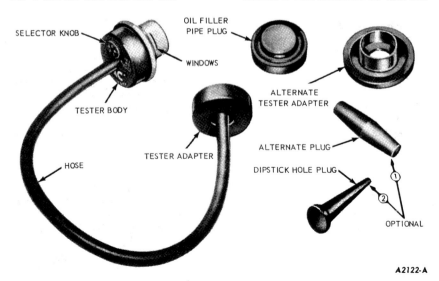

FIG. 6—AC Position Crankcase Ventilation System Tester

CRANKCASE VENTILATION SYSTEM DIAGNOSIS WITH AC TESTER

COLOR	CAUSE
GREEN	SYSTEM OPERATING PROPERLY.
GREEN AND YELLOW	REGULATOR VALVE OR SYSTEM PARTIALLY PLUGGED. SLIGHT KINK IN TESTER HOSE. SLIGHT ENGINE BLOW-BY. PLUGS FROM THE KIT OR THE ENGINE VACUUM LINES ARE NOT PROPERLY SEALED. TESTER KNOB IMPROPERLY SET.
YELLOW	REGULATOR VALVE OR SYSTEM PARTIALLY PLUGGED. TESTER HOSE KINKED OR BLOCKED. BLOW-BY AT MAXIMUM CAPACITY OF REGULATOR VALVE. PLUGS FROM THE KIT OR THE ENGINE VACUUM LINES ARE NOT PROPERLY SEALED. TESTER KNOB IMPROPERLY SET.
YELLOW AND RED	REGULATOR VALVE OR SYSTEM PARTIALLY OR FULLY PLUGGED. MORE ENGINE BLOW-BY THAN REGULATOR VALVE CAN HANDLE. VENT HOSE PLUGGED OR COLLAPSED.
RED	REGULATOR VALVE OR SYSTEM FULLY PLUGGED OR STUCK. VENT HOSE PLUGGED OR COLLAPSED. EXTREME BLOW-BY.

A2126-A

FIG. 7—Diagnosis of Air Intake Test

indicator point bears against the flywheel face (Fig. 9). Turn the flywheel making sure that it is full forward or rearward so that crankshaft end play will not be indicated as flywheel runout.

If the clutch face runout exceeds the specifications, remove the flywheel and check for burrs between the flywheel and the face of the crankshaft mounting flange. If no burrs exist, check the runout of the crankshaft mounting flange. Replace the flywheel or machine the crankshaft flywheel mounting face if the mounting flange runout is excessive.

If the ring gear runout exceeds specifications, replace it or reinstall it on the flywheel, following the procedure under Ring Gear Replacement (Part 8-1, Section 2).

FLYWHEEL RUNOUT— AUTOMATIC TRANSMISSION

Remove the spark plugs.

Install a dial indicator so that the indicator point rests on the face of the ring gear adjacent to the gear teeth.

Push the flywheel and crankshaft forward or backward as far as possible to prevent crankshaft end play from being indicated as flywheel runout.

Set the indicator dial on the zero mark. Turn the flywheel one complete revolution while observing the total indicator reading (T.I.R.). If the T.I.R. exceeds specifications, the flywheel and ring gear assembly must be replaced.

FLYWHEEL RING GEAR RUNOUT

Install the dial indicator so that the point rests on a tooth of the ring gear (Fig. 10), and check the outside diameter (O.D.) of the assembled flywheel and ring gear. **For this check, carefully adjust the indicator on the gear tooth so that the indicator point is near the extreme limit of its travel. This will prevent the indicator point from catching between the gear teeth as the flywheel is turned.** Set the indicator dial on the zero mark and slowly turn the flywheel through one revolution while observing the total indicator reading. The T.I.R. must be within specifications, or the ring gear (standard transmission) or flywheel and ring gear assembly (automatic transmission) must be replaced.

CAMSHAFT END PLAY

Push the camshaft toward the rear of the engine. Install a dial indicator so that the indicator point is on the camshaft sprocket retaining screw (Fig. 11). Zero the dial indicator. Position a large screw driver between the camshaft sprocket and the block. Pull the camshaft forward and release it. Compare the dial indicator reading with specifications. If the end play is excessive, replace the

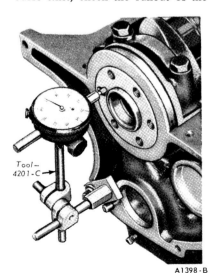

Tool—4201-C

A1398-B

FIG. 8—Typical Crankshaft End Play

Tool—4201-C   A1408-B

FIG. 9—Typical Flywheel Face Runout

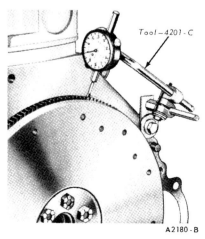

Tool—4201-C

A2180-B

FIG. 10—Typical Flywheel Ring Gear Runout

FIG. 11—Typical Camshaft End Play

thrust plate. Remove the dial indicator.

TIMING CHAIN DEFLECTION

1. Rotate the crankshaft in a clockwise direction (as viewed from the front) to take up the slack on the left side of the chain.
2. Establish a reference point on

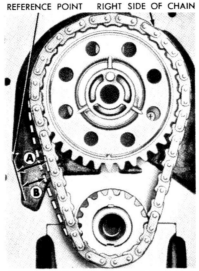

TAKE UP SLACK ON LEFT SIDE, ESTABLISH REFERENCE POINT. MEASURE DISTANCE **A.** TAKE UP SLACK ON RIGHT SIDE. FORCE LEFT SIDE OUT. MEASURE DISTANCE **B.** DEFLECTION IS **A** MINUS **B.**   A1284-C

FIG. 12—Typical Timing Chain Deflection

the block and measure from this point to the chain (Fig. 12).

3. Rotate the crankshaft in the opposite direction to take up the slack on the right side of the chain. Force the left side of the chain out with the fingers and measure the distance between the reference point and the chain. The deflection is the difference between the two measurements.

If the deflection exceeds specifications, replace the timing chain and sprockets.

---

2 COMMON ADJUSTMENTS AND REPAIRS

ADJUSTMENTS

VALVE CLEARANCE— HYDRAULIC VALVE LIFTERS, 170 and 200 SIX

A 0.060-inch shorter push rod or a 0.060-inch longer push rod are available for service to provide a means of compensating for dimensional changes in the valve mechanism. Refer to the Master Parts List or the specifications for the pertinent color code. Valve stem to valve rocker arm clearance should be to the specified clearance with the hydraulic lifter completely collapsed. Repeated valve reconditioning operations (valve and/or valve seat refacing) will decrease the clearance to the point that if not compensated for, the hydraulic valve lifter will cease to function.

To determine whether a shorter or a longer push rod is necessary, make the following check:

1. Disconnect the brown lead (I terminal) and the red and blue lead (S terminal) at the starter relay. Install an auxiliary starter switch between the battery and S terminals of the starter relay. **Crank the engine with the ignition switch OFF** until the No. 1 piston is on TDC after the compression stroke.

By using the procedure in step 3, check the following valves:

No. 1 Intake   No. 3 Exhaust
No. 1 Exhaust   No. 4 Intake
No. 2 Intake   No. 5 Exhaust

2. Now rotate the crankshaft until the No. 6 piston is on TDC after the compression stroke (1 revolution of the crankshaft). By using the procedure in step 3, check the following valves:

No. 2 Exhaust   No. 5 Intake
No. 3 Intake   No. 6 Intake
No. 4 Exhaust   No. 6 Exhaust

3. Using Tool—6513-K apply pressure to the push rod end of the rocker arm (Fig. 13) to slowly bleed down the valve lifter until the plunger is completely bottomed. Hold the lifter in this position and check the available clearance between the rocker arm and the valve stem tip with a feeler gauge.

If the clearance is less than specifications, install an undersize push rod. If the clearance is greater than specifications, install an oversize push rod.

VALVE CLEARANCE— HYDRAULIC VALVE LIFTERS, 289 REGULAR V-8

The cylinders are numbered from

FIG. 13—Valve Clearance Check —170 and 200 Six

front to rear—right bank, 1-2-3-4; left bank, 5-6-7-8.

The valves on the right bank are arranged from front to rear, I-E-I-E-I-E-I-E.

The valves on the left bank are arranged from front to rear, E-I-E-I-E-I-E-I.

1. Disconnect the brown lead (I terminal) and the red and blue lead (S terminal) at the starter relay. Install an auxiliary starter switch between the battery and "S" terminals of the starter relay. **Crank**

the engine with the ignition switch OFF.

2. Make three chalk marks on the crankshaft damper (Fig. 14). Space the marks approximately 90° apart so that with the timing mark, the damper is divided into four equal parts (90° represents ¼ of the distance around the damper circumference).

3. Rotate the crankshaft until No. 1 piston is on TDC at the end of the compression stroke. **Check the breaking torque (torque required to turn nut in a counterclockwise direction)** of the No. 1 intake and exhaust stud nuts. Replace the stud nut if the breaking torque does not meet specifications. If the breaking torque still is not within specifications, replace the stud.

4. With No. 1 piston on TDC at the end of the compression stroke, adjust the intake and exhaust valve clearance for No. 1 cylinder. Loosen the rocker arm stud nut until there is end clearance in the push rod, then tighten the nut to just remove all the push rod to rocker arm clearance. This may be determined by rotating and/or moving the push rod with the fingers as the stud nut is tightened (Fig 15). When the push rod to rocker arm clearance has been eliminated, tighten the stud nut an additional ¾ turn to place the hydraulic lifter plunger in the desired operating range.

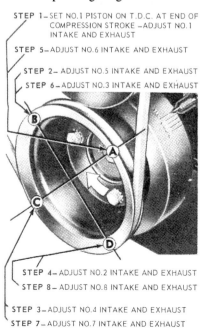

STEP 1– SET NO.1 PISTON ON T.D.C. AT END OF COMPRESSION STROKE –ADJUST NO.1 INTAKE AND EXHAUST

STEP 5– ADJUST NO.6 INTAKE AND EXHAUST

STEP 2– ADJUST NO.5 INTAKE AND EXHAUST

STEP 6– ADJUST NO.3 INTAKE AND EXHAUST

STEP 4– ADJUST NO.2 INTAKE AND EXHAUST

STEP 8– ADJUST NO.8 INTAKE AND EXHAUST

STEP 3– ADJUST NO.4 INTAKE AND EXHAUST

STEP 7– ADJUST NO.7 INTAKE AND EXHAUST

A2198-A

FIG. 14—289 V-8 Valve Clearance

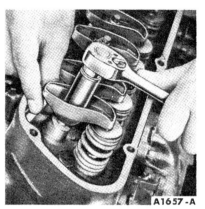

A1657-A

FIG. 15—Typical Valve Clearance Adjustment—289 V-8

5. Repeat this procedure for the remaining set of valves, turning the crankshaft with an auxiliary starter switch, ¼ turn at a time, in the direction of rotation, while adjusting the valves in the firing order sequence. The firing order is 1-5-4-2-6-3-7-8.

An alternate method is to remove the distributor cap and turn the crankshaft with an auxiliary starter switch until the breaker points are on the next peak of the distributor cam lobe. When the breaker points are on the next distributor cam lobe, the valves for the cylinder next in the firing order can be adjusted.

These procedures require two complete turns of the crankshaft.

6. Operate the engine and check for rough engine idle or a noisy lifter(s). Valve clearance set too tight will cause rough engine idle, and valve clearance set too loose will cause a noisy lifter(s). If it has been determined that these conditions are caused by improper valve clearance, adjust the affected valve(s) using the following procedure:

Position the piston(s) on TDC after the compression stroke (See Step 2 above). Apply pressure to slowly bleed down the valve lifter until the plunger is completely bottomed (Fig. 16). While holding the valve lifter in the fully collapsed position, check the available clearance between the rocker arm and valve stem tip (Fig. 16). If the clearance is not within specifications, rotate the rocker arm stud nut clockwise to decrease the clearance and counterclockwise to increase the clearance. **Normally one turn of the rocker arm stud will vary the clearance by 0.006 inch:**

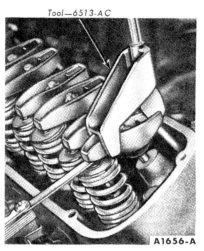

Tool—6513-A C

A1656-A

FIG. 16—Typical Valve Clearance Check—289 V-8

VALVE CLEARANCE– HYDRAULIC VALVE LIFTERS, 390 V-8

The valve arrangement is E-I-E-I-I-E-I-E from front to rear on both cylinder banks.

A 0.060-inch shorter push rod or a 0.060-inch longer push rod are available for service to provide a means of compensating for dimensional changes in the valve mechanism. Refer to the Master Parts List or the specifications for the pertinent color code.

Valve stem to valve rocker arm clearance should be within specifications with the hydraulic lifter completely collapsed. Repeated valve reconditioning operations (valve and/or valve seat refacing) will decrease the clearance to the point that, if not compensated for, the hydraulic valve lifter will cease to function.

To determine whether a shorter or a longer push rod is necessary, make the following check:

1. **Disconnect the brown lead (I terminal) and the red and blue lead (S terminal) at the starter relay.** Install an auxiliary starter switch between the battery and S terminals of the starter relay. **Crank the engine with the ignition switch OFF.**

2. **Position the crankshaft as outlined in steps 3 and 4.** Position the hydraulic lifter compressor tool on the rocker arm and slowly apply pressure to bleed down the hydraulic lifter until the plunger is completely bottomed (Fig. 17). Hold the lifter in the fully collapsed position and insert the clearance gauge between the valve stem and the rocker

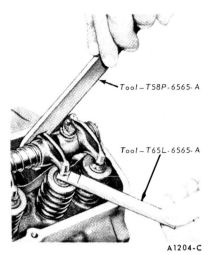

FIG. 17—390 V-8 Valve Clearance

arm of the valve being checked. If the first step of the gauge enters, the old push rod may be used. If the first step will not enter, replace the standard push rod with a shorter service push rod. If the second step of the gauge enters, the operating range of the lifter is excessive, which indicates that the incorrect push rod has been installed or severe wear has occurred at the push rod ends, rocker arm, or valve stem. In this case, it will be necessary to determine the area of discrepancy, and the incorrect or defective part(s) should be replaced. If all the valve train components except the push rod are within limits, install a 0.060-inch longer push rod.

3. Rotate the crankshaft until No. 1 piston is on TDC at the end of the compression stroke and check the following valves:

No. 1 Intake	No. 1 Exhaust
No. 3 Intake	No. 4 Exhaust
No. 7 Intake	No. 5 Exhaust
No. 8 Intake	No. 8 Exhaust

4. After these valves have been checked, rotate the crankshaft 360° (one revolution) to position No. 6 piston on TDC and check the following valves:

No. 2 Intake	No. 2 Exhaust
No. 4 Intake	No. 3 Exhaust
No. 5 Intake	No. 6 Exhaust
No. 6 Intake	No. 7 Exhaust

When compressing the valve spring to remove the push rods, be sure the piston in the individual cylinder is below TDC to avoid contact between the valve and the piston.

To replace a push rod, it will be

necessary to remove the valve rocker arm shaft assembly, following the procedure in Part 8-4.

Upon replacement of a valve push rod and/or valve rocker arm shaft assembly, the engine should not be cranked or rotated until the hydraulic lifters have had an opportunity to leak down to their normal operating position. The leakdown rate can be accelerated by using the tool shown in Fig. 17 on the valve rocker arm and applying pressure in a direction to collapse the lifter.

VALVE LASH — MECHANICAL TAPPETS, 289 HIGH PERFORMANCE V-8

Preliminary (Cold). If the valve rocker arm(s) has been removed and installed, it will be necessary to make a preliminary (cold) valve lash adjustment before starting the engine. If the adjustment is made for an engine tune-up, follow the final (hot) adjustment procedure.

1. Follow steps 1 thru 3 under Valve Clearance—Hydraulic Valve Lifters, 289 Regular V-8.

2. With the No. 1 piston on TDC at the end of the compression stroke, adjust the intake and exhaust valve lash to the specified cold setting.

3. Follow step 5 under Valve Clearance—Hydraulic Valve Lifters, 289 Regular V-8.

Final (Hot). It is very important that the valve lash be held to the correct specifications because:

If the lash is set too close, the valve will open too early and close too late, resulting in rough engine idle. Burning and warping of the valves will occur also because the valves cannot make firm contact with the seats long enough to cool properly. If the lash is excessive, it will cause the valve to open too late and close too early causing valve bounce. In addition, damage to the camshaft lobe is likely because the tappet foot will not follow the pattern of the camshaft lobe causing a shock contact between these two parts.

1. Be sure the engine is at normal operating temperature before attempting to set the valve lash.

2. With the engine idling, set the valve lash (Fig. 18) using a step-type feeler gauge only (GO and NO GO). The final (hot) intake and exhaust valve lash settings are listed in the Specification Section.

Step-Type Feeler Gauge   A2053-A

FIG. 18—Final Valve Lash Adjustment—289 High Performance V-8

For example, to obtain the correct setting if the valve lash is 0.019 inch, use a step-type gauge of 0.018 inch (GO) and 0.020 inch (NO GO). The GO step should enter, and the NO GO step should not enter. The resultant setting will be to the required setting (0.019 inch).

REPAIRS

VALVE ROCKER ARM AND/OR SHAFT ASSEMBLY

Dress up minor surface defects on the rocker arm shaft and in the rocker arm bore with a hone.

If the pad at the valve end of the rocker arm has a grooved radius, replace the rocker arm. **Do not attempt to true this surface by grinding.**

For a 289 V-8 engine, refer to Cylinder Head Repair for the rocker arm stud replacement procedure.

PUSH RODS

Following the precedures in Section 3 under Push Rod Inspection check the push rods for straightness.

If the runout exceeds the maximum limit at any point, discard the rod. **Do not attempt to straighten push rods.**

CYLINDER HEADS

Thermactor Exhaust Emission Control System. On engines so equipped, replace any air nozzle that is eroded, burned or damaged to the extent that air flow is restricted or increased.

Replace the head if it is cracked. **Do not plane or grind more than 0.010 inch from the cylinder head gasket surface.** Remove all burrs or scratches with an oil stone.

Rocker Arm Stud Nut Replacement—289 V-8. If the rocker arm stud nut breaking torque is less than specified, install a new standard stud nut and recheck the breaking torque. Refer to Valve Clearance Adjustment for the torque procedure.

Rocker Arm Stud Replacement— 289 Regular V-8. If it is necessary to remove a rocker arm stud, a rocker arm stud kit (tool T62F-6A527-B) is available which contains the following: a stud remover, a 0.006-inch O.S. reamer, and a 0.015-inch O.S. reamer. Use stud replacer T65P-6A527-A to press in replacement studs.

Rocker arm studs that are broken or have damaged threads may be replaced with standard studs. Loose studs in the head may be replaced with 0.006 or 0.015-inch oversize studs which are available for service. The standard studs have no identification markings, whereas the 0.006-inch oversize stud has two grooves around the pilot end of the stud and the 0.015 inch oversize stud has a step produced by the increased diameter of the stud approximately $1\frac{5}{32}$ inches from the pilot end.

When going from a standard size rocker arm stud to a 0.015-inch oversize stud, always use the 0.006-inch reamer before finish reaming with the 0.015-inch reamer.

1. Position the sleeve of the rocker arm stud remover (tool T62F-6A527-B) over the stud with the bearing end down. Thread the puller into the sleeve and over the stud until it is fully bottomed. Hold the sleeve with a wrench; then rotate the puller clockwise to remove the stud (Fig. 19).

If the rocker arm stud was broken off flush with the stud boss, use an easy-out to remove the broken stud following the instructions of the tool manufacturer.

2. If a loose rocker arm stud is being replaced, ream the stud bore using the proper reamer (or reamers in sequence) for the selected oversize stud (Fig. 20). **Make sure the metal particles do not enter the valve area.**

3. Screw the new stud into the sliding driver of the rocker arm stud installer (tool T65P-6A527-A) and coat the end of the stud with Lubriplate. Align the stud and installer with the stud bore; then tap the sliding driver until it bottoms (Fig. 21). When the installer contacts the stud boss, the stud is installed to its correct height.

Valve Rocker Arm Stud Replacement—289 High Performance V-8.

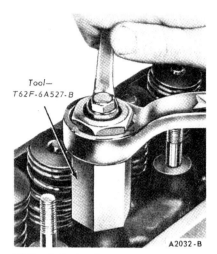

FIG. 19—Rocker Arm Stud Removal

The valve rocker arm and stud assembly is shown in Fig. 22.

REMOVAL.
1. Remove the air cleaner.
2. Disconnect the spark plug wires at the spark plugs. Remove the wires from the bracket(s) on the rocker arm cover(s) and position the wires out of the way.
3. If a rocker arm and stud is being removed from the right cylinder head, pull the regulator valve out of the rubber grommet and position the hose and valve out of the way. Also remove the automatic choke heat tube.
4. Remove the valve rocker arm cover(s).
5. Remove the valve rocker arm stud nut, fulcrum seat, and rocker arm.

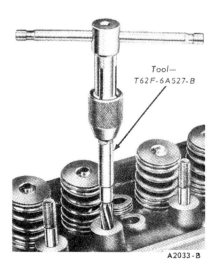

FIG. 20—Reaming Rocker Arm Stud Bore

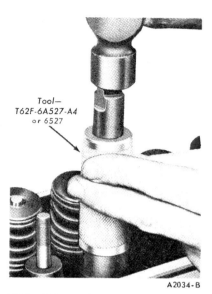

FIG. 21—Rocker Arm Stud Installation

6. Remove the rocker arm stud.

INSTALLATION.

1. Apply water-resistant sealer to the rocker arm stud threads (side that screws into the head only). Install the rocker arm stud and torque to specifications.

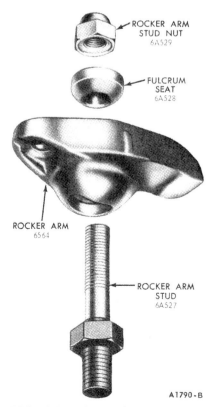

FIG. 22—Valve Rocker Arm and Stud Assembly

2. Apply Lubriplate to the top of the valve stem and at the push rod guide in the cylinder head.

3. Install the valve rocker arm, fulcrum seat, and stud nut. Perform a preliminary (cold) valve lash adjustment.

4. Temporarily lay the valve rocker arm covers in place and connect the spark plug wire to the spark plugs. Operate the engine at 1200 rpm for 30 minutes to stabilize engine temperatures. Remove the valve rocker arm covers and perform a hot valve lash adjustment with the engine idling.

5. Clean the valve rocker arm cover(s) and the cylinder head gasket surface. Apply oil-resistant sealer to one side of a new cover gasket(s). Lay the cemented side of the gasket(s) in place in the cover(s).

6. Position the cover(s) on the cylinder head(s). Make sure that the gasket seats evenly around the head. Install the valve cover bolts. Torque the bolts to specifications. Two minutes later, torque the bolts to the same specifications.

If the right valve rocker arm cover was removed, install the automatic choke heat tube and the crankcase ventilation regulator valve.

Reaming Valve Guides. If it becomes necessary to ream a valve guide (Fig. 23) to install a valve with an oversize stem, a reaming kit is available which contains the following reamer and pilot combinations: a 0.003-inch O.S. reamer with a standard diameter pilot, a 0.015-inch O.S. reamer with a 0.003-inch O.S. pilot, and a 0.030-inch reamer with a 0.015-inch O.S. pilot.

When going from a standard size valve to an oversize valve, always use the reamers in sequence. **Always reface the valve seat after the valve guide has been reamed.**

Refacing Valve Seats. Refacing of the valve seats should be closely coordinated with refacing of the valve face so that the finished seat and valve face will be concentric and the specified interference fit will be maintained. This is important so that the valve and seat will have a compression tight fit. Be sure that the refacer grinding wheels are properly dressed.

Grind the valve seats to a true 45° angle (Fig. 24). Remove only enough stock to clean up pits, grooves, or to correct the valve seat runout. After the seat has been refaced, use a seat width scale to measure the seat

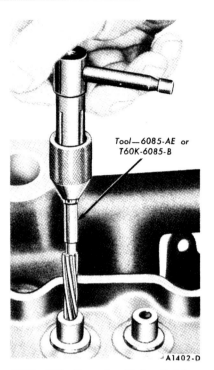

Tool—6085-AE or
T60K-6085-B

FIG. 23—Reaming Valve Guides

width (Fig. 25). Narrow the seat, if necessary, to bring it within specifications.

If the valve seat width exceeds the maximum limit, remove enough stock from the top edge and/or bottom edge of the seat to reduce the width to specifications (Fig. 24).

Use a 30° angle grinding wheel to remove stock from the top of the seats (lower the seats) and use a 60° angle wheel to remove stock from the bottom of the seats (raise the seats).

The finished valve seat should contact the approximate center of the valve face. It is good practice to determine where the valve seat contacts the face. To do this, coat the seat with Prussian blue, then set the valve in place. Rotate the valve with light pressure. If the blue is transferred to the center of the valve face, the contact is satisfactory. If the blue is trans-

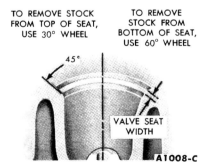

TO REMOVE STOCK
FROM TOP OF SEAT,
USE 30° WHEEL

TO REMOVE
STOCK FROM
BOTTOM OF SEAT,
USE 60° WHEEL

45°

VALVE SEAT
WIDTH

FIG. 24—Valve Seat Refacing

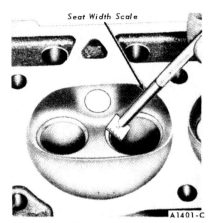

Seat Width Scale

FIG. 25—Valve Seat Width

ferred to the top edge of the valve face, lower the valve seat. If the blue is transferred to the bottom edge of the valve face, raise the valve seat.

VALVES

For inspection procedures refer to Section 3.

Valve defects, such as minor pits, grooves, etc., may be removed. Discard valves that are severely damaged, or if the face runout or stem clearance exceeds specifications.

Discard any defective part of the valve assembly.

Refacing Valves. The valve refacing operation should be closely coordinated with the valve seat refacing operation so that the finished angles of the valve face and of the valve seat will provide a compression-tight fit. Be sure that the refacer grinding wheels are properly dressed.

If the valve face runout is excessive and/or to remove pits and grooves, reface the valves to a true 44° angle. Remove only enough stock to correct the runout or to clean up the pits and grooves. If the edge of the valve head is less than $\frac{1}{32}$ inch thick after grinding, replace the valve as the valve will run too hot in the engine. **The interference fit of the valve and seat should not be lapped out.**

Remove all grooves or score marks from the end of the valve stem, and chamfer it as necessary. Do not remove more than 0.010 inch from the end of the valve stem.

If the valve and/or valve seat has been refaced, it will be necessary to check the clearance between the rocker arm pad and the valve stem with the valve train assembly installed in the engine.

Select Fitting Valves. If the valve

stem to valve guide clearance exceeds the wear limit, ream the valve guide for the next oversize valve stem. Valves with oversize stem diameters of 0.003, 0.015 and 0.030 inch are available for service. **Always reface the valve seat after the valve guide has been reamed.** Refer to Reaming Valve Guides.

CAMSHAFT

Remove light scuffs, scores or nicks from the camshaft machined surfaces with a smooth oil stone.

CRANKSHAFT

Dress minor imperfections with an oil stone. If the journals are severely marred or exceed the wear limit, they should be refinished to size for the next undersize bearing.

Refinishing Journals. Refinish the journal to give the proper clearance with the next undersize bearing. If the journal will not clean up to give the proper clearance with the maximum undersize bearing available, replace the crankshaft.

Always reproduce the same journal shoulder radius that existed originally. Too small a radius will result in fatigue failure of the crankshaft. Too large a radius will result in bearing failure due to radius ride of the bearing.

After refinishing the journals, chamfer the oil holes, then polish the journal with a No. 320 grit polishing cloth and engine oil. Crocus cloth may be used also as a polishing agent.

PISTONS, PINS AND RINGS

Fitting Pistons. Pistons are available for service in standard sizes and the oversizes shown in Table 2.

The standard-size pistons are color coded red or blue on the dome. Refer to the specifications for the standard-size piston dimensions. Piston pins and retainers are provided with new pistons, except retainers are not used on the 170 and 200 Six and 289 V-8.

Follow the procedures in Section 3 to measure the piston O.D. and cylinder bore I.D. The dimensions should be within specifications, and the piston to bore clearance (bore I.D. minus piston O.D.) must be within the specified limits.

If the clearance is greater than the maximum limit, recheck calculations to be sure that the proper size piston has been selected, check for a damaged piston; then, try a new piston. If the clearance is less than the

TABLE 2—Oversize Service Piston

ENGINE	PISTON OVERSIZE (inches)
170 Six	0.003, 0.020, 0.030, 0.040, 0.060
200 Six 289 390 V-8 (2-V and 4-V)	0.003, 0.020, 0.030, 0.040
289 High Performance V-8	Standard Only

minimum limit, recheck calculations before trying another piston. If none can be fitted, refinish the cylinder for the next size piston.

When a piston has been fitted, mark it for assembly in the cylinder to which it was fitted.

If the taper, out-of-round and piston to cylinder bore clearance conditions of the cylinder bore are within specified limits, new piston rings will give satisfactory service. If the new rings are to be installed in a used cylinder that has not been refinished, remove the cylinder wall glaze. Be sure to clean the cylinder bore thoroughly, following the procedure in Section 3.

To Fit a Piston:

1. Calculate the size piston to be used by taking a cylinder bore check. Follow the procedures outlined in Section 3.
2. Select the proper size piston to provide the desired clearance (refer to the specifications). Measure the piston diameter in line with the centerline of the piston pin and at 90° to the piston pin axis.
3. Make sure the piston and cylinder block are at room temperature (70°F). **After any refinishing operation, allow the cylinder bore to cool and make sure the piston and bore are clean and dry before the piston fit is checked.**

Fitting Piston Rings

1. Select the proper ring set for the size piston to be used.
2. Position the ring in the cylinder bore in which it is going to be used.
3. Push the ring down into the bore area where normal ring wear is not encountered.
4. Use the head of a piston to position the ring in the bore so that the ring is square with the cylinder

FIG. 26—Piston Ring Gap

wall. **Use caution to avoid damage to the ring or cylinder bore.**

5. Measure the gap between the ends of the ring with a feeler gauge (Fig. 26). If the ring gap is less or greater than the specified limits, try another ring set.

6. Check the ring side clearance of the compression rings with a feeler gauge inserted between the ring and its lower land (Fig. 27). The gauge should slide freely around the entire ring circumference without binding. Any wear that occurs will form a step at the inner portion of the lower land. **If the lower lands have high steps, the piston should be replaced.**

Fitting Piston Pins. On the 390 V-8, the piston pin should be a light thumb press fit at normal temperature (70°F). Standard piston pins are color coded green. Pins of 0.001-inch oversize (color coded blue) and 0.002-inch oversize (color coded yellow) are available.

Install the piston pin in the piston and rod. Install a new retainer at each end of the pin to hold it in place. Make sure the retainers are properly seated in their grooves.

On the 170 and 200 Six or 289 V-8, install the piston pin, following the procedure under Piston Assembly (Part 8-2 or 8-3).

FIG. 27—Ring Side Clearance

If the pin hole in the piston must be reamed or honed on the 390 V-8, use precision honing equipment or an expansion-type piloted reamer. **Piston pin bores must not be reamed with hand-driven reamers. Use motor-driven reamers, but do not exceed the cutting speed (rpm) recommended by the reamer manufacturer.**

If a reamer is used, set the reamer to the size of the pin bore; then expand the reamer slightly and trial ream the pin bore. Take a light cut. Use a pilot sleeve of the nearest size to maintain alignment of the bores.

Check the hole size, using the new piston pin. If the bore is small, expand the reamer slightly and make another cut. Repeat the procedure until the proper fit is obtained. Check the piston pin for fit in the respective rod or rod bushing. On the 390 V-8, if necessary, ream or hone the rod bushing to fit the pin to specifications.

CYLINDER BLOCK

Refinishing Cylinder Walls. Honing is recommended for refinishing cylinder walls only when the walls have minor imperfections, such as light scuffs and scratches or for fitting pistons to the specified clearance. The grade of hone to be used is determined by the amount of metal to be removed. Follow the instructions of the hone manufacturer.

If coarse stones are used to start the honing operation, leave enough material so that all hone marks can be removed with the finishing hone which is used to obtain the proper piston clearance.

Cylinder walls that are severely marred and/or worn beyond the specified limits should be refinished. Before any cylinder is refinished, all main bearing caps must be in place and tightened to the proper torque so that the crankshaft bearing bores will not become distorted from the refinishing operation.

Refinish only the cylinder or cylinders that require it. **All pistons are the same weight, both standard and oversize; therefore, various sizes of pistons can be used without upsetting engine balance.**

Refinish the cylinder with the most wear first to determine the maximum oversize. If the cylinder will not clean up when refinished for the maximum oversize piston recommended, replace the cylinder block.

Refinish the cylinder to within approximately 0.0015 inch of the required oversize diameter. This will allow enough stock for the final step of honing so that the correct surface finish and pattern are obtained. Use clean sharp hones of No. 180-220 grit for this operation.

For the proper use of the refinishing equipment, follow the instructions of the manufacturer. **Only experienced personnel should be allowed to perform this work.**

After the final operation in either of the two refinishing methods described and prior to checking the piston fit, thoroughly clean and oil the cylinder walls, following the procedure in Section 3. Check the piston fit, following the procedure in this section and Section 3. Mark the pistons to correspond to the cylinders in which they are to be installed. When the refinishing of all cylinders that require it has been completed and all pistons are fitted, thoroughly clean the entire block and oil the cylinder walls following the procedure under Cylinder Block Cleaning in Section 3.

FLYWHEEL RING GEAR— MANUAL-SHIFT TRANSMISSIONS

To replace a defective ring gear, heat the defective ring gear with a blow torch on the engine side of the gear, and knock it off the flywheel. **Do not hit the flywheel when removing the ring gear.**

Heat the new ring gear evenly until the gear expands enough to slip onto the flywheel. Make sure the gear is seated properly against the shoulder. **Do not heat any portion of the gear to a temperature higher than 500°F. If this limit is exceeded, the temper will be removed from the ring gear teeth.**

---

3 CLEANING AND INSPECTION

The cleaning and inspection procedures in this section are for a complete engine overhaul; therefore, for partial engine overhaul or parts replacement, follow the pertinent cleaning or inspection procedure.

INTAKE MANIFOLD CLEANING

Remove all gasket material from the machined surfaces of the manifold. Clean the manifold in a suitable solvent and dry it with compressed air.

INSPECTION

Inspect the manifold for cracks, damaged gasket surfaces, or other defects that would make it unfit for further service. Replace all studs that are stripped or otherwise damaged. **Remove all filings and foreign matter that may have entered the manifold as a result of repairs.**

On the 390 V-8 engine, check the baffle plate on the underside of the manifold; it should be securely fastened at all retaining points.

EXHAUST MANIFOLDS CLEANING

Remove all gasket material from the manifolds. Make sure the automatic choke air inlet and outlet holes (right exhaust manifold on V-8 engines) are completely open and the cover does not leak.

Blow out the automatic choke air heat tube with compressed air.

INSPECTION

Inspect the cylinder head joining flanges of the exhaust manifold(s) for evidence of exhaust gas leaks.

Inspect the manifold(s) for cracks, damaged gasket surfaces, or other defects that would make them unfit for further service.

VALVE ROCKER ARM AND/OR SHAFT ASSEMBLY CLEANING

Clean all the parts thoroughly. Make sure all oil passages are open.

On ball stud rocker arms, make sure the oil passage in the push rod end of the rocker arm is open.

INSPECTION

On rocker arm shaft assemblies, check the clearance between each rocker arm and the shaft by checking the ID of the rocker arm bore and the OD of the shaft. If the clearance between any rocker arm and the shaft exceeds the wear limit, replace the shaft and/or the rocker arm. Inspect the shaft and the rocker arm bore for nicks, scratches, scores or scuffs.

Inspect the pad at the valve end of the rocker arm for indications of scuffing or abnormal wear. If the pad is grooved, replace the rocker arm. **Do not attempt to true this surface by grinding.**

On ball stud rocker arms, check the rocker arm and fulcrum seat for excessive wear, cracks, nicks or burrs. Check the rocker arm stud and nut for stripped or broken threads.

On a 289 High Performance V-8, check the rocker arm adjusting screws and the push rod end of the rocker arms for stripped or broken threads, and the ball end of the adjusting screw for nicks, scratches, or excessive wear.

PUSH RODS
CLEANING

On a 289 V-8, clean the push rods in a suitable solvent. Blow out the oil passage in the push rods with compressed air.

INSPECTION

Check the ends of the push rods for nicks, grooves, roughness or excessive wear.

The push rods can be visually checked for straightness while they are installed in the engine by rotating them with the valve closed. They also can be checked with a dial indicator (Fig. 28).

CYLINDER HEADS
CLEANING

On engines equipped with Thermactor exhaust emission control system, clean the air nozzle tips with a wire brush. Clean the nozzle air hole with a 5/16-inch-diameter, stiff wire brush.

With the valves installed to protect the valve seats, remove deposits from the combustion chambers and valve heads with a scraper and a wire brush. **Be careful not to damage the cylinder head gasket surface.** After the valves are removed, clean the valve guide bores with a valve guide cleaning tool. Use cleaning solvent to remove dirt, grease and other deposits. Clean all bolt holes; be sure the oil transfer passage is clean.

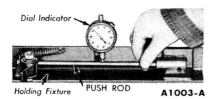

Dial Indicator · *Holding Fixture* · **PUSH ROD** · A1003-A

FIG. 28—Push Rod Runout

Remove all deposits from the valves with a fine wire brush or buffing wheel.

INSPECTION

On engines equipped with a Thermactor exhaust emission control system, inspect the air nozzles for eroded, burned or damaged tips that would restrict the normal air flow. Inspect the connections for stripped or damaged threads and damaged tube nut seats. Inspect the cylinder heads for cracks or excessively burned areas in the exhaust outlet ports.

Check the cylinder head for cracks, and inspect the gasket surface for burrs and nicks. Replace the head if it is cracked.

The following inspection procedures are for a cylinder head that is to be completely overhauled. For individual repair operations, use only the pertinent inspection procedure.

Cylinder Head Flatness. When a cylinder head is removed because of gasket leaks, check the flatness of the cylinder head gasket surface (Fig. 29) for conformance to specifications.

If necessary to refinish the cylinder head gasket surface, **do not plane or grind off more than 0.010 inch.**

Valve Seat Runout. Check the valve seat runout with an accurate gauge (Fig. 30). Follow the instructions of the gauge manufacturer. If the runout exceeds the wear limit, reface the valve and valve seat.

Valve Seat Width. Measure the valve seat width (Fig. 25). Reface the valve seats if the width is not within specifications.

Valves. The critical inspection points and tolerances of the valves are illustrated in Fig. 31. Refer to the specifications for the wear limits. Inspect the valve face and the edge of the valve head for pits, grooves, scores or other defects. Inspect the stem for a bent condition and the end of the stem for grooves

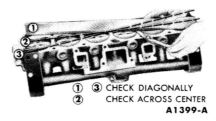

① ③ CHECK DIAGONALLY
② CHECK ACROSS CENTER
A1399-A

FIG. 29—Typical Cylinder Head Flatness

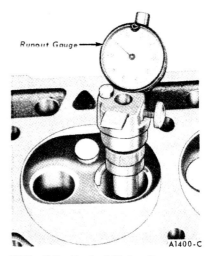

Runout Gauge · A1400-C

FIG. 30—Typical Valve Seat Runout

or scores. Check the valve head for signs of burning, erosion, warpage and cracking. Defects, such as minor pits, grooves, etc., may be removed. Discard valves that are severely damaged.

Inspect the valve springs, valve spring retainers, locks and sleeves for defects.

Valve Face Runout. Check the valve face runout (Fig. 32). It should not exceed the specified wear limit. If the runout exceeds the wear limits, the valve should be refaced or replaced as outlined under Refacing Valves in Section 2.

Valve Stem Clearance. Check the valve stem to valve guide clearance of each valve in its respective valve guide with the tool shown in Fig. 33 or its equivalent.

Install the tool on the valve stem until it is fully seated, and tighten the knurled set screw firmly. Permit the valve to drop away from its seat until the tool contacts the

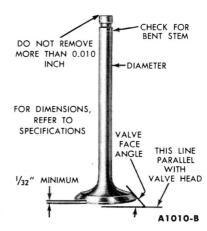

CHECK FOR BENT STEM · DO NOT REMOVE MORE THAN 0.010 INCH · DIAMETER · FOR DIMENSIONS, REFER TO SPECIFICATIONS · VALVE FACE ANGLE · THIS LINE PARALLEL WITH VALVE HEAD · 1/32" MINIMUM · A1010-B

FIG. 31—Critical Valve Tolerances

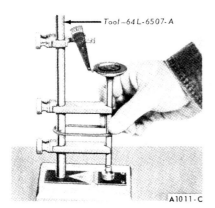

FIG. 32—Valve Race Runout

upper surface of the valve guide.

Position the dial indicator with its flat tip against the center portion of the tool's spherical section at approximately 90° to the valve stem axis. Move the tool back and forth in line with the indicator stem. Take a reading on the dial indicator without removing the tool from the valve guide upper surface. Divide the reading by two, the division factor for the tool.

Valve Spring Pressure. Check the springs for proper pressure (Fig. 34) at the specified spring lengths. Weak valve springs cause poor engine performance; therefore, if the pressure of any spring approaches the wear limit, replace the spring.

Valve Spring Squareness. Check each spring for squareness using a steel square and a surface plate (Fig. 35). Stand the spring and square on end on the surface plate. Slide the spring up to the square. Revolve the spring slowly and observe the space between the top coil of the spring and the square. If

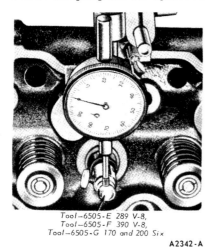

Tool–6505-E 289 V-8,
Tool–6505-F 390 V-8,
Tool–6505-G 170 and 200 Six

FIG. 33—Typical Valve Stem Clearance

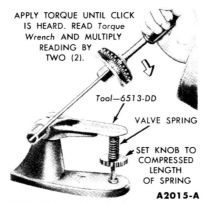

FIG. 34—Valve Spring Pressure

the spring is out of square more than ⅟₁₆ inch, replace it.

Follow the same procedure to check new valve springs before installation.

Make certain the proper spring (color coded) is installed.

Visually inspect the valve spring retainer to determine if the damper spring coil has been hitting the retainer. This interference will also cause a clicking noise when the engine is operating. The damper spring is properly installed in the valve spring when positioned so that the end of the damper spring bottom coil is 135° counterclockwise from the end of the valve spring lower coil.

HYDRAULIC VALVE LIFTERS

The valve lifter assemblies should be kept in proper sequence so that they can be installed in their original position. Inspect and test each lifter separately so as not to intermix the internal parts. **If any part of the lifter assembly needs replacing, replace the entire assembly.**

CLEANING

Thoroughly clean all the parts in

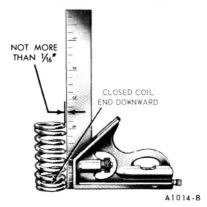

FIG. 35—Valve Spring Squareness

clean solvent and wipe them with a clean, lint-free cloth.

INSPECTION

Inspect the parts and discard the entire lifter assembly if any part shows pitting, scoring, galling or evidence of non-rotation. Replace the entire assembly if the plunger is not free in the body. The plunger should drop to the bottom of the body by its own weight when assembled dry.

Assemble the lifter assembly and check for freeness of operation by pressing down on the push rod cup. The lifters can also be checked with a hydraulic tester to test the leak down rate. Follow the instructions of the test unit manufacturer or the procedure in Section 1.

MECHANICAL TAPPETS
CLEANING

Thoroughly clean the tappets in clean solvent and wipe them with a clean, lint-free cloth.

INSPECTION

Inspect the tappets, and discard any that show signs of pitting, scoring or galling. Replace any tappets that show evidence of non-rotation.

TIMING CHAIN AND SPROCKETS
CLEANING

Clean all parts in solvent and dry them with compressed air.

Lubricate the timing chain with engine oil before installing it on the engine.

INSPECTION

Inspect the chain for broken links. Inspect the sprockets for cracks and worn or damaged teeth. Replace all components of the timing chain and sprocket assembly if any one item needs replacement.

On the 289 and 390 V-8, inspect the fuel pump drive eccentric for scores, nicks and excessive wear. If the eccentric is scored, replace it.

CAMSHAFT
CLEANING AND INSPECTION

Clean the camshaft in solvent and wipe it dry. Inspect the camshaft lobes for scoring and signs of abnormal wear. Lobe wear characteristics may result in pitting in the general area of the lobe toe. This pitting is not detrimental to the operation of the camshaft; therefore, the camshaft should not be replaced until the lobe lift loss has exceeded 0.005 inch.

The lift of the camshaft lobes can be checked with the camshaft installed in the engine or on centers. Refer to Camshaft Lobe Lift.

Check the distributor drive gear for broken or chipped teeth.

CRANKSHAFT VIBRATION DAMPER AND SLEEVE
CLEANING

Clean the oil seal contact surface on the crankshaft damper or sleeve (390 V-8) with solvent to remove any corrosion, sludge or varnish deposits. Excess deposits that are not readily removed with solvent may be removed with crocus cloth. Use crocus cloth to remove any sharp edges, burrs or other imperfections which might damage the oil seal during installation or cause premature seal wear. **Do not use crocus cloth to the extent that the seal surface becomes polished. A finely polished surface may produce poor sealing or cause premature seal wear.**

INSPECTION

Inspect the crankshaft damper or sleeve (390 V-8) oil seal surface for nicks, sharp edges or burrs that might damage the oil seal during installation or cause premature seal wear.

CRANKSHAFT
CLEANING

Handle the crankshaft with care to avoid possible fractures or damage to the finished surfaces. Clean the crankshaft with solvent, then blow out all oil passages with compressed air.

INSPECTION

Inspect main and connecting rod journals for cracks, scratches, grooves or scores.

Measure the diameter of each journal in at least four places to determine out-of-round, taper or undersize condition (Fig. 36).

On engines used with a manual-shift transmission, check the fit of the clutch pilot bushing in the bore of the crankshaft. The bushing is pressed into the crankshaft and should not be loose. Inspect the inner surface of the bushing for wear or a bell-mouth condition. Check the ID of the bushing (Fig. 37). Replace the bushing if it is worn or damaged or the ID is not within specifications.

Inspect the pilot bearing, when used, for roughness, evidence of

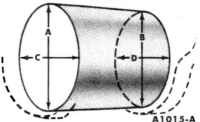

A VS B = VERTICAL TAPER
C VS D = HORIZONTAL TAPER
A VS C AND B VS D = OUT-OF-ROUND
CHECK FOR OUT-OF-ROUND AT
EACH END OF JOURNAL

A1015-A

FIG. 36—Crankshaft Journal Measurements

overheating or loss of lubricant. Replace it if any of these conditions are found.

FLYWHEEL—MANUAL-SHIFT TRANSMISSIONS
INSPECTION

Inspect the flywheel for cracks, heat checks, or other defects that would make it unfit for further service. Machine the friction surface of the flywheel if it is scored or worn. If it is necessary to remove more than 0.045 inch of stock from the original thickness, replace the flywheel.

Inspect the ring gear for worn, chipped or cracked teeth. If the teeth are damaged, replace the ring gear.

With the flywheel installed on the crankshaft, check the flywheel face runout, following the procedure in Section 1.

FLYWHEEL—AUTOMATIC TRANSMISSION
INSPECTION

Inspect the flywheel for cracks or other defects that would make it unfit for further service. Inspect

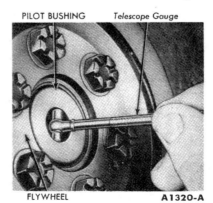

PILOT BUSHING   *Telescope Gauge*

FLYWHEEL   A1320-A

FIG. 37—Typical Clutch Pilot Bushing Wear Check

the starter ring gear for worn, chipped or cracked teeth. If the teeth are damaged, replace the ring gear and flywheel assembly.

With the flywheel installed on the crankshaft, check the gear face runout and outside diameter runout of the flywheel (refer to Section 1 for the proper procedure).

CONNECTING RODS
CLEANING

Remove the bearings from the rod and cap. Identify the bearings if they are to be used again. Clean the connecting rod in solvent, including the rod bore and the back of the inserts. **Do not use a caustic cleaning solution.** Blow out all passages with compressed air.

INSPECTION

The connecting rods and related parts should be carefully inspected and checked for conformance to specifications. Various forms of engine wear caused by these parts can be readily identified.

A shiny surface on the pin boss side of the piston usually indicates that a connecting rod is bent or the piston pin hole is not in proper relation to the piston skirt and ring grooves.

Abnormal connecting rod bearing wear can be caused by either a bent connecting rod, an improperly machined crankpin, or a tapered connecting rod bore.

Twisted connecting rods will not create an easily identifiable wear pattern, but badly twisted rods will disturb the action of the entire piston, rings and connecting rod assembly and may be the cause of excessive oil consumption.

Inspect the connecting rods for signs of fractures and the bearing bores for out-of-round and taper. If the bore exceeds the recommended limits and/or if the connecting rod is fractured, it should be replaced.

Check the piston pin to connecting rod bushing clearance. Replace the connecting rod if the bushing is so worn that it cannot be reamed or honed for an oversize pin.

On the 170 and 200 Six and 289 V-8, check the I.D. of the connecting rod piston pin bore. Replace the connecting rod if the pin bore is not within specifications.

Replace defective connecting rod nuts and bolts.

If the connecting rod has been removed from the piston it should be checked for bend or twist before assembling it to the piston. Connecting rods can be checked for bend or twist while assembled to the piston. Check the connecting rods for bend or twist on a suitable alignment fixture. Follow the instructions of the fixture manufacturer. If the bend and/or twist exceeds specifications, the connecting rod must be straightened or replaced.

PISTONS, PINS AND RINGS
CLEANING

Remove deposits from the piston surfaces. Clean gum or varnish from the piston skirt, piston pins and rings with solvent. **Do not use a caustic cleaning solution or a wire brush to clean pistons.** Clean the ring grooves with a ring groove cleaner (Fig. 38). Make sure the oil ring slots (or holes) are clean.

INSPECTION

Carefully inspect the pistons for fractures at the ring lands, skirts and pin bosses, and for scuffed, rough or scored skirts. If the lower inner portion of the ring grooves has a high step, replace the piston. The step will interfere with ring operation and cause excessive ring side clearance.

Spongy, eroded areas near the edge of the top of the piston are usually caused by detonation or pre-ignition. A shiny surface on the thrust surface of the piston, offset from the centerline between the piston pin holes, can be caused by a bent connecting rod. Replace pistons that show signs of excessive wear, wavy ring lands or fractures or damage from detonation or pre-ignition.

Check the piston to cylinder bore

clearance by measuring the piston and bore diameters. Refer to the specifications for the proper clearance. Refer to Cylinder Block Inspection for the bore measurement procedure. **Measure the O.D. of the piston with micrometers at the centerline of the piston pin bore and at 90° to the pin bore axis.**

Check the ring side clearance following the procedure under Fitting Piston Rings in Section 2.

Replace piston pins showing signs of fracture, etching or wear. Check the piston pin fit in the piston and rod. Refer to Pistons and Connecting Rods Assembly in the pertinent engine section.

Check the O.D. of the piston pin and the I.D. of the pin bore in the piston. Replace any piston pin or piston that is not within specifications.

Replace all rings that are scored, chipped or cracked. Check the end gap and side clearance. It is good practice to always install new rings when overhauling an engine. Rings should not be transferred from one piston to another regardless of mileage.

MAIN AND CONNECTING ROD BEARINGS
CLEANING

Clean the bearing inserts and caps thoroughly in solvent, and dry them with compressed air. **Do not scrape gum or varnish deposits from the bearing shells.**

INSPECTION

Inspect each bearing carefully. Bearings that have a scored, chipped or worn surface should be replaced. Typical examples of bearing failures and their causes are shown in Fig. 39. The copper lead bearing base may be visible through the bearing overlay. This does not mean that the

bearing is worn. It is not necessary to replace the bearing if the bearing clearance is within recommended limits. Check the clearance of bearings that appear to be satisfactory with Plastigage. Fit new bearings following the recommended procedure in the pertinent part of Group 8.

CYLINDER BLOCK
CLEANING

After any cylinder bore repair operation, such as honing or deglazing, clean the bore(s) with soap or detergent and water. **Then, thoroughly rinse the bore(s) with clean water to remove the soap or detergent, and wipe the bore(s) dry with a clean, lint-free cloth. Finally, wipe the bore(s) with a clean cloth dipped in engine oil. If these procedures are not followed, rusting of the cylinder bore(s) may occur.**

If the engine is disassembled, thoroughly clean the block in solvent. Remove old gasket material from all machined surfaces. Remove all pipe plugs that seal oil passages; then clean out all the passages. Blow out all passages, bolt holes, etc., with compressed air.

On the 390 V-8, be sure the jiggle pin in the main oil gallery front plug operates freely.

Make sure the threads in the cylinder head bolt holes are clean. Dirt in the threads may cause binding and result in a false torque reading. Use a tap to true-up threads and to remove any deposits.

INSPECTION

After the block has been thoroughly cleaned, make a check for cracks. Minute cracks not visible to the naked eye may be detected by coating the suspected area with a mixture of 25% kerosene and 75% light motor oil. Wipe the part dry

Ring Groove Cleaner

A1404-C

FIG. 38—Cleaning Ring Grooves —Typical

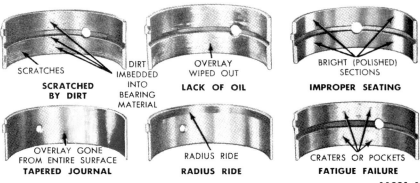

SCRATCHES | DIRT IMBEDDED INTO BEARING MATERIAL | OVERLAY WIPED OUT | BRIGHT (POLISHED) SECTIONS

SCRATCHED BY DIRT | **LACK OF OIL** | **IMPROPER SEATING**

OVERLAY GONE FROM ENTIRE SURFACE | RADIUS RIDE | CRATERS OR POCKETS

TAPERED JOURNAL | **RADIUS RIDE** | **FATIGUE FAILURE**

A1021-A

FIG. 39—Typical Bearing Failures

and immediately apply a coating of zinc oxide dissolved in wood alcohol. If cracks are present, the coating will become discolored at the defective area. Replace the block if it is cracked.

Check all machined gasket surfaces for burrs, nicks, scratches and scores. Remove minor imperfections with an oil stone. Check the flatness of the cylinder block gasket surface following the procedure and specifications recommended for the cylinder head. The cylinder block can be machined to bring the cylinder head gasket surface within the flatness specifications, **but not to exceed 0.010 inch stock removal.**

Replace all expansion-type plugs that show evidence of leakage.

Inspect the cylinder walls for scoring, roughness or other signs of wear. Check the cylinder bore for out-of-round and taper. Measure the bore with an accurate gauge following the instructions of the manufacturer. Measure the diameter of each cylinder bore at the top, middle and bottom with the gauge placed at right angles and parallel to the centerline of the engine (Fig. 40). **Use only the measurements obtained at 90° to the engine centerline when calculating the piston to cylinder bore clearance.**

Refinish cylinders that are deeply scored and/or when out-of-round and/or taper exceed the wear limits.

If the cylinder walls have minor surface imperfections, but the out-of-round and taper are within limits, it may be possible to remove the imperfections by honing the cyl-

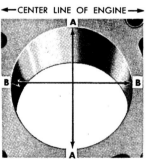

←CENTER LINE OF ENGINE→ **A**
A
AT RIGHT ANGLE TO CENTER LINE OF ENGINE
B
B PARALLEL TO CENTER LINE OF ENGINE

1. OUT-OF-ROUND = DIFFERENCE BETWEEN **A** AND **B**
2. TAPER = DIFFERENCE BETWEEN THE **A** MEASUREMENT AT TOP OF CYLINDER BORE AND THE **A** MEASUREMENT AT BOTTOM OF CYLINDER BORE   A1025-A

FIG. 40—Cylinder Bore Out-of-Round and Taper

inder walls and installing new service piston rings providing the piston clearance is within specified limits. Use the finest grade of honing stone for this operation.

OIL PAN
CLEANING

Scrape any dirt or metal particles from the inside of the pan. Scrape all old gasket material from the gasket surface. Wash the pan in a solvent and dry it thoroughly. Be sure all foreign particles are removed from below the baffle plate.

INSPECTION

Check the pan for cracks, holes, damaged drain plug threads, a loose baffle, and a nicked or warped gasket surface.

Repair any damage, or replace the pan if repairs can not be made.

OIL PUMP
CLEANING

Wash all parts in a solvent and dry them thoroughly with compressed air. Use a brush to clean the inside of the pump housing and the pressure relief valve chamber. Be sure all dirt and metal particles are removed.

INSPECTION

Refer to the specifications for clearances and wear limits.

Check the inside of the pump housing and the outer race and rotor for damage or excessive wear.

Check the mating surface of the pump cover for wear. If the cover mating surface is worn, scored or grooved, replace the cover.

Measure the outer race to housing clearance (Fig. 41) which should be to specifications.

With the rotor assembly installed in the housing so that the identification mark on the outer race is toward the bottom of the pump, place a straight edge over the rotor assembly and the housing. Measure the clearance (rotor end play) between the straight edge and the rotor and outer race (Fig. 42).

The outer race, shaft and rotor are replaceable only as an assembly.

Check the drive shaft to housing bearing clearance by measuring the OD of the shaft and the ID of the housing bearing.

Inspect the relief valve spring for a collapsed or worn condition. Check the relief valve spring tension. If the spring tension is not within specifications and/or the spring is

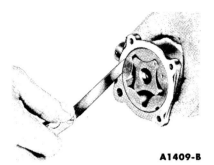

FIG. 41—Outer Race to Housing Clearance

defective, replace the spring.

Check the relief valve piston for scores and free operation in the bore.

POSITIVE CRANKCASE VENTILATION SYSTEM

Refer to Group 19 for the correct mileage interval for maintenance.

CLEANING

Do not attempt to clean the crankcase ventilation regulator valve. It should be replaced at the specified mileage intervals (Group 19).

The oil filler tube breather cap, located on the valve rocker arm cover should be cleaned at the specified interval. Remove the cap and wash it in a low-volatilty, petroleum-base solvent. Probe the breather hole(s) to assure removal of any accumulated deposits. Shake the cap dry and install it. **Do not dry with compressed air as air pressure may damage the filter element.**

Clean the crankcase ventilation system connection on the carburetor spacer by probing the inlet nipple with a flexible wire or bottle brush.

Clean the rubber hoses with a low-volatilty, petroleum-base solvent and dry with compressed air.

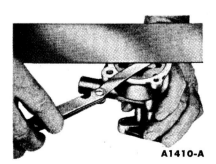

FIG. 42—Rotor End Play

PART 8-2

170 AND 200 SIX

Section	Page
1 Description and Operation	8-24
Manifolds	8-24
Cylinder Heads	8-25
Cylinder Block	8-25
Valve Train	8-25
Lubrication System	8-26
Crankcase Ventilation	8-27
Cooling System	8-27
2 In-Car Adjustments and Repairs	8-29
Engine Supports	8-30
Exhaust Manifold	8-31
Positive Crankcase Ventilation System	8-31
Valve Rocker Arm Shaft Assembly	8-31
Cylinder Head	8-32
Valve Spring, Retainer and Stem Seal Replacement	8-34
Cylinder Front Cover and Timing Chain	8-34
Camshaft	8-35

Section	Page
Camshaft Rear Bearing Bore Plug Replacement	8-36
Hydraulic Valve Lifter	8-37
Main and Connecting Rod Bearing Replacement	8-37
Pistons and Connecting Rods	8-39
Flywheel	8-40
Clutch Pilot Bushing Replacement	8-41
Oil Filter Replacement	8-41
Oil Pan	8-41
Oil Pump	8-42
3 Engine Removal and Installation	8-43
4 Major Repair Operations	8-44
Crankshaft	8-44
Camshaft Bearing Replacement	8-46
Cylinder Assembly Replacement	8-47
Cylinder Block Replacement	8-47
Engine Disassembly	8-47
Engine Assembly	8-48

1 DESCRIPTION AND OPERATION

The 170 and 200 Six engines (Figs. 1, 2, 3, and 4) have compression ratios of 9.1 and 9.2 respectively. The 170 Six engine has a piston displacement of 170 cubic inches and the patent plate identification symbol is U. The 200 Six engine has a piston displacement of 200 cubic inches and the patent plate symbol is T.

THERMACTOR EXHAUST EMISSION CONTROL SYSTEM

For engines equipped with Thermactor exhaust emission control system, refer to Group 12 for description and adjustment and repair procedures.

MANIFOLDS

Exhaust gases provide the heat necessary to assist in vaporizing the incoming fuel mixture.

To prevent carburetor icing at the throttle plate, a spacer, heated by engine coolant, is located between the carburetor and the intake manifold (Fig. 5). The coolant flows from the front of the engine through the spacer inlet hose into the carburetor coolant spacer. The coolant circu-

FIG. 1—Typical ¾ Left Front View

A2045-B

top compression ring is molybdenum coated and the lower compression ring is phosphate-coated. The oil control ring assembly consists of a serrated spring and two chrome-plated steel rails.

VALVE TRAIN

The 170 and 200 Six engines utilize hydraulic valve lifters to provide zero lash. The operation and parts identification of the hydraulic valve lifters are shown in Fig. 6. When the valve is closed, the lifter assembly is on the base circle of the camshaft lobe and the valve push rod is in its lowest position. With the lifter assembly in this position, the plunger spring expands, forcing the plunger upward. This action is transmitted to the valve rocker arm via the valve push rod until there is solid contact between the valve and the valve end of valve rocker arm (zero valve lash).

As the lifter plunger moves upward, the volume of the compression chamber is increased, resulting in reduced oil pressure in the compression chamber. Therefore, to equalize the resulting pressure differential between the supply chamber and the compression chamber, the disc valve moves off its seat and permits oil to

FIG. 2—¾ Right Front View

A2046-B

lates through the spacer and flows into the heater inlet hose and into the heater. On cars that do not have a heater the coolant flows through the spacer and flows into the return hose and into the water pump.

CYLINDER HEAD

The cylinder head carries the valves, valve rocker arm shaft assembly, integrally cast intake manifold, the coolant outlet and thermostat. Valve guides are integral with the head. The valves are arranged from front to rear E-I-I-E-I-E-E-I-E-I-I-E.

CYLINDER BLOCK

The cylinders are numbered from 1 to 6 starting at the front of the engine. The firing order is 1-5-3-6-2-4.

The distributor, located on the left front of the engine, drives the oil pump through an intermediate drive shaft.

The crankshaft used on the 170 engine is supported by four main bearings. Crankshaft end thrust is controlled by the flanges of the No. 3 main bearing.

The crankshaft used on the 200 engine is supported by seven main bearings. Crankshaft end thrust is controlled by the flanges of the No. 5 main bearing.

The pistons have two compression rings and one oil control ring. The

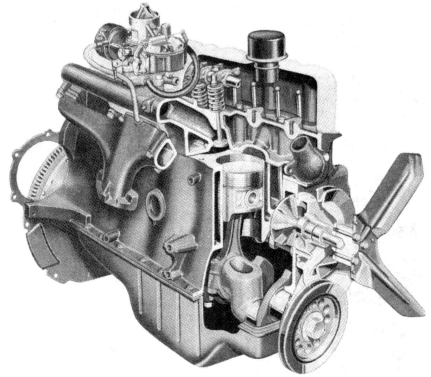

A2047-C

FIG. 3—¾ Sectional View—170 Six Engine

leakage of oil past the plunger occurs (calibrated leak down rate).

As the high point of the camshaft lobe rotates and passes by the foot of the valve lifter, the valve in the cylinder head seats and the valve lifter assembly is forced downward. Reduced force on the lifter plunger at this time relieves the pressure on the lifter plunger and it is free to be moved upward by the plunger spring. This action allows oil to flow once again through the oil holes in the lifter body and plunger.

The operating cycle is completed for each revolution of the camshaft. Zero clearance (lash) in the valve train mechanism is maintained at all times by the hydraulic force and expansion of the plunger spring between the lifter body and plunger.

LUBRICATION SYSTEM

Oil from the oil pan sump is forced through the pressure-type lubrication system (Fig. 7) by a rotor pump. A spring-loaded relief valve in the pump limits the maximum pressure of the system. Oil relieved by the valve is directed back to the intake side of the pump.

All the oil discharged by the pump passes through a full flow-type Rotunda filter before it enters the engine. The filter has an integral by-pass valve and mounting gasket. The by-pass valve permits oil to by-pass the filter if it becomes clogged, thereby maintaining an emergency supply of oil to the engine at all

A2293-A

FIG. 4—¾ Sectional View—200 Six Engine

flow from the supply chamber to the compression chamber. When the compression chamber becomes filled with oil, the pressures in the two chambers are equalized. The oil flow ceases and the disc valve spring seats the disc valve and closes the disc valve port.

As the camshaft rotates, the lifter assembly is raised by the camshaft lobe. This increases the push rod force against the lifter plunger and

hydraulic pressure immediately builds up in the compression chamber until it acts as a solid member of the valve operating mechanism. The lifter then becomes a hydraulic ram which forces the valve in the cylinder head to open. During this period, a slight

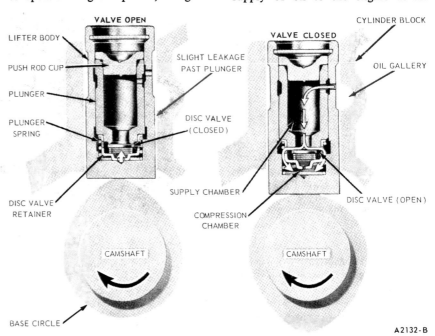

FIG. 6—Hydraulic Valve Lifter Operation

A2048-C

FIG. 5—Typical Coolant-Heated Carburetor Spacer

A 2049-B

FIG. 7—Typical Lubrication System

times. An anti-drain back diaphragm prevents a reverse flow of oil when the engine is stopped.

From the filter, the oil flows into the main oil gallery. The oil gallery supplies oil to all the camshaft and main bearings through a drilled passage in each main bearing web.

The timing chain and sprockets are splash-lubricated from the oil pan.

Oil slingers prevent leakage by directing oil away from the crankshaft front and rear oil seals.

Cylinder walls, pistons and piston pins are lubricated through a drilled hole in each connecting rod which indexes with a drilled hole in the connecting rod journal of the crankshaft.

Oil from the main gallery feeds pressure oil to the hydraulic valve lifters and lubricates the lifter bores in the cylinder block. A reservoir at each valve lifter bore boss traps oil so that oil is available for valve lifter lubrication as soon as the engine starts.

Oil under reduced pressure is fed to the valve rocker arm shaft assembly through a drilled passage in the cylinder block at the No. 4 camshaft bearing. The oil is metered by a groove in the camshaft journal. The

passage in the block indexes with a hole in the cylinder head. The oil passage in the cylinder head is drilled from the cylinder head bolt bore to the No. 6 valve rocker arm shaft support. The rocker arm shaft supports have a square cored bolt mounting hole for more positive lubrication of the rocker arms, shafts and valves. The oil flows through the valve rocker arm shaft through drilled holes in each rocker arm to lubricate the valve and the push rod end of the rocker arm. The excess oil spirals down the rotating push rod and assists in lubricating the tappet and push rod seat. An oil outlet in the No. 1 rocker arm shaft support, exhausts excess oil from the valve rocker arm shaft. The oil from each rocker arm drains into the push rod chamber through the push rod bore holes in the cylinder head.

The oil in the push rod chamber drains back into the oil pan through cored openings in the block.

POSITIVE CRANKCASE VENTILATION

The engines are equipped with either an open positive crankcase ventilation system or a closed positive crankcase ventilation system. In

either system the crankcase vapors are directed to the intake manifold.

OPEN VENTILATION SYSTEM

The air flow in the positive crankcase ventilation system is shown in Fig. 8.

Ventilating air enters the engine through the oil filler cap located on the front of the valve rocker arm cover. The filler cap contains a filtering element which filters the incoming air.

From the oil filler cap, the air flows into the front section of the valve rocker arm shaft chamber. The ventilating air moves down past the push rods and into the crankcase. Air is diverted from the front section of the crankcase through holes in the front of the cylinder block wall to ventilate the timing chain chamber.

The rotating action of the crankshaft causes the air to flow towards the rear of the crankcase and up into the rear section of the valve rocker arm cover. The air then enters a spring-loaded regulator valve that regulates the amount of air flow to meet changing operating conditions. The air is then directed to the intake manifold through the crankcase vent hose and the spacer fitting.

During idle, intake manifold vacuum is high. The high vacuum overcomes the tension of the spring pressure and moves the valve to a low flow position (Fig. 9). With the valve in this position, all the ventilating air passes through the restricted passage in the valve. With the valve in this position, there is minimum ventilation. As engine speed increases and manifold vacuum decreases, the spring forces the valve out of the passage and to the full open position (Fig. 9). This increases the flow of ventilating air.

CLOSED VENTILATION SYSTEM

The closed ventilation system is the same as the open ventilation system except for the following:

The ventilating air is picked up at the air cleaner and transferred through a tube to the oil filler cap.

The oil filler cap is otherwise closed to the atmosphere.

COOLING SYSTEM

The coolant is drawn from the bottom of the radiator by the water pump which delivers the coolant to the cylinder block (Fig. 10).

As the coolant enters the block, it

INLET HOSE
(CLOSED SYSTEM)

travels through cored passages to cool the entire length of each cylinder wall. Upon reaching the rear of the cylinder block, the coolant is directed upward into the cylinder head where it cools the combustion chambers, valves, and valve seats on its return to the front of the engine.

At this point, the coolant flows into the coolant outlet connection, past the thermostat if it is open, and into the top of the radiator. If the thermostat is closed, a small portion of the coolant is returned to the water pump for recirculation. The entire system is pressurized to 13-15 psi.

A2050-B

FIG. 8—Typical Positive Crankcase Ventilation System

FROM CRANKCASE AND/OR ROCKER ARM COVER

TO INTAKE MANIFOLD

LOW SPEED OPERATION — HIGH MANIFOLD VACUUM

HIGH SPEED OPERATION — LOW MANIFOLD VACUUM

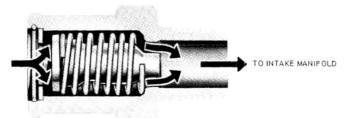

FROM CRANKCASE AND/OR ROCKER ARM COVER

TO INTAKE MANIFOLD

A2121-B

FIG. 9—Positive Crankcase Ventilation Regulator Valve Operation

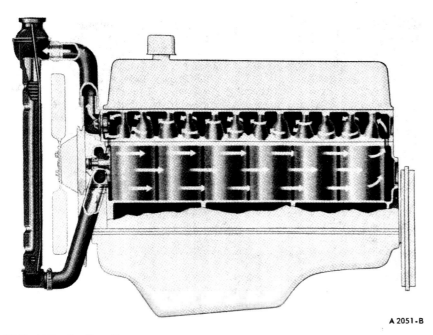

A 2051-B

FIG. 10—Cooling System

2 IN-CAR ADJUSTMENTS AND REPAIRS

For adjustment and repair procedures of all components of the Thermactor exhaust emission control system, (if so equipped), refer to Group 12.

When installing nuts or bolts that must be torqued (refer to Part 8-5 for torque specifications), oil the threads with light weight engine oil. **Do not oil threads that require oil-resistant or water-resistant sealer.**

ENGINE FRONT SUPPORT

The procedures given apply to either a right or left installation.

The engine front supports are located on each side of the cylinder block (Figs. 11 and 12).

MUSTANG

Removal

1. Remove the insulator to support bracket nuts and washers from both insulators (Fig. 11).

2. Raise the engine with a jack and wood block placed under the oil pan.

3. Remove the insulator to engine bolts and washers and remove the insulator.

Installation

1. Position the insulator assembly on the engine and install the insulator to engine bolts and washers

finger-tight.

2. Lower the engine carefully to make sure the insulator stud engages the hole in the support bracket.

3. Install the insulator to support bracket washer and nut on both engines front mounts. Tighten the insulator bolts and nuts to specifications.

FAIRLANE, COMET, AND FALCON

Removal

1. Remove the insulator to support bracket retaining nut.

2. Using a wood block placed under the oil pan raise the engine only enough to clear the insulator bolt at the frame bracket.

3. Remove the retaining screws and nuts from the insulator to engine front support insulator bracket, and remove the insulator.

Installation

1. Position the insulator to the engine front support insulator bracket and install the retaining screws and nuts. Torque to specifications.

2. Carefully lower the engine guiding the insulator bolt into the frame bracket.

3. Install the insulator to frame bracket retaining nut, and torque to specifications.

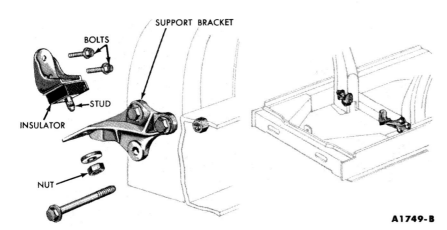

SUPPORT BRACKET

BOLTS

STUD

INSULATOR

NUT

A1749-B

FIG. 11—Mustang Engine Front Supports

ENGINE REAR SUPPORT

The rear support is located at the transmission extension housing (Fig. 13).

FAIRLANE, COMET, and FALCON

Removal

1. Support the transmission with a floor jack to relieve weight from the supporting crossmember.

2. Remove the retaining nuts, washers, and cotter keys from the supporting crossmember, and remove the supporting crossmember.

3. Remove the screws and washers which retain the engine rear support insulator assembly beneath the transmission.

4. Remove the insulator assembly.

Installation

1. Position the engine rear support insulator assembly in place beneath the transmission, and install the retaining screws. Torque them to specifications.

2. Position the supporting crossmember and install the retaining washers and nuts. Torque them to specifications.

3. Install the cotter keys. If necessary, continue tightening the two outer nuts as required to align the castellations.

MUSTANG

Removal

1. Remove the insulator to rear support nuts and washers (Fig. 14).

2. Raise and support the transmission with a transmission jack.

3. Loosen one of the rear support to crossmember bolts.

4. Remove the other rear support to crossmember bolt, washer (right side only) and nut, and swing the rear support down and out of the way.

5. On a 3-speed, manual-shift transmission, remove the support extension to transmission bolts and lockwashers, and remove the insulator and the support extension. Separate the support extension to insulator nuts and bolts.

On a 4-speed, manual-shift or an automatic transmission, remove the insulator to transmission bolts and washers and remove the insulator.

Installation

1. On a 4-speed, manual-shift or an automatic transmission, position the insulator against the transmission and install the insulator to transmission bolts and washers (Fig. 14). Torque the bolts to specifications.

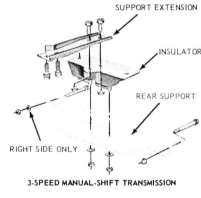

3-SPEED MANUAL-SHIFT TRANSMISSION

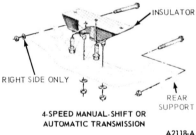

4-SPEED MANUAL-SHIFT OR AUTOMATIC TRANSMISSION

A2118-A

FIG. 14—Mustang Engine Rear Support

On a 3-speed, manual-shift transmission, attach the support extension to the insulator with the support extension to insulator nuts and bolts. Torque the nuts to specifications. Position the support extension and insulator assembly against the transmission and install the support extension to transmission bolts and lockwashers. Torque the bolts to specifications.

2. Swing the rear support up into position and install the rear support to crossmember bolt, washer (right side only) and nut. Torque *both* rear support to crossmember nuts to specifications.

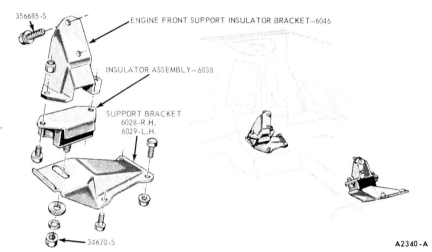

FIG. 12—Fairlane, Comet, and Falcon Engine Front Supports

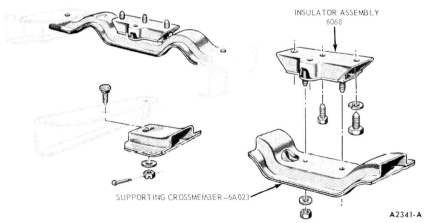

FIG. 13—Fairlane, Comet, Falcon, Engine Rear Support

3. Lower the transmission and install the insulator to rear support nuts and washers. Torque the nuts to specifications.

EXHAUST MANIFOLD REMOVAL

1. Remove the air cleaner. Disconnect the muffler inlet pipe from the exhaust manifold.

2. Bend the exhaust manifold retaining bolt lock tabs back and remove the retaining bolts. Remove the exhaust manifold.

CLEANING AND INSPECTION

Refer to Part 8-1, Section 3 for the cleaning and inspection procedures.

INSTALLATION

1. Clean the mating surfaces of the exhaust manifold and cylinder head. Scrape the gasket material from the mounting flange of the exhaust manifold and muffler inlet pipe.

2. Apply graphite grease to the mating surface of the exhaust manifold.

3. Position the exhaust manifold on the cylinder head and install the retaining bolts and tab washers. Working from the center to the ends, torque the bolts to specifications.

Lock the bolts by bending one tab of the washer over a flat on the bolt.

4. Place a new gasket on the muffler inlet pipe. Position the muffler inlet pipe to the manifold. Install and torque the retaining nuts to specifications.

5. Install the air cleaner. Start the engine and check for exhaust leaks.

POSITIVE CRANKCASE VENTILATION SYSTEM

The positive crankcase ventilation system components are shown in Fig. 15.

REMOVAL

1. On a closed ventilation system, remove the inlet hose from the air cleaner and the oil filler cap.

2. Remove the air cleaner.

3. Grasp the crankcase vent hose near the rocker arm cover grommet and pull to remove the regulator valve from the rocker arm cover.

4. Using hose clamp pliers, slide both hose clamps towards the center of the vent hose. Remove the regulator valve from the vent hose and remove the vent hose from the hose fitting in the carburetor spacer.

CLEANING AND INSPECTION

Refer to Part 8-1, Section 3 for the cleaning and inspection procedures.

INSTALLATION

1. Position the hose clamps on the vent hose. Install the hose on the fitting in the carburetor spacer and the regulator valve in the hose. Using hose clamp pliers, slide the clamps into position.

2. Insert the regulator valve into the rocker arm cover mounting grommet.

3. Install the air cleaner.

4. On a closed ventilation system, connect the inlet hose to the air cleaner and the oil filler cap.

5. Operate the engine and check for leaks.

VALVE ROCKER ARM SHAFT ASSEMBLY REMOVAL

1. Remove the air cleaner and the crankcase ventilation system.

2. If equipped with a Thermactor exhaust emission control system, disconnect the air hoses as necessary for accessibility and position them out of the way.

3. Remove the valve rocker arm cover and discard the gasket.

4. Remove the rocker arm shaft support bolts by loosening the bolts two turns at a time in sequence. Remove the rocker arm shaft assembly (Fig. 16). Remove the valve push rods.

FIG. 16—Valve Rocker Arm Shaft Removal

INSTALLATION

1. Apply Lubriplate to both ends of the push rods and to the valve stem tip.

2. Install the valve push rods. Position the valve rocker arm shaft assembly on the cylinder head.

3. Install and tighten all valve rocker arm support bolts, two turns at a time in sequence, until the supports fully contact the cylinder head. Torque the bolts to specifications.

4. If any part which could affect the valve clearance has been changed, check the valve clearance following the procedure outlined under Valve Clearance—170 and 200 Six (Part 8-1, Section 2).

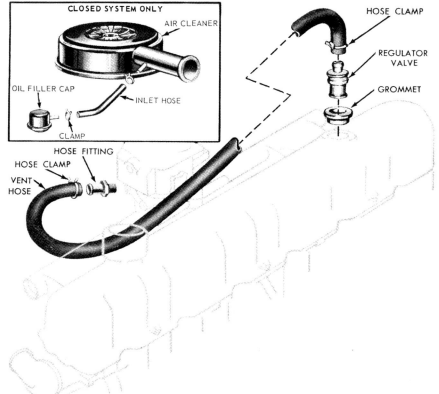

A2012-C

FIG. 15—Positive Crankcase Ventilation System Components

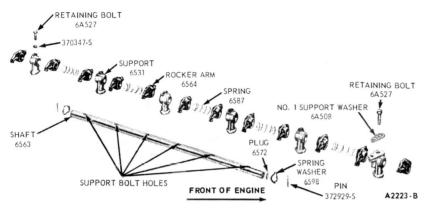

FIG. 17—Valve Rocker Arm Shaft Assembly

FIG. 18—Valve Push Rod Removal

push rods in sequence (Fig. 18).

11. Remove the remaining cylinder head bolts and remove the cylinder head. **Do not pry between the cylinder head and block as the gasket surfaces may become damaged.**

INSTALLATION

1. Clean the head and block gasket surfaces. If the cylinder head was removed for a gasket change, check the flatness of the cylinder head and block. Install guide studs at each end of the cylinder block (Fig. 19).

FIG. 19—Cylinder Head Guide Studs

2. On the 170 Six engine, apply cylinder head gasket sealer to both sides of a new gasket. Use the brush furnished to spread the sealer evenly over the entire gasket surface. **Do not apply sealer to a 200 Six engine head gasket.** Position the gasket over the guide studs on the cylinder block.

3. Install a new gasket on the flange of the muffler inlet pipe.

4. Lift the cylinder head over the guides and slide it down carefully, guiding the exhaust manifold studs into the muffler inlet pipe.

5. Coat the threads of the Nos. 1 and 6 bolts for the right side of the cylinder head with a small amount of water resistant sealer. Install, but do not tighten two bolts at opposite

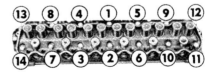

FIG. 20—Cylinder Head Bolt Torque Sequence

5. Clean the valve rocker arm cover and cylinder head gasket surfaces. Coat one side of a new gasket with an oil resistant sealer and lay the cemented side of the gasket in place on the cover. Install the cover, making sure the gasket seats evenly around the head. Tighten the cover retaining bolts in two steps. First, torque the bolts to specifications; then, retorque to the same specifications two minutes after initial tightening.

6. If equipped with a Thermactor exhaust emission control system, connect the air hoses.

7. Install the crankcase ventilation system and the air cleaner.

DISASSEMBLY

1. Remove the pin and spring washer from each end of the valve rocker arm shaft.

2. Slide the valve rocker arms, springs, and supports off the shaft. Be sure to identify the parts.

3. If it is necessary to remove the plugs from each end of the shaft, drill or pierce the plug on one end. Use a steel rod to knock out the plug on the opposite end. Working from the open end, knock out the remaining plug.

CLEANING AND INSPECTION

Refer to Part 8-1, Section 3 for the cleaning and inspection procedures.

REPAIRS

Refer to Part 8-1, Section 2 for the repair procedures.

ASSEMBLY

1. Lubricate all parts with engine oil. Apply Lubriplate to the valve and push rod ends of the rocker arm.

2. If the plugs were removed

from the ends of the shaft, use a blunt tool or large diameter pin punch and install a plug, cup side out, in each end of the shaft.

3. Install the spring washer and pin on one end of the shaft.

4. Install the valve rocker arms, supports, and springs in the order shown in Fig. 17. **Be sure the oil holes in the shaft are facing downward. Complete the assembly by installing the remaining spring washer and pin.**

CYLINDER HEAD
REMOVAL

1. Drain the cooling system. Remove the air cleaner.

2. Disconnect the muffler inlet pipe at the exhaust manifold. Pull the muffler inlet pipe down. Remove the gasket.

3. Disconnect the accelerator rod retracting spring. Disconnect the accelerator rod at the carburetor.

4. Disconnect the fuel inlet line at the fuel filter hose, and the distributor vacuum line at the carburetor.

5. Disconnect the coolant lines at the carburetor spacer. Remove the radiator upper hose at the coolant outlet housing.

6. Disconnect the distributor vacuum line at the distributor. Disconnect the carburetor fuel inlet line at the fuel pump. Remove the lines as an assembly.

7. Disconnect the spark plug wires at the spark plugs and the temperature sending unit wire at the sending unit.

8. Remove the crankcase ventilation system. Remove hoses from the Thermactor exhaust emission control system as necessary for accessibility.

9. Remove the valve rocker arm cover.

10. Remove the valve rocker arm shaft assembly. Remove the valve

ends of the head to hold the head and gasket in position. Remove the guides and install the remaining bolts.

6. The cylinder head bolts are tightened in three progressive steps. Torque all the bolts in sequence (Fig. 20) to 55 ft-lbs, then to 65 ft-lbs, and finally to specifications. **After the cylinder head bolts have been torqued to specifications, the bolts should not be disturbed.**

7. Apply Lubriplate to both ends of the push rods. Install the push rods in their original bores, positioning the lower end of the rods into the tappet sockets. Apply Lubriplate to the valve stem tips and to the rocker arm pads.

8. Install the valve rocker arm shaft assembly following steps 1 thru 7 under Valve Rocker Arm Shaft Installation.

Check the valve clearance, following the procedure outlined under Valve Clearance (Part 8-1, Section 2).

9. Install a new gasket on the muffler inlet pipe. Install the muffler inlet pipe lock washers and retaining nuts. Torque the nuts to specifications.

10. Connect the radiator upper hose at the coolant outlet housing. Connect the coolant hoses at the carburetor spacer.

11. Position the distributor vacuum line and the carburetor fuel inlet line on the engine. Connect the fuel line at the fuel filter using a new clamp; then connect the distributor vacuum line at the carburetor.

12. Connect the accelerator rod retracting spring. Connect the accelerator rod at the carburetor.

13. Connect the distributor vacuum line at the distributor. Connect the carburetor fuel inlet line at the fuel pump.

14. Connect the temperature sending unit wire at the sending unit. Connect the spark plug wires. **Be sure the wires are forced all the way down into their sockets.**

15. Fill and bleed the cooling system.

16. Install the crankcase ventilation system. Install the hoses on the Thermactor exhaust emission control system.

17. Start the engine and check for coolant and oil leaks.

DISASSEMBLY

1. Remove the Thermactor exhaust emission control system components. Remove deposits from the combustion chambers and valve heads with a scraper and a wire brush before removing the valves. **Be careful not to scratch the cylinder head gasket surfaces.**

Valve Spring Compressor

A1387-B

FIG. 21—Compressing Valve Spring—On Bench

2. Compress the valve springs (Fig. 21). Remove the valve retainer locks and release the spring. If the valve locks are stuck, place a piece of steel tubing (¾-inch OD, ½-inch ID and 3-inches long) over the end of the valve stem squarely against the sleeve surface. Tap the tube with a steel hammer to dislodge the locks.

3. Remove the sleeve, spring retainer, stem seal, and valve. Discard the valve stem seals. Identify all valve parts. If the cylinder head is to be replaced, remove the manifold assembly.

CLEANING AND INSPECTION

Refer to Part 8-1, Section 3 for the cleaning and inspection procedures.

REPAIRS

Refer to Part 8-1, Section 2 for repair procedures.

ASSEMBLY

1. If the cylinder head is being replaced, install the manifold assembly. Lubricate the valve guides and valve stems with engine oil. Apply Lubriplate to the tip of the valve stems.

2. Install each valve (Fig. 22) in the valve guide from which it was removed or to which it was fitted. Install a new stem seal on the valve.

3. Install the valve spring assembly over the valve. Install the spring retainer and sleeve.

4. Compress the spring and install the retainer locks (Fig. 21).

5. Measure the assembled height

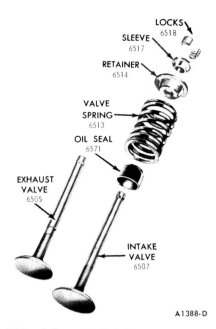

A1388-D

FIG. 22—Typical Valve Assembly

of the valve spring from the surface of the cylinder head spring pad to the underside of the spring retainer with dividers (Fig. 23).

6. Check the dividers against a scale. If the assembled height is greater than specifications, install the necessary 0.030-inch thick spacer(s) between the cylinder head spring pad and the valve spring to bring the assembled height to the recommended dimension. **Do not install spacers unless necessary. Use of spacers in excess of recommendations will result in overstressing the valve springs and overloading the camshaft lobes which would lead to spring breakage and worn camshaft lobes.**

Install the Thermactor exhaust emission control components.

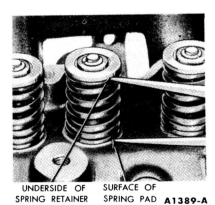

UNDERSIDE OF SPRING RETAINER   SURFACE OF SPRING PAD   A1389-A

FIG. 23—Valve Spring Assembled Height

VALVE SPRING, RETAINER AND STEM SEAL REPLACEMENT

Broken valve springs or defective valve stem seals and retainer may be replaced without removing the cylinder head, provided damage to the valve or valve seat has not occurred.

1. Remove the air cleaner. Remove the crankcase ventilation regulator valve from the valve rocker arm cover. If equipped with a Thermactor exhaust emission control system, disconnect the air hoses as necessary for accessibility. Remove the valve rocker arm cover. Remove the applicable spark plug.

2. Loosen the valve rocker arm shaft support bolts 2 turns at a time, in sequence, until the valve spring pressure is relieved. Remove both valve push rods of the cylinder to be serviced.

3. Install an air line with an adapter in the spark plug hole.

4. Tighten the retaining bolts just enough to seat the rocker arm shaft supports on the cylinder head. Push the rocker arm to one side and secure it in this position (Fig. 24). To move the rocker arm on either end of the shaft, it will be necessary to remove the retaining pin and spring washer and slide the rocker arm off the shaft.

FIG. 24—Compressing Valve Spring—In Chassis

5. Turn *on the air supply*. **Air pressure may turn the crankshaft until the piston reaches the bottom of its stroke.** Using the valve spring compression tool shown in Fig. 24, compress the valve and remove the valve spring retainer locks, the sleeve, spring retainer and the valve spring. **If air pressure fails to hold the valve in the closed position during this operation, it can be presumed that the valve is not seating or is damaged. If this condition occurs, remove the**

cylinder head for further inspection.

6. Remove the valve stem seal (Fig. 25). **If air pressure has forced the piston to the bottom of the cylinder, any removal of air pressure will allow the valve(s) to fall into the cylinder. A rubber band, tape or string wrapped around the end of the valve stem will prevent this condition and will still allow enough travel to check the valve for binds.**

FIG. 25—Valve Stem Seal Removal

7. Install a new valve stem seal. Position the spring over the valve. Install the spring retainer and sleeve. Compress the valve spring and install the valve spring retainer locks.

8. Apply Lubriplate to both ends of the push rod, the valve and push rod ends of the rocker arm, and the valve stem tip. Remove the rocker arm shaft and install the push rod(s), making sure the lower end of the rod is positioned in the valve lifter push rod cup.

9. Remove the wire securing the valve rocker arm and slide the rocker arm into position. If an end valve rocker arm was removed, slide it into position on the shaft and install the spring washer and retaining pin. Turn off the air and remove the air line and adapter. Install the spark plug and spark plug wire.

10. Install the rocker arm shaft by following the instructions under Rocker Arm Shaft Assembly Installation.

11. Install the valve rocker arm cover.

12. If equipped with a Thermactor exhaust emission control system, connect the air hoses.

13. Insert the crankcase ventilation regulator valve into the valve rocker arm cover mounting grommet. Install the air cleaner.

CYLINDER FRONT COVER AND TIMING CHAIN
REMOVAL

1. Drain the cooling system and the crankcase. Disconnect the radiator upper hose at the coolant outlet housing and the radiator lower hose at the water pump. On a car with automatic transmission, disconnect the transmission oil cooler lines from the radiator.

2. Remove the radiator. Remove the drive belt, fan and pulley. On a car with air conditioning remove the condenser retaining bolts and position the condenser forward. **Do not disconnect the refrigerant lines.** Remove the compressor drive belt. On a car equipped with Thermactor exhaust emission control system remove the air supply pump drive belt. If so equipped, remove the accessory drive pulley. Using tool T58P-6316-A, remove the crankshaft damper.

3. Remove the cylinder front cover and gasket. Remove the crankshaft front oil slinger.

4. Rotate the crankshaft in a clockwise direction (as viewed from the front) to take up the slack on the left side of the chain.

5. Establish a reference point on the block and measure from this point to the chain. Rotate the crankshaft in the opposite direction to take up the slack on the right side of the chain. Force the left side of the chain out with the fingers and measure the distance between the reference point and the chain. The deflection is the difference between the two measurements. If the deflection extends ½ inch, replace the timing chain and sprockets.

6. Crank the engine until the timing marks are aligned as shown in Fig. 26. Remove the camshaft sprocket retaining bolt and washer. Slide both sprockets and timing chain forward and remove them as an assembly (Fig. 27).

7. Remove the oil pan and related parts.

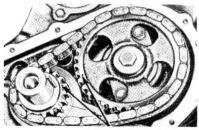

TIMING MARKS A1370-B

FIG. 26—Aligning Timing Marks

FIG. 27—Timing Chain and Sprockets Removal

FRONT OIL SEAL REPLACEMENT

It is good practice to replace the oil seal each time the cylinder front cover is removed.

1. Drive out the oil seal with a pin punch. Clean the recess in the cover.

2. Coat a new seal with grease and install the seal. Drive the seal in until it is fully seated in the recess. (Fig. 28). Check the seal after installation to be sure the spring is properly positioned in the seal.

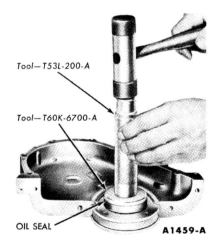

FIG. 28—Crankshaft Front Oil Seal Replacement

CLEANING AND INSPECTION

Refer to Part 8-1, Section 3 for the cleaning and inspection procedures. Clean the crankshaft damper following the referenced procedures.

INSTALLATION

1. Oil the timing chain. Position the sprockets and timing chain on the camshaft and crankshaft. Be sure the timing marks on the sprockets and chain are positioned as shown in Fig. 26. Install the camshaft sprocket retaining bolt and washer. Torque the bolt to specifications. Install the oil slinger so that the raised side of

the embossed pointer is facing outward.

2. Clean the cylinder front and the gasket surface of the cylinder block. Apply oil-resistant sealer to a new cylinder front cover gasket and position the gasket on the cylinder front cover. Install the cylinder front cover using the tool shown in Fig. 29. Torque the retaining bolts to specifications.

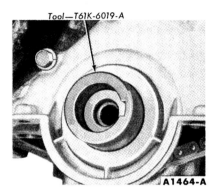

FIG. 29—Cylinder Front Cover

3. Lubricate the hub of the crankshaft damper with Lubriplate to prevent damage to the seal during installation or initial engine start. Using tool T52L-6306-AEE, install the crankshaft damper. Torque the retaining bolt to specifications.

4. Install the oil pan and related parts.

5. Install the fan, pulley and drive belt. Adjust the drive belt.

6. Install the radiator. Connect the radiator upper and lower hoses.

7. Fill and bleed the cooling system. Fill the crankcase with the proper quantity and grade of engine oil.

8. Start the engine and check the ignition timing. Operate the engine at fast idle and check all hose connections and gaskets for leaks.

CAMSHAFT

The camshaft and related parts are shown in Fig. 30.

REMOVAL

1. Drain the cooling system and the crankcase. Remove the air cleaner. If equipped with a Thermactor exhaust emission control system, disconnect the air hoses as necessary for accessibility, and position them out of the way.

2. Disconnect the radiator hoses from the coolant outlet housing and the water pump. Remove the radiator. Remove the grille. On a car with air conditioning, remove the condenser retaining bolts, and position the condenser to one side. **Do not** disconnect the condenser refrigerant lines.

3. On a Mustang, remove the grille center support bracket. Remove the bolts from the left side of the upper and lower stone shields. If necessary, loosen the bolts on the right side of the stone shields and raise the stone shields out of the way to remove the camshaft.

4. Disconnect the accelerator rod retracting spring. Disconnect the accelerator rod from the carburetor.

5. Disconnect the fuel inlet line at the fuel filter, and the distributor vacuum line from the carburetor.

6. Disconnect the coolant hoses from the carburetor spacer.

7. Disconnect the muffler inlet pipe from the exhaust manifold. Pull the muffler inlet pipe down. Remove the gasket.

8. Disconnect the distributor vacuum line from the distributor. Disconnect the carburetor fuel inlet line from the fuel pump. Remove the lines as an assembly.

9. Disconnect the spark plug wires from the spark plugs and the coil high tension lead at the coil. Remove the distributor cap and spark plug wires as an assembly. Disconnect the primary wire from the coil and remove it from the retaining clip on the cylinder head.

10. Disconnect the engine temperature sending unit wire from the sending unit. Disconnect the flexible fuel line from the fuel tank line and

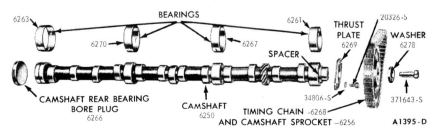

FIG. 30—Camshaft and Related Parts

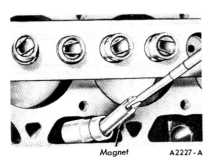

FIG. 31—Valve Lifter Removal

plug the line. Remove the distributor, the fuel pump, and the oil filter.

11. Remove the crankcase vent hose, regulator valve, valve rocker arm cover and cylinder head by following steps 8 thru 11 under Cylinder Head Removal.

12. Using a magnet, remove the valve lifters and keep them in order so that they can be installed in their original location (Fig. 31).

13. Loosen and remove the drive belt, fan and pulley. Remove the crankshaft damper using tool T58P-6316-A.

14. Remove the oil level dipstick. Remove the oil pan. Remove the oil pump and inlet tube assembly.

15. Remove the cylinder front cover and gasket. Remove the crankshaft front oil slinger.

16. Push the camshaft toward the rear of the engine. Install a dial indicator so that the indicator point is on the camshaft sprocket cap screw (Fig. 32). Zero the dial indicator. Position a large screw driver between the camshaft sprocket and the block. Pull the camshaft forward and release it. Compare the dial indicator reading with specifications. If the end play is excessive, replace the thrust plate.

17. Remove the dial indicator. Remove the timing chain and

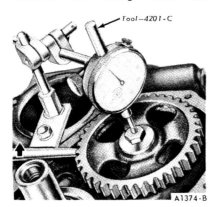

FIG. 32—Camshaft End Play

sprockets following steps 4 and 5 under "Cylinder Front Cover and Timing Chain Removal."

18. Remove the camshaft thrust plate. Carefully remove the camshaft by pulling it toward the front of the engine. **Use caution to avoid damaging the journals and lobes.**

INSTALLATION

1. Clean the oil passage that feeds the rocker arm shaft by blowing compressed air into the opening in the block. Oil the camshaft journals and apply Lubriplate to all the camshaft lobes. Carefully slide the camshaft through the bearings.

2. Install the thrust plate with the oil groove toward the rear of the engine and torque the retaining bolts to specifications. Replace the crankshaft front oil seal.

3. Follow steps 1, 2 and 3 under Cylinder Front Cover and Timing Chain Installation and install the sprockets and timing chain, oil slinger, cylinder front cover and crankshaft damper.

4. Clean the oil pump inlet tube screen, and oil the pan and block gasket surfaces. Prime the oil pump and install the oil pump inlet tube and oil pump and the oil pan and related parts. Install the oil level dipstick.

5. Install the fan and fan pulley and drive belt. Adjust the belt tension. Install the radiator and the grille.

On a Mustang, install the bolts in the upper and lower stone shields, and install the grille, grille center support bracket and bumper.

6. Dip the valve lifter foot in Lubriplate. Coat the remainder of each valve lifter with engine oil. Install the valve lifters in their original bores.

7. Install the cylinder head, push rods and the valve rocker arm shaft assembly by following steps 1 thru 9 under Cylinder Head Installation.

8. Using a new gasket, install the fuel pump and connect the flexible fuel line. Install the oil filter.

9. Position the No. 1 piston at TDC after the compression stroke. Position the distributor in the block with the rotor at the No. 1 firing position and the breaker points open. Install the distributor hold down clamp.

10. Connect the engine temperature sending unit wire. Connect the coil primary wire. Install the distributor cap. Connect the spark plug

wires and the coil high tension lead.

11. Install the carburetor fuel inlet line, using a new clamp on the filter tubing. Connect the distributor vacuum line to the carburetor.

12. On a car with air conditioning, position the condenser and install the retaining bolts. Install the radiator and connect the radiator upper and lower hoses. Connect the coolant hoses to the carburetor spacer.

13. Connect the accelerator rod retracting spring. Connect the accelerator rod at the carburetor. If equipped with a Thermactor exhaust emission control system, connect the air hoses.

14. Fill and bleed the cooling system. Fill the crankcase.

15. Start the engine and check and adjust the ignition timing. Connect the distributor vacuum line to the distributor. Check for coolant and oil leaks. Adjust the engine idle speed and the idle fuel mixture.

CAMSHAFT REAR BEARING BORE PLUG REPLACEMENT

1. On a car with a manual-shift transmission, slide the transmission to the rear and remove the clutch pressure plate and disc following the procedure in Group 5.

On a car with automatic transmission, remove the transmission and converter housing following the procedure in Group 7.

2. Remove the flywheel retaining bolts and remove the flywheel and engine rear cover plate.

3. Drill a ½-inch hole in the camshaft rear bearing bore plug and use tool T58L-101-A to remove the plug (Fig. 33).

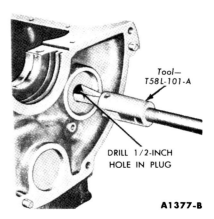

FIG. 33—Camshaft Rear Bearing Bore Plug Removal

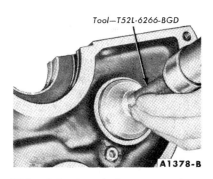

Tool—T52L-6266-BGD

A1378-B

FIG. 34—Camshaft Rear Bearing Bore Plug Installation

4. Clean out the plug bore recess thoroughly.

5. Coat the flange of a new plug with oil resistant sealer and install it with the flange facing out and slightly below the chamfer in the bore (Fig. 34).

6. Install the engine rear cover plate, apply oil-resistant sealer to the flywheel bolts and install the flywheel.

On a car with a manual-shift transmission, install the clutch pressure plate, disc, and transmission following the procedure in Group 5.

On a car with automatic transmission install the transmission and converter housing following the procedure in Group 7.

HYDRAULIC VALVE LIFTER REPLACEMENT

1. Remove the cylinder head and related parts following the procedure under Cylinder Head Removal.

2. Using a magnet, remove the valve lifters (Fig. 31). Place the lifters in a rack so they can be installed in their original positions.

If the lifters are stuck in their bores by excessive varnish or gum, it may be necessary to use a plier-type tool to remove the lifters. Rotate the lifter back and forth to loosen the gum and varnish which may have formed on the lifter.

The internal parts of each hydraulic valve lifter assembly are matched sets. Do not intermix the parts. Keep the assemblies intact until they are to be cleaned.

3. Install new (or cleaned) hydraulic valve lifters through the push rod openings with a magnet (Fig. 31).

4. Install the cylinder head and related parts.

DISASSEMBLY

Each valve lifter is a matched as-sembly; therefore, the parts are not interchangeable. Disassemble and assemble each lifter carefully, keeping the assemblies in proper sequence so they will be installed in their original bores.

1. Grasp the lock ring with needle nose pliers to release it from the groove. It may be necessary to depress the plunger to fully release the lock ring.

2. Remove the push rod cup, plunger and spring.

3. Invert the plunger assembly and remove the check valve retainer by carefully prying up on it with a screwdriver. Remove the check valve and spring.

CLEANING AND INSPECTION

Refer to Part 8-1, Section 3 for the cleaning and inspection procedures.

ASSEMBLY

A typical hydraulic valve lifter assembly is shown in Fig. 35.

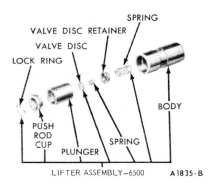

SPRING
VALVE DISC RETAINER
VALVE DISC
LOCK RING
BODY
PUSH ROD CUP
SPRING
PLUNGER
LIFTER ASSEMBLY—6500   A1835-B

FIG. 35—Typical Valve Lifter Assembly

1. Place the plunger upside down on a clean work bench.

2. Place the check valve in position over the oil hole on the bottom of the plunger. Set the check valve spring on top of the check valve.

3. Position the check valve retainer over the check valve and spring and push the retainer down into place on the plunger.

4. Place the plunger spring and then the plunger (open end up) into the tappet body.

5. Place the push rod seat in the plunger.

6. Depress the plunger and position the closed end of the lock ring in the lifter body groove. Release the plunger; then depress it again to fully seat the lock ring.

CLEANING AND INSPECTION

Refer to Part 8-1, Section 3 for the cleaning and inspection procedures.

MAIN AND CONNECTING ROD BEARING REPLACEMENT

The main bearing inserts are selective fit. **Do not file or lap bearing caps or use bearing shims to obtain the proper bearing clearance.**

Selective fit main bearings are available for service in standard sizes and 0.002 inch undersize. Standard bearings are divided into two sizes and are identified by a daub of red or blue paint. Refer to the Parts Catalog for the available sizes. **Red marked bearings increase the clearance; blue marked bearings decrease the clearance.** Undersize bearings, which are not selective fit, are available for use on journals that have been refinished.

MAIN BEARING

1. Drain the crankcase. Remove the oil level dipstick. Remove the oil pan and related parts.

2. Remove the oil pump inlet tube assembly and the oil pump.

3. **Replace one bearing at a time, leaving the other bearings securely fastened.** Remove the main bearing cap to which new bearings are to be installed.

4. Insert the upper bearing removal tool (tool 6331) in the oil hole in the crankshaft.

5. Rotate the crankshaft in the direction of engine rotation to force the bearing out of the block.

6. Clean the crankshaft journal. **When replacing standard bearings with new bearings, it is good practice to first try to obtain the proper clearance with two blue bearing halves.**

7. To install the upper main bearing, place the plain end of the bearing over the shaft on the locking tang side of the block and partially install the bearing so that tool 6331 can be inserted in the oil hole in the crankshaft. With tool 6331 positioned in the oil hole in the crankshaft, rotate the crankshaft in the opposite direction of engine rotation until the bearing seats itself. Remove the tool.

8. Install the cap bearing.

9. Support the crankshaft so that its weight will not compress the Plastigage used in Step 10 and provide an erroneous reading. Position

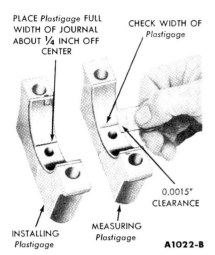

PLACE *Plastigage* FULL WIDTH OF JOURNAL ABOUT ¼ INCH OFF CENTER

CHECK WIDTH OF *Plastigage*

0.0015" CLEARANCE

INSTALLING *Plastigage*

MEASURING *Plastigage*

A1022-B

FIG. 36—Installing and Measuring Plastigage—Engine Installed

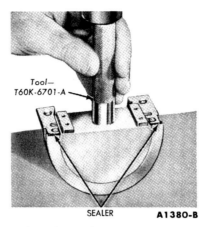

Tool— T60K-6701-A

SEALER   A1380-B

FIG. 37—Seal to Rear Bearing Cap Installation

a jack so that it will bear against the counterweight adjoining the bearing which is being checked.

10. Place a piece of Plastigage on the bearing surface the full width of the bearing cap and about ¼ inch off center (Fig. 36).

11. Install the cap and torque the bolts to specifications. **Do not turn the crankshaft while the Plastigage is in place.**

12. Remove the cap. Using the Plastigage scale, check the width of the Plastigage. **When checking the width of the Plastigage, check at the widest point in order to get the minimum clearance. Check at the narrowest point in order to get the maximum clearance. The difference between the two readings is the taper.**

13. If the clearance is less than the specified limits, try two red bearing halves or a combination of red and blue, depending upon the condition.

If the clearance exceeds specified limits, try 0.002 inch undersize bearings in combination with blue or red bearings. **The bearing clearance must be within specified limits. If 0.002 inch undersize main bearings are used on more than one journal, be sure they are all installed on the same side (cap or cylinder block) of the crankshaft.**

If the standard and 0.002 inch undersize bearings do not bring the clearance within the desired limits, refinish the crankshaft journal; then install undersize bearings.

14. If the rear main bearing is replaced, replace the lower oil seal in the rear main bearing cap as follows:

Remove and discard the rear seal. If there is evidence of oil seal leakage, the upper half of the oil seal must also be replaced to assure satisfactory sealing.

Clean the mating surfaces of the block and rear main bearing cap, and the rear journal oil seal groove. Preform the new seal by hand to the approximate radius of the cap.

Insert the seal in the oil seal groove, seating the center of the seal first with the seal extending equally on both ends. Press the seal down firmly with the thumb at the center of the seal, then press both ends of the seal into the groove working from the ends to the center.

Position the seal forming tool as shown in Fig. 37 and complete the seal installation. After installation, cut the ends of the seal flush.

Apply a thin coating of oil resistant sealer to the rear main bearing cap at the rear of the top mating surface (Fig. 37). **Do not apply sealer to the area forward of the oil slinger groove.**

The upper oil seal in the block cannot be replaced with the crankshaft installed.

15. After the bearing has been fitted, apply a light coat of engine oil to the journal and bearings, then install the bearing cap. Torque the cap bolts to specifications.

16. Repeat the procedure for the remaining bearings that require replacement.

17. If the thrust bearing cap (No. 3 main bearing) has been removed, install it as follows:

Install the thrust bearing cap with the bolts finger-tight. Pry the crankshaft forward against the thrust surface of the upper half of the bearing

(Fig. 57). Hold the crankshaft forward and pry the thrust bearing cap to the rear (Fig. 57). This will align the thrust surfaces of both halves of the bearing. Retain the forward pressure on the crankshaft. Torque the cap bolts to specification (Fig. 57).

18. Clean the oil pump inlet tube screen. Prime the oil pump; then install the oil pump and the inlet tube assembly.

19. Position the oil pan gaskets on the oil pan. Position the oil pan front seal on the cylinder front cover. Position the oil pan rear seal on the rear main bearing cap. Install the oil pan and related parts. Install the oil level dipstick.

20. Fill the crankcase. Start the engine and check for oil pressure. Operate the engine at fast idle and check for oil leaks.

CONNECTING ROD BEARING

1. Follow steps 1 and 2 under Main Bearing Replacement.

2. Turn the crankshaft until the connecting rod to which new bearings are to be fitted is down. Remove the connecting rod cap. Remove the bearing inserts from the rod and cap.

3. Be sure the bearing inserts and the bearing bore in the connecting rod and cap are clean. Foreign material under the inserts will distort the bearing and cause a failure.

4. Clean the crankshaft journal.

5. Install the bearing inserts in the connecting rod and cap with the tangs fitting in the slot provided.

6. Pull the connecting rod assembly down firmly on the crankshaft journal.

7. Place a piece of Plastigage on the lower bearing surface, the full width of the cap and about ¼ inch off center.

8. Install the cap and torque the connecting rod nuts to specification. **Do not turn the crankshaft while the Plastigage is in place.**

9. Remove the cap; then, using the Plastigage scale, check the width of the Plastigage. **When checking the width of the Plastigage, check at the widest point in order to get the minimum clearance. Check at the narrowest point in order to get the maximum clearance. The difference between the two readings is the taper.**

10. If the clearance is less than the specified limits, try two red bearing halves or a combination of red and blue depending upon the condition.

If the clearance exceeds the specified limits, try 0.002 inch undersize bearings in combination with blue or red bearings. **The bearing clearance must be within specified limits.**

If proper clearance cannot be achieved with standard or 0.002 undersize bearings, the crankshaft will have to be ground undersize and fitted with undersize bearings.

After the bearing has been fitted, clean and apply a light coat of engine oil to the journal and bearings. Install the connecting rod cap. Torque the nuts to specifications.

11. Repeat the procedure for the remaining connecting rods that require new bearings.

12. Follow steps 18 thru 20 under Main Bearing Replacement.

CLEANING AND INSPECTION

Refer to Part 8-1, Section 3 for the cleaning and inspection procedures.

PISTONS AND CONNECTING RODS

REMOVAL

1. Drain the cooling system and the crankcase.

2. Refer to Cylinder Head Removal and remove the cylinder head and related parts.

3. Remove the oil pan and related parts. Remove the oil pump inlet tube and the oil pump.

4. Turn the crankshaft until the piston to be removed is at the bottom of its travel and place a cloth on the piston head to collect the cuttings. Remove any ridge and/or deposits from the upper end of the cylinder bores. Remove the cylinder ridge with a ridge cutter. Follow the instructions furnished by the tool manufacturer. **Never cut into the ring travel area in excess of 1/32 inch when removing ridges.**

5. Make sure all the connecting rod caps are marked so that they can be installed in their original positions. Remove the connecting rod cap.

6. Push the connecting rod and piston assembly out the top of the cylinder with the handle end of a hammer. Avoid damage to the crankpin or the cylinder wall when removing the piston and rod.

INSTALLATION

1. Clean the oil pump inlet tube screen, and the oil pan and block gasket surfaces.

2. Oil the piston rings, pistons and

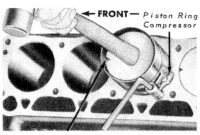

FIG. 38—Piston Installation

cylinder walls with light engine oil.

3. **Be sure to install the pistons in the same cylinders from which they were removed, or to which they were fitted. The connecting rod and bearing caps are numbered from 1 to 6 beginning at the front of the engine. The numbers on the connecting rod and bearing cap must be on the same side when installed in the cylinder bore. If a connecting rod is ever transposed from one block or cylinder to another, new bearings should be fitted and the connecting rod should be numbered to correspond with the new cylinder.**

4. Make sure the ring gaps are properly spaced around the circumference of the piston. Install a piston ring compressor on the piston and push the piston in with a hammer handle until it is slightly below the top of the cylinder (Fig. 38). Be sure to guide the connecting rods to avoid damaging the crankshaft journals. **Install the piston with the notch in the piston head toward the front of the engine.**

5. Check the clearance of each bearing following the procedure under "Connecting Rod Bearing Replacement."

6. After the bearings have been fitted, apply a light coat of engine oil to the journals and bearings.

7. Turn the crankshaft throw to the bottom of its stroke, then push the piston all the way down until the connecting rod bearing seats on the crankshaft journal. Install the connecting rod cap. Torque the nuts to specifications.

8. After the piston and connecting rod assemblies have been installed, check the connecting rod side clearance on each crankshaft journal (Fig. 39).

9. Prime the oil pump. Install the oil pump and the oil pump inlet tube. Install the oil pan and related parts.

10. Install the cylinder head by following steps 1 through 17 under

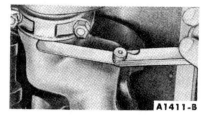

FIG. 39—Typical Connecting Rod Side Clearance

Cylinder Head Installation.

11. Fill the crankcase.

12. Start the engine and check for oil pressure. Operate the engine at fast idle and check for oil and coolant leaks.

13. Check and adjust the ignition timing, engine idle speed and the fuel mixture.

14. Install the air cleaner.

DISASSEMBLY

1. Remove the bearing inserts from the connecting rod and cap.

2. Mark the pistons and pins to assure assembly with the same rod and installation in the same cylinders from which they were removed.

3. Remove the piston pin from the piston and connecting rod using the tool shown in Fig. 40. Remove the piston rings.

CLEANING AND INSPECTION

Refer to Part 8-1, Section 3 for the cleaning and inspection procedures.

REPAIRS

To fit new pistons, pins or rings, refer to Part 8-1, Section 2.

ASSEMBLY

The piston, connecting rod and related parts are shown in Fig. 41. **Check the fit of a new piston in the cylinder bore before assembling the piston and piston pin to the connecting rod.**

The piston pin bore of a connecting rod and the diameter of the piston pin must be within specifications. Refer to Part 8-4.

1. Apply a light coat of engine oil to all parts. **Assemble the piston to the connecting rod with the oil squirt hole in the connecting rod and the indentation in the piston positioned as shown in Fig. 42.**

2. Start the piston pin in the piston and connecting rod. Draw the piston pin through the piston and connecting rod until the end of the pin seats in Detail 2 (Fig. 43).

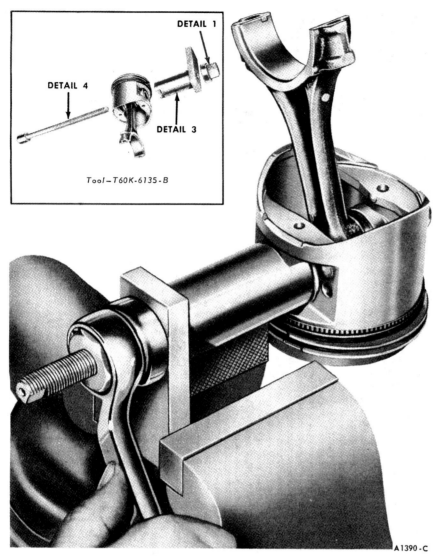

FIG. 40—Piston Pin Removal

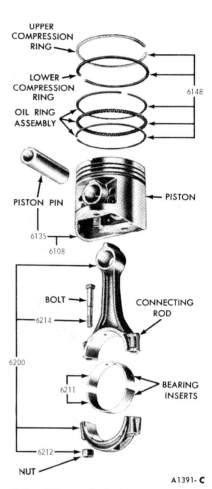

FIG. 41—Typical Piston, Connecting Rod and Related Parts

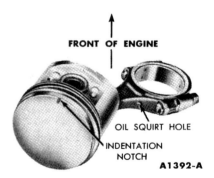

FIG. 42—Typical Piston and Connecting Rod Assembly

3. Check the end gap of all piston rings (Part 8-1). It must be within specifications (Part 8-4). Follow the instructions contained on the piston ring package and install the piston rings.

4. Check the ring side clearance of the compression rings with a feeler gauge. Refer to Fitting Piston Rings in Part 8-1, Section 2.

5. Be sure the bearing inserts and the bearing bore in the connecting rod and cap are clean. Foreign material under the inserts will distort the bearing and cause a failure. Install the bearing inserts in the connecting rod and cap with the tangs fitting in the slots provided.

FLYWHEEL

REMOVAL

1. On a manual-shift transmis-

sion, remove the transmission, clutch pressure plate and disc, following the procedures in Group 5. Do not drain the transmission.

On a car with automatic transmission, remove the transmission and converter housing following the procedure in Group 7. Do not drain the transmission.

2. Remove the flywheel retaining bolts and remove the flywheel.

CLEANING AND INSPECTION

Refer to Part 8-1, Section 3 for the cleaning and inspection procedures.

REPAIRS

To check flywheel face runout, refer to Part 8-1, Section 1.

INSTALLATION

1. Position the flywheel on the

crankshaft flange. Apply oil-resistant sealer to the retaining bolts. Install and torque the bolts in sequence across from each other to specifications.

2. On a manual-shift transmission, *install the clutch pressure plate, disc,* and the transmission following the procedures in Group 5.

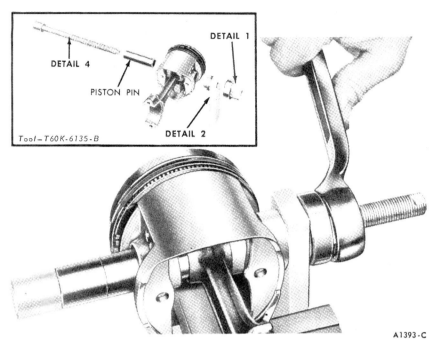

FIG. 43—Piston Pin Installation

On a car with automatic transmission, install the converter housing and transmission following the procedure in Group 7. It is not necessary to adjust the transmission, when it has been removed only for flywheel removal.

CLUTCH PILOT BUSHING REPLACEMENT

Inspection procedures are outlined under Flywheel Cleaning and Inspection in Part 8-1, Section 3.

1. Remove the transmission, clutch pressure plate, and disc following the procedures in Group 5.

2. Using tools T59L-100-B and T58L-101-A, remove the pilot bushing (Fig. 44).

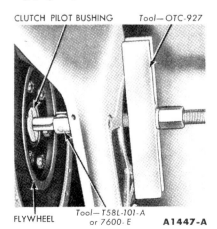

FIG. 44—Typical Clutch Pilot Bushing Removal

3. Coat the pilot bushing bore in the crankshaft with a small quantity of wheel bearing lubricant. **Avoid using too much lubricant as it may be thrown onto the clutch disc when the clutch revolves.**

4. Using tool T52T-12175-AJD, install the pilot service bearing (Fig. 45).

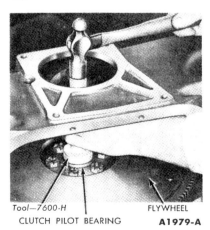

FIG. 45—Typical Clutch Pilot Service Bearing Installation

5. Install the clutch pressure plate, disc, and the transmission following the procedures in Group 5.

OIL FILTER REPLACEMENT

1. Place a drip pan under the filter. Unscrew the filter from the adapter fitting. Clean the adapter filter recess.

2. Coat the gasket on the replacement filter with oil. Position the filter on the adapter fitting. Hand tighten the filter until the gasket contacts the adapter face, then advance it ½ turn.

3. Operate the engine at fast idle, and check for oil leaks. If oil leaks are evident, perform the necessary repairs to correct the leakage. Check the oil level and fill the crankcase if necessary.

OIL PAN

REMOVAL

1. Drain the crankcase.

2. Remove the oil level dipstick and the flywheel housing inspection cover.

3. On a Mustang, remove the stabilizer bar.

4. Remove the oil pan and gasket.

5. Remove the oil pump inlet tube and screen assembly.

CLEANING AND INSPECTION

Refer to Part 8-1, Section 3 for the cleaning and inspection procedures.

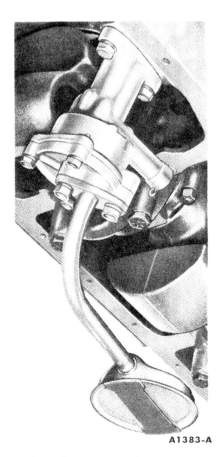

FIG. 46—170 Six Oil Pump Inlet Tube Installed

INSTALLATION

1. Clean and install the oil pump inlet tube and screen assembly (Fig. 46 or 47).

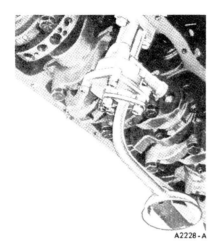

FIG. 47—200 Six Oil Pump Inlet Tube Installed

2. Clean the gasket surfaces of the block and oil pan. The oil pan has a two-piece gasket. Coat the block surface and the oil pan gasket surface with oil-resistant sealer. Position the oil pan gaskets on the cylinder block (Fig. 48 or 49).

3. Position the oil pan front seal on the cylinder front cover (Fig. 48 or 49). **Be sure the tabs on the seal are over the oil pan gasket.**

4. Position the oil pan rear seal on the rear main bearing cap (Fig. 48 or 49). **Be sure the tabs on the seal are over the oil pan gasket.**

5. Hold the oil pan in place against the block and install a bolt, finger-tight, on each side of the oil pan. Install the remaining bolts. Torque the bolts from the center outward in each direction to specifications.

6. On a Mustang, install the stabilizer bar.

7. Install the oil level dipstick. Fill the crankcase with the proper grade and quantity of engine oil. Operate the engine and check for oil leaks.

OIL PUMP

REMOVAL

1. Remove the oil pan and related parts as outlined under Oil Pan Removal.

2. Remove the oil pump retaining bolts and remove the oil pump, gasket, and intermediate drive shaft.

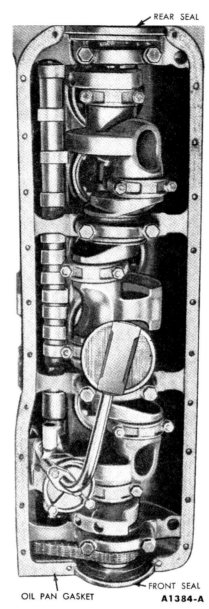

FIG. 48—170 Six Oil Pan Gaskets and Seals Installed

INSTALLATION

1. Prime the oil pump by filling either the inlet or outlet port with engine oil. Rotate the pump shaft to distribute the oil within the pump body.

2. Position the intermediate drive shaft into the distributor socket.

3. Position a new gasket on the pump housing. Insert the intermediate drive shaft into the oil pump. Install the pump and shaft as an assembly. **Do not attempt to force the pump into position if it will not seat readily. The drive shaft hex may be misaligned with the distributor shaft. To align, rotate the intermediate**

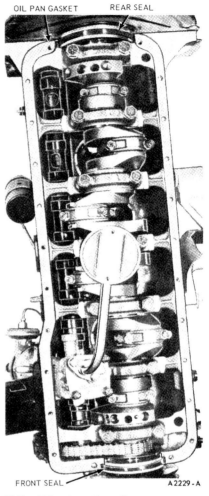

FIG. 49—200 Six Oil Pan Gaskets and Seals Installed

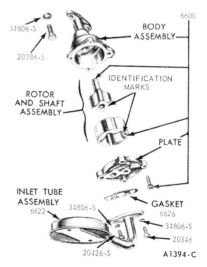

FIG. 50—Typical Oil Pump Assembly

drive shaft into a new position. Torque the oil pump retaining screws to specifications.

4. Install the oil pan and related parts as outlined under Oil Pan Installation.

DISASSEMBLY

1. Remove the oil inlet tube from the oil pump and remove the gasket.

2. Remove the cover retaining screws, and remove the cover. Remove the inner rotor and shaft assembly, and remove the outer race.

3. Insert a self-threading sheet metal screw of the proper diameter into the oil pressure relief valve chamber cap and pull the cap out of

the chamber. Remove the spring and plunger.

CLEANING AND INSPECTION

Refer to Part 8-1, Section 3 for the cleaning and inspection procedures.

ASSEMBLY

The oil pump assembly is shown in Fig. 50.

1. Oil all parts thoroughly.

2. Install the oil pressure relief valve plunger, spring, and a new cap.

3. Install the outer race, and the inner rotor and shaft assembly. **Be sure the identification mark on the rotor and on the outer race both face to the bottom of the pump. The inner rotor and shaft, and the outer race are serviced as an assembly. One part should not be replaced without replacing the other.** Install the cover and torque the cover retaining screws to specifications.

4. Position a new gasket and the oil inlet tube on the oil pump and install the retaining bolts.

---

3 ENGINE REMOVAL AND INSTALLATION

REMOVAL

1. Remove the hood.

2. Drain the cooling system and the crankcase.

3. Remove the air cleaner. Disconnect the battery ground cable at the cylinder head, and at the battery. Disconnect the radiator upper hose at the water outlet housing and the radiator lower hose at the water pump. On a car with automatic transmission disconnect the transmission oil cooler lines from the radiator.

4. Remove the radiator. Remove the drive belt, fan, and pulley.

5. Disconnect the heater hoses from the water pump and the carburetor spacer. Disconnect the alternator wires from the alternator, the starter cable from the starter, the accelerator rod and the choke control cable from the carburetor. On a car with air conditioning, remove the compressor from the mounting bracket, and position it out of the way, **leaving the refrigerant lines attached.**

6. Disconnect the flexible fuel line at the fuel tank line and plug the fuel tank line.

7. Disconnect the coil primary wire at the coil. Disconnect the oil pressure and the water temperature sending unit wires at the sending units. On a car with intermittent windshield wipers, disconnect the vacuum hose from the engine fitting.

8. Remove the starter and dust seal.
On a car with a manual-shift transmission, disconnect the clutch retracting spring. Disconnect the clutch equalizer shaft and arm bracket at the underbody rail and remove the arm bracket and equalizer shaft.

9. Raise the car. Remove the flywheel or converter housing upper retaining bolts through the access holes in the underbody.

10. Disconnect the muffler inlet pipe at the exhaust manifold. Loosen the inlet pipe clamp and slide it off the support bracket on the engine. Disconnect the engine right and left mount at the underbody bracket. Remove the flywheel or converter housing cover.
On a car with a manual-shift transmission, remove the flywheel housing lower retaining bolts.
On a car with automatic transmission, disconnect the converter from the flywheel. Remove the converter housing lower retaining bolts.

11. Lower the car. Support the transmission and flywheel or converter housing with a jack.

12. Attach the engine lifting hook (Fig. 51). Carefully lift the engine out of the engine compartment. In-

Tool—T60K-6000-A

A2017-A

FIG. 51—Engine Lifting Hook

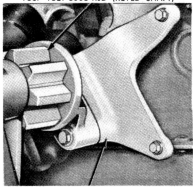

Tool—T52T-6005-CJD (SPLINED SHAFT)
Tool—T52T-6005-KJD (KEYED SHAFT)

Tool—6001-FBA   A1364-B

FIG. 52—Engine Work Stand

stall the engine on a work stand (Fig. 52).

INSTALLATION

1. Install guide pins in the flywheel or converter housing bolt holes in the rear of the engine. Place a new gasket over the studs of the exhaust manifold.

2. Carefully lower the engine into the engine compartment.

3. Make sure the studs on the exhaust manifold are aligned with the holes in the muffler inlet pipe and the guide pins in the block engage the holes in the flywheel housing.
On a car with automatic transmission, start the converter pilot into the crankshaft.
On a car with a manual-shift transmission, start the transmission main drive gear into the clutch disc. It may be necessary to adjust the position of the transmission in relation to the engine if the input shaft will not enter the clutch disc. If the

engine hangs up after the shaft enters, turn the crankshaft slowly (transmission in gear) until the shaft splines mesh with the clutch disc splines.

4. Remove the engine lifting hooks. Install the flywheel or converter housing upper retaining bolts.

5. Remove the jack from the transmission. Raise the car.

6. Remove the guide pin and install the flywheel or converter housing lower retaining bolts.

On a car with automatic transmission, attach the converter to the flywheel and torque the retaining nuts to specifications.

7. Install the flywheel or converter housing dust cover.

On a car with a manual-shift transmission, install the clutch equalizer shaft and arm bracket. Connect the clutch retracting spring.

8. Install the engine left and right mount to the underbody bracket. Install the sediment bowl on the fuel pump.

9. Remove the plug from the fuel tank line and connect the flexible fuel line to the fuel tank line. Install the exhaust manifold to muffler inlet pipe retaining lock washers and nuts. Torque the nuts to specifications. Position the inlet pipe clamp on the support bracket on the engine and tighten the clamp.

10. Lower the car. Connect the oil pressure and the engine temperature sending unit wires. Connect the coil primary wire. Connect the windshield wiper vacuum hose to the engine fitting. Connect the accelerator rod. Connect and adjust the choke control cable.

11. Install the starter motor and dust seal. Connect the starter cable.

Connect the alternator wires. Connect the heater hose at the water pump and carburetor spacer. Connect the battery ground cable.

12. Install the pulley, fan, and drive belt. Adjust the drive belt tension. On a car with air conditioning, install the compressor on the mounting bracket, and adjust the belt tension to specifications. Install the radiator. Connect the radiator upper and lower hoses. Fill and bleed the cooling system. Fill the crankcase with the proper grade and quantity of engine oil.

13. Install and adjust the hood.

14. Operate the engine at fast idle and check all gaskets and hose connections for leaks.

On a car with automatic transmission, adjust the transmission control linkage (Group 7).

15. Install the air cleaner.

4 MAJOR REPAIR OPERATIONS

To perform the operations in this section, it will be necessary to remove the engine from the car and install it on a work stand.

When installing nuts or bolts that must be torqued (refer to Part 8-5 for torque specifications), oil the threads with light weight engine oil. **Do not oil threads that require oil-resistant or water-resistant sealer.**

CRANKSHAFT
REMOVAL

The crankshaft and related parts are shown in Fig. 53 or 54.

1. Loosen the alternator adjusting bolts and remove the fan belt. Remove the oil level dipstick.

2. Remove the accessory drive

pulley (if so equipped). Remove the crankshaft damper retaining bolt and washer. Remove the crankshaft vibration damper using tool T58P-6316-A.

3. Remove the cylinder front cover and air conditioning idler pulley assembly (if so equipped). Remove the cover gasket.

4. Remove the oil slinger. Check the timing chain deflection, then remove the timing chain and sprockets by following steps 4 and 5 under Cylinder Front Cover and Timing Chain Removal.

5. Invert the engine on the work stand. Remove the flywheel. Remove the oil pan and gasket. Remove the oil pump.

6. Make sure all bearing caps (main and connecting rod) are marked so that they can be installed in their original locations. Turn the crankshaft until the connecting rod from which the cap is being removed is down. Remove the connecting rod cap. Push the connecting rod and piston assembly up in the cylinder. Repeat for the remaining caps.

7. Remove the main bearing caps.

8. Carefully lift the crankshaft out of the block so that the thrust bearing surfaces are not damaged. **Handle the crankshaft with care to avoid possible fracture or damage to the finished surfaces.**

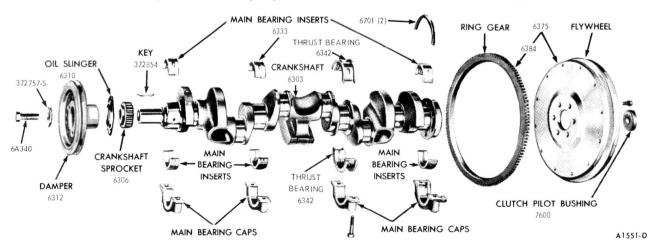

FIG. 53—Typical 170 Six Crankshaft and Related Parts

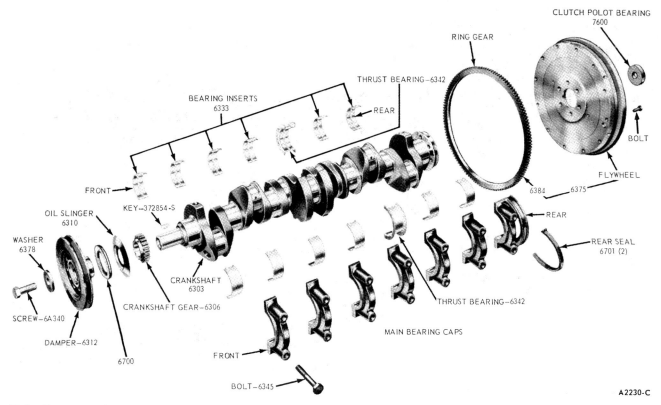

FIG. 54—Typical 200 Six Crankshaft and Related Parts

CLEANING AND INSPECTION

Refer to Part 8-1, Section 3, for the cleaning and inspection procedures. **Be sure the oil seal surfaces on the crankshaft and crankshaft damper are properly cleaned.**

REPAIRS

To refinish journals, dress minor imperfections, etc., refer to Part 8-1, Section 2.

INSTALLATION

1. Remove the rear journal oil seal from the block and rear main bearing cap.
2. Remove the main bearing inserts from the block and bearing caps.
3. Remove the connecting rod bearing inserts from the connecting rods and caps.
4. Clean the rear journal oil seal grooves. Install a new rear journal oil seal in the block (Fig. 55) and rear main bearing cap (Fig. 37). After installation, cut the ends of the seals flush.
5. Apply a thin coating of oil resistant sealer to the rear main bearing cap at the rear of the top mating surface (Fig. 37). **Do not apply sealer to the area forward of the oil slinger groove.**

6. If the crankshaft main bearing journals have been refinished to a definite undersize, install the correct undersize bearings. Be sure the bearing inserts and bearing bores are clean. Foreign material under the inserts will distort the bearing and cause a failure.

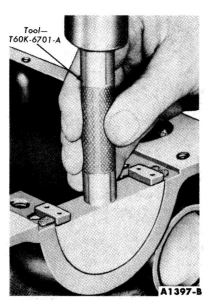

FIG. 55—Rear Oil Seal to Block Installation

7. Place the upper main bearing inserts in position in the bores with the tang fitting in the slot provided.
8. Install the lower main bearing inserts in the bearing caps.
9. Carefully lower the crankshaft into place. **Be careful not to damage the bearing surfaces.**
10. Check the clearance of each main bearing. Place a piece of Plastigage on the crankshaft journal the full width of the journal and about ¼ inch off center (Fig. 56). Follow steps 11 thru 13 under Main Bearing Replacement.
11. After the bearings have been fitted, apply a light coat of engine oil to the journals and bearings. Install all the bearing caps, except the

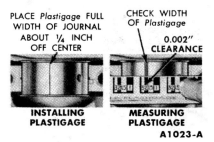

FIG. 56—Installing and Measuring Plastigage—Engine on Work Stand

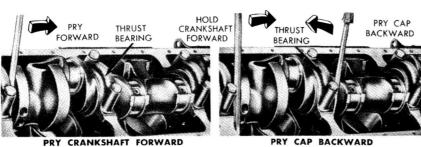

PRY CRANKSHAFT FORWARD   PRY CAP BACKWARD   TIGHTEN CAP   A1381-A

FIG. 57—Typical Thrust Bearing Alignment

thrust bearing cap (No. 3 bearing on a 170 Six engine or No. 5 bearing on a 200 Six engine). **Be sure that the main bearing caps are installed in their original locations.** Torque the bearing cap bolts to specifications.

12. Install the thrust bearing cap with the bolts finger-tight.

13. Pry the crankshaft forward against the thrust surface of the upper half of the bearing (Fig. 57).

14. Hold the crankshaft forward and pry the thrust bearing cap to the rear (Fig. 57). This will align the thrust surfaces of both halves of the bearing.

15. Retain the forward pressure on the crankshaft. Torque the cap bolts to specifications (Fig. 57).

16. Force the crankshaft toward the rear of the engine.

17. Install a dial indicator so that the contact point rests against the crankshaft flange and the indicator axis is parallel to the crankshaft axis (Fig. 58).

18. Zero the dial indicator. Push the crankshaft forward and note the reading on the dial.

19. If the end play exceeds speci-

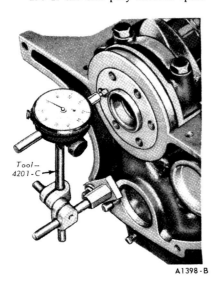

Tool—
4201-C →

A1398-B

FIG. 58—Crankshaft End Play

fications, replace the thrust bearing. If the end play is less than the minimum limit, inspect the thrust bearing faces for scratches, burrs, nicks, or dirt. If the thrust faces are not defective or dirty, they probably were not aligned properly. Install the thrust bearing and align the faces following the recommended procedure (steps 12, 13, 14, and 15). Check the end play which should be within specifications.

20. Install new bearing inserts in the connecting rods and caps. Check the clearance of each bearing following the procedure under Connecting Rod Bearing Replacement.

21. If the bearing clearances are to specifications, apply a light coat of engine oil to the journals and bearings.

22. Turn the crankshaft throw to the bottom of its stroke. Push the piston all the way down until the rod bearing seats on the crankshaft journal.

23. Install the connecting rod cap. Torque the nuts to specifications.

24. After the piston and connecting rod assemblies have been installed, check the connecting rod side clearance on each connecting rod crankshaft journal (Fig. 39).

25. Turn the engine on the work stand so that the front end is up. Install the timing chain and sprockets, cylinder front cover and crankshaft pulley or damper, following steps 1 thru 3 under Cylinder Front Cover and Timing Chain Installation.

26. Clean the oil pan, oil pump, and oil pump screen.

27. Prime and install the oil pump following steps 1, 2, and 3 under Oil Pump Installation. Install the oil pan following steps 2 thru 5 under Oil Pan Installation.

28. Position the flywheel on the crankshaft. Apply oil-resistant sealer to the flywheel retaining bolts. Install and torque the retaining bolts to specifications.

On a flywheel for a manual-shift

transmission, use tool 7563 to locate the clutch disc. Install the pressure plate.

29. Turn the engine on the work stand so that the engine is in the normal position. Install the oil level dipstick. Install and adjust the drive belt.

30. Remove the engine from the work stand and install it in the car.

CAMSHAFT BEARING REPLACEMENT

The camshaft bearings are available pre-finished to size and require no reaming for standard and 0.015-inch undersize journal diameters.

1. Remove the flywheel and the camshaft. Remove the rear bearing bore plug (Fig. 33).

2. Remove the camshaft bearings with the tool shown in Fig. 59.

3. Select the proper size expanding collet and back-up nut and assemble on the expanding mandrel. With the expanding collet collapsed, install the collet assembly in the camshaft bearing, and tighten the back-up nut on the expanding mandrel until the collet fits the camshaft bearing.

4. Assemble the puller screw and extension (if necessary) as shown and install on the expanding mandrel. Wrap a cloth around the threads of the puller screw to protect the front bearing or journal. Tighten the pulling nut against the thrust bearing and pulling plate to remove the camshaft bearing. Be sure to hold a wrench on the end of the puller screw to prevent it from turning.

5. Repeat the procedure for each bearing. To remove the front bearing, install the puller screw from the rear of the cylinder block.

6. Position the new bearings at the bearing bores, and press them in place with the tool shown in Fig. 59. Be sure to center the pulling plate and puller screw to avoid damage to the bearing. **Failure to use the**

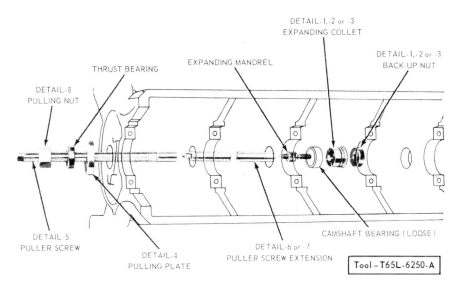

FIG. 59—Typical Camshaft Bearing Replacement

correct expanding collet can cause severe bearing damage. Align the oil holes in the bearings with the oil holes in the cylinder block when the bearings are installed. **Be sure the front bearing is installed 0.020-0.035 inch below the front face of the cylinder block.**

7. Clean out the camshaft rear bearing bore plug recess thoroughly. Coat the flange of a new plug with oil-resistant sealer and install the plug (Fig. 34) with the flange edge of the plug facing outward.

8. Install the camshaft, crankshaft, flywheel and related parts, following the appropriate procedures in Part 8-2, Section 2 or Section 4, except do not check connecting rod and main bearing clearances as a part of Camshaft Bearing Replacement. Install the engine in the car.

CYLINDER ASSEMBLY REPLACEMENT

DISASSEMBLY

Follow steps 1 thru 3, 5 thru 13, and 24 under Engine Disassembly. Remove the cylinder assembly from the work stand.

CLEANING

Clean the gasket and seal surfaces of all parts and assemblies (refer to Part 8-1, Section 3).

ASSEMBLY

Install the replacement cylinder block assembly on a work stand. Transfer all parts removed from the

old cylinder assembly to the new cylinder assembly, following the procedures in steps 28 thru 44, 47 thru 50, 53 and 56 thru 58 under Engine Assembly. Check all assembly clearances.

CYLINDER BLOCK REPLACEMENT

DISASSEMBLY

Follow steps 1 thru 3, 5 thru 19, 21 and 24 under Engine Disassembly. Remove the cylinder assembly from the work stand.

CLEANING

Clean the gasket and seal surfaces of all parts and assemblies (refer to Part 8-1, Section 3).

ASSEMBLY

Install the replacement cylinder block assembly on a work stand. Transfer all parts removed from the old cylinder assembly to the new cylinder assembly, following the procedures in steps 1 thru 4, 6 thru 9, 11 thru 21, 28 thru 50, 53 and 56 thru 58 under Engine Assembly. Check all assembly clearances.

ENGINE DISASSEMBLY

1. Disconnect the distributor vacuum line at the carburetor.

2. Disconnect the carburetor fuel inlet line at the fuel filter, and at the fuel pump. Disconnect the distributor vacuum line at the distributor. Remove the fuel inlet line and distributor vacuum line as an assembly.

3. Remove the crankcase ventilation system by following the pro-

cedures under Crankcase Ventilation System Removal in Section 2 of this part of the manual.

On a car with Thermactor exhaust emission control system (Group 12), disconnect the air and vacuum lines. Remove the air supply pump, air manifold assembly, air pump, air cleaner assembly, anti-backfire valve, and air and vacuum lines and brackets.

4. Remove the automatic choke heat tube; then remove the carburetor and gasket. Remove the exhaust manifold.

5. Remove the coil. Remove the distributor cap and spark plug wires as an assembly. Remove the distributor, fuel pump, oil pressure sending unit, oil filter and oil filter mounting insert. Remove the spark plugs.

6. Remove the valve rocker arm cover. Remove the valve rocker arm shaft assembly (Fig. 17) by removing the support bolts evenly and equally 2 turns at a time.

7. Remove the valve push rods in sequence and identify them so that they can be installed in their original positions (Fig. 18).

8. Remove all cylinder head bolts. Lift the cylinder head assembly off the engine. **Do not pry between the head and block as the gasket surfaces may become damaged.** Using a magnet, remove the valve lifters and keep them in order so they can be installed in their original location (Fig. 30).

On a flywheel for a manual-shift transmission, mark the pressure plate cover so that it can be replaced in the same position. Remove the clutch pressure plate and cover assembly.

Remove the flywheel. Remove the clutch pilot bushing (Fig. 44) and engine rear cover plate.

9. Remove the dipstick and the oil pan. Discard the gasket and seals.

10. Remove the oil pump and inlet tube assembly. Discard the oil pump gasket.

11. Loosen the alternator mounting bolts and disconnect the alternator adjusting arm at the water pump. Remove the drive belt.

12. Remove the alternator, the water pump and the accessory drive pulley (if so equipped). Remove the crankshaft damper. Remove the damper by using tool T58P-6316-A.

13. Remove the cylinder front cover. Discard the gasket. Remove the crankshaft front oil slinger.

Check the camshaft end play by following step 15 under Camshaft Removal. Check timing chain deflection by following step 4 under Cylinder Front Cover Removal.

14. Remove the camshaft sprocket retaining bolt and washer. Slide both sprockets and the timing chain forward and remove them as an assembly (Fig. 27).

15. Remove any ridges and/or deposits from the upper end of the cylinder bores. Remove the cylinder ridges with a ridge cutter. Follow the instructions furnished by the tool manufacturer. **Never cut into the ring travel area in excess of $\frac{1}{32}$ inch when removing ridges.**

16. **Make sure all bearing caps (main and connecting rod) are marked so they can be installed in their original locations.** Turn the crankshaft until the connecting rod being removed is down. Remove the connecting rod cap.

17. Push the connecting rod and piston assembly out the top of the cylinder with the handle end of a hammer. **Avoid damage to the crankpin or the cylinder wall when removing the piston and rod.**

18. Remove the bearing inserts from the connecting rods and caps. Remove the main bearing caps.

19. Carefully lift the crankshaft out of the cylinder block so that the thrust bearing surfaces are not damaged. **Handle the crankshaft with care to avoid possible fracture or damage to the finished surfaces.**

20. Remove the rear journal oil seal from the block and rear main bearing cap. Remove the main bearing inserts from the block and bearing caps.

21. Remove the camshaft thrust plate. Carefully remove the camshaft by pulling it toward the front of the engine. **Use caution to avoid damaging the journals and lobes.**

22. Remove the camshaft rear bearing bore plug (Fig. 33).

23. Remove the camshaft bearings (Fig. 59).

24. Remove the dipstick tube and the plug or drain.

ENGINE ASSEMBLY

1. Install the camshaft bearings and rear bore plug by following steps 3 and 4 under Camshaft Bearing Replacement.

2. The camshaft and related parts are shown in Fig. 30. Oil the camshaft journals and apply Lubriplate to all camshaft lobes. Carefully slide the camshaft through the bearings.

3. Install the thrust plate. Torque the retaining screws to specifications.

4. The crankshaft and related parts are shown in Fig. 53 or 54. Be sure that the rear journal oil seal grooves are clean. Install a new rear journal oil seal in the block (Fig. 55) and rear main bearing cap (Fig. 37). After installation, cut the ends of the seals flush.

5. If the crankshaft main bearing journals have been refinished to a definite undersize, install the correct undersize bearings. Be sure the bearing bores are clean. Place the upper main bearing inserts in position in the bore with the tang fitting in the slot provided.

6. Install the lower main bearing inserts in the bearing caps.

7. Carefully lower the crankshaft into place. **Be careful not to damage the bearing surfaces.**

8. Check the clearance of each main bearing following steps 10 thru 13 under Main Bearing Replacement. In step 10, place the Plastigage on the crankshaft journal instead of in the bearing cap (Fig. 56).

9. After the bearings have been fitted, apply a light coat of engine oil to the journals and bearings. Install all the bearing caps, except the thrust bearing cap (No. 3 bearing on 170 six engine or No. 5 bearing on 200 six engine). **Be sure that the main bearing caps are installed in their original locations.** Torque the bearing cap bolts to specifications.

10. Install the thrust bearing cap by following steps 12 thru 15 under Crankshaft Installation.

11. Check the crankshaft end play by following steps 17 thru 19 under "Crankshaft Installation."

12. Turn the engine on the work stand so that the front end is up.

13. Oil the piston rings, pistons, and cylinder walls with light engine oil.

14. **Be sure to install the pistons in the same cylinders from which they were removed, or to which they were fitted. The connecting rod and bearing cap are numbered from 1 to 6 beginning at the front of the engine. The numbers on the connecting rod and bearing cap must be on the same side when installed in the cylinder bore. If a connecting rod is ever transposed from one block or cylinder to another, new bearings should be fitted and the connecting rod should be numbered to correspond with the new cylinder number.**

15. Make sure the ring gaps are properly spaced around the circumference of the piston.

16. Install a piston ring compressor on the piston and push the piston in with a hammer handle until it is slightly below the top of the cylinder (Fig. 38). Be sure to guide the connecting rods to avoid damaging the crankshaft journals. **Install the piston with the notch in the piston head toward the front of the engine.**

17. Check the clearance of each bearing following the procedure under Connecting Rod Bearing Replacement.

18. After the bearings have been fitted, apply a light coat of engine oil to the journals and bearings.

19. Turn the crankshaft throw to the bottom of its stroke. Push the piston all the way down until the connecting rod bearing seats on the crankshaft journal.

20. Install the connecting rod cap. Torque the nuts to specifications.

21. After the piston and connecting rod assemblies have been installed, check the connecting rod side clearance on each crankshaft journal (Fig. 39).

22. Lubricate the timing chain and sprockets with engine oil. Place the keys in position in the slots on the crankshaft and camshaft.

23. Oil the timing chain. Position the sprockets and timing chain on the camshaft and crankshaft. Be sure the timing marks on the sprockets and chain are positioned as shown in Fig. 26.

24. Install the camshaft sprocket retaining bolt and washer. Torque the bolt to specifications. Install the oil slinger.

25. Clean the cylinder front cover and the gasket surface of the cylinder block.

26. Install a new crankshaft front oil seal.

27. Coat the gasket surface of the block and the cover with oil-resistant sealer. Position a new gasket on the block.

28. Using tool T61K-6019-A, install the cylinder front cover on the block. Torque the screws to specifications. Apply Lubriplate to the seal surface, and to the seal running surface of the damper.

29. Line up the crankshaft damper keyway with the key on the crankshaft.

30. Install the crankshaft damper using tool T52L-6306-AEE. Torque the retaining bolt to specifications. Install the accessory drive pulley

if so equipped.

31. Install the water pump, alternator, fan pulley, and fan. Install and adjust the drive belt.

32. Prime the oil pump by filling either the inlet or outlet port with engine oil. Rotate the pump shaft to distribute the oil within the pump body.

33. Using a new gasket, install the oil pump. Clean and install the oil inlet tube assembly.

34. Make sure the gasket surfaces of the block and oil pan are clean.

35. Coat the block surface and oil pan gasket surface with oil-resistant sealer and position the gasket on the block (Fig. 48 or 49).

36. Install the oil pan front seal on the cylinder front cover and the oil pan rear seal on the rear main bearing cap (Fig. 48 or 49). **Be sure the tabs on the seals are over the oil pan gasket.**

37. Position the oil pan on the block. Install the retaining screws. Torque the screws from the center outward in each direction to specifications.

38. Install the clutch pilot bushing (Fig. 45). Install the engine rear cover plate, position the flywheel on the crankshaft and install the retaining bolts. Torque the bolts to specifications.

On a flywheel for a manual-shift transmission, use tool 7563 to locate the clutch disc. Install the pressure plate. Torque the retaining bolts to specifications.

39. Using a new gasket, install the fuel pump.

40. Turn the crankshaft until No. 1 cylinder is at TDC after the compression stroke. Position the distributor and intermediate drive shaft into the block with the rotor at the No. 1 firing position and the breaker points open. Install the hold down clamp. **Make sure the oil pump intermediate drive shaft is properly seated in the oil pump. It may be necessary to reposition the inter-mediate shaft in order to engage it in the oil pump.**

41. Install the oil filter insert and oil filter assembly.

42. Dip the valve lifter foot in Lubriplate. Coat the remainder of each valve lifter with engine oil. Install the lifters in their original bores.

43. Clean the head and block gasket surfaces.

44. Inspect the head for any damage and repair as necessary.

45. On a 170 six engine, apply cylinder head gasket sealer to both sides of a new gasket. **Do not apply sealer to the gasket on a 200 six engine.** Install the cylinder head guide studs (Fig. 19). Position the gasket over the guide studs on the cylinder block.

46. Lift the cylinder head over the guides and slide it down carefully. Before installing the cylinder head bolts, coat the threads of the end bolts for the right side of the cylinder head with a small amount of water resistant sealer. Install, but do not tighten, two bolts at opposite ends of the head to hold the head and gasket in position. Remove the guides, then install the remaining bolts.

47. The cylinder head bolts are torqued in three progressive steps. Follow the sequence shown in Fig. 20. Torque the bolts to 55 ft-lbs; then torque them to 65 ft-lbs. Finally, torque the bolts to specifications. **After the cylinder head bolts have been torqued to specifications, the bolts should not be disturbed.**

48. Apply Lubriplate to both ends of the push rods. Install the push rods in their proper sequence, positioning the lower end of the rods in the lifter sockets.

49. Apply Lubriplate to the valve tips and the rocker arm pads. Position the valve rocker arm shaft assembly on the head. **Be sure the oil holes in the shaft are facing downward.**

50. Install the valve rocker arm shaft bolts. Tighten them evenly and equally 2 turns at a time until the specified torque is obtained.

51. Refer to Part 8-1, Section 2 and check the valve clearance.

52. Clean the gasket surfaces on the valve rocker arm cover and cylinder head. Coat one side of a new gasket with an oil-resistant sealer and lay the cemented side of the gasket on the cover. Install the cover making sure the gasket seats evenly around the head. Torque the cover bolts to specifications. Torque the cover bolts to specifications again two minutes later.

53. Install the spark plugs. Install the distributor cap and spark plug wire assembly. Connect the spark plug wires. Install the coil on the block and connect the coil high tension lead.

54. Position the exhaust manifold on the cylinder head. Install the tab washers and bolts. Torque the bolts to specifications. Lock the bolts by bending one tab of the washer over a flat on the bolt.

55. Position the carburetor gasket on the spacer. Install the carburetor.

56. Install the carburetor fuel inlet line, the manifold vacuum line and the distributor vacuum line, and the choke heat tube.

57. Install the crankcase ventilation system by following the procedure under Crankcase Ventilation System Installation in Section 2 of this part of the manual. On a car with Thermactor exhaust emission control system, install the anti-back-fire valve, air pump, air cleaner assembly, air manifold assembly and air supply pump. Install the air and vacuum lines and brackets.

58. Install the oil pressure sending unit, dipstick tube and dipstick.

59. Install the engine in the car.

60. Check the ignition timing and adjust if necessary. Adjust the engine idle fuel mixture and idle speed.

PART 8-3   289 V-8

Section	Page
1 Description and Operation	8-50
Thermactor Exhaust Emission Control System	8-50
Manifolds	8-50
Cylinder Heads	8-51
Cylinder Block	8-51
Valve Train	8-51
Lubrication System	8-53
Air Intake System	8-54
Crankcase Ventilation	8-54
Cooling System	8-55
2 In-Car Adjustments and Repairs	8-56
Engine Supports	8-56
Valve Rocker Arm Assembly	8-58
Intake Manifold	8-58
Exhaust Manifolds	8-60
Positive Crankcase Ventilation System	8-60
Cylinder Heads	8-61
Valve Spring, Retainer and Stem Seal Replacement	8-62
Cylinder Front Cover and Timing Chain	8-63

Section	Page
Camshaft	8-65
Camshaft Rear Bearing Bore Plug Replacement	8-66
Valve Lifter	8-66
Crankshaft Rear Oil Seal Replacement	8-67
Main and Connecting Rod Bearing Replacement	8-67
Pistons and Connecting Rods	8-68
Flywheel	8-69
Clutch Pilot Bushing Replacement	8-70
Oil Filter Replacement	8-70
Oil Pan	8-71
Oil Pump	8-72
3 Engine Removal and Installation	8-72
4 Major Repair Operations	8-74
Crankshaft	8-74
Camshaft Bearing Replacement	8-76
Cylinder Assembly Replacement	8-77
Cylinder Block Replacement	8-77
Engine Disassembly	8-77
Engine Assembly	8-78

1 DESCRIPTION AND OPERATION

The 289 V-8 engines are shown in Figs. 1, 2, 3 and 4. Differences in the engine are called out when they exist. Refer to Table 1 for the engine identification and application.

An engine identification tag is attached to the ignition coil bracket; refer to Part 8-1, Section 1.

THERMACTOR EXHAUST EMISSION CONTROL SYSTEM

For engines equipped with Thermactor exhaust emission control system, refer to Group 12 for description and adjustment and repair procedures.

MANIFOLDS

Coolant flows from the front of the engine through the intake manifold into the heater inlet hose and circulates through the heater. On cars that do not have a heater, the coolant is returned to the water pump through a by-pass hose.

Exhaust gases flowing through the crossover passage (Fig. 5) provide the initial heat necessary to assist in vaporizing the incoming fuel mixture.

A1718-D

FIG. 1—Typical 289 V-8

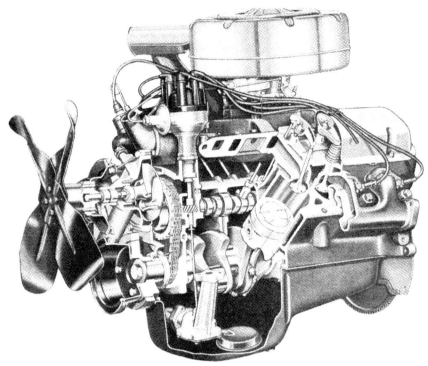

A1717-D

FIG. 2—Typical 289 V-8 Engine Sectional

The intake manifold has two sets of fuel passages, each with its own separate inlet connection to the carburetor (Fig. 6). The right barrel(s) of the carburetor feeds Nos. 1, 4, 6 and 7 cylinders and the left barrel(s) feeds Nos. 2, 3, 5 and 8 cylinders.

Filtered air is drawn from the air cleaner, through an air inlet tube, into the heat chamber in the right exhaust manifold. Here the air is heated and then directed to the automatic choke through the air outlet choke tube (Fig. 7).

CYLINDER HEADS

The cylinder head assemblies contain the valves and the valve rocker arm assemblies. The valve guides and push rod guides are machined in the head with a cast combustion chamber. The valve arrangement from front to rear on the left bank is E-I-E-I-E-I-E-I and on the right bank I-E-I-E-I-E-I-E (Fig. 8).

CYLINDER BLOCK

The cylinders are numbered from front to rear, on the right bank 1, 2, 3 and 4 and on the left bank 5, 6, 7 and 8. The firing order is 1-5-4-2-6-3-7-8.

The oil pump, mounted inside the oil pan at the left front, is driven by

the distributor through an intermediate drive shaft.

The oil filter is mounted on the left lower front of the block.

The crankshaft is supported by five main bearings. Crankshaft end thrust is controlled by the flanges of the No. 3 main bearing.

The pistons have two compression rings and one oil control ring. The top compression ring is chrome-plated and the lower compression ring is phosphate-coated. The oil control ring assembly consists of a serrated spring and two chrome-plated steel rails.

VALVE TRAIN

The push rods are tubular steel with ball ends. The push rods supply oil from a metering valve (disc) in the valve lifters through drilled holes in the ball ends for independent lubrication of each rocker arm.

The rocker arms have a drilled hole in the push rod end for lubrication. They are individually mounted on a stud that is either pressed into the cylinder head on regular performance engines or threaded into the cylinder head on high performance engines. A fulcrum seat permits the rocker motion and a nut secures the rocker arm on the stud.

The camshaft is supported by five stepped diameter bearings pressed

A2055-C

FIG. 3—Typical 289 High Performance V-8

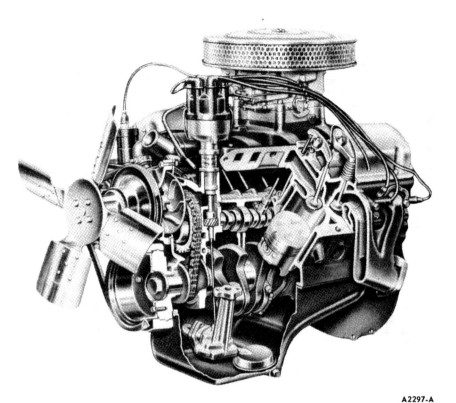

A2297-A

FIG. 4—Typical 289 High Performance V-8 Engine Sectional

A1578-B

FIG. 5—Intake Manifold Exhaust Gas Crossover Passage

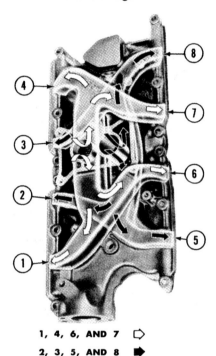

1, 4, 6, AND 7 ▷

2, 3, 5, AND 8 ➡

A1579-C

FIG. 6—Typical Intake Manifold Fuel Passages

into the block. A dowel is used for positioning the camshaft sprocket. The camshaft is driven by a sprocket and timing chain in mesh with a sprocket on the crankshaft. Camshaft end play is controlled by a thrust plate attached to the cylinder block. An eccentric, bolted to the front end of the camshaft, operates the fuel pump.

On the 289 high performance V-8 engine, mechanical valve lifters are used. Valve lash is maintained by self-locking adjusting screws.

On all other engines, hydraulic valve lifters are used. These lifters provide zero valve lash. The operation and parts identification of the

hydraulic valve lifters are shown in Fig. 9.

When the valve is closed, the lifter assembly is on the base circle of the camshaft lobe and the valve push rod is in its lowest position. With the lifter assembly in this position, the plunger spring expands, forcing the plunger upward. This action is transmitted to the valve rocker arm via the valve push rod until there is solid contact between the valve and the valve end of the valve rocker arm (zero valve lash).

As the lifter plunger moves upward, the volume of the compression chamber is increased, resulting in reduced oil pressure in the compression

chamber. Therefore, to equalize the resulting pressure differential between the supply chamber and the

TABLE 1—Engine Identification and Application

Engine	Patent Plate Code	Engine Prefix	Piston Displacement	Bore and Stroke	Compression Ratio	Valve Lifters	Carburetor	Distributor	Fuel Required	Model Application
289	C	EGA	289	4.00 x 2.87	9.0:1	Hydraulic	2-V Ford	Dual Advance	Regular	All
289	A	EGA	289	4.00 x 2.87	9.0:1	Hydraulic	4-V Ford	Dual Advance	Premium	Mustang and Ranchero
289 High Performance	K	EGA	289	4.00 x 2.87	10.5:1	Mechanical	4-V Ford	Centrifugal Advance	Premium	Mustang

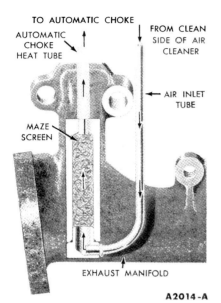

TO AUTOMATIC CHOKE

AUTOMATIC CHOKE HEAT TUBE

FROM CLEAN SIDE OF AIR CLEANER

AIR INLET TUBE

MAZE SCREEN

EXHAUST MANIFOLD

A2014-A

FIG. 7—Automatic Choke Heat Chamber

compression chamber, the disc valve moves off its seat and permits oil to flow from the supply chamber to the compression chamber. When the compression chamber becomes filled with oil, the pressures in the two chambers are equalized. The oil flow ceases and the disc valve spring seats the disc valve and closes the disc valve port.

As the camshaft rotates, the lifter assembly is raised by the camshaft lobe. This increases the push rod force against the lifter plunger and hydraulic pressure immediately builds up in the compression chamber until it acts as a solid member of the valve operating mechanism. The lifter then becomes a hydraulic ram which forces the valve in the cylinder head to open. During this period, a slight leakage of oil past the plunger occurs (calibrated leak down rate).

As the high point of the camshaft

lobe rotates and passes by the foot of the valve lifter, the valve in the cylinder head seats and the valve lifter assembly is forced downward. Reduced force on the lifter plunger at this time relieves the pressure on the lifter plunger and it is free to be moved upward by the plunger spring. This action allows oil to flow once again through the oil holes in the lifter body and plunger.

The operating cycle is completed for each revolution of the camshaft. Zero clearance (lash) in the valve train mechanism is maintained at all times by the hydraulic force and expansion of the plunger spring between the lifter body and plunger.

LUBRICATION SYSTEM

Oil from the oil pan sump, located in the front of the oil pan, is forced through the pressure-type lubrication system (Fig. 10) by a rotor oil pump. A spring-loaded relief valve in the pump limits the maximum pressure of the system. Oil relieved by the valve is directed back to the intake side of the pump.

All the oil discharged by the pump passes through an exclusive design full flow-type Rotunda filter before it enters the engine. The filter is mounted at the lower left front of the engine.

On a cartridge-type oil filter, a relief valve in the filter permits oil to bypass the filter if the element becomes clogged.

On an element-type oil filter, a by-

pass in the center bolt provides oil to the engine in case the filter element becomes clogged. The bypass is located in the hollow center bolt of the filter and consists of a spring-loaded valve. When the element is clean and oil will flow through it, the pressure difference between the inner and outer faces of the valve is not great enough to overcome the spring pressure behind the valve. Therefore, no oil flows through the bypass. When the element is dirty and will not permit a sufficient flow of oil, the pressure acting on the inner face of the valve drops. If the pressure difference between the valve faces is great enough to overcome spring pressure, the valve will open. Oil then bypasses the element, maintaining an emergency supply of oil to the engine.

From the filter, the oil flows into the main oil gallery which is located to the right side of the camshaft. The oil gallery supplies oil to each individual main bearing, through drilled passages in the block. Passages are drilled from each main bearing to each camshaft bearing. Number 1 main bearing feeds No. 1 camshaft bearing, and No. 2 main bearing feeds No. 2 camshaft bearing, etc. The oil then flows through notches or grooves in the main bearings to lubricate the crankshaft journals. The timing chain and sprockets are lubricated by oil deflected from the front camshaft bearing by an oil drip trough on the cylinder front cover.

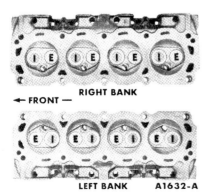

RIGHT BANK

← FRONT —

LEFT BANK   A1632-A

FIG. 8—Valve Port Arrangement

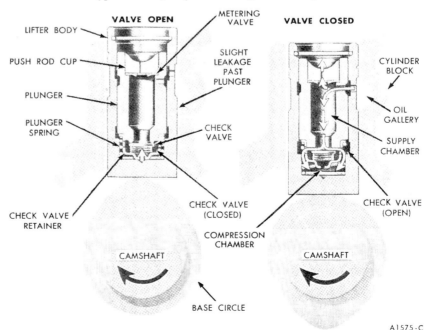

VALVE OPEN

LIFTER BODY

PUSH ROD CUP

PLUNGER

PLUNGER SPRING

CHECK VALVE RETAINER

METERING VALVE

SLIGHT LEAKAGE PAST PLUNGER

CHECK VALVE

CHECK VALVE (CLOSED)

COMPRESSION CHAMBER

CAMSHAFT

BASE CIRCLE

VALVE CLOSED

CYLINDER BLOCK

OIL GALLERY

SUPPLY CHAMBER

CHECK VALVE (OPEN)

CAMSHAFT

A1575-C

FIG. 9—Typical Hydraulic Valve Lifter Operation

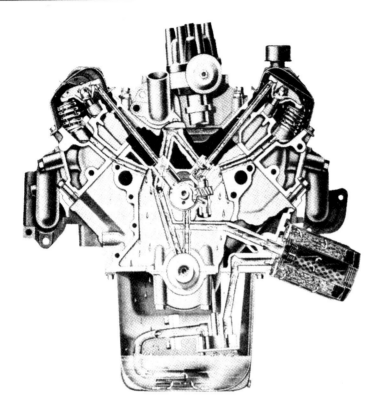

A1581-E

FIG. 10—Lubrication System

The crankshaft is drilled from the main bearings to the connecting rod bearings.

A small groove is located in the connecting rod at the mating face where the cap contacts the connecting rod. This groove is used as an oil squirt hole for cylinder wall lubrication. Oil from the connecting rod squirt hole lubricates the opposite cylinder wall. For example, the No. 1 connecting rod oils No. 5 cylinder, etc. As the crankshaft turns, the hole in the connecting rod bearing aligns with the hole in the journal causing a direct squirt of oil onto the cylinder wall (Fig. 10).

Oil passages are drilled from the main oil gallery to each valve lifter oil gallery. Oil from here feeds the valve lifter assemblies. A reservoir at each valve lifter bore boss traps oil so that oil is available for valve lifter lubrication as soon as the engine starts.

The oil hole in the hydraulic lifter is indexed with the lifter oil gallery and oil flows into the lifter. Oil in the lifter is then metered through the metering valve (disc), through the oil passages in the push rod cup and then flows up the hollow push rod. In this position, the drilled hole in the ball end of the push rod is indexed with a drilled hole in the rocker arm and the oil lubricates the upper valve train bearing areas (Fig. 10). Excess oil is returned to the oil pan through drain back holes located at each end of the cylinder heads and block (Fig. 10).

AIR INTAKE SYSTEM

The temperature of the air entering the air cleaner is thermostatically controlled by an air intake duct and thermostat assembly (Fig. 2). This system supplies warm air to the engine during the warm-up period, resulting in better fuel vaporization and reducing the possibility of carburetor icing. The air duct shroud and tube assembly together with the air duct and thermostat assembly direct warm air into the air cleaner and carburetor.

If the temperature of the air passing over the thermostat is less than 75°F., the valve plate in the air duct is held in an up or heat on position by a valve plate tension spring. When the valve plate is in the "heat on" position, the air entering the air cleaner is drawn through the shroud and tube assembly. The air passing through the shroud and tube is first directed over the exhaust manifold and heated.

A wax-filled thermostat is connected to the valve plate by a thermostat rod. The incoming air passes over the thermostat before entering the air cleaner. As the temperature of the air passing over the thermostat approaches 85°F., the wax begins to expand and pushes the thermostat rod against the valve plate. The tension of the valve plate spring is overcome and the valve plate is moved downward to partially close off the warm air duct to allow the cooler air from the engine compartment to mix with the warm air directed from the exhaust manifold.

If the temperature of the incoming air is approximately 105°F., the valve plate moves downward to a heat off position to close off the warm air duct. Cooler air from the engine compartment is then directed to the air cleaner without passing over the exhaust manifold.

POSITIVE CRANKCASE VENTILATION SYSTEM

The engine is equipped with a positive crankcase ventilation system. In the *positive system,* the crankcase vapors are directed to the intake manifold.

OPEN VENTILATION SYSTEM

The air flow in the positive crankcase ventilation system is shown in Fig. 11.

Ventilating air enters the engine through the oil filler cap located on the front of the left valve rocker arm cover. The filler cap contains a filtering element which filters the incoming air.

From the oil filler cap, the air flows into the front section of the valve rocker arm chamber. The ventilating air moves down past the push rods into the front of the lower crankcase and into the timing chain chamber.

The rotating action of the crankshaft causes the air to flow towards the rear of the crankcase and up into the rear section of the right valve rocker arm cover. The air then enters a spring-loaded regulator valve that regulates the amount of air to meet changing operating conditions. The air is then directed to the intake manifold through the crankcase vent hose.

During idle, intake manifold vacuum is high. The high vacuum overcomes the tension of the spring pressure and moves the valve to the Low Speed Operation position (Fig.

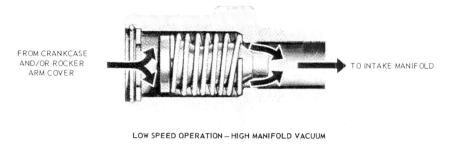

LOW SPEED OPERATION — HIGH MANIFOLD VACUUM

HIGH SPEED OPERATION — LOW MANIFOLD VACUUM

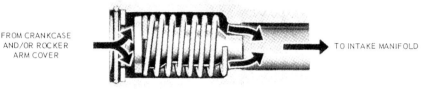

A2121-B

FIG. 12—Positive Crankcase Ventilation Regulator Valve Operation

12). With the valve in this position, the ventilating air passes between the valve (jiggle pin) and the outlet port. With the valve in this position, there is minimum ventilation.

As engine speed increases and manifold vacuum decreases, the spring forces the valve to the full open position (Fig. 12). This increases the flow of ventilating air.

CLOSED VENTILATION SYSTEM

The closed ventilation system is the same as the open ventilation system except for the following:

The crankcase ventilating air source is the carburetor air cleaner. The air passes through a hose connecting the air cleaner to the oil filler cap. The oil filler cap is sealed at the filler opening to prevent the entrance of atmospheric air. A restriction in the air cleaner at the hose connection, assists the crankcase ventilation regulator valve in maintaining a slight vacuum in the crankcase.

COOLING SYSTEM

The coolant is drawn from the bottom of the radiator by the water pump which delivers the coolant to the cylinder block (Fig. 13).

The coolant travels through cored passages to cool the entire length of each cylinder wall. Upon reaching the rear of the cylinder block, the coolant is directed upward into the cylinder heads, where it cools the

CLOSED SYSTEM ONLY

A2195-B

FIG. 11—Positive Crankcase Ventilation System

combustion chambers, valves and valve seats on its return to the front of the engine.

The coolant from each cylinder head flows through the water passages in the intake manifold past the water thermostat, if it is open, into the top of the radiator. If the thermostat is closed, a small portion of the coolant is returned to the water pump for recirculation. The entire system is pressurized to 12-15 psi.

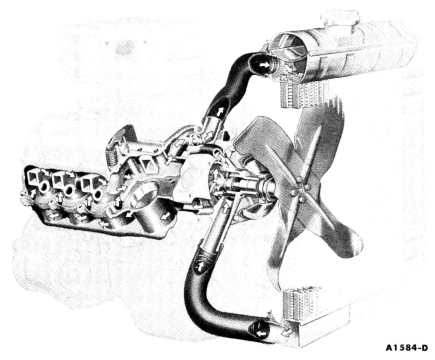

A1584-D

FIG. 13—Cooling System

2 IN-CAR ADJUSTMENTS AND REPAIRS

When installing nuts or bolts that must be torqued (refer to Part 8-5 for torque specifications), oil the threads with light weight engine oil. **Do not oil threads that require oil-resistant or water-resistant sealer.**

ENGINE FRONT SUPPORT INSULATORS

The front supports are located on each side of the cylinder block (Figs. 14, 15 and 16). The procedures given apply to either a right or left installation.

MUSTANG (EXCEPT *HIGH PERFORMANCE* ENGINE)

To ensure installing the right and left insulator brackets in their proper locations, the right insulator bracket is identified by a yellow stripe painted on the bracket.

Removal.

1. Remove the insulator assembly bracket to support lock nuts and washers from both insulator assembly brackets.

2. Raise the engine with a jack and wood block placed under the oil pan.

3. Remove the insulator assembly to engine bolts and lock washers. Remove the insulator assembly, insulator assembly bracket and heat shield as an assembly. Remove the insulator assembly to insulator assembly bracket nuts and washers to separate the insulator assembly from the insulator bracket.

Installation.

1. Position the insulator assembly bracket to the insulator assembly and install the nut and washer. Torque the nut to specifications.

2. Position the insulator assembly, insulator assembly bracket and heat shield on the engine and install the bolts and lock washers. Torque the bolts to specifications.

3. Lower the engine carefully to make sure the insulator assembly bracket studs engage the holes in each support.

4. Install the insulator assembly

bracket to support lock nuts and washers on both engine front mounts. Torque the nuts to specifications.

MUSTANG—HIGH PERFORMANCE ENGINE

Removal.

1. Remove the heat shield to engine bolts and lock washers from both heat shields.

2. Raise the engine with a jack and wood block placed under the oil pan.

3. Remove the nut and washer from the insulator assembly to support bolt and remove the rebound insulator, heat shield, insulator assembly and insulator assembly bracket as as assembly.

4. Remove the insulator assembly bracket to rebound insulator assembly bolt and nut and separate the insulators from the heat shield and the insulator assembly bracket.

Installation

1. Position the insulators on the

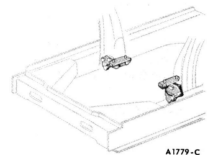

FIG. 14—Falcon, Comet and Mustang (Except High Performance) Engine Front Supports

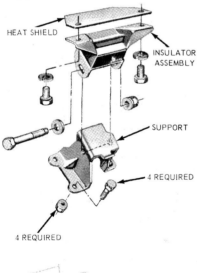

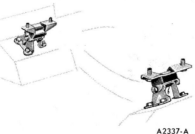

FIG. 15—Fairlane Engine Front Supports

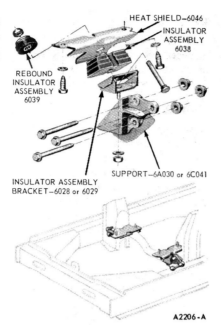

FIG. 16—Mustang High Performance Engine Front Supports

heat shield and the insulator assembly bracket. Install the insulator assembly bracket to rebound insulator assembly bolt and nut. Torque the nut to specifications.

2. Position the heat shield, rebound insulator assembly, insulator assembly and insulator assembly bracket on the engine and install the bolts and lock washers. Torque the bolts to specifications.

3. Lower the engine carefully to make sure the insulator assembly bracket bolts engage the holes in each support.

4. Install the insulator assembly bracket to support nut on both mounts. Torque the nuts to specifications.

COMET, FALCON AND FAIRLANE

Removal

1. Support the engine with a jack and a piece of wood placed under the oil pan.

2. Remove the insulator assembly to support bolt, washer and nut from both front supports.

3. Using the jack and block of wood placed under the oil pan, raise the engine enough to allow for removal of the insulator assembly.

4. Remove the bolts and lock washers retaining the insulator assembly and heat shield to the engine.

Installation

1. Place the heat shield and insulator assembly in position on the engine block and install the bolts and washers. Torque the bolts to specifications.

2. Lower the engine enough to allow installation of the insulator assembly to support bolt, washer and nut.

3. Install the insulator assembly to support bolt, washer and nut. Torque the bolt to specifications.

4. Remove the jack and block of wood from under the oil pan.

ENGINE REAR SUPPORT INSULATOR

REMOVAL

1. Remove the insulator assembly to crossmember retaining nuts and washers (Fig. 17).

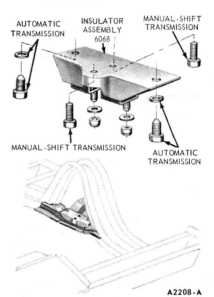

FIG. 17—Engine Rear Support

2. Raise the transmission with a floor jack.

3. Remove the insulator assembly to transmission extension housing bolts and washers (if so equipped).

4. Remove the insulator assembly.

Installation

1. Position the insulator assembly on the transmission extension housing and install the insulator assembly to transmission extension housing bolts and washers (if so equipped). Torque the bolts to specifications.

2. Lower the transmission carefully to make sure the insulator assembly studs engage the holes in the crossmember.

3. Install the insulator assembly

to crossmember nuts and washers. Torque the nuts to specfications.

VALVE ROCKER ARM ASSEMBLY

The valve rocker arm assembly is shown in Fig. 18.

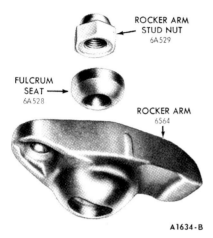

ROCKER ARM
STUD NUT
6A529

FULCRUM
SEAT
6A528

ROCKER ARM
6564

A1634-B

FIG. 18—Valve Rocker Arm Assembly

REMOVAL

1. To remove a valve rocker arm assembly from the right cylinder head, disconnect the automatic choke heat chamber air inlet hose at the inlet tube near the right valve rocker arm cover.

Remove the air cleaner and intake duct assembly.

Remove the automatic choke heat tube. Remove the crankcase ventilation regulator valve from the valve rocker arm cover.

2. Disconnect the spark plug wires at the spark plugs by grasping, twisting and pulling the moulded cap only. Remove the wires from the bracket on the valve rocker arm cover(s) and position the wires out of the way.

3. If the engine is equipped with a Thermactor exhaust emission control system, disconnect the air hose(s) at the air manifold(s). To remove the right rocker arm cover, remove the check valve from the air manifold.

4. Remove the valve rocker arm cover(s).

5. Remove the valve rocker arm stud nut, fulcrum seat and rocker arm.

CLEANING AND INSPECTION

Refer to Part 8-1, Section 3 for the cleaning and inspection procedures.

REPAIRS

If removal of the rocker arm stud is necessary, refer to the procedure under Cylinder Head Repairs in Part 8-1, Section 2.

INSTALLATION

1. Apply Lubriplate to the top of the valve stem and at the push rod guide in the cylinder head.

2. Install the valve rocker arm, fulcrum seat and stud nut. Adjust the valve clearance following the procedure in Part 8-1, Section 2.

3. Clean the valve rocker arm cover(s) and the cylinder head gasket surface(s). Apply oil-resistant sealer to one side of new cover gasket(s). Lay the cemented side of the gasket(s) in place in the cover(s).

4. Position the cover(s) on the cylinder head(s). Make sure the gasket seats evenly all around the head. Install the bolts. The cover is tightened in two steps. Torque the bolts

to specifications. Two minutes later, torque the bolts to the same specifications.

If the engine is equipped with a Thermactor exhaust emission control system, connect the air hose(s) to the air manifold(s).

If the right rocker arm cover was removed, install the check valve to the air manifold.

If the right cover was removed, install the automatic choke heat tube and the crankcase ventilation regulator valve.

Connect the automatic choke heat chamber air inlet hose.

Install the air cleaner and intake duct assembly.

5. Install the spark plug wires in the bracket on the valve rocker arm cover(s). Connect the spark plug wires.

INTAKE MANIFOLD

The intake manifold assembly is shown in Fig. 19.

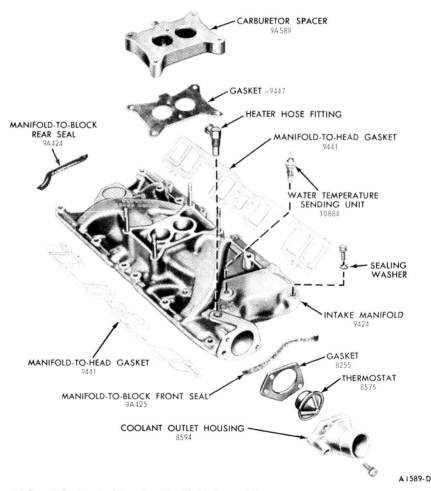

CARBURETOR SPACER
9A589

GASKET –9447

HEATER HOSE FITTING

MANIFOLD-TO-HEAD GASKET
9441

WATER TEMPERATURE
SENDING UNIT
10884

SEALING
WASHER

INTAKE MANIFOLD
9424

MANIFOLD-TO-BLOCK
REAR SEAL
9A424

MANIFOLD-TO-HEAD GASKET
9441

MANIFOLD-TO-BLOCK FRONT SEAL
9A425

COOLANT OUTLET HOUSING
8594

GASKET
8255

THERMOSTAT
8575

A1589-D

FIG. 19—Typical Intake Manifold Assembly

REMOVAL

1. Drain the cooling system. Disconnect the automatic choke heat chamber air inlet hose at the inlet tube near the right valve rocker arm cover. Remove the air cleaner and intake duct assembly.

2. Disconnect the accelerator rod at the carburetor. Remove the accelerator retracting spring.

On a car equipped with vacuum operated accessories, disconnect any vacuum lines that are connected to the intake manifold.

3. Disconnect the high tension lead and wires at the coil.

4. Disconnect the spark plug wires at the spark plugs by grasping, twisting and pulling the moulded cap only. Remove the wires from the harness brackets on the valve rocker arm covers. Remove the distributor cap and spark plug wire assembly.

5. Remove the carburetor fuel inlet line and the automatic choke heat tube.

6. Disconnect the distributor vacuum line (if so equipped) at the carburetor. Remove the distributor hold down bolt and remove the distributor.

7. Disconnect the radiator upper hose at the coolant outlet housing, and the water temperature sending unit wire at the sending unit. Remove the heater hose from the automatic choke housing and disconnect the hose at the intake manifold.

8. Loosen the clamp on the water pump bypass hose at the coolant outlet housing and slide the hose off the outlet housing.

9. Disconnect the crankcase vent hose at the valve rocker arm cover.

10. If equipped with Thermactor exhaust emission control system, remove the air pump to left air manifold hose at the air pump and position it out of the way.

Remove the air hose at the antibackfire valve. Remove the air hose bracket from the right valve rocker arm cover and position the air hose out of the way.

11. If the car is equipped with air conditioning, remove the compressor to intake manifold brackets.

12. Remove the intake manifold and carburetor as an assembly. It may be necessary to pry the intake manifold away from the cylinder heads. Remove the intake manifold gaskets and seals. Discard the intake manifold retaining bolt sealing washers.

13. If the manifold is to be disassembled, remove the coolant out-

let housing, gasket and thermostat. Remove the ignition coil, temperature sending unit, carburetor, spacer and gaskets.

If equipped with Thermactor exhaust emission control system, remove the anti-backfire valve and bracket.

CLEANING AND INSPECTION

Refer to Part 8-1, Section 3 for the cleaning and inspection procedures.

INSTALLATION

Intake manifold alignment tools are required when installing the intake manifold on the cylinder block and cylinder heads. Fabricate two alignment tools according to the specifications shown in Fig. 20.

1. If the intake manifold assembly was disasembled, install the temperature sending unit (threads coated with electrical conductive sealer), ignition coil, carburetor, spacer and gaskets. Position the thermostat in the coolant outlet housing. Coat the thermostat gasket with water-resistant sealer and position it on the coolant outlet housing. Install the coolant outlet housing, thermostat and gasket assembly.

If equipped with Thermactor exhaust emission control system, install the anti-backfire valve and bracket.

2. Clean the mating surfaces of the intake manifold, cylinder heads and cylinder block. Use a suitable solvent to remove all traces of oil. Coat the cylinder block seal surfaces with quick-drying sealer.

3. Position new seals on the cylinder block and new gaskets on the cylinder heads with the gaskets interlocked with the seal tabs. Be sure the holes in the gaskets are aligned with the holes in the cylinder heads.

Apply non-hardening sealer at the four junction points of the gaskets and seals.

4. Carefully lower the intake manifold into position on the cylinder block and cylinder heads. **After the intake manifold is in place, run a finger around the seal area to make sure the seals are in place. If the seals are not in place, remove the intake manifold and position the seals.**

5. Be sure the holes in the manifold gaskets and manifold are in alignment. Position the intake manifold alignment tools (Fig. 20) in the front and rear bolt holes (Nos. 10 and 12) on the left bank of the manifold.

6. Using new sealing washers, install the intake manifold retaining bolts. Torque the bolts in two steps. First, torque the bolts in sequence (Fig. 21) to 15-17 ft-lbs.

7. Remove the manifold alignment tools from the front and rear bolt holes (Nos. 10 and 12). Using new sealing washers, install the two remaining bolts and torque to 15-17 ft-lbs.

8. Then, torque all the manifold retaining bolts in sequence to specifications.

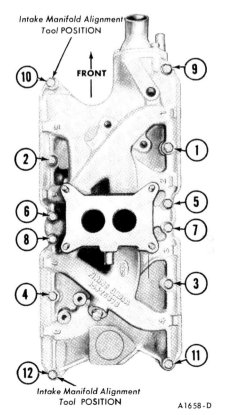

FIG. 21—Intake Manifold Torque Sequence

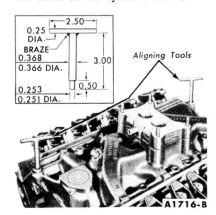

FIG. 20—Intake Manifold Alignment

9. Install the water pump bypass hose on the coolant outlet housing. Slide the clamp into position and tighten the clamp.

10. Connect the radiator upper hose. Install the heater hose against the automatic choke housing and connect the hose at the intake manifold.

11. Install the carburetor fuel inlet line and the automatic choke heat tube.

12. Rotate the crankshaft damper until the No. 1 piston is on TDC at the end of the compression stroke. Position the distributor in the block with the rotor at the No. 1 firing position and the points open. Install the hold down clamp.

13. Install the distributor cap. Position the spark plug wires in the harness brackets on the valve rocker arm covers, and connect the spark plug wires.

14. Connect the crankcase vent hose. Connect the high tension lead and coil wires.

15. Connect the accelerator rod and retracting spring.

On a car equipped with vacuum operated accessories, connect any vacuum lines that were disconnected from the intake manifold during removal.

On a car with air conditioning, install the compressor to intake manifold brackets.

16. If equipped with Thermactor exhaust emission control system, connect the hose from the left air manifold to the air pump, connect the air hose to the anti-backfire valve and install the air hose bracket on the right valve rocker arm cover.

17. Fill and bleed the cooling system.

18. Start the engine and check and adjust the ignition timing. Connect the distributor vacuum line at the carburetor.

19. Operate the engine at fast idle and check all hose connections and gaskets for leaks. Operate the engine until engine temperatures have stabilized and adjust the engine idle speed and idle fuel mixture.

20. Connect the automatic choke heat chamber air inlet hose.

21. Adjust the transmission throttle linkage. Install the air cleaner and intake duct assembly.

EXHAUST MANIFOLDS
REMOVAL

1. On a right exhaust manifold, disconnect the automatic choke heat chamber air inlet hose at the inlet tube near the right valve rocker arm cover.

Remove the automatic choke heat tube from the right exhaust manifold.

2. Remove the air cleaner and intake duct assembly.

3. Disconnect the exhaust manifold at the muffler inlet pipe.

4. Remove the retaining bolts and tab washers and remove the exhaust manifold.

CLEANING AND INSPECTION

Refer to Part 8-1, Section 3 for the cleaning and inspection procedures.

INSTALLATION

1. Clean the mating surfaces of the exhaust manifold and cylinder head. Clean the mounting flange of the exhaust manifold and muffler inlet pipe.

2. Apply graphite grease to the mating surface of the exhaust manifold.

3. Position the exhaust manifold on the cylinder head and install the retaining bolts and tab washers. Working from the center to the ends, torque the bolts to specifications. Lock the bolts by bending one tab of the washer over a flat on the bolt.

4. Place new gaskets on the muffler inlet pipe. Position the muffler inlet pipe to the manifold. Install and torque the retaining nuts to specifications.

5. Install the automatic choke heat tube on the right exhaust manifold. Install the air cleaner and intake duct assembly.

6. Connect the automatic choke heat chamber air inlet hose.

7. Start the engine and check for exhaust leaks.

POSITIVE CRANKCASE VENTILATION SYSTEM

The positive crankcase ventilation system components are shown in Fig. 22.

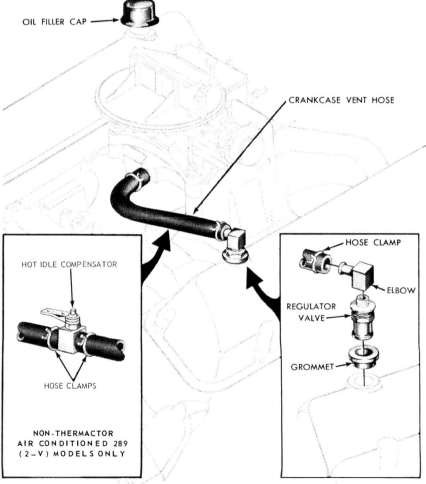

FIG. 22—Positive Crankcase Ventilation System Components

REMOVAL

1. On a closed ventilation system, remove the ventilation system air intake hose from the air cleaner and the oil filler cap.

2. Remove the air cleaner and intake duct assembly.

3. Using hose clamp pliers, slide both crankcase vent hose clamps towards the center of the vent hose.

Slide the vent hose clamps away from the hot idle compensator (if so equipped).

Disconnect the crankcase vent hose at the carburetor spacer, regulator valve and hot idle compensator (if so equipped).

4. Pull the regulator valve and fitting (elbow) out of the valve rocker arm cover mounting grommet.

INSTALLATION

1. Insert the regulator valve and fitting (elbow) into the valve rocker arm cover mounting grommet.

2. Position the hose clamps on the vent hose. Connect the vent hose to the carburetor spacer regulator valve and hot idle compensator (if so equipped). Using hose clamp pliers, slide the clamps into position.

3. Install the air cleaner and intake duct assembly.

4. On a closed ventilation system, install the closed ventilation system air intake hose to the air cleaner and the oil filler cap.

5. Operate the engine and check for leaks.

CLEANING AND INSPECTION

Refer to Part 8-1, Section 3 for the cleaning and inspection procedures.

TESTING

Refer to Part 8-1, Section 1 for the test procedures.

CYLINDER HEADS

If a cylinder head is to be replaced, follow the procedures under Cylinder Head Disassembly and Assembly, and transfer all valves, springs, spark plugs, etc., to the new cylinder head. Clean and inspect all parts, reface the valves (refer to Part 8-1) and check all assembly clearances before assembling the new or used parts to the new cylinder head.

REMOVAL

1. Remove the intake manifold and carburetor as an assembly following the procedure under Intake Manifold Removal.

2. Disconnect the battery ground cable at the cylinder head.

If the left cylinder head is to be removed, on a car with an air conditioner, isolate and remove the compressor as outlined in Group 15.

If the left cylinder head is to be removed, on a car with power steering, disconnect the power steering pump bracket from the left cylinder head and remove the drive belt from the pump pulley. Wire the power steering pump out of the way and in a position that will prevent the oil from draining out.

If the left cylinder head is to be removed on an engine with Thermactor exhaust emission control system, disconnect the hose from the air manifold on the left cylinder head.

3. If the right cylinder head is to be removed, remove the alternator mounting bracket bolt and spacer, ignition coil and air cleaner inlet duct from the right cylinder head assembly.

If the right cylinder head is to be removed on an engine with Thermactor exhaust control emission system, remove the air pump and bracket. Disconnect the hose from the air manifold on the right cylinder head.

4. Disconnect the exhaust manifold(s) at the muffler inlet pipe(s).

Remove the rocker arm covers. If the right rocker arm cover is to be removed on an engine equipped with a thermactor exhaust emission control system, remove the check valve from the air manifold.

5. Loosen the rocker arm stud nuts so that the rocker arms can be rotated to the side. Remove the push rods in sequence (Fig 23) so that they may be installed in their original positions.

6. Install the cylinder head holding fixtures (Fig. 24). Remove the cylinder head retaining bolts and lift the cylinder head off the block. Remove and discard the cylinder head gasket.

FIG. 23—Valve Push Rod Removal

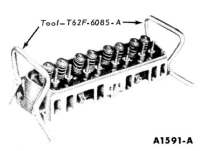

FIG. 24—Cylinder Head Holding Fixtures

INSTALLATION

1. Clean the cylinder head, intake manifold, valve rocker arm cover and cylinder block gasket surfaces. If the cylinder head was removed for a cylinder head gasket replacement, check the flatness of the cylinder head and block gasket surfaces.

2. Position the new cylinder head gasket over the cylinder dowels on the block. Coat the head bolts with water-resistant sealer. Position the cylinder head on the block and install the retaining bolts. Remove the holding fixtures.

3. The cylinder head bolts are tightened in three progressive steps. Torque all the bolts in sequence (Fig. 25) to 50 ft-lbs., then to 60 ft-lbs., and finally to specifications. **After the cylinder head bolts have been torqued to specifications, the bolts should not be disturbed.**

4. Clean the push rods in a suitable solvent. Blow out the oil passage in the push rod with compressed air. Check the ends of the push rods for nicks, grooves, roughness or excessive wear. Visually check the push rods for straightness or check push rod runout with a dial indicator. If runout exceeds the maximum limit at any point, discard the rod. **Do not attempt to straighten push rods.**

5. Install the push rods in their original positions. Apply Lubriplate to the valve stem tips and the push rod guides in the cylinder head.

6. Install the rocker arms. Perform a valve clearance adjustment as outlined in Part 8-1, Section 2.

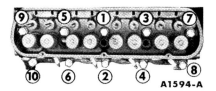

FIG. 25—Cylinder Head Bolt Torque Sequence

7. Position a new gasket(s) on the muffler inlet pipe(s). Connect the exhaust manifold(s) at the muffler inlet pipe(s). Torque the nuts to specifications.

8. If the right cylinder head was removed, install the alternator retaining bolt and spacer, ignition coil and air cleaner inlet duct on the right cylinder head assembly. Adjust the drive belt tension to specifications.

9. Apply oil-resistant sealer to one side of new cover gaskets. Lay the cemented side of the gaskets in place in the cover(s). Install the valve rocker arm cover(s).

If the right cylinder head was removed on an engine equipped with Thermactor exhaust emission control system, install the check valve and connect the hose to the air manifold on the right cylinder head. Install the air pump and alternator.

If the left cylinder head was removed, on a car with an air conditioner, install the compressor as outlined in Group 15.

If the left cylinder head was removed, on a car with power steering, install the drive belt and power steering pump bracket. Install the bracket retaining bolts. Adjust the drive belt to specifications.

10. Install the intake manifold and related parts following the procedure under Intake Manifold Installation.

11. If the left cylinder head was removed on an engine equipped with Thermactor exhaust emission control system, connect the hose to the air manifold on the left cylinder head.

DISASSEMBLY

1. Remove the exhaust manifolds and the spark plugs.

2. Clean the carbon out of the cylinder head combustion chambers before removing the valves.

3. Compress the valve springs (Fig. 26). Remove the spring retainer locks and release the spring.

4. Remove the spring retainer, spring, stem seal and valve. Discard valve stem seals. Identify all valve parts.

CLEANING AND INSPECTION

Refer to Part 8-1, Section 3 for the cleaning and inspection procedures.

REPAIRS

Cylinder head repair and rocker arm stud replacement procedures, and checks such as valve and valve

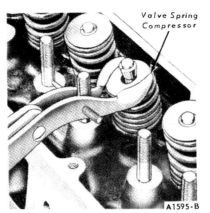

FIG. 26—Compressing Valve Spring—On Bench

seat refacing, cylinder head flatness checks, etc., are covered in Part 8-1, Section 2.

ASSEMBLY

1. Install each valve (Fig. 27) in the port from which it was removed or to which it was fitted. Install a new stem seal on the valve.

2. Install the valve spring over the valve, and install the spring retainer. Compress the spring and install the retainer locks (Fig. 26).

3. Measure the assembled height of the valve spring from the surface of the cylinder head spring pad to the underside of the spring retainer with dividers (Fig. 28). Check the dividers against a scale. If the assembled height is greater than specifications, install the necessary 0.030-inch thick spacer(s) between the cylinder head spring pad and the valve spring to bring the assembled height to the recommended height.

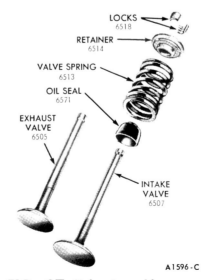

FIG. 27—Valve Assembly

FIG. 28—Valve Spring Assembled Height

Do not install the spacers unless necessary. Use of spacers in excess of recommendations will result in overstressing the valve springs and overloading the camshaft lobes which could lead to spring breakage and worn camshaft lobes.

4. Install the exhaust manifolds and the spark plugs.

VALVE SPRING, RETAINER AND STEM SEAL REPLACEMENT

Broken valve springs, or defective valve stem seals and retainers may be replaced without removing the cylinder head, providing damage to the valve or valve seat has not occurred.

1. Disconnect the automatic choke heat chamber air inlet hose at the inlet tube near the right valve rocker arm cover.

2. Remove the air cleaner and intake duct assembly.

To remove the right valve rocker arm cover, remove the automatic choke heat tube. Remove the crankcase ventilation regulator valve from the valve rocker arm cover. If the engine is equipped with Thermactor exhaust emission control system, disconnect the anti-backfire valve air line and position it out of the way. Remove the check valve.

To remove the left valve rocker arm cover on an engine with Thermactor exhaust emission control system, disconnect the air hose from the left air manifold.

3. Remove the valve rocker arm cover and the applicable spark plug.

4. Remove the valve rocker arm stud nuts, fulcrum seats, valve rocker arms and push rods from the applicable cylinder.

5. Install an air line with an

FIG. 29—Compressing Valve Spring—In Chassis

adapter in the spark plug hole and turn on the air supply.

6. Install the stud nut and position the compressor tool as shown in Fig. 29. Compress the valve spring and remove the retainer locks, spring retainer and valve spring.

7. Remove and discard the valve stem seal (Fig. 30). **If air pressure fails to hold the valve in the closed position during this operation, it can be presumed that the valve is not seating or is damaged. If this condition occurs, remove the cylinder head for further inspection.**

8. **If air pressure has forced the piston to the bottom of the cylinder, any removal of air pressure will allow the valve(s) to fall into the cylinder. A rubber band, tape or string wrapped around the end of the valve stem will prevent this condition and will still allow enough travel to check the valve for binds.**

9. Inspect the valve stem for damage. Rotate the valve and check the valve stem tip for eccentric movement during rotation. Move the valve up and down through normal travel in the valve guide and check

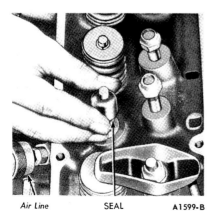

FIG. 30—Valve Stem Seal Removal or Installation

the stem for binds. **If the valve has been damaged, it will be necessary to remove the cylinder head for repairs as outlined in Part 8-1, Section 2.**

10. If the condition of the valve proved satisfactory, hold the valve in the closed position and apply the air pressure within the cylinder.

11. Install a new valve stem seal (Fig. 30). Place the spring in position over the valve and install the valve spring retainer. Compress the valve spring and install the valve spring retainer locks. Remove the compressor tool and stud nut.

12. Install the push rod. Apply Lubriplate to the tip of the valve stem and at the push rod guide in the cylinder head.

13. Install the valve rocker arms fulcrum seats and stud nuts. Adjust the valve clearance following the procedure in Part 8-1, Section 2.

14. Turn off the air and remove the air line and adapter. Install the spark plug and connect the spark plug wire.

15. Clean and install the rocker arm cover.

If the right cover was removed install the automatic choke heat tube and the crankcase ventilation regulator valve. If the engine is equipped with Thermactor exhaust emission control system, install the check valve and connect the anti-backfire valve air line.

If the left cover was removed on an engine with Thermactor exhaust emission control system, connect the air hose to the left air manifold.

16. Install the air cleaner and intake duct assembly.

17. Connect the automatic choke heat chamber air inlet hose.

CYLINDER FRONT COVER AND TIMING CHAIN
REMOVAL

1. Drain the cooling system and the crankcase.

2. Disconnect the radiator lower hose at the water pump.

3. Disconnect the heater hose at the water pump. Slide the water pump bypass hose clamp toward the water pump.

4. Loosen the alternator to cylinder head mounting bolt. Remove the alternator bracket bolts at the water pump and position the alternator and brackets out of the way.

If the engine is equipped with a Thermactor exhaust emission control system, remove the air pump and brackets.

5. On a car with power steering and/or air conditioning, loosen the drive belt tension and remove the belt(s).

6. Remove the fan, spacer, pulley and drive belt.

7. Remove the crankshaft pulley from the crankshaft vibration damper. Remove the damper retaining screw and washer. Install the puller on the crankshaft vibration damper (Fig. 31) and remove the vibration damper.

8. Disconnect the fuel pump outlet line at the fuel pump. Remove the fuel pump retaining bolts and lay the pump to one side with the flexible fuel line still attached.

9. Remove the oil level dipstick.

10. Remove the oil pan to cylinder front cover retaining bolts. Remove the cylinder front cover and water pump as an assembly.

If a new cylinder front cover is to be installed, remove the water pump and dipstick tube from the old cylinder front cover and install them on the new cover.

11. Discard the cylinder front cover gasket. Remove the crankshaft front oil slinger.

12. Check the timing chain deflection (refer to Part 8-1, Section 2).

13. Crank the engine until the timing marks on the sprockets are positioned as shown in Fig. 32.

14. Remove the camshaft sprocket cap screw, washers and fuel pump eccentric. Slide both sprockets and the timing chain forward, and remove them as an assembly (Fig. 33).

15. Remove the oil pan and oil pump pickup tube by following the procedure under Oil Pan Removal.

CLEANING AND INSPECTION

Refer to Part 8-1, Section 3 for the cleaning and inspection procedures. Clean the crankshaft damper,

FIG. 31—Crankshaft Vibration Damper Removal

TIMING MARKS   A1603-C

FIG. 32—Aligning Timing Marks

following the referenced procedure.

FRONT OIL SEAL REPLACEMENT

It is good practice to replace the oil seal each time the cylinder front cover is removed.

REMOVAL

1. Drive out the old seal with a pin punch. Clean out the recess in the cover.
2. Coat a new seal with grease, then install the seal in the cover (Fig. 34). Drive the seal in until it is fully seated in the recess. Check the seal after installation to be sure the spring is properly positioned in the seal.

INSTALLATION

1. Position the sprockets and timing chain on the camshaft (Fig. 33). Be sure the timing marks on the sprockets are positioned as shown in Fig. 32.
2. Install the fuel pump eccentric, washers and camshaft sprocket cap screw. *Torque the sprocket* cap screw to specifications. Install the crankshaft front oil slinger (Fig. 35).
3. Clean the cylinder front cover, oil pan and the block gasket surfaces.
4. Lubricate the timing chain with engine oil.
5. Coat the gasket surfaces of the block and cover with sealer. Position a new gasket on the block.
6. Install the alignment pilot tool on the cylinder front cover so that the keyway in the pilot aligns with

A1604-C

FIG. 33—Timing Chain Removal or Installation

the key in the crankshaft. Position the cover and pilot over the end of the crankshaft and against the block (Fig. 36). Coat the threads of the retaining screws with oil-resistant sealer and install the screws. While pushing in on the pilot, torque the screws to specifications. Remove the pilot.

7. Apply Lubriplate to the oil seal rubbing surface of the vibration damper inner hub to prevent damage to the seal. Apply a white lead and oil mixture to the front of the crankshaft damper for installation.
8. Line up the crankshaft vibration damper keyway with the key on the crankshaft. Install the vibration damper on the crankshaft (Fig. 37). Install the cap screw and washer. Torque the screw to specifications. Install the crankshaft pulley.

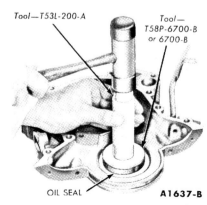

Tool—T53L-200-A   Tool—T58P-6700-B or 6700-B

OIL SEAL   A1637-B

FIG. 34—Crankshaft Front Oil Seal Replacement

FUEL PUMP ECCENTRIC   DOWEL

CRANKSHAFT FRONT OIL SLINGER   A1638-C

FIG. 35—Fuel Pump Eccentric and Front Oil Slinger Installed

9. Install the oil pump pickup tube and oil pan following the procedure under Oil Pan Installation.
10. Install the fuel pump using a new gasket. Connect the fuel pump outlet pipe.
11. Install the water pump pulley, drive belt, spacer and fan.
12. On an engine equipped with Thermactor exhaust emission control system, install the air pump and brackets.
13. Install the alternator bracket. Adjust the drive belt tension to specifications and tighten the alternator mounting bolts.
14. Connect the heater hose and the water pump bypass hose. Slide

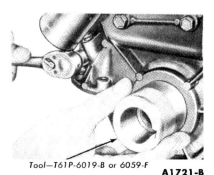

Tool—T61P-6019-B or 6059-F   A1721-B

FIG. 36—Cylinder Front Cover Alignment

FIG. 37—Crankshaft Vibration Damper Installation

the bypass hose clamp into position.

15. Connect the radiator hose.

16. On a car with power steering and/or air conditioning, install and adjust the drive belts.

17. Fill and bleed the cooling system. Fill the crankcase with the proper grade and quantity of engine oil.

18. Operate the engine at fast idle and check for coolant and oil leaks. Check and adjust the ignition timing.

CAMSHAFT

The camshaft and related parts are shown in Fig. 38.

REMOVAL

1. Remove the cylinder front cover and the timing chain following the procedure under Cylinder Front Cover and Timing Chain Removal.

2. Disconnect the spark plug wires at the spark plugs and remove the wires from the ignition harness brackets on the valve rocker arm covers. Disconnect the coil high tension lead at the coil. Remove the distributor

cap and spark plug wire assembly.

3. Disconnect the ignition coil wires at the coil.

4. Disconnect the distributor vacuum line at the carburetor. Remove the distributor hold down bolt and clamp and remove the distributor.

5. Disconnect the automatic choke heat tube at the carburetor. Remove the heater hose from the automatic choke and disconnect the hose at the intake manifold.

On a car with an automatic transmission, disconnect the throttle valve vacuum line at the intake manifold. Disconnect the transmission oil cooler lines at the radiator.

6. Disconnect the radiator upper hose and remove the radiator.

7. Disconnect the accelerator rod at the carburetor. Remove the accelerator retracting spring.

8. Disconnect the water temperature sending unit wire at the sending unit and the engine ground strap at the engine.

9. Remove the crankcase ventilation regulator valve from the valve rocker arm cover. Remove the valve rocker arm covers. Loosen the valve rocker arm stud nuts and rotate the rocker arms to the side.

10. Remove the intake manifold and carburetor as an assembly, following the procedure under Intake Manifold Removal. Remove the intake manifold gaskets and seals.

11. Remove the valve push rods in sequence so that they can be installed in their original positions.

12. Using a magnet, remove the valve lifters and place them in a rack so that they can be installed in their original bores (Fig. 39).

If the valve lifters are stuck in their bores by excessive varnish, etc. it may be necessary to use a plier-type tool (T52T-6500-DJD or 6500-

FIG. 39—Valve Lifter Removal

D) to remove the lifters. Rotate the lifter back and forth to loosen it from the gum or varnish that may have formed at the lifter.

13. Remove the camshaft thrust plate. Carefully remove the camshaft by pulling it toward the front of the engine. **Use caution to avoid damaging the camshaft bearings.**

CLEANING AND INSPECTION

Refer to Part 8-1, Section 3 for the cleaning and inspection procedures.

REPAIRS

Refer to Part 8-1, Section 2 for the repair procedures.

INSTALLATION

1. Oil the camshaft journals and apply Lubriplate to the lobes. Carefully slide the camshaft through the bearings. Install the camshaft thrust plate.

2. Install the valve lifters in the bores from which they were removed.

3. Install the push rods in their original position. Apply Lubriplate to the valve stem tips and the push rod guides in the cylinder head. Position the rocker arms over the push rods.

4. Install the intake manifold and related parts by following steps 1 thru 8 under Intake Manifold Installation.

5. Connect the water temperature sending unit and the engine ground strap.

6. Connect the accelerator rod and accelerator retracting spring.

7. Install the radiator.

On a car with an automatic transmission, connect the transmission oil

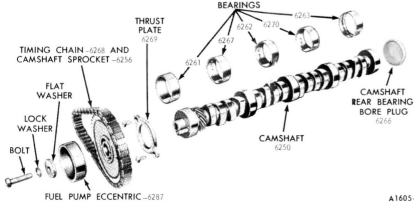

FIG. 38—Camshaft and Related Parts

cooler lines and throttle valve vacuum line.

8. Connect the heater hose at the intake manifold. Position and connect the fuel line.

9. Replace the crankshaft front oil seal. Install the timing chain, cylinder front cover and related parts following steps 1 thru 16 under Cylinder Front Cover and Timing Chain Installation.

10. With No. 1 piston on TDC at the end of the compression stroke, position the distributor in the block with the rotor at the No. 1 firing position and the points open. Install the hold down clamp.

11. Perform a valve clearance adjustment as outlined in Part 8-1, Section 2.

12. Clean the valve rocker arm covers and the cylinder head gasket surface. Apply oil-resistance sealer to one side of new cover gaskets. Lay the cemented side of the gaskets in place in the covers.

13. Position the covers on the cylinder heads. Make sure the gasket seats evenly all around the head. Install the bolts. The cover is tightened in two steps. Torque the bolts to specifications. Two minutes later, torque the bolts to the same specifications.

14. Clean and install the crankcase ventilation system.

15. Install the automatic choke heat tube. Connect the ignition coil wires.

16. Install the distributor cap. Position the spark plug wires in the harness brackets on the valve rocker arm covers and connect the spark plug wires. Connect the high tension lead at the coil.

17. Fill and bleed the cooling system. Fill the crankcase with the proper grade and quantity of engine oil.

18. Start the engine and check and adjust the ignition timing. Connect the distributor vacuum line at the carburetor.

19. Operate the engine at fast idle and check all hose connections and gaskets for leaks. Operate the engine until engine temperatures have stabilized and adjust the engine idle speed and idle fuel mixture.

20. Adjust the transmission throttle linkage. Install the air cleaner and intake duct assembly.

21. Connect the automatic choke heat chamber air inlet hose.

CAMSHAFT REAR BEARING BORE PLUG REPLACEMENT

1. On a car with a manual-shift transmission, remove the transmission, clutch pressure plate and disc following the procedures in Group 5.

On a car with an automatic transmission, remove the transmission and converter housing following the procedure in Group 7.

2. Remove the flywheel retaining bolts and remove the flywheel. Remove the engine rear cover plate.

3. Drill a ½-inch hole in the camshaft rear bearing bore plug and remove the plug using the tools shown in Fig. 60.

4. Clean out the plug bore recess thoroughly and coat the flange of a new plug with oil-resistant sealer. Install the new plug with the flange facing outward. Drive the plug in until it is slightly below the chamfer in the bore (Fig. 63).

5. Coat the flywheel retaining bolts with oil-resistant sealer. Position the engine rear cover plate on the cylinder block dowels. Position the flywheel on the crankshaft flange. Install and torque the retaining bolts in sequence across from each other to specifications.

On a car with a manual-shift transmission, install the clutch pressure plate, disc and the transmission following the procedures in Group 5.

On a car with an automatic transmission, install the transmission and converter housing following the procedure in Group 7.

VALVE LIFTERS
REPLACEMENT

1. Remove the intake manifold and related parts by following steps 1 thru 12 under Intake Manifold Removal.

2. Remove the crankcase ventilation regulator valve from the valve rocker arm cover. Remove the valve rocker arm covers. Loosen the valve rocker arm stud nuts and rotate the rocker arms to the side.

3. Remove the valve push rods in sequence so that they can be installed in their original positions.

4. Using a magnet, remove the valve lifters and place them in a rack so that they can be installed in their original bores (Fig. 39).

If the valve lifters cannot be removed from their bores because of excessive varnish, etc., it may be necessary to use a plier-type tool (T52T-6500-DJD or 6500-D) to remove the lifters. Rotate the lifter

back and forth to loosen it from the gum or varnish that may have formed at the lifter.

On hydraulic valve lifters, the internal parts of each lifter assembly are matched sets. Do not intermix the parts. Keep the assemblies intact until they are to be cleaned.

5. Clean and install the valve lifters in the bores from which they were removed. If a new lifter(s) is being installed, test the new lifter(s) for a free fit in the bore in which it is to be installed.

6. Install the push rods in their original position. Apply Lubriplate to the valve stem tips and the push rod guides in the cylinder head.

7. Position the rocker arms over the push rods. Perform a valve clearance adjustment as outlined in Part 8-1, Section 2.

8. Install the valve rocker arm covers. Install the crank case ventilation regulator valve in the valve rocker arm cover.

9. Install the intake manifold and related parts by following steps 2 thru 20 under Intake Manifold Installation.

DISASSEMBLY

Each valve lifter is a matched assembly. If the parts of one lifter are intermixed with those of another, improper valve operation may result. Disassemble and assemble each lifter separately. Keep the lifter assemblies in proper sequence so that they can be installed in their original bores.

1. Grasp the lock ring with needle nose pliers to release it from the groove. It may be necessary to depress the plunger to fully release the lock ring.

2. Remove the push rod cup, metering valve (disc), plunger and spring.

3. Invert the plunger assembly and remove the check valve retainer by carefully prying up on it with a screw driver. Remove the check valve (disc or ball check) and spring.

CLEANING AND INSPECTION

Refer to Part 8-1, Section 3 for the cleaning and inspection procedures.

ASSEMBLY

A typical hydraulic valve lifter assembly is shown in Fig. 40.

1. Place the plunger upside down on a clean work bench.

2. Place the check valve (disc or ball check) in position over the oil hole on the bottom of the plunger.

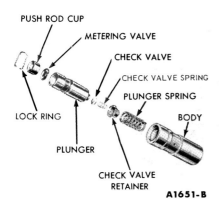

FIG. 40—Typical Hydraulic Valve Lifter Assembly

Set the check valve spring on top of the check valve (disc or ball check).

3. Position the check valve retainer over the check valve and spring and push the retainer down into place on the plunger.

4. Place the plunger spring, and then the plunger (open end up) into the lifter body.

5. Position the metering valve (disc) in the plunger, then place the push rod seat in the plunger.

6. Depress the plunger, and position the closed end of the lock ring in the groove of the lifter body. With the plunger still depressed, position the open ends of the lock ring in the groove. Release the plunger, then depress it again to fully seat the lock ring.

TESTING

Refer to Part 8-1, Section 1 for the testing procedures.

CRANKSHAFT REAR OIL SEAL REPLACEMENT

Replacement of a crankshaft rear oil seal because of oil leakage requires replacement of both the upper and lower seals. Remove the engine; then remove the crankshaft and replace the seals by following the procedure under Crankshaft Removal and Installation (Section 4).

MAIN AND CONNECTING ROD BEARING REPLACEMENT

The main and connecting rod bearing inserts are selective fit. **Do not file or lap bearing caps or use bearing shims to obtain the proper bearing clearance.**

Selective fit bearings are available for service in standard sizes and 0.002 inch undersize. Standard bearings are divided into two sizes and are identified by a daub of red or blue

paint. Refer to the Parts Catalog for the available sizes. **Red marked bearings increase the clearance; blue marked bearings decrease the clearance.** Undersize bearings, which are not selective fit, are available for use on journals that have been refinished.

MAIN BEARING

1. Drain the crankcase. Remove the oil level dipstick. Remove the oil pan and related parts.

2. Remove the oil pump inlet tube assembly and the oil pump.

3. **Replace one bearing at a time, leaving the other bearings securely fastened.** Remove the main bearing cap to which new bearings are to be installed.

4. Insert the upper bearing removal tool (tool 6331) in the oil hole in the crankshaft.

5. Rotate the crankshaft in the direction of the engine rotation to force the bearing out of the block.

6. Clean the crankshaft journals. Inspect the journals and thrust faces (thrust bearing) for nicks, burrs or bearing pick-up that would cause premature bearing wear. **When replacing standard bearings with new bearings, it is good practice to fit the bearing to the minimum specified clearance and to first try to obtain the proper clearance with two blue bearing halves.**

7. To install the upper main bearing, place the plain end of the bearing over the shaft on the locking tang side of the block and partially install the bearing so that tool 6331 can be inserted in the oil hole in the crankshaft. With tool 6331 positioned in the oil hole in the crankshaft, rotate the crankshaft in the opposite direction of engine rotation until the bearing seats itself. Remove the tool.

8. Replace the cap bearing.

9. Support the crankshaft so that its weight will not compress the Plastigage and provide an erroneous reading. Position a jack so that it will bear against the counterweight adjoining the bearing which is being checked.

10. Place a piece of Plastigage on the bearing surface the full width of the bearing cap and about ¼ inch off center (Fig. 41).

11. Install the cap and torque the bolts to specifications. **Do not turn the crankshaft while the Plastigage is in place.**

12. Remove the cap. Using the Plastigage scale, check the width of the Plastigage. When checking the

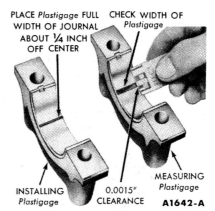

FIG. 41—Installing and Measuring Plastigage—Engine Installed

width of the Plastigage, check at the widest point in order to get the minimum clearance. Check at the narrowest point in order to get the maximum clearance. The difference between the two readings is the taper.

13. If the clearance is less than the specified limits, try two red bearing halves or a combination of red and blue depending upon the condition.

If the clearance exceeds specified limits, try 0.002 inch undersize bearings in combination with red or blue bearings. **The bearing clearance must be within specified limits.** If 0.002 undersize main bearings are used on more than one journal, be sure they are all installed on the same side (cap or cylinder block) of the crankshaft. If the standard and 0.002 inch undersize bearings do not bring the clearance within the desired limits, refinish the crankshaft journal, then install undersize bearings.

14. After the bearing has been fitted, apply a light coat of engine oil to the journal and bearings; then install the bearing cap. Torque the cap bolts to specifications.

15. Repeat the procedure for the remaining bearings that require replacement.

16. If the rear main bearing is to be replaced, remove the rear main bearing cap. Remove and discard the rear oil seal.

17. Clean the rear journal oil seal groove and the mating surfaces of the block and rear main bearing cap. Preform the new seal by hand to the approximate radius of the cap.

18. Insert the seal in the oil seal groove, seating the center of the seal first and allowing the seal to extend equally on both ends. Press the seal

down firmly with the thumb at the center of the seal, then press both ends of the seal into the groove, working from the ends to the center.

19. Position the seal forming tool as shown in Fig. 42 and complete the seal installation. After installation, cut the ends of the seal flush.

20. Apply a thin coating of oil-resistant sealer to the rear main bearing cap at the rear of the top mating surface (Fig. 42). **Do not apply sealer to the area forward of the oil slinger groove.** Install the rear main bearing cap and torque the cap bolts to specifications.

21. If the thrust bearing cap (No. 3 main bearing) has been removed, install it as follows:

Install the thrust bearing cap with the bolts finger-tight. Pry the crankshaft forward against the thrust surface of the upper half of the bearing (Fig. 59). Hold the crankshaft forward and pry the thrust bearing cap to the rear (Fig. 59). This will align the thrust surfaces of both halves of the bearing. Retain the forward pressure on the crankshaft. Torque the cap bolts to specifications (Fig. 59).

22. Clean the oil pump inlet tube screen. Prime and install the oil pump and the inlet tube assembly.

23. Position the oil pan gaskets on the oil pan. Position the oil pan front seal on the cylinder front cover. Position the oil pan rear seal on the rear main bearing cap. Install the oil pan and related parts. Install the oil level dipstick.

24. Fill the crankcase. Start the engine and check for oil pressure.

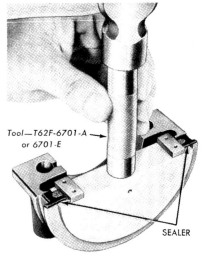

Tool—T62F-6701-A or 6701-E

SEALER

A1641-C

FIG. 42—Seal to Rear Bearing Cap Installation

Operate the engine at fast idle and check for oil leaks.

CONNECTING ROD BEARING

1. Follow steps 1 and 2 under Main Bearing Replacement.

2. Turn the crankshaft until the connecting rod to which new bearings are to be fitted is down. Remove the connecting rod cap. Remove the bearing inserts from the rod and cap.

3. Be sure the bearing inserts and the bearing bore in the connecting rod and cap are clean. Foreign material under the inserts may distort the bearing and cause a failure.

4. Clean the crankshaft journal. **When replacing standard bearings with new bearings, it is good practice to fit the bearing to the minimum specified clearance and to first try to obtain the proper clearance with two blue bearing halves.**

5. Install the bearing inserts in the connecting rod and cap with the tangs fitting in the slots provided.

6. Pull the connecting rod assembly down firmly on the crankshaft journal.

7. Place a piece of Plastigage on the lower bearing surface, the full width of the cap and about ¼ inch off-center.

8. Install the cap and torque the connecting rod nuts to specifications. **Do not turn the crankshaft while the Plastigage is in place.**

9. Refer to steps 12 and 13 under Main Bearing Replacement.

10. After the bearing has been fitted, clean and apply a light coat of engine oil to the journal and bearings. Install the connecting rod cap. Torque the nuts to specifications.

11. Repeat the procedure for the remaining connecting rods that require new bearings.

12. Follow steps 22 thru 24 under Main Bearing Replacement.

CLEANING AND INSPECTION

Refer to Part 8-1, Section 3 for the cleaning and inspecting procedures.

PISTONS AND CONNECTING RODS
REMOVAL

1. Drain the cooling system and the crankcase. Remove the intake manifold, cylinder heads, oil pan and oil pump following the procedures in this section.

2. Remove any ridge and/or deposits from the upper end of the cylinder bores as follows:

Turn the crankshaft until the piston to be removed is at the bottom

of its travel and place a cloth on the piston head to collect the cuttings. Remove any ridge and/or deposits from the upper end of the cylinder bores. Remove the cylinder ridge with a ridge cutter. Follow the instructions furnished by the tool manufacturer. **Never cut into the ring travel area in excess of 1/32 inch when removing ridges.**

3. Make sure all connecting rod caps are marked so that they can be installed in their original positions.

4. Turn the crankshaft until the connecting rod being removed is down.

5. Remove the connecting rod nuts and cap.

6. Push the connecting rod and piston assembly out the top of the cylinder with the handle end of a hammer. **Avoid damage to the crankshaft journal or the cylinder wall when removing the piston and rod.**

7. Remove the bearing inserts from the connecting rod and cap.

8. Install the cap on the connecting rod from which it was removed.

INSTALLATION

1. If new piston rings are to be installed, remove the cylinder wall glaze. Follow the instructions of the tool manufacturer.

2. Oil the piston rings, pistons and cylinder walls with light engine oil. **Be sure to install the pistons in the same cylinders from which they were removed or to which they were fitted. The connecting rod and bearing caps are numbered from 1 to 4 in the right bank and from 5 to 8 in the left bank, beginning at the front of the engine. The numbers on the connecting rod and bearing cap must be on the same side when installed in the cylinder bore. If a connecting rod is ever transposed from one block or cylinder to another, new bearings should be fitted and the connecting rod should be numbered to correspond with the new cylinder number.**

3. Make sure the ring gaps are properly spaced around the circumference of the piston (Fig. 43).

4. Install a piston ring compressor on the piston and push the piston in with a hammer handle until it is slightly below the top of the cylinder (Fig. 44). Be sure to guide the connecting rods to avoid damaging the crankshaft journals. **Install the piston with the indentation notch in the piston head toward the front of the engine.**

5. Check the clearance of each

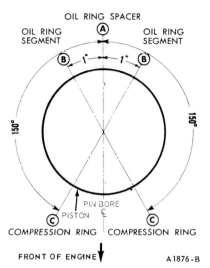

FIG. 43—Piston Ring Spacing

bearing following the procedure under Connecting Rod Bearing Replacement.

6. After the bearings have been fitted, apply a light coat of engine oil to the journals and bearings.

7. Turn the crankshaft throw to the bottom of its stroke. Push the piston all the way down until the connecting rod bearing seats on the crankshaft journal.

8. Install the connecting rod cap. The high performance engine uses ⅜-inch-diameter connecting rod bolts. **The bolts must be installed with the flat on the outside of the connecting rod. If improperly installed, the bolt will loosen and eventually fail.** Torque the nuts to specifications.

9. After the piston and connecting rod assemblies have been installed, check the side clearance between the connecting rods on each crankshaft journal (Fig. 45).

10. Disassemble, clean and assemble the oil pump. Clean the oil

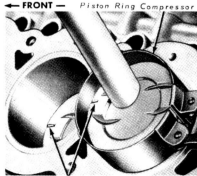

FIG. 44—Piston Installation

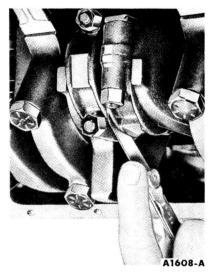

FIG. 45—Connecting Rod Side Clearance

pump inlet tube screen, and the oil pan and block gasket surfaces.

11. Prime the oil pump by filling either the inlet port or outlet port with engine oil and rotating the pump shaft to distribute the oil within the housing. Install the oil pump and the oil pan.

12. Install the cylinder heads following steps 1 thru 9 under Cylinder Head Installation.

13. Install the intake manifold following steps 2 thru 15 under Intake Manifold Installation.

14. Fill and bleed the cooling system. Fill the crankcase with the proper grade and quantity of engine oil.

15. Start the engine and check and adjust the ignition timing. Connect the distributor vacuum line at the carburetor.

16. Operate the engine at fast idle and check for oil and coolant leaks. Operate the engine until engine temperatures have stabilized and adjust the engine idle speed and idle fuel mixture.

17. Adjust the transmission throttle linkage. Install the air cleaner and intake duct assembly.

18. Connect the automatic choke heat chamber air inlet hose.

DISASSEMBLY

1. Remove the bearing inserts from the connecting rod and cap.

2. Mark the pistons and pins to assure assembly with the same rod and installation in the same cylinders from which they were removed.

3. Remove the piston pin from the piston and connecting rod (Fig.

46). Remove the piston rings.

CLEANING AND INSPECTION

Refer to Part 8-1, Section 3 for the cleaning and inspection procedures.

REPAIRS

Refer to Part 8-1, Section 2 for the repair procedures.

ASSEMBLY

The piston, connecting rod and related parts are shown in Fig. 47. **Check the fit of a new piston in the cylinder bore before assembling the piston and piston pin to the connecting rod.**

The piston pin bore of a connecting rod and the diameter of the piston pin must be within specifications. Refer to Part 8-4.

1. Apply a light coat of engine oil to all parts. **Assemble the piston to the connecting rod with the oil squirt hole in the connecting rod and the indentation notch in the piston positioned as shown in Fig. 48.**

2. Start the piston pin in the piston and connecting rod. Draw the piston pin through the piston and connecting rod until the end of the pin seats in Detail 2 (Fig. 49).

3. Follow the instructions contained on the piston ring package and install the piston rings.

4. Check the ring side clearance of the compression rings with a feeler gauge inserted between the ring and its lower land. (Part 8-1, Section 2). The gauge should slide freely around the entire ring circumference without binding. Any wear that occurs will form a step at the inner portion of the lower land. **If the lower lands have high steps, the piston should be replaced.**

5. Be sure the bearing inserts and the bearing bore in the connecting rod and cap are clean. Foreign material under the inserts will distort the bearing and cause a failure. Install the bearing inserts in the connecting rod and cap with the tangs fitting in the slots provided.

FLYWHEEL
REMOVAL

1. On a car with a manual-shift transmission, remove the transmission, clutch pressure plate and disc following the procedures in Group 5.

On a car with an automatic transmission, remove the transmission and converter housing following the procedure in Group 7.

2. Remove the flywheel retaining bolts and remove the flywheel.

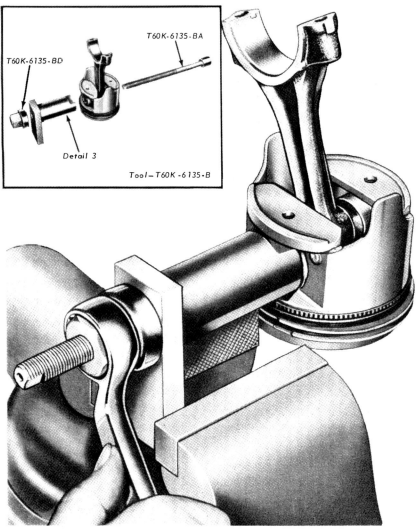

FIG. 46—Piston Pin Removal

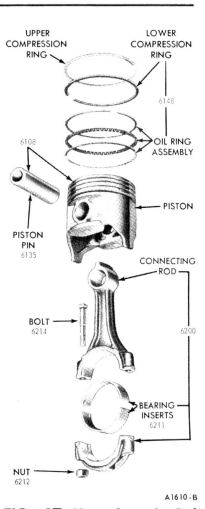

FIG. 47—Piston, Connecting Rod and Related Parts

CLEANING AND INSPECTION

Refer to Part 8-1, Section 3 for the cleaning and inspection procedures for manual-shift transmissions.

REPAIRS

To check flywheel face runout refer to Part 8-1, Section 1.

INSTALLATION

1. Coat the threads of the flywheel retaining bolts with oil-resistant sealer. Position the flywheel on the crankshaft flange. Install and torque the bolts in sequence across from each other to specifications.

2. On a car with a manual-shift transmission check the flywheel runout, following the procedure in Part 8-1, Section 1 and install the clutch pressure plate, disc and the transmission following the procedures in Group 5.

On a car with an automatic transmission check the flywheel runout, following the procedure in Part 8-1, Section 1 and install the transmission and converter housing following the procedure in Group 7.

CLUTCH PILOT BUSHING REPLACEMENT

1. Remove the transmission, clutch pressure plate and disc following the procedures in Group 5.
2. Remove the pilot bushing as shown in Fig. 64.
3. Coat the pilot bushing bore in the crankshaft with a small quantity of wheel bearing lubricant. **Avoid using too much lubricant as it may be thrown onto the clutch disc when the clutch revolves.**
4. Install the clutch pressure plate, disc and the transmission following the procedures in Group 5.

OIL FILTER REPLACEMENT
CARTRIDGE-TYPE OIL FILTER

The Rotunda oil filter assembly is shown in Fig. 50.

1. Place a drip pan under the filter. Unscrew the filter from the adapter fitting and clean the adapter recess.
2. Coat the gasket on a new Rotunda filter with oil. Place the new Rotunda filter in position on the

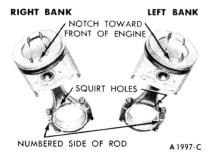

FIG. 48—Correct Piston and Rod Positions

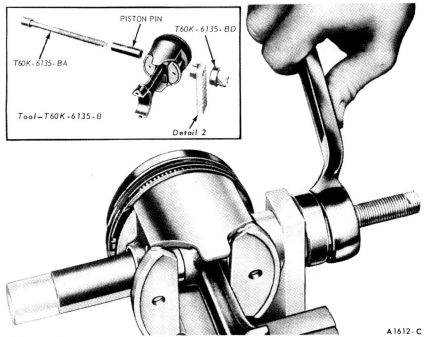

FIG. 49—Piston Pin Installation

adapter fitting. Hand tighten the filter until the gasket contacts the adapter face, and then advance it ½ turn.

3. Operate the engine at fast idle, and check for oil leaks. If oil leaks are evident, perform the necessary repairs to correct the leakage. Check the oil level and fill the crankcase if necessary.

ELEMENT-TYPE OIL FILTER

The oil filter assembly is shown in Fig. 51.

1. Place a drip pan under the filter. Loosen the filter center bolt, and remove the filter assembly and gasket.

2. Remove the filter element, neoprene gasket, spring and seat. Remove the center bolt from the filter cover and the fiber gasket from the bolt. Discard the filter element and all gaskets.

3. Wash all parts in solvent. Make sure all the openings in the center bolt are clean.

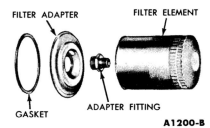

FIG. 50—Cartridge-Type Oil Filter

4. Install a new Rotunda filter element in the filter cover following the instructions furnished with the new element.

5. Clean the oil filter cover mounting surface on the adapter. Position a new gasket in the adapter recess.

6. Place the filter assembly in

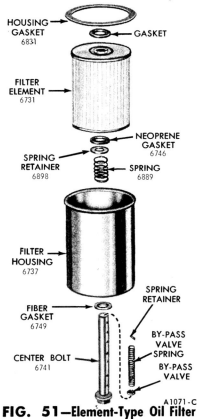

FIG. 51—Element-Type Oil Filter

position, and thread the center bolt into the adapter finger-tight. Rotate the filter slightly, in each direction, to make sure the gasket is seated evenly.

7. Torque the center bolts to specifications. **Do not overtighten the center bolt.**

8. Add oil to the crankcase if necessary. Operate the engine at fast idle, and check for leaks.

9. If oil leaks are evident, perform the necessary repair to correct the leakage.

OIL PAN
REMOVAL

1. Drain the crankcase. Remove the oil level dipstick.

2. Lower the stabilizer bar. On a Mustang, the idler arm will also have to be lowered.

3. Remove the oil pan retaining bolts and crank the engine as required to obtain clearance and remove the oil pan.

4. Remove the oil pump inlet tube and screen assembly.

5. Remove and discard the inlet tube to pump gasket.

CLEANING AND INSPECTION

Refer to Part 8-1, Section 3 for the cleaning and inspection procedures.

INSTALLATION

1. Clean the oil pump inlet tube and screen assembly.

2. Using a new inlet tube to pump gasket, install the inlet tube and screen assembly.

3. Clean the gasket surfaces of the block and oil pan. The oil pan has a two-piece gasket. Coat the block surface and the oil pan gasket surface with sealer. Position the oil pan gaskets on the cylinder block (Fig. 52).

4. Position the oil pan front seal on the cylinder front cover (Fig. 52). **Be sure the tabs on the seal are over the oil pan gasket.**

5. Position the oil pan rear seal on the rear main bearing cap (Fig. 52). **Be sure the tabs on the seal are over the oil pan gasket.**

6. Hold the oil pan in place against the block and install a bolt, finger-tight, on each side of the oil pan. Install the remaining bolts. Torque the bolts from the center outward in each direction to specifications.

7. Connect the stabilizer bar. On a Mustang, the idler arm must be installed.

8. Install the oil level dipstick. Fill the crankcase with the proper grade

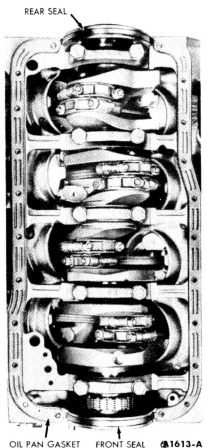

FIG. 52—Oil Pan Gaskets and Seals Installed

and quantity of engine oil. Operate the engine and check for oil leaks.

OIL PUMP
REMOVAL

1. Remove the oil pan and related parts as outlined under Oil Pan Removal.

2. Remove the oil pump inlet tube and screen assembly. Discard the gasket.

3. Remove the oil pump retaining bolts and remove the oil pump, gasket and intermediate drive shaft.

INSTALLATION

1. Prime the oil pump by filling either the inlet or outlet port with engine oil. Rotate the pump shaft to distribute the oil within the pump body.

2. Position the intermediate drive shaft into the distributor socket. With the shaft firmly seated in the distributor socket, the stop on the shaft should touch the roof of the crankcase. Remove the shaft and position the stop as necessary.

3. Position a new gasket on the pump housing. With the stop properly positioned, insert the intermediate drive shaft into the oil pump. Install the pump and shaft as an assembly. **Do not attempt to force the pump into position if it will not seat readily. The drive shaft hex may be misaligned with the distributor shaft. To align, rotate the intermediate drive shaft into a new position.** Torque the oil pump retaining screws to specifications.

4. Clean the oil pump inlet tube and screen assembly (Fig. 53).

5. Using a new gasket, install the oil pump inlet tube and screen assembly.

6. Install the oil pan and related parts as outlined under Oil Pan Installation.

DISASSEMBLY

1. Remove the oil inlet tube from the oil pump and remove the gasket.

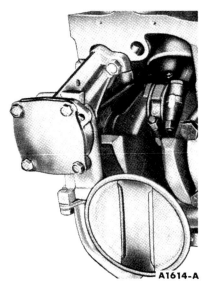

FIG. 53—Oil Pump and Inlet Tube Installed

2. Remove the cover retaining screws and the cover. Remove the inner rotor and shaft assembly, then remove the outer race.

3. Insert a self-threading sheet metal screw of the proper diameter into the oil pressure relief valve chamber cap and pull the cap out of the chamber. Remove the spring and plunger.

CLEANING AND INSPECTION

Refer to Part 8-1, Section 3 for the cleaning and inspection procedures.

ASSEMBLY

The oil pump assembly is shown in Fig. 54.

1. Oil all parts thoroughly.

2. Install the oil pressure relief valve plunger, spring and a new cap.

3. Install the outer race, and the inner rotor and shaft assembly. **The inner rotor and shaft, and the outer race are serviced as an assembly. One part should not be replaced without replacing the other. Be certain that the dimple (identification mark) on the outer race is facing outward on the same side as the identification mark on the rotor.** Install the cover and torque the cover retaining screws to specifications.

4. Position a new gasket and the oil inlet tube on the oil pump and install the retaining bolts.

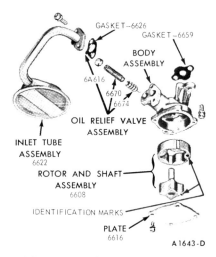

FIG. 54—Oil Pump Assembly

---

3 **ENGINE REMOVAL AND INSTALLATION**

The engine removal and installation procedures are for the engine only without the transmission attached.

REMOVAL

1. Drain the cooling system and the crankcase. Remove the oil filter.

2. Remove the hood. Disconnect

the battery ground cable at the cylinder block.

3. Disconnect the automatic choke heat chamber air inlet hose at the

inlet tube near the right valve rocker arm cover. Remove the air cleaner and intake duct assembly.

4. Disconnect the radiator upper hose at the coolant outlet housing and the radiator lower hose at the water pump.

On a car with an automatic transmission, disconnect the transmission oil cooler lines at the radiator.

5. Remove the radiator. Remove the fan, spacer, belt and pulley.

6. Disconnect the wires at the alternator. Loosen the alternator adjusting bolts to allow the alternator to swing down and out of the way.

7. Disconnect the oil pressure sending unit wire at the sending unit, and the flexible fuel line at the fuel tank line. Plug the fuel tank line.

8. Disconnect the accelerator rod.

On a car with an automatic transmission, disconnect the throttle valve vacuum line at the intake manifold. Disconnect the manual shift rod and remove the retracting spring. Disconnect the transmission filler tube bracket at the cylinder block.

On a car with an air conditioner, isolate and remove the compressor as outlined in Group 16.

On a car with power steering, disconnect the power steering pump bracket from the cylinder head. Remove the drive belt. Wire the power steering pump out of the way and in a position that will prevent the oil from draining out.

On a car with power brakes, disconnect the brake vacuum line at the intake manifold.

On an engine equipped with Thermactor exhaust emission control system, remove the air pump air filter if it is not connected to the engine.

9. Remove the heater hose from the automatic choke housing. Disconnect the heater hoses at the water pump and intake manifold. Disconnect the water temperature sending unit wire at the sending unit.

10. Remove the flywheel or converter housing to engine upper bolts.

11. Disconnect the primary wire at the ignition coil and position the wire out of the way.

12. Raise the front of the car. Disconnect the starter cable at the starter. Remove the starter and dust seal.

13. Disconnect the muffler inlet pipes from the exhaust manifolds. Disconnect the engine support insulators at the brackets on the frame underbody.

On a car with a manual-shift transmission, remove the remaining flywheel housing to engine bolts.

On a car with an automatic transmission, remove the converter housing inspection cover. Disconnect the flywheel from the converter. Secure the converter assembly in the housing. Remove the remaining converter housing to engine bolts.

14. Lower the car, then support the transmission. Install the engine left lifting bracket at the front of the left cylinder head, and install the engine right lifting bracket at the rear of the right cylinder head; then attach the engine lifting sling (Fig. 55).

15. Remove the air cleaner duct stud from the exhaust manifold. Remove the battery.

16. Raise the engine slightly and carefully pull it from the transmission. Carefully lift the engine out of the engine compartment so that the rear cover plate is not bent or other components damaged. Install the engine on a work stand.

INSTALLATION

1. Position new gaskets on the muffler inlet pipes.

2. Attach the engine lifting brackets and sling (Fig. 55). Remove the engine from the work stand.

3. Lower the engine carefully into the engine compartment. Make sure the exhaust manifolds are properly aligned with the muffler inlet pipes and the dowels in the block are through the rear cover plate and engage the holes in the flywheel housing.

On a car with an automatic transmission, start the converter pilot into the crankshaft.

On a car with a manual-shift transmission, start the transmission main drive gear into the clutch disc.

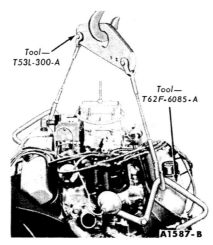

Tool—
T53L-300-A

Tool—
T62F-6085-A

A1587-B

FIG. 55—Engine Lifting Brackets and Sling—Typical

It may be necessary to adjust the position of the transmission in relation to the engine if the input shaft will not enter the clutch disc. **If the engine hangs up after the shaft enters, turn the crankshaft slowly (transmission in gear) until the shaft splines mesh with the clutch disc splines.**

4. Install the flywheel or converter housing upper bolts.

5. Install the engine support insulator to bracket retaining nuts. Disconnect the engine lifting sling and remove the lifting brackets.

6. Raise the front of the car. Connect both exhaust manifolds to the muffler inlet pipes. Torque the nuts to specifications.

7. Position the dust seal and install the starter.

On a car with a manual-shift transmission, install the remaining flywheel housing to engine bolts.

On a car with an automatic transmission, remove the retainer securing the converter in the housing. Attach the converter to the flywheel. Install the converter housing inspection cover. Install the remaining converter housing retaining bolts.

8. Remove the support from the transmission and lower the car.

9. Connect the engine ground strap and coil primary wire.

10. Connect the water temperature sending unit wire. Install the heater hose on the automatic choke housing and connect the hose at the intake manifold.

11. Connect the accelerator rod.

On a car with an automatic transmission, connect the transmission filler tube bracket. Connect the manual shift rod and install the retracting spring. Connect the throttle valve vacuum line.

On a car with an air conditioner, install the compressor as outlined in Group 16.

On a car with power steering, install the drive belt and power steering pump bracket. Install the bracket retaining bolts. Adjust the drive belt tension to specifications.

On a car with power brakes, connect the brake vacuum line.

12. Remove the plug from the fuel tank line. Connect the flexible fuel line and the oil pressure sending unit wire.

13. Install the pulley, belt, spacer and fan. Adjust the belt tension to specifications.

14. Install the battery. Install the air cleaner duct stud on the exhaust manifold.

15. Tighten the alternator adjust-

ing bolts. Connect the alternator wires and the battery ground cable.

16. Install the radiator. Connect the radiator upper and lower hoses.

On a car with an automatic transmission, connect the transmission oil cooler lines.

17. Install the oil filter. Fill and bleed the cooling system. Connect the heater hose at the water pump. Fill the crankcase with the proper grade and quantity of oil.

18. Adjust the transmission throttle linkage.

19. Operate the engine at fast idle and check all gaskets and hose connections for leaks.

20. Install the air cleaner and intake duct assembly. Connect the automatic choke heat chamber air inlet hose.

On an engine equipped with Thermactor exhaust emission control system, install the air pump air filter if it was removed.

21. Install and adjust the hood.

4 MAJOR REPAIR OPERATIONS

When installing nuts or bolts that must be torqued (refer to Part 8-5 for torque specifications), oil the threads with light weight engine oil. **Do not oil threads that require oil-resistant or water-resistant sealer.**

To perform the operations in this section, it will be necessary to remove the engine from the car and install it on a work stand.

CRANKSHAFT

The crankshaft and related parts are shown in Fig. 56.

REMOVAL

1. Disconnect the spark plug wires at the spark plugs and remove the wires from the ignition harness brackets on the valve rocker arm covers. Disconnect the coil to distributor high tension lead at the coil. Remove the distributor cap and spark plug wire assembly. Remove the spark plugs to allow easy rotation of the crankshaft.

2. Remove the fuel pump and oil filter. Slide the water pump bypass hose clamp toward the water pump. Remove the alternator and mounting brackets.

If the engine is equipped with Thermactor exhaust emission control system, remove the air pump and brackets from the right cylinder head.

3. Remove the crankshaft pulley from the crankshaft vibration damper. Remove the cap screw and washer from the end of the crankshaft. Install the puller on the crankshaft vibration damper (Fig. 37) and remove the damper.

4. Remove the cylinder front cover and water pump as an assembly.

5. Remove the crankshaft front oil slinger. Check the timing chain deflection; then remove the timing chain and sprockets by following steps 12 through 16 under Cylinder Front Cover and Timing Chain Removal.

Remove the counterweight (high performance engines only).

6. Invert the engine on the work stand. Remove the clutch pressure plate and disc (manual-shift transmission). Remove the flywheel and engine rear cover plate. Remove the oil pan and gasket. Remove the oil pump.

7. Make sure all bearing caps (main

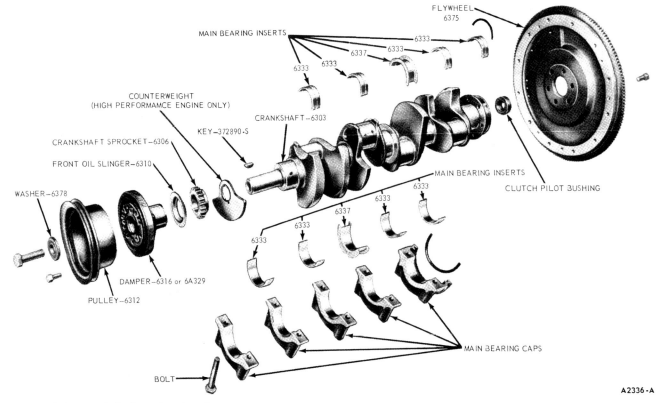

FIG. 56—Crankshaft and Related Parts

and connecting rod) are marked so that they can be installed in their original locations. Turn the crankshaft until the connecting rod from which the cap is being removed is down and remove the bearing cap. Push the connecting rod and piston assembly up into the cylinder. Repeat this procedure until all the connecting rod bearing caps are removed.

8. Remove the main bearing caps.

9. Carefully lift the crankshaft out of the block so that the thrust bearing surfaces are not damaged. **Handle the crankshaft with care to avoid possible fracture or damage to the finished surfaces.**

CLEANING AND INSPECTION

Refer to Part 8-1, Section 3 for the cleaning and inspection procedures. Clean the crankshaft damper, following the referenced procedure.

REPAIRS

To refinish journals, dress minor imperfections, etc., refer to Part 8-1, Section 2.

INSTALLATION

1. Remove the rear journal oil seal from the block and rear main bearing cap.

2. Remove the main bearing inserts from the block and bearing caps.

3. Remove the connecting rod bearing inserts from the connecting rods and caps.

4. If the crankshaft main bearing journals have been refinished to a definite undersize, install the correct undersize bearings. Be sure the bearing inserts and bearing bores are clean. Foreign material under the inserts will distort the bearing and cause a failure.

5. Place the upper main bearing inserts in position in the bores with the tang fitting in the slot provided.

6. Install the lower main bearing inserts in the bearing caps.

7. Clean the rear journal oil seal groove and the mating surfaces of the block and rear main bearing cap. Preform the new seal by hand to the approximate radius of the cap.

8. Insert the seal in the oil seal groove, seating the center of the seal first and allowing the seal to extend equally on both ends. Press the seal down firmly with the thumb at the center of the seal; then press both ends of the seal into the groove, working from the ends to the center.

9. Position the seal forming tool as shown in Fig. 57 and complete the seal installation. After installa-

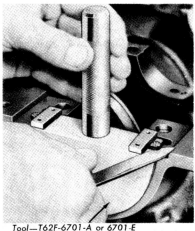

Tool—T62F-6701-A or 6701-E   **A1644-B**

FIG. 57—Rear Oil Seal to Block Installation

tion, cut the ends of the seal flush.

10. Carefully lower the crankshaft into place. **Be careful not to damage the bearing surfaces.**

11. Check the clearance of each main bearing as follows:

Place a piece of Plastigage on the crankshaft journal the full width of the journal and about ¼ inch off-center (Fig. 58). Follow steps 11 thru 15 under Main Bearing Replacement.

12. After the bearings have been fitted, apply a light coat of engine oil to the journals and bearings. Install a new seal in the rear main bearing cap and install the rear main bearing cap by following steps 17 thru 20 under Main Bearing Replacement. Install all the bearing caps, except the thrust bearing cap (No. 3 bearing). **Be sure that the main bearing caps are installed in their original locations.**

13. Install the thrust bearing cap with the bolts finger-tight.

14. Pry the crankshaft forward against the thrust surface of the upper half of the bearing (Fig. 59).

15. Hold the crankshaft forward

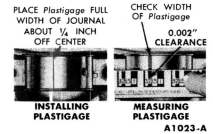

PLACE *Plastigage* FULL WIDTH OF JOURNAL ABOUT ¼ INCH OFF CENTER

CHECK WIDTH OF *Plastigage*

0.002" CLEARANCE

INSTALLING PLASTIGAGE   **MEASURING PLASTIGAGE**

A1023-A

FIG. 58—Installing and Measuring Plastigage—Engine on Work Stand

and pry the thrust bearing cap to the rear (Fig. 59). This will align the thrust surfaces of both halves of the bearing.

16. Retain the forward pressure on the crankshaft. Tighten the cap bolts to specifications (Fig. 59).

17. Force the crankshaft toward the rear of the engine.

18. Check the crankshaft end play (refer to Part 8-1, Section 2).

19. Install new bearing inserts in the connecting rods and caps. Check the clearance of each bearing following the recommended procedure.

20. After the connecting rod bearings have been fitted, apply a light coat of engine oil to the journals and bearings.

21. Turn the crankshaft throw to the bottom of its stroke. Push the piston all the way down until the rod bearing seats on the crankshaft journal.

22. Install the connecting rod cap. Torque the nuts to specifications.

23. After the piston and connecting rod assemblies have been installed, check the side clearance between the connecting rods on each connecting rod crankshaft journal (Fig. 45).

24. Install the crankshaft counterweight (high performance engines only). Install the timing chain and sprockets, cylinder front cover and crankshaft pulley and adapter, following steps 1 through 8 under Cylinder Front Cover and Timing Chain Installation.

25. Coat the threads of the flywheel retaining bolts with oil-resistant sealer. Position the flywheel on the crankshaft flange. Install and torque the bolts to specifications.

On a flywheel for a manual-shift transmission, use tool 6392-N to locate the clutch disc. Install the pressure plate. Tighten the retaining bolts.

26. Clean the oil pan, oil pump and oil pump screen. Prime the oil pump by filling either the inlet or outlet port with engine oil and rotating the pump shaft to distribute oil within the housing. Install the oil pump and oil pan by following the procedures under Oil Pan and Oil Pump Installation.

27. Install the Rotunda oil filter, fuel pump and connect the fuel lines. Install the alternator, shield, and mounting bracket.

If the engine is equipped with a Thermactor exhaust emission control system, install the air pump and mounting bracket.

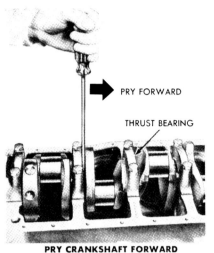
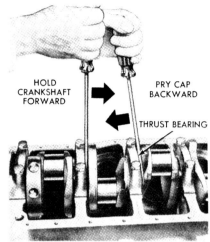
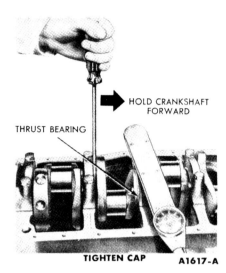

PRY CRANKSHAFT FORWARD   PRY CAP BACKWARD   TIGHTEN CAP   A1617-A

FIG. 59—Thrust Bearing Alignment

28. Install the spark plugs, distributor cap and spark plug wires. Connect the spark plug wires and high tension lead.

29. Install the engine in the car.

CAMSHAFT BEARING REPLACEMENT

Camshaft bearings are available pre-finished to size for standard and 0.015-inch undersize journal diameters. The bearings are not interchangeable from one bore to another.

1. Remove the camshaft, flywheel and crankshaft, following the appropriate procedures in Section 2 or Section 4. Push the pistons to the top of the cylinders.

2. Remove the camshaft rear bearing bore plug (Fig. 60). Remove the camshaft bearings (Fig. 61).

3. Select the proper size expanding collet and back-up nut and assemble on the expanding mandrel.

With the expanding collet collapsed, install the collet assembly in the camshaft bearing, and tighten the back-up nut on the expanding mandrel until the collet fits the camshaft bearing.

4. Assemble the puller screw and extension (if necessary) as shown and install on the expanding mandrel. Wrap a cloth around the threads of the puller screw to protect the front bearing or journal. Tighten the pulling nut against the thrust bearing and pulling plate to remove the camshaft bearing. Be sure to hold a wrench on the end of the puller screw to prevent it from turning.

5. Repeat the procedure for each bearing. To remove the front bearing, install the puller screw from the rear of the cylinder block.

6. Position the new bearings at the bearing bores, and press them in place with the tool shown in Fig. 61. Be sure to center the pulling plate and puller screw to avoid damage to the bearing. **Failure to use the correct expanding collett can cause severe bearing damage.** Align the oil holes in the bearings with the oil holes in the cylinder block when the bearings are installed. **Be sure the front bearing is installed 0.005-0.020 inch below the front face of the cylinder block (Fig. 62).**

7. Clean out the camshaft rear bearing bore plug recess thoroughly. Coat the flange of a new plug with oil-resistant sealer and install the plug (Fig. 63) with the flange edge of the plug facing outward.

8. Install the camshaft, crankshaft,

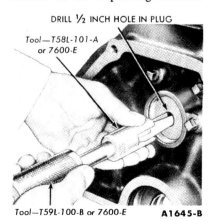

DRILL ½ INCH HOLE IN PLUG

Tool—T58L-101-A or 7600-E

Tool—T59L-100-B or 7600-E   A1645-B

FIG. 60—Camshaft Rear Bearing Bore Plug Removal

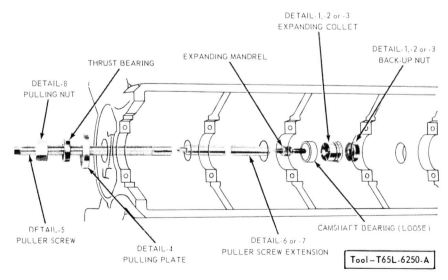

DETAIL-1,-2 or -3 EXPANDING COLLET

DETAIL-1,-2 or -3 BACK-UP NUT

EXPANDING MANDREL

THRUST BEARING

DETAIL-8 PULLING NUT

DETAIL-5 PULLER SCREW

DETAIL-4 PULLING PLATE

DETAIL-6 or -7 PULLER SCREW EXTENSION

CAMSHAFT BEARING (LOOSE)

Tool—T65L-6250-A

A2133-A

FIG. 61—Typical Camshaft Bearing Replacement

INSTALL FRONT BEARING 0.005-0.020 INCH
BELOW FRONT FACE OF BLOCK

A1647-A

**FIG. 62—Camshaft Front
Bearing Measurement**

flywheel and related parts, following
the appropriate procedures in Section 2 or Section 4, except do not
check connecting rod and main bearing clearances as a part of Camshaft
Bearing Replacement. Install the
engine in the car.

CYLINDER ASSEMBLY REPLACEMENT
DISASSEMBLY

Follow steps 1 thru 9, 11 thru 13,
and 16 thru 18 under Engine Disassembly. Remove 4 cylinder head
dowels from the cylinder block. Remove the cylinder block drain plugs,
and remove the cylinder assembly
from the work stand.

CLEANING

Clean the gasket and seal surfaces
of all parts and assemblies (refer to
Part 8-1, Section 3).

ASSEMBLY

Install the replacement cylinder
block assembly on a work stand. Install the cylinder block drain plugs
and cylinder head dowels. Transfer

Tool—T62F-6266-A or 6266-B
Tool—T53L-200-A

A1648-B

**FIG. 63—Camshaft Rear Bearing
Bore Plug Installation**

all parts removed from the old cylinder assembly to the new cylinder
assembly, following the procedures
in steps 21 through 31 and 35 through
59 under Engine Assembly. Check
all assembly clearances and correct
as necessary.

CYLINDER BLOCK REPLACEMENT
DISASSEMBLY

Follow steps 1 through 9, 11
through 14, 17 through 24, 27 and
28 under Engine Disassembly. Remove the 4 cylinder head dowels and
the cylinder block drain plugs from
the cylinder block. Remove the cylinder block from the work stand.

CLEANING AND INSPECTION

Clean the crankshaft damper and
the gasket and seal surfaces of all the
parts and assemblies (refer to Part
8-1, Section 3).

ASSEMBLY

Install the replacement cylinder
block on the work stand. Install the
cylinder block drain plugs and cylinder head dowels. Transfer the parts
removed from the old cylinder block
to the new cylinder block by following steps 5, 6, 9 through 12, 14
through 31 and 34 through 59 under
Engine Assembly. Check all assembly
clearances and correct as necessary.

ENGINE DISASSEMBLY

1. Install the engine on the workstand.
2. Remove the distributor cap and
spark plug wire assembly.
3. Disconnect the distributor vacuum line at the distributor. Remove
the carburetor fuel inlet line and fuel
pump outlet line. Remove the fuel
pump and discard the gasket. Remove the oil filter and adapter.
4. Slide the clamp on the water
pump bypass hose toward the water
pump. Remove the automatic choke-heat tube.
5. Remove the valve rocker arm
covers and the crankcase ventilation
system.
If the engine is equipped with a
Thermactor exhaust emission control
system, remove the anti-backfire valve
and bracket, the air pump and brackets and all the hoses.
6. Remove the alternator mounting brackets. Remove the ignition coil.
Remove the distributor hold-down
bolt and remove the distributor.
7. Remove the intake manifold
retaining bolts. Raise the manifold
and carefully remove it from the

engine. Discard the intake manifold
gaskets, seals and sealing washers.

8. Loosen the valve rocker arm
stud nuts so that the valve rocker
arms can be rotated to the side.
Remove the valve push rods in sequence and put them in a rack or
holder so that they can be installed
in their original position.
9. Using a magnet, remove the
valve lifters and place them in a rack
so that they can be installed in their
original bores (Fig. 39).
If the valve lifters are stuck in
their bores by excessive varnish, etc.,
it may be necessary to use a plier-type tool (T52T-6500-DJD or 6500-D) to remove the lifters. Rotate the
lifter back and forth to loosen it
from the gum or varnish that may
have formed at the lifter.
**The internal parts of each hydraulic valve lifter assembly are matched
sets. Do not intermix the parts. Keep
the assemblies intact until they are
to be cleaned.**
10. Remove the exhaust manifolds and the spark plugs.
11. Install the cylinder head holding fixtures (Fig. 24). Remove the
cylinder head bolts and lift the cylinder heads off the block. Discard the
cylinder head gaskets.
12. Remove the crankshaft pulley
from the crankshaft vibration damper. Remove the cap screw and washer from the end of the crankshaft.
Install the puller on the crankshaft
vibration damper (Fig. 31) and remove the vibration damper.
13. Remove the oil pan to cylinder front cover retaining bolts. Remove the cylinder front cover retaining screws. Remove the cylinder
front cover and water pump as an
assembly. Discard the gasket and remove the crankshaft front oil slinger.
14. Check the timing chain deflection and remove the timing chain
and sprockets by following steps 12
thru 16 under Cylinder Front Cover
and Timing Chain Removal. Remove
the crankshaft counterweight (high
performance engines only). Remove
the crankshaft sprocket key.
15. Remove any ridge and/or
carbon deposits from the upper end
of the cylinder bores. Move the piston to the bottom of its travel and
place a cloth on the piston head to
collect the cuttings. Remove the
cylinder ridge with a ridge cutter.
Follow the instructions furnished by
the tool manufacturer. **Never cut
into the ring travel area in excess
of 1/32 inch when removing ridges.**
After the ridge has been removed,

remove the cutter from the cylinder bore.

16. On a flywheel for a manual-shift transmission, remove the clutch pressure plate and disc.

17. Remove the flywheel and rear cover plate. Remove the clutch pilot bushing (Fig. 64).

18. Invert the engine. Remove the oil pan and discard the gaskets and seals.

19. Remove the oil pump and inlet tube as an assembly. Remove the intermediate drive shaft. Discard the oil pump gasket.

20. Make sure all connecting rods and caps are marked so that they can be installed in their original locations. Turn the crankshaft until the connecting rod being removed is down. Remove the rod cap.

21. Push the connecting rod and piston assembly out the top of the cylinder with the handle end of a hammer. **Avoid damage to the connecting rod journal or the cylinder wall when removing the piston and rod.**

22. Remove the bearing inserts from the connecting rods and caps. Install the rod caps on the connecting rods from which they were removed.

23. Remove the main bearing caps.

24. Carefully lift the crankshaft out of the cylinder block so that the thrust bearing surfaces are not damaged. **Handle the crankshaft with care to avoid possible fracture or damage to the finished surfaces.**

25. Remove the rear journal oil seal from the block and rear bearing cap.

26. Remove the main bearing inserts from the block and bearing caps. Install the main bearing caps in their original positions.

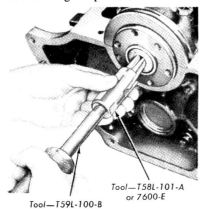

Tool—T58L-101-A or 7600-E
Tool—T59L-100-B or 7600-E   A1649-B

FIG. 64—Clutch Pilot Bushing Removal

27. Remove the camshaft thrust plate. Carefully remove the camshaft by pulling it toward the front of the engine. Use caution to avoid damaging the journals and lobes.

28. Remove the oil filter adapter.

29. Remove the camshaft rear bearing bore plug (Fig. 60). Remove the camshaft bearings (Fig. 61).

ENGINE ASSEMBLY

If the cylinder block is to be replaced, transfer the cylinder head dowels and cylinder block drain plugs to the new cylinder block and start the assembly procedures with step 5.

1. If the original block is used, remove the glaze from the cylinder bores by following the instructions of the tool manufacturer.

2. Invert the engine on the work stand.

3. Position the new camshaft bearings at the bearing bores, and press them in place with the tool shown in Fig. 61. Align the oil holes in the cylinder block when the bearings are installed. **Be sure the camshaft front bearing is installed 0.005-0.020 inch below the front face of the cylinder block (Fig. 62).**

4. Clean out the camshaft rear bearing bore plug recess thoroughly. Coat the flange of a new plug with oil-resistant sealer and install it with the cup side facing out (Fig. 63). Drive the plug in until it is slightly below the chamfer in the bore.

5. Oil the camshaft journals and apply Lubriplate to all lobes, then carefully slide it through the bearings.

6. Clean the rear journal oil seal groove and the mating surfaces of the block and rear main bearing cap. Preform the new seal by hand to the approximate radius of the cap.

7. Insert the seal in the oil seal groove, seating the center of the seal first and allowing the seal to extend equally on both ends. Press the seal down firmly with the thumb at the center of the seal, then press both ends of the seal into the groove, working from the ends to the center.

8. Position the seal forming tool as shown in Fig. 57 and complete the seal installation. After installation, cut the ends of the seal flush.

9. If the crankshaft main bearing journals have been refinished to a definite undersize, install the correct undersize bearings. Be sure the bearing inserts and bearing bores are clean. Foreign material under the in-

serts will distort the bearing and cause a failure.

Place the upper main bearing inserts in position in the bore with the tang fitting in the slot provided.

10. Install the lower main bearing inserts in the bearing caps.

11. Carefully lower the crankshaft into place. **Be careful not to damage the bearing surfaces.**

12. Check the clearance of each main bearing following the procedure under Main Bearing Replacement.

13. After the bearings have been fitted, apply a light coat of engine oil to the journals and bearings.

14. Install a new journal oil seal in the cap (Fig. 42) by following steps 6, 7 and 8. Apply a thin coating of oil-resistant sealer to the rear main bearing cap at the rear of the top mating surface (Fig. 42). **Do not apply sealer to the area forward of the oil slinger groove.** Install the rear main bearing cap and the remainder of the caps, except the thrust bearing cap (No. 3 bearing). **Be sure that the main bearing caps are installed in their original positions.** Torque the bearing cap bolts to specifications.

15. Install the thrust bearing cap and check crankshaft end play by following steps 13 thru 20 under Crankshaft Installation.

16. Turn the engine on the work stand so that the front end is up.

17. Install the pistons and connecting rods by following steps 1 thru 9 under Piston and Connecting Rod Installation.

18. Install the crankshaft counterweight (high performance engines only.) Position the sprockets and timing chain on the camshaft and crankshaft (Fig. 33). Be sure the timing marks on the sprockets are positioned as shown in Fig. 32.

19. Lubricate the timing chain and sprockets with engine oil.

20. Install the fuel pump eccentric, washer and camshaft sprocket cap screw. Torque the sprocket cap screw to specifications. Install the crankshaft front oil slinger (Fig. 35).

21. Clean the cylinder front cover and the cylinder block gasket surfaces. Install a new crankshaft front oil seal (Fig. 34).

22. Coat the gasket surface of the block and cover and the cover bolt threads with oil-resistant sealer. Position a new gasket on the block.

23. *Install the alignment pilot tool on the cylinder front cover so that the keyway in the pilot aligns with* the key in the crankshaft. Position the cover (and water pump) and pilot over the end of the crankshaft and against the block (Fig. 36).

24. Install the cylinder front cover screws finger tight. While pushing in on the pilot, torque the cover bolts to specifications. Remove the pilot.

25. Lubricate the crankshaft with a white lead and oil mixture and apply lubriplate to the oil seal rubbing surface of the vibration damper inner hub to prevent damage to the oil seal.

26. Line up the crankshaft vibration damper keyway with the key on the crankshaft, then install the vibration damper on the crankshaft (Fig. 37). Install the damper cap screw and washer, and torque the screw to specifications. Install the crankshaft pulley.

27. Using a new gasket, install the fuel pump.

28. Turn the engine on the work stand so that the top of the engine is up.

29. Clean the cylinder head and block gasket surfaces. Install the head gasket over the cylinder head dowels.

30. Place the cylinder head on the engine, then remove the holding fixtures. Coat the head bolt threads with water-resistant sealer, and then install the bolts.

31. The cylinder head bolt tightening procedure is performed in three progressive steps. Torque the bolts in sequence (Fig. 25) to 50 ft-lbs, then to 60 ft-lbs and finally to specifications. **After the cylinder head bolts have been torqued to specifications, the bolts should not be disturbed.**

32. Coat the mating surfaces of the exhaust manifold with a light film of graphite grease. Position new gaskets on the muffler inlet pipe.

33. Position the exhaust manifolds on the cylinder heads and install the retaining bolts and tab washers. Torque the retaining bolts to specifications, working from the center to the ends. Lock the bolts by bending one tab of the washer over a flat on the bolt.

34. Install the spark plugs.

35. Coat the outside of each valve lifter with engine oil to provide initial lubrication. **Do not fill the lifters with oil. The lifters will fill much faster after the engine is started, if they are free of any oil film which may cause an oil seal between the plunger and the lifter body.** Place each lifter in the bore from which it was removed.

36. Install the push rods in their original positions. Apply Lubriplate over the valve stem tips and the push rod guides in the cylinder head. Install the rocker arms over the push rods. Perform a valve clearance adjustment as outlined in Part 8-1, Section 2.

37. Clean the mating surfaces of the intake manifold, cylinder heads and cylinder block.

38. Coat the intake manifold and cylinder block seal surfaces with quick-setting adhesive.

39. Position new seals on the cylinder block and new gaskets on the cylinder heads with the gaskets interlocked with the seal tabs. Apply non-hardening sealer at the four junction points of the seals and gaskets. Be sure the holes in the gaskets are aligned with the holes in the cylinder heads.

40. Carefully lower the intake manifold on the cylinder block and cylinder heads. **After the intake manifold is in place, run a finger around the seal area to make sure the seals are in place. If the seals are not in place, remove the intake manifold and position the seals.**

41. Be sure the holes in the manifold gaskets and manifold are in alignment. Position the intake manifold alignment tools (Fig. 20) in the front and rear (Nos. 10 and 12) bolt holes on the left bank of the manifold.

42. Using new sealing washers, install the intake manifold retaining bolts. Torque the bolts in two steps. First, torque the bolts in sequence (Fig. 21) to 15-17 ft-lbs.

43. Remove the manifold alignment tools from the front and rear bolt holes (Nos. 10 and 12). Using new sealing washers, install the two remaining bolts and torque to 15-17 ft-lbs.

44. Torque all the manifold retaining bolts in sequence to specifications.

45. Install the water pump bypass hose on the coolant outlet housing. Slide the clamp into position and tighten the clamp.

46. Rotate the crankshaft until the No. 1 piston is on TDC after the compression stroke, then position the distributor in the block with the rotor at the No. 1 firing position and the points open. Install the hold down clamp.

47. Install the ignition coil. Position and install the alternator, shield and mounting bracket.

If the engine is equipped with a Thermactor exhaust emission control system, install the anti-backfire valve and bracket, the air pump and bracket and the hoses.

48. Clean the valve rocker arm covers and the cylinder head gasket surface. Apply oil-resistant sealer to one side of new cover gaskets. Lay the cemented side of the gaskets in place in the covers.

49. Position the covers on the cylinder heads. Make sure the gasket seats evenly all around the head. Install the bolts. The cover is tightened in two steps. Torque the bolts to specifications. Two minutes later, torque the bolts to the same specifications.

50. Install the crankcase ventilation system.

51. Install the automatic choke heat tube. Install the distributor cap. Position the spark plug wires in the brackets on the valve rocker arm covers. Connect the spark plug wires and the coil wire.

52. Connect the carburetor fuel inlet line and pump inlet line.

53. Prime the oil pump by filling either the inlet or outlet port with engine oil. Rotate the pump shaft to distribute the oil within the pump body.

54. Invert the engine on the work stand. Position the intermediate drive shaft into the distributor socket. With the shaft firmly seated in the distributor socket, the stop on the shaft should touch the roof of the crankcase. Remove the shaft and position the stop as necessary.

55. With the stop properly positioned, insert the intermediate drive shaft into the oil pump.

56. Position a new gasket on the pump housing and install the pump and shaft as an assembly. **Do not attempt to force the pump into position if it will not seat readily. The drive shaft hex may be misaligned with the distributor shaft. To align, rotate the intermediate shaft into a new position.** Torque the oil pump retaining screws to specifications.

57. Clean the gasket surfaces of the block and oil pan. Coat the block surface and the oil pan gasket surface with sealer. Position new gaskets on the block and position a new seal on the cylinder front cover and rear main bearing cap. Make sure the tabs on the seal are over the oil pan gasket. Install the retaining screws and torque them from the center outward to specifications

(one screw retains the fuel line bracket).

58. Install the oil filter adapter. Clean the oil filter gasket surface. Coat the gasket on the filter with oil. Place the Rotunda filter in position on the adapter fitting. Hand tighten the filter until the gasket contacts the adapter face; then advance it ½ turn.

59. Install the clutch pilot service bearing (Fig. 65). Coat the threads of the flywheel retaining bolts with oil-resistant sealer. Position the rear cover plate on the block and the flywheel on the crankshaft flange. Install and torque the bolts to specifications.

On a flywheel for a manual-shift transmission, use tool T58P-7563-A to locate the clutch disc. Install the

Tool—7600-H

A1650-C

FIG. 65—Clutch Pilot Bearing Installation

pressure plate.

60. Install the engine in the car. Fill and bleed the cooling system. Fill the crankcase with the proper grade and quantity of engine oil.

61. Operate the engine and check for oil and coolant leaks. Check and adjust the ignition timing. Connect the distributor vacuum line at the distributor.

62. Adjust the engine idle speed, fuel mixture and anti-stall dashpot (if applicable). Adjust the transmission throttle linkage (Group 7).

PART 8-4

390 V-8 ENGINE

Section	Page
1 Description and Operation	8-81
Manifolds	8-81
Cylinder Heads	8-82
Cylinder Block	8-82
Valve Train	8-82
Lubrication System	8-83
Positive Crankcase Ventilation System	8-84
Cooling System	8-85
2 In-Car Adjustments and Repairs	8-86
Engine Supports	8-86
Valve Rocker Arm Shaft Assembly	8-86
Intake Manifold	8-87
Exhaust Manifold	8-89
Positive Crankcase Ventilation System	8-90
Cylinder Heads	8-90
Valve Spring, Retainer and Stem Seal Replacement	8-91
Cylinder Front Cover and Timing Chain	8-92

Section	Page
Camshaft	8-94
Camshaft Rear Bearing Bore Plug Replacement	8-95
Hydraulic Valve Lifter Replacement	8-95
Main and Connecting Rod Bearing Replacement	8-96
Piston and Connecting Rod Assembly	8-97
Flywheel	8-99
Oil Filter Replacement	8-100
Oil Pan and Oil Pump	8-100
3 Engine Removal and Installation	8-101
4 Major Repair Operations	8-102
Crankshaft	8-102
Camshaft Bearing Replacement	8-104
Cylinder Assembly Replacement	8-105
Cylinder Block Replacement	8-105
Engine Disassembly	8-105
Engine Assembly	8-106

1 DESCRIPTION AND OPERATION

The 390 V-8 engine (Figs. 1 and 2) has a 4.05-inch bore and a 3.78-inch stroke and a total piston displacement of 390 cubic inches. It has a compression ratio of 10.5:1. The warranty plate identification symbol for the engine is Z.

An engine identification tag is attached to the ignition coil bracket; refer to Part 8-1, Section 1.

THERMACTOR EXHAUST EMISSION CONTROL SYSTEM

For engines equipped with Thermactor exhaust emission control system, refer to group 12 for description and adjustment and repair procedures.

MANIFOLDS

Exhaust gases provide the initial heat necessary to assist in vaporizing the incoming fuel mixture. An exhaust control valve located between the right exhaust manifold and the muffler inlet pipe, remains closed during engine warmup. This directs exhaust gases through a heat crossover passage in the intake manifold (Fig. 3).

The intake manifold has two sets of fuel passages, each with its own separate inlet connection to the carburetor (Fig. 4). The right barrels of the carburetor feed Nos. 1, 4, 6 and 7 cylinders and the left barrels feed Nos. 2, 3, 5 and 8 cylinders.

The distributor is mounted at the left front of the intake manifold.

Warm air for the automatic choke is drawn from the heat chamber of the right exhaust manifold.

FIG. 1—¾ Left Front View

A2294-A

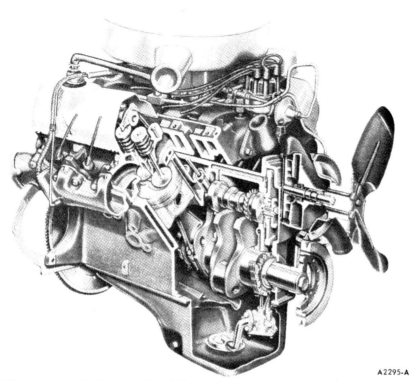

FIG. 2—¾ Right Front Sectional View

CYLINDER HEADS

The cylinder head assemblies contain the valves and the valve rocker arm shaft assembly. The combustion chambers are machined in the head. Valve guides are an integral part of the head. The valves are arranged from front to rear on both banks E-I-E-I-I-E-I-E (Fig. 5).

CYLINDER BLOCK

The cylinders are numbered from front to rear, on the right bank 1, 2, 3 and 4 and on the left bank 5, 6, 7 and 8. The firing order is 1-5-4-2-6-3-7-8.

The oil pump, mounted inside the oil pan at the front, is driven by the distributor through an intermediate drive shaft.

The crankshaft is supported by five main bearings. Crankshaft end thrust is controlled by the flanges of the No. 3 main bearing.

The pistons have two compression rings and one oil control ring. The top compression ring is molybdenum coated, and the lower compression ring is phosphate-coated. The oil control ring assembly consists of a serrated spring and two chrome-plated steel rails.

VALVE TRAIN

The intake and exhaust valve assemblies are the rotating-type which rotate slightly each time the valve opens and closes.

The push rods are solid steel with oil cushioned sockets.

The camshaft is supported by five bearings pressed into the block. It is driven by a sprocket and timing chain in mesh with a sprocket on the crankshaft. Camshaft thrust is controlled by a thrust plate bolted to the front of the cylinder block. An eccentric, bolted to the front end of the camshaft, operates the fuel pump.

Hydraulic valve lifters are used in the engine. The valve lifters are housed in bores located in the cylinder block valve lifter chamber. The valve lifters operate directly on the camshaft lobes, thereby transmitting the thrust of the camshaft lobes, by the means of hydraulic pressure, to the push rods which actuate the valve train. Figure 6 shows the various components and operation of a hydraulic lifter.

When either an exhaust valve or an intake valve is closed, the actuating valve lifter is on the base circle (lowest position) of the camshaft lobe.

When the valve lifter is in this position, the lifter plunger spring expands. This action forces the lifter plunger and valve push rod upward, forcing the valve end of the rocker arm to maintain solid contact with the valve (zero valve lash).

As the lifter plunger moves upward, the volume of the compression chamber is increased, resulting in reduced oil pressure in the compression chamber. Therefore, to equalize the resulting pressure differential between the supply chamber and the compression chamber, the disc valve moves off its seat and permits oil to flow from the supply chamber to

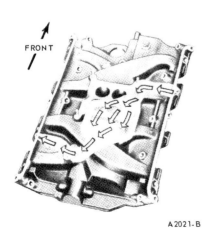

FIG. 3—Typical Intake Manifold Exhaust Gas Passages

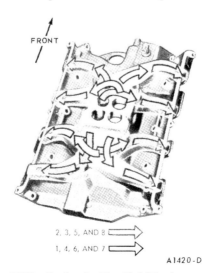

2, 3, 5, AND 8 ⇨
1, 4, 6, AND 7 ⇨

FIG. 4—Intake Manifold Fuel Passages

FIG. 5—Valve Port Arrangement

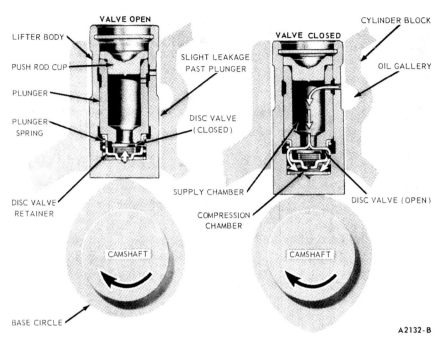

FIG. 6—Typical Hydraulic Valve Lifter Operation

the compression chamber. When the compression chamber becomes filled with oil, the pressures in the two chambers are equalized. The oil flow ceases and the disc valve spring seats the disc valve and closes the disc valve port.

As the camshaft rotates, the lifter assembly is raised by the camshaft lobe. This increases the push rod force against the lifter plunger and hydraulic pressure immediately builds up in the compression chamber until it acts as a solid member of the valve operating mechanism. The lifter then becomes a hydraulic ram which forces the valve in the cylinder head to open. During this period, a slight leakage of oil past the plunger occurs (calibrated leak down rate).

As the high point of the camshaft lobe rotates and passes by the foot of the valve lifter, the valve in the cylinder head seats and the valve lifter assembly is forced downward. Reduced force on the lifter plunger at this time relieves the pressure on the lifter plunger and it is free to be moved upward by the plunger spring. This action allows oil to flow once again through the oil holes in the lifter body and plunger.

The operating cycle is completed for each revolution of the camshaft. Zero clearance (lash) in the valve train mechanism is maintained at all times by the hydraulic force and expansion of the plunger spring between the lifter body and plunger.

LUBRICATION SYSTEM

Oil from the oil pan sump, located in the front of the oil pan, is forced through the pressure-type lubrication system (Fig. 7) by a rotor oil pump. A spring-loaded relief valve in the pump limits the maximum pressure

of the system. Oil relieved by the valve is directed back to the intake side of the pump.

All the oil discharged by the pump passes through a full flow-type filter before in enters the engine. The filter is mounted in a vertical position at the lower left front of the engine. A relief valve in the filter permits oil to by-pass the filter element if it becomes clogged.

From the filter, the oil flows into the main oil gallery which is located in the center of the valve push rod chamber floor. The oil gallery supplies oil to each individual camshaft bearing, through drilled passages in the block. Passages are drilled from each camshaft bearing to each main bearing. The camshaft No. 1 bearing feeds No. 1 main bearing, and the camshaft No. 2 bearing feeds No. 2 main bearing, etc. The oil then flows through notches or grooves in the main bearings to lubricate the crankshaft journals. A jiggle pin in the main oil gallery front plug allows any air that may be trapped in the oil to escape. The timing chain and sprockets are splash lubricated by oil from the jiggle pin.

The crankshaft is drilled from the main bearings to the connecting rod bearings.

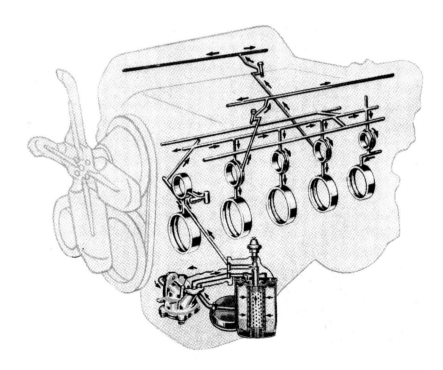

FIG. 7—Lubrication System

A small groove is located in the connecting rod at the mating face where the cap contacts the connecting rod. This groove is used as an oil squirt hole for cylinder wall lubrication. Oil from the connecting rod squirt hole lubricates the opposite cylinder wall. For example, the No. 1 connecting rod oils No. 5 cylinder, etc. As the crankshaft turns, the hole in the connecting rod bearing aligns with the hole in the journal causing a direct squirt of oil onto the cylinder wall.

Oil passages are drilled from the main oil gallery to each valve lifter oil gallery. Oil from here feeds the valve lifter assemblies. A reservoir at each valve lifter bore boss traps oil so that oil is available for valve lifter lubrication as soon as the engine starts.

An oil passage is drilled from the camshaft No. 2 bearing web to the left cylinder head between Nos. 5 and 6 cylinders to lubricate the valve rocker arm shaft assembly (Fig. 8). The oil passage in the cylinder head is drilled from the cylinder head bolt bore to the No. 2 valve rocker arm shaft support.

The oil flows through the valve rocker arm shaft through drilled holes in each valve rocker arm to

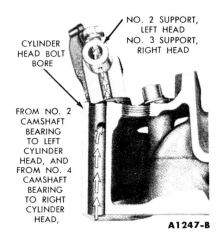

FIG. 8—Valve Rocker Arm Shaft Lubrication

lubricate the bushing and both ends of the valve rocker arm. The excess oil spirals down the rotating push rods and lubricates the push rod seats. The right valve rocker arm shaft assembly is similarly lubricated from No. 4 camshaft bearing via the No. 3 valve rocker arm shaft support.

A baffle located under the valve rocker arm shaft assembly shields the valve stems from oil splash. Excess oil is returned to the oil pan through drain-back holes located at each end of the cylinder head and

in the push rod chamber floor.

POSITIVE CRANKCASE VENTILATION SYSTEM

The engine is equipped with either an open positive crankcase ventilation system or a closed positive crankcase ventilation system. In either system the crankcase vapors are directed to the intake manifold.

OPEN VENTILATION SYSTEM

The positive crankcase ventilation system is shown in Fig. 9.

Ventilating air enters the engine through the oil filler cap located on the front of the left valve rocker arm cover. The filler cap contains a filtering element which filters the incoming air.

From the oil filler cap, the air flows into the front section of the valve rocker arm chamber. The ventilating air moves down past the push rods into the front of the lower crankcase and into the timing chain chamber.

The rotating action of the crankshaft causes the air to flow towards the rear of the crankcase and up into the rear section of the right valve rocker arm cover. The air then enters a spring-loaded regulator valve that regulates the amount of air to meet

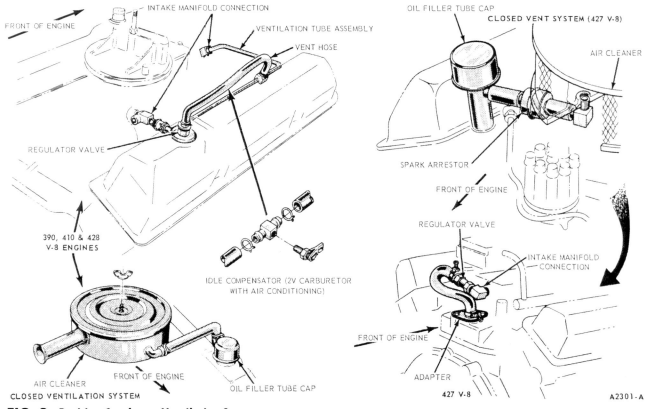

FIG. 9—Positive Crankcase Ventilation System

changing operating conditions (Fig. 10). The air is then directed to the intake manifold through the crankcase vent hose tube and fittings.

During idle, intake manifold vacuum is high. The high vacuum overcomes the tension of the spring pressure and moves the valve to the Low Speed Operation position (Fig. 10). With the valve in this position, the ventilating air passes between the valve (jiggle pin) and the outlet port. With the valve in this position, there is minimum ventilation.

As engine speed increases and manifold vacuum decreases, the spring forces the valve to the full open position (Fig. 10). This increases the flow of ventilating air.

CLOSED VENTILATION SYSTEM

The closed ventilation system is the same as the open ventilation system except for the following:

The crankcase ventilating air source is the carburetor air cleaner. The air passes through a hose connecting the air cleaner to the oil filler cap (Fig. 9). The oil filler cap is sealed at the filler opening to prevent the entrance of atmospheric air. A restriction in the air cleaner at the hose connection, assists the crankcase ventilation regulator valve in maintaining a slight vacuum in the crankcase.

COOLING SYSTEM

The coolant is drawn from the bottom of the radiator by the water pump which delivers the coolant to the cylinder block (Fig. 11).

The coolant travels through cored passages to cool the entire length of each cylinder wall. Upon reaching the rear of the cylinder block, the coolant is directed upward into the cylinder heads where it cools the combustion chambers, valves, and valve seats on its return to the front of the engine.

The coolant from each cylinder head flows through the water pas-

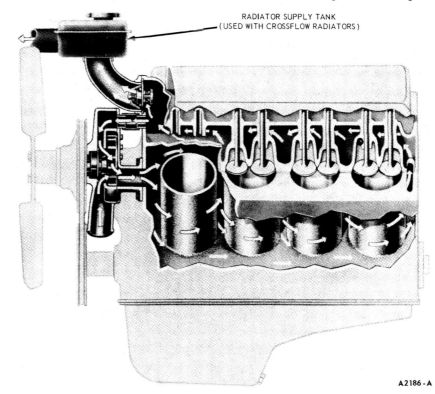

RADIATOR SUPPLY TANK
(USED WITH CROSSFLOW RADIATORS)

A2186-A

FIG. 11—Typical Cooling System

sages in the intake manifold past the water thermostat, if it is open, into the radiator header tank or supply tank. If the thermostat is closed, a small portion of the coolant is returned to the water pump for recirculation. The entire system is pressurized to 12-15 psi.

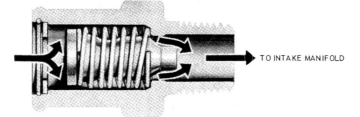

FROM CRANKCASE AND/OR ROCKER ARM COVER

TO INTAKE MANIFOLD

LOW SPEED OPERATION — HIGH MANIFOLD VACUUM

HIGH SPEED OPERATION — LOW MANIFOLD VACUUM

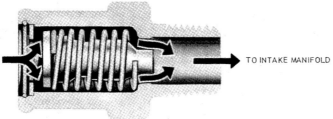

FROM CRANKCASE AND/OR ROCKER ARM COVER

TO INTAKE MANIFOLD

A2121-B

FIG. 10—Positive Crankcase Ventilation Regulator Valve Operation

2 IN-CAR ADJUSTMENTS AND REPAIRS

For adjustment and repair procedures of all components of the Thermactor exhaust emission system (if so equipped), refer to group 12.

When installing nuts or bolts that must be torqued (refer to Part 8-5 for torque specifications), oil the threads with light weight engine oil. **Do not oil threads that require oil-resistant or water-resistant sealer.**

ENGINE SUPPORTS

The front supports are located on each side of the cylinder block and the rear support is located at the transmission extension housing.

FRONT SUPPORT INSULATOR

The engine front support is shown in Fig. 12.

Removal

1. Position a jack and wood block under the engine oil pan, and raise the engine sufficiently to unload the engine front support insulators.

2. Remove the insulator assembly to engine retaining bolts and lock washers. Remove the intermediate support bracket retaining nuts and washers on both engine supports.

3. Raise the engine about 1 inch and remove the right side insulator assembly. Remove the assembly nuts and separate the insulator from the intermediate support bracket.

4. On the left side engine support, move the insulator and intermediate support bracket forward, and remove the assembly nuts. Separate the insulator and intermediate support bracket, and remove them from the engine compartment.

Installation

1. On a left side engine support, position the insulator and intermediate support bracket between the engine and frame crossmember bracket. Assemble the insulator and support bracket and torque the nuts to specifications.

2. On a right side engine support, assemble the support insulator to the intermediate support bracket, and torque the nuts to specifications.

3. Position the insulator assembly(ies) to the engine and install the retaining bolts and lock washers. Torque the retaining bolts to specifications.

4. Lower the engine and install the insulator assembly to support bracket retaining nut and washer on both supports. Torque the retaining nuts to specifications.

REAR SUPPORT INSULATOR

The engine rear support is shown in Fig. 13.

Removal

1. Position a jack under the transmission extension housing. Remove the insulator assembly to support bracket retaining bolts and nuts. Remove the insulator to transmission extension housing bolts and lock washers.

2. Raise the transmission extension housing slightly to gain clearance and remove the insulator assembly.

3. If necessary, loosen the support bracket to rail retaining bolts, washers and nuts. Remove the support bracket.

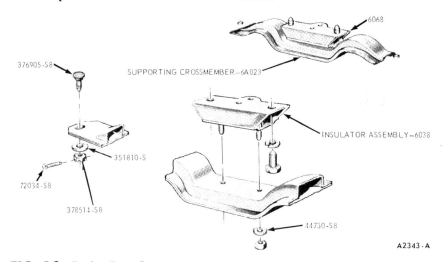

FIG. 13—Engine Rear Support

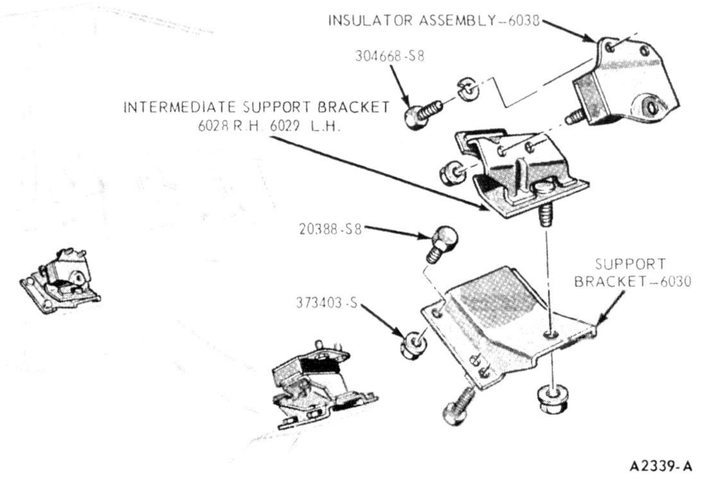

Installation

1. Position the insulator assembly to the transmission extension housing and to the support bracket, and install the bolts and lock washers. Torque the bolts to specifications.

2. Lower the transmission extension housing and tighten the support assembly to rail bolts and nuts to specifications. Remove the jack.

VALVE ROCKER ARM SHAFT ASSEMBLY

REMOVAL

1. Remove the air cleaner.

2. Disconnect the spark plug wires at the spark plugs. Remove the wires from the bracket on the valve rocker arm cover(s) and position the wires

INSULATOR ASSEMBLY—6038

304668-S8

INTERMEDIATE SUPPORT BRACKET
6028 R.H. 6029 L.H.

20388-S8

373403-S

SUPPORT BRACKET—6030

A2339-A

FIG. 12—Engine Front Supports

out of the way. If equipped with a Thermactor exhaust emission control system, disconnect the air hoses as necessary for accessibility and position them out of the way.

To remove the right valve rocker arm cover, remove the carburetor choke air heat tube, and the heat chamber air inlet tube. Remove the crankcase ventilation regulator valve.

To remove the left valve rocker arm cover, disconnect the brake booster vacuum line and position the line out of the way.

3. Remove the valve rocker arm cover(s).

If the left cover is removed, position the wire loom out of the way.

4. Starting at the No. 4 cylinder, loosen the right valve rocker arm shaft support bolts in sequence, two turns at a time. After the bolts are all loosened, remove the valve rocker arm shaft assembly and the oil baffle plate. Starting at the No. 5 cylinder, follow the same procedure on the left valve rocker arm shaft support bolts. **This procedure must be followed to avoid damage to the valve mechanism.**

INSTALLATION

1. Apply Lubriplate to the pad end of the rocker arms, to the tip of the valve stems, and to both ends of the push rods.

2. Crank the engine until the No. 1 piston is on TDC at the end of the compression stroke.

3. Rotate the crankshaft damper an additional 45° (identified by XX on the damper).

4. Position the baffle plate and the valve rocker arm shaft assembly(ies) on the cylinder head(s) with the valve push rods in place and the rocker shaft support bolts finger-tight. **Be sure the shaft is positioned so that the oil holes are to the bottom. Also, the identification notch (Fig. 14) must be downward and toward the front on the right bank, or toward the rear on the left bank.**

5. Starting at the No. 4 cylinder, tighten the bolts in sequence, two turns at a time, until the supports fully contact the cylinder head. Torque the bolts in sequence to specifications.

6. Starting at the No. 5 cylinder, follow the same procedure for the left valve rocker arm shaft support bolts. The additional time consumed in this procedure will permit the hydraulic lifters to leak down. This will minimize the possibility of bending

NOTCH   A1832-A

FIG. 14—Typical Installation Identification Mark—Rocker Arm Shaft Assembly

the push rods, valves or rocker arms. **Be sure that the hydraulic lifters have leaked down to their normal operating position before cranking the engine. This is necessary in order to avoid possible damage to the valves, push rods or valve rocker arms.**

7. Clean the valve rocker arm cover(s). Apply oil-resistant sealer to one side of new cover gasket(s). Lay the cemented side of the gasket(s) in place in the cover(s).

8. Position the cover(s) on the cylinder head(s). Make sure the gasket seats evenly all around the head. Install the bolts (and the wire loom clamps on the left cover). The cover is tightened in two steps. First, torque the bolts to specifications. Two minutes later, torque the bolts to the same specifications.

If the left cover was removed, connect the brake booster vacuum line.

If the right cover was removed, install the carburetor choke air heat tube, and connect the automatic choke heat chamber air inlet tube. Install the crankcase ventilation regulator valve in the rocker cover. If equipped with a Thermactor exhaust emission control system, connect the air hoses.

9. Connect the spark plug wires. Install the air cleaner.

DISASSEMBLY

1. Remove the cotter pins from each end of the valve rocker arm shaft. Remove the flat washer and spring washer from each end of the shaft.

2. Slide the rocker arms, springs and supports off the shaft. Be sure to identify all the parts.

3. If it is necessary to remove the plugs from each end of the shaft,

drill a hole in one plug. Insert a steel rod through the drilled plug and knock out the plug on the opposite end. Working from the open end, knock out the remaining plug.

CLEANING AND INSPECTION

Refer to Part 8-1, Section 3 for the cleaning and inspection procedures.

REPAIRS

Refer to Part 8-1, Section 2 for the repair procedures.

ASSEMBLY

1. Oil all the moving parts with engine oil. Apply Lubriplate to the pad of the valve rocker arms.

2. If the plugs were removed from the ends of the shaft, use a blunt tool or large diameter pin punch, and install a plug, cup side out, in each end of the rocker arm shaft.

3. Install the rocker arms, supports and springs in the order shown in Fig. 15. **Be sure the oil holes in the shaft are facing downward.**

When properly asembled, the identification notch (Fig. 14) on the right rocker shaft assembly must be facing downward and toward the front of the engine. On the left rocker shaft assembly, the notch is downward and toward the rear. Complete the assembly by installing the remaining flat washer and spring washer and install the cotter pin.

INTAKE MANIFOLD
REMOVAL

1. Drain the cooling system. Remove the air cleaner. Disconnect the automatic choke heat chamber air inlet tube.

2. Disconnect the accelerator rod at the carburetor. Remove the accelerator cross shaft bracket from the intake manifold and position it out of the way.

3. Remove the carburetor fuel inlet line at the fuel filter, and the automatic choke air heat tube. Disconnect the brake booster vacuum line at the intake manifold and at the flexible hose. Remove the vacuum line.

4. Disconnect the coil high tension lead and the coil wires at the coil. Disconnect the oil pressure sending unit wire at the sending unit. Remove the wire loom from the retaining clips on the left valve rocker arm cover and position it out of the way.

5. Disconnect the spark plug wires at the spark plugs and remove

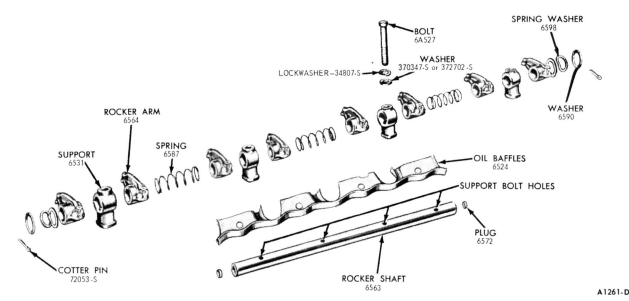

FIG. 15—Valve Rocker Arm Shaft Assembly

the wires from the ignition harness brackets on the valve rocker arm covers.

6. Remove the distributor cap and spark plug wire assembly. Disconnect the distributor vacuum line at the distributor.

7. Remove the distributor hold-down bolt and clamp. Remove the distributor.

8. Disconnect the radiator upper hose at the coolant outlet elbow. Disconnect the water temperature sending unit wire at the sending unit. Disconnect the heater hose at the automatic choke housing and at the manifold. Position the hoses out of the way.

9. Slide the clamp on the water pump bypass hose toward the water pump. Remove the crankcase ventilation regulator valve from the right valve rocker arm cover. Remove or disconnect the necessary components of the Thermactor exhaust emission control system.

10. Remove the valve rocker arm covers.

11. Refer to Valve Rocker Arm Shaft Assembly Removal and remove the valve rocker arm shaft assembly by following step 4.

12. Remove the valve push rods in sequence.

13. Remove the intake manifold retaining bolts.

14. Install standard eye bolts with $\frac{5}{16}$-18 threads in the left front and right rear rocker arm cover screw holes. Attach the engine lifting sling (Fig. 16).

15. Remove the intake manifold assembly. **It may be necessary to pry the intake manifold away from the cylinder head(s).** Remove the intake manifold gaskets and seals.

16. If the intake manifold assembly is to be disassembled, remove the coolant outlet elbow thermostat and gasket. Remove the heater hose fitting. Remove the carburetor, spacer and gasket. Remove the coolant temperature sending unit. Remove the crankcase ventilation inlet tube and fittings.

Remove the Thermactor exhaust emission control system fittings.

CLEANING AND INSPECTION

Refer to Part 8-1, Section 3 for the cleaning and inspection procedures.

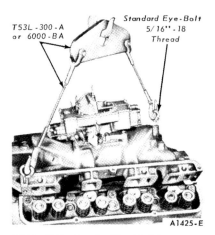

FIG. 16—Intake Manifold Removal or Installation

INSTALLATION

The intake manifold assembly is shown in Fig. 17.

1. If the intake manifold assembly was disassembled, install the carburetor, spacer and gasket. Coat the thermostat gasket and heater hose fitting with water-resistant sealer. Install the heater hose fitting. Coat the coolant temperature sending unit with electrical-conductive sealer and install it in the intake manifold. Install the crankcase ventilation inlet tube and fitting. Install the Thermactor exhaust emission control system fittings. Position the thermostat gasket on the intake manifold. Install the thermostat and coolant outlet elbow.

2. Clean the mating surfaces of the intake manifold, cylinder heads and cylinder block. Use a suitable solvent to remove all traces of oil.

3. Coat the cylinder block seal surfaces with a quick-setting seal adhesive. Apply a non-hardening sealer to the mating lines of the cylinder heads and cylinder block.

4. Position new seals on the cylinder block and new gaskets on the cylinder heads. **Be sure the seals are properly positioned during installation as the adhesive sticks to the seals immediately on contact.** Position the manifold gasket slots over the end tabs on the seals. Coat these four connections with a non-hardening sealer. Be sure the holes in the gaskets are aligned with the holes in the cylinder heads.

5. Install the eye bolts in the intake manifold and attach the engine

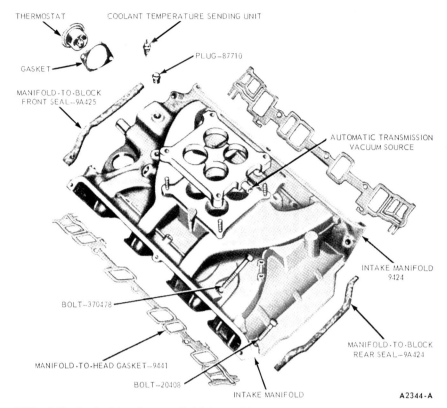

FIG. 17—Typical Intake Manifold Assembly

lifting sling. Carefully lower the intake manifold on the engine (Fig. 16) and at the same time engage the coolant outlet nipple with the water pump bypass hose.

6. Position the intake manifold by inserting the distributor in place. **After the intake manifold is in place, run a finger around the seal area to make sure the seals are in place. If the seals are not in place, remove the intake manifold and reposition the seals.**

7. Be sure the holes in the manifold gaskets and manifold are in alignment. **Apply a non-hardening, oil-resistant sealer under the head of each bolt,** and install the manifold retaining bolts. Torque the bolts to specifications in sequence as shown in Fig. 18.

8. Remove the distributor.

9. Remove the engine lifting sling and eye bolts.

10. Slide the water pump bypass hose clamp into position. Connect the water temperature sending unit, and the radiator upper hose. Install the heater hose on the automatic choke housing and connect the heater hose to the manifold.

11. Refer to Valve Rocker Arm Shaft Assembly Installation, and install the valve rocker arm shaft as-

sembly by following steps 1 thru 7.

12. Rotate the crankshaft damper until the No. 1 piston is on **TDC** at the end of the compression stroke. Position the distributor in the block with the rotor at the No. 1 firing position and the points open. Install the hold down clamp.

13. Install the valve rocker arm covers; refer to steps 8 and 9 under Valve Rocker Arm Shaft Assembly Installation. Install the crankcase ventilation regulator valve on the right valve rocker arm cover. Install

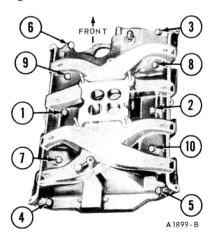

FIG. 18—Intake Manifold Torque Sequence

or connect the necessary components of the Thermactor exhaust emission control system.

14. Connect the brake booster vacuum line and the flexible hose.

15. Using a new clamp, install the carburetor fuel inlet line and connect the distributor vacuum line. Install the automatic choke air heat tube.

16. Install the distributor cap. Connect the spark plug wires. Install the wire loom in the retaining clips on the left valve rocker arm cover.

17. Connect the oil pressure sending unit wire, coil high tension lead, coil primary wire, and coolant temperature sending unit wire.

18. Install the accelerator cross shaft bracket. Connect the accelerator rod.

19. Fill and bleed cooling system.

20. Start the engine and check and adjust the ignition timing. Operate the engine until engine temperatures have stabilized, and adjust the engine idle speed and idle fuel mixture.

21. Adjust the transmission control linkage. Connect the automatic choke heat chamber air inlet tube, and install the air cleaner.

EXHAUST MANIFOLD
REMOVAL

1. On a right exhaust manifold, disconnect the automatic choke heat chamber air inlet tube at the carburetor. Remove the air cleaner. Remove the automatic choke air heat tube and air inlet tube.

2. On a left exhaust manifold, disconnect the power steering pump bracket from the cylinder block and move it out of the way. Position the pump so that the oil will not drain out. Disconnect the power steering hose bracket and position the hoses out of the way. Remove the dipstick and tube assembly.

3. Disconnect the exhaust manifold at the muffler inlet pipe. Remove the retaining bolts and tab washers and remove the exhaust manifolds.

On a right exhaust manifold, remove the exhaust control valve assembly, and discard the gaskets.

CLEANING AND INSPECTION

Refer to Part 8-1, Section 3 for the cleaning and inspection procedures.

INSTALLATION

1. Clean the mating surfaces of

the exhaust manifold(s) and cylinder head(s). Scrape the gasket material from the mounting flange of the exhaust manifold and muffler inlet pipe.

2. Apply graphite grease to the mating surface(s) of the exhaust manifold(s) and cylinder head(s).

3. On a right exhaust manifold install the exhaust control valve and a new gasket on the manifold studs. Place a new gasket on the muffler inlet pipe.

4. Position the exhaust manifold(s) on the cylinder head(s) and install the retaining bolts and tab washers. Working from the center to the ends torque the retaining bolts to specifications. Lock the bolts by bending one tab of the washer over a flat on the bolt.

5. On a left exhaust manifold, install the dipstick and tube assembly. Use oil-resistant sealer on the dipstick tube threads. Position the power steering pump bracket on the cylinder block and install the retaining bolts. Adjust the belt tension. Position the hoses and install the power steering hose bracket.

6. On a right exhaust manifold, install the automatic choke air heat tube and air inlet tube.

7. On a left manifold, position a new gasket on the muffler inlet pipe(s) and connect the exhaust manifold(s) to the inlet pipe(s). Install and torque the muffler inlet pipe retaining nuts to specifications.

8. Install the air cleaner.

POSITIVE CRANKCASE VENTILATION SYSTEM
REMOVAL

1. Remove the carburetor air cleaner, and disconnect the vent tube assembly at the two elbow fittings on the intake manifold. If equipped with a closed system, remove the vent hose from the air cleaner and/ or the filler tube breather.

2. Grasp the crankcase ventilation regulator valve and pull it straight upwards and out of the grommet in the right valve rocker arm cover.

3. Use a hose clamp tool to slide both hose clamps off the ends of the inlet hose. Remove the inlet hose from the carburetor spacer, and separate the hose from the regulator valve.

CLEANING AND INSPECTION

Refer to Part 8-1, Section 3 for cleaning and inspection procedures on the inlet hose, and oil filler tube breather cap. **Do not clean the reg-**

ulator valve. It should be replaced at the specified interval.

INSTALLATION

1. Install the inlet hose and hose clamp on the regulator valve. Position the hose clamp.

2. Install the crankcase ventilation regulator valve in the right valve rocker arm cover, and connect the vent tube assembly at the two elbow fittings on the intake manifold. Install the air cleaner. If equipped with a closed system install the vent hose.

CYLINDER HEADS
REMOVAL

If a cylinder head is to be replaced, follow the procedures under Cylinder Head Disassembly and Assembly, and transfer all valves, springs, spark plugs, etc., to the new cylinder head. Clean and inspect all parts and reface the valves (refer to Part 8-1) before assembling the used parts to the new cylinder head. Check all assembly clearances.

1. If equipped with a Thermactor exhaust emission control system, disconnect the air hoses as necessary for accessibility, and position them out of the way. Remove the intake manifold and carburetor as an assembly following the procedure under Intake Manifold Removal.

2. Disconnect the exhaust manifolds at the muffler inlet pipes.

If the left cylinder head it to be removed, remove the ignition coil and engine identification tag, and remove the power steering pump mounting bolt from the cylinder head.

3. Remove the cylinder head bolts.

4. Lift the cylinder heads off the block. **Do not pry between the head and the block.** Remove and discard the cylinder head gasket.

INSTALLATION

1. Clean the cylinder head and cylinder block gasket surfaces.

2. Inspect the cylinder head, following the procedures in Part 8-1, Section 3.

3. Guided by the word FRONT on the cylinder head gasket, install the gasket on the cylinder block. **Do not use cylinder head gasket sealer on a composition gasket.**

4. Place the cylinder head on the engine.

On the left cylinder head, install the ignition coil, engine identification tag, and the power steering pump mounting bolt.

5. Install the cylinder head bolts.

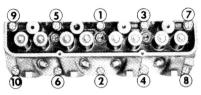

A1292-B

FIG. 19—Cylinder Head Bolt Torque Sequence

The cylinder head bolts are tightened in three progressive steps. Torque all the bolts in sequence (Fig. 19) to 70 ft-lbs., then torque them to 80 ft-lbs., and finally torque to specifications. **After the cylinder head bolts have been torqued to specifications, the bolts should not be disturbed.**

6. Position new gaskets on the muffler inlet pipes. Connect the exhaust manifolds to the muffler inlet pipes. Torque the nuts to specifications.

7. Install the intake manifold and related parts following the procedure under Intake Manifold Installation. If equipped with Thermactor exhaust emission control system, connect the air hoses.

DISASSEMBLY

1. Remove the Thermactor exhaust emission control system components. Remove the spark plugs. Clean the carbon out of the cylinder head combustion chambers before removing the valves.

2. Remove the exhaust manifolds.

3. Compress the valve springs (Fig. 20). Remove the spring retainer locks and release the spring.

4. Remove the sleeve, spring retainer, spring (and damper spring if applicable), stem seal and valve. Discard the valve stem seals. Identify all valve parts.

CLEANING AND INSPECTION

Refer to Part 8-1, Section 3 for the cleaning and inspection procedures.

REPAIRS

Cylinder head repair procedures and checks such as valve and valve seat refacing, cylinder head flatness checks, etc., are covered in Part 8-1, Sections 2 and 3.

ASSEMBLY

1. Install each valve (Fig. 21) in the port from which it was removed or to which it was fitted. Install a new stem seal on the valve. **The**

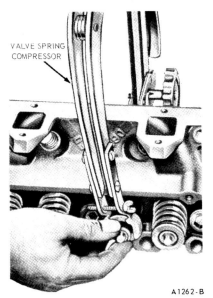

FIG. 20—Compressing Valve
Spring—On Bench

exhaust valve stem seal is approximately 0.025 inch shorter in overall height than the intake valve stem seal; therefore, be sure the seals are installed on the proper valves.

2. Install the valve spring (closed coils downward) over the valve, and install the spring retainer and sleeve.

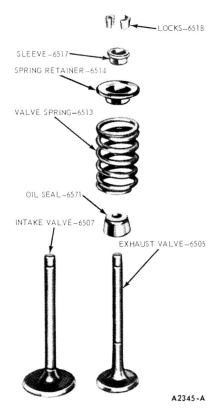

FIG. 21—Valve Assembly

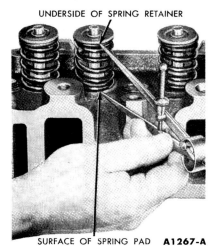

FIG. 22—Valve Spring Assembled Height

3. Compress the spring and install the retainer locks (Fig. 20).

4. Measure the assembled height of the valve spring from the surface of the cylinder head spring pad to the underside of the spring retainer with dividers (Fig. 22). Check the dividers against a scale. If the assembled height is greater than specified, install the necessary 0.030-inch thick spacer(s) between the cylinder head spring pad and the valve spring (Fig. 23) to bring the assembled height to the recommended specifications.

Do not install spacers unless necessary. Use of spacers in excess of recommendations will result in overstressing the valve springs and overloading the camshaft lobes which could lead to spring breakage and worn cam shaft lobes.

5. Install the exhaust manifolds.

6. Install the spark plugs.

7. Install the Thermactor exhaust emission control components.

FIG. 23—Valve Spring Spacer Installation

VALVE SPRING, RETAINER AND STEM SEAL REPLACEMENT

Broken valve springs, or defective valve stem seals and retainers may be replaced without removing the cylinder head, providing damage to the valve or valve seat has not occurred.

1. Disconnect the automatic choke heat chamber air inlet tube and remove the air cleaner. Remove the valve rocker arm cover(s), following steps 2 and 3 under Valve Rocker Arm Shaft Assembly Removal.

2. Loosen the valve rocker arm support bolts evenly and alternately, two turns at a time, until the valve spring tension has been released. Remove the push rods of the cylinder to be serviced.

3. Tighten the valve rocker arm support bolts evenly and alternately, two turns at a time, until they are snug. Push the rocker arm to one side and secure it in this position (Fig. 24). If an end valve is to be worked on, it will be necesary to remove the rocker arm from the shaft.

4. Remove the applicable spark plug. Install an air adapter in the spark plug hole and connect the air supply hose to the adapter (Fig. 25). Turn on the air supply. **Air pressure may turn the crankshaft until the piston reaches the bottom of its stroke.**

5. Compress the valve spring and remove the valve retainer locks from the valve (Fig. 26). **If air pressure fails to hold the valve in the closed position during this operation, it can be presumed that the valve is**

FIG. 24—Valve Stem Seal Removal

Tool—6513-AB or 6513-ABA

A1845-B

FIG. 25—Installation of Air Adapter Tool in Spark Plug Hole

not seating, or is damaged. If this condition occurs, remove the cylinder head for further inspection.

6. Remove the valve spring and related parts. Remove the valve stem seal (Fig. 24). **If air pressure has forced the piston to the bottom of the cylinder, any removal of air pressure will allow the valve(s) to fall into the cylinder A rubber band, tape or string wrapped around the end of the valve stem will prevent this condition and still allow enough travel to check the valve for binds.**

7. Inspect the valve stem for damage. Rotate the valve and check the valve stem tip for eccentric movement during rotation. Move the valve up and down through normal travel in the valve guide and check the stem for binds. **If the valve has been damaged, it will be necessary to**

SECURE ROCKER ARM

Tool—6513-J

Air Line Adapter

A1451-E

FIG. 26—Compressing Valve Spring—In Chassis

remove the cylinder head for repairs as outlined in Part 8-1, Section 2.

8. If the condition of the valve proved satisfactory, hold the valve in the closed position and apply the air pressure within the cylinder.

9. Inspect the valve stem seal for a cracked, torn or brittle condition, and replace it if necessary. Install the seal on the valve stem. **The exhaust valve stem is approximately 0.025 inch shorter in overall height than the intake valve stem seal; therefore, be sure the proper seal is installed.**

10. Install the valve springs, retainer and sleeve over the valve stem. **Make sure the valve damper spring is installed in the valve spring so that the coil end of the damper spring is 135° counterclockwise from the coil end of the valve spring.**

11. Compress the valve spring (Fig. 26) and install the valve retainer locks. Tap the valve stem tip with a soft mallet to make certain that the retainer locks are properly seated.

12. Remove the air line and adapter. Install the spark plug. Remove the wire securing the valve rocker arm and slide the rocker arm in position. Install the end rocker arm(s), if they were removed.

13. Loosen the valve rocker arm support bolts evenly and alternately, two turns at a time, until spring tension is removed. Apply Lubriplate to both ends of the push rod. Position the push rod within the rocker arm socket and the valve lifter seat.

14. Tighten the rocker arm shaft support bolts evenly and alternately, two turns at a time, until they are snug. Torque the bolts to specifications.

15. Remove the remote control starter switch. Install the high tension lead wire in the ignition coil terminal.

16. Install the spark plug wires. Check the valve clearances and correct if necessary (Part 8-1, Section 2).

17. Install the valve rocker arm cover(s), following steps 8 and 9 under Valve Rocker Arm Shaft Assembly Installation.

18. If equipped with a Thermactor exhaust emission control system, connect the air hoses.

19. Connect the automatic choke heat chamber air inlet tube, and heat tube. Install the air cleaner.

CYLINDER FRONT COVER AND TIMING CHAIN

If the cylinder front cover is being removed to replace the gasket or to replace the fuel pump drive eccentric, it is not necessary to check the timing chain deflection. For cylinder front cover gasket replacement, it is not necessary to remove the timing chain and sprockets.

REMOVAL

1. Raise the car on a hoist. Drain the cooling system and crankcase. Disconnect the battery ground cable.

2. Disconnect the fuel pump outlet line and remove the fuel pump retaining bolts. Position the fuel pump to one side, leaving it attached to the flexible fuel line.

3. Remove the oil pan and oil pump inlet screen, following the procedure under Oil Pan Removal.

4. Remove the cooling fan.

5. Disconnect the radiator upper hose at the coolant outlet elbow. Disconnect the radiator lower hose at the water pump. Disconnect the transmission oil cooler line at the radiator. Remove the radiator.

On a car with air conditioning remove the condenser retaining bolts, and position the condenser forward. **Do not disconnect the refrigerant lines.** Remove the compressor drive belt.

On a car equipped with Thermactor exhaust emission control system remove the air supply pump drive belt.

6. On a car with air conditioning, remove the compressor bracket to water pump bolts. Remove the power steering pump brackets to compressor bracket bolts. Loosen the remaining compressor bracket bolts.

7. Disconnect the power steering pump bracket from the water pump and remove the drive belt. Wire the power steering pump assembly to the left side of the car in a position that will prevent the oil from draining out.

8. Disconnect the heater hose at the water pump. Slide the water pump bypass hose clamp toward the engine.

9. Loosen the alternator mounting bolts at the alternator. Remove the drive belt. Remove the alternator support bolt at the water pump. Remove the water pump.

10. Remove the cap screw and washer from the end of the crankshaft. Remove the power steering

FIG. 27—Crankshaft Damper Removal

pulley from the crankshaft damper. Install the puller on the crankshaft damper (Fig. 27) and remove the damper.

11. Remove the crankshaft sleeve as shown in Fig. 28.

12. Remove the screws fastening the cylinder front cover to the block. Remove the cylinder front cover.

13. Discard the cylinder front cover gasket. Remove the oil slinger.

14. Check the timing chain deflection by following the procedure in Part 8-1, Section 1. If the deflection exceeds ½ inch, replace the timing chain and/or sprockets.

15. Crank the engine until the timing marks on the sprocket are positioned as shown in Fig. 29.

16. Remove the camshaft sprocket cap screw and the fuel pump eccentric.

17. Slide both sprockets and the timing chain forward, and remove the sprockets and timing chain as an assembly (Fig. 30).

CLEANING AND INSPECTION

Refer to Part 8-1, Section 3 for the cleaning and inspection procedures.

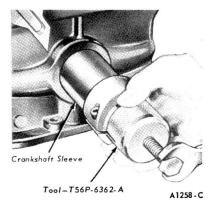

FIG. 28—Crankshaft Sleeve Removal

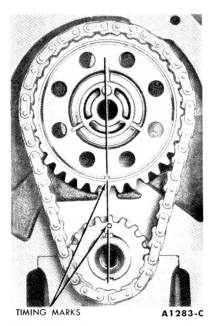

FIG. 29—Aligning Timing Marks

FRONT OIL SEAL REPLACEMENT

It is good practice to replace the oil seal each time the cylinder front cover is removed.

1. Drive out the old seal with a pin punch. Clean out the recess in the cover.

2. Coat a new seal with grease; then install the seal (Fig. 31). Drive the seal in until it is fully seated in the recess. Check the seal after installation to be sure the spring is properly positioned in the seal.

INSTALLATION

1. Oil the timing chain. Position the sprockets and timing chain on

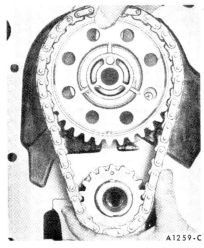

FIG. 30—Timing Chain Removal or Installation

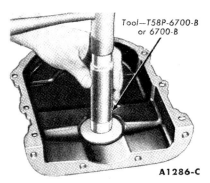

FIG. 31—Oil Seal Installation

the camshaft and crankshaft (Fig. 30). Be sure the timing marks on the sprockets are positioned as shown in Fig. 29.

2. Install the fuel pump eccentric and the camshaft sprocket cap screw (Fig. 32). Torque the sprocket cap screw to specifications. Install the crankshaft front oil slinger.

3. Clean the cylinder front cover, oil pan and cylinder block gasket surfaces.

4. Coat the gasket surface of the block and cover and the cover bolt threads with sealer. Position a new gasket on the block.

5. Lubricate and install the alignment pilot tool on the cylinder front cover so that the keyway in the pilot aligns with the key in the crankshaft. Position the cover and pilot over the end of the crankshaft and against the block (Fig. 33). Install the retaining screws.

While pushing in on the pilot

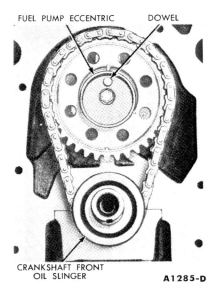

FIG. 32—Fuel Pump Eccentric and Front Oil Slinger Installed

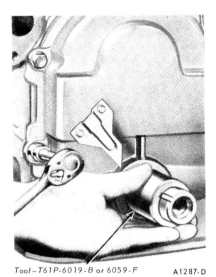

Tool—T61P-6019-B or 6059-F   A1287-D

FIG. 33—Cylinder Front Cover Alignment

torque the screws to specifications. Remove the pilot.

6. Install the crankshaft sleeve.

7. Lubricate the inside diameter of the hub and line up the damper keyway with the key on the crankshaft. Install the damper on the crankshaft (Fig. 34), using the illustrated tool.

8. Install the damper cap screw and washer, and torque the screw to specifications. Install the power steering drive pulley on the damper. Torque the screws to specification.

9. Clean the water pump gasket surfaces. Coat new gaskets with water-resistant sealer and position the gaskets on the block. Install the water pump and position the bypass hose and clamp on the water pump.

If equipped with air conditioning, attach the compressor bracket with the water pump bolts.

Install the alternator brackets.

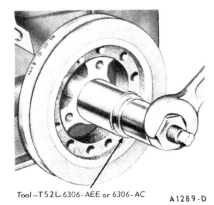

Tool—T52L-6306-AEE or 6306-AC   A1289-D

FIG. 34—Crankshaft Damper Installation

Torque all bolts to specifications.

10. Install the power steering pump.

11. Install the alternator on the mounting brackets.

12. Install the drive belts and adjust the belt tension to specifications.

13. Raise the car on a hoist. Clean the oil pan and the oil pump screen. Install the oil pump screen and oil pan following the procedure under Oil Pan and Oil Pump Installation.

14. Install the fuel pump, using a new gasket.

15. Connect the carburetor fuel inlet line, using a new clamp.

16. Install the radiator and support as an assembly. Connect the radiator lower hose at the water pump and the radiator upper hose at the coolant outlet elbow. Connect the battery ground cable. Connect the transmission oil cooler lines. Install the cooling fan and drive belt. Adjust the belt tension to specifications.

17. Fill and bleed the cooling system. Fill the crankcase with the proper grade and quantity of engine oil.

18. Operate the engine at fast idle and check for coolant and oil leaks. Adjust the ignition timing. Install the automatic choke heat chamber air inlet tube, and air cleaner.

CAMSHAFT

The camshaft and related parts are shown in Fig. 35.

REMOVAL

1. Remove the grille assembly. Remove the hood lock assembly.

2. Remove the cylinder front cover following steps 1 thru 13 under Cylinder Front Cover and Timing Chain Removal.

3. Refer to Valve Rocker Arm Shaft Assembly Removal and remove the valve rocker arm covers and the valve rocker arm shaft assemblies.

4. Remove the intake manifold and baffle plate, following the procedures under Intake Manifold Removal.

5. Remove the valve lifters and push rods in sequence and place them in a rack so that they can be installed in their original positions.

6. Remove the oil pan and oil pump screen by following the procedure under Oil Pan Removal.

7. Remove the timing chain and sprockets following steps 14 thru 17 under Cylinder Front Cover and Timing Chain Removal.

8. Remove the camshaft thrust plate and spacer. Carefully remove the camshaft by pulling it toward the front of the engine. **Use caution to avoid damaging the camshaft bearings.**

CLEANING AND INSPECTION

Refer to Part 8-1, Section 3 for the cleaning and inspection procedures.

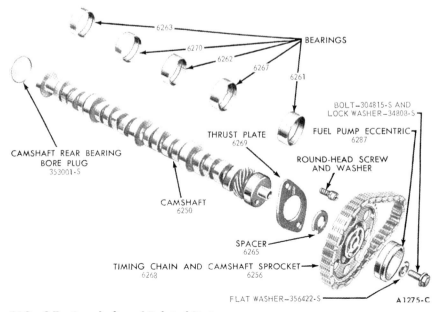

FIG. 35—Camshaft and Related Parts

REPAIRS

Refer to Part 8-1, Section 2 for the repair procedure.

INSTALLATION

1. Oil the camshaft and apply Lubriplate to the lobes. Carefully slide the camshaft through the bearings. Install the thrust plate and install the spacer. **The chamfered ID of the spacer must be toward the camshaft front journal. Be sure the thrust plate oil groove is up and toward the front (next to camshaft sprocket).**

2. Check the camshaft end play. Install a dial indicator so the indicator point is on the camshaft sprocket retaining screw. Push the camshaft toward the rear of the engine and set the dial indicator on zero. Pull the camshaft forward and release it. Compare the indicator reading with the specifications. If the end play is excessive, check the spacer for correct installation. If the spacer is installed correctly, replace the thrust plate.

3. Position the sprockets and timing chain on the camshaft and crankshaft (Fig. 30) with the timing marks on the sprockets aligned as shown in Fig 29.

4. Install the fuel pump eccentric and the camshaft sprocket cap screw (Fig. 32). Torque the sprocket cap screw to specifications. Install the front oil slinger.

5. Replace the crankshaft front oil seal. Install the cylinder front cover, crankshaft damper and related parts following steps 3 thru 16 under Cylinder Front Cover and Timing Chain Installation.

6. Install the valve lifters in the bores from which they were removed. Install the intake manifold, following the procedures under Engines With Hydraulic Valve Lifters.

7. Install the push rods in their original positions. Refer to Valve Rocker Arm Shaft Assembly Installation and install the valve rocker arm shaft assembly following steps 1 thru 9.

8. Refer to Valve Rocker Arm Shaft Assembly Installation and install the valve rocker arm shaft assembly following steps 1 thru 10.

9. Install and adjust the hood lock assembly. Install the grille assembly.

10. Fill and bleed the cooling system. Fill the crankcase with the proper grade and quantity of engine oil.

11. Start the engine and check and adjust the ignition timing. Connect the distributor vacuum line. Operate the engine at fast idle and check all hose connections and gaskets for leaks.

CAMSHAFT REAR BEARING BORE PLUG REPLACEMENT

1. On a car with a manual-shift transmission, slide the transmission to the rear and remove the clutch pressure plate, disc and flywheel housing following the procedure in Group 5.

On a car with an automatic transmission, remove the transmission and converter housing following the procedure in Group 7.

2. Remove the flywheel retaining bolts and remove the flywheel. Remove the rear cover plate.

3. Drill a ½-inch hole in the camshaft rear bearing bore plug and use tool T59L-100-B with puller attachment T58L-101-A to remove the plug.

4. Clean out the plug bore recess thoroughly.

5. Coat the flange of a new plug with oil-resistant sealer and install it with the flange facing inward (Fig. 61).

6. Install the rear cover plate. Install the flywheel.

On a car with a manual-shift transmission, install the clutch pressure plate, disc and flywheel housing and install the transmission following the procedure in Group 5.

On a car with an automatic transmission, install the transmission and converter housing following the procedure in Group 7.

HYDRAULIC VALVE LIFTER REPLACEMENT

The following procedure is applicable for removing one or all of the valve lifters.

1. Remove the intake manifold, following the procedures under Intake Manifold Removal.

2. Remove the valve lifters with a magnet through the push rod openings. Place the lifters in a rack so that they can be installed in their original positions.

The internal parts of each hydraulic valve lifter assembly are matched sets. Do not intermix the parts. Keep the assemblies intact until they are to be cleaned.

3. Install the new (or cleaned) hydraulic valve lifters through the push rod openings with a magnet.

4. Install the intake manifold, following the procedures under Intake Manifold Installations.

HYDRAULIC VALVE LIFTER DISASSEMBLY

Each valve lifter is a matched assembly. If the parts of one lifter are intermixed with those of another, improper valve operation may result. Disassemble and assemble each lifter separately. Keep the lifter assemblies in proper sequence so that they can be installed in their original bores.

1. Grasp the lock ring with needle nose pliers to release it from the groove. It may be necessary to depress the plunger to fully release the lock ring.

2. Remove the push rod cup. Remove the plunger (Fig. 36) and spring.

3. Invert the plunger assembly and remove the disc valve retainer by carefully prying up on it with a screw driver. Remove the disc valve and spring.

CLEANING AND INSPECTION

Refer to Part 8-1, Section 3 for the cleaning and inspection procedures.

HYDRAULIC VALVE LIFTER ASSEMBLY

A typical hydraulic valve lifter assembly is shown in Fig. 37.

1. Place the plunger upside down on a clean work bench.

2. Place the disc valve in position over the oil hole on the bottom of the plunger. Set the disc valve spring on top of the disc.

3. Position the disc valve retainer over the disc and spring, and push the retainer down into place on the plunger.

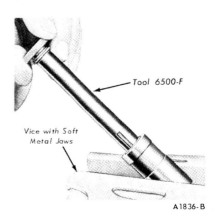

A1836-B

FIG. 36—Lifter Plunger Removal

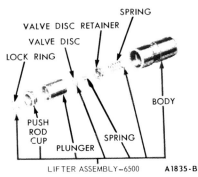

FIG. 37—Typical Hydraulic Valve Lifter Assembly

4. Place the plunger spring and then the plunger (open end up) into the lifter body.

5. Place the push rod seat in the plunger.

6. Depress the plunger, and position the closed end of the lock ring in the groove of the lifter body. With the plunger still depressed, position the open ends of the lock ring in the groove. Install the lock ring (Fig. 38). Release the plunger, then depress it again to fully seat the lock ring.

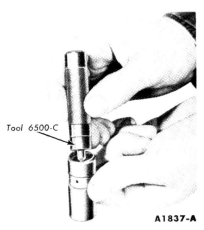

FIG. 38—Valve Lifter Lock Ring Installation

TESTING

Refer to Part 8-1, Section 1 for the testing procedures.

CRANKSHAFT REAR OIL SEAL REPLACEMENT

Replacement of a crankshaft rear oil seal requires replacement of both the upper and lower seals. Remove the engine; then remove the crankshaft and replace the seals following the procedure under Crankshaft Removal and Installation (Section 4).

MAIN AND CONNECTING ROD BEARING REPLACEMENT

The main and connecting rod bearing inserts are selective fit. **Do not file or lap bearing caps or use shims to obtain the proper bearing clearance.**

Selective fit bearings are available for service in standard sizes and 0.002 inch undersize only. Standard bearings are divided into two sizes and are identified by a daub of red or blue paint. Refer to the Parts Catalog for the available sizes. **Red marked bearings increase the clearance; blue marked bearings decrease the clearance.** Undersize bearings, which are not selective fit, are available for use on journals that have been refinished.

MAIN BEARING REPLACEMENT

1. Drain the crankcase. Remove the oil level dipstick. Remove the oil pan and oil pump. Remove the spark plugs to allow easy rotation of the crankshaft.

2. **Replace one bearing at a time leaving the other bearing securely fastened.** Remove the main bearing cap to which new bearings are to be installed.

3. Insert the upper bearing removal tool (tool 6331) in the oil hole in the crankshaft (Fig. 39).

4. Rotate the crankshaft in the direction of engine rotation to force the bearing out of the block.

5. Clean the crankshaft journal and bearing inserts. **When replacing standard bearings with new bearings, it is good practice to first try to obtain the proper clearance with two blue bearing halves.**

6. To install the upper main bearing, place the plain end of the bearing over the shaft on the locking

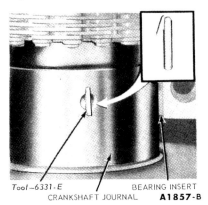

FIG. 39—Upper Main Bearing Insert Removal or Installation

tang side of the block and partially install the bearing so that tool 6331 can be inserted in the oil hole in the crankshaft (Fig. 39). With tool 6331 positioned in the oil hole in the crankshaft, rotate the crankshaft in the opposite direction of engine rotation until the bearing seats itself. Remove the tool.

7. Install the cap bearing.

8. Support the crankshaft so that its weight will not compress the Plastigage and provide an erroneous reading. Position a small jack so that it will bear against the counterweight adjoining the bearing which is being checked.

9. Place a piece of Plastigage on the bearing surface the full width of the bearing cap and about ¼ inch off center (Fig. 40).

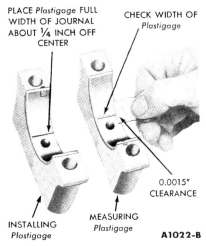

FIG. 40—Installing and Measuring Plastigage—Engine in Chassis

10. Install the cap and torque the bolts to specifications. **Do not turn the crankshaft while the Plastigage is in place. When checking the width of the Plastigage, check at the widest point in order to get the minimum clearance. Check at the narrowest point in order to get the maximum clearance. The difference between the two readings is the taper.**

11. If the clearance is less than the specified limits, try two red bearing halves or a combination of red and blue depending upon the condition. If the clearance exceeds specified limits, try 0.002 inch undersize bearings in combination with blue or red bearings. *The bearing clearance must be within specified limits. If 0.002 inch undersize main*

bearings are used on more than one journal, be sure they are all installed on the same side (cap or cylinder block) of the crankshaft. If the standard and 0.002 inch undersize bearings do not bring the clearance within the desired limits, refinish the crankshaft journal. Then install undersize bearings.

12. After the bearing has been checked and found to be satisfactory, apply a light coat of engine oil to the journal and bearings; then install the bearing cap. Torque the cap bolts to specifications.

13. Repeat the procedure for the remaining bearings that require replacement.

14. If the thrust bearing cap (No. 3 main bearing) has been removed, install it as follows:

Install the thrust bearing cap with the bolts finger-tight. Pry the crankshaft forward against the thrust surface of the upper half of the bearing (Fig. 58). Hold the crankshaft forward and pry the thrust bearing cap to the rear (Fig. 58). This will align the thrust surfaces of both halves of the bearing. Retain the forward pressure on the crankhaft. Torque the cap bolts to specifications.

15. If the rear main bearing is replaced, remove the rear main bearing cap. Remove and discard the rear seal and side seals.

16. Clean the rear journal oil seal

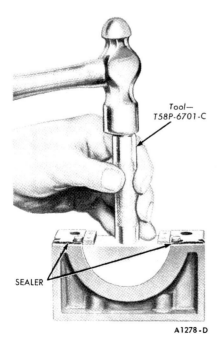

Tool—
T58P-6701-C

SEALER

A1278-D

FIG. 41—Seal to Rear Bearing Cap Installation

groove.

17. Install a new rear journal oil seal in the rear main bearing cap (Fig. 41). After installation, cut the end of the seals flush.

18. Apply a thin coating of oil-resistant sealer to the rear main bearing cap at the rear of the top mating surface (Fig. 41). **Do not apply sealer to the area forward of the side seal groove.** Install the rear main bearing cap. Torque the cap bolts to specifications.

19. Dip the side seals in light engine oil; then immediately install them in the grooves. **Do not use sealer on the side seals. The seals are designed to expand when dipped in oil. Using sealer may retard this expansion.** It may be necessary to tap the seals into place for the last ½ inch of travel. Do not cut the seal projecting ends.

20. Check the retainer side seals for leaks by squirting a few drops of oil into the parting lines between the rear main bearing cap and the cylinder block from the outside. Blow compressed air against the seals from the inside of the block. If air bubbles appear in the oil, it indicates possible oil leakage. **This test should not be performed on newly installed seals until sufficient time has been allowed for the seals to expand into the seal grooves.**

21. Disassemble, clean and assemble the oil pump.

22. Install the oil pump and oil pan. Install the oil level dipstick. Fill the crankcase with the proper amount and viscosity oil. Install the spark plugs.

23. Operate the engine and check for oil leaks.

CONNECTING ROD BEARING REPLACEMENT

1. Follow step 1 under Main Bearing Replacement.

2. Turn the crankshaft until the connecting rod to which new bearings are to be fitted is down.

3. Remove the connecting rod cap. Push the connecting rod up into the cylinder and remove the bearing insert from the rod and cap.

4. Follow step 5 under Main Bearing Replacement.

5. Install the new bearings in the connecting rod and cap. Pull the connecting rod assembly down firmly on the chankshaft journal.

6. Place a piece of Plastigage on the lower bearing surface, the full width of the cap and about ¼ inch off-center.

7. Install the cap and torque the connecting rod nuts to specifications. **Do not turn the crankshaft while the Plastigage is in place.**

8. Remove the cap; then, using the Plastigage scale, check the width of the Plastigage. **When checking the width of the Plastigage, check at the widest point in order to get the minimum clearance. Check at the narrowest point in order to get the maximum clearance. The difference between the two readings is the taper.**

9. If the clearance is less than the specified limits, try two red bearing halves or a combination of red and blue depending upon the condition.

If the clearance exceeds the specified limits, try 0.002 inch undersize bearings in combination with blue or red bearings. **The bearing clearance must be within specified limits.**

If the proper clearance cannot be achieved with standard or 0.002 undersize bearings, the crankshaft will have to be ground undersize and fitted with undersize bearings.

10. After the bearing clearance has been checked and found to be satisfactory, apply a light coat of engine oil to the journal and bearings. Install the connecting rod cap.

11. Repeat the procedure for the remaining connecting rods that require new bearings.

12. Follow steps 21, 22 and 23 under Main Bearing Replacement.

CLEANING AND INSPECTION

Refer to Part 8-1, Section 3 for the cleaning and inspection procedures.

PISTON AND CONNECTING ROD ASSEMBLY
REMOVAL

1. Drain the cooling system and the crankcase. Remove the intake manifold, cylinder heads, oil pan and oil pump following the procedures in this section.

2. Remove any ridge and/or deposits from the upper end of the cylinder bores as follows.

Turn the crankshaft until the piston to be removed is at the bottom of its travel and place a cloth on the piston head to collect the cuttings. Remove any ridge and/or deposits from the upper end of the cylinder bores. Remove the cylinder ridge with a ridge cutter. Follow the instructions furnished by the tool manufacturer. **Never cut into the ring** travel area in excess of $\frac{1}{32}$ inch when removing ridges.

3. Make sure all connecting rod caps are marked so that they can be installed in their original locations.

4. Turn the crankshaft until the connecting rod being removed is down.

5. Remove the connecting rod cap.

6. Push the connecting rod and piston assemby out the top of the cylinder with the handle end of a hammer. **Avoid damage to the crankshaft journal or the cylinder wall when removing the piston and rod.**

7. Remove the bearing inserts from the connecting rod and cap.

8. Install the cap on the connecting rod from which it was removed.

INSTALLATION

1. If new piston rings are to be installed, remove the cylinder wall glaze. Follow the instructions of the tool manufacturer.

2. Oil the piston rings, pistons and cylinder walls with light engine oil. **Be sure to install the pistons in the same cylinders from which they were removed or to which they were fitted. The connecting rods and bearing caps are numbered from 1 to 4 in the right bank and from 5 to 8 in the left bank, beginning at the front of the engine. The numbers on the connecting rod and bearing cap must be on the same side when installed in the cylinder bore. If a connecting rod is ever transposed from one block or cylinder to another, new bearings should be fitted, and the connecting rod should be numbered to correspond with the**

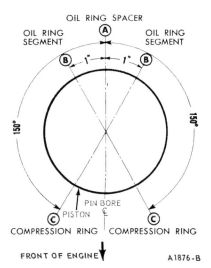

FIG. 42—Piston Ring Gap Spacing

new cylinder number.

Check the end gap of all piston rings (Part 8-1). It must be within specifications (Part 8-4).

3. Make sure the ring gaps are properly spaced around the circumference of the piston (Fig. 42).

4. Install a piston ring compressor on the piston and push the piston in with a hammer handle until it is slightly below the top of the cylinder (Fig. 43). Be sure to guide the connecting rods to avoid damaging the crankshaft journals. **Install the piston with the indentation in the piston head toward the front of the engine.**

5. Check the clearance of each

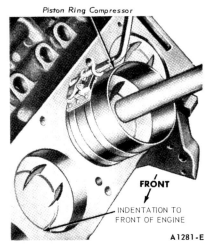

FIG. 43—Piston Installation

bearing following the procedure under Connecting Rod Bearing Replacement.

6. After the bearings have been fitted, apply a light coat of engine oil to the journals and bearings.

7. Turn the crankshaft throw to the bottom of its stroke. Push the piston all the way down until the connecting rod bearing seats on the crankshaft journal.

8. Install the connecting rod cap. Torque the nuts to specifications.

9. After the piston and connecting rod assemblies have been installed, check the side clearance between the connecting rods on each crankshaft journal (Fig. 44).

10. Disassemble, clean and assemble the oil pump. Clean the oil pump inlet tube screen and the oil pan and block gasket surfaces.

11. Prime the oil pump by filling either the inlet port or outlet port with engine oil and rotating the pump shaft to distribute the oil within the housing. Install the oil pump

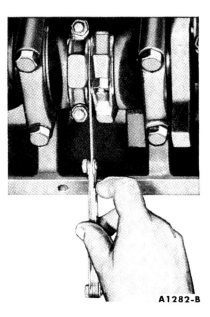

FIG. 44—Connecting Rod Side Clearance

and the oil pan.

12. Install the cylinder heads by following steps 1 thru 6 under Cylinder Head Installation.

13. Refer to Intake Manifold Installation and install the intake manifold by following steps 2 through 18.

14. Fill and bleed the cooling system. Fill the crankcase with the proper grade and quantity of engine oil.

15. Operate the engine and check for oil and coolant leaks. Check and adjust the ignition timing. Adjust the engine idle speed and fuel mixture.

16. Install the air cleaner and connect the automatic choke heat chamber air inlet tube.

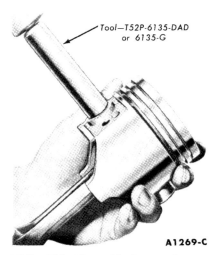

FIG. 45—Piston Pin Removal

DISASSEMBLY

1. Mark the pistons and pins to assure assembly with the same rod and installation in the same cylinder from which they were removed.

2. Remove the piston rings. Remove the piston pin retainers. Drive the pin out of the piston and connecting rod (Fig. 45). Discard the retainers.

CLEANING AND INSPECTION

Refer to Part 8-1, Section 3 for the cleaning and inspection procedures.

REPAIR

Refer to Part 8-1, Section 2 for the repair procedures.

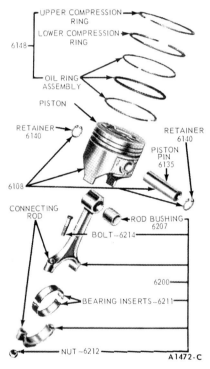

FIG. 46—Piston, Connecting Rod and Related Parts

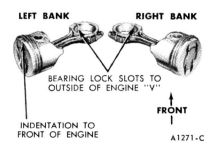

FIG. 47—Connecting Rod and Piston Assembly

ASSEMBLY

The piston, connecting rod and related parts are shown in Fig. 46.

1. Lubricate all parts with light engine oil. Position the connecting rod in the piston and push the pin into place. Assemble the piston and connecting rod as shown in Fig. 47.

2. Install new piston pin retainers in the piston. Follow the instructions contained on the piston ring package and install the piston rings.

3. Check the ring side clearance of the compression rings with a feeler gauge (step 6 under Fitting Piston Rings in Part 8-1, Section 2).

Be sure the piston ring gaps are properly spaced (Fig. 42).

4. Be sure the bearing inserts and the bearing bore on the connecting rod and cap are clean. Foreign material under the inserts may distort the bearing and cause a failure. Install the bearing inserts in the connecting rod and cap with the tangs fitting in the slots provided.

FLYWHEEL
REMOVAL

1. Disconnect the transmission from the engine and slide it to the rear as outlined in Group 5 (manual-shift transmissions) or on an automatic transmission remove the transmission (Group 7).

On a manual-shift transmission, remove the pressure plate and cover assembly as outlined in Group 5.

2. Remove the flywheel retaining bolts and remove the flywheel.

CLEANING AND INSPECTION

Refer to Part 8-1, Section 3 for the cleaning and inspection procedures.

REPAIRS

To check flywheel face runout or replace flywheel ring gear, refer to Part 8-1, Section 2.

INSTALLATION

1. Install the flywheel on the crankshaft flange and install the retaining bolts. Torque the bolts in sequence across from each other to specifications.

2. Check the flywheel runout, following the procedure in Part 8-1, Section 1.

3. On a manual-shift transmission, install the pressure plate and cover assembly (Group 5).

4. Connect the transmission to the engine as outlined in Group 5

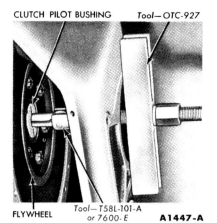

FIG. 48—Typical Clutch Pilot Bushing Removal

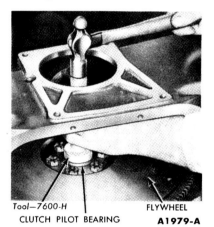

FIG. 49—Typical Clutch Pilot Service Bearing Installation

(manual-shift transmissions) or on an automatic transmission, install the transmission (Group 7). It is not necessary to adjust the transmission, when it has been removed only for flywheel removal.

CLUTCH PILOT BUSHING REPLACEMENT

Inspection procedures are outlined under Crankshaft Cleaning and Inspection in Part 8-1, Section 3.

1. Disconnect the transmission from the engine and slide it to the rear as outlined in Group 5.

2. Remove the pressure plate and cover assembly and the clutch disc as outlined in Group 5.

3. Remove the pilot bushing (Fig. 48).

4. Coat the pilot bushing bore in the crankshaft with a small quantity of wheel bearing lubricant. **Avoid using too much lubricant as it may be thrown onto the clutch disc when the clutch revolves.**

5. Install the pilot service bearing (Fig. 49).

6. Install the clutch disc and the pressure plate and cover assembly as outlined in Group 5.

7. Connect the transmission to the engine as outlined in Group 5.

OIL FILTER REPLACEMENT

The Rotunda oil filter assembly is shown in Fig. 50.

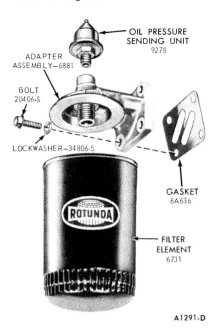

FIG. 50—Rotunda Oil Filter Assembly

1. Place a drip pan under the filter. Unscrew the filter from the adapter fitting. Clean the adapter filter recess.

2. Coat the gasket on the new filter with oil. Place the filter in position on the adapter (Fig. 51). Hand tighten the filter until the gasket contacts the adapter face. Then advance it ½-turn.

3. Operate the engine at fast idle and check for leaks. If oil leaks are evident, perform the necessary repairs to correct the leakage. Check the oil level and fill the crankcase if necessary.

OIL PAN AND OIL PUMP
REMOVAL

1. Drain the crankcase and remove the oil level dipstick.

2. Remove the oil pan retaining screws and lower the oil pan to the cross member. Position the crankshaft so that the counterweight will clear the oil pan.

3. Remove the oil pump retaining

FIG. 51—Rotunda Oil Filter Replacement

bolts and place the oil pump, inlet tube screen and intermediate drive shaft in the oil pan. Remove the oil pan and oil pump. Remove the inlet tube and screen assembly from the oil pump. Discard the gasket. Clean the oil pump inlet tube and screen.

CLEANING AND INSPECTION

Refer to Part 8-1, Section 3 for the cleaning and inspection procedures.

INSTALLATION

1. Clean the oil pan and cylinder block gasket surfaces. Position a new gasket on the oil pan.

2. Position a new oil pump inlet tube gasket on the oil pump and install the inlet tube and screen. Prime the oil pump by filling either the inlet or outlet port with engine oil. Rotate the pump shaft to distribute the oil within the pump body.

3. Place the oil pump in the oil pan and position the oil pan on the cross member. Position a new oil pump gasket on the cylinder block. Insert the intermediate drive shaft into the oil pump housing and install the oil pump and shaft as an assembly (Fig. 52). **Do not attempt to force the pump into position if it will not seat readily. The drive shaft hex may be misaligned with the distributor shaft. To align, rotate the intermediate shaft into a**

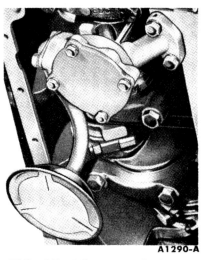

FIG. 52—Oil Pump and Inlet Tube Installed

new position. Torque the oil pump retaining screws to specifications.

4. Hold the oil pan in place against the cylinder block and install a retaining screw on each side of the oil pan. **Install the oil pan sealer bolts that retain the oil pan to the rear main bearing cap.** Install the remaining screws and torque them, from the center outward, to specifications.

5. Replace the engine oil filter. Fill the crankcase with the proper grade and quantity of engine oil. Operate the engine and check for leaks.

OIL PUMP DISASSEMBLY

1. Remove the oil inlet tube from the oil pump and remove the gasket.

2. Remove the cover retaining

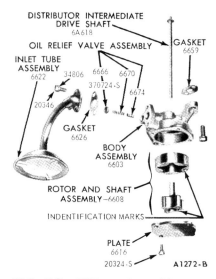

FIG. 53—Oil Pump Assembly

screws, then remove the cover. Remove the inner rotor and shaft assembly and the outer race.

3. Remove the staking marks at the relief valve chamber cap. Drill a hole in the relief valve chamber cap, and install a self-threading sheet metal screw of the proper diameter into the oil pressure relief valve chamber cap and pull the cap out of the chamber. Remove the spring and plunger.

CLEANING AND INSPECTION
Refer to Part 8-1, Section 3 for the cleaning and inspection procedures.

OIL PUMP ASSEMBLY
The oil pump assembly is shown in Fig. 53.
1. Oil all parts thoroughly.
2. Install the oil pressure relief valve plunger, spring and a new cap. Stake the cap.

3. Install the outer race, and the inner rotor and shaft assembly. **The inner rotor and shaft, and the outer race are serviced as an assembly. One part should not be replaced without replacing the other.** Install the cover. Torque the cover retaining screws to specifications.
4. Position a new gasket and the oil inlet tube on the oil pump and install the retaining bolts.

---

3 ENGINE REMOVAL AND INSTALLATION

The procedures given are for the engine without the transmission attached.

REMOVAL
1. Drain the cooling system and the crankcase. Remove the hood. Disconnect the automatic choke heat chamber air inlet tube and remove the air cleaner.
2. Disconnect the radiator upper hose at the coolant outlet elbow and the radiator lower hose at the water pump.
3. Disconnect the transmission oil cooler lines at the radiator. Remove the radiator and support as an assembly.
4. Disconnect the battery ground cable at the alternator mounting bracket. Remove the ignition coil and engine identification tag.
5. Disconnect the oil pressure sending unit wire at the sending unit and the flexible fuel line at the fuel tank line.
6. Remove the wire loom from the clips on the left valve rocker arm cover and position the wires out of the way.
7. Disconnect the accelerator rod at the carburetor. Remove the accelerator retracting spring. Remove the accelerator cross shaft bracket from the intake manifold and position it out of the way. On a car with air conditioning, remove the compressor from the mounting bracket, and position it out of the way, **leaving the refrigerant lines attached.**
8. Disconnect the power steering pump bracket from the water pump; then wire the power steering pump to the hood left hinge in a position that will prevent the oil from draining out.
9. Disconnect the power brake line at the intake manifold and at the flexible line. Release the line from the brackets on the left valve rocker

arm cover and remove the line.
On a car with an air conditioner, disconnect the magnetic clutch wire. Isolate the compressor.
10. Remove the heater hose from the automatic choke housing and disconnect the hoses at the water pump, and at the intake manifold. Position the heater hoses out of the way.
11. Disconnect the alternator wires at the alternator (Part 13-2).
12. Disconnect the coolant temperature sending unit wire at the sending unit.
13. Remove the engine ground strap. Remove the starter cable retaining bracket from the alternator mounting bracket.
14. Raise the front of the car.
15. Remove the No. 2 cross member to underbody brace on the right side to provide clearance for starter removal. Remove the starter and dust seal and the transmission fluid filler tube bracket.
16. Disconnect the muffler inlet pipes from the exhaust manifolds. Remove the engine intermediate support bracket to cross member retaining nut on the right and left engine front supports.
17. Remove the converter housing lower access cover and the cover assembly. Remove the flywheel to converter nuts. Secure the converter assembly in the housing. Remove the converter housing to engine lower bolts, and remove the oil cooler lines retaining clamp from the engine block.
18. Lower the car and support the transmission. Remove the converter housing upper retaining bolts. Remove the front fender to upper dash braces.
19. Install the engine left lifting bracket on the front of the left cylinder head where the coil mounts. Install the engine right lifting bracket at the rear of the right cylinder

head. Attach the engine lifting sling (Fig. 54).
20. Raise the engine slightly and carefully pull it from the transmission.

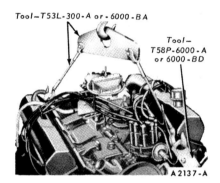

FIG. 54—Engine Lifting Brackets and Sling

21. Lift the engine out of the engine compartment and install it on a work stand.
22. Remove the exhaust control valve and gaskets. Clean the valve and inlet pipe gasket surfaces.

INSTALLATION
1. Place a new gasket on the muffler inlet pipes. Place the exhaust control valve and a new gasket on the right exhaust manifold studs.
2. Attach the engine lifting brackets and sling (Fig. 54). Remove the engine from the work stand.
3. Lower the engine carefully into the engine compartment. Make sure the exhaust manifolds are properly aligned with the muffler inlet pipes and the dowels in the block engage the holes in the converter housing. Start the converter pilot into the crankshaft.
4. Install the front fender to upper dash braces. Install the converter housing upper bolts. Torque the bolts to specifications.

5. Start the engine intermediate support bracket to cross member retaining nut on the right and left engine front supports. Disconnect the engine lifting sling and remove the lifting brackets.

6. Raise the front of the car. Install the converter housing lower retaining bolts. Torque the bolts to specifications.

7. Remove the retainer securing the converter in the housing. Install the flywheel to converter lock washers and nuts. Torque the nuts to specifications. Install the converter lower access plate and the housing cover assembly. Install the oil cooler lines retaining clamp.

8. Torque the engine intermediate support bracket to cross member retaining nuts to specifications.

9. Connect both exhaust manifolds to the muffler inlet pipes. Torque the nuts to specifications.

10. Position the dust seal and install the starter and the transmission fluid filter tube bracket. Install the No. 2 cross member to underbody brace.

11. Remove the support from the

transmission and lower the car.

12. Connect the alternator wires (Part 13-2).

13. Connect the water temperature sending unit wire.

14. Connect the engine ground strap. Install the starter cable retaining clamp.

15. Connect the flexible fuel line and the oil pressure sending unit wire.

16. Install the ignition coil and engine identification tag. Connect the coil primary and high tension wires.

17. Position the wire loom in the retaining clips on the left valve rocker arm cover.

18. Install the accelerator cross shaft bracket and the accelerator retracting spring. Connect the accelerator rod.

19. Connect the power steering pump bracket to the water pump.

20. Connect the power brake line to the intake manifold and to the flexible line. Install the line in the retaining clips on the left valve rocker arm cover.

On a car with an air conditioner, connect the magnetic clutch wire

and the compressor lines.

21. Install the radiator and support as an assembly. Connect the radiator upper and lower hoses. Connect the transmission oil cooler lines.

22. Install the heater hose on the automatic choke housing.

On a car with an air conditioner, connect the heater hose at the intake manifold.

23. Fill and bleed the cooling system. Connect the heater hose at the water pump, and at the intake manifold.

24. Fill the crankcase with the proper grade and quantity of engine oil. On a car with air conditioning, install the compressor on the mounting bracket, and adjust the belt tension to specifications.

25. Operate the engine at fast idle and check all gaskets and hose connections for leaks.

26. Adjust the transmission control linkage. Adjust the accelerator linkage. Install the air cleaner and connect the automatic choke heat chamber air inlet tube.

27. Install and adjust the hood.

4 MAJOR REPAIR OPERATIONS

To perform the operations in this section, it will be necessary to remove the engine from the car and install it on a work stand.

When installing nuts or bolts that must be torqued (refer to Part 8-5 for torque specifications), oil the threads with light weight engine oil. **Do not oil threads that require oil-resistant or water-resistant sealer.**

CRANKSHAFT

The crankshaft and related parts are shown in Fig. 55.

REMOVAL

1. Remove the alternator adjusting arm bracket bolt from the alternator and the upper support bracket bolt at the water pump. Remove the spark plugs to allow easy rotation of the crankshaft.

2. Remove the fuel pump. Slide the water pump bypass hose clamp toward the rear of the engine. Remove the water pump and fan as an assembly.

3. Remove the accessory drive pulley (if so equipped). Remove the crankshaft damper cap screw and washer. Remove the power steering pump pulley. Install the puller on

the damper (Fig. 27) and remove the damper.

4. Remove the crankshaft sleeve as shown in Fig. 28.

5. Remove the cylinder front cover and air conditioning idler pulley assembly (if so equipped). Remove the cover gasket.

6. Remove the crankshaft front oil slinger. Check the timing chain deflection, Part 8-1, Section 1. Then remove the timing chain and sprockets by following the applicable steps under Cylinder Front Cover Removal.

7. Invert the engine on the work stand. Remove the flywheel. Remove the oil pan and gasket. Remove the oil pump.

8. Make sure all bearing caps (main and connecting rod) are marked so that they can be installed in their original locations. Remove the connecting rod bearing caps. Turn the crankshaft until the connecting rod from which the cap is being removed is down and remove the cap. Push the connecting rod and piston assembly up into the cylinder.

9. Remove the main bearing caps.

10. Carefully lift the crankshaft out of the block so that the thrust bearing surfaces are not damaged. **Handle the crankshaft with care to avoid possible fracture or damage to the finished surfaces.**

CLEANING AND INSPECTION
Refer to Part 8-1, Section 3 for the cleaning and inspection procedures.

REPAIRS
To refinish journals, dress minor imperfections, etc., refer to Part 8-1, Section 2.

INSTALLATION
1. Remove the rear journal oil seal from the block and rear main bearing cap. Remove the rear main bearing cap to block side seals.

2. Remove the main bearing inserts from the block and bearing caps.

3. Remove the connecting rod bearing inserts from the connecting rods and caps.

4. If the crankshaft main bearing journals have been refinished to a *definite undersize, install the correct* undersize bearings. Be sure the bearing inserts and bearing bores are

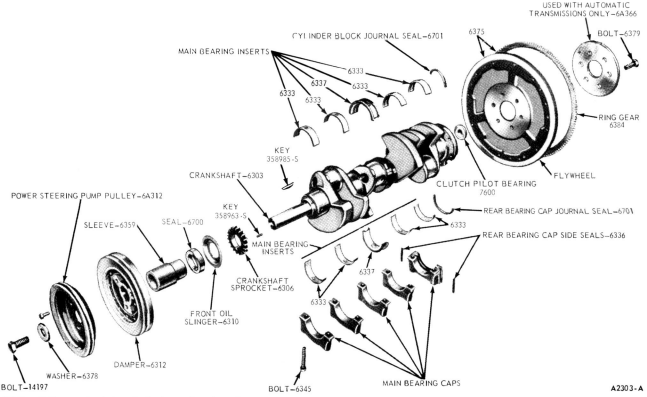

FIG. 55—Typical Crankshaft and Related Parts

clean. Foreign material under the inserts may distort the bearing and cause a failure.

5. Place the upper main bearing inserts in position in the bores with the tang fitting in the slot provided.

If the oil hole does not line up with the cylinder block oil passage, check the holes with a rod corresponding to the following diameters:

No. 1 Bearing—$\frac{7}{64}$ inch
No. 2 Bearing—$\frac{9}{64}$ inch
No. 3 Bearing—$\frac{9}{32}$ inch
No. 4 Bearing—$\frac{5}{32}$ inch
No. 5 Bearing—$\frac{9}{32}$ inch

If the rod passes through both the bearing and the block, sufficient lubrication is assured.

6. Install the lower main bearing inserts in the bearing caps.

7. Install a new rear journal oil seal in the block (Fig. 56). After installation, cut the ends of the seals flush. **It is very important that the seal be cut flush with the surface of the cylinder block. This prevents rough edges which may project from the groove and lodge between the bearing cap and cylinder block.**

8. Carefully lower the crankshaft into place. **Be careful not to damage the bearing surfaces.**

9. Check the clearance of each main bearing as follows:

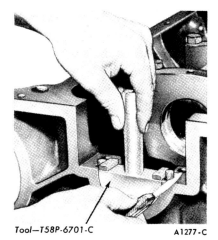

Tool—T58P-6701-C   A1277-C

FIG. 56—Seal to Block Installation

Place a piece of Plastigage on the crankshaft journal the full width of the journal and about ¼ inch off center (Fig. 57). Follow steps 10 and 11 under Main Bearing Replacement in Part 8-2, Section 2.

10. After the bearings have been fitted, apply a light coat of engine oil to the journals and bearings. Install a new seal in the rear main bearing cap and install the rear main bearing cap by following steps 15 thru 19 under Main Bearing Replacement in Part 8-2, Section 2.

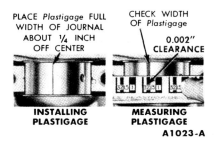

FIG. 57—Installing and Measuring Plastigage—Engine on Work Stand

Install all the bearing caps, except the thrust bearing cap (No. 3 bearing). **Be sure that the main bearing caps are installed in their original locations.** Torque the bearing cap bolts to specifications.

11. Install the thrust bearing cap with the bolts finger-tight.

12. Pry the crankshaft forward against the thrust surface of the upper half of the bearing (Fig. 58).

13. Hold the crankshaft forward and pry the thrust bearing cap to the rear (Fig. 58). This will align the thrust surfaces of both halves of the bearing.

14. Retain the forward pressure on the crankshaft. Torque the cap bolts to specifications (Fig. 58).

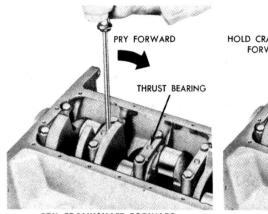
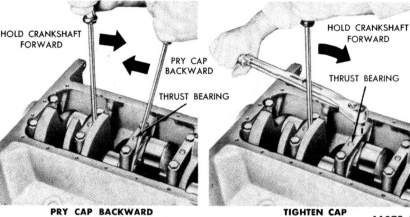

FIG. 58—Thrust Bearing Alignment

15. Check the crankshaft end play by following the procedure in Part 8-1, Section 1.

16. Install new bearing inserts in the connecting rods and caps. Check the clearance of each bearing following the procedure under Main Bearing Replacement.

17. After the connecting rod bearings have been fitted, apply a light coat of engine oil to the journals and bearings.

18. Turn the crankshaft throw to the bottom of its stroke. Push the piston all the way down until the rod bearing seats on the crankshaft journal.

19. Install the connecting rod cap. Torque the nuts to specifications.

20. After the piston and connecting rod assemblies have been installed, check the side clearance be-

tween the connecting rods on each connecting rod crankshaft journal (Fig. 44).

21. Install the cover plate and position the flywheel on the crankshaft. Install the retaining bolts. Torque the bolts to specifications.

22. Install the timing chain and sprockets, cylinder front cover and crankshaft damper, following steps 1 thru 12 under Cylinder Front Cover Installation.

23. Clean the oil pan, oil pump and oil pump inlet screen. Prime the oil pump by filling either the inlet or outlet port with engine oil and rotating the pump shaft to distribute oil within the housing. Install the oil pump and oil pan, following the procedures under Oil Pan and Oil Pump Installation.

24. Install the oil filter, fuel pump

and carburetor fuel inlet line. Install the alternator. Install the spark plugs.

25. Install the engine in the car.

CAMSHAFT BEARING REPLACEMENT

Camshaft bearings are available pre-finished to size for standard and 0.015-inch undersize journal diameters. The bearings are not interchangeable from one bore to another.

1. Remove the camshaft, flywheel and crankshaft, following the appropriate procedures in Section 2 or Section 4. Push the pistons to the top of the cylinders.

2. Remove the camshaft rear bearing bore plug. Remove the camshaft bearings (Fig. 59).

If the camshaft bearings are being removed with the tool shown in Fig. 61, the following procedure will apply: Select the proper size expanding collet and back-up nut and assemble on the expanding mandrel. With the expanding collet collapsed, install the collet assembly in the camshaft bearing, and tighten the back-up nut on the expanding mandrel until the collet fits the camshaft bearing. Assemble the puller screw and extension (if necessary) as shown and install on the expanding mandrel. Tighten the pulling nut against the thrust bearing and pulling plate to remove the camshaft bearing. Be sure to hold a wrench on the end of the puller screw, to prevent it from turning. Repeat the procedure for each bearing. To remove the front bearing, install the puller screw from the rear of the cylinder block.

3. Position the new bearings at the bearing bores, and press them in place with the tool shown in Fig. 61. Be sure to center the pulling

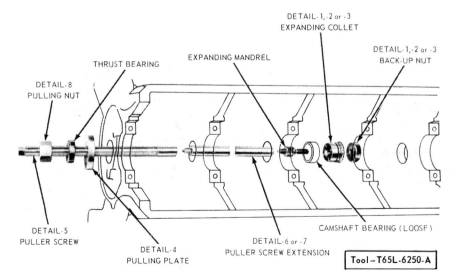

FIG. 59—Typical Camshaft Bearing Replacement

plate and the puller screw to avoid damage to the bearing. Wrap a cloth around the threads of the puller screw to protect the front bearing or journal. **Failure to use the correct expanding collet can cause severe bearing damage.** Align the oil holes in the bearings with the oil holes in the cylinder block when the bearings are installed. **Be sure the front bearing is installed 0.005-0.020 inch below the front face of the cylinder block (Fig. 60).**

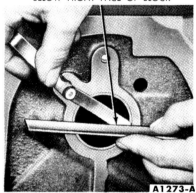

INSTALL FRONT BEARING 0.005-0.020 INCH BELOW FRONT FACE OF BLOCK

FIG. 60—Camshaft Front Bearing Measurement

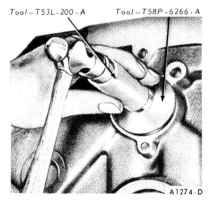

Tool—T53L-200-A   Tool—T58P-6266-A

FIG. 61—Camshaft Rear Bearing Bore Plug Installation

4. Clean out the camshaft rear bearing bore plug recess thoroughly. Coat the flange of a new plug with oil-resistant sealer and install the plug (Fig. 61) with the flange edge of the plug facing inward.

5. Install the camshaft, crankshaft, flywheel and related parts, following the appropriate procedures in Section 2 or Section 4, except do not check connecting rod and main bearing clearances as a part of Camshaft Bearing Replacement. Install the engine in the car.

CYLINDER ASSEMBLY REPLACEMENT
DISASSEMBLY

Follow steps 1 thru 11, 13 thru 19, and 23 thru 25 under Engine Disassembly. Remove 4 cylinder head dowels from the cylinder block. Remove the cylinder block drain plugs, and remove the cylinder assembly from the work stand.

CLEANING

Clean the gasket and seal surfaces of all parts and assemblies (refer to Part 8-1, Section 3).

ASSEMBLY

Install the replacement cylinder block assembly on a work stand. Install the cylinder block drain plugs and cylinder head dowels. Transfer all parts removed from the old cylinder assembly to the new cylinder assembly, following the procedures in steps 21 thru 34 and 41 thru 62 under Engine Assembly. Check all assembly clearances and correct as required.

CYLINDER BLOCK REPLACEMENT
DISASSEMBLY

Follow steps 1 thru 33 under Engine Disassemby. Remove the cyinder head dowels and cylinder block drain plugs. Remove the intake and exhaust manifolds and cylinder heads as an assembly. Remove the cylinder block from the work stand.

CLEANING

Clean the gasket and seal surfaces of all parts and assemblies (Part 8-1, Section 3).

ASSEMBLY

Install the replacement cylinder block on a work stand. Install the cylinder block drain plugs and cylinder head dowels. Transfer all parts removed from the old cylinder block to the new cylinder block, following steps 7 thru 62 under Engine Assembly. Install the manifolds and cylinder head as an assembly.

ENGINE DISASSEMBLY

1. Install the engine on the work stand.

2. Remove the distributor cap and spark plug wire assembly.

3. Disconnect the distributor vacuum line at the distributor. Remove the carburetor fuel inlet line at the fuel filter, and at the fuel pump. Re-

move the fuel pump and discard the gasket.

4. Slide the clamp on the water pump bypass hose toward the water pump. Remove the automatic choke air heat tube and air inlet tube. Remove the valve rocker arm covers and crankcase ventilation tube. On a car with Thermactor exhaust emission control system (Group 12), disconnect the air and vacuum lines. Remove the air supply pump, air manifold assembly, air cleaner assembly, anti-backfire valve, and air and vacuum lines and brackets.

Starting at the No. 4 cylinder, loosen the right rocker arm shaft support bolts in sequence, two turns at a time. After the bolts are all loosened, remove the valve rocker arm shaft assembly and the oil baffle plate. Starting at the No. 5 cylinder, follow the same procedure on the left valve rocker arm shaft support bolts.

5. Remove the valve push rods in sequence and put them in a rack so that they can be installed in their original bore.

6. Remove the distributor hold down bolt and clamp and remove the distributor.

7. Remove the intake manifold retaining bolts.

8. Install standard eye bolts with $\frac{5}{16}$-18 threads in the left front and right rear rocker arm cover screw holes and attach the engine lifting sling (Fig. 54).

9. Raise the intake manifold and carefully remove it from the engine. Discard the intake manifold gaskets and seals.

10. Remove the baffle plate from the valve push rod chamber floor by prying up on the baffle with a screw driver (Fig. 62).

FIG. 62—Baffle Plate Removal

11. Lift the valve lifters from the cylinder block and place them in a rack so that they can be installed in their original bore (Fig. 63). **The internal parts of each hydraulic valve lifter assembly are matched sets. Do not intermix the parts. Keep the assemblies intact until they are to be cleaned.**

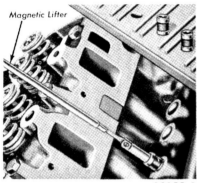

Magnetic Lifter

A1255-A

FIG. 63—Valve Lifter Removal— Intake Manifold Removed

12. Remove the exhaust manifolds and the spark plugs. Remove the automatic choke air chamber cover from the right exhaust manifold.

13. Remove the cylinder head bolts.

14. Lift the cylinder heads off the block. **Do not pry between the head and the block.** Discard the cylinder head gaskets.

15. Remove the oil filter. Remove the oil filter adapter assembly and oil pressure sending unit as an assembly. Discard the gasket.

16. Remove the alternator, brackets and drive belts.

17. Remove the water pump, pulley and fans as an assembly, and the accessory drive pulley (if so equipped).

18. Remove the power steering pulley. Remove the crankshaft damper (Fig. 27).

19. Remove the crankshaft sleeve as shown in Fig. 28.

20. Remove the cylinder front cover. Discard the gasket. Remove the crankshaft front oil slinger.

21. Check the timing chain deflection by following the procedure in Part 8-1, Section 1.

22. Remove the camshaft sprocket cap screw and the fuel pump eccentric. Remove the crankshaft sprocket key. Remove the sprockets

and timing chain as an assembly (Fig. 31).

23. Remove any ridge and/or carbon deposits from the upper end of the cylinder bores. Move the piston to the bottom of its travel and place a cloth on the piston head to collect the cuttings. Remove the cylinder ridge with a ridge cutter. Follow the instructions furnished by the tool manufacturer. **Never cut into the ring travel area in excess of 1/32 inch when removing ridges.** After the ridge has been removed, remove the cutter from the cylinder bore.

24. Remove the flywheel.

25. Invert the engine. Remove the oil pan. Discard the gasket.

26. Remove the oil pump and inlet tube as an assembly. Remove the oil pump drive shaft. Discard the oil pump gasket.

27. Make sure all connecting rods and caps are marked so that they can be installed in their original locations. Turn the crankshaft until the connecting rod being removed is down. Remove the rod cap.

28. Push the connecting rod and piston assembly out the top of the cylinder with the handle end of a hammer. **Avoid damage to the crankpin or the cylinder wall when removing the piston and rod.**

29. Remove the bearing inserts from the connecting rods and caps. Install the rod caps on the connecting rods from which they were removed.

30. Remove the main bearing caps.

31. Carefully lift the crankshaft out of the cylinder block so that the thrust bearing surfaces are not damaged. **Handle the crankshaft with care to avoid possible fracture or damage to the finished surfaces.**

32. Remove the rear journal oil seal from the block and rear bearing cap, and remove the cap to block side seals.

33. Remove the main bearing inserts from the block and bearing caps. Install the main bearing caps in their original positions.

34. Carefully remove the camshaft by pulling it toward the front of the engine. Use caution to avoid damaging the journals and lobes.

35. Remove the camshaft rear bearing bore plug. Remove the camshaft bearings (Fig. 59).

CLEANING AND INSPECTION

For cleaning and inspection procedures, refer to Part 8-1, Section 3.

ENGINE ASSEMBLY

If the cylinder block is to be replaced, transfer the cylinder head dowels and cylinder block drain plugs to the new cylinder block.

1. Remove the glaze from the cylinder bores by following the instructions of the tool manufacturer.

2. Invert the engine on the work stand.

3. Position the new camshaft bearings at the bearing bores, and press them in place with the tool shown in Fig. 59. Align the oil holes in the cylinder block when the bearings are installed. **Be sure the camshaft front bearing is installed 0.005-0.020 inch below the front face of the cylinder block (Fig. 60).**

4. Check the oil passage that feeds the rocker arm shafts for obstructions by squirting oil into the opening on each cylinder bank and observing the flow through the oil holes at Nos. 2 and 4 bearings.

5. Clean out the camshaft rear bearing bore plug recess thoroughly.

6. Coat the flange of a new plug with oil-resistant sealer and install it with the flange facing inward (Fig. 61). Drive the plug in until it is flush or slightly below the casting surface.

7. Oil the camshaft and apply Lubriplate to all lobes; then carefully slide it through the bearings.

8. Be sure that the rear oil seal grooves are clean. Install a new rear journal oil seal in the block. (Fig. 56). After installation, cut the ends of the seals flush.

9. If the crankshaft main bearing journals have been refinished to a definite undersize, install the correct undersize bearings. Be sure the bearing inserts and bearing bores are clean. Foreign material under the inserts may distort the bearing and cause a failure.

Place the upper main bearing inserts in position in the bore with the tang fitting in the slot provided.

10. Install the lower main bearing inserts in the bearing caps.

11. Carefully lower the crankshaft into place. **Be careful not to damage the bearing surfaces.**

12. Check the clearance of each

main bearing following the procedure under Main Bearing Replacement.

13. After the bearings have been fitted, apply a light coat of engine oil to the journals and bearings.

14. Be sure that the oil seal grooves in the rear main bearing cap are clean. Install a new journal seal in the cap (Fig. 40). After installation, cut the ends of the seal flush. Apply a thin coating of oil-resistant sealer to the rear main bearing cap at the rear of the top mating surface (Fig. 41). **Do not apply sealer to the area forward of the side seal groove.** Install the rear main bearing cap and the remainder of the caps, except the thrust bearing cap (No. 3 bearing). **Be sure that the main bearing caps are installed in their original locations.** Torque the bearing cap bolts to specifications.

15. Install the thrust bearing cap and check crankshaft end play by following steps 11 thru 18 under Crankshaft Installation.

16. Turn the engine on the work stand so that the front end is up.

17. Install the pistons and connecting rods by following steps 1 thru 9 under Piston and Connecting Rod Assembly Installation.

18. Position the sprockets and timing chain on the camshaft and crankshaft (Fig. 30). Be sure the timing marks on the sprockets are positioned as shown in Fig. 29).

19. Lubricate the timing chain and sprockets with engine oil.

20. Install the fuel pump eccentric (Fig. 32) and the camshaft sprocket cap screw. Torque the sprocket cap screw to specifications. Install the crankshaft front oil slinger.

21. Clean the cylinder front cover and the cylinder block against surfaces. Install a new crankshaft front oil seal (Fig. 31).

22. Coat the gasket surface of the block and cover and the cover bolt threads with sealer. Position a new gasket on the block.

23. Install the alignment pilot tool on the cylinder front cover so that the keyway in the pilot aligns with the key in the crankshaft. Position the cover and pilot over the end of the crankshaft and against the block (Fig. 33).

24. Install the cylinder front cover bolts finger-tight. Position the alternator support bracket and the alternator adjusting arm bracket; then

install the bolts (on a car equipped with an air conditioner, connect the compressor and brackets to the cylinder front cover). While pushing in on the pilot, torque the cover bolts to specifications. Remove the pilot.

25. Lubricate the crankshaft with a white lead and oil mixture and lubricate the oil seal rubbing surface with grease.

26. Install the crankshaft sleeve.

27. Line up the damper keyway with the key on the crankshaft, and install the damper on the crankshaft (Fig. 34). Install the damper cap screw and washer, and torque the screw to specifications.

28. Install the power steering pump pulley on the crankshaft damper.

29. Clean the water pump gasket surfaces and apply sealer. Position new gaskets on the pump and install the water pump, pulley and fan as an assembly.

30. Using a new gasket, install the fuel pump. Install the alternator, brackets and drive belts.

31. Turn the engine on the work stand so that the top of the engine is up.

32. Clean the cylinder head and block gasket surfaces. Apply sealer to both sides of a new gasket. Guided by the word FRONT on the gasket install the head gasket over the cylinder head dowels.

33. Place the cylinder head on the engine and remove the holding fixtures. Coat the head bolt threads with water-resistant sealer and install the bolts.

34. The cylinder head bolt tightening procedure is performed in three progressive steps. Torque the bolts in sequence (Fig. 19) to 70 ft-lbs, then to 80 ft-lbs. and finally to specifications. **After the cylinder head bolts have been torqued to specifications, the bolts should not be disturbed.**

35. Coat the mating surfaces of the exhaust manifold with a light film of graphite grease.

36. Using a new gasket, install the automatic choke air chamber cover on the right exhaust manifold. **Be sure the cover is securely fastened.**

37. Position a new gasket over the muffler inlet pipe studs of the exhaust manifolds.

38. Position the exhaust manifolds on the cylinder heads and install the retaining bolts and tab washers. Torque the retaining bolts to specifications, working from the center to

the ends. Lock the bolts by bending one tab of the washer over a flat on the bolt.

39. Install the spark plugs.

40. Install the baffle plate in the valve push rod chamber. Position one side of the baffle plate and press the other side into place.

41. Coat the outside of each valve lifter with engine oil to provide initial lubrication. **Do not fill the lifters with oil. The lifters will fill much faster after the engine is started, if they are free of any oil film which may cause an oil seal between the plunger and the lifter body.** Place each lifter in the bore from which it was removed.

42. Clean the mating surfaces of the intake manifold, cylinder heads and cylinder block.

43. Coat the intake manifold and cylinder block seal surfaces with oil-resistant sealer.

44. Position new seals on the cylinder block and new gaskets on the cylinder heads. Position the gasket slots in the end tabs over the ribs on the seals. Be sure the holes in the gaskets are aligned with the holes in the cylinder heads.

45. Install the eye bolts in the intake manifold and attach the engine lifting sling and carefully lower the intake manifold on the engine.

46. Position the intake manifold by inserting the distributor in place. **After the intake manifold is in place, run a finger around the seal area to make sure the seals are in place. If the seals are not in place, remove the intake manifold and position the seals.**

47. Start the water pump bypass hose on the intake manifold.

48. Be sure the holes in the manifold gaskets and manifold are in alignment. Install the manifold retaining bolts and torque them to specifications, in sequence as shown in Fig. 18.

49. Remove the distributor and the engine lifting sling and eye bolts.

50. Refer to Valve Rocker Arm Shaft Assembly Installation and install the valve rocker arm shaft assembly by following steps 1 thru 6.

51. Install the automatic choke air heat tube and air inlet tube.

52. Rotate the crankshaft damper until the No. 1 piston is on TDC then position the distributor in the block with the rotor at the No. 1 firing position and the points open. Install the hold down clamp.

53. Connect the distributor vacuum line. Install the distributor cap. Install the valve rocker arm covers.

54. Connect the spark plug wires. Install the carburetor fuel inlet line at the fuel filter and at the fuel pump.

55. Invert the engine on the work stand. Position the oil pump drive shaft into the distributor socket. With the shaft firmly seated in the distributor socket, the stop on the shaft should touch the roof of the crankcase. Remove the shaft and position the stop as necessary.

56. With the stop properly positioned, insert the oil pump drive shaft into the oil pump.

57. Prime the oil pump by filling either the inlet or outlet port with engine oil. Rotate the pump shaft to distribute the oil within the pump body.

58. Position a new gasket on the pump housing and install the pump and shafts as an assembly. **Do not attempt to force the pump into position if it will not seat readily. The drive shaft hex may be misaligned with the distributor shaft. To align, rotate the intermediate shaft into a new position.**

59. Install the oil pan assembly on the block following the procedure under Oil Pan and Oil Pump Installation. Install the retaining screws and torque them from the center outward to specifications.

60. Position the flywheel on the crankshaft and install the retaining bolts. Torque the bolts alternately to specifications.

61. Clean the oil filter adapter gasket surfaces. Apply sealer to a new adapter gasket and install the adapter assembly and gasket.

62. Clean the adapter filter recess. Coat the gasket on a new filter with oil. Place the filter in position on the adapter. Hand tighten the filter until the gasket contacts the adapter face, and then advance it ½-turn. On a car with Thermactor exhaust emission control system, install the anti-backfire valve, air cleaner assembly, air manifold assembly and air supply pump. Install the air and vacuum lines and brackets.

63. Install the engine in the car. Operate the engine and check for oil and coolant leaks. Check the ignition timing, and adjust the engine idle speed, idle fuel mixture and anti-stall dashpot.

64. Adjust the transmission control linkage.

PART 8-5

SPECIFICATIONS

NOTE: All specifications are given in inches unless otherwise noted.

GENERAL ENGINE

MODEL PREFIX
170	EET
200	EFZ
289	EGA
390	EES

ENGINE MODELS AND PISTON DISPLACEMENT—Cubic Inches
170 Six	170
200 Six	200
289 V-8	289
390 V-8	390

COMPRESSION RATIO
170	9.1:1
200 Six	9.2:1
289 V-8 (2-V)	9.3:1
289 V-8 (4-V)	10.0:1
289 V-8 High Performance	10.5:1
390 V-8 (2-V)	9.5:1
390 V-8 (4-V)	10.5:1

BRAKE HORSEPOWER @ Specified rpm
170 Six	105 @ 4400
200 Six	120 @ 4400
289 V-8 (2-V)	200 @ 4400
289 V-8 (4-V)	225 @ 4800
289 V-8 High Performance	271 @ 6000
390 V-8 (2-V)	265 @ 4400
390 V-8 (4-V)	315 @ 4600

TORQUE—Ft-lbs @ Specified rpm
170 Six	158 @ 2400
200 Six	190 @ 2400
283 V-8 (2-V)	282 @ 2400
289 V-8 (4-V)	305 @ 3200
289 V-8 High Performance	312 @ 3400
390 V-8 (2-V)	401 @ 2600
390 V-8 (4-V)	427 @ 2800

BORE AND STROKE
170 Six	3.50 x 2.940
200 Six	3.68 x 3.126
289 V-8	4.00 x 2.870
390 V-8	4.05 x 3.984

COMPRESSION PRESSURE—psi (Sea Level @ Cranking Speed)
170 and 200 Six	155-195
289 V-8	130-170
390 V-8	160-200
Allowable tolerance between cylinders	20 psi

TAXABLE HORSEPOWER
170 Six	29.40
200 Six	32.50
289 V-8	51.20
390 V-8	52.49

FIRING ORDER
170 and 200 Six	1-5-3-6-2-4
289 and 390 V-8	1-5-4-2-6-3-7-8

VALVE ARRANGEMENT—Front to Rear
170 and 200 Six	E-I-I-E-I-E-E-I-E-I-I-E
289 V-8	Right I-E-I-E-I-E-I-E
	Left E-I-E-I-E-I-E-I
390 V-8	E-I-E-I-I-E-I-E

GENERAL ENGINE (Continued)

ENGINE IDLE RPM①
Manual-Shift Transmissions
170, 200, 289 and 390	575-600
170 and 200 with Thermactor	625-650
289 and 390 with Thermactor	610-635
289 V-8 High Performance	750-775

Automatic Transmissions—Drive Range
170 and 200	500-525
170 and 200 with Thermactor	550-575
289 and 390	475-500

①Refer to Group 10, Part 10-1, Section 2, for proper procedures in setting idle speed.

ENGINE IDLE MANIFOLD VACUUM—Minimum Inches of Mercury @ Specified Engine Neutral Idle rpm (Sea Level)
170, 200 Six and 390 V-8	17
289 V-8 (Except High Performance)	18
289 V-8 High Performance	15

INITIAL IGNITION TIMING—BTDC②
Manual-Shift Transmission
170①, 200①, and 289	6°
170, 200 and 289 with Thermactor	TDC
289 High Performance	12°
390①	10°
390 with Thermactor	6°

Automatic Transmission
170① and 200①	12°
289	6°
170, 200 and 289 with Thermactor	TDC
390①	10°
390 with Thermactor	6°

①For altitude operation, and/or to obtain optimum engine performance and fuel economy, the initial ignition timing may be advanced 5° over the "normal" setting. No further improvement in engine performance or fuel economy will be achieved by advancing beyond this point. Advance the timing progressively until engine detonation (spark knock) is evident under actual road test acceleration. Retard the timing until the detonation (spark knock) is eliminated.

②If the individual requirements of the car and/or the use of sub-standard fuels dictate, the initial timing may have to be retarded from the recommended setting to eliminate detonation (spark knock). If retarding is necessary, it should be done progressively and not to exceed 2° BTDC.

OIL CAPACITY①
	U.S. MEASURE	IMPERIAL MEASURE
170 and 200 Six	4.50 quarts	3.75 quarts
289 and 390 V-8	5.00 quarts	4.25 quarts

①Includes one U.S. quart required with oil filter replacement.

OIL PRESSURE—Hot @ 2000 rpm
All Engines	35-55 psi

CYLINDER HEAD

GASKET SURFACE FLATNESS
170 and 200	0.003 inch in any 6 inches or 0.007 inch overall
289 and 390	0.003 inch in any 6 inches or 0.006 inch overall

VALVE GUIDE BORE DIAMETER—Standard
Intake and Exhaust
170 and 200	0.3115-0.3125
289	0.3433-0.3443
390	0.3728-0.3735

GENERAL ENGINE (Continued)

VALVE SEAT WIDTH
Intake and Exhaust
170 and 200....................................0.070-0.080
289...0.060-0.080
390 Intake....................................0.040-0.060
     Exhaust.....................................0.070-0.090

VALVE SEAT ANGLE
Intake and Exhaust
All Engines..45°

VALVE SEAT RUNOUT
Maximum 289...................................0.0015
Maximum Other Engines......................0.002

ROCKER ARM STUD BORE DIAMETER
289..0.3685-0.3695

COMBUSTION CHAMBER VOLUME—CC
170 and 200....................................48.5-50.5
289...52.0-55.0
390...73.1-76.1

VALVE MECHANISM

VALVE CLEARANCE①
170 and 200....................................0.066-0.216
289...0.082-0.152
390...0.050-0.150
①Hydraulic Valve Lifters—Clearance specified is obtained at the valve stem tip with the tappet collapsed.

VALVE LASH
Cold
Intake and Exhaust
289 High Performance......................0.022
Hot
Intake and Exhaust
289 High Performance......................0.018

VALVE STEM DIAMETER
Standard
INTAKE
170 and 200................................0.3100-0.3107
289...0.3416-0.3423
390...0.3711-0.3718
EXHAUST
170 and 200................................0.3098-0.3105
289...0.3406-0.3413
390...0.3711-0.3718
0.003 Oversize
INTAKE
170 and 200................................0.3130-0.3137
289...0.3446-0.3453
390...0.3741-0.3748
EXHAUST
170 and 200................................0.3125-0.3135
289...0.3436-0.3443
390...0.3741-0.3748
0.015 Oversize
INTAKE
170 and 200................................0.3250-0.3257
289...0.3566-0.3573
390...0.3861-0.3868
EXHAUST
170 and 200................................0.3248-0.3255
289...0.3556-0.3563
390...0.3861-0.3868
0.030 Oversize
INTAKE
170 and 200................................0.3400-0.3407
289...0.3716-0.3723
390...0.4011-0.4018
EXHAUST
170 and 200................................0.3398-0.3405
289...0.3706-0.3713
390...0.4011-0.4018

VALVE FACE ANGLE
All Engines..44°

VALVE MECHANISM (Continued)

VALVE STEM TO VALVE GUIDE CLEARANCE
Intake
170 and 200.............0.0008-0.0025—Wear Limit 0.0045
289.....................0.0010-0.0027—Wear Limit 0.0045
390.....................0.0010-0.0024—Wear Limit 0.0045
Exhaust
170 and 200.............0.0010-0.0027—Wear Limit 0.0047
289.....................0.0020-0.0037—Wear Limit 0.0055
390.....................0.0010-0.0024—Wear Limit 0.0055

VALVE HEAD DIAMETER
Intake
170 and 200................................1.642-1.657
289...1.662-1.677
390...2.022-2.037
Exhaust
170 and 200................................1.381-1.396
289...1.442-1.457
390...1.551-1.566

VALVE FACE RUNOUT
Intake and Exhaust
170 and 200....................................0.0015
289 and 390.....................................0.0020

VALVE SPRING FREE LENGTH—Approximate
170 and 200...1.79
289 (Except High Performance).....................2.09
289 High Performance...............................2.04
390..2.15

VALVE SPRING OUT OF SQUARE—Maximum
All Engines.......................................0.072

VALVE SPRING PRESSURE—Lbs. @ Specified Length
170 and 200...............................51-57 @ 1.590
Wear Limit 46 @ 1.590
142-158 @ 1.222
Wear Limit 128 @ 1.222
289 (Except High Performance)............71-79 @ 1.780
Wear Limit 64 @ 1.780
161-177 @ 1.390
Wear Limit 145 @ 1.390
289 High Performance.................83.5-92.5 @ 1.770
Wear Limit 75 @ 1.770
234.5-259.5 @ 1.320
Wear Limit 211 @ 1.320
390......................................80-90 @ 1.820
Wear Limit 72 @ 1.820
233-257 @ 1.380
Wear Limit 210 @ 1.380

VALVE SPRING ASSEMBLED HEIGHT
170 and 200.................................1⁹⁄₁₆-1³⁹⁄₆₄
289...1¾-1²⁵⁄₃₂
390...1¹³⁄₁₆-1²⁷⁄₃₂

VALVE PUSH ROD MAXIMUM RUNOUT
289..0.015
Other Engines....................................0.025

VALVE TAPPET DIAMETER—Standard
All Engines...............................0.8740-0.8745

VALVE TAPPET TO TAPPET BORE CLEARANCE
All Engines..................0.0005-0.0020—Wear Limit 0.005

HYDRAULIC VALVE LIFTER LEAK DOWN RATE—Wear Limit
All Engines (measured at 1/16 inch Plunger Travel).....5-50 Seconds

ROCKER ARM TO ROCKER ARM SHAFT CLEARANCE
170 and 200.................0.002-0.0045—Wear Limit 0.006
390........................0.003-0.0055—Wear Limit 0.006

ROCKER ARM SHAFT O.D.
170 and 200................................0.780-0.781
390...0.838-0.839

ROCKER ARM BORE DIAMETER
170 and 200................................0.783-0.784
390...0.843-0.844

CAMSHAFT AND TIMING CHAIN

CAMSHAFT JOURNAL DIAMETER—Standard	
170 and 200	1.8095-1.8105
289 #1	2.0805-2.0815
#2	2.0655-2.0665
#3	2.0505-2.0515
#4	2.0355-2.0365
#5	2.0205-2.0215
390	2.1238-2.1248

CAMSHAFT JOURNAL TO BEARING CLEARANCE	
All Engines	0.001-0.003—Wear Limit 0.006

CAMSHAFT JOURNAL MAXIMUM OUT-OF-ROUND	
All Engines	0.0005

TIMING CHAIN MAXIMUM DEFLECTION	
All Engines	0.5

CAMSHAFT LOBE LIFT	
170 Intake and Exhaust	0.232—Wear Limit 0.227
200 Intake and Exhaust	0.245—Wear Limit 0.240
289 Intake	0.2302—Wear Limit 0.2253
Exhaust	0.2375—Wear Limit 0.2325
289 High Performance Intake and Exhaust	0.2983—Wear Limit 0.2933
390 Intake and Exhaust	0.2530—Wear Limit 0.2480

CAMSHAFT END PLAY	
All Engines	0.001-0.007—Wear Limit 0.012

CAMSHAFT BEARINGS

INSIDE DIAMETER	
170 and 200	1.8115-1.8125

No. 1 bearing is installed with the front edge 0.115 to 0.125 inch toward the rear from the front face of the cylinder block.

289 #1	2.0825-2.0835
#2	2.0675-2.0685
#3	2.0525-2.0535
#4	2.0375-2.0385
#5	2.0225-2.0235
390	2.1258-2.1268

No. 1 bearing is installed with the front edge 0.005 to 0.020 inch toward the rear from the front face of the cylinder block.

CRANKSHAFT

MAIN BEARING JOURNAL DIAMETER	
Standard	
170 and 200	2.2482-2.2490
289	2.2482-2.2490
390	2.7484-2.7492

MAIN BEARING JOURNAL RUNOUT—Maximum	
170 and 200	0.0025—Wear Limit 0.0035
289 and 390	0.002—Wear Limit 0.003

MAIN BEARING JOURNALS MAXIMUM OUT-OF-ROUND	
All Engines	0.0004

CONNECTING ROD BEARING JOURNALS MAXIMUM TAPE	
170, 200 and 390	0.0003 per inch
289	0.0004 per inch

CONNECTING ROD AND MAIN BEARING JOURNALS MAXIMUM TAPER	
All Engines	0.0003 per inch

THRUST BEARING JOURNAL LENGTH	
170 and 200	1.275-1.277
289	1.137-1.139
390	1.124-1.126

MAIN BEARING JOURNAL THRUST FACE RUNOUT	
390	0.0004
All Other Engines	0.001

CONNECTING ROD JOURNAL DIAMETER	
Standard	
170 and 200	2.1232-2.1240
289	2.1228-2.1236
390	2.4380-2.4388

CRANKSHAFT (Continued)

CRANKSHAFT FREE END PLAY	
390	0.004-0.010—Wear Limit 0.014
All Other Engines	0.004-0.008—Wear Limit 0.012

ASSEMBLED FLYWHEEL CLUTCH FACE MAXIMUM RUNOUT	
All Six	0.007
All V-8	0.010

ASSEMBLED FLYWHEEL O.D. MAXIMUM RUNOUT	
Standard Transmission	
390	0.020
All Other Engines	0.018
Automatic Transmission	
All Engines	0.020

MAIN BEARINGS

BEARING TO CRANKSHAFT CLEARANCE	Desired	Allowable
170 and 200	0.0005-0.0015	0.0005-0.0022
289	0.0005-0.0015	0.0005-0.0025
390	0.0005-0.0015	0.0005-0.0025

WALL THICKNESS	Standard	0.002 U.S.
170 and 200	0.0758-0.0761	0.0768-0.0771
289	0.0957-0.0962	0.0967-0.0972
390	0.0956-0.0961	0.0966-0.0971

CONNECTING ROD

PIN BORE STANDARD DIAMETER	
Standard	
170 and 200	0.9107-0.9112
289	0.9104-0.9112
390	0.9752-0.9755

BEARING BORE DIAMETER—Standard	
390	2.5907-2.5915
All Other Engines	2.2390-2.2398

BEARING BORE MAXIMUM OUT-OF-ROUND	
170 and 200	0.0003-0.0004
289 and 390	0.0004

BEARING BORE MAXIMUM TAPER	
All Engines	0.0004

CONNECTING ROD LENGTH—Center to Center	
170 and 200	4.7145-4.7165
289	5.1535-5.1565
390	6.4860-6.4900

CONNECTING ROD①	
Twist Maximum Total Difference	
All Six	0.008
All V-8	0.012
Bend Maximum Total Difference	
All Engines	0.004

①Piston pin bore and crankshaft bearing bore must be parallel and in the same vertical plane within the specified total difference at ends of 8-inch long bar measured 4-inches on each side of rod.

CONNECTING ROD ASSEMBLY—Assembled to Crankshaft	
Side Clearance	
170 and 200	0.0035-0.0105—Wear Limit 0.014
289 and 390	0.010-0.020—Wear Limit 0.023

CONNECTING ROD BEARINGS

BEARING TO CRANKSHAFT CLEARANCE	Desired	Allowable
All Six	0.0008-0.0015	0.0008-0.0024
All V-8	0.0008-0.0015	0.0008-0.0026

CONNECTING ROD (Continued)

BEARING WALL THICKNESS FOR STANDARD AND UNDERSIZE JOURNAL		
	Standard	0.002 U.S.
170 and 200	0.0571-0.0574	0.0583-0.0588
289	0.0572-0.0577	0.0582-0.0587
390	0.0755-0.0760	0.0765-0.0770

PISTON

PISTON DIAMETER—At Right Angle to Pin Centerline
Color Coded Red
170 . . . . 3.4982-3.4987
200 . . . . 3.6778-3.6784
289 (Except High Performance) 3.9984-3.9990
289 High Performance 3.9978-3.9984
390 . . . . 4.0484-4.0490
Color Coded Blue
170 . . . . 3.4993-3.4999
200 . . . . 3.6790-3.6796
289 (Except High Performance) 3.9996-4.0002
289 High Performance 3.9990-3.9996
390 . . . . 4.0496-4.0502

PISTON TO CYLINDER BORE CLEARANCE
170 and 200 . . . . 0.0014-0.0020
289 (Except High Performance) 0.0014-0.0022
289 High Performance 0.0030-0.0038
390 . . . . 0.0015-0.0023

PISTON PIN BORE DIAMETER
170 and 200 . . . . 0.9122-0.9125
289 . . . . 0.9124-0.9127
390 . . . . 0.9752-0.9755

RING GROOVE WIDTH
Upper Compression Ring
All Engines 0.080-0.081
Lower Compression Ring
All Engines 0.080-0.081
Oil Ring
All Engines 0.1880-0.1890

PISTON PIN

PISTON PIN DIAMETER
Standard
390 . . . . 0.9750-0.9753
All Other Engines 0.9119-0.9124

PISTON PIN LENGTH
390 . . . . 3.156-3.170
All Other Engines 3.010-3.040

PISTON PIN TO PISTON CLEARANCE—Loose
390 . . . . 0.0001-0.0003—Wear Limit 0.0008
All Other Engines . . . . 0.0003-0.0005—Wear Limit 0.0008

PISTON RINGS

RING WIDTH
Compression Ring
UPPER
390 . . . . 0.0770-0.0780
All Other Engines 0.0774-0.0781
LOWER
170, 200 and 289 . . . . 0.0770-0.0780

SIDE CLEARANCE
Compression Ring
UPPER
170 . . . . 0.009-0.0026—Wear Limit 0.006
200 and 289 . . . . 0.0019-0.0036—Wear Limit 0.006
390 . . . . 0.0020-0.0040—Wear Limit 0.006
LOWER
All Engines . . . . 0.0020-0.0040—Wear Limit 0.006
Oil Ring
All Engines . . . . Snug

PISTON RINGS (Continued)

RING GAP WIDTH
Compression Ring—Standard Bore—Upper
170, 200 and 289 . . . . 0.010-0.020
390 . . . . 0.010-0.031
Compression Ring—Standard Bore—Lower
All Engines 0.010-0.020
Oil Ring*—Standard Bore
170 and 200 . . . . 0.015-0.055
289 . . . . 0.015-0.069
390 . . . . 0.015-0.066
*Steel Rail

CYLINDER BLOCK

CYLINDER BORE DIAMETER—Standard Spreads for 8 Grades
170 . . . . 3.5000-3.5024
200 . . . . 3.6800-3.6824
289 . . . . 4.0000-4.0024
390 . . . . 4.0500-4.0524

CYLINDER BORE MAXIMUM OUT-OF-ROUND
All Engines . . . . 0.001—Wear Limit 0.005

CYLINDER BORE TAPER
All Engines . . . . 0.001—Wear Limit 0.010

HEAD GASKET SURFACE FLATNESS
All Six . . . . 0.003 inch in any 6 inches or 0.007 inch overall
All V-8 . . . . 0.003 inch in any 6 inches or 0.006 inch overall

MAIN BEARING BORE DIAMETER
170 and 200 . . . . 2.4012-2.4020
289 . . . . 2.4412-2.4420
390 . . . . 2.9412-2.9420

OIL PUMP—Rotor Type

RELIEF VALVE SPRING TENSION—Lbs. @ Specified Length
170 and 200 . . . . 9.0-10.1 @ 1.078
289 . . . . 11.15-11.75 @ 1.704
390 . . . . 9.0-9.6 @ 1.53

RELIEF VALVE CLEARANCE
All Engines 0.0015-0.0029

DRIVE SHAFT TO HOUSING BEARING CLEARANCE
All Engines 0.0015-0.0029

ROTOR ASSEMBLY END CLEARANCE—Pump Assembled
All Engines 0.0011-0.0041

OUTER RACE TO HOUSING—Radial Clearance
All Engines 0.006-0.012

TORQUE LIMITS—Ft-Lbs

Oil the threads with lightweight engine oil, except do not oil threads that require oil-resistant or water-resistant sealer.

MAIN BEARING CAP BOLTS
390 95-105
All Other Engines 60-70

CYLINDER HEAD BOLTS
170 and 200
Step 1 55
Step 2 65
Step 3 70-75
289
Step 1 50
Step 2 60
Step 3 65-70
390
Step 1 70
Step 2 80
Step 3 80-90

OIL PAN TO CYLINDER BLOCK
170 and 200 7-9
289 ¼-20 Bolt 7-9
5/16-18 Bolt 9-11
390 9-11

TORQUE LIMITS—Ft-Lbs (Continued)

MANIFOLDS TO CYLINDER HEAD
Intake
289—Step 1 15-17
Step 2 20-22
390 32-35
Exhaust
390 12-18
All Other Engines..................................13-18

FLYWHEEL TO CRANKSHAFT
All Engines..75-85

OIL PUMP TO CYLINDER BLOCK
170 and 200..12-15
289 23-28
390 20-25

OIL PUMP COVER PLATE
All Engines..6-9

OIL FILTER ADAPTER TO CYLINDER BLOCK
170 and 200..10-15
289 60-100
390 12-15

OIL FILTER TO ADAPTER OR CYLINDER BLOCK
All Engines   With grease on the gasket surface, hand tighten until gasket contacts adapter face. Then tighten ½ turn more.

CYLINDER FRONT COVER
170 and 200..7-9
289 and 390..12-15

WATER OUTLET HOUSING
All Engines..12-15

OIL PAN DRAIN PLUG
All Engines..15-20

CAMSHAFT THRUST PLATE TO CYLINDER BLOCK
170, 200 and 390......................................12-15
289 6-9

WATER PUMP TO CYLINDER BLOCK OR FRONT COVER
390 20-25
All Other Engines....................................12-15

CAMSHAFT SPROCKET TO CAMSHAFT
170, 200 and 390......................................35-45
289 40-45

DAMPER OR PULLEY TO CRANKSHAFT
170 and 200..85-100
289 and 390..70-90

CONNECTING ROD NUTS
All Except 289 High Performance and 390 19-24
289 High Performance and 390 40-45

VALVE ROCKER ARM COVER
390 4-7
All Other Engines......................................3-5

VALVE ROCKER SHAFT SUPPORT TO CYLINDER HEAD
170 and 200..30-35
390 40-45

VALVE ROCKER ARM ADJUSTING NUT
289 ....4.5-15
With tappet on camshaft base circle turn adjusting nut counterclockwise.

VALVE ROCKER ARM STUD TO CYLINDER HEAD
289 High Performance.............................60-70

TORQUE LIMITS—Ft-Lbs (Continued)

OIL INLET TUBE TO OIL PUMP
All Engines..12-15

FUEL PUMP TO CYLINDER BLOCK OR CYLINDER FRONT COVER
All Engines..12-15

ENGINE FRONT SUPPORT—Nuts or Bolts
Insulator Assembly to Engine
Mustang
6 cyl..18-24
289 V-8...25-40
Comet, Falcon and Fairlane
289 and 390 V-8.......................................35-50
Insulator Assembly to Support Bracket
Mustang
6 cyl..25-35
289 V-8...25-40
Comet, Falcon and Fairlane
6 cyl..24-34
289 V-8...35-50
Support Bracket to Body
Mustang
6 cyl..20-28
289 V-8...20-30
289 High Performance V-8.....................20-28
Comet, Falcon and Fairlane
6 cyl..18-25
289 V-8...20-30
390 V-8...18-25
Support Bracket to Intermediate Support Bracket
Mustang
289 V-8...20-30
289 High Performance V-8.....................26-35
Comet, Falcon and Fairlane......................45-60
Insulator Bracket to Engine
Mustang—289 High Performance V-8......35-50
Comet, Falcon and Fairlane
6 cyl..18-25
Insulator to Insulator Bracket and Support Bracket
Mustang—289 High Performance V-8......35-50
Insulator to Insulator Bracket
Comet, Falcon and Fairlane
6 cyl..18-25
390 V-8...45-60

ENGINE REAR SUPPORT—Nuts or Bolts
Insulator to Rear Support
All Engines..25-35
Insulator to Support Extension—Automatic Transmission
Mustang—6 cyl..20-30
Rear Support Extension to Transmission (Automatic)
Mustang—6 cyl..20-30
Rear Support to Body
Mustang
6 cyl. (automatic transmission).............15-20
6 cyl. (standard transmission)...............10-20
289 V-8 (standard transmission)...........20-30
289 V-8 (automatic transmission).........30-42
289 High Performance V-8.....................10-20
Comet, Falcon and Fairlane
All Engines..50-70
Insulator to Transmission
Mustang
6 cyl..20-30
289 V-8...30-42
289 High Performance V-8.....................20-30
Comet, Falcon and Fairlane
170 Six—Standard Transmission...........15-25
170 Six—Automatic Transmission.........30-60
200 Six and 289 V-8.................................30-60
390 V-8...30-42

SPECIAL TOOLS

Description	Ford Tool No.	Former No.	Application in engine size		
			170-200 Six	289 V-8	390 V-8
Impact Hammer	T50T-100-A	—	X	X	X
Impact Slide Hammer	T59L-100-B	—	X	X	X
Puller Attachment Use with T50T-100-A or T59L-100-B	T58L-101-A	—	X	X	X
Handle Adapter	T53L-200-A	—	X	X	X
Engine Lifting Sling	T53L-300-A	6000-BA	X	X	X
Differential Backlash and Runout Gauge, with Universal Bracket and Dial Indicator (1¼ inch range). Includes indicator TOOL-6565	TOOL-4201-C	4201-C	X	X	X
Engine Lifting Bracket Use with T53L-300-A	T58P-6000-A	6000-BD			X
Adapter Mount To fit K. R. Wilson 1009 or Manzel 6001-TES	T64L-6001-B	—		X	X
Cylinder Front Cover Pilot	T61P-6019-B	6059-F	X	X	X
Valve Guide Reamer Kit	T58P-6085-B				X
Valve Guide Reamer Kit	T60K-6085-B			X	
Engine Lifting and Head Holding Brackets	T62F-6085-A	6005-BDA	X		
Piston Pin Remover	T52P-6135-DAD	—			X
Piston Pin Remover and Replacer Press	T60K-6135-B	6135-J		X	
Camshaft Bearings Remover and Replacer Adapters	T65L-6250-A	T52L-6261-CEE	X	X	X
Camshaft Bearing Bore Plug Replacer-Adapter Use with T53L-208-A	T58P-6266-A				X
Camshaft Rear Bearing Bore Plug Replacer-Adapter Use with T53L-200-A	T62F-6266-A	—		X	
Crankshaft Sprocket and Crankshaft Damper Replacer	T52L-6306-AEE	3355-D		X	
Crankshaft Damper Replacer	T64T-6306-A	—	X	X	X
Crankshaft Damper Remover	T58P-6316-B	—			X
Crankshaft Damper Remover Adapter Screw Use with T58P-6316-B	T62F-6316-C	—		X	
Upper Main Bearing Insert Remover and Replacer	TOOL-6331	6331		X	
Upper Main Bearing Remover and Replacer	TOOL-6331-E	6331-E			X
Crankshaft Pulley Spacer Remover	T56P-6362-A	—			X
Solid Tappet Remover	T52T-6500-DJD	6500-D		X[1]	
Hydraulic Tappet Clip Replacer	TOOL-6500-C	6500-C	X	X	X
Hydraulic Tappet Leakdown Tester	TOOL-6500-E	6500-E	X	X	X
Hydraulic Tappet Plunger Remover and Replacer	TOOL-6500-F	6500-F	X	X	X
Valve Stem Clearance Checking Tool	TOOL-6505-F	6505-F			X
Valve Stem Clearance Checking Tool	TOOL-6505-G	6505-G	X	X	
Valve Face Runout Gauge	T64L-6507-A	—	X	X	X
Valve Spring Compressor	T65P-6513-A		X[2]		
Air Adapter and Hose-Valve Holdup	TOOL-6513-ABA	6513-AB	X	X	X
Compressor—Tappet Bleed-Down	TOOL-6513-AC	6513-AC	X	X	
Valve and Clutch Spring Tester	TOOL-6513-DD	6513-DD	X	X	X
Valve Spring and Rocker Arm Compressor	TOOL-6513-J	6513-J			X
Push Rod Check Compressor	TOOL-6513-K	6513-K	X		
Rocker Arm Stud Kit	T62F-6A527-B		X	X	X

[1]High Performance Only
[2]200 Six Only

SPECIAL TOOLS (Continued)

Description	Ford Tool No.	Former No.	Application in engine size		
			170-200 Six	289 V-8	390 V-8
Rocker Arm Stud Installer (Supplements T56F-6A527-B)	T65P-6A527-A			X	
Cam Lift and Push Rod Stroke Dial Indicator (1 inch range) Use with bracket from TOOL-4201-C	TOOL-6565	6565	X	X	X
Cup Shaped Adapter to TOOL-6565	TOOL-6565-AB	6565-AB	X	X	X
Valve Spring Compressor	T62F-6565-A	6513-HH		X	
Valve Stem to Rocker Arm Clearance Compressor and Gauge	T58P-6565-A	—			X
Crankcase Ventilation System Tester (Kit)		AC spark plug	X	X	X
Cylinder Block Front Cover Oil Seal Replacer Adapter	T60K-6700-A	6700-C	X		
Cylinder Block Front Cover Oil Seal Replacer Adapter Use with T53L-200-A	T58P-6700-B	6700-B	X	X	X
Crankshaft Rear Oil Seal Forming Tool	T58P-6701-C	6701-C			X
Crankshaft Rear Seal Replacer	T62F-6701-A	6701-E	X	X	
Clutch Disc Pilot	T58P-7563-A	—		X	
Clutch Disc Alignment Pilot	TOOL-7563-E	7563-E	X		
Clutch Pilot Bearing Replacer	TOOL-7600-H	7600-H	X	X	X

IGNITION SYSTEM

GROUP 9

PART 9-1   **PAGE**
GENERAL IGNITION SYSTEM SERVICE . . **9-1**

PART 9-2
LOADOMATIC DISTRIBUTORS **9-20**

PART 9-3
DUAL ADVANCE DISTRIBUTORS **9-24**

PART 9-4   **PAGE**
CENTRIFUGAL ADVANCE
DISTRIBUTORS **9-30**

PART 9-5
SPECIFICATIONS **9-35**

PART 9-1   GENERAL IGNITION SYSTEM SERVICE

Section	Page
1 Diagnosis and Testing	9-1
General Information	9-1
Ignition System Tests—Conventional Test Equipment	9-2
Ignition System Tests—Rotunda Oscilloscope Testers	9-4
Distributor Checks	9-9
Distributor Tests—Rotunda RE-27-44 Dwell Tester	9-10
Distributor Tests—Rotunda RE-236 Distributor Tester	9-10
Distributor Tests—Rotunda RE-1416 Distributor Tester	9-12

Section	Page
2 Common Adjustments and Repairs	9-14
Breaker Points and Condenser	9-14
Ignition Timing	9-16
Spark Plug Wire Replacement	9-16
Spark Plugs	9-17
Resistance Wire Replacement	9-17
3 Cleaning and Inspection	9-18
Spark Plugs	9-18
Distributors	9-18
Secondary Wiring	9-18
Coil	9-18
Distributor Cap	9-18
Rotor	9-18

This part covers ignition system description and operation, general ignition system diagnosis, tests, adjustments and repair operations. In addition, the cleaning and inspection procedures are covered.

For distributor removal, disassembly, assembly, installation, major repair procedures and specifications, refer to the pertinent part of this group.

The distributor identification number is stamped on the distributor housing. The basic part number for ungoverned distributors is 12127. To procure replacement parts, it is necessary to know the part No. prefix and suffix and, in some cases, the design code change (Fig. 1).

Always refer to the Master Parts Catalog for parts usage and interchangeability before replacing a distributor or a component part for a distributor.

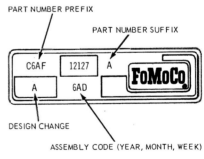

B2574-A

FIG. 1—Distributor Identification

⬛ DIAGNOSIS AND TESTING

GENERAL INFORMATION

The ignition system consists of a primary (low voltage) and a secondary (high voltage) circuit (Fig. 2).

The primary circuit consists of the:
1. Battery.
2. Ignition switch.
3. Primary circuit resistance wire.
4. Primary windings of the ignition coil.
5. Breaker points.
6. Condenser.

The secondary circuit consists of the:
1. Secondary windings of the ignition coil.
2. Distributor rotor.
3. Distributor cap.

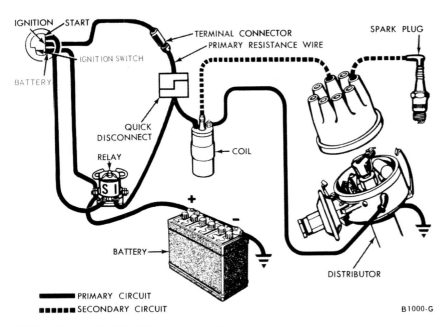

PRIMARY CIRCUIT
SECONDARY CIRCUIT

B1000-G

FIG. 2—Typical Ignition System Circuit

4. High tension wires.

5. Spark plugs.

When the breaker points are closed, the primary or low voltage current flows from the battery through the ignition switch to the primary windings in the coil, then to ground through the closed breaker points. When the breaker points open, the magnetic field built up in the primary windings of the coil moves through the secondary windings of the coil producing high voltage current. **High voltage current is produced each time the breaker points open.** The high voltage flows through the coil high tension lead to the distributor cap where the rotor distributes it to one of the spark plug terminals in the distributor cap. This process is repeated for every power stroke of the engine.

IGNITION SYSTEM TESTS— CONVENTIONAL TEST EQUIPMENT

TROUBLE ISOLATION

Ignition *system troubles* are caused by a failure in the primary and/or the secondary circuit or incorrect ignition timing. If an engine trouble has been traced to the ignition system from the "Engine Trouble Diagnosis Guide," the trouble can be found by performing an ignition system test on a scope or by further isolating the trouble to the primary or secondary circuit as follows:

1. Disconnect the brown wire from the starter relay I terminal and

the red and blue wire from the starter relay S terminal.

2. Remove the coil high tension lead from the distributor cap.

3. Turn on the ignition switch.

4. While holding the high tension lead approximately $3/16$ inch from the cylinder head or any other good ground, crank the engine by using an auxiliary starter switch between the starter relay battery and S terminals.

If the spark is good, the trouble lies in the secondary circuit.

If there is no spark or a weak spark, the trouble is in the primary circuit, coil to distributor high tension lead, or the coil.

Primary Circuit

A breakdown or energy loss in the primary circuit can be caused by:

1. Defective primary wiring, or loose or corroded terminals.

2. Burned, shorted, sticking or improperly adjusted breaker points.

3. A defective coil.

4. A defective condenser.

To isolate a trouble in the primary circuit, proceed as follows:

Turn the ignition switch off and remove the auxiliary starter switch from the starter relay.

Install the coil high tension lead in the distributor cap, the red and blue wire on the starter relay S terminal and the brown wire on the starter relay I terminal.

Now perform a primary circuit test.

Secondary Circuit

A breakdown or energy loss in the

secondary circuit can be caused by:

1. Fouled or improperly adjusted spark plugs.

2. Defective high tension wiring.

3. High tension leakage across the coil, distributor cap or rotor resulting from an accumulation of dirt.

To isolate a trouble in the secondary circuit, proceed as follows:

Turn the ignition switch off and remove the auxiliary starter switch from the starter relay.

Install the coil high tension lead in the distributor cap, the red and blue wire on the starter relay S terminal and the brown wire on the starter relay I terminal.

Now perform a secondary circuit test.

PRIMARY CIRCUIT TESTS

A complete test of the primary circuit consists of checking the circuit from the battery to the coil, the circuit from the coil to ground, and the starting ignition circuit.

Excessive voltage drop in the primary circuit will reduce the secondary output of the ignition coil, resulting in hard starting and poor performance.

Battery to Coil Test

1. Connect the voltmeter leads as shown in Fig. 3.

2. Install a jumper wire from the distributor terminal of the coil to a good ground on the distributor housing.

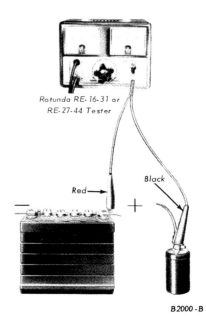

Rotunda RE-16-31 or RE-27-44 Tester

Red→ Black

B2000-B

FIG. 3—Battery to Coil and Starting Ignition Circuit Test

3. Turn the lights and accessories off.

4. Turn the ignition switch on.

5. If the voltmeter reading is 6.9 volts or less, the primary circuit from the battery to the coil is satisfactory.

6. If the voltmeter reading is greater than 6.9 volts, check the following:

The battery and cables for loose connections or corrosion.

The primary wiring for worn insulation, broken strands, and loose or corroded terminals.

The resistance wire for defects.

The starter relay to ignition switch for defects.

Starting Ignition Circuit Test

1. Connect the voltmeter leads as shown in Fig. 3.

2. Disconnect and ground the coil to distributor high tension lead at the distributor.

3. With the ignition switch off, crank the engine by installing a jumper wire between the battery and the "S" terminal of the starter relay while observing the voltage drop.

4. If the voltage drop is 0.1 volt or less, the starting ignition circuit is satisfactory.

5. If the voltage drop is greater than 0.1 volt, clean and tighten the terminals in the circuit or replace the wiring as necessary.

Ignition Switch Test

1. Connect the voltmeter leads as shown in Fig. 4.

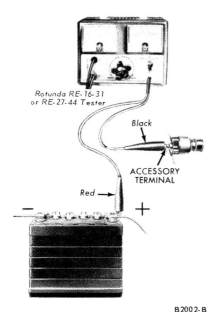

Rotunda RE-16-31 or RE-27-44 Tester

Black

ACCESSORY TERMINAL

Red

B2002-B

FIG. 4—Ignition Switch Test

2. Install a jumper wire from the distributor terminal of the coil to a good ground on the distributor body.

3. Turn all of the accessories and lights off.

4. Turn the ignition switch on.

5. If the voltmeter reading is 0.3 volt or less, the ignition switch and the relay to switch wire are satisfactory.

6. If the voltmeter reading is greater than 0.3 volt, either the ignition switch and/or the wire are defective.

Resistance Wire Test

1. Connect the voltmeter leads as shown in Fig. 5.

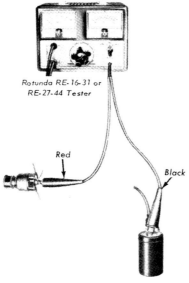

Rotunda RE-16-31 or RE-27-44 Tester

Red

Black

B2004-B

FIG. 5—Resistance Wire Test

2. Install a jumper wire from the distributor terminal of the coil to a good ground on the distributor housing.

3. Turn all of the accessories and lights off.

4. Turn the ignition switch on.

5. If the voltmeter reading is 6.6 volts or less, the resistance wire is satisfactory.

6. If the voltmeter reading is greater than 6.6 volts, replace the resistance wire.

Coil to Ground Test

1. Connect the voltmeter leads as shown in Fig. 6.

2. Close the breaker points.

3. Turn all lights and accessories off.

4. Turn the ignition switch on.

5. If the voltmeter reading is 0.1

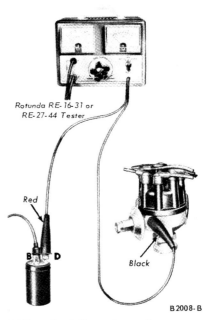

Rotunda RE-16-31 or RE-27-44 Tester

Red

Black

B2008-B

FIG. 6—Coil to Ground Test

volt or less, the primary circuit from coil to ground is satisfactory.

6. If the voltmeter reading is greater than 0.1 volt, test the voltage drop between each of the following:

The coil and breaker point terminals of the coil to distributor primary wire.

The movable breaker point and the breaker plate.

The breaker plate and the distributor housing.

The distributor housing and engine ground.

Breaker Points

Clean and inspect the breaker points by following the procedure under Cleaning and Inspection (Section 3 of this part).

The breaker point dwell can be checked with a distributor tester or a dwell meter by following the procedure under Distributor Tests in this section of the manual.

The breaker point resistance can be checked with a Rotunda RE-1416 distributor tester by following the procedure under Distributor Tests in this section of the manual.

Coil

Clean and inspect the coil by following the procedure under Cleaning and Inspection (Section 3 of this part).

Check the coil on a coil tester by following the manufacturers instructions.

SECONDARY CIRCUIT TESTS

Distributor Cap

Clean and inspect the distributor cap by following the procedure under Cleaning and Inspection (Section 3 of this part).

Rotor

Clean and inspect the rotor by following the procedure under Cleaning and Inspection (Section 3 of this part).

Secondary (High Tension) Wires

The secondary wires include the wires connecting the distributor cap to the spark plugs and the wire connecting the center terminal of the distributor cap to the center terminal of the ignition coil.

Clean and inspect the secondary wiring by following the procedure under Cleaning and Inspection (Section 3 of this part).

These wires are the radio resistance-type which filter out the high frequency electrical impulses that are the source of ignition noise interference. The resistance of each wire should not exceed 7000 ohms per foot.

When checking the resistance of the wires or setting ignition timing, do not puncture the wires with a probe. The probe may cause a separation in the conductor.

When removing the wires from the spark plugs, grasp and twist the moulded cap, then pull the cap off the spark plug. Do not pull on the wire because the wire connection inside the cap may become separated or the insulator seal may be damaged.

To check the spark intensity at the spark plugs, proceed as follows:

1. Disconnect a spark plug wire. **Check the spark intensity of one wire at a time.**

2. Install a terminal adapter in the terminal of the wire to be checked. Hold the adapter approximately 3/16-inch from the exhaust manifold and crank the engine, using a remote starter switch. The spark should jump the gap regularly.

3. If the spark intensity of all the wires is satisfactory, the coil, condenser, rotor, distributor cap and secondary wires are probably satisfactory.

If the spark is good at only some wires, check the resistance of the faulty leads.

If the spark is equal at all wires,

but weak or intermittent, check the coil, distributor cap and the coil to distributor high tension wire.

Spark Plugs

Inspect, clean and gap the plugs following the instructions in sections 2 and 3. After the proper gap is obtained, check the plugs on a testing machine. Compare the sparking efficiency of the cleaned and gapped plug with a new plug. Replace the plug if it fails to meet 70% of the new plug performance.

Test the plugs for compression leakage at the insulator seal. Apply a coating of oil to the shoulder of the plug where the insulator projects through the shell, and to the top of the plug, where the center electrode and terminal project from the insulator. Place the spark plug under pressure with the tester's high tension wire removed from the spark plug. Leakage is indicated by air bubbling through the oil. If the test indicates compression leakage, replace the plug. If the plug is satisfactory, wipe it clean.

Ignition Timing

Incorrect ignition timing can be caused by:

1. Timing incorrectly adjusted.
2. Distributor bushing and/or shaft worn, or a bent distributor shaft.
3. Defective vacuum advance system.
4. Defective centrifugal advance system.

IGNITION SYSTEM TESTS— ROTUNDA OSCILLOSCOPE TESTERS

The following is a complete step-by-step procedure for connecting the scope, checking the ignition system primary and secondary circuits and checking the engine dynamic compression (RE-881 only).

The primary and secondary superimposed pattern checks can be performed with the engine cranking. This allows the dwell, coil and condenser to be checked if the engine will not start.

TEST CONNECTIONS—RE-27-55, AND RE-881

The test connections for the RE-27-55 tester are shown in Fig. 7 and the test connections for the RE-881 tester are shown in Fig. 8.

1. With the tester turned off, plug

the power plug into a proper AC outlet.

2. Connect the green lead to the distributor terminal of the coil.

3. Remove the No. 1 plug wire from the distributor cap; place the blue pickup in the cap, and place the plug wire in the pickup.

4. On the RE-27-55 tester, connect the black lead to a good ground.

5. Clip the red pickup over the coil-to-distributor high tension wire.

6. If the engine timing is to be checked, plug the timing light into its socket.

The following steps pertain to the RE-881 tester only.

7. Disconnect the battery positive and negative cables at the battery.

8. Install the battery adapter on the positive battery post.

9. Connect the battery positive cable to the battery adapter.

10. Connect the shunt spade terminal and the yellow lead to the battery cable post on the battery adapter.

11. Connect the shunt to the adapter.

12. Connect the battery negative cable to the battery negative terminal and connect the black lead to the battery negative terminal.

13. Turn the ground polarity switch to the minus position. Turn the VOLTS switch to the 20-volt position.

POINT RESISTANCE TEST— RE-881 TESTER

This test checks the voltage drop from the distributor terminal of the coil, through the primary wire and the breaker points and to ground.

1. Remove and ground the high tension wire from the center of the distributor.

2. Depress the VOLT AMP push-button and turn the VOLTS switch to the PT. RES. position.

3. Disconnect the brown wire (I terminal) and the red and blue wire (S terminal) at the starter relay. Install an auxiliary starter switch between the battery and S terminals of the starter relay. With the ignition switch ON, tap the auxiliary starter switch until the lowest voltmeter reading is obtained.

4. Depress the PT. RES. push-button.

5. The voltmeter pointer should read in the 12V black, PT. RES. area. If it doesn't, check for improper breaker point spring tension, a loose or defective primary or ground wire

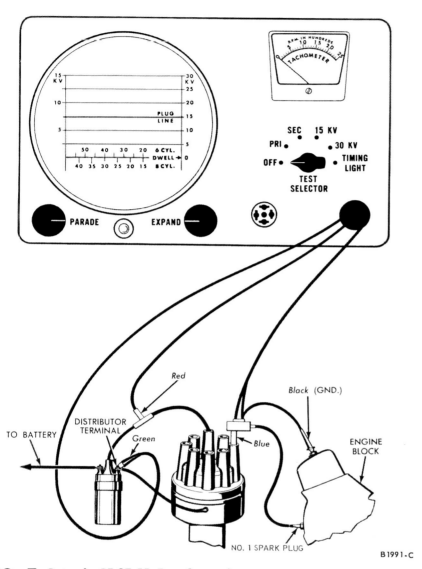

FIG. 7—Rotunda RE-27-55 Test Connections

or for burned or pitted points.

6. Connect the high tension wire to the distributor.

7. Turn the ignition switch OFF and turn the VOLTS switch to the 20V position.

8. Remove the auxiliary starter switch from the starter relay and connect the brown wire and the red and blue wire to the starter relay.

IGNITION TIMING

The following procedure checks the initial ignition timing and the ignition advance mechanism.

Section 2 of this part gives the ignition timing mark locations.

Disconnect the distributor vacuum line (if so equipped). Clean and mark the desired timing mark if using the RE-27-55 tester or the TDC timing mark if using the RE-881 tester.

RE-27-55 Tester

1. Start the engine and allow it to warm up.

2. Turn the TEST SELECTOR to the TIMING LIGHT position.

3. Operate the engine at the specified idle rpm and point the timing light toward the pointer. The desired timing mark should line up with the pointer. If it doesn't, loosen the distributor hold-down bolt and rotate the distributor until the mark lines up with the pointer. Now tighten the hold down bolt and check the timing again in case the timing changed while the distributor hold-down bolt was being tightened.

4. Connect the distributor vacuum line (if so equipped).

5. With the timing light pointed towards the timing marks, accelerate

the engine to see if the timing advances.

RE-881 Tester

1. Turn the RPM selector to the 800 position.

2. Depress the ADVANCE TIMING pushbutton.

3. Start the engine and allow it to warm up.

4. Operate the engine at the specified idle rpm.

5. Point the timing light toward the timing pointer and turn the ADVANCE control until the TDC mark lines up with the pointer. The IGNITION ADVANCE scale of the VOLTS meter will indicate the initial timing. If the initial timing is incorrect, loosen the distributor hold-down bolt and rotate the distributor until the desired timing is obtained. Tighten the distributor hold-down bolt and check the timing again in case the timing changed while the distributor hold-down bolt was being tightened.

6. Connect the distributor vacuum line (if so equipped).

7. Turn the RPM switch to the 8000 position and adjust the engine speed to 2000 rpm.

8. Point the timing light toward the timing pointer and turn the ADVANCE control until the TDC mark lines up with the pointer. The IGNITION ADVANCE scale of the VOLTS meter will indicate the total ignition advance for 2000 rpm. The total ignition advance should be the sum of the initial ignition timing, twice the centrifugal advance at 1000 distributor rpm and twice the maximum vacuum advance. If it isn't, the distributor advance should be checked on a distributor tester.

**PRIMARY CIRCUIT
SUPERIMPOSED PATTERN**

This pattern shows the individual firing patterns as seen by the primary circuit. The individual firing patterns are superimposed to give the appearance of one firing pattern.

The primary circuit superimposed pattern will indicate incorrect battery polarity, incorrect dwell angle, excessive primary circuit resistance, partially shorted condenser, uneven distributor cam lobes, bent distributor shaft or worn distributor bushings.

Procedure

RE-27-55 Tester

1. With the engine running at

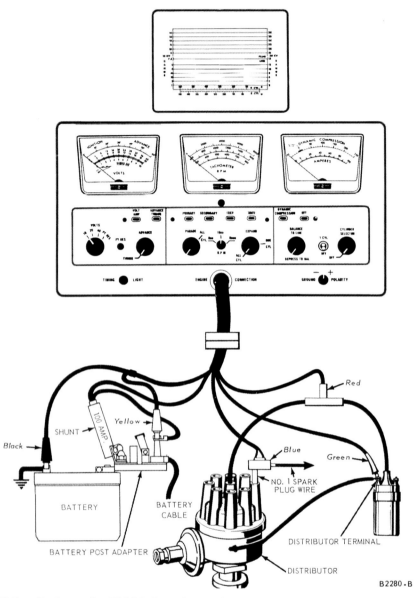

FIG. 8—Rotunda RE-881 Test Connections

1000 rpm, turn the TEST SELECTOR switch to the PRI. position.

2. Adjust the PARADE control to position the left end of the pattern at the 6-cyl 60° dwell mark on the scope screen.

3. Adjust the EXPAND control so that the right end of the pattern is at the 6 cyl 0° dwell mark on the scope screen.

RE-881 Tester

1. Turn the RPM selector to the 1600 rpm position. Start the engine and adjust it to 1000 rpm.

2. Depress the PRI. pushbutton on the console panel.

3. Adjust the PARADE control to position the left end of the pattern at the 6-cyl 60° dwell mark on the

scope screen.

4. Adjust the EXPAND control so that the right end of the pattern is at the 6-cyl 0° dwell mark on the scope screen.

Results

A normal test pattern is shown in Fig. 9. Point A indicates the spark plug line which is the time when the points open. At B, the coil energy is used up sufficiently so that the plug no longer fires and only the energy stored in the breaker point condenser remains. The coil/condenser oscillation which is indicated in the pattern between B and C is completely used up at C which is the points close mark. The portion of the pattern between C and D is the points close

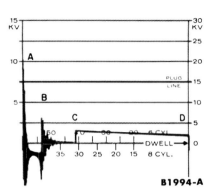

B1994-A

FIG. 9—Normal Superimposed Primary Circuit Pattern

time, which is cam angle or dwell time. At D, the points again open and the firing cycle repeats.

If points A and C are below the 0 line, the battery polarity is incorrect. This could be caused by a battery that is either installed incorrectly or improperly charged, causing a polarity reversal.

If the firing line is not below the 0 horizontal line and there are no oscillations at point C, there is an open circuit at the coil high tension tower. This could be caused by a broken wire inside the coil tower, or a broken center contact on the distributor rotor.

If the dwell time is too long or short, the breaker points are incorrectly set (the larger the gap, the smaller the dwell).

If point A is at a reduced height, and the distance to B is short or non-existent, there is a high resistance in the coil primary circuit. This could be caused by a fouled plug, defective ignition switch, or a bad wire or connection. If the scope pattern is still the same after the above ignition parts have been checked and proven satisfactory, run the 15 KV test to check for a gasket leak or a lean fuel mixture.

If point A is at a greatly reduced height and there are no oscillations at point B, the condenser is partially shorted.

If there is a variation of more than 3° at point C, the cam lobes are uneven, the distributor shaft is bent, or the distributor bushings are worn.

SECONDARY CIRCUIT SUPERIMPOSED PATTERN

This pattern shows the individual firing patterns as seen by the secondary circuit. The individual firing patterns are superimposed to give the appearance of one firing pattern.

The secondary circuit superimposed pattern will indicate arcing breaker points, defective coil or coil high tension wire, excessive resistance in the distributor cap, rotor, secondary wiring or spark plugs or a loose connection in the primary circuit.

The ignition system, as seen by the secondary circuit, can be further checked by checking the 15 KV and 30KV patterns.

Procedure

RE-27-55 Tester

1. With the engine running at 1000 rpm, turn the TEST SELECTOR switch to the SEC. position.

2. Adjust the PARADE control so that the left end of the pattern is at the 6-cyl 60° dwell mark on the scope screen.

3. Adjust the EXPAND control so that the right end of the pattern is at the 6-cyl 0° dwell mark on the scope screen.

RE-881 Tester. The procedure is the same as the procedure for the primary (superimposed) except, the SEC. pushbutton is depressed instead of the PRI. pushbutton.

Results

A normal test pattern is shown in Fig. 10.

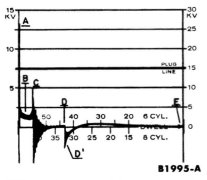

FIG. 10—Normal Superimposed Secondary Circuit Pattern

Point A is the points open time. The height of the pattern at point A indicates the high tension voltage required to overcome the spark plug gap resistance.

Point B is the plug firing line. Notice that this portion of the pattern is quite thick. Remember that this pattern is actually 6 or 8 firing patterns superimposed one on top of the other. This increase in thickness of the pattern at B is caused by slight vari-

ations in the plug gap, distributor rotor gap and slight differences in the resistance of the individual spark plug circuits.

The pattern area between points C and D shows the coil/condenser oscillations to be correct. No point bounce at D indicates correct breaker point spring tension.

The few so-called damped oscillations appearing at D are normal and are caused by the surge of current through the coil primary winding when the breaker points first close.

This current levels off and decreases slightly toward the points open position at E as indicated by the slight downward slope of the curve at about the 8-cyl 15° mark on the cam angle scale.

To observe the coil/condenser oscillations and the damped oscillations at D in the greater detail, adjust the expand control so that the pattern area between points C and D nearly fills the screen.

If there is erratic action at points C and D, and there is a blotch above point E, the breaker points are burned or badly pitted.

If there are no condenser oscillations between C and D and no damped oscillations at point D, there are shorted primary windings in the coil.

If the line at B is sloping downward greatly from A to C (resistor plugs will cause a slight slope), there is a high resistance in the spark plug wires, distributor cap or rotor. If the line at B is sloping upward, there is a high resistance in the spark plugs. If some of the firing patterns are correct and others are sloping incorrectly, perform a 15 KV pattern check to find out which cylinder has the defective part.

If the dwell line between points D and E is not the smooth line shown, there is a loose connection in the primary circuit. Check the primary circuit for loose connections, damaged wires or a defective starter switch.

SECONDARY CIRCUIT 15 KV PATTERN

This pattern shows the individual firing patterns as seen by the secondary circuit. The individual firing patterns are paraded from left to right in order of firing order.

The secondary circuit 15 KV pattern will indicate weak breaker point spring tension, improper breaker point contact, incorrect condenser capacitance, excessive resistance in

the distributor cap terminal or a spark plug wire, shorted or improperly adjusted spark plugs, partially shorted coil primary windings or an incorrect idle fuel mixture.

Procedure

RE-27-55 Tester

1. With the engine operating at 1000 rpm, turn the test selector switch to the 15 KV position.

2. Adjust the PARADE control so that the left end of the pattern is at the 6-cyl 60° dwell mark on the scope screen.

3. Adjust the EXPAND control so that the right end of the pattern is at the 6-cyl 0° dwell mark on the scope screen (Fig. 11).

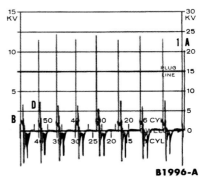

FIG. 11—Normal Secondary Circuit 15 KV Pattern

RE-881 Tester

1. With the RPM selector at the 1600 position and the engine operating at 1000 rpm, depress the 15 KV pushbutton.

2. Adjust the PARADE control so that the left end of the pattern is at the 6-cyl 60° dwell mark on the scope screen.

3. Adjust the EXPAND control so that the right end of the pattern is at the 6-cyl 0° dwell mark on the scope screen (Fig. 11).

Results

A normal eight cylinder engine 15 KV pattern is shown in Fig. 11. The six cylinder pattern would have six similar images. The spark plug line (A) for the No. 1 spark plug is on the extreme right hand side of the screen. The remainder of the No. 1 firing pattern is on the left side of the screen. The remainder of the patterns are shown from left to right in their firing order.

With the exception of the No. 1 spark plug line (which should be shorter than the others), the patterns should be similar. If one of the patterns differs from the others, adjust the expand and parade controls until that pattern fills the screen in the same manner as in the secondary test (Fig. 10).

The following list of symptoms will refer to Fig. 10.

If there is a fluctuation at point C, the points may have incorrect spring tension.

The condenser oscillation signal from C to D should diminish to a straight line at D. If it doesn't, the condenser capacitance is incorrect.

If the points open line (A) is higher than the rest and the plug firing line (B) is sloped downward at an unusually large slope, there is excessive resistance in the high tension wire to that cylinder or in the distributor cap.

If the points open line (A) is low and the firing line (B) is long and nearly straight, the spark plug is shorted out.

If the points open line (A) is low and the firing line (B) is long and wide, the spark plug gap is out of adjustment.

If there are no oscillations at points C or D, the coil primary windings are partially shorted.

If all of the points open lines (A) are at varied heights, check the idle adjustment of the carburetor (always adjust the idle mixture on the rich side).

SECONDARY CIRCUIT 30 KV PATTERN

This pattern is like the 15 KV pattern with the exception of the height. The height has been reduced to allow for checking the coil reserve.

The secondary circuit 30 KV pattern will indicate excessive resistance in the plugs, insufficient coil reserve voltage or leakage at the rotor, distributor cap or spark plug wire.

Procedure

RE-27-55 Tester

1. With the engine running at 600 rpm, turn the test selector switch to the 30 KV position.

2. Adjust the PARADE control so that the left end of the pattern is at the 6-cyl 60° dwell mark on the scope screen.

3. Adjust the EXPAND control so that the right end of the pattern is at the 6-cyl 0° dwell mark on the scope screen (Fig. 12).

RE-881 Tester

1. With the RPM selector at the

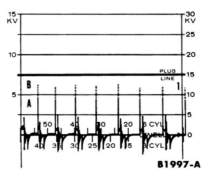

FIG. 12—Normal Secondary Circuit 30 KV Pattern

1600 position and the engine operating at 600 rpm, depress the 30 KV pushbutton.

2. Adjust the PARADE control so that the 6-cyl 60° dwell mark on the scope screen.

3. Adjust the EXPAND control so that the right end of the pattern is at the 6-cyl 0° dwell mark on the scope screen (Fig. 12).

Results

A normal eight cylinder engine 30 KV pattern is shown in Fig. 12. The six cylinder pattern would have six similar images. The spark plug line (A) for the No. 1 spark plug is on the extreme right hand side of the screen. The remainder of the No. 1 firing pattern is on the left side of the screen. The remainder of the patterns are shown from left to right in their firing order.

Notice the average height of the solid part of the points open line. Increase the speed of the engine and notice the height of the dotted lines. The difference is the required ignition output under load. The maximum should be between 13.5 and 15 KV.

If the maximum for one or more of the plugs is above 15 KV, check the complete circuit(s) of the plug(s) for any trouble that would cause resistance. If the maximum does not increase during the increase in engine speed, check for a fouled or improperly gapped spark plug or for very low compression.

Remove the high tension wire at the distributor cap for any plug except No. 1. Notice the change between the average points open line and the points open line of the cylinder with the high tension wire removed. This height difference is the coil reserve. The coil reserve should be at least 20 KV. If it is less than 20 KV, replace the coil.

Remove and do not ground one

spark plug wire at the spark plug. If a plug firing line shows up on the scope for that cylinder, check the plug wire, rotor and distributor cap for bad insulation.

DYNAMIC COMPRESSION TEST—RE-881 TESTER

Procedure

1. Turn the RPM selector to the 1600 position and depress the DYNAMIC COMPRESSION pushbutton.

2. Adjust the engine to 1500 rpm.

3. Adjust the EXPAND and PARADE controls so that the six patterns (6-cyl) or eight patterns (8-cyl) fill the scope screen dwell range.

4. Press and turn the BALANCE TO LINE control to position the needle on the DYNAMIC COMPRESSION scale at the 0 mark.

5. The pattern indication as shown at 5 in Fig. 13 will appear at point A.

6. Turn the CYLINDER SELECTOR control clockwise from its OFF position. As the switch is turned clockwise, the pattern indication will move to the right across the scope.

7. When the pattern indication passes through the firing pattern for cylinder number 5, the plug firing line will disappear (Fig. 13) and the engine will miss on the number 5 cylinder.

8. Observe the dynamic compression meter reading for the number 5 cylinder.

9. Continue to rotate the CYLINDER SELECTOR control to duplicate the above condition for each cylinder in the system except number one (last plug firing line).

10. Turn the CYLINDER SELECTOR control to its maximum clockwise rotation.

11. Turn the NO. 1 CYL. switch on.

12. Slowly turn the CYLINDER SELECTOR control counterclockwise until the pattern shown in Fig. 14 is obtained.

13. Observe the dynamic compression meter reading for the number 1 cylinder.

NOTE: If the engine rpm should change from 1500 rpm, set the speed back to 1500 rpm and repeat step 5.

Results

The readings obtained are relative readings. However, if the engine compression and firing conditions are normal, the readings for all cylinders will be approximately the same.

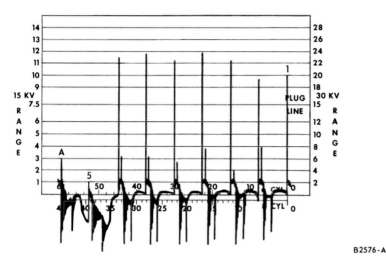

B2576-A

FIG. 13—Typical Dynamic Compression Pattern—All Except No. 1 Cylinder

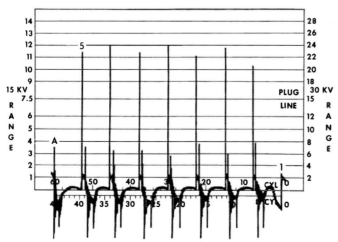

B2577-A

FIG. 14—Typical Dynamic Compression Pattern—No. 1 Cylinder

If the readings are not within 3 divisions of each other, the cylinder(s) with the low reading(s) are not operating as efficiently as the other cylinders.

A cylinder (or cylinders) that is not operating efficiently indicates one or more of the following causes:

Low Compression caused by worn piston rings, leaking valves, leaking cylinder head gasket and/or damaged piston or rings.

Intake Vacuum Leak caused by leaking manifold, carburetor or carburetor spacer gaskets.

Malfunctioning Crankcase Ventilation Regulator Valve.

Carburetor Air Cleaner Restricted.

DISTRIBUTOR CHECKS

DISTRIBUTOR GEAR BACKLASH—LOADOMATIC DISTRIBUTOR

The distributor gear backlash can not be accurately checked on the dual advance or centrifugal advance distributor.

1. Mount a dial indicator on the distributor so that the indicator point rests on the rotor, ⅝-inch from the center.

2. Turn the rotor as far as it will go and set the indicator on zero.

3. Turn the rotor in the opposite direction and note the reading on the dial indicator. This is the backlash.

4. The backlash should be 0.003 to 0.005 inch. If the backlash is not to specifications, it indicates an incorrect number of teeth on the distributor or camshaft gear, or excessively worn gears.

DISTRIBUTOR SHAFT END PLAY

If the shaft end play is not to specifications, check the location of the gear on the shaft (loadomatic distributor), or the distributor shaft collar (dual advance or centrifugal advance distributor).

Loadomatic Distributor

The shaft end play can be checked with the distributor installed on the engine.

1. Mount a dial indicator on the distributor so that the indicator tip rests on the top of the distributor shaft.

2. Push the shaft down as far as it will go and set the dial indicator on zero.

3. Pull the distributor shaft upward as far as it will go and read the end play. The end play should be within specifications with the distributor removed or installed.

Dual Advance and Centrifugal Advance Distributor

1. Remove the distributor from the engine.

2. Place the distributor in the holding tool and clamp it in a vise with the gear end up.

3. Push the distributor shaft upward as far as it will go, and check the end play with a feeler gauge placed between the collar and the distributor base. The end play should be within the specified limits.

DISTRIBUTOR TESTS— ROTUNDA RE-27-44 DWELL TESTER

TEST CONNECTIONS

1. Connect the red lead to the distributor terminal of the coil.

2. Connect the black lead to a good ground on the engine.

DWELL ANGLE CHECK

1. Connect the tester.

2. Turn the test control knob to the set position.

3. Adjust the set control knob until the needle on the dwell meter lines up with the set line.

4. Start the engine and let it idle.

5. Turn the test control knob to the 8 CYL position for eight cylinder engines or to the 6 CYL position for 6 cylinder engines.

6. Read the dwell angle on the dwell meter and compare the reading to specifications.

7. Turn off the engine.

8. If the dwell angle was below the specified amount, the breaker point gap is too large. If the dwell angle was above the specified amount, the breaker point gap is too small.

On dual point distributors, the gaps of both breaker point assemblies should be the same.

If the dwell is to specifications, turn the test selector knob to the OFF position and disconnect the tester leads.

DWELL ANGLE ADJUSTMENT

If the dwell angle is not within specifications, proceed as follows:

1. Remove the coil high tension lead from the distributor and ground it.

2. Remove the distributor cap and place it out of the way.

3. Disconnect the brown wire (I terminal) and the red and blue wire (S terminal) from the starter relay.

4. Loosen the breaker point assembly retaining screw near the breaker point contacts.

5. With the ignition on, crank the engine with an auxiliary starter switch connected between the battery and S terminals of the starter relay and adjust the gap to specifications.

6. Release the auxiliary starter switch and tighten the breaker point assembly retaining screw.

7. Since the adjustment may have changed when the retaining screw was tightened, crank the engine again with the auxiliary starter switch and check the dwell.

On dual-point distributors, when the combined dwell has been set to specifications, the individual dwell settings should be checked. To check the individual dwell settings, block one set of points open with a piece of insulating material and check the dwell of the other set. The individual dwell settings should be the same.

DISTRIBUTOR TESTS— ROTUNDA RE-236 DISTRIBUTOR TESTER

MOUNTING DISTRIBUTOR

1. Adjust the distributor support arm in relation to the distributor shaft length.

2. Set the distributor in the support arm and enter the lower end of the distributor shaft in the Syncrograph chuck.

3. Tighten the chuck on the distributor shaft, using the wrench located near the support arm column.

4. Align the distributor shaft by shifting the support arm and distributor, and tighten the clamp screw.

5. Clamp the distributor securely in the distributor support arm clamp so that it will not turn in its mounting.

6. Connect the synchrograph test lead to the primary wire of the distributor.

MECHANICAL OPERATIONS

1. Turn the OFF, SET, CAM, SYNC. switch to the SET position.

2. Adjust the SET TACH control so the tachometer pointer is on the SET line.

3. Turn the OFF, SET, CAM, SYNC. switch to the SYNC. position.

4. Turn the MOTOR switch to the LEFT for 8 cylinder cars or to the RIGHT for 6 cylinder cars.

5. Adjust the speed control to vary the distributor speed between 400 and 4000 engine rpm, or at the maximum speed of the engine on which the distributor is used. Erratic or thin faint flashes of light preceding the regular flashes as the speed of rotation is increased can be due to weak breaker arm spring tension or binding of the breaker arm on the pivot pin.

6. Operate the distributor at approximately 2500 engine rpm and move the protractor scale so that the zero degree mark on the scale is opposite one of the neon flashes. The balance of all the flashes should come within 1°, plus or minus, evenly around the protractor scale. A variation larger than 1° or erratic or wandering flashes may be caused by a worn cam or distributor shaft or a bent distributor shaft.

DWELL ANGLE

Single Point Distributors

1. Turn the OFF, SET, CAM, SYNC. switch to the CAM position. Operate the distributor at about 1000 rpm.

2. Adjust the breaker point gap until the dwell angle is to specifications.

Dual Point Distributors

1. Turn the OFF, SET, CAM, SYNC. switch to the CAM position. Operate the distributor at about 1000 rpm.

2. Adjust the breaker points until the combined dwell is to specifications and the individual dwells are the same.

The individual dwell settings are checked by isolating one set of points from the circuit. This is done by placing a piece of insulating material between the contacts.

BREAKER PLATE WEAR

A worn breaker plate on the loadomatic or dual advance distributors will cause the breaker point gap and contact dwell to change as engine speed and load conditions are varied.

On the loadomatic distributor, there should not be over a 3° variation in dwell between engine idle speed and 2500 rpm. If the contact dwell changes more than 3°, the plate and bushing should be replaced.

On the dual advance distributor, adjust the test set to 0° advance, 0 inches vacuum, and 1000 rpm. Adjust the dwell angle to 26°. Apply vacuum to the distributor diaphragm and increase it very slowly while observing the indicated dwell angle. The maximum dwell angle variation should not exceed 6° when going from zero to maximum vacuum at constant rpm. If the dwell angle variation exceeds this limit, there is excessive wear at the stationary subplate pin or the diaphragm rod is bent or distorted.

DISTRIBUTOR SPARK ADVANCE

The spark advance is checked to determine if the ignition timing advances in proper relation to engine speed and load.

Loadomatic Distributor

1. Check the breaker point contact dwell. If the contact dwell is not within specifications, adjust the breaker points.
2. Check the breaker arm spring tension. Adjust if necessary.
3. Adjust the test set to 0° advance, 0 inch vacuum and the initial rpm setting listed in the specifications.
4. Check the operation of the vacuum advance at the lowest and highest vacuum and rpm settings given in the specifications.

If the spark advance is not within the limits under low vacuum, the primary spring adjustment is at fault. If the spark advance is not within the limits under high vacuum, the secondary spring adjustment is at fault.

To adjust the spark advance, release the tension on the retard springs by turning the adjusting posts as required (Fig. 15). Adjust the primary spring (spring closest to the vacuum chamber) first, for the low vacuum settings. Adjust the secondary spring last, for the high vacuum settings. As a final check, check the advance throughout the entire range.

If it is impossible to adjust both springs to give the correct spark advance throughout the range, one or both springs should be replaced and the spark advance readjusted.

If the advance characteristics still cannot be brought within specifications, check the diaphragm assembly as follows:

Adjust the vacuum pressure of the distributor tester to its maximum position. Hold your hand over the end of the tester's vacuum hose and note the maximum reading obtained. **Do not exceed 25 inches Hg.**

If the maximum reading is 25 inches Hg or less, connect the test-

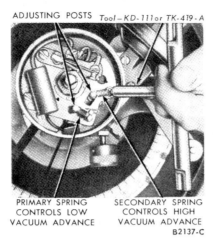

FIG. 15—Spark Advance Adjustment

er's vacuum line to the vacuum fitting on the diaphragm **without changing any of the adjustments.** The maximum gauge reading should not be less than it was above. If it is less, the diaphragm is leaking and should be replaced.

Dual Advance Distributor

1. Check the contact dwell. If the contact dwell is not within specifications, adjust the breaker points.
2. Check the breaker arm spring tension and adjust it, if necessary.

The dual advance distributor has two independently operated spark advance systems. Each system is adjusted separately. **Adjust the centrifugal advance before adjusting the vacuum advance.**

Centrifugal Advance

1. Operate the distributor in the direction of rotation (counterclockwise) and adjust the speed to the initial rpm setting listed in the specifications. Move the protractor scale so that one of the flashes lines up with the zero degree mark.
2. Slowly increase the rpm to the setting specified for the first advance reading listed in the specifications.

If the correct advance is not indicated at this rpm, stop the distributor and bend one spring adjustment bracket to change its tension (Fig. 16). Bend the adjustment bracket away from the distributor shaft to decrease advance (increase spring tension) and toward the shaft to increase advance (decrease spring tension). After the adjustment is made, identify the bracket.

3. After an adjustment has been made to one spring, check the mini-

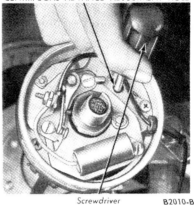

FIG. 16—Centrifugal Advance Adjustment

mum advance point again.

4. Operate the distributor at the specified rpm to give an advance just below the maximum. If this advance is not to specifications, stop the distributor and bend the other spring bracket to give the correct advance.
5. Check the advance at all rpm settings listed in the specifications. Operate the distributor both up and down the rpm range.

Vacuum Advance

1. Connect the test set vacuum line to the fitting on the diaphragm.
2. Set the test set to 0° advance, 0 vacuum, and at 1000 rpm.
3. Check the advance at the first vacuum setting given in the specifications.
4. If the advance is incorrect, change the calibration washers between the vacuum chamber spring and nut (Fig. 17). After installing or removing the washers, position the gasket in place and tighten the nut. **The addition of a washer will decrease advance and the removal of a washer will increase advance.**
5. After one vacuum setting has been adjusted, the others should be

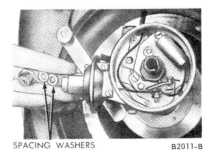

FIG. 17—Vacuum Advance Adjustment

checked. **Do not change the original rpm setting when going to a different vacuum setting.** If the other settings are not within limits, there is incorrect spring tension, leakage in the vacuum chamber and/or line, or the wrong fibre stop has been installed in the vacuum chamber of the diaphragm housing.

To check the diaphragm for leakage:

Remove the vacuum line from the distributor. Adjust the vacuum pressure of a distributor tester to its maximum position. Hold your hand over the end of the tester's vacuum hose and note the maximum reading obtained. **Do not exceed 25 inches Hg.**

If the maximum reading is 25 inches Hg or less, connect the tester's vacuum line to the vacuum fitting on the diaphragm **without changing any of the adjustments.** The maximum gauge reading should not be less than it was above. If it is less, the diaphragm is leaking and should be replaced.

Centrifugal Advance Distributor

1. On a high performance centrifugal advance distributor, check the gap of the breaker point assemblies or the combined dwell.

2. Check the breaker arm spring tension and adjust it if necessary.

3. Turn the OFF, SET, CAM, SYNC. switch to SYNC. position.

4. Operate the distributor in the direction of rotation (counterclockwise) and adjust the speed to the initial rpm setting listed in the specifications. Move the protractor scale so that one of the flashes lines up with the zero degree mark.

5. Slowly increase the rpm to the setting specified for the first advance reading listed in the specifications.

If the correct advance is not indicated at this rpm, stop the distributor and bend one spring adjustment bracket to change its tension (Fig. 18). **Bend the adjustment bracket away from the distributor shaft to decrease advance (increase spring tension) and toward the shaft to increase advance (decrease spring tension).** After the adjustment is made, identify the bracket.

6. After an adjustment has been made to one spring, check the minimum advance point again.

7. Operate the distributor at the specified rpm to give an advance just below the maximum. If this advance is not to specifications, stop the distributor and bend the other spring

CENTRIFUGAL ADVANCE ADJUSTMENT HOLE

Screwdriver B2326-B

FIG. 18—Dual Point Distributor Centrifugal Advance Adjustment

bracket to give the correct advance.

8. Check the advance at all rpm settings listed in the specifications. Operate the distributor both up and down the rpm range.

Lack of synchronization, excessive cam wear, worn bearings, or weak breaker arm spring tension causing contact point chatter are all disclosed by uneven or intermittent flashes around the protractor scale.

DISTRIBUTOR TESTS— ROTUNDA RE-1416 DISTRIBUTOR TESTER

MOUNTING DISTRIBUTOR

1. Clamp the distributor securely in the distributor support arm clamp so that it will not turn in its mounting.

2. Loosen the hand-operated locking screw on the side of the distributor support arm and adjust the support arm column up or down by turning the crank on the knob at the top of the column until the distributor shaft or adapter shaft can be securely fastened in the driving chuck.

3. Securely tighten the drive chuck to the distributor drive shaft by means of the chuck key, attached by a chain to the Syncrograph.

4. Rotate the drive chuck by hand to make sure the distributor shaft turns freely and then tighten the locking screw on the distributor support arm.

5. Connect the Syncrograph test lead to the primary lead wire of the distributor.

BREAKER POINT RESISTANCE

1. Turn the test selector to

POINT RES. position.

2. Revolve the chuck by hand until the distributor breaker points are closed.

3. The meter pointer on the cam angle meter should read in the OK zone at the left side of the meter scale. If the meter pointer does not fall in the OK zone, there is excessive resistance caused by a faulty contact across the distributor points, a faulty primary lead, or a poorly grounded base plate. A faulty contact across the distributor points indicates improper spring tension or burned or pitted points.

INSULATION AND LEAKAGE

1. Turn the test selector to the cam angle position and revolve the chuck by hand until the distributor breaker contacts are open.

2. The cam angle meter should show a zero reading. If a zero reading is not obtained, a short circuit to ground exists.

A short could be caused by poor primary lead wire insulation, a shorted condenser, or a short between the breaker arm and breaker plate.

MECHANICAL OPERATION

1. Turn the test selector to the SYNCHRO. position and check to make sure the drive chuck is securely tightened on the distributor shaft.

2. Turn the motor control switch to the left for an eight cylinder car or to the right for a six cylinder car. **If it is necessary to reverse the rotation of the drive motor, turn the motor control switch to the OFF position and allow the chuck to come to a complete stop before reversing the switch.**

3. Adjust the rpm control to vary the distributor speed between 400 and 4000 engine rpm or at the maximum speed of the engine on which the distributor is used. Erratic or thin faint flashes of light preceding the regular flashes as the speed of rotation is increased can be due to weak breaker arm spring tension or binding of the breaker arm on the pivot pin.

4. Operate the distributor at approximately 2500 engine rpm.

5. Move the protractor scale with the adjustment control so that the zero degree mark on the scale is opposite one of the neon flashes. The balance of all the flashes should come within 1°, plus or minus, evenly around the protractor scale. A variation larger than 1° or erratic or wan-

dering flashes may be caused by a worn cam or distributor shaft or a bent distributor shaft.

DWELL ANGLE

Single Point Distributor

1. Turn the cylinder selector to the figure corresponding to the number of lobes on the cam of the distributor being tested.

2. Turn the test selector switch to the cam angle position and operate the distributor at approximately 1000 engine rpm.

3. Adjust the distributor breaker point gap to the dwell angle shown in the specifications.

Dual Point Distributor

1. Follow steps 1 and 2 under "Single Point Distributor."

2. Adjust the breaker points until the combined dwell is to specifications and the individual dwell settings are the same.

The individual dwell settings are checked by isolating one set of points from the circuit. This is done by placing a piece of insulating material between the contacts.

BREAKER PLATE WEAR

A worn breaker plate on the loadomatic or dual advance distributors will cause the breaker point dwell to change as engine speed and load conditions are varied.

On the loadomatic distributor there should not be over a 3° variation in dwell between engine idle speed and 2500 rpm. If the contact dwell changes more than 3°, the plate bushing should be replaced.

On the dual advance distributor adjust the test set to 0° advance, 0 inches vacuum, and 1000 rpm. Adjust the dwell angle to 26°. Apply vacuum to the distributor diaphragm and increase it very slowly while observing the indicated dwell angle. The maximum dwell angle variation should not exceed 6° when going from zero to maximum vacuum at constant rpm. If the dwell angle variation exceeds this limit, there is excessive wear at the stationary subplate pin or the diaphragm.

DISTRIBUTOR SPARK ADVANCE

The spark advance is checked to determine if the ignition timing advances in proper relation to engine speed and load.

Loadomatic Distributor

1. Check the breaker point contact dwell. If the contact dwell is not within specifications, adjust the breaker points.

2. Check the breaker arm spring tension. Adjust if necessary.

Attach the vacuum adapter fitting to the vacuum unit and attach the vacuum hose between the distributor vacuum control and the vacuum outlet located at the upper right of the front panel. Check the zero setting of the vacuum gauge and, if necessary, adjust the small knob at the lower edge of the dial rim so that the vacuum gauge hand rests on zero. Turn the vacuum supply switch to the ON position.

3. Adjust the test set to 0° advance, 0 inch vacuum and the initial rpm setting listed in the specifications.

4. Check the operation of the vacuum advance at the lowest and highest vacuum and rpm settings given in the specifications.

If the spark advance is not within the limits under low vacuum, the primary spring adjustment is at fault. If the spark advance is not within the limits under high vacuum, the secondary spring adjustment is at fault.

To adjust the spark advance, release the tension on the retard springs by turning the adjusting posts as required (Fig. 15). Adjust the primary spring (spring closest to the vacuum chamber) first, for the low vacuum settings. Adjust the secondary spring last, for the high vacuum settings. As a final check, check the advance throughout the entire range.

If it is impossible to adjust both springs to give the correct spark advance throughout the range, one or both springs should be replaced and the spark advance readjusted. If the advance characteristics still cannot be brought within specifications, check the diaphragm assembly as follows:

Adjust the vacuum pressure of a distributor tester to its maximum position. Hold your hand over the end of the tester's vacuum hose and note the maximum reading obtained. **Do not exceed 25 inches Hg.**

If the maximum reading is 25 inches Hg or less, connect the tester's vacuum line to the vacuum fitting on the diaphragm **without changing any of the adjustments.** The maximum gauge reading should not be less than it was above. If it is less, the diaphragm is leaking and should be replaced.

Dual Advance Distributor

1. Check the contact dwell. If the contact dwell is not within specifications, adjust the breaker points.

2. Check the breaker arm spring tension and adjust it if necessary.

The dual advance distributor has two independently operated spark advance systems. Each system is adjusted separately. **Adjust the centrifugal advance before adjusting the vacuum advance.**

Centrifugal Advance

1. Operate the distributor in the direction of rotation (counterclockwise) and adjust the speed to the initial rpm setting listed in the specifications. Move the protractor scale so that one of the flashes lines up with the zero degree mark.

2. Slowly increase the rpm to the setting specified for the first advance reading listed in the specifications.

If the correct advance is not indicated at this rpm, stop the distributor and bend one spring adjustment bracket to change its tension (Fig. 16). **Bend the adjustment bracket away from the distributor shaft to decrease advance (increase spring tension) and toward the shaft to increase advance (decrease spring tension).** After the adjustment is made, identify the bracket.

3. After an adjustment has been made to one spring, check the minimum advance point again.

4. Operate the distributor at the specified rpm to give an advance just below the maximum. If this advance is not to specifications, stop the distributor and bend the other spring bracket to give the correct advance.

5. Check the advance at all rpm settings listed in the specifications. Operate the distributor both up and down the rpm range.

Vacuum Advance

1. Connect the test set vacuum line to the fitting on the diaphragm and turn the vacuum supply switch on.

2. Set the test set to 0° advance, 0 vacuum, and at 1000 rpm.

3. Check the advance at the first vacuum setting given in the specifications.

4. If the advance is incorrect, change the calibration washers between the vacuum chamber spring and nut (Fig. 17). After installing or removing the washers, position the gasket in place and tighten the nut. **The addition of a washer will decrease advance and the removal of a**

washer will increase advance.

5. After one vacuum setting has been adjusted, the others should be checked. **Do not change the original rpm setting when going to a different vacuum setting.** If the other settings are not within limits, it indicates incorrect spring tension, leakage in the vacuum diaphragm and/or line, or the wrong fiber stop has been installed in the vacuum chamber of the diaphragm housing.

To check the diaphragm for leakage:

Remove the vacuum line from the distributor. Adjust the vacuum pressure of a distributor tester to its maximum position. Hold your hand over the end of the tester's vacuum hose and note the maximum reading obtained. **Do not exceed 25 inches Hg.**

If the maximum reading is 25 inches Hg or less, connect the tester's vacuum line to the vacuum fitting on the diaphragm **without changing any of the adjustments.** The maximum

gauge reading should not be less than it was above. If it is less, the diaphragm is leaking and should be replaced.

Centrifugal Advance Distributor

1. On a high performance centrifugal advance distributor, check the combined dwell. If it is not within specifications, adjust the gap.
2. Check the breaker arm spring tension and adjust it if necessary.
3. Turn the test selector to the SYNCRO. position.
4. Operate the distributor in the direction of rotation (counterclockwise) and adjust the speed to the initial rpm setting listed in the specifications. Move the protractor scale so that one of the flashes lines up with the zero degree mark.
5. Slowly increase the rpm to the setting specified for the first advance reading listed in the specifications.

If the correct advance is not indicated at this rpm, stop the distributor and bend one spring adjustment

bracket to change its tension (Fig. 18). **Bend the adjustment bracket away from the distributor shaft to decrease advances (increase spring tension) and toward the shaft to increase advance (decrease spring tension).** After the adjustment is made, identify the bracket.

6. After an adjustment has been made to one spring, check the minimum advance point again.
7. Operate the distributor at the specified rpm to give an advance just below the maximum. If this advance is not to specifications, stop the distributor and bend the other spring bracket to give the correct advance.
8. Check the advance at all rpm settings listed in the specifications. Operate the distributor both up and down the rpm range.

Lack of synchronization, excessive cam wear, worn bearings, or weak breaker arm spring tension causing contact point chatter are all disclosed by uneven or intermittent flashes around the protractor scale.

2 COMMON ADJUSTMENTS AND REPAIRS

BREAKER POINTS AND CONDENSER

REPLACEMENT

Loadomatic Distributors

Removal

1. Remove the distributor cap and rotor.
2. Disconnect the condenser and primary lead wires from the breaker point assembly.
3. Remove the breaker point assembly and condenser retaining screws and lift the breaker point assembly and condenser out of the distributor.

Installation

1. Place the breaker point assembly and condenser in position on the breaker plate and install the screws. Be sure that the ground wire is under the breaker point assembly screw nearest the breaker point contacts. Align and adjust the breaker points.
2. Connect the primary and condenser wires to the breaker point assembly.
3. Install the rotor and distributor cap.

Dual Advance Distributors

Removal

1. Remove the distributor cap and the rotor.
2. Disconnect the primary and the condenser wires from the breaker point assembly.
3. Remove the breaker point assembly and condenser retaining screws. Lift the breaker point assembly and condenser out of the distributor.

Installation

1. Place the breaker point assembly and the condenser in position and install the retaining screws. Be sure to place the ground wire under the breaker point assembly screw farthest from the breaker point contacts.
2. Align and adjust the breaker point assembly.
3. Connect the primary and condenser wires to the breaker point assembly.
4. Install the rotor and the distributor cap.

Centrifugal Advance Distributor

Removal

1. Remove the distributor cap and the rotor.

2. Disconnect the primary lead, the jumper strap, and the condenser lead from the breaker point assemblies.
3. Remove the retaining screws from the breaker point assemblies and the condenser. Lift the breaker point assemblies and the condenser out of the distributor.

Installation

1. Place the breaker point assemblies and the condenser in position and install the retaining screws.
2. Align and adjust the breaker point assemblies.
3. Connect the primary lead, the jumper strap, and the condenser lead to the breaker point assemblies.
4. Install the rotor and the distributor cap.

BREAKER POINT ALIGNMENT

The vented-type breaker points must be accurately aligned and strike squarely in order to realize the full advantages provided by this design and assure normal breaker point life. Any misalignment of the breaker point surfaces will cause premature wear, overheating and pitting.

1. Turn the cam so that the breaker points are closed and check the alignment of the points (Fig. 19).

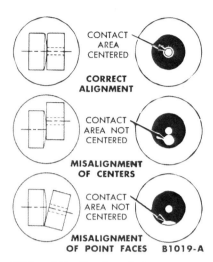

FIG. 19—Breaker Point Alignment

If the distributor is in the engine, close the points by proceeding as follows:

Disconnect the brown wire and the red and blue wire from the starter relay and, with the ignition switch off, crank the engine by using an auxiliary starter switch between the S and the battery terminals of the starter relay.

2. Align the breaker points to make full face contact by bending the stationary breaker point bracket (Fig. 20). **Do not bend the breaker arm.**

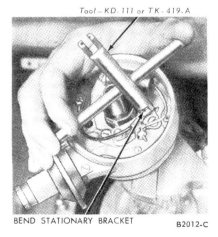

BEND STATIONARY BRACKET B2012-C

FIG. 20—Aligning Breaker Points

3. After the breaker points have been properly aligned, adjust the breaker point gap or dwell.

BREAKER POINT GAP ADJUSTMENT

A scope, a dwell meter, or a feeler gauge can be used to check the gap of new breaker points.

A scope or a dwell meter can be used to check the gap of used breaker points. Due to the roughness of used points, it is not advisable to use a feeler gauge to check the gap.

To check and adjust the breaker points with a feeler gauge:

1. Check and adjust the breaker point alignment.

2. Rotate the distributor until the rubbing block rests on the peak of a cam lobe.

If the distributor is in the engine place the rubbing block on the peak of the cam by proceeding as follows:

Disconnect the brown wire and the red and blue wire from the starter relay and, with the ignition switch off, crank the engine by using an auxiliary starter switch between the S and battery terminals of the starter relay.

Insert the correct blade of a clean feeler gauge between the breaker points (Fig. 21).

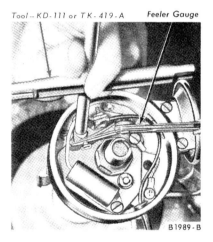

FIG. 21—Adjusting New Breaker Point Gap

Apply a light film of distributor cam lubricant (C4AZ-19D530-A) to the cam when new points are installed. **Do not use engine oil to lubricate the distributor cam.**

Set the ignition timing.

If a scope or a dwell meter is used to adjust new points, be sure the points are in proper alignment. Also, set the contact dwell to the low setting. New points must be set to the low dwell as the rubbing block will wear down slightly while seating to the cam.

To check and adjust the breaker points with a scope, refer to Ignition System Tests—Rotunda Oscilloscope Testers.

To check and adjust the breaker points with a dwell meter, refer to

Distributor Tests—Rotunda RE-27-55 Dwell Tester.

BREAKER POINT SPRING TENSION ADJUSTMENT

Correct breaker point spring tension is essential to proper engine operation and normal breaker point life. If the spring tension is too great, rapid wear of the breaker arm rubbing block will result, causing the breaker point gap to close up and retard the spark timing. If the spring tension is too weak, the breaker arm will flutter at high engine rpm resulting in an engine miss.

To check the spring tension on either the pivot-type or the pivotless breaker points, place the hooked end of the spring tension gauge over the movable breaker point. Pull the gauge at a right angle (90°) to the movable arm until the breaker points just start to open (Fig. 22). If the tension is not within specifications, adjust the spring tension on the pivot-type points or replace the breaker point assembly on the pivotless points.

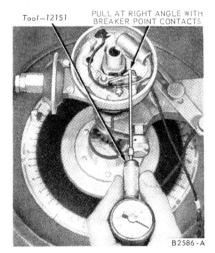

FIG. 22—Checking Breaker Point Spring Tension

To adjust the spring tension (Fig. 23):

1. Disconnect the primary or distributor-transistor lead wire and the condenser lead if so equipped, and the jumper strap on the centrifugal advance distributor at the breaker point assembly primary terminal.

2. Loosen the nut holding the spring in position. **Move the spring toward the breaker arm pivot to decrease tension and in the opposite direction to increase tension.**

3. Tighten the lock nut, and then check spring tension. Repeat the ad-

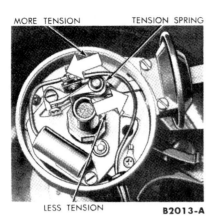

FIG. 23—Adjusting Breaker Point Spring Tension

justment until the specified spring tension is obtained.

4. Install the primary or distributor-transistor lead wire, the condenser lead (if so equipped) and the jumper strap on the centrifugal advance distributor with the lockwasher and tighten the nut securely.

On the centrifugal advance distributor with dual breaker points, loosen the lock nut holding the jumper strap to the other breaker point assembly and follow steps 2 and 3. After the adjustment has been completed, connect the jumper strap.

IGNITION TIMING

TIMING MARK LOCATIONS

There are two methods of showing the timing position. Both methods use the crankshaft damper and a timing pointer.

One method uses degree marks on the crankshaft pulley (Fig. 24). These degree marks range from 0° or top dead center (TDC) to some value before top dead center (BTDC). When checking the timing, the correct degree mark should be in line with the timing pointer when the timing light flashes.

The other method uses degree marks on the timing pointer (Fig. 25). These also range from 0° or top dead center (TDC) to some value before top dead center (BTDC). When checking the timing, the correct degree mark should be in line with the timing mark on the crankshaft pulley when the timing light flashes.

ADJUSTMENT

The procedure for checking and adjusting the ignition timing with a scope is given in Section 1 of this part.

To check and adjust the timing

FIG. 24—Typical V-8 Engine Timing Marks

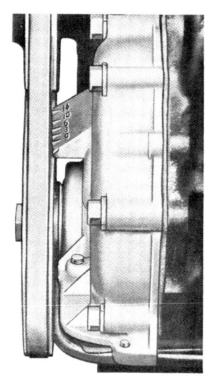

FIG. 25—Typical Six Cylinder Engine Timing Marks

with a Rotunda 13-07 power timing light, proceed as follows:

1. Remove the plug wire from the number 1 spark plug.

2. Install the spark plug adaptor on the spark plug.

3. Connect the plug wire to the spark plug adaptor.

4. Clamp the timing light spark plug lead to the spark plug adaptor.

5. Connect the timing light battery leads to the battery terminals.

6. Disconnect the distributor vacuum line (if so equipped).

7. If necessary, clean and mark the timing marks.

8. Operate the engine at the specified idle rpm and point the timing light at the timing pointer.

9. If the timing is incorrect, loosen the distributor hold down bolt and rotate the distributor until the desired initial advance is obtained.

10. Tighten the distributor hold down bolt and check the timing again.

11. Turn off the engine.

12. Remove the timing light and connect the vacuum line.

SPARK PLUG WIRE REPLACEMENT

When removing the wires from the spark plugs, grasp, twist and pull the moulded cap only. Do not pull on the wire because the wire connection inside the cap may become separated or the weather seal may be damaged.

170 AND 200 C.I.D. SIX CYLINDER ENGINES

The ignition wire installation is shown in Fig. 26.

Removal

1. Disconnect the wires at the spark plugs and at the distributor cap.

2. Remove the coil high tension lead.

Cleaning and Inspection

Refer to section 3 of this part for the cleaning and inspection procedures.

Installation

1. Connect the wires to the proper spark plugs.

2. Insert the ends of the wires in the correct sockets in the distributor cap. Be sure the wires are forced all the way down into their sockets and that they are held firmly in position. The No. 1 socket is identified on the cap. Install the wires in a clockwise direction in the firing order (1-5-3-6-2-4) starting at the No. 1 socket.

3. Install the coil high tension lead. Push all weatherseals into position.

ALL V-8 ENGINES

A typical ignition wiring installation is shown in Fig. 27.

Removal

1. Disconnect the wires from the spark plugs and distributor cap.

2. Pull the wires from the brackets

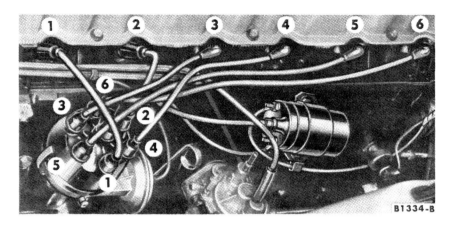

FIG. 26—6-Cylinder Engine Ignition Wiring

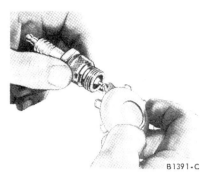

FIG. 28—Checking Spark Plug Gap

on the valve rocker arm covers and remove the wires.

3. Remove the coil high tension lead.

Cleaning and Inspection

Refer to section 3 of this part for the cleaning and inspection procedures.

Installation

1. Insert each wire in the proper socket of the distributor cap. Be sure the wires are forced all the way down into their sockets. The No. 1 socket is identified on the cap. Install the wires in a counterclockwise direction in the firing order (1-5-4-2-6-3-7-8) starting at the No. 1 socket. Cylinders are numbered from front to rear; right bank 1-2-3-4, left bank 5-6-7-8.

2. Remove the brackets from the old spark plug wire set and install them on the new set in the same relative position. Install the wires in the brackets on the valve rocker arm covers. (Fig. 27). Connect the wires to the proper spark plugs. Install the coil high tension lead. **Be sure the No. 7 spark plug wire is positioned in the bracket as shown in Fig. 27.**

SPARK PLUGS

REMOVAL

1. Remove the wire from each spark plug by grasping, twisting and pulling the moulded cap of the wire only. **Do not pull on the wire because the wire connection inside the cap may become separated or the weather seal may be damaged.**

2. Clean the area around each spark plug port with compressed air, and then remove the spark plugs.

CLEANING AND INSPECTION

Refer to section 3 of this part for

the cleaning and inspection procedures.

ADJUSTMENT

Set the spark plug gap to specifications by bending the ground electrode (Fig. 28).

INSTALLATION

1. Install the spark plugs and torque each plug to 15-20 ft-lbs.

When a new spark plug is installed in a new replacement cylinder head, torque the plug to 20-30 ft-lbs.

2. Connect the spark plug wires.

RESISTANCE WIRE REPLACEMENT

1. Cut the brown wire and the red wire (with a green stripe) from the upper quick disconnect at the dash panel. Cut the wires as close to the quick disconnect as possible.

2. Solder a male bullet-type terminal to the brown wire and to the red wire (with a green stripe). Make a single terminal of the two wires. Using a female bullet terminal connector, connect the wires to one end of the service replacement resistance wire. **Do not splice the resistance wire.**

3. Drill a ¾-inch hole through

FIRING ORDER-1-5-4-2-6-3-7-8

FIG. 27—Typical V-8 Engine Ignition Wiring

one of the accessory dimples in the dash panel.

4. Install a grommet into the hole drilled in the dash panel.

5. Thread one end of the service replacement resistance wire through the grommet in the dash panel and connect it to the quick disconnect near the ignition switch. Make sure the wire is routed through the retaining clips.

3 CLEANING AND INSPECTION

SPARK PLUGS

Examine the firing ends of the spark plugs, noting the type of deposits and the degree of electrode erosion. Refer to Fig. 30 for the various types of spark plug fouling and their causes.

Clean the plugs on a sand blast cleaner, following the manufacturer's instructions. **Do not prolong the use of the abrasive blast as it will erode the insulator and electrodes.**

Clean the electrode surfaces with a small file (Fig. 31). Dress the electrodes to obtain flat parallel surfaces on both the center and side electrodes.

After cleaning, examine the plug carefully for cracked or broken insulators, badly pitted electrodes, and other signs of failure. Replace as required.

DISTRIBUTORS

Soak all parts of the distributor assembly (except the condenser, breaker point assembly, lubricating wick, vacuum diaphragm, distributor base oil seal and electrical wiring) in a mild cleaning solvent or mineral spirits. Do not use a harsh cleaning solution. Wipe all parts that can not be immersed in a solvent with a clean dry cloth.

After foreign deposits have been loosened by soaking, scrub the parts with a soft bristle brush. **Do not use a wire brush, file, or other abrasive object.** Dry the parts with compressed air.

Examine the bushing surface(s) of the distributor shaft and the bushing(s) for wear.

Inspect the distributor cam lobes for scoring and signs of wear. If any lobe is scored or worn, replace the cam assembly (dual advance and centrifugal advance distributor) or the shaft (loadmatic distributor).

Inspect the breaker plate assembly for signs of distortion. In addition, on the dual advance distributor, inspect the stationary sub-plate for worn nylon contact buttons. Replace the breaker plate assembly if it is defective.

The breaker point assembly(ies) and condenser (if so equipped) should be replaced whenever the distributor is overhauled.

Inspect all electrical wiring for fraying, breaks, etc., and replace any that are not in good condition.

Check the distributor base for cracks or other damage.

On a loadmatic or dual advance distributor, check the diaphragm housing, bracket, and rod for damage. Check the vacuum line fitting for stripped threads or other damage. Test the vacuum fittings, case, and diaphragm for leakage as explained under Distributor Tests. Replace all defective parts.

The breaker point assembly consists of the stationary point bracket assembly, breaker arm and the primary wire terminal.

Breaker points should be inspected, cleaned and adjusted as necessary. Breaker points can be cleaned with chloroform and a stiff bristle brush. Replace the breaker point assembly if the contacts are badly burned or excessive metal transfer between the points is evident (Fig. 29). Metal transfer is considered excessive when it equals or exceeds the gap setting.

SECONDARY WIRING

Wipe the wire with a damp cloth and check for fraying, breaks or cracked insulation. Inspect the terminals and weather seals for looseness or corrosion. Replace any wires that are not in good condition.

COIL

Wipe the coil with a damp cloth and check for any cracks or other defects.

DISTRIBUTOR CAP

Clean the distributor cap with a soft bristle brush and mild cleaning solvent or mineral spirits. Dry the cap with compressed air. Inspect the cap for cracks, burned contacts, permanent carbon tracks or dirt or corrosion in the sockets. Replace the cap if it is defective.

ROTOR

Clean the rotor with a soft bristle brush and mild cleaning solvent or mineral spirits. Dry the rotor with compressed air. Inspect the rotor for cracks or burning. Replace the rotor if it is defective.

CONDITION	CAUSED BY
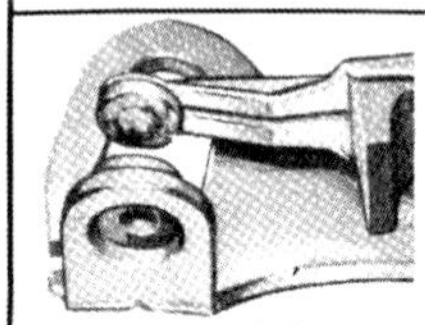 **BURNED**	Any discoloration other than a frosted slate grey shall be considered as burned points.
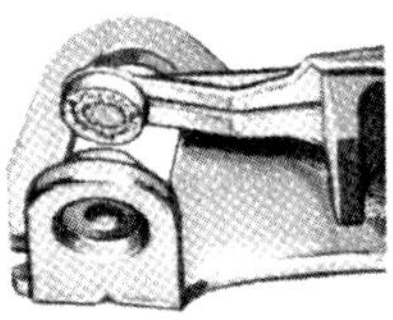 **EXCESSIVE METAL TRANSFER OR PITTING**	Incorrect alignment. Incorrect voltage regulator setting. Radio condenser installed to the distributor side of the coil. Ignition condenser of improper capacity. Extended operation of the engine at speeds other than normal.

B1443-B

FIG. 29—Breaker Point Inspection

CARBON FOULED	OIL FOULED	GAP BRIDGED

IDENTIFIED BY BLACK, DRY FLUFFY CARBON DEPOSITS ON INSULATOR TIPS, EXPOSED SHELL SURFACES AND ELECTRODES. CAUSED BY TOO COLD A PLUG, WEAK IGNITION, DIRTY AIR CLEANER, DEFECTIVE FUEL PUMP, TOO RICH A FUEL MIXTURE, IMPROPERLY OPERATING HEAT RISER OR EXCESSIVE IDLING. CAN BE CLEANED.	IDENTIFIED BY WET, BLACK DEPOSITS ON THE INSULATOR, SHELL BORE AND ELECTRODES. CAUSED BY EXCESSIVE OIL ENTERING COMBUSTION CHAMBER THROUGH WORN RINGS AND PISTONS, EXCESSIVE CLEARANCE BETWEEN VALVE GUIDES AND STEMS, OR WORN OR LOOSE BEARINGS. CAN BE CLEANED.	IDENTIFIED BY DEPOSIT BUILD-UP CLOSING GAP BETWEEN ELECTRODES. CAUSED BY OIL OR CARBON FOULING. IF DEPOSITS ARE NOT EXCESSIVE, THE PLUG CAN BE CLEANED.
LEAD FOULED	NORMAL	WORN

IDENTIFIED BY DARK GRAY, BLACK, YELLOW OR TAN DEPOSITS OR A FUSED GLAZED COATING ON THE INSULATOR TIP. CAUSED BY HIGHLY LEADED GASOLINE. CAN BE CLEANED.	IDENTIFIED BY LIGHT TAN OR GRAY DEPOSITS ON THE FIRING TIP. CAN BE CLEANED.	IDENTIFIED BY SEVERELY ERODED OR WORN ELECTRODES. CAUSED BY NORMAL WEAR. SHOULD BE REPLACED.
FUSED SPOT DEPOSIT	OVERHEATING	PRE-IGNITION

IDENTIFIED BY MELTED OR SPOTTY DEPOSITS RESEMBLING BUBBLES OR BLISTERS. CAUSED BY SUDDEN ACCELERATION. CAN BE CLEANED.	IDENTIFIED BY A WHITE OR OR LIGHT GRAY INSULATOR WITH SMALL BLACK OR GRAY BROWN SPOTS AND WITH BLUISH-BURNT APPEARANCE OF ELECTRODES. CAUSED BY ENGINE OVERHEATING, WRONG TYPE OF FUEL, LOOSE SPARK PLUGS, TOO HOT A PLUG, LOW FUEL PUMP PRESSURE OR INCORRECT IGNITION TIMING.	IDENTIFIED BY MELTED ELECTRODES AND POSSIBLY BLISTERED INSULATOR. METALLIC DEPOSITS ON INSULATOR INDICATE ENGINE DAMAGE. CAUSED BY WRONG TYPE OF FUEL, INCORRECT IGNITION TIMING OR ADVANCE, TOO HOT A PLUG, BURNT VALVES OR ENGINE OVERHEATING. REPLACE THE PLUG.

B2581-A

FIG. 30—Spark Plug Inspection

B1390-C

FIG. 31—Cleaning Spark Plug Electrode

PART 9-2

LOADOMATIC DISTRIBUTORS

Section	Page
1 Description and Operation	9-20
2 In-Car Adjustments and Repairs	9-20
Breaker Point and Condenser Replacement	9-20
Vacuum Diaphragm Replacement	9-20
3 Removal and Installation	9-21

Section	Page
Removal	9-21
Installation	9-21
4 Major Repair Operations	9-21
Bench Disassembly	9-21
Bench Assembly	9-21

1 DESCRIPTION AND OPERATION

The direction of distributor rotation is clockwise as viewed from the top of the distributor.

Engine speed and load requirements are satisfied by the action of the breaker plate which is controlled by a vacuum-actuated diaphragm working against the tension of two calibrated breaker plate springs (Figs. 1 and 2). The breaker plate is free to rotate on the shaft bushing. The diaphragm moves the breaker plate in a counterclockwise direction to advance the spark, and the springs move the plate in a clockwise direction to retard the spark. The degree of spark advance is determined by the strength of the vacuum acting on the diaphragm.

Vacuum is transmitted to the distributor diaphragm from two interconnected passages in the carburetor. The opening of one passage is in the throat of the venturi and the opening(s) of the other passage is in the throttle bore just above the closed throttle plate.

All manifold vacuum to the distributor passes through a spark control valve located in the carburetor throttle body or main body. Under steady part throttle operation, the spark valve is held open against the pressure of a calibrated spring. A combi-

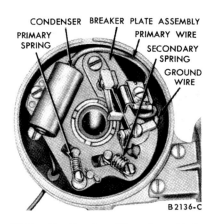

FIG. 1—Breaker Plate Installed

nation of atmospheric pressure outside the spark valve diaphragm and manifold vacuum from within holds the spark valve open. When accelerating, manifold vacuum momentarily drops below a predetermined point and the calibrated spring closes the spark valve shutting off the manifold vacuum port. Vacuum from the venturi prevents full spark retard.

As engine speed approaches the throttle setting, manifold vacuum increases sufficiently to open the spark valve and allow a higher vacuum to operate the distributor.

At high engine speed, manifold

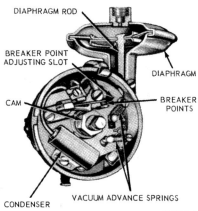

FIG. 2—Spark Advance Mechanism

vacuum falls and the valve closes. This prevents loss of venturi vacuum due to bleed back caused by the lower manifold vacuum. This assures full spark advance at high engine speed.

The spark valve functions in a similar manner to provide an intermediate spark retard whenever the load on the engine is increased to a degree where normal road load spark advance would be too great and the wide-open throttle spark retard would reduce the efficiency of the engine.

2 IN-CAR ADJUSTMENTS AND REPAIRS

BREAKER POINT AND CONDENSER REPLACEMENT

The replacement procedures are covered in Part 9-1, Section 2.

VACUUM DIAPHRAGM REPLACEMENT

REMOVAL

1. Remove the distributor cap and rotor.

2. Remove the vacuum line from the diaphragm.

3. Remove the spring *clip* that secures the diaphragm link to the breaker plate.

4. Remove the diaphragm retain-

ing screws and remove the diaphragm.

INSTALLATION

1. Install the vacuum unit on the distributor body. Insert the tip of the vacuum rod through the breaker plate and attach the rod with the spring clip.

2. Install the vacuum line in the diaphragm assembly and tighten the fitting.

3. Install the rotor and distributor cap.

ADJUSTMENTS

Refer to Part 9-1 for the proper procedures for adjusting the breaker points and spark advance.

3 REMOVAL AND INSTALLATION

REMOVAL

1. Disconnect the primary wire at the coil and remove the distributor cap.

2. Disconnect the vacuum line at the distributor.

3. Scribe a mark on the distributor body, indicating the position of the rotor, and scribe another mark on the body and engine block, indicating position of the body in the block. These lines will be used as guides when installing the distributor in the correctly timed engine.

4. Remove the retaining bolt and lock washer and lift the distributor out of the block.

Do not rotate the crankshaft while the distributor is removed, or it will be necessary to time the engine.

INSTALLATION

1. If the crankshaft has not been rotated while the distributor was removed, position the distributor in the block with the rotor aligned with the mark previously scribed on the distributor body.

Install the distributor retaining screw.

2. If the crankshaft has been rotated while the distributor was removed, rotate the crankshaft until the No. 1 piston is on TDC after the compression stroke. Position the distributor in the block with the rotor at the No. 1 firing position. **Make sure the oil pump intermediate drive shaft is properly seated in the oil pump.** Install, but do not tighten, the distributor retaining bolt. Rotate the distributor body clockwise until the breaker points are just starting to open. Tighten the retaining bolt.

3. Connect the distributor primary wire and install the distributor cap.

4. Start the engine and adjust the ignition timing to specifications with a timing light. Connect the distributor vacuum line, and check the advance with the timing light when the engine is accelerated.

4 MAJOR REPAIR OPERATIONS

To perform the operations in this section, it will be necessary to remove the distributor from the car.

BENCH DISASSEMBLY

The distributor assembly is shown in Fig. 3.

1. Install the distributor in a vise.

2. Remove the rotor and retaining clip.

3. Remove the vacuum diaphragm rod and spring clip. Push the diaphragm rod out of the plate. Remove the vacuum diaphragm unit from the distributor.

4. Disconnect the primary and condenser wires from the breaker point terminal. Working from the inside of the distributor, pull the primary wire through the opening in the distributor.

5. Remove the condenser.

6. Remove the breaker point assembly.

7. Release the tension on the return springs and disconnect the springs. **Do not stretch the springs as distortion may result, making it impossible to obtain an adjustment. If the springs are distorted, discard them.**

8. Remove the distributor from the vise. Remove the distributor cap clamps.

9. Drive out the drive gear pin with a punch (Fig 4).

10. If the gear and shaft are to be used again, mark the gear and shaft so that the pin holes can be easily aligned for assembly.

11. Press the gear off the shaft (Fig. 5). Slide the distributor shaft out of the body.

12. Position the distributor in a vise.

13. Remove the lock ring attaching the breaker plate to the upper bushing. Lift the breaker plate from the body.

14. Remove the ground wire.

15. Remove the oil filler cap and the oil wick.

16. Compress and insert the slotted end of the bushing removal tool in the distributor body. Allow it to expand and butt against the bushing. Drive out the bushing (Fig. 6).

BENCH ASSEMBLY

1. Oil the bushing and position it in the body with the lock ring end up. Install the bushing (Fig. 7). Press the tool until the bushing bottoms firmly against the distributor body.

2. Burnish the bushing to the proper size (Fig. 8).

3. Install the ground wire. Position the breaker plate in the body. Install the lock ring to secure the plate.

4. Position a new breaker point assembly on the breaker plate. Be sure the pivot pin enters the hole in the breaker plate.

5. Connect the ground wire under the breaker point screw at the end closest to the adjustment slot. Install the other screw and lock washer at the opposite end of the assembly.

6. Install a new condenser. Pass the primary wire assembly through the opening in the distributor, working from the inside to the outside of the distributor housing. Pull the wire through the opening until the locating stop is flush with the inside of the distributor. Place the condenser lead, primary lead, lock washer, and nut on the primary terminal.

7. Install the return springs on the adjustment and breaker plate posts. **Make certain that the primary spring is installed closest to the condenser.**

8. Install the vacuum diaphragm on the distributor body.

9. Insert the tip of the vacuum dia-

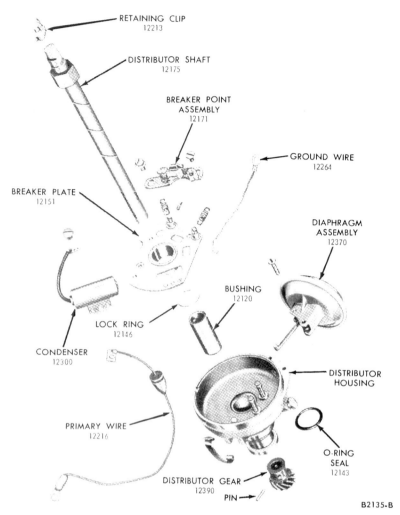

FIG. 3—Distributor Assembly

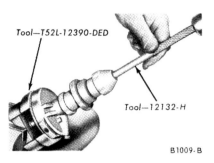

FIG. 6—Bushing Removal

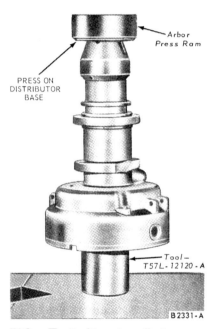

FIG. 7—Bushing Installation

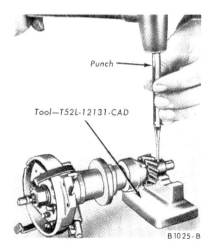

FIG. 4—Gear Pin Removal or Installation

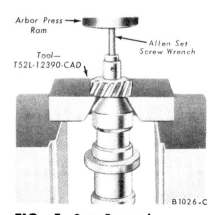

FIG. 5—Gear Removal

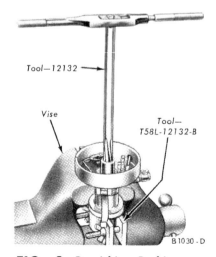

FIG. 8—Burnishing Bushing

phragm rod through the breaker plate. Attach the rod with the spring clip.

10. Slide the shaft into the body using care not to damage the rubbing

block on the breaker points. **The shaft and gear are replaced as an assembly. One part should not be replaced without replacing the other.**

11. Place the distributor locating and installing fixture on the distributor. Place a 0.022 feeler gauge between the backing screw and the shaft. Tighten the backing screw

enough to remove all shaft end play and remove the feeler gauge.

12. Place the spacer on the gear end of the shaft. Press the gear on the shaft (Fig. 9). If a new shaft is being installed, drill the shaft with a

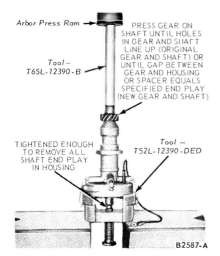

Arbor Press Ram →

PRESS GEAR ON SHAFT UNTIL HOLES IN GEAR AND SHAFT LINE UP (ORIGINAL GEAR AND SHAFT) OR UNTIL GAP BETWEEN GEAR AND HOUSING OR SPACER EQUALS SPECIFIED END PLAY (NEW GEAR AND SHAFT)

Tool — T65L-12390-B

TIGHTENED ENOUGH TO REMOVE ALL SHAFT END PLAY IN HOUSING

Tool — T52L-12390-DED

B2587-A

FIG. 9—Gear Installation

⅛-inch drill using the pin hole in the gear shoulder as a guide.

13. Install the pin through the gear and shaft. Install the distributor cap clamps. Lubricate the cam with distributor cam lubricant.

14. Fill the oil reservoir with approximately 40 drops of engine oil. Install the oil wick and the filler cap.

15. Refer to Part 9-1 and adjust the breaker point spring tension, align the breaker points, and adjust the gap. Check the vacuum advance, and the breaker point dwell and resistance.

PART 9-3

DUAL ADVANCE DISTRIBUTORS

Section	Page
1 Description and Operation	9-24
2 In-Car Adjustments and Repairs	9-25
Breaker Point and Condenser Replacement	9-25
Vacuum Diaphragm Replacement	9-25
Breaker Plate and Sub-Plate Replacement	9-25
Cam and Centrifugal Advance Mechanism	
Replacement	9-25

Section	Page
3 Removal and Installation	9-27
Removal	9-27
Installation	9-27
4 Major Repair Operations	9-27
Bench Disassembly	9-27
Bench Assembly	9-28

1 DESCRIPTION AND OPERATION

The dual advance distributor has two independently operated spark advance systems. A centrifugal advance mechanism (Fig. 1) is located below the stationary sub-plate assembly, and a vacuum operated spark control diaphragm is located on the side of the distributor base (Fig. 2). As speed increases, the centrifugal weights cause the cam to advance or move ahead with respect to the distributor drive shaft. The rate of advance is controlled by calibrated springs.

The vacuum advance mechanism has a spring-loaded diaphragm which is connected to the breaker plate. The spring-loaded side of the diaphragm is airtight and is connected through a vacuum line to the carburetor throttle bore. When the throttle plates open, the distributor vacuum passage is exposed to manifold vacuum, which causes the diaphragm to move against the tension of the spring. This action causes the movable breaker plate to pivot on the stationary sub-plate. The breaker point rubbing block, which is positioned on the opposite side of the cam from the pivot pin, then moves against distributor rotation and advances the spark timing. As the movable breaker plate is rotated from retard position to full advance position, the dwell decreases slightly. This is because the breaker point rubbing block and the cam rotate on different axes.

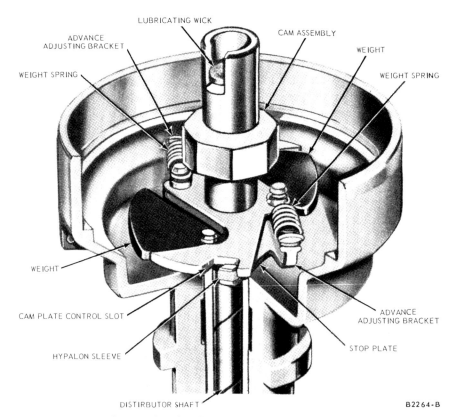

FIG. 1—Typical Centrifugal Advance Mechanism

LUBRICATING WICK

CAM ASSEMBLY

WEIGHT

WEIGHT SPRING

ADVANCE ADJUSTING BRACKET

WEIGHT SPRING

WEIGHT

CAM PLATE CONTROL SLOT

HYPALON SLEEVE

ADVANCE ADJUSTING BRACKET

STOP PLATE

DISTIRBUTOR SHAFT

B2264-B

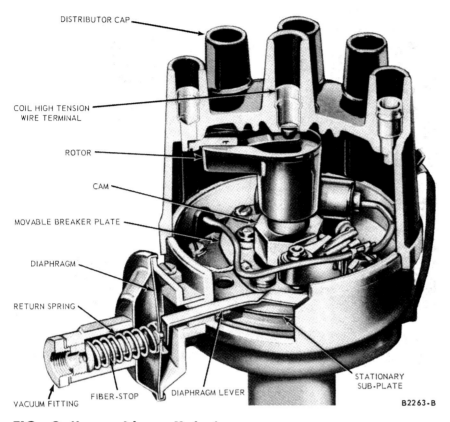

DISTRIBUTOR CAP

COIL HIGH TENSION
WIRE TERMINAL

ROTOR

CAM

MOVABLE BREAKER PLATE

DIAPHRAGM

RETURN SPRING

VACUUM FITTING

FIBER-STOP

DIAPHRAGM LEVER

STATIONARY
SUB-PLATE

B2263-B

FIG. 2—Vacuum Advance Mechanism

2 IN-CAR ADJUSTMENTS AND REPAIRS

BREAKER POINT AND CONDENSER REPLACEMENT

The replacement procedures are covered in Part 9-1, Section 2.

VACUUM DIAPHRAGM REPLACEMENT

REMOVAL

1. Remove the distributor cap and the rotor.
2. Remove the vacuum line from the diaphragm fitting.
3. Remove the spring clip that secures the diaphragm link to the movable breaker plate.
4. Remove the diaphragm retaining screws and slide the diaphragm out of the distributor.

INSTALLATION

1. Slide the diaphragm into the opening in the distributor and place the link in its position.
2. Install the spring clip that secures the diaphragm link to the movable breaker plate and the diaphragm retaining screws.
3. Install the vacuum line on the diaphragm fitting.

4. Install the rotor and the distributor cap.

BREAKER PLATE AND SUB-PLATE REPLACEMENT

Refer to Figs. 3 and 4 for the proper location of parts.

REMOVAL

1. Remove the distributor cap and the rotor.
2. Remove the breaker point assembly, the condenser, and the vacuum diaphragm.
3. Working from the inside of the distributor, pull the primary wire through the opening in the distributor.
4. Remove the spring clip, the flat washer, and the spring washer securing the breaker plate to the sub-plate.
5. Remove the sub-plate retaining screws and lift both plates out of the distributor.

INSTALLATION

1. Place the breaker plate in position on the sub-plate.
2. Install the spring washer, the flat washer, and the spring clip that

secures the breaker plate to the sub-plate.
3. Install the sub-plate hold down screws (the ground wire should be under the sub-plate hold down screw near the primary wire opening in the distributor).
4. Working from the inside of the distributor, push the primary wire through the opening in the distributor.
5. Install the breaker point assembly, the condenser and the vacuum diaphragm.
6. Install the rotor and the distributor cap.

CAM AND CENTRIFUGAL ADVANCE MECHANISM REPLACEMENT

REMOVAL

1. Remove the distributor cap and the rotor.
2. Working from the inside of the distributor, pull the primary wire through the opening in the distributor.
3. Remove the sub-plate retaining

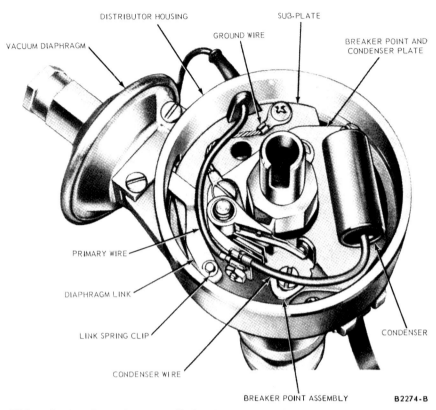

FIG. 3—Breaker Plate Installed—Pivot-Type Points

screws and lift the plate assembly out of the distributor.

4. Mark one of the distributor

weight springs and its brackets. Also mark one of the weights and its pivot pin.

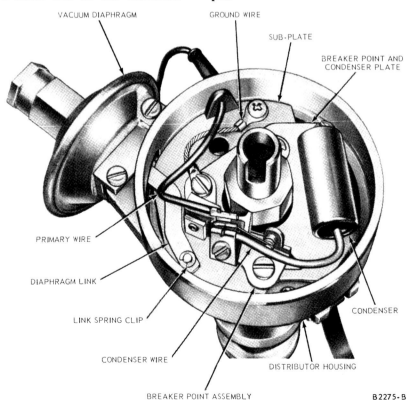

FIG. 4—Breaker Plate Installed—Pivotless Points

5. Carefully unhook and remove the weight springs.

6. Lift the lubricating wick from the cam assembly. Remove the cam assembly retainer and lift the cam assembly off the distributor shaft. Remove the thrust washer.

7. Remove the weight retainers and lift the weights out of the distributor.

INSTALLATION

1. Fill the grooves in the weight pivot pins with distributor cam lubricant (C4AZ-19D530-A).

2. Position the weights in the distributor **(the marked weight is placed on the marked pivot pin)** and install the weight retainers.

3. Place the thrust washer on the shaft.

4. Fill the grooves in the upper portion of the distributor shaft with distributor cam lubricant (C4AZ-19D530-A).

5. Install the cam assembly. **Be sure that the marked spring bracket on the cam assembly is near the marked spring bracket on the stop plate.**

If a new cam is being installed, make sure that the cam is installed with the hypalon covered stop in the correct cam plate control slot. This can be done by measuring the length of the slot used on the old cam and by using the corresponding slot on the new cam. Some of the cams will have the size of the slot in degrees stamped near the slot. **If the wrong slot is used, an incorrect maximum advance will be obtained.**

Place a light film of distributor cam lubricant on the distributor cam lobes. Install the retainer and the wick. Saturate the wick with SAE 10W engine oil.

6. Install the weight springs. **Be sure that the marked spring is attached to the marked spring brackets.**

7. Install the sub-plate assembly.

8. Working from the inside of the distributor, push the primary wire through the opening in the distributor.

9. Install the rotor and the distributor cap.

ADJUSTMENTS

Refer to Part 9-1, Section 2 for the adjustment procedures.

3 REMOVAL AND INSTALLATION

REMOVAL

1. Disconnect the primary wire at the coil. Disconnect the vacuum advance line at the distributor. Remove the distributor cap.

2. Scribe a mark on the distributor body and engine block indicating the position of the body in the block, and scribe another mark on the distributor body indicating the position of the rotor. These marks can be used as guides when installing the distributor in a correctly timed engine.

3. Remove the distributor hold down bolt and clamp. Lift the distributor out of the block.

Do not rotate the crankshaft while the distributor is removed, or it will be necessary to time the engine.

INSTALLATION

1. If the crankshaft was rotated while the distributor was removed from the engine, it will be necessary to time the engine. Rotate the crankshaft until No. 1 piston is on TDC after the compression stroke. Align the TDC mark on the timing pointer with the timing pin on the crankshaft damper. Position the distributor in the block with the rotor at the No. 1 firing position.

Make sure the oil pump intermediate shaft properly engages the distributor shaft. It may be necessary to crank the engine with the starter, after the distributor drive gear is partially engaged, in order to engage the oil pump intermediate shaft.

Install, but do not tighten, the re-taining clamp and bolt. Rotate the distributor body counterclockwise until the breaker points are just starting to open. Tighten the clamp.

2. If the crankshaft has not been rotated, position the distributor in the block with the rotor aligned with the mark previously scribed on the distributor body, and the marks on the distributor body and engine block in alignment. Install the retaining clamp.

3. Install the distributor cap.

4. Connect the primary wire to the coil.

5. Check the ignition timing with a timing light and adjust to specifications if necessary. Connect the vacuum line, and check the advance with the timing light when the engine is accelerated.

4 MAJOR REPAIR OPERATIONS

To perform the operations in this section, it will be necessary to remove the distributor from the engine and place it in a vise.

BENCH DISASSEMBLY

The distributor assembly is shown in Fig. 5.

1. Remove the rotor.

2. Disconnect the primary and the condenser wires from the breaker point assembly.

3. Remove the breaker point assembly and condenser retaining screws. Lift the breaker point assembly and condenser out of the distributor.

4. Remove the spring clip that se-cures the diaphragm link to the moveable breaker plate.

5. Remove the diaphragm retaining screws and slide the diaphragm out of the distributor.

6. Working from the inside of the distributor, pull the primary wire through the opening in the distributor.

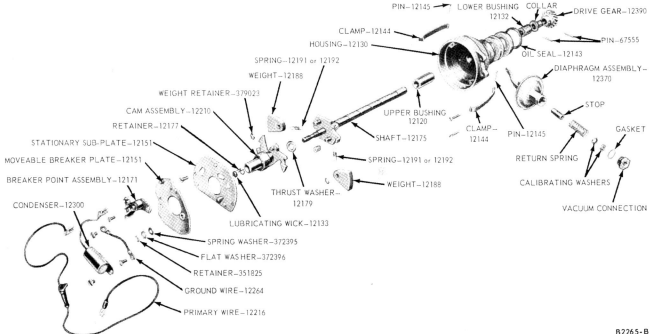

FIG. 5—Distributor Assembly

B2265-B

7. Remove the spring clip, the flat washer, and the spring washer securing the breaker plate to the sub-plate.

8. Remove the sub-plate retaining screws and lift both plates out of the distributor.

9. Mark one of the distributor weight springs and its brackets. Also mark one of the weights and its pivot pin.

10. Carefully unhook and remove the weight springs.

11. Lift the lubricating wick from the cam assembly. Remove the cam assembly retainer and lift the cam assembly off the distributor shaft. Remove the thrust washer.

12. Remove the weight retainers and lift the weights out of the distributor.

13. Remove the distributor cap clamps.

14. If the gear and shaft are to be used again, mark the gear and the shaft so that the pin holes can be easily aligned for assembly. Remove the gear roll pin (Fig. 6), and then remove the gear (Fig. 7).

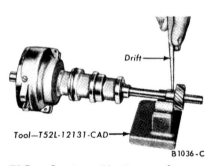

FIG. 6—Gear Pin Removal or Installation

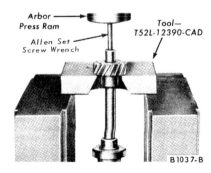

FIG. 7—Gear Removal

15. Remove the shaft collar roll pin (Fig. 8).

16. Invert the distributor and place it on a support plate in a position that will allow the distributor shaft to clear the support plate and press the shaft out of the collar and distributor housing (Fig. 9).

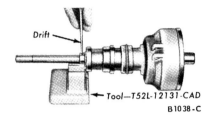

FIG. 8—Collar Pin Removal or Installation

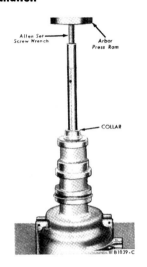

FIG. 9—Shaft Removal

17. Refer to Figs. 10 and 11 and remove the distributor shaft upper and lower bushings.

BENCH ASSEMBLY

ORIGINAL SHAFT AND GEAR

1. Oil the new upper bushing, and position it on the bushing replacer tool. Install the bushing (Fig. 12). When the tool bottoms against the distributor base, the bushing will be installed to the correct depth.

2. Burn the bushing to the proper size (Fig. 13).

3. Invert the distributor and install and burnish the lower bushing in a similar manner.

4. Oil the shaft and slide it into the distributor body.

5. Place the collar in position on the shaft and align the holes in the collar and the shaft, then install a new pin. Install the distributor cap clamps.

6. Check the shaft end play with a feeler gauge placed between the collar and the base of the distributor. If the end play is not within specifications, replace the shaft and gear.

7. Attach the distributor shaft supporting tool to the distributor. Tighten the backing screw in the tool enough to remove all shaft end play.

8. Install the assembly in a press.

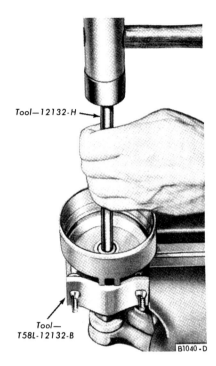

FIG. 10—Lower Bushing Removal

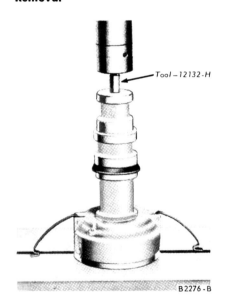

FIG. 11—Upper Bushing Removal

Press the gear on the shaft (Fig. 14), using the marks made on the gear and shaft as guides to align the pin holes.

9. Remove the distributor from the press. Install the gear retaining pin (Fig. 6).

10. Position the distributor in a vise. Fill the grooves in the weight pivot pins with a distributor cam lubricant.

11. Position the weights in the dis-

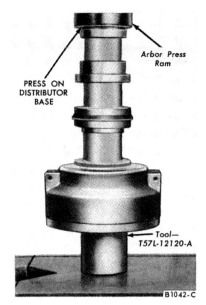

FIG. 12—Upper Bushing Installation

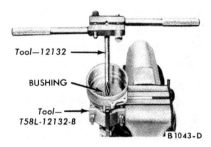

FIG. 13—Burnishing Bushing

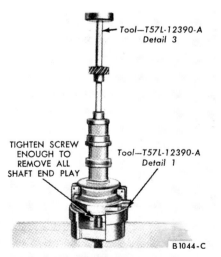

FIG. 14—Original Shaft and Gear Installation

tributor (the marked weight is placed on the marked pivot pin) and install the weight retainers.

12. Place the thrust washer on the shaft.

13. Fill the grooves in the upper portion of the distributor shaft with distributor cam lubricant (C4AZ-19D530-A).

14. Install the cam assembly. **Be sure that the marked spring bracket on the cam assembly is near the marked spring bracket on the stop plate.**

If a new cam is being installed, make sure that the cam is installed with the hypalon covered stop in the correct cam plate control slot. This can be done by measuring the length of the slot used on the old cam and by using the corresponding slot on the new cam. Some of the cams will have the size of the slot in degrees stamped near the slot. **If the wrong slot is used, an incorrect maximum advance will be obtained.**

Place a light film of distributor cam lubricant on the distributor cam lobes. Install the retainer and the wick. Saturate the wick with SAE 10W engine oil.

15. Install the weight springs. **Be sure that the marked spring is attached to the marked spring brackets.**

16. Place the breaker plate in position on the sub-plate.

17. Install the spring washer, the flat washer, and the spring clip that secures the breaker plate to the sub-plate.

18. Install the sub-plate hold down screws (the ground wire should be under the sub-plate hold down screw near the primary wire opening in the distributor).

19. Working from the inside of the distributor, push the primary wire through the opening in distributor.

20. Slide the diaphragm into the opening in the distributor and place the link in its position.

21. Install the spring clip that secures the diaphragm link to the moveable breaker plate.

22. Place the breaker point assembly and the condenser in position and install the retaining screws. Be sure to place the ground wire under the breaker point assembly screw farthest from the breaker point contacts. Align and adjust the breaker point assembly by following the procedure in Part 9-1.

23. Connect the primary and condenser leads to the breaker point assembly.

24. Install the rotor and the distributor cap.

25. Check and adjust (if necessary) the centrifugal and vacuum advance (Refer to Part 9-1, Section 1).

NEW SHAFT AND GEAR

The shaft and gear are replaced as an assembly. One part should not be replaced without replacing the other. Refer to Fig. 5 for the correct location of the parts.

1. Follow steps 1, 2, 3, and 4 under "Installing Original Shaft and Gear—Conventional Ignition System Distributor."

2. Attach the distributor shaft supporting tool to the distributor and install the assembly in a vise. Insert a 0.024-inch feeler gauge between the backing screw and the shaft. Tighten the backing screw on the tool enough to remove all shaft end play. Remove the feeler gauge and allow the shaft to rest on the backing screw. Slide the collar on the shaft. While holding the collar in place against the distributor base (Fig. 15), drill a ⅛-inch hole through the shaft using the access opening in the collar as a pilot.

3. Position the gear on the end of the shaft. Install the assembly in a press.

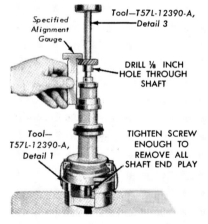

FIG. 15—New Shaft and Gear Installation

4. With the backing screw on the support tool tightened enough to remove all end play, press the gear on the shaft to the specified distance from the bottom face of the gear to the bottom face of the distributor mounting flange (Fig. 15). Drill a ⅛-inch hole through the shaft using the hole in the gear as a pilot.

5. Remove the distributor from the press and remove the support tool. Install the collar retaining pin (Fig. 8) and the gear retaining pin (Fig. 6).

6. Complete the assembly by following steps 9 thru 25 under Installing Original Shaft and Gear.

PART 9-4

CENTRIFUGAL ADVANCE DISTRIBUTORS

Section	Page
1 Description and Operation	9-30
2 In-Car Adjustments and Repairs	9-30
Breaker Point and Condenser Replacement	9-30
Breaker Point and Condenser Plate Replacement	9-30
Cam and Centrifugal Advance	

Section	Page
Mechanism Replacement	9-31
3 Removal and Installation	9-31
Removal	9-31
Installation	9-32
4 Major Repair Operations	9-32
Bench Disassembly	9-32
Bench Assembly	9-33

1 DESCRIPTION AND OPERATION

The centrifugal advance distributor is a straight mechanical-type unit. A governor-type centrifugal advance is located below the stationary breaker plate (Fig. 1). Two centrifugal weights cause the cam to advance or move ahead with respect to the distributor drive shaft. The rate of advance is controlled by two calibrated springs.

The breaker points are located on the stationary breaker plate and are connected in parallel with an insulated jumper strap. One breaker point assembly closes the primary circuit and the other opens the primary circuit. This type of construction results in a greater amount of dwell with approximately the same amount of gap spacing as the single breaker point distributor. The breaker arm spring tension is greater than on the loadomatic or dual advance distributors. This increased dwell and breaker arm spring tension assures reserve spark plug voltage for high speed performance.

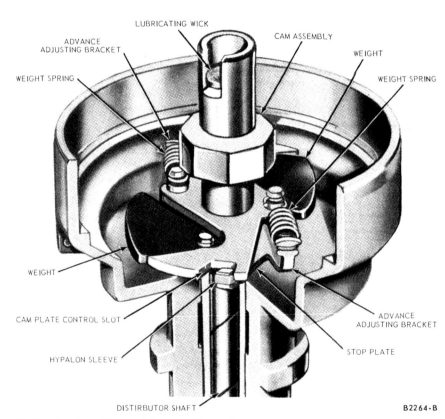

FIG. 1—Centrifugal Advance Mechanism

2 IN-CAR ADJUSTMENTS AND REPAIRS

BREAKER POINT AND CONDENSER REPLACEMENT

The replacement procedures are in Part 9-1, Section 2.

BREAKER POINT AND CONDENSER PLATE REPLACEMENT

REMOVAL

1. Remove the distributor cap and the rotor.

2. Remove the breaker point assemblies and the condenser.

3. Working from the inside of the distributor, pull the primary wire *through the opening* in the distributor.

4. Remove the breaker point and

condenser plate retaining screws and lift the plate out of the distributor.

INSTALLATION

The breaker point and condenser plate assembly installation is shown in Fig. 2.

1. Place the breaker point and condenser plate in position and install the retaining screws.

2. Working from the inside of the distributor, push the primary wire through the opening in the distributor housing.

3. Install the breaker point assemblies and the condenser.

4. Install the rotor and the distributor cap.

CAM AND CENTRIFUGAL ADVANCE MECHANISM REPLACEMENT

REMOVAL

1. Remove the distributor cap and the rotor.

2. Working from the inside of the distributor, pull the primary wire through the opening in the distributor.

3. Remove the breaker point and condenser plate retaining screws and lift the plate assembly out of the distributor.

4. **Mark one of the distributor weight springs and its brackets. Also mark one of the weights and its pivot pin.**

5. Carefully unhook and remove the weight springs.

6. Lift the lubricating wick from the cam assembly. Remove the cam assembly retainer and lift the cam assembly off the distributor shaft. Remove the thrust washer.

7. Remove the weight retainers and lift the weights out of the distributor.

INSTALLATION

1. Fill the grooves in the weight pivot pins with distributor cam lubricant (C4AZ-19D530-A).

2. Position the weights in the distributor **(the marked weight is**

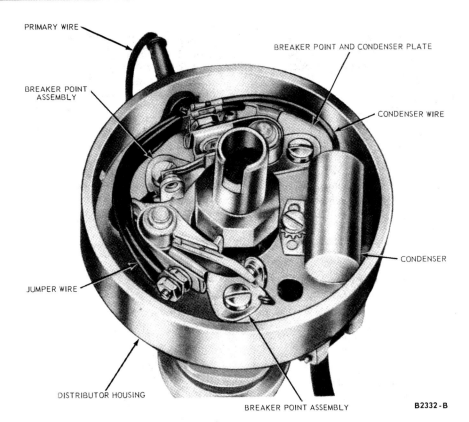

PRIMARY WIRE

BREAKER POINT AND CONDENSER PLATE

BREAKER POINT ASSEMBLY

CONDENSER WIRE

CONDENSER

JUMPER WIRE

DISTRIBUTOR HOUSING

BREAKER POINT ASSEMBLY

B2332-B

FIG. 2—Breaker Plate Installed

placed on the marked pivot pin) and install the weight retainers.

3. Place the thrust washer on the shaft.

4. Fill the grooves in the upper portion of the distributor shaft with distributor cam lubricant (C4AZ-19D530-A).

5. Install the cam assembly. **Be sure that the marked spring bracket on the cam assembly is near the marked spring bracket on the stop plate.**

If a new cam assembly is being installed, make sure that the cam is installed with the hypalon covered stop in the correct cam plate control slot. This can be done by measuring the length of the slot used on the old cam and by using the corresponding slot on the new cam. Some of the cams will have the size of the slot in degrees stamped near the slot. **If the**

wrong slot is used, an incorrect maximum advance will be obtained.

Place a light film of distributor cam lubricant (C4AZ-19D530-A) on the distributor cam lobes. Install the retainer and the wick. Saturate the wick with SAE 10W engine oil.

6. Install the weight springs. **Be sure that the marked spring is attached to the marked spring brackets.**

7. Install the breaker point and condenser plate assembly.

8. Working from the inside of the distributor, push the primary wire through the opening in the distributor.

9. Install the rotor and the distributor cap.

ADJUSTMENTS

Refer to Part 9-1, Section 3 for the adjustment procedures.

⬛ 3 REMOVAL AND INSTALLATION

REMOVAL

1. Disconnect the primary wire at the coil. Remove the distributor cap.

2. Scribe a mark on the distributor body and engine block indicating the position of the body in the block, and scribe another mark on the distributor body indicating the position of the rotor. These marks can be used as guides when installing the distributor in a correctly timed engine.

3. Remove the distributor hold down cap bolt and clamp, and then

lift the distributor out of the block.

Do not rotate the crankshaft while the distributor is removed, or it will be necessary to time the engine.

INSTALLATION

1. If the crankshaft was rotated while the distributor was removed from the engine, it will be necessary to time the engine. Rotate the crankshaft until No. 1 piston is on TDC (after the compression stroke). Align the TDC mark on the timing pointer with the timing pin on the

crankshaft damper. Position the distributor in the block with the rotor at the No. 1 firing position.

If the crankshaft has not been rotated, position the distributor in the block with rotor aligned with the mark previously scribed on the distributor body, and the marks on the distributor body and engine block in alignment. Install the retaining clamp.

Make sure the oil pump intermediate shaft properly engages the distributor shaft. It may be necessary to crank the engine with the

starter, after the distributor drive gear is partially engaged, in order to engage oil pump intermediate shaft.

2. Install, but do not tighten, the retaining clamp and bolt. Rotate the distributor body counterclockwise until one set of breaker points are just starting to open. Tighten the clamp.

3. Install the distributor cap.

4. Connect the primary wire to the coil.

5. Check the ignition timing with a timing light and adjust it if necessary.

---

4 MAJOR REPAIR OPERATIONS

To perform the operations in this section, it will be necessary to remove the distributor from the car and place it in a vise.

BENCH DISASSEMBLY

Refer to Fig. 3 for the location of parts.

1. Remove the rotor.

2. Disconnect the primary wire, the jumper strap, and the condenser wire from the breaker point assemblies.

3. Remove the retaining screws from the breaker point assemblies and condenser. Lift the breaker point assemblies and the condenser out of the distributor.

4. Working from the inside of

the distributor, pull the primary wire through the opening in the distributor.

5. Remove the breaker point and condenser plate retaining screws and lift the plate out of the distributor.

6. Mark one of the distributor weight springs and its brackets. Also mark one of the weights and its pivot pin.

7. Carefully unhook and remove the weight springs.

8. Lift the lubricating wick from the cam assembly. Remove the cam assembly retainer and lift the cam assembly off the distributor shaft. Remove the thrust washer.

9. Remove the weight retainers and lift the weights out of the distributor.

10. Remove the distributor cap clamps.

11. If the gear and shaft are to be used again, mark the gear and the shaft so that the pin holes can be easily aligned for assembly. Remove the gear roll pin (Fig. 4), and then remove the gear (Fig. 5).

12. Remove the shaft collar roll pin (Fig. 6).

13. Invert the distributor and place it on a support in a position that will allow the distributor shaft to clear the support plate and press the shaft out of the collar and the distributor housing (Fig. 7).

14. Remove the distributor shaft upper bushing (Fig. 8).

15. Remove the distributor shaft lower bushing (Fig. 9).

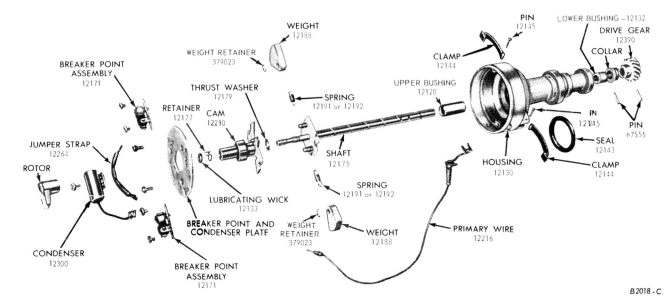

B2018-C

FIG. 3—Distributor Assembly

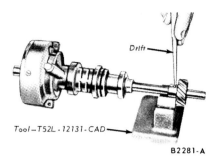

FIG. 4—Gear Pin Removal or Installation

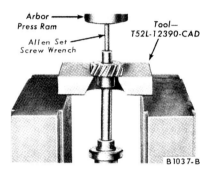

FIG. 5—Gear Removal

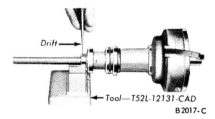

FIG. 6—Collar Pin Removal or Installation

BENCH ASSEMBLY

ORIGINAL SHAFT AND GEAR

1. Oil the new upper bushing, and install it on the bushing replacer tool. Then install the upper bushing (Fig. 10). When the tool bottoms against the distributor base, the bushing will be installed to the correct depth.

2. Burnish the bushing to the proper size (Fig. 11).

3. Invert the distributor and install the lower bushing in a similar manner.

4. Oil the shaft and slide it into the distributor body.

5. Place the collar in position on the shaft and align the holes in the collar and shaft, then install a new pin (Fig. 6). Install the distributor cap clamps.

6. Check the shaft end play with a feeler gauge placed between the collar and the base of the distribu-

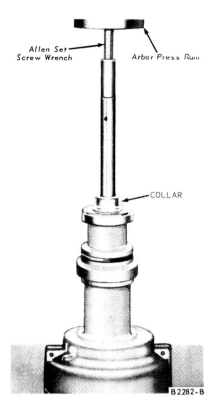

FIG. 7—Shaft Removal

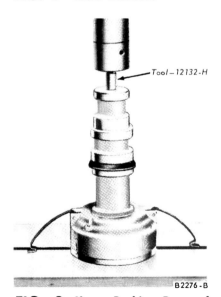

FIG. 8—Upper Bushing Removal

tor. If the end play is not within limits, replace the shaft and gear.

7. Attach the distributor shaft supporting tool to the distributor. Tighten the backing screw in the tool enough to remove all shaft end play.

8. Install the assembly in a press. Press the gear on the shaft (Fig. 12), using the marks made on the gear and shaft as guides to align the pin holes.

FIG. 9—Lower Bushing Removal

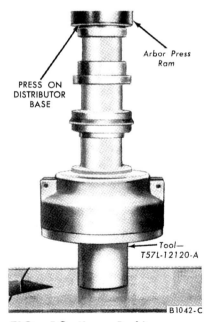

FIG. 10—Upper Bushing Installation

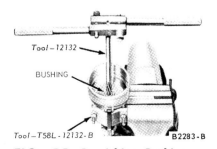

FIG. 11—Burnishing Bushing

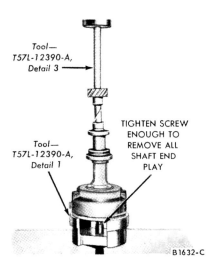

FIG. 12—Original Shaft and Gear Installation

9. Remove the distributor from the press. Install the gear retaining pin (Fig. 4).

10. Position the distributor in a vise. Fill the grooves in the weight pivot pins with distributor cam lubricant (C4AZ-19D530-A).

11. Position the weights in the distributor **(the marked weight is placed on the marked pivot pin)** and install the weight retainers.

12. Place the thrust washer on the shaft.

13. Fill the grooves in the upper portion of the distributor shaft with distributor cam lubricant (C4AZ-19D530-A).

14. Install the cam assembly. **Be sure that the marked spring bracket on the cam assembly is near the marked spring bracket on the stop plate.**

If a new cam assembly is being installed, make sure that the cam is installed with the hypalon covered stop in the correct cam plate control slot. This can be done by measuring the length of the slot used on the

old cam and by using the corresponding slot on the new cam. Some of the cams will have the size of the slot in degrees stamped near the slot. **If the wrong slot is used, an incorrect maximum advance will be obtained.**

Place a light film of distributor cam lubricant on the distributor cam lobes. Install the retainer and the wick. Saturate the wick with SAE 10W engine oil.

15. Install the weight springs. **Be sure that the marked spring is attached to the marked spring brackets.**

16. Place the breaker point and condenser plate in position and install the retaining screws.

17. Working from the inside of the distributor, push the primary wire through the opening in the distributor housing.

18. Place the breaker point assemblies and the condenser in position and install the retaining screws.

19. Align and adjust the breaker point assemblies by following the procedure in Part 9-1.

20. Connect the primary wire, the jumper strap, and the condenser wire to the breaker point assemblies.

21. Install the rotor and the distributor cap.

22. Check and adjust (if necessary) the centrifugal advance mechanism (Refer to Part 9-1).

NEW SHAFT AND GEAR

The shaft and gear are replaced as an assembly. One part should not be replaced without replacing the other.

1. Follow steps 1, 2, 3, and 4 under Installing Original Shaft and Gear.

2. Attach the distributor shaft supporting tool to the distributor and install the assembly in a vise. Insert a 0.024-inch feeler gauge between the backing screw and the shaft.

Tighten the backing screw on the tool enough to remove all shaft end play, then remove the feeler gauge and allow the shaft to rest on the backing screw. Slide the collar on the shaft. While holding the collar in place against the distributor base, drill a 1/8-inch hole through the shaft using the hole in the collar as a pilot.

3. Position the gear on the end of the shaft. Install the assembly in a press.

4. With the backing screw on the support tool tightened enough to remove all end play, press the gear on the shaft to the specified distance from the bottom face of the gear to the bottom face of the distributor mounting flange (Fig. 13). Drill a 1/8-inch hole through the shaft using the hole in the gear as a pilot.

5. Remove the distributor from the press and remove the support tool. Install the collar retaining pin (Fig. 6) and the gear retaining pin (Fig. 4).

6. Complete the assembly by following steps 10 thru 22 under Installing Original Shaft and Gear.

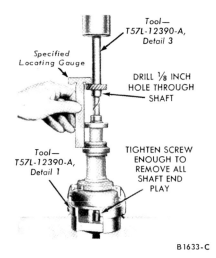

FIG. 13—New Shaft and Gear Installation

PART 9-5
SPECIFICATIONS

DISTRIBUTOR

GENERAL

170 and 200 Six
Breaker Arm Spring Tension (Ounces) 17-21
Contact Spacing (Inches) 0.025
Dwell Angle at Idle Speed ....37°-42°

289 V-8 (Except High Performance) and 390 V-8
Breaker Arm Spring Tension (Ounces) 17-21
Contact Spacing (Inches) 0.017
Dwell Angle at Idle Speed ....26°-31°

289 High Performance V-8
Breaker Arm Spring Tension (Ounces) 27-30
Contact Spacing (Inches) 0.020
Combined Dwell Angle at Idle Speed ....30°-33°

DIMENSIONS

Shaft End Play — Distributor Removed (Inches)
170 and 200 Six 0.022-0.033
289 V-8 ....0.024-0.035
390 V-8 ....0.022-0.032
Distance From Bottom of Mounting Flange to Bottom of Gear (Inches)
170 and 200 Six① 2.510-2.515
289 V-8 ....4.031-4.038
390 V-8 ....3.071-3.077
①Does not apply to dual advance distributors.

IGNITION TIMING

Manual-Shift Transmission — BTDC②
170①, 200①, and 289 ....6°
170, 200 and 289 with Thermactor ....TDC
289 High Performance ....12°
390① ....10°
390 with Thermactor ....6°

Automatic Transmission — BTDC②
170① and 200① ....12°
289 ....6°
170, 200 and 289 with Thermactor ....TDC
390① ....10°
390 with Thermactor ....6°

① For altitude operation, and/or to obtain optimum engine performance and fuel economy, the initial ignition timing may be advanced 5° over the "normal" setting. No further improvement in engine performance or fuel economy will be achieved by advancing beyond this point. Advance the timing progressively until engine detonation (spark knock) is evident under actual road test acceleration. Retard the timing until the detonation (spark knock) is eliminated.

② If the individual requirements of the car and/or the use of sub-standard fuels dictate, the initial timing may have to be retarded from the recommended setting to eliminate detonation (spark knock). If retiming is necessary, it should be done progressively and not to exceed 2° BTDC.

CONDENSER

Capacity (Microfarads) 0.21-0.25
Minimum Leakage (Megohms) ..,................5
Maximum Series Resistance (Ohms) 1

APPLICATION TABLE

Engine	Transmission		Thermactor Emission System		Distributor	
	Std.	Auto.	With	Without	Type	No. (12127)
170 Six	X			X	①	C5DF-C
170 Six	X		X		②	C6DF-A
170 Six		X		X	①	C5DF-K
170 Six		X	X		②	C6DF-D
200 Six	X			X	①	C5DF-E
200 Six	X		X		②	C6DF-C
200 Six		X		X	①	C5DF-K
200 Six		X	X		②	C6DF-E
289 2-V	X			X	②	C5AF-M
289 2-V	X		X		②	C6AF-J
289 2-V		X		X	②	C5AF-N
289 2-V		X	X		②	C6AF-S
289 4-V	X	X		X	②	C5GF-A
289 4-V	X		X		②	C6ZF-A
289 4-V		X	X		②	C6ZF-B
289 HP	X			X	③	C5OF-E
390 2-V	X			X	②	C6AF-A
390 2-V	X		X		②	C6AF-K
390 2-V		X		X	②	C6AF-B
390 2-V		X	X		②	C6AF-T
390 4-V	X			X	②	C6AF-C
390 4-V		X		X	②	C6AF-D
390 4-V	X	X	X		②	C6AF-L
① Loadomatic ② Dual Advance ③ Centrifugal						

ADVANCE CHARACTERISTICS

Note: The advance characteristics given apply to the distributor with the indicated number only. The distributor number is stamped on the distributor housing or on a plate attached to the distributor housing.

C5AF-12127-M

CENTRIFUGAL ADVANCE: Set the test stand to 0° at 250 rpm and 0 inches of mercury.

Distributor (rpm)	Advance (Degrees)	Vacuum (Inches) of Mercury)
650	1½-2½	0
800	4¾-5¾	0
1200	8½-9½	0
1600	10¼-11¾	0
2000	12-13¾	0
Maximum Advance Limit . . . . .14°		

VACUUM ADVANCE: Set the test stand to 0° at 1000 rpm and 0 inches of mercury.

Distributor (rpm)	Advance (Degrees)	Vacuum (Inches of Mercury)
1000	1½-4½	8
1000	3½-6½	10
1000	6¾-9¾	14
Maximum Advance Limit . . . . .11°		

C5AF-12127-N

CENTRIFUGAL ADVANCE: Set the test stand to 0° at 250 rpm and 0 inches of mercury.

Distributor (rpm)	Advance (Degrees)	Vacuum (Inches of Mercury)
450	1½-2½	0
600	5¼-6¼	0
800	7¼-8¼	0
1400	8¾-10	0
2000	10½-12	0
Maximum Advance Limit . . . . .14°		

VACUUM ADVANCE: Set the test stand to 0° at 1000 rpm and 0 inches of mercury.

Distributor (rpm)	Advance (Degrees)	Vacuum (Inches of Mercury)
1000	1½-4¾	8
1000	5-8	10
1000	8¼-11	14
Maximum Advance Limit . . . . .12½°		

C5DF-12127-C

VACUUM ADVANCE: Set the test stand to 0° at 250 rpm and 0 inches of mercury.

Distributor (rpm)	Advance (Degrees)	Vacuum (Inches of Mercury)
800	2½-3½	0.8
1200	6½-7½	1.8
1800	8¾-10	3.0
2000	10¼-11½	3.9
Maximum Advance Limit . . . . .14½°		

C5DF-12127-E

VACUUM ADVANCE: Set the test stand to 0° at 250 rpm and 0 inches of mercury.

Distributor (rpm)	Advance (Degrees)	Vacuum (Inches of Mercury)
600	1-2	0.44
800	5-6	1.80
1200	8¼-9¼	1.90
2000	10¼-11½	3.80
Maximum Advance Limit . . . . .15½°		

C5DF-12127-K

VACUUM ADVANCE: Set the test stand to 0° at 250 rpm and 0 inches of mercury.

Distributor (rpm)	Advance (Degrees)	Vacuum (Inches of Mercury)
800	¾-1¾	0.79
1200	3¾-4¾	1.90
1600	5¾-7	3.00
2000	7-8¼	3.80
Maximum Advance Limit . . . . .12¾°		

C5GF-12127-A

CENTRIFUGAL ADVANCE: Set the test stand to 0° at 250 rpm and 0 inches of mercury.

Distributor (rpm)	Advance (Degrees)	Vacuum (Inches of Mercury)
550	1½-2¼	0
700	5-6	0
1000	6¾-7¾	0
1400	7½-8¼	0
2000	8½-10	0
Maximum Advance Limit . . . . .14°		

VACUUM ADVANCE: Set the test stand to 0° at 1000 rpm and 0 inches of mercury.

Distributor (rpm)	Advance (Degrees)	Vacuum (Inches of Mercury)
1000	1½-4½	8
1000	3½-6¾	10
1000	6¾-9¾	14
1000	8-11	20
Maximum Advance Limit . . . . .11°		

C5OF-12127-E

CENTRIFUGAL ADVANCE: Set the test stand to 0° at 250 rpm and 0 inches of mercury.

Distributor (rpm)	Advance (Degrees)	Vacuum (Inches of Mercury)
650	2¼-3¾	0
750	4-5½	0
1000	6½-7½	0
1600	7½-8¾	0
2000	8¼-9¾	0
Maximum Advance Limit . . . . .14°		

C6AF-12127-A

CENTRIFUGAL ADVANCE: Set the test stand to 0° at 250 rpm and 0 inches of mercury.

Distributor (rpm)	Advance (Degrees)	Vacuum (Inches of Mercury)
400	0-½	0
800	2½-3½	0
1200	4½-5½	0
1800	7¼-8¾	0

Maximum Advance Limit .14°

VACUUM ADVANCE: Set the test stand to 0° at 1000 rpm and 0 inches of mercury.

Distributor (rpm)	Advance (Degrees)	Vacuum (Inches of Mercury)
1000	0-1	5
1000	3½-6½	10
1000	7-10	15

Maximum Advance Limit . . . . .12°

C6AF-12127-D

CENTRIFUGAL ADVANCE: Set the test stand to 0° at 250 rpm and 0 inches of mercury.

Distributor (rpm)	Advance (Degrees)	Vacuum (Inches of Mercury)
500	2¼-3	0
1200	5¾-7	0
1850	8-9½	0
2000	8½-10	0

Maximum Advance Limit .14°

VACUUM ADVANCE: Set the test stand to 0° at 1000 rpm and 0 inches of mercury.

Distributor (rpm)	Advance (Degrees)	Vacuum (Inches of Mercury)
1000	0-1	6
1000	1-4½	10
1000	9-12	18

Maximum Advance Limit .12½°

C6AF-12127-B

CENTRIFUGAL ADVANCE: Set the test stand to 0° at 250 rpm and 0 inches of mercury.

Distributor (rpm)	Advance (Degrees)	Vacuum (Inches of Mercury)
625	1¾-2¾	0
1200	5¾-7	0
1500	7-8¼	0
2000	9-10½	0

Maximum Advance Limit .14°

VACUUM ADVANCE: Set the test stand to 0° at 1000 rpm and 0 inches of mercury.

Distributor (rpm)	Advance (Degrees)	Vacuum (Inches of Mercury)
1000	0-1	5
1000	2-5½	9
1000	6-9	13

Maximum Advance Limit .12°

C6AF-12127-J

CENTRIFUGAL ADVANCE: Set the test stand to 0° at 250 rpm and 0 inches of mercury.

Distributor (rpm)	Advance (Degrees)	Vacuum (Inches of Mercury)
600	6-7	0
1000	11-12	0
1800	13½-15	0

Maximum Advance Limit .16°

VACUUM ADVANCE: Set the test stand to 0° at 1000 rpm and 0 inches of mercury.

Distributor (rpm)	Advance (Degrees)	Vacuum (Inches of Mercury)
1000	0-1	7
1000	2-5	13
1000	5-8	16

Maimum Advance Limit . . . . .8°

C6AF-12127-C

CENTRIFUGAL ADVANCE: Set the test stand to 0° at 250 rpm and 0 inches of mercury.

Distributor (rpm)	Advance (Degrees)	Vacuum (Inches of Mercury)
600	2¼-3¼	0
1200	5¾-7	0
1600	7¼-8½	0
2000	8¾-10¼	0

Maximum Advance Limit .14°

VACUUM ADVANCE: Set the test stand to 0° at 1000 rpm and 0 inches of mercury.

Distributor (rpm)	Advance (Degrees)	Vacuum (Inches of Mercury)
1000	0-1	5
1000	6-9	13
1000	8¼-10¼	17

Maximum Advance Limit .12°

C6AF-12127-K

CENTRIFUGAL ADVANCE: Set the test stand to 0° at 250 rpm and 0 inches of mercury.

Distributor (rpm)	Advance (Degrees)	Vacuum (Inches of Mercury
500	2-3	0
1000	6½-7¼	0
1300	7¾-9	0
2000	11½-13	0

Maximum Advance Limit .16°

VACUUM ADVANCE: Set the test stand to 0° at 1000 rpm and 0 inches of mercury.

Distributor (rpm)	Advance (Degrees)	Vacuum (Inches of Mercury)
1000	0-1	5
1000	6-9	13
1000	8¼-11¼	17

Maximum Advance Limit .12°

C6AF-12127-L

CENTRIFUGAL ADVANCE: Set the test stand to 0° at 250 rpm and 0 inches of mercury.

Distributor (rpm)	Advance (Degrees)	Vacuum (Inches of Mercury)
500	2-3	0
900	6¼-7	0
1400	8¾-10	0
2000	10¾-12¼	0

Maximum Advance Limit . . . . .16°

VACUUM ADVANCE: Set the test stand to 0° at 1000 rpm and 0 inches of mercury.

Distributor (rpm)	Advance (Degrees)	Vacuum (Inches of Mercury)
1000	0-1	6
1000	3-6	11
1000	7-10	15

Maximum Advance Limit . . . . .12½°

C6DF-12127-A

CENTRIFUGAL ADVANCE: Set the test stand to 0° at 250 rpm and 0 inches of mercury.

Distributor (rpm)	Advance (Degrees)	Vacuum (Inches of Mercury)
500	0-½	0
900	6¼-7¼	0
1200	9½-10½	0
1800	12½-13¾	0

Maximum Advance Limit . . . . .16°

VACUUM ADVANCE: Set the test stand to 0° at 1000 rpm and 0 inches of mercury.

Distributor (rpm)	Advance (Degrees)	Vacuum (Inches of Mercury)
1000	0-1	5
1000	3¼-6¼	10
1000	7-10¼	15

Maximum Advance Limit . . . . .12°

C6AF-12127-S

CENTRIFUGAL ADVANCE: Set the test stand to 0° at 250 rpm and 0 inches of mercury.

Distributor (rpm)	Advance (Degrees)	Vacuum (Inches of Mercury)
600	2-3	0
800	6¼-7¼	0
1200	11¼-12¼	0
1800	13-14½	0

Maximum Advance Limit . . . . .16°

VACUUM ADVANCE: Set the test stand to 0° at 1000 rpm and 0 inches of mercury.

Distributor (rpm)	Advance (Degrees)	Vacuum (Inches of Mercury)
1000	0-1	5
1000	2-5	7
1000	7-10	12

Maximum Advance Limit . . . . .10°

C6DF-12127-C

CENTRIFUGAL ADVANCE: Set the test stand to 0° at 250 rpm and 0 inches of mercury.

Distributor (rpm)	Advance (Degrees)	Vacuum (Inches of Mercury)
300	0-½	0
600	2¼-3¼	0
900	6¼-7¼	0
1200	9-10	0
1800	11¾-13¼	0

Maximum Advance Limit . . . . .16°

VACUUM ADVANCE: Set the test stand to 0° at 1000 rpm and 0 inches of mercury.

Distributor (rpm)	Advance (Degrees)	Vacuum (Inches of Mercury)
1000	0-1	4
1000	7-10	10
1000	9½-12½	15

Maximum Advance Limit . . . . .12½°

C6AF-12127-T

CENTRIFUGAL ADVANCE: Set the test stand to 0° at 250 rpm and 0 inches of mercury.

Distributor (rpm)	Advance (Degrees)	Vacuum (Inches of Mercury)
475	1¼-2¼	0
700	3¾-4¾	0
1300	7-8¼	0
1800	9¾-11	0

Maximum Advance Limit . . . . .16°

VACUUM ADVANCE: Set the test stand to 0° at 1000 rpm and 0 inches of mercury.

Distributor (rpm)	Advance (Degrees)	Vacuum (Inches of Mercury)
1000	0-1	5
1000	6-9	13
1000	8½-11½	18

Maximum Advance Limit . . . . .12°

C6DF-12127-D

CENTRIFUGAL ADVANCE: Set the test stand to 0° at 250 rpm and 0 inches of mercury.

Distributor (rpm)	Advance (Degrees)	Vacuum (Inches of Mercury)
300	0-½	0
600	2½-3½	0
900	7¾-8¾	0
1200	9¼-10½	0
1800	12½-13¾	0

Maximum Advance Limit . . . . .16°

VACUUM ADVANCE: Set the test stand to 0° at 1000 rpm and 0 inches of mercury.

Distributor (rpm)	Advance (Degrees)	Vacuum (Inches of Mercury)
1000	0-1	5
1000	3-6	10
1000	3-6	15

Maximum Advance Limit . . . . .6°

C6DF-12127-E

CENTRIFUGAL ADVANCE: Set the test stand to 0° at 250 rpm and 0 inches of mercury.

Distributor (rpm)	Advance (Degrees)	Vacuum (Inches of Mercury)
300	0-½	0
500	2-3	0
900	6½-7¾	0
1200	8¼-9½	0
1800	10¾-12¼	0

Maximum Advance Limit . . . . .16°

VACUUM ADVANCE: Set the test stand to 0° at 1000 rpm and 0 inches of mercury.

Distributor (rpm)	Advance (Degrees)	Vacuum (Inches of Mercury)
1000	0-1	5
1000	3½-6¼	10
1000	7-10¼	15

Maximum Advance Limit . . . . .12°

C6ZF-12127-A

CENTRIFUGAL ADVANCE: Set the test stand to 0° at 250 rpm and 0 inches of mercury.

Distributor (rpm)	Advance (Degrees)	Vacuum (Inches of Mercury)
475	2½-3½	0
625	7-8	0
1200	10¼-11½	0
1850	11-12¼	0

Maximum Advance Limit . . . . .14°

VACUUM ADVANCE: Set the test stand to 0° at 1000 rpm and 0 inches of mercury.

Distributor (rpm)	Advance (Degrees)	Vacuum (Inches of Mercury)
1000	0-1	5
1000	5-8	10
1000	6½-9½	15

Maximum Advance Limit. . . . . .9½°

C6ZF-12127-B

CENTRIFUGAL ADVANCE: Set the test stand to 0° at 250 rpm and 0 inches of mercury.

Distributor (rpm)	Advance (Degrees)	Vacuum (Inches of Mercury)
650	3-4	0
900	9-10	0
1200	10½-11½	0
2000	11½-13	0

Maximum Advance Limit . . . . .14°

VACUUM ADVANCE: Set the test stand to 0° at 1000 rpm and 0 inches of mercury.

Distributor (rpm)	Advance (Degrees)	Vacuum (Inches of Mercury)
1000	0-1	5
1000	2-5	9
1000	4½-7½	14

Maximum Advance Limit . . . . .7½°

SPARK PLUGS

Engines	Type	Size	Gap (Inches)	Torque (Ft-lbs)[1]
170-200	BF-82	18MM	0.032-0.036	15-20
289-390	BF-42	18MM	0.032-0.036	15-20
289 H.P.	BF-32	18MM	0.028-0.032	15-20

[1] When a new spark plug is installed in a new replacement cylinder head, torque the spark plug to 20-30 ft-lbs.

COIL

Primary Resistance (Ohms) . . . . .1.40-1.54(75°F.)
Secondary Resistance (Ohms) . . . . .8000-8800(75°F.)
Amperage Draw—Engine Stopped 4.5
          —Engine Idling 2.5
Primary Circuit Resistor . . . . .1.30-1.40(75°F.)

SPECIAL TOOLS

DESCRIPTION	TOOL NO.
Breaker point aligning tool	KD-111 or TK-419-A
Breaker point spring tension scale	12151
Bushing burnisher	12132
Bushing installer	T57L-12120-A or 12132-A
Bushing remover	12132-H
Distributor holding clamp	T58L-12132-B
Distributor testers	RE-236
	RE-1416
Drive gear installing fixture	T57L-12390-A
Drive gear remover kit	T52L-12390-CAD
Ignition scopes	RE-27-55
	RE-881
Pin removing fixture	T60K-12131-A or T52L-12131-CAD
Tach-dwell tester	RE-27-44
Timing light	13-07

FUEL SYSTEM

GROUP 10

PART 10-1   PAGE
GENERAL FUEL SERVICE 10-1

PART 10-2
FORD 1-V CARBURETOR 10-25

PART 10-3
FORD 2-V CARBURETORS 10-36

PART 10-4
FORD 4-V CARBURETORS 10-46

PART 10-5   PAGE
AIR CLEANER 10-60

PART 10-6
FUEL PUMP AND FUEL FILTER 10-62

PART 10-7
FUEL TANK AND LINES 10-65

PART 10-8
SPECIFICATIONS 10-70

PART 10-1 GENERAL FUEL SYSTEM SERVICE

Section   Page
1 Diagnosis and Testing 10-2
Diagnosis 10-2
Fuel Pump, Tank and Lines Diagnosis
  Guide 10-2
Carburetor Diagnosis Guide 10-3
Tests 10-5
  Fuel Pump Tests 10-5
  Air Intake Duct Valve Test 289 V-8 10-6
  Carburetor Tests 10-6
2 Common Adjustments and Repairs 10-7
Carburetor Adjustments 10-7
  Float Adjustment—Dry 10-7
  Secondary Throttle Plate Adjustment—
    Ford 4-V 10-7
  Automatic Choke Plate Clearance
    (Pull-Down) and Fast Idle Cam
    Linkage Adjustment 10-8
  Manual Choke Plate Clearance
    (Pull-Down) Adjustment—Ford 4-V 10-9
  Automatic Choke Thermostatic Spring
    Housing Adjustment 10-9
  Fuel Level Float Adjustment (Wet)—
    Ford 2-V and 4-V 10-10
  Idle Fuel Mixture and Idle (Hot Engine)
    Speed Adjustments 10-11
  Fast (Cold Engine) Idle Speed Adjustment
    —Automatic Choke 10-12
  Fast (Cold Engine) Idle Speed
    Adjustment—Manual Choke 10-12
  Anti-Stall Dashpot (Automatic
    Transmissions) Adjustment 10-13
  Accelerating Pump Adjustments 10-13
  Vent Valve Adjustment—Ford 1-V 10-14
Throttle Linkage Adjustment 10-14
  Manual-Shift Transmissions 10-14
  Accelerator Pedal Idle Height
    Adjustment 10-14
  Automatic Transmission 10-18
Carburetor Repairs .10-18
  Air Horn to Main Body Gasket
    Replacement 10-18
  Float or Needle Valve Replacement—
    Ford 1-V 10-18

Section   Page
  Main Jet Replacement—Ford 1-V 10-18
  Float, Needle Valve and Seat, Inlet
    Screen, or Main Jet Replacement—
    Ford 2-V or 4-V 10-18
  Accelerating Pump Diaphragm
    Replacement—Ford 1-V 10-19
  Accelerating Pump Diaphragm and/or
    Elastomer Valve Replacement—
    Ford 2-V and 4-V 10-19
  Secondary Diaphragm Replacement—
    Ford 4-V 10-19
  Anti-Stall Dashpot Replacement 10-19
  Thermostatic Choke Spring Housing
    and Gasket Replacement 10-20
  Thermostatic Choke Assembly Removal
    and Installation—Clean and Overhaul . .10-20
  Vent Valve Replacement—Ford 1-V 10-21
  Spark Valve or Gasket Replacement—
    Ford 1-V 10-21
  Power Valve or Gaskets Replacement—
    Ford 4-V 10-21
  Carburetor Spacer and Gaskets
    Replacement 10-21
Throttle Linkage Repair—Manual Shift
  Transmissions 10-21
  Accelerator Pedal Cover Replacement 10-21
  Accelerator Pedal Pad Replacement 10-21
  Accelerator Pedal Replacement 10-21
  Accelerator Shaft Replacement 10-22
  Accelerator Control Shaft Rod or
    Accelerator Bellcrank to Carburetor
    Rod Replacement 10-22
  Accelerator Shaft to Bellcrank Rod
    Replacement 10-22
  Bellcrank Stabilizer Replacement 10-23
  Accelerator Bellcrank Replacement
    Assembly 10-23
Throttle Linkage Repair—Automatic
  Transmission 10-23
3 Cleaning and Inspection 10-23
  Carburetor 10-23
  Fuel Pump 10-24
  Air Cleaner 10-24

This part covers general fuel system diagnosis, tests, adjustment and repair procedures. In addition, the cleaning and inspection procedures are covered.

For fuel system component removal, disassembly, assembly, installation, major repair procedures and specifications, refer to the pertinent part of this group.

The carburetor identification tag is attached to the carburetor. The basic part number for all carburetors is 9510. To procure replacement parts, it is necessary to know the part number prefix and suffix and, in some instances, the design change code (Fig. 1).

Always refer to the Master Parts Catalog for parts usage and interchangeability before replacing a carburetor or a component part for a carburetor.

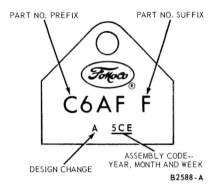

FIG. 1—Typical Carburetor Identification Tag

1 DIAGNOSIS AND TESTING

DIAGNOSIS

FUEL TANK, LINES AND FILTER

Water and dirt that accumulate in the fuel tank can cause a restricted fuel line or filter and malfunction of fuel pump, or carburetor. Condensation, which is the greatest source of water entering the fuel tank, is formed by moisture in the air when it strikes the cold interior walls of the fuel tank.

If the accumulation of sediment in the filter is excessive, the fuel tank should be removed and flushed, and the line from the fuel pump to the tank should be blown out.

Leakage in the fuel inlet line can cause low vacuum, and volume conditions, and loss of fuel.

A restricted fuel tank vent can cause low fuel pump pressure and volume and may, in some instances, result in collapsed inlet hoses or a collapsed fuel tank.

FUEL PUMP

Incorrect fuel pump pressure and low volume (flow rate) are the two most likely fuel pump troubles that will affect engine performance. Low pressure will cause a lean mixture and fuel starvation at high speeds and excessive pressure will cause high fuel consumption and carburetor flooding. Low volume will cause fuel starvation at high speeds.

FUEL PUMP, TANK AND LINES DIAGNOSIS GUIDE

LOW FUEL PUMP PRESSURE OR VOLUME	Diaphragm stretched or leaking. Fuel pump diaphragm spring is weak. Rocker arm or eccentric worn or undersize. Excessive clearance between rocker arm and fuel pump link. Fittings loose or cracked.	Fuel filter clogged (low volume). Fuel line cracked or broken. Fuel pump valves improperly seating. Dirt in fuel tank and/or lines. Fuel tank vent restricted. Diaphragm ruptured. Main body retaining screws loose.
HIGH FUEL PUMP PRESSURE OR VOLUME	Diaphragm spring too strong or improper spring. Diaphragm surface too tight (over-tensioned).	Pump link has no free play (frozen). Diaphragm vent opening plugged or omitted.
LOW FUEL PUMP VACUUM	Diaphragm stretched or leaking. Fuel pump springs weak. Fuel pump valves improperly seating. Diaphragm ruptured.	Rocker arm or eccentric worn. Excessive clearance between rocker arm and fuel pump link. Main body retaining screws loose.
LOW FUEL PUMP VOLUME WITH NORMAL PRESSURE	Fuel filter clogged. Fuel pump to carburetor inlet line obstructed, crimped or leaks.	Restriction in fuel supply line to fuel pump.
FUEL PUMP LEAKS FUEL	Diaphragm defective. Fittings loose.	Threads on fittings stripped. Body cracked.

FUEL PUMP, TANK AND LINES DIAGNOSIS GUIDE—Continued

FUEL PUMP LEAKS OIL	Fuel pump retaining bolts loose. Mounting gasket defective.	Diaphragm pull rod oil seal ruptured or improperly installed.
FUEL PUMP NOISE	Rocker arm or eccentric worn. Mounting bolts loose. Rocker arm springs weak or broken.	Rocker arm bumper pad defective.
FUEL TANK AND/OR INLET LINE HOSES COLLAPSED	Fuel tank vent restricted.	

CARBURETORS

Prior to performing an extensive diagnosis of carburetor malfunction on a Thermactor exhaust emission control equipped car, disconnect the anti-backfire valve vacuum sensing and air supply lines at the intake manifold. Plug the manifold connections to prevent leakage. Normal fuel system diagnosis procedures can then be performed.

Dirt accumulation in the fuel and air passages, improper idle adjustments and improper fuel level are the major sources of carburetor troubles.

CARBURETOR DIAGNOSIS GUIDE

FLOODING OR LEAKING CARBURETOR	Cracked carburetor body. Defective main body and/or fuel bowl gasket. High fuel level or float setting. Fuel inlet needle not seating properly or worn needle and/or seat.	Ruptured accelerating pump diaphragm. Excessive fuel pump pressure. Defective power valve gasket. Ruptured power valve diaphragm.
HARD STARTING	Anti-backfire valve stuck open (if equipped with Thermactor exhaust emission control). Improper starting procedure causing a flooded engine. Improper carburetor fuel level. Improper idle adjustments. Sticking or incorrectly seating fuel inlet needle. Incorrect fuel pump pressure.	Improper carburetor gasket and/or spacer combination. Incorrect setting of choke thermostatic spring housing. Choke linkage or plate binding. Binding or broken manual choke linkage. Restrictions or air leaks in the choke vacuum or hot air passages. Dirty air cleaner element.
STALLING	**ENGINE HOT OR COLD** Incorrect idle fuel mixture. Engine idle speed too slow (fast or cold idle adjustments). Dirt, water or ice in fuel filter. Positive crankcase ventilation system malfunctioning. Fuel lines restricted or leaking air. Fuel tank vent restricted. Leakage intake manifold or carburetor gaskets. Carburetor icing (cold, wet or humid weather). Incorrect throttle linkage adjust-	ment to carburetor. Clogged air bleeds or idle passages. Defective fuel pump. **ENGINE HOT ONLY** Improperly adjusted or defective carburetor dashpot (if so equipped). Idle compensator malfunctioning (if so equipped). Coolant control thermostat defective. Excessive looseness of throttle shaft in bore(s) of throttle body.
ROUGH IDLE	Anti-backfire valve stuck open (if equipped with Thermactor exhaust emission control). Positive crankcase ventilation system malfunctioning or restricted.	Incorrect idle mixture adjustment. Idle compensator malfunction (if so equipped). Idle adjusting needle(s) grooved, worn, or otherwise damaged.

CARBURETOR DIAGNOSIS GUIDE—Continued

ROUGH IDLE (Continued)	Idle air bleeds restricted. Idle air or fuel passages restricted. Idle discharge holes restricted. Idle discharge holes not in proper relation to throttle plate(s). Excessive dirt in air cleaner. High or low fuel level or float setting. Fuel inlet needle not seating properly, or worn needle or seat. Power valve leaking. Restricted air bleeds.	Plugged idle fuel channel restrictor. Worn or damaged main metering jet. Accelerating pump discharge ball check and/or weight not seating properly. Fuel pump pressure too low, or excessive. Fuel siphoning from secondary main fuel system (Ford 4-V carburetor). Restriction in main fuel passage.
POOR ACCELERATION	Poor acceleration complaints fall under one of three headings: the engine is sluggish on acceleration, the engine stalls when accelerated, or the engine hesitates or develops a flat	spot when accelerated. Poor acceleration is caused by either an excessively lean or rich mixture on acceleration and/or defects or improper adjustments in the ignition system.
	A LEAN MIXTURE ON ACCELERATION CAN BE CAUSED BY: Low fuel pump pressure. Sticking fuel inlet needle. Low fuel level or float setting. Restriction in main fuel passage. Air leak between the carburetor and the manifold caused by loose mounting bolts or defective gasket. Air leak at the throttle shaft caused by a worn throttle shaft. Accelerating pump diaphragm defective. Incorrect accelerating pump stroke adjustment. Accelerating pump fuel inlet valve (Elastomer valve or ball check—Ford 2-V or 4-V carburetor) not seating on acceleration. Restriction in the accelerating pump discharge passage. Accelerating pump discharge Elastomer valve (Ford 2-V or 4-V carburetor), ball check or weight not	coming fully off its seat, or failing to seat properly on the reverse stroke of the pump diaphragm. Air leak at the accelerating pump cover caused by a defective gasket or warped pump cover. **4-V CARBURETORS** Defective secondary diaphragm. Air leak where secondary vacuum pick-up tube fits into air horn, between air horn and main body, or between the secondary diaphragm housing cover and housing. Secondary throttle plates wedged in barrels. Bent secondary throttle shaft. Secondary throttle plates operating rod binding, or disconnected from secondary diaphragm or secondary throttle lever. Secondary vacuum passage ball check stuck on its seat. Secondary vacuum probe restricted or not properly positioned. Defective power valve spring.
	A RICH MIXTURE ON ACCELERATION CAN BE CAUSED BY: Excessive fuel pump pressure. High fuel level or float setting. Fuel inlet needle not seating properly or worn needle and/or seat. Malfunctioning automatic choke. Excessively dirty air cleaner.	Incorrect accelerating pump stroke adjustment. Power valve leakage. Restricted air bleeds. Worn or damaged main metering jet. Accelerating pump Elastomer valve (Ford 2-V or 4-V carburetor) ball check and/or weight not seating properly.
INCONSISTENT ENGINE IDLE SPEED	Anti-backfire valve stuck open (if equipped with Thermactor exhaust emission control). Fast idle screw contacting low	step of cam at curb idle. *Incorrect throttle linkage adjustment to carburetor.* Binding or sticking throttle link-

CARBURETOR DIAGNOSIS GUIDE (Continued)

INCONSISTENT ENGINE IDLE SPEED (Continued)	age or accelerator pedal. Sticking carburetor throttle shaft. Excessive looseness of throttle shaft in bores of throttle body. Improperly adjusted or defective carburetor dashpot (if so equipped). Incorrectly installed throttle plates.	Idle compensator malfunctioning (if so equipped). Positive crankcase ventilation system restricted. Sticking fuel inlet needle. Defective spark valve or gasket (170 and 200 Six only). Defective power valve or gasket.
AUTOMATIC CHOKE SLOW WARM-UP, ON TOO OFTEN	Thermostatic choke setting too rich. Choke linkage sticking or binding. Incorrect choke linkage adjustment. Choke plate misaligned or binding in air horn.	Defective coolant thermostat. Restricted coolant line at carburetor. Restriction or air leak in the choke vacuum or hot air passage. Choke heat inlet tube restricted. Choke clean air tube restricted.
SEVERE TRANSMISSION ENGAGEMENT AFTER COLD ENGINE START	Carburetor fast idle speed setting too high. Throttle operating on starting step	(highest step) of the fast idle cam. Binding or sticking throttle linkage.
SURGING (CRUISING SPEEDS TO TOP SPEEDS)	Clogged main jets. Improper size main jets. Low fuel level or float setting. Low fuel pump pressure or volume. Clogged fuel filter or carburetor	filter screen. Distributor vacuum passage clogged. Defective spark valve or gasket (170 and 200 Six only).
REDUCED TOP SPEED	Anti-backfire valve stuck open (if equipped with Thermactor exhaust emission control). Float setting too high or too low. Fuel pump pressure or volume too high or too low. Improper size or obstructed main jets. Power valve spring weak, or power valve restricted. Restricted air bleeds. Restriction in main fuel passages. Excessive dirt in air cleaner. Throttle plate(s) not fully open. Faulty choke operation. Improper throttle linkage adjustment.	**4-V CARBURETORS** Air leak where secondary vacuum pick-up tube fits into air horn and main body, or air leakage between the secondary diaphragm housing cover and housing or the air horn mounting gasket. Secondary diaphragm return spring too stiff. Secondary throttle plates wedged in barrels. Bent secondary throttle shaft. Secondary throttle plate operating rod binding. Secondary vacuum passage ball check sticking on its seat.

TESTS

FUEL PUMP TESTS

Two tests: fuel pump static pressure and fuel volume are necessary to determine that the fuel pump is in satisfactory condition.

If both the fuel pump volume and pressure are within specifications (Part 10-8) and the pump and lines are in satisfactory condition, a vacuum test is not required.

If the pump volume is low, but the pressure is within specifications, a fuel pump capacity test must be

made with the in-line filter removed. If the pump volume meets specifications with the filter removed, replace the filter. If the pump volume is still below specifications, repeat the capacity test, using an auxiliary fuel supply. If the pump volume still does not meet specifications, replace the pump. If the pump does meet specifications, there is a restriction in the fuel supply from the tank or the tank is not venting properly.

The tests are performed with the fuel pump installed on the engine and the engine temperature stabi-

lized at the normal operating temperature. **Make certain the replaceable fuel filter is not restricted or clogged.** When in doubt, install a new fuel filter prior to performing the tests. A clogged or restricted filter is often the cause of fuel system malfunction.

Pressure Test

1. Remove the carburetor air cleaner assembly (Part 10-5). Disconnect the fuel inlet hose at the fuel filter. Unscrew the filter from the carburetor. Connect the fuel hose to the filter and tighten the retaining clamp. **Use care to prevent combustion due to fuel spillage.**

2. Connect a pressure gauge, restrictor and flexible hose (Fig. 2) between the carburetor inlet port and the fuel filter connections.

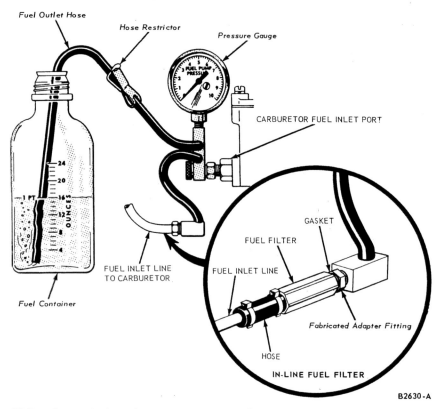

FIG. 2—Typical Fuel Pump Pressure and Capacity Tests

3. Position the flexible hose restrictor so that the fuel can be expelled into a suitable container (Fig. 2) for the capacity (volume) test.

4. Operate the engine at 500 rpm. Vent the system into the container by opening the hose restrictor momentarily before taking a pressure reading.

5. Operate the engine at 500 rpm. After the fuel pump pressure has stabilized, it should be to specification (Part 10-8).

Capacity (Volume) Test

Perform this test only when the fuel pump pressure is within specifications (Part 10-8).

1. Operate the engine at 500 rpm.

2. Open the hose restrictor and expel the fuel into the container (Fig. 2), while observing the time required to expel one pint; then close the restrictor. One pint of fuel should be expelled within the specified time limit (Part 10-8).

3. Remove the test equipment, and connect the fuel inlet line and fuel filter assembly to the carburetor.

AIR INTAKE DUCT VALVE TEST 289 V-8

Proper operation of the air intake duct thermostatic valve can be determined by the following test:

1. Remove the air duct (Part 10-5). Place the air duct assembly in a container of cool water (below 75° F). Be sure that the thermostat is covered by the water.

2. Place the thermometer in the water and observe the temperature.

3. With water temperature at 75°F or below, the valve should be in the heat-on position.

4. Using a hot plate or other suitable device, heat the water slowly.

5. When the water temperature reaches 85°F the valve should start to open. **If the valve does not start to open at this time, stabilize the water temperature at 85°F for eight minutes before condemning the unit.**

6. When the water temperature reaches 100°F or higher, the valve should be in the full heat-off position.

7. If the operation of the valve is unsatisfactory, remove the thermostat and spring assembly and check

the valve plate shaft for binding.

8. If the valve plate moves freely, replace the thermostat and spring assembly. Retest the heat-on and the heat-off temperatures.

9. If the valve does not operate correctly, adjust the thermostat rod. By increasing the rod length, the valve plate will be moved toward the heat-off position. By decreasing the rod length the valve plate will be moved toward the heat-on position.

CARBURETOR TESTS

Accelerating Pump Discharge Test

1. Remove the air cleaner (Part 10-5).

2. Open the primary throttle plates and observe the fuel flow from the accelerating pump discharge nozzles. If the system is operating correctly, a quick steady stream of fuel will flow from the discharge nozzles.

Power Valve Tests

A power valve must not be replaced unless it is leaking sufficiently to cause an unadjustable rough engine idle condition. Fuel accumulation in the power valve cover does not necessarily indicate a defective power valve. Fuel vapors will be drawn into the vacuum side of the power valve and condense during periods of deceleration. Leakage in the power valve area can be caused by an improperly tightened cover or defective gaskets. Any defect in the gasket sealing qualities must be corrected before the power valve is replaced.

Power valve leakage that causes an unadjustable rough engine idle condition can be diagnosed, in most instances, by the fact that the idle mixture needle(s) must be nearly, or completely seated in order to obtain a relatively smooth engine idle condition. If power valve leakage is suspected, the following test procedure must be performed.

Ford 2-V and 4-V Carburetors

1. Remove the carburetor from the intake manifold. Invert the carburetor.

2. Remove the glass bowl from the fixture (Fig. 3). Fill the bowl half-full of water. Install the bowl on the fixture.

3. Connect a line from the vacuum pump to the fitting on top of the fixture. Insert the large OD end of the wand into the tube and attach

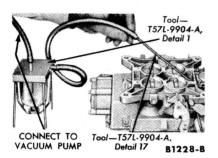

CONNECT TO VACUUM PUMP   Tool—T57L-9904-A, Detail 17   B1228-B

FIG. 3—Ford Carburetor Power Valve Test

the other end of the tube to the fitting on the side of the fixture. Slip the rubber gasket (furnished with the tool) over the small OD end of the wand. Hold this end against the power valve vacuum pick-up port (Fig. 3).

4. Look for bubble formations in the water in the bowl. A continuous stream of bubbles indicates leakage through the power valve diaphragm or gasket, or the cover or gasket.

If leakage is encountered, the power valve, power valve gasket, cover, and cover gasket should be

replaced one at a time with a new part and the test repeated until the source of leakage has been found. If the source of leakage can not be found, the gasket seats are damaged and the defective parts should be replaced.

A few bubbles may be noticed immediately upon attaching the vacuum line. The bubbling should stop within approximately 15 seconds or after the air has been removed from the system. If no bubbles are seen, the power valve, gaskets and cover are sealing properly.

2. COMMON ADJUSTMENTS AND REPAIRS

CARBURETOR ADJUSTMENTS

FLOAT ADJUSTMENT—DRY

Ford 1-V

The dry float fuel level adjustment for the Ford 1-V carburetor is a final float or fuel level adjustment.

1. Remove the carburetor air horn and gasket from the carburetor. Refer to Air Horn to Main Body Gasket Replacement in this section for the proper procedure.

2. Measure the distance from the gasket surface of the upper body (air horn) to the top of the float (Fig. 4). If the float adjustment is not within the specified dimension, bend the float arm tab, as necessary, to obtain the specified dimension. **Do not apply pressure on the fuel inlet needle. The viton tip of the fuel inlet needle may be damaged through undue pressure exerted on it and thus cause an improper fuel level within the bowl.**

3. Install the carburetor air horn and a new gasket on the carburetor.

Refer to Carburetor Air Horn to Main Body Gasket Replacement in this section for the proper procedure.

Ford 2-V and 4-V

The dry float adjustment is a preliminary fuel level adjustment only. The final adjustment (Fuel Level Float Adjustment—Wet) must be made after the carburetor is mounted on the engine.

With the air horn removed, float raised and the fuel inlet needle seated, check the distance between the top surface of the main body and the top surface of the float for conformance to specifications (Part 10-8). Take the measurement near the center of the float at a point approximately ⅛ inch from the free end of the float. **If the cardboard float gauge is used, place the gauge in the corner of the enlarged end section of**

the fuel bowl (Fig. 5). The gauge should touch the float near the end, but not on the end radius.

Depress the float tab to seat the fuel inlet needle. The float height is measured from the gasket surface of the main body with the gasket removed. If necessary, bend the tab on the float to bring the setting within the specified limits. This should provide the proper preliminary fuel level setting.

SECONDARY THROTTLE PLATE ADJUSTMENT— FORD 4-V

1. Hold the secondary throttle plates closed.

2. Turn the secondary throttle shaft lever adjusting screw out (counterclockwise) (Fig. 6) until the secondary throttle plates stick in the throttle bores.

3. Turn the screw in (clockwise) until the screw JUST contacts the secondary lever.

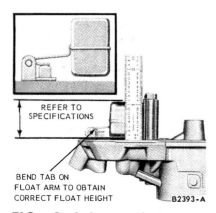

REFER TO SPECIFICATIONS

BEND TAB ON FLOAT ARM TO OBTAIN CORRECT FLOAT HEIGHT   B2393-A

FIG. 4—Carburetor Float Adjustment—Ford 1-V

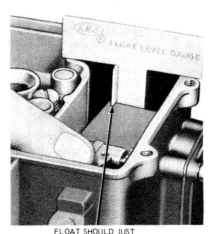

FLOAT SHOULD JUST TOUCH AT THIS POINT   B2590-A

FIG. 5—Fuel Level Float Adjustment (Dry)—Ford 2-V and 4-V

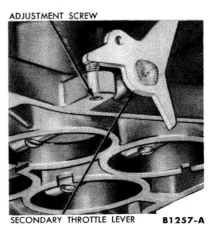

ADJUSTMENT SCREW

SECONDARY THROTTLE LEVER   B1257-A

FIG. 6—Secondary Throttle Plate Adjustment—Ford 4-V

4. Turn the screw in (clockwise) the specified distance (Part 10-8).

AUTOMATIC CHOKE PLATE CLEARANCE (PULL-DOWN) AND FAST IDLE CAM LINKAGE ADJUSTMENT

Ford 1-V

The automatic choke fast idle cam linkage must be properly adjusted before performing the choke plate clearance (pull-down) adjustment, because the position of the pull-down rod is one of the determining factors affecting the throttle-to-choke opening relationship.

1. Insert a gauge pin or drill of the specified clearance (Part 10-8) thickness between the throttle plate and the side of the throttle bore. Hold the throttle plate against the gauge pin or drill (Fig. 7). Close the choke plate and turn the fast idle screw inward until it just contacts the fast idle cam.

2. Place a drill or gauge of the same thickness as the specified clearance (Part 10-8) between the choke plate and the upper body wall (Fig. 8). Close the choke plate on the drill or gauge and hold it securely.

3. Close the throttle until the fast idle screw touches the fast idle cam. Adjust the plastic nut to just contact

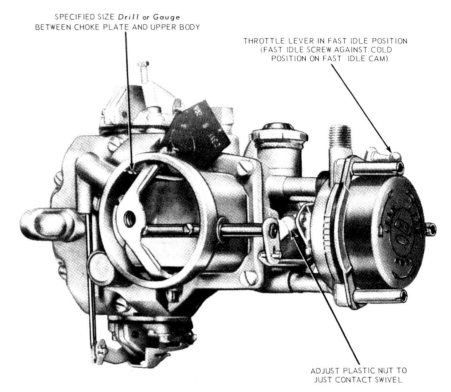

SPECIFIED SIZE *Drill or Gauge* BETWEEN CHOKE PLATE AND UPPER BODY

THROTTLE LEVER IN FAST IDLE POSITION (FAST IDLE SCREW AGAINST COLD POSITION ON FAST IDLE CAM)

ADJUST PLASTIC NUT TO JUST CONTACT SWIVEL

B2414-B

FIG. 8—Choke Plate Clearance (Pull-Down) Adjustment—Ford 1-V

the swivel on the choke lever assembly.

Ford 2-V and 4-V

1. If the air cleaner, heater hose and mounting bracket have not been removed previously, remove them from the carburetor.

2. Position the fast *idle (rpm)* adjustment screw on the index mark of the fast idle cam (Fig. 9).

3. Turn the choke thermostatic spring housing cover 90° rich (counterclockwise) and check the clearance between the front of the choke plate and the air horn (Fig. 9). Adjust the clearance to specification (Part 10-8), if required. **Turn the fast idle cam lever adjusting screw clockwise (inward) to increase the clearance and counterclockwise (outward) to decrease the clearance. Make certain the fast idle screw remains on the index mark (kickdown step) of the fast idle cam during the adjustment procedure.**

4. Bend a specified size (Part 10-8) wire gauge (tool) at a 90° angle, approximately ⅛ inch from its end (Fig. 10).

5. Remove the choke thermostatic spring housing. Block the throttle about half-open so that the fast idle cam does not contact the fast idle adjustment screw.

6. Insert the bent end of the gauge between the lower edge of the

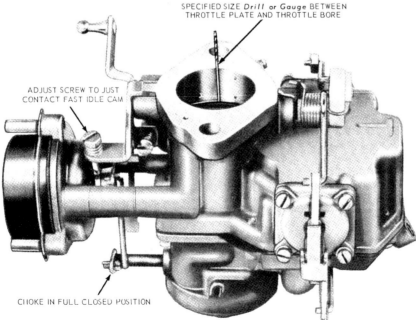

SPECIFIED SIZE *Drill or Gauge* BETWEEN THROTTLE PLATE AND THROTTLE BORE

ADJUST SCREW TO JUST CONTACT FAST IDLE CAM

CHOKE IN FULL CLOSED POSITION

B2413-B

FIG. 7—Fast Idle Cam Linkage Adjustment—Ford 1-V

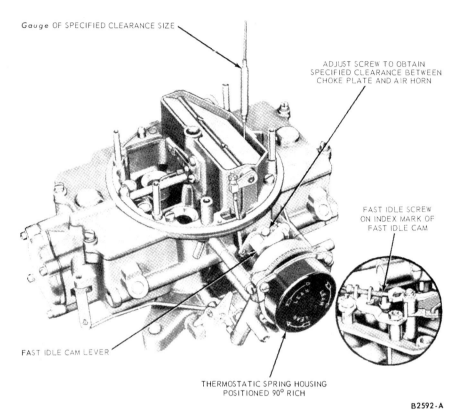

FIG. 9—Fast Idle Cam Linkage Adjustment (Typical)—Ford 2-V and 4-V

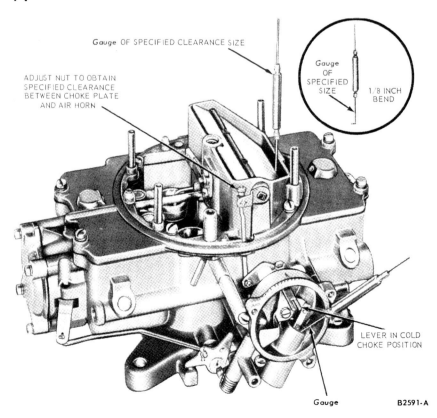

FIG. 10—Choke Plate Clearance (Pull-Down) Adjustment—(Typical) Ford 2-V and 4-V

piston slot and the upper edge of the right hand slot in the choke housing (Fig. 10), and pull the choke countershaft lever counterclockwise until the gauge is snug in the piston slot. Hold the wire gauge in place by exerting light pressure on the countershaft lever, and adjust the choke plate clevis (pull-down) adjusting nut to obtain the specified clearance (Part 10-8) between the front of the choke plate and the air horn (Fig. 10).

7. Install the choke thermostatic spring housing and gasket. Install the housing retainer and the retaining screws.

8. Set the choke thermostatic spring housing to the specified index mark. Refer to Automatic Choke Thermostatic Spring Housing Adjustment in this section. If no other carburetor adjustments are required, adjust the engine idle speed and idle fuel mixture, and the dashpot (if so equipped).

MANUAL CHOKE PLATE CLEARANCE (PULL-DOWN) ADJUSTMENT—FORD 4-V

1. Remove the air cleaner assembly (Part 10-5) if it has not been previously removed.

2. Pull the choke cam and lever to the full choke position. Insert the specified size gauge or drill (Part 10-8) between the downward side of the choke plate and the air horn wall. The gauge or drill will open the choke plate against the pull-down spring tension. Adjust the choke operating (pull-down) rod adjusting nut to just contact the plastic swivel (Fig. 11).

3. If the choke plate clearance adjustment was performed with the carburetor installed on the car, install the air cleaner assembly (Part 10-5) if other carburetor adjustments are not required.

AUTOMATIC CHOKE THERMOSTATIC SPRING HOUSING ADJUSTMENT

The automatic choke has an adjustment to control its reaction to engine temperature. By loosening the clamp screws that retain the thermostatic spring housing to the choke housing, the spring housing can be turned to alter the adjustment. Turning the housing in a counterclockwise direction will require a higher thermostatic spring temperature (cold weather operation) to fully open the choke plate. Turning the spring housing in the opposite direc-

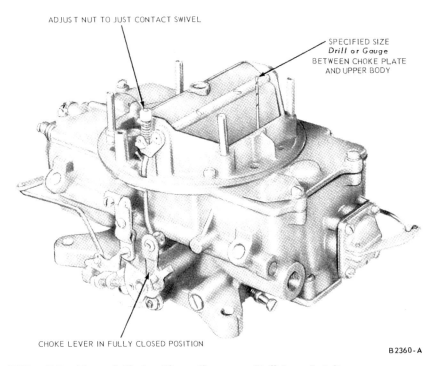

ADJUST NUT TO JUST CONTACT SWIVEL

SPECIFIED SIZE
Drill or Gauge
BETWEEN CHOKE PLATE
AND UPPER BODY

CHOKE LEVER IN FULLY CLOSED POSITION

B 2360-A

FIG. 11—Manual Choke Plate Clearance (Pull-Down) Adjustment—Ford 4-V

tion (clockwise) will cause the choke plate to be fully open at a lower thermostatic spring temperature (hot weather operation). This is the lean direction, as indicated by the arrow on the choke thermostatic spring housing. Refer to the specifications (Part 10-8) for the proper setting for normal ambient temperatures.

1. Remove the air cleaner assembly (Part 10-5), heater hose and mounting bracket (if so equipped) from the carburetor, if they have not been previously removed.

2. Loosen the thermostatic spring housing clamp retaining screws. Set the spring housing to the specified (Part 10-8) index mark (Fig. 12) and tighten the clamp retaining screws.

3. If other carburetor adjustments are not required, install the heater hose and mounting bracket (if so equipped) and the air cleaner assembly (Part 10-5, Section 2) on the carburetor.

**FUEL LEVEL FLOAT
ADJUSTMENT (WET)—FORD
2-V AND 4-V**

The fuel pump pressure and volume must be to specification (Part 10-8) prior to performing the following adjustments:

1. Operate the engine to normalize engine temperatures, and place

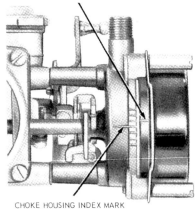

THERMOSTATIC SPRING HOUSING INDEX MARK

CHOKE HOUSING INDEX MARK

B 2358-A

FIG. 12—Automatic Choke Thermostatic Spring Housing Adjustment—Typical

the car on a flat surface as near level as possible. Stop the engine.

2. Remove the carburetor air cleaner assembly (Part 10-5, Section 2) and anchor screw, if they have not been previously removed.

3. On an automatic choke equipped carburetor, disconnect the automatic choke clean air tube at the carburetor. Remove the automatic choke plate operating rod to choke lever retainer.

On a manual choke equipped carburetor, disconnect the choke cable from the fast idle cam. Remove the fast idle cam retainer and washer, and remove the fast idle cam.

4. Remove the air horn retaining screws and lock washers, and the carburetor identification tag.

5. Temporarily place the air horn gasket in position on the carburetor main body and start the engine. Let the engine idle for several minutes, then rotate the air horn and remove the air horn gasket to provide accessability to the float assembly(ies).

6. While the engine is idling, use a standard depth scale to measure the vertical distance from the top machined surface of the carburetor main body to the level of the fuel in the fuel bowl (Fig. 13). The measurement must be made at least ¼ inch away from any vertical surface to assure an accurate reading, because the surface of the fuel is concave (higher at the edges than in the center). Care must be exercised to measure the fuel level at the point of contact with the fuel. Refer to the specifications (Part 10-8), for the correct fuel level (wet) setting.

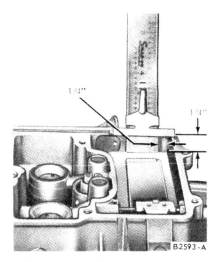

1/4"　　1/4"

B 2593-A

FIG. 13—Fuel Level Float Adjustment (Wet)—Typical for 2-V and 4-V Carburetors

7. If any adjustment is required, stop the engine to minimize the hazard of fire due to fuel spray when the float setting is disturbed. To adjust the fuel level, bend the float tab (contacting the fuel inlet valve) upward in relation to the original position to raise the fuel level, and downward to lower it. Each time an adjustment is made to the float tab to alter the fuel level, the engine

must be started and permitted to idle for at least three minutes to stabilize the fuel level. Check the fuel level after each adjustment until the specified (Part 10-8) level is achieved.

8. Position the new air horn gasket and air horn on the main body.

On an automatic choke equipped carburetor, position the air horn on the main body and gasket so that the choke plate operating rod fits into the opening in the choke housing lever. Install the choke plate rod retainer.

On a manual choke equipped carburetor, position the air horn on the main body and gasket.

On a 4-V carburetor, use care to prevent damage to the secondary throttle control vacuum tube(s) during the air horn installation.

9. Install the air horn retaining screws and lock washers and the carburetor identification tag. Install the air cleaner anchor screw.

10. On an automatic choke equipped carburetor, connect the automatic choke clean air tube to the carburetor.

On a manual choke equipped carburetor, install the fast idle cam on the choke operating rod and the fast idle cam shaft on the carburetor. Install the flat washer and fast idle cam retainer. Connect the choke cable to the fast idle cam clevis. With the choke fully-closed, adjust the choke cable to remove all slack.

11. Check the idle fuel mixture and the idle speed adjustment, and the carburetor dashpot (if so equipped). Adjust the carburetor as required.

12. Install the air cleaner assembly (Part 10-5, Section 2).

IDLE FUEL MIXTURE AND IDLE (HOT ENGINE) SPEED ADJUSTMENTS

It is of utmost importance that the idle fuel system on 2-V and 4-V carburetors be balanced as closely as possible in order to obtain a satisfactory, stable, idle and fuel mixture adjustment. This is achieved by establishing initial idle speed and mixture adjustments before proceeding with the final idle speed and mixture adjustment, and the fast (cold engine) idle speed adjustment.

With the air cleaner removed, make the idle adjustments in the following sequence:

Initial Idle Speed and Fuel Mixture Adjustments

Refer to Figs. 14 and 15 for views of the Ford 1-V carburetor idle fuel mixture and idle (hot engine) speed adjustment screws.

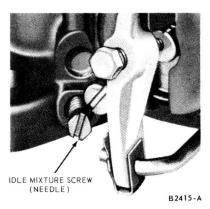

IDLE MIXTURE SCREW
(NEEDLE)

B2415-A

FIG. 14—Idle Fuel Mixture Adjustment—Ford 1-V

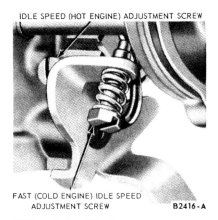

IDLE SPEED (HOT ENGINE) ADJUSTMENT SCREW

FAST (COLD ENGINE) IDLE SPEED
ADJUSTMENT SCREW   B2416-A

FIG. 15—Idle Speed Adjustments—Ford 1-V

The idle fuel mixture and idle (hot engine) speed adjustment screws for the Ford 2-V and 4-V carburetors are shown in Figs. 16 and 17.

1. Set the initial idle fuel mixture

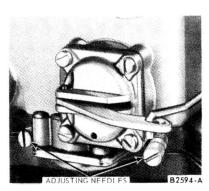

ADJUSTING NEEDLES   B2594-A

FIG. 16—Idle Fuel Mixture Adjustments—Typical For Ford 2-V or 4-V

by turning the idle mixture screw(s) (needle) inward (clockwise) until lightly seated; then, turn the screw(s) outward (counterclockwise) the specified turns (Part 10-8). **Do not turn the needle(s) tightly against their seat(s) as they may groove the end(s). If a needle is damaged, it must be replaced before a satisfactory fuel mixture can be obtained.**

2. Position the choke mechanism so that the choke plate is fully open. Seat the throttle plate in the throttle bore. **It may be necessary to back off on the dashpot (if so equipped) adjustment screw to seat the throttle plate in the throttle bore.** Set the idle speed adjustment screw to just make contact with the stop on the carburetor lower body, and turn the screw inward (clockwise) the specified (Part 10-8) turns.

Final Idle (Hot Engine) Speed and Mixture Adjustments

The engine idle speed is adjusted to settings for a hot engine and a cold engine fast idle speed during choke operation. All final idle speed and mixture adjustments must be made on a hot, normalized engine.

Refer to Figs. 14, 15, 16 and 17 for views of the idle fuel mixture and idle (hot engine) speed screws for the various carburetor applications.

1. Operate the engine until engine temperatures are stabilized. **On a car with an air conditioner, operate the engine for twenty minutes before setting the engine idle speed. The engine idle speed is adjusted with the air conditioner operating.**

2. Position the transmission lever in neutral. Allow the throttle to drop back to the normal idle speed position. Attach a tachometer to the engine. Set the parking brake.

3. Turn on the headlamps. **It is necessary to place the alternator under a load condition in this manner in order to obtain the specified engine idle speed during the adjustment procedure.**

4. **On a car with a manual shift transmission, the engine idle speed is checked and adjusted with the gear shift lever in neutral position. On a car with an automatic transmission, the engine idle speed is checked and adjusted first with the transmission selector lever in the neutral position and adjusted with the transmission selector lever in the drive range position.** Adjust and check the engine

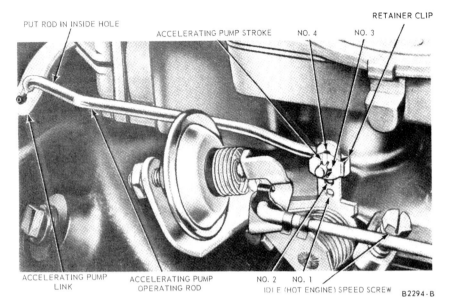

PUT ROD IN INSIDE HOLE ACCELERATING PUMP STROKE NO. 4 NO. 3 RETAINER CLIP

ACCELERATING PUMP LINK ACCELERATING PUMP OPERATING ROD NO. 2 NO. 1 IDLE (HOT ENGINE) SPEED SCREW B2294-B

FIG. 17—Accelerating Pump Stroke and Idle (Hot Engine) Speed Adjustments—Typical for Ford 2-V and 4-V

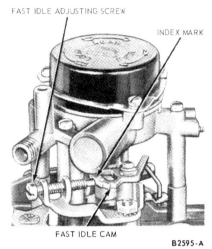

FAST IDLE ADJUSTING SCREW INDEX MARK FAST IDLE CAM B2595-A

FIG. 18—Fast (Cold Engine) Idle Speed Adjustment—Ford 2-V and 4-V

idle speed. **Be sure the dashpot (if so equipped) is not interfering with the throttle lever. On an automatic choke equipped carburetor, make sure the fast idle screw is not contacting the fast idle cam. On a manual choke equipped carburetor, make sure the choke cam and lever is in the slow position, with the fast idle screw not contacting the cam.**

On carburetors equipped with a hot idle compensator, be sure the compensator is seated to allow for proper idle adjustment.

Adjust the engine idle speed to specifications (Part 10-8) by turning the engine idle speed screw (Figs. 15 or 17) inward to increase the speed or outward to decrease the speed.

5. Turn the idle mixture needle(s) (Figs. 14 or 16) inward until the engine rpm begins to drop, due to the lean mixture. Turn the needle(s) outward until the rpm increases and begins to drop. **On cars equipped with a Thermactor exhaust emission system, the outward adjustment of the idle fuel mixture needle(s) is the final fuel mixture needle adjustment required.** On cars without the Thermactor system, turn the idle mixture needle(s) inward for maximum rpm and engine smoothness. Always favor a slightly rich mixture. **On Ford 2-V and 4-V carburetors, the needles should be turned evenly and alternately approximately the same amount. The final setting may vary about ½ turn difference between needles.**

6. After the correct engine idle

mixture has been obtained, **check the idle speed with the transmission selector lever in neutral and manually opening and closing the throttle.** Adjust the idle speed to specification, if required.

If the car is equipped with an automatic transmission, position the selector lever in drive range to check and adjust the idle speed to specification (Part 10-8), if necessary.

The final engine idle speed may be varied to suit the conditions under which the car is to be operated.

7. Shut off the engine. Check the fast (cold engine) idle speed.

FAST (COLD ENGINE) IDLE SPEED ADJUSTMENT—AUTOMATIC CHOKE

On a Ford 1-V carburetor, the fast (cold engine) idle adjustment screw (Fig. 15) is located on the left side of the carburetor.

On a Ford 2-V and 4-V carburetor, the fast (cold engine) idle adjustment screw (Fig. 18) is located on the right side of the carburetor.

The fast idle adjusting screw contacts one edge of the fast idle cam. The cam permits a faster engine idle speed for smoother running when the engine is cold during choke operation. As the choke plate is moved through its range of travel from the closed to the open position, the fast idle cam pick-up lever rotates the fast idle cam. Each position on the fast idle cam permits a slower idle rpm as engine temperature rises and choking is reduced.

Make certain the idle (hot engine) speed and mixture is adjusted to specification before attempting to set the fast idle speed.

1. With the engine operating temperature normalized (hot), air cleaner removed and the tachometer attached, manually rotate the fast idle cam until the fast idle adjusting screw rests adjacent to the shoulder of the highest step (screw aligned with arrow mark) on the cam.

2. Start the engine and turn the fast idle adjusting screw inward or outward as required to obtain the specified idle rpm (Part 10-8).

3. Place the transmission selector lever in neutral and turn off the engine. Switch off the headlamps and the air conditioner (if so equipped). Remove the tachometer.

4. If the car is equipped with an automatic transmission, check the anti-stall dashpot for proper adjustment.

FAST (COLD ENGINE) IDLE SPEED ADJUSTMENT—MANUAL CHOKE

The adjusting screw on the right side of the carburetor contacts one edge of the choke cam and lever (Fig. 19). The cam permits a faster engine idle speed for smoother running when the engine is cold during choke operation. As the choke cam and lever is moved through its range of travel from the open to the closed position, the fast idle pick-up lever rotates the throttle shaft.

1. Manually rotate the choke cam and lever until the fast idle adjusting screw rests on the index mark (arrow) on the cam (Fig. 19).

2. Turn the fast idle adjusting screw inward or outward (as required) so that the fast idle adjusting screw just contacts the fast idle cam at the index mark to obtain the specified fast idle rpm (Part 10-8).

3. If the car is equipped with an automatic transmission, check the dashpot for proper adjustment.

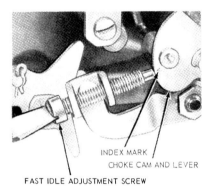

FIG. 19—Manual Choke Fast (Cold Engine) Idle Speed Adjustment

ANTI-STALL DASHPOT (AUTOMATIC TRANS-MISSIONS) ADJUSTMENT

The anti-stall dashpot adjustment is made with the air cleaner removed (Part 10-5, Section 2) from the car.

Ford 1-V

1. Adjust the throttle position to the hot idle setting. Turn the dashpot adjusting screw outward until it is clear of the dashpot plunger assembly (Fig. 20).

2. Turn the dashpot adjusting screw inward until it initially contacts the dashpot plunger assembly; then, turn the adjusting screw inward (clockwise) the specified (Part 10-8) number of turns against the dashpot diaphragm plunger assembly.

3. Check the accelerating pump lever and stroke for proper adjustment, if required. Install the air cleaner (Part 10-5, Section 2).

Ford 2-V and 4-V

1. With the engine idle speed and mixture properly adjusted, and the engine at normal operating temperature, loosen the anti-stall dashpot lock nut (Fig. 21).

2. Hold the throttle in the closed position and depress the plunger with a screwdriver blade. Check the clearance between the throttle lever and

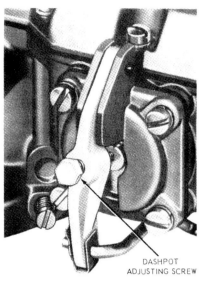

ADJUST THROTTLE TO HOT IDLE POSITION PRIOR TO ADJUSTING DASHPOT   B2417-A

FIG. 20—Anti-Stall Dashpot Adjustment—Ford 1-V

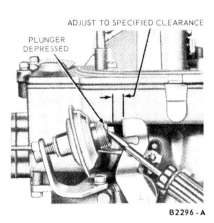

                                                    B2296-A

FIG. 21—Anti-Stall Dashpot Adjustment—Typical For Ford 2-V and 4-V

the plunger tip with a feeler gauge of the specified clearance dimension (Part 10-8). Turn the anti-stall dashpot in its bracket in a direction to provide the specified clearance between the tip of the plunger and the throttle lever. Tighten the lock nut to secure the adjustment.

3. Check the accelerating pump stroke for proper adjustment, if required. Install the air cleaner assembly (Part 10-5, Section 2).

ACCELERATING PUMP ADJUSTMENTS

Acceleration requirements in various climates are satisfied by controlling the amount of fuel discharged

by the accelerating pump. This is accomplished by adjusting the pump clearance to specification; then, adjusting the pump stroke to suit the ambient temperature in which the car is to be operated. **An accelerating pump clearance adjustment is not required on Ford 2-V or 4-V carburetors.**

The accelerating pump adjustments are performed with the carburetor air cleaner removed from the car (Part 10-5, Section 2).

Accelerating Pump Clearance —Ford 1-V

1. Insert the roll pin in the lower hole (HI) position in the lever stop hole (Fig. 22).

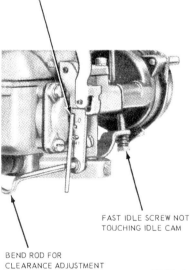

WITH THROTTLE PLATE FULLY CLOSED, INSERT A *Gauge* THAT EQUALS THE SPECIFIED CLEARANCE BETWEEN THE PIN AND COVER

FAST IDLE SCREW NOT TOUCHING IDLE CAM

BEND ROD FOR CLEARANCE ADJUSTMENT

                                                    B2418-A

FIG. 22—Accelerating Pump Clearance Adjustment—Ford 1-V

2. Position the throttle and choke linkage so that the throttle plate will seat in the throttle bore. Hold the throttle plates in the closed position. Position a gauge or drill of the specified thickness (Part 10-8) between the roll pin and the cover surface. Bend the accelerating pump actuating rod to obtain the specified gauge or drill clearance between the pump cover and the roll pin in the pump lever (Fig. 22).

Accelerating Pump Stroke Ford 1-V

The pump stroke is controlled by changing location of the roll pin in the lever stop hole (Fig. 23).

1. For operation in ambient temperatures 50°F and below, place the roll pin in the lever hole marked HI (lower hole).

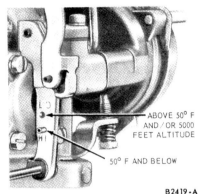

ABOVE 50° F
AND/OR 5000
FEET ALTITUDE

50° F AND BELOW

B2419-A

FIG. 23—Accelerating Pump Stroke Adjustment—Ford 1-V

For best performance and economy at normal ambient temperatures and high altitude (above 50°F and/or above 5,000 feet altitude), place the roll pin in the LO (upper hole) of the lever.

2. Check the vent valve for proper adjustment.

Accelerating Pump Stroke— Ford 2-V and 4-V

The primary throttle shaft lever (overtravel lever) has 4 holes and the accelerating pump link has 2 holes (Fig. 17) to control the accelerating pump stroke for various ambient temperatures and operating conditions of the engine.

The accelerating pump operating rod should be in the specified (Part 10-8) hole in the overtravel lever and the inboard hole (hole closest to the pump plunger) in the accelerating pump link (Fig. 17).

1. To release the rod from the retainer clip, press the tab end of the clip toward the rod; then, at the same time, press the rod away from the clip until *it is disengaged*.

2. Position the clip over the specified (Part 10-8) hole in the overtravel lever. Press the ends of the clip together and insert the operating rod through the clip and the overtravel lever. Release the clip to engage the rod.

VENT VALVE ADJUSTMENT— FORD 1-V

The vent valve adjustment is always performed after the accelerat-

ing pump adjustment has been completed.

1. With the air cleaner removed, set the throttle linkage to the hot idle position. The groove in the vent valve rod should now be even with the open end of the vent (Fig. 24). Bend the arm on the vent valve rod actuating lever (where it contacts the accelerating pump lever) to align the groove with the edge of the bore.

2. Install the air cleaner (Part 10-5, Section 2).

NOTCH ON VENT VALVE ROD TO ALIGN WITH EDGE OF HOLE, WITH THROTTLE IN HOT IDLE POSITION

BEND ACTUATING LEVER TO OBTAIN CORRECT ROD POSITION

B1810-B

FIG. 24—Vent Valve Adjustment

THROTTLE LINKAGE ADJUSTMENT

MANUAL-SHIFT TRANSMISSIONS

The engine idle speed and fuel mixture (Part 10-1, Section 2) must be adjusted to specification prior to performing throttle linkage adjustments.

On cars equipped with a bellcrank stabilizer, it will be necessary to perform a bellcrank stabilizer adjustment before adjusting the throttle (accelerator) linkage.

Views of the throttle (accelerator) linkage for the various car models are shown in Figs. 25 through 30.

Bellcrank Stabilizer Adjustment —Fairlane and Comet 289 and 390 V-8

Refer to Figs. 29 or 30 for views of the bellcrank stabilizer for the applicable car model(s).

The bellcrank stabilizer must be properly adjusted prior to adjusting the carburetor throttle (accelerator) linkage.

1. Disconnect the retaining clip and bellcrank stabilizer clevis from the bellcrank assembly.

2. Insert a ¼ inch adjustment pin (fabricated out of cold rolled steel) through the adjustment holes in the bellcrank assembly. Adjust the bellcrank stabilizer clevis so that it centers (fits freely) in the bore of the bellcrank.

3. Connect the retaining clip and bellcrank stabilizer clevis to the bellcrank. Secure the stabilizer into position with the retaining clip. Make sure the clip is positioned securely. Remove the adjustment pin.

ACCELERATOR PEDAL IDLE HEIGHT ADJUSTMENT

Mustang Six

Refer to Fig. 25 for a view of the accelerator linkage and the accelerator pedal specified idle height for the car model.

1. Adjust the idle (hot engine) speed (Part 10-1, Section 2) to specification (Part 10-8), if required.

2. With the engine stopped, make sure the carburetor choke plate is fully opened and the carburetor throttle plate is fully closed. **Be sure the fast idle cam is not contacting the fast idle screw.**

3. Check the accelerator pedal for the specified idle height. **Make sure the floor mat is properly positioned when performing this operation.**

4. If the pedal height requires adjustment, disconnect the accelerator retracting spring and return spring at the accelerator shaft. Disconnect the accelerator control shaft rod at the carburetor accelerator shaft lever.

5. With the carburetor throttle plate closed, adjust the accelerator control shaft rod assembled length to obtain the specified accelerator pedal idle height.

6. Connect the accelerator control shaft rod so that it centers over the *retaining ball stud* on the carburetor accelerator shaft lever. **Make sure it is secure.** Install the return spring and accelerator retracting spring.

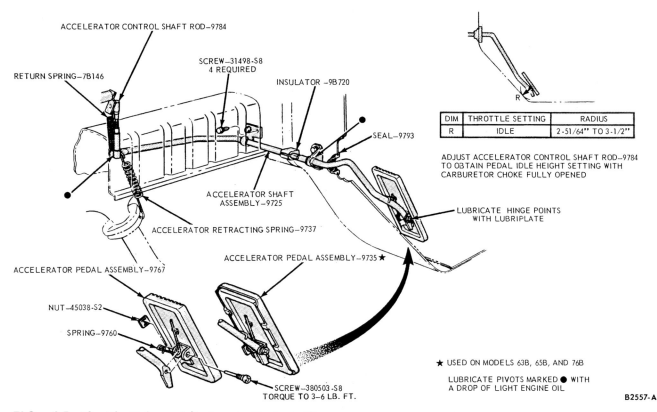

FIG. 25—Throttle Linkage Adjustment—Mustang Six

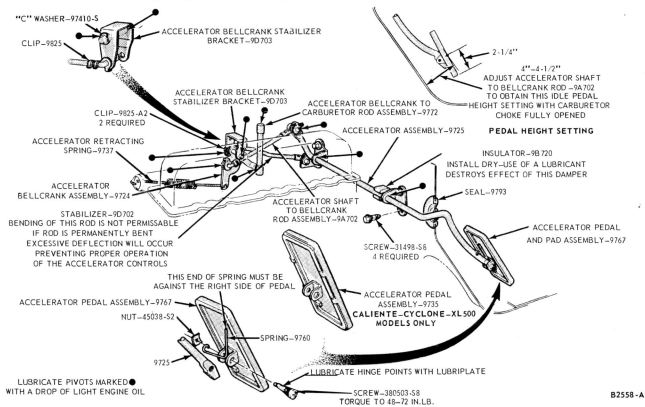

FIG. 26—Throttle Linkage Adjustment—Falcon, Comet and Fairlane Six

All Models Except Mustang Six

Refer to Figs. 26 through 30 for views of the accelerator linkage and the accelerator pedal specified idle height for the applicable car model(s):

1. Adjust the idle (hot engine) speed (Part 10-1, Section 2) to specification (Part 10-8), if required.

2. With the engine stopped, make

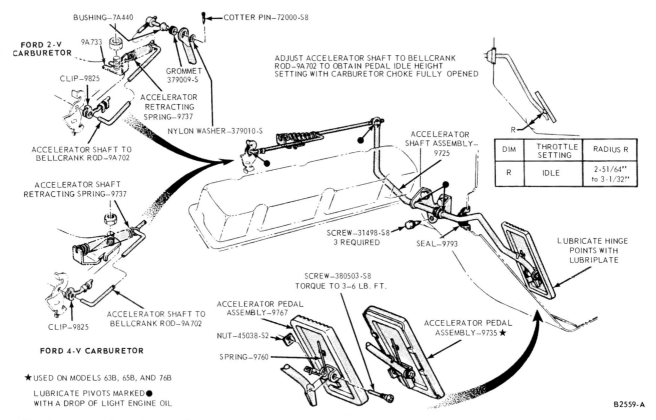

FIG. 27—Throttle Linkage Adjustment—Mustang V-8

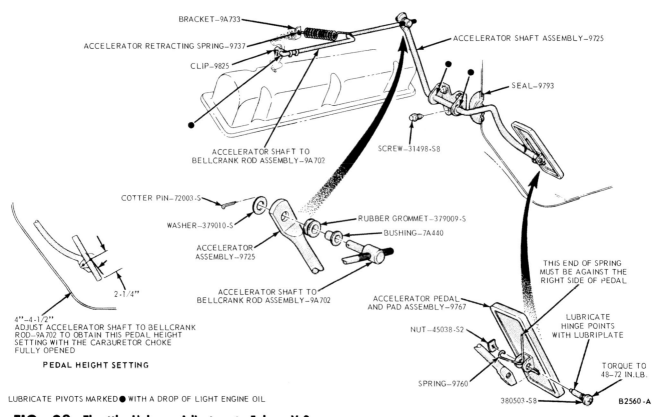

FIG. 28—Throttle Linkage Adjustment—Falcon V-8

sure the carburetor choke plate is fully opened and the throttle plate(s) is closed. **Be sure the fast idle cam is not contacting the fast idle screw.**

3. Check the accelerator pedal for the specified idle height. **Make sure**

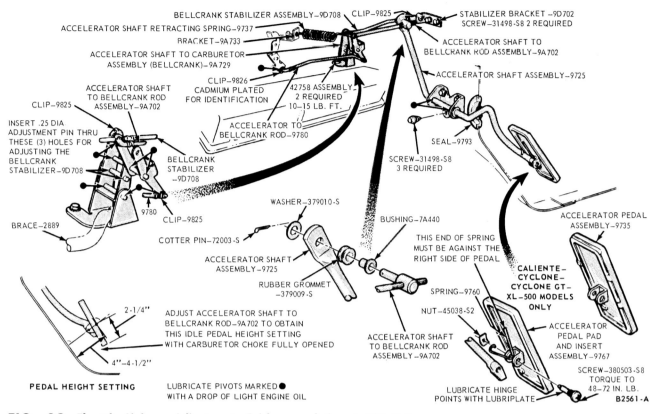

FIG. 29—Throttle Linkage Adjustment—Fairlane and Comet 289 V-8

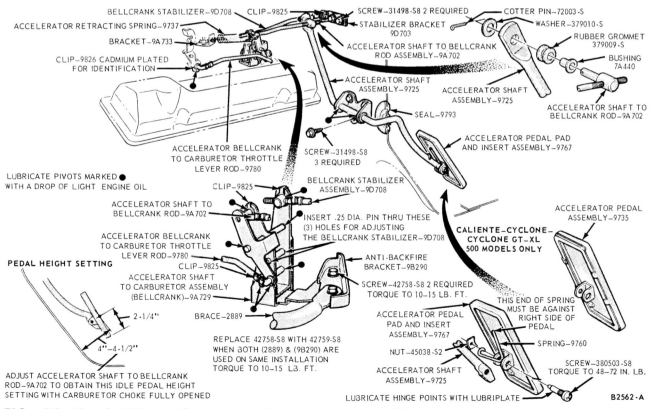

FIG. 30—Throttle Linkage Adjustment—Fairlane and Comet 390 V-8

the floor mat is properly positioned when performing this operation.

4. If the pedal height requires adjustment, disconnect the accelerator

retracting spring at the accelerator shaft or bellcrank (if so equipped).

Disconnect the accelerator shaft at the carburetor throttle lever or accelerator bellcrank lever, if so equipped.

5. With the throttle plate(s) closed, lengthen or shorten the assembled length of the accelerator shaft to bellcrank rod to obtain the accelerator pedal specified height.

6. Install the retaining clip and connect the accelerator shaft to bellcrank rod at the carburetor throttle lever or accelerator bellcrank lever, if so equipped. **Make sure the clip is properly seated.** Install the accelerator retracting spring.

AUTOMATIC TRANSMISSION

The throttle linkage adjustments for the automatic transmissions are covered in Group 7.

CARBURETOR REPAIRS

AIR HORN TO MAIN BODY GASKET REPLACEMENT

Ford 1-V

1. Remove the air cleaner assembly (Part 10-5, Section 2).

2. Remove the fuel filter from the carburetor.

3. Depress the tab on the retaining clip that secures the fuel bowl vent rod to the actuating lever, and remove the rod and the retainer from the lever.

4. Remove the upper body (air horn) to lower body retaining screws and the carburetor identification tag.

5. Tilt the fuel bowl vent side of the upper body to allow clearance between the float assembly and the lower body, using a twisting motion to disconnect the choke plate lever from the actuating rod. Remove and discard the gasket.

6. Install a new gasket on the carburetor lower body. **Make sure all holes in the new gasket have been punched and that no foreign material has adhered to the gasket. Make certain the word Top (inscribed on the gasket) is facing upward.**

7. Insert the choke plate lever actuating rod through the choke plate lever. Use a twisting motion to position the carburetor upper body on the mounting gasket. **During the installation, observe the float shaft to make certain it does not dislodge.** Install the upper to lower body retaining screws and the carburetor identification tag. Tighten the screws.

8. Position the fuel bowl vent rod

retaining clip on the vent rod actuating lever. Depress the tab on the retaining clip and install the vent rod in the clip and the lever. Release the tab.

9. Connect the fuel filter and inlet line to the carburetor.

10. Adjust the idle fuel mixture and engine idle speed as outlined in this section.

Ford 2-V and 4-V

1. Remove the air cleaner assembly (Part 10-5, Section 2). Remove the air cleaner anchor screw.

2. On an automatic choke equipped carburetor, disconnect the automatic choke clean air tube at the carburetor. Remove the automatic choke plate operating rod to choke lever retainer. Remove the choke plate operating rod from the choke lever.

On a manual choke equipped carburetor, disconnect the choke cable from the fast idle cam. Remove the fast idle cam retainer and washer, and remove the fast idle cam.

3. Remove the air horn retaining screws and lock washers and the carburetor identification tag.

4. Remove the air horn to main body gasket. Discard the gasket.

5. Install a new air horn to main body gasket. **Make sure all holes in the new gasket have been properly punched and that no foreign material has adhered to the gasket.**

6. On an automatic choke equipped carburetor, position the air horn on the main body and gasket so that the choke plate operating rod fits into the opening in the choke housing lever. Install the choke plate rod retainer.

On a manual choke equipped carburetor, position the air horn on the main body and gasket.

On a 4-V carburetor, use care to prevent damage to the secondary throttle control vacuum tubes during the air horn installation.

7. Install the air horn retaining screws and lock washers and the carburetor identification tag. Install the air cleaner anchor screw.

8. On an automatic choke equipped carburetor, connect the automatic choke clean air tube to the carburetor.

On a manual choke equipped carburetor, install the fast idle cam on the choke operating rod and the fast idle cam shaft on the carburetor. Install the flat washer and the fast idle cam retainer. Connect the choke ca-

ble to the fast idle cam clevis. With the choke fully-closed, adjust the choke cable to remove all slack.

9. Perform the idle fuel mixture and idle speed adjustments, and the dashpot (if so equipped) adjustment as outlined in this section.

10. Install the carburetor air cleaner (Part 10-5, Section 2).

FLOAT OR NEEDLE VALVE REPLACEMENT—FORD 1-V

1. Remove the carburetor upper body and gasket by following steps 1 thru 5 under Air Horn to Main Body Gasket Replacement in this section.

2. Remove the carburetor float shaft and float assembly.

3. If necessary, remove the fuel inlet needle valve, seat and gasket. Discard the gasket.

4. If the needle valve and seat were removed, install the new gasket and the needle valve seat. Tighten the seat with a wrench. Insert the needle valve into the bore, with the viton tip toward the seat.

5. Position the float assembly in the upper body (air horn), with the tab on the arm located over the needle valve and the hinge of the arm lined up between the hinge bracket holes in the casting. Insert the float shaft through the holes in the upper body and float assembly.

6. Check the float setting. Refer to Float Adjustment—Dry in this section for the proper procedure.

7. Install the carburetor air horn and gasket by following steps 6 thru 10 under Carburetor Air Horn to Main Body Gasket Replacement in this section.

MAIN JET REPLACEMENT— FORD 1-V

1. Remove the carburetor upper body and gasket by following steps 1 through 5 under Air Horn to Main Body Gasket Replacement, in this section.

2. Remove and replace the carburetor main jets with a jet wrench or wide bladed screwdriver.

3. Install the carburetor air horn and gasket by following steps 6 through 10 under Air Horn to Main Body Gasket Replacement—Ford 1-V, in this section.

FLOAT, NEEDLE VALVE AND SEAT, INLET SCREEN, OR MAIN JET REPLACEMENT—FORD 2-V AND 4-V

1. Remove the carburetor air horn

to main body gasket by following steps 1 through 4 under Air Horn to Main Body Gasket Replacement— Ford 2-V and 4-V, in this section.

2. With the use of a screwdriver, pry the float shaft retainer(s) from the fuel inlet seat(s). Remove the float, float shaft retainer(s) and fuel inlet needle assembly(ies).

3. If required, remove the fuel inlet needle seat(s), filter screen(s) and the main jets with a jet wrench. **Be sure the correct (specified) jets are installed for the primary and secondary (4-V carburetor) systems (Part 10-8).**

4. If required, install the fuel inlet filter(s) in the inlet valve seat bore(s). Install the valve seat(s) and gasket(s). Install the fuel inlet needle valve(s).

5. Slide the float shaft(s) into the float lever(s). Position the float shaft retainer(s) on the float shaft(s).

6. Insert the float assembly(ies) into the fuel bowl(s) and hook the float lever tab(s) under the fuel inlet needle clip(s). Insert the float shaft(s) into the guides at the sides of the fuel bowl(s).

7. With the use of a screwdriver, position the float shaft retainer(s) in the groove of the fuel inlet needle seat(s).

8. Refer to Float Adjustment— Dry, in this section, and perform dry float fuel level adjustment on the float(s).

9. Install the carburetor air horn and gasket and related parts. Refer to Air Horn to Main Body Gasket Replacement—Ford 2-V and 4-V, Steps 5 through 8 (in this section) for the proper procedure.

10. Refer to Fuel Level Float Adjustment—Wet, in this section, and perform the wet fuel level adjustment procedures.

ACCELERATING PUMP DIAPHRAGM REPLACEMENT— FORD 1-V

1. Remove the air cleaner assembly (Part 10-5, Section 2).

2. Depress the tab on the accelerating pump lever to control rod retaining clip with pliers, and slide the rod out of the lever. Remove the clip from the lever.

3. Remove the accelerator pump cover retaining screws. Lift the cover upward and remove the diaphragm and return spring.

4. Position the new diaphragm on the diaphragm cover, with the diaphragm plunger facing the lever, and line up the holes. While holding the

diaphragm in place, position the small diameter of the diaphragm return spring on the boss in the accelerator pump chamber; then, position the cover and the diaphragm over the return spring and onto the lower body. Install the cover retaining screws finger-tight.

5. Push the diaphragm inward with the lever and tighten the cover screws.

6. Position the accelerating pump actuating rod retaining clip over the hole in the accelerating pump lever, with the tab side of the clip toward the carburetor barrel. Depress the tab and insert the end of the rod through the lever and clip. Release the tab when the rod is inserted. Perform the Accelerating Pump Adjustments outlined in this section.

7. Install the air cleaner assembly (Part 10-5, Section 2).

ACCELERATING PUMP DIAPHRAGM AND/OR ELASTOMER VALVE REPLACEMENT—FORD 2-V AND 4-V

1. Remove the carburetor air horn to main body gasket by following steps 1 through 4 under Air Horn to Main Body Gasket Replacement— Ford 2-V and 4-V, in this section.

2. Remove the accelerating pump operating rod retainer. To release the rod from the retainer, press the tab ends of the clip together; then, at the same time, press the rod away from the clip until it is disengaged. Remove the rod. Remove the accelerating pump cover, diaphragm assembly and spring.

3. If inspection proves it necessary to remove the Elastomer valve, grasp it firmly and pull it out. **If the Elastomer valve tip broke off during removal, be sure to remove the tip from the fuel bowl. An Elastomer valve must be replaced whenever it is removed from the main body.**

4. If the Elastomer valve was removed, lubricate the tip of a new valve and insert the tip into the accelerator pump cavity. Using needle nosed pliers, reach into the fuel bowl and grasp the valve tip. Pull the valve in until it seats, and cut off the tip forward of the retaining shoulder. Remove the tip from the bowl.

5. Position the new accelerating pump diaphragm assembly to the cover and place the cover and diaphragm assembly in position on the return spring and main body. Install the cover screws finger-tight. Push the accelerating pump plunger the

full length of its travel and tighten the cover screws.

6. Position the accelerating pump operating rod in the inboard hole (hole closest to the pump plunger).

7. Adjust the accelerating pump stroke to specification (Part 10-8).

8. Install the carburetor air horn and gasket. Refer to the Air Horn to Main Body Gasket Replacement—Ford 2-V and 4-V Carburetor, Steps 5 through 9, in this section for the proper procedure.

SECONDARY DIAPHRAGM REPLACEMENT—FORD 4-V

1. Remove the carburetor air horn to main body gasket by following steps 1 through 4 under Air Horn to Main Body Gasket Replacement— Ford 2-V and 4-V, in this section.

2. Remove the secondary operating rod retainer and remove the rod. Remove the diaphragm cover, return spring and diaphragm.

3. Install the new secondary diaphragm on the secondary operating lever. Install the diaphragm return spring on the cover. Install the cover retaining screws finger-tight. With the diaphragm in the extended position, tighten the cover screws.

4. Install the secondary operating rod in the operating lever, and secure the rod to the secondary throttle shaft with the retaining clip.

5. Check the operation and seal of the secondary vacuum system by opening the primary and secondary throttle plates. Hold the secondary throttle plates open. Place a finger over the secondary vacuum inlet hole in the main body and release the secondary throttle plates. **This is a check for vacuum leakage at the diaphragm.** The throttle plates should not close fully. They will move slightly when released, but they must stop and should not move toward the closed position after the initial movement. Replace the diaphragm or tighten the cover screws as necessary to correct the vacuum leakage.

6. Install the carburetor air horn and gasket by following steps 5 through 9 under Air Horn to Main Body Gasket Replacement—Ford 2-V and 4-V Carburetors, in this section.

ANTI-STALL DASHPOT REPLACEMENT

Diaphragm Replacement Ford 1-V

1. Remove the air cleaner assembly (Part 10-5, Section 2).

2. Depress the tab on the dashpot lever to control rod retaining clip with pliers and slide the rod out of the lever. Remove the clip from the lever.

3. Remove the dashpot cover retaining screws. Remove the cover, diaphragm and return spring.

4. Position the new diaphragm on the dashpot cover, with the diaphragm plunger facing the lever, and line up the holes. Position the small diameter of the spring on the boss in the dashpot chamber; then, position the cover and diaphragm over the return spring and onto the lower body. Install the cover retaining screws finger-tight.

5. Push the diaphragm inward with the lever and tighten the cover screws.

6. Position the dashpot actuating rod retaining clip over the hole in the accelerating pump lever, with the tab side of the clip toward the carburetor barrel. Depress the tab and insert the end of the rod through the lever and clip. Release the tab when the rod is inserted. Adjust the dashpot. Refer to Anti-Stall Dashpot— Automatic Transmissions, in this section, for the proper adjustment procedure.

7. Install the air cleaner assembly (Part 10-5, Section 2).

Ford 2-V and 4-V

1. Remove the air cleaner assembly (Part 10-5, Section 2.

2. Remove the retaining nut and the dashpot from the mounting bracket.

3. Install the new dashpot and retaining nut on the mounting bracket.

4. Adjust the anti-stall dashpot. Refer to Anti-Stall Dashpot—Automatic Transmissions, in this section, for the proper procedure.

5. Install the air cleaner (Part 10-5, Section 2).

THERMOSTATIC CHOKE SPRING HOUSING AND GASKET REPLACEMENT

1. Remove the carburetor air cleaner assembly (Part 10-5, Section 2).

2. Remove the heater hose and mounting bracket from the carburetor.

3. Remove the choke thermostatic spring housing clamp retaining screws, and remove the spring housing and gasket. Discard the gasket.

4. Replace the spring housing, if required.

5. Position the thermostatic choke

spring housing gasket on the choke housing. **On a Ford 1-V carburetor, make sure the loop at the end of the thermostatic spring is on the thermostatic spring lever. On a Ford 2-V or 4-V carburetor, make sure the slot in the arm of the thermostatic spring lever is inserted into the loop of the thermostatic spring.** Position the retainer over the thermostatic spring housing and loosely install the retaining screws.

6. Rotate the spring housing in a counterclockwise, rich direction, and set the thermostatic spring housing index mark to the specified index mark (Part 10-9) on the choke housing. Tighten the retaining screws.

7. Install the heater hose mounting bracket, heater hose and the air cleaner assembly (Part 10-5, Section 2) on the carburetor.

THERMOSTATIC CHOKE ASSEMBLY REMOVAL AND INSTALLATION—CLEAN AND OVERHAUL

Ford 1-V

1. Remove the carburetor assembly from the car. Refer to Removal and Installation (Part 10-2, Section 2) for the procedures.

2. Remove the choke pull-down rod to throttle lever retainer (Fig. 12 in Part 10-2, Section 3). Remove the rod from the lever.

3. Remove the choke thermostatic spring housing to choke housing retaining screws. Remove the thermostat spring housing clamp, housing and the gasket. Discard the gasket.

4. Remove the choke housing to lower body retaining screws. Rotate the choke housing to disconnect the choke control rod and remove the choke housing and the gasket. Discard the gasket.

5. Remove the choke control lever to thermostatic choke shaft screw. Remove the choke control lever assembly and the spring. Slide the choke shaft out of the choke housing.

6. Remove the choke control rod from the lever.

7. Remove the choke pulldown rod adjusting nut from the rod. Slide the rod out of the swivel.

8. Clean and inspect the automatic choke. Refer to Cleaning and Inspection (Part 10-1, Section 3) for the procedures. Replace all worn or damaged parts.

9. When facing the cam side of the choke housing (Figs. 12 and 13 in Part 10-2, Section 3), position the choke shaft spring over the bushing

hub with the hook of the spring on the cam finger (spring windup will rotate the cam counterclockwise).

10. Hold the cam finger clockwise and against the stop of the housing; then rotate the spring counterclockwise until the spring straight end passes the cam finger. Position the choke control lever over the fast idle cam, with the pulldown swivel away from the housing and the short tang between the cam finger and the spring straight end.

11. Insert the thermostatic choke shaft assembly into the choke housing from the bimetal spring side of the housing and into the choke control lever (the pull-down swivel and the thermostatic spring arm should be aligned and not opposite), and install the retaining screw.

12. Insert the threaded end of the choke pull-down rod through the swivel (from the bottom) and install the adjusting nut.

13. Position the short end of the choke control rod into the keyhole in the choke housing choke lever.

14. Insert the choke assembly retaining screws into the choke housing. Position the new choke control gasket and the choke housing onto the lower body, connecting the rod to the choke plate shaft. Start the retaining screws into the body.

15. Insert the end of the choke pull-down rod into the throttle shaft lever hole and install the retainer.

16. Check the position of the choke control gasket and tighten the retaining screws.

17. Position the thermostatic spring housing, new gasket and cover to the choke housing, making sure the loop at the end of the thermostatic spring is on the choke lever. Loosely install the thermostatic spring housing clamp and the retaining screws. Rotate the spring housing in a counterclockwise (rich) direction and align the index mark on the spring housing with the specified index mark (Part 10-8) on the choke housing. Tighten the retaining screws.

18. Perform the Automatic Choke Plate Clearance (Pull-Down) and Fast Idle Cam Linkage Adjustment —Ford 1-V, outlined in this section of the manual.

19. Install the carburetor assembly. Refer to Removal and Installation (Part 10-2, Section 2) for the procedures.

Ford 2-V and 4-V

1. Remove the carburetor air

cleaner assembly (Part 10-5, Section 2).

2. Remove the heater hose and mounting bracket from the carburetor. Disconnect the choke heat tube from the carburetor.

3. Remove the fast idle cam retainer.

4. Remove the choke control rod retainer. Remove the choke housing retaining screws. Remove the choke housing assembly, gasket and fast idle cam as a unit. Remove the fast idle cam and rod from the fast idle cam lever.

5. If it is necessary to clean and overhaul the thermostatic choke housing assembly, remove the choke lever retaining screw and washer. Remove the choke piston lever from the housing. If necessary, remove the pin securing the choke piston to the choke lever link. Remove the choke lever and fast idle cam lever from the choke housing.

6. Clean and inspect the component parts. Refer to Cleaning and Inspection (Part 10-1, Section 3) for the proper procedure.

7. If it was necessary to clean and overhaul the thermostatic choke assembly, perform the following procedure:

If the choke piston and link was disassembled, install the choke piston on the choke thermostatic spring lever link and install the retaining pin.

Position the fast idle cam lever on the thermostatic choke shaft and lever assembly. **The bottom of the fast idle lever adjusting screw must rest against the tang on the choke shaft lever.** Insert the choke shaft assembly into the rear of the choke housing. Position the choke shaft lever so that the hole in the lever is to the left side of the choke housing.

Insert the choke piston into the choke housing. Position the choke thermostatic spring lever on the flange of the choke shaft, and install the retaining screw and washer.

8. Install the fast idle cam rod on the fast idle cam lever. Place the fast idle cam on the fast idle cam rod and install the retainer. Place the choke housing vacuum pickup port to main body gasket on the choke housing flange.

9. Position the choke housing on the main body, and at the same time, install the fast idle cam on the hub of the main body. Position the gasket and install the choke housing retaining screws. Install the fast idle cam retainer.

10. Connect the choke heat inlet

tube to the carburetor thermostatic choke housing.

11. Refer to the Automatic Choke Plate Clearance (Pull-Down) and Fast Idle Cam Linkage Adjustment—Ford 2-V and 4-V in this section, and perform steps 2 through 8.

VENT VALVE REPLACEMENT —FORD 1-V

1. Remove the air cleaner assembly (Part 10-5, Section 2).

2. Depress the tab on the retaining clip that secures the fuel bowl vent rod to the actuating lever and remove the rod and retainer from the lever.

3. Remove the stake marks from the vent valve opening with a scraper or a small file.

4. Remove the vent rod and valve assembly by pulling it outward. Remove the return spring.

5. Insert the fuel vent valve return spring in the vent passage. Insert the piston end of the fuel vent rod in the passage.

6. Punch 3 indentations in the vent valve passage opening with a center punch and a hammer. The indentations must distort the inside edge of the opening sufficiently to act as a stop for the piston end of the vent rod.

7. Position the fuel bowl vent rod retaining clip on the vent rod actuating lever. Depress the tab on the retaining clip with pliers and install the vent rod in the clip and the lever. Release the tab.

8. Perform a Vent Valve Adjustment as outlined in this section.

9. Install the air cleaner assembly (Part 10-5, Section 2).

SPARK VALVE OR GASKET REPLACEMENT—FORD 1-V

1. Remove the spark valve with a wrench. Remove and discard the gasket.

2. Install a new gasket on the spark valve. Install the spark valve and tighten it securely with a wrench.

POWER VALVE OR GASKETS REPLACEMENT—FORD 4-V

1. Remove the carburetor from the car. Refer to Part 10-4, Section 2 for the proper procedure.

2. Test the power valve. Refer to steps 1 through 4 under Power Valve (Part 10-1, Section 1) for the proper procedure.

3. If it is necessary to replace the cover gaskets or power valve, invert the main body. Remove the power valve cover and gasket. Discard the

gasket. Remove the power valve with a box wrench or socket wrench. Discard the power valve gasket.

Install a new gasket on the power valve. Install the power valve and gasket. **Tighten the power valve securely.** Position a new cover gasket on the main body. Install the cover. **Tighten the retaining screws securely.**

4. Install the carburetor assembly on the car. Refer to Part 10-4, Section 2 for the proper procedure.

CARBURETOR SPACER AND GASKETS REPLACEMENT

It is necessary to remove the carburetor from the car to replace a carburetor spacer and gaskets. Refer to the Carburetor Removal and Installation procedure steps in this group that pertain to the type of carburetor installed on the car.

THROTTLE LINKAGE REPAIR —MANUAL SHIFT TRANSMISSIONS

ACCELERATOR PEDAL COVER REPLACEMENT

Refer to Figs. 25 through 27 and Figs. 29 and 30 for views of the accelerator pedal cover for the applicable car models.

1. Hold the accelerator pedal in a manner that will prevent strain on the accelerator linkage and uncrimp the pedal cover to pedal retaining tabs. Remove the pedal cover.

2. Position the new pad on the accelerator pedal and carefully crimp the retaining tabs in a manner that will prevent distortion of the tabs and movement of the cover on the accelerator pedal pad.

ACCELERATOR PEDAL PAD REPLACEMENT

Refer to Figs. 25 through 30 for views of the accelerator pedal pad for the applicable car models.

1. Pry the edges of the accelerator pedal pad from the accelerator pedal with the fingers and remove the pad from the pedal.

2. Position the new accelerator pad on the accelerator pedal. Fold the pedal pad edges over the pedal with the fingers. **Make sure the pedal pad is properly seated on the pedal and that the pedal spring has not been dislodged.**

ACCELERATOR PEDAL REPLACEMENT

Refer to Figs. 25 through 30 for views of the accelerator pedal for the applicable car model(s).

1. Remove the retaining screw and nut securing the accelerator pedal assembly to the accelerator shaft. Remove the accelerator pedal and spring. Remove the accelerator pedal pad or cover (if so equipped) and discard it if it needs to be replaced.

2. Install the accelerator pedal pad or cover (if so equipped) on the accelerator pedal. Insert the pedal spring into position in the slot on the lower surface of the pedal.

3. Lubricate the accelerator pedal hinge points with the specified lubricant (Group 21) and position the accelerator pedal and spring assembly on the accelerator shaft and install the retaining screw. **Make sure the spring is properly seated on the pedal and the accelerator shaft. Install the retaining nut.**

ACCELERATOR SHAFT REPLACEMENT

Refer to Figs. 25 through 30 for views of the accelerator linkage components for the applicable car model(s).

1. Remove the accelerator pedal assembly. Refer to Accelerator Pedal Replacement, in this section, for the proper procedures.

2. Disconnect the accelerator retracting spring.

3. On all models except the Mustang, Falcon, Comet and Fairlane Six engines, remove the accelerator shaft to bellcrank rod retaining cotter pin, washer, rubber grommet, bushing and clevis from the accelerator shaft assembly.

On Falcon, Fairlane and Comet Six engines, loosen the accelerator shaft to bellcrank rod retaining clip. Disconnect the accelerator shaft to bellcrank rod from the accelerator shaft assembly. Remove the retaining clip.

On a Mustang Six engine, disconnect the accelerator control shaft rod from the accelerator shaft assembly.

4. On a Fairlane, Falcon and Comet Six engine, disconnect the stabilizer rod from the accelerator shaft assembly inner bracket.

5. Remove the retaining screws securing the accelerator shaft assembly bracket(s) to the dashpanel within the engine compartment. Remove the accelerator shaft assembly, seal and insulator as a unit. Discard the seal and the insulator if they are worn or damaged.

6. Lubricate the accelerator shaft hinge points with the specified lubricant (Group 21). Install the seal and insulator on the accelerator shaft as-

sembly. Position the accelerator shaft bracket(s) seal and insulator on the dashpanel. **Make sure the seal is properly installed to prevent the entrance of air, dirt and foreign material.** Secure the accelerator shaft assembly bracket(s) to the dashpanel with the retaining screws.

6. On a Fairlane, Falcon and Comet Six engine, connect the stabilizer rod to the accelerator shaft assembly inner bracket.

7. On a Mustang Six engine, connect the accelerator control shaft rod to the accelerator shaft. **Make sure the rods are properly connected.**

On a Falcon, Fairlane and Comet Six engine, install the retaining clip on the accelerator shaft. Connect the accelerator bellcrank clevis to the accelerator shaft, and secure the retaining clip to bellcrank rod.

On all models except the Mustang, Falcon, Fairlane and Comet Six engines, install the bushing and rubber grommet on the accelerator shaft to bellcrank rod clevis, and install the clevis on the accelerator shaft assembly. Install the washer and cotter pin on the clevis. Spread the ends of the retaining cotter pin.

8. Install the accelerator shaft retracting spring.

9. Install the accelerator pedal assembly. Refer to Accelerator Pedal Replacement in this section for the proper procedure.

10. Check the accelerator pedal for the specified idle height from the dash panel. Refer to Throttle Linkage Adjustment in this section for the proper procedure. Adjust the throttle linkage, if required.

ACCELERATOR CONTROL SHAFT ROD OR ACCELERATOR BELLCRANK TO CARBURETOR ROD REPLACEMENT

Refer to Figs. 25 through 26 for views of the accelerator linkage components for the applicable car model(s).

1. Remove the accelerator retracting spring and return spring (if so equipped).

2. Disconnect and remove the accelerator control shaft rod (Mustang Six) or accelerator bellcrank to carburetor rod.

3. Lubricate the accelerator control shaft rod or accelerator bellcrank to carburetor rod hinge point(s) with the specified lubricant (Group 21).

4. Install the accelerator control shaft rod (Mustang Six) or bellcrank to carburetor rod. **If the accelerator**

control shaft or bellcrank to carburetor rod is equipped with ball retaining clips, make sure the clips are properly seated over the ball.

5. Install the accelerator retracting spring and return spring (if so equipped).

6. On a Mustang Six engine, check the accelerator pedal for the specified idle height from the dash panel. Refer to Throttle Linkage Adjustment in this section for the proper procedure. Adjust the throttle linkage if required.

ACCELERATOR SHAFT TO BELLCRANK ROD REPLACEMENT

Refer to Figs. 26 through 30 for views of the accelerator linkage components for the applicable car model(s).

1. Disconnect the accelerator retracting spring.

2. On all models except the Mustang, Falcon, Comet and Fairlane Six engines, remove the accelerator shaft to bellcrank rod retaining cotter pin, washer, rubber grommet, bushing and clevis from the accelerator shaft assembly. Disconnect the accelerator shaft to bellcrank rod at the carburetor throttle lever or bellcrank (if so equipped) lever.

On Falcon, Fairlane and Comet Six engines, loosen the accelerator shaft to bellcrank rod retaining clip. Disconnect the accelerator shaft to bellcrank rod from the accelerator shaft assembly. Remove the retaining clip. Disconnect the accelerator shaft to bellcrank rod at the bellcrank lever.

3. Replace all worn or damaged parts. Lubricate the accelerator shaft to bellcrank rod hinge points with the specified lubricant (Group 21).

4. On a Fairlane or Comet 289 or 390 V-8 engine, check the bellcrank stabilizer for proper adjustment. Refer to Bellcrank Stabilizer Adjustment—289 and 390 V-8 in this section, for the proper procedure.

5. On a Falcon, Fairlane and Comet Six engine, install the retaining clip on the accelerator shaft. Connect the accelerator bellcrank clevis to the accelerator shaft, and secure the retaining clip to bellcrank rod.

On all models except the Mustang, Falcon, Fairlane and Comet Six engines, install the bushing and rubber grommet on the accelerator shaft to bellcrank rod clevis, and install the clevis on the accelerator shaft assembly. Install the washer and cotter pin on the clevis. Spread the ends of the retaining cotter pin.

6. Adjust the throttle (accelerator) linkage to obtain the specified accelerator pedal idle height, and connect the accelerator shaft to bellcrank rod to the carburetor throttle lever or bellcrank lever (if so equipped). Refer to Throttle Linkage Adjustments, in this section, for the proper procedure.

BELLCRANK STABILIZER REPLACEMENT

Refer to Figs. 29 and 30 for views of the accelerator linkage components for the applicable car model(s).

1. Loosen the bellcrank stabilizer rod retaining clips and disconnect the stabilizer rod from the retaining brackets.

2. Replace all worn or damaged parts.

3. Install the retaining clips on the bellcrank stabilizer brackets and connect the stabilizer rod to the brackets.

4. On a Fairlane or Comet 289 or 390 V-8 engine, perform a bellcrank stabilizer adjustment. Refer to Bellcrank Stabilizer Adjustment—Fairlane and Comet 289 and 390 V-8, in this section, for the proper procedure.

ACCELERATOR BELLCRANK REPLACEMENT ASSEMBLY

Refer to Figs. 26, 29 and 30 for views of the accelerator linkage components for the applicable car model(s).

1. Disconnect the accelerator shaft retracting spring.

2. On a Falcon, Comet and Fairlane Six engine, disconnect the accelerator shaft to bellcrank rod at the bellcrank. Disconnect the bellcrank stabilizer rod from the bellcrank stabilizer bracket. Disconnect the accelerator shaft to bellcrank rod at the accelerator shaft. Remove the bellcrank stabilizer bracket retaining washer. Remove the bellcrank assembly.

3. On a Fairlane and Comet V-8 engine, disconnect the bellcrank stabilizer rod, accelerator shaft to bellcrank rod and the accelerator bellcrank to carburetor rod from the bellcrank assembly. Remove the bellcrank retaining screws and remove the bellcrank assembly.

4. Replace all worn or damaged parts. Lubricate the accelerator linkage hinge points with the specified lubricant (Group 21).

5. On A Falcon, Comet, Fairlane Six engine, install the bellcrank stabilizer bracket assembly and retaining washer. Connect the accelerator shaft to bellcrank rod at the accelerator shaft. Connect the bellcrank stabilizer rod to the bellcrank stabilizer bracket. Connect the accelerator shaft to bellcrank rod at the

bellcrank. **Make sure the accelerator linkage retaining clips are securely fastened.**

6. On a Fairlane and Comet V-8 engine, install the bellcrank assembly on the engine; position the anti-backfire bracket and brace (if so equipped) on the bellcrank and install the retaining screws. Torque the screws to specification. Connect the bellcrank to carburetor rod to the bellcrank.

Perform a bellcrank stabilizer adjustment and connect the stabilizer rod to the bellcrank. Refer to Bellcrank Stabilizer Adjustment—Fairlane and Comet 289 V-8, in this section, for the proper procedure.

Connect the accelerator shaft to bellcrank rod to the bellcrank.

Make sure the accelerator linkage retaining clips are securely fastened.

7. Check the accelerator pedal idle height and adjust the linkage, if required. Refer to Throttle Linkage Adjustment in this section for the proper procedure.

8. Connect the accelerator retracting spring.

THROTTLE LINKAGE REPAIR—AUTOMATIC TRANSMISSION

The throttle linkage repair procedures for automatic transmissions are covered in Group 7.

3 CLEANING AND INSPECTION

CARBURETOR

Dirt, gum, water or carbon contamination in the carburetor or the exterior moving parts of the carburetor are often responsible for unsatisfactory performance. For this reason, efficient carburetion depends upon careful cleaning and inspection.

The cleaning and inspection of only those parts not included in the carburetor overhaul repair kit are covered here. All gaskets and parts included in the repair kit should be installed when the carburetor is assembled and the old gaskets and parts should be discarded.

Wash all the carburetor parts except the accelerating pump diaphragm, spark control valve (2-V carburetors), the power valve (2-V or 4-V carburetors), the secondary operating diaphragm (4-V carburetors), and the anti-stall dashpot assembly

(automatic transmission) in clean commercial carburetor cleaning solvent. If a commercial solvent is not available, lacquer thinner or denatured alcohol may be used.

Rinse the parts in kerosene to remove all traces of the cleaning solvent, then dry them with compressed air. Wipe all parts that can not be immersed in solvent with a clean, soft, dry cloth. Be sure all dirt, gum, carbon and other foreign matter are removed from all parts.

Force compressed air through all passages of the carburetor. **Do not use a wire brush to clean any parts or a drill or wire to clean out any openings or passages in the carburetor.** A drill or wire may enlarge the hole or passage, changing the calibration of the carburetor.

Check the choke shaft for grooves, wear and excessive looseness or

binding. Inspect the choke plate for nicked edges and for ease of operation and free it if necessary. Make sure all carbon and foreign material has been removed from the automatic choke housing and the piston. Check the operation of the automatic choke piston in the choke housing to make certain it has free movement.

Check the throttle shafts in their bores for excessive looseness or binding and check the throttle plates for burrs which prevent proper closure.

Inspect the main body, air horn, nozzle bars and booster venturi assemblies (2-V and 4-V carburetors), automatic choke housing and thermostatic spring housing, power valve cover, (2-V and 4-V carburetors), accelerating pump cover, secondary operating diaphragm cover (4-V carburetors) for cracks.

On Ford 1-V carburetors, check the metallic float for leaks by holding it under water that has been heated to just below the boiling point. Bubbles will appear if there is a leak. If a float leaks, replace it.

Replace the float(s) if the arm needle contact surface is grooved. If the float is serviceable, polish the needle contact surface with crocus cloth or steel wool. Replace the float shaft(s) if they are worn.

Replace all screws and nuts that have stripped threads. Replace all distorted or broken springs.

Inspect all gasket mating surfaces for nicks and burrs. Repair or replace any parts that have a damaged gasket surface.

On 2-V and 4-V carburetors, inspect the idle tubes in each nozzle bar assembly. If they are plugged, bent or broken, replace the booster venturi and nozzle bar assembly.

Inspect the rubber boot of the anti-stall dashpot (2-V and 4-V carburetors), if so equipped, for proper installation in the groove of the stem bushing. Check the stem movement for smooth operation. Do not lubricate the stem. Replace the assembly if it is defective.

FUEL PUMP

On all fuel pumps, except the Carter permanently sealed type, clean the fuel pump body, valve housing and cover. Blow out all body, housing and cover passages. Inspect the pump body, valve housing, cover, rocker arm, spring and pin for cracks or damage and replace them if necessary. If the fuel valves are not serviceable and replacement is necessary, replace the valve housing and valves as an assembly. Inspect

the mounting flange for distortion. Remove the pump body or lap the distorted flange if necessary.

On all Carter permanently sealed fuel pumps, clean the fuel pump with a cloth. Inspect the fuel pumps for cracks or damage. Inspect the mounting flange for distortion. Lap the distorted flange, if necessary. Inspect the rocker arm spring, pin and the rocker arm for wear, cracks or damage. **The rocker arm spring, pin and the rocker arm are the only components on the permanently sealed fuel pumps that are replaceable. If any other fuel pump components are damaged beyond repair, replace the fuel pump.**

AIR CLEANER

MAINTENANCE

Refer to Group 19 for the recommended air cleaner assembly maintenance mileage interval.

REMOVAL AND INSTALLATION

Refer to Part 10-5, Section 2 for the air cleaner assembly removal and installation procedures.

FILTER ELEMENT

The polyeurethene filter element on a "closed" crankcase ventilation system equipped car cannot be cleaned; it must be replaced.

The cellulose fiber filter element used on an "open" crankcase ventilation system equipped car must never be cleaned with a solvent or cleaning solution. Also, oil must not be added to the surfaces of the filter element or air cleaner body.

There are two alternate procedures that can be used to clean the

air filter element. One method is performed with the use of compressed air.

The other is performed by tapping the element on a smooth horizontal surface.

Compressed Air Method

Direct a stream of compressed air through the element in the direction opposite that of the intake air flow, that is from the inside outward. **Extreme care must be exercised to prevent rupture of the element material.**

Tapping Method

Hold the element in the vertical position and tap it lightly against a smooth, horizontal surface to shake the dust and dirt out. **Do not deform the element or damage the gasket surfaces by tapping too hard.** Rotate the filter after each tap until the entire outer surface has been cleaned.

Inspection

Hold the filter in front of a backup light and carefully inspect it for any splits or cracks. If the filter is split or cracked, replace it.

BODY AND COVER

Clean the air cleaner body and the cover with a solvent or compressed air. If the air cleaner contains an opening for the crankcase ventilation system air flow, probe the opening to assure removal of deposits. Wipe the air cleaner dry if a solvent is used. Inspect the air cleaner body and cover for distortion or damage at the gasket mating surfaces. Replace the cover or body if they are damaged beyond repair.

PART 10-2 FORD 1-V CARBURETOR

Section	Page
1 Description and Operation	10-25
Description	10-25
Operation	10-25
Fuel Inlet System	10-25
Idle Fuel System	10-25
Main Fuel Metering System	10-26
Accelerating Pump System	10-26
Power Fuel System	10-27
Fuel Bowl Vent System	10-30
Spark (Distributor Vacuum) Control System	10-30
2 Removal and Installation	10-31
Removal	10-31
Installation	10-31
3 Major Repair Operations	10-31

Section	Page
Disassembly	10-31
Automatic Choke	10-31
Upper Air Horn and Lower Body	10-33
Upper Body (Air Horn)	10-33
Fuel Vent Valve Rod	10-33
Lower Body	10-33
Cleaning and Inspection	10-33
Assembly	10-33
Fuel Vent Valve Rod	10-33
Upper Body (Air Horn)	10-33
Lower Body	10-34
Upper (Air Horn) to Lower Body Assembly	10-34
Automatic Choke	10-34

1 DESCRIPTION AND OPERATION

DESCRIPTION

The carburetor (Figs. 1 and 2) consists of two main assemblies, the main (upper) body and the throttle (lower) body.

The upper body (air horn) assembly contains the major metering components of the carburetor: the main and idle fuel system, which consists of the power valve, float chamber vent, and the fuel inlet system.

The lower body assembly contains: the fuel bowl, the accelerating pump assembly, the idle mixture adjusting screw (needle), and the spark valve. An hydraulic dashpot is also included in the lower body for use on car models that are equipped with an automatic transmission.

This section applies to all carburetors. Differences in carburetor operation are given when they exist.

OPERATION

The engine speed is regulated and controlled by the proportion of fuel and air delivered to the cylinders for all engine operating condition. Operation is based on the principle of pressure differences or vacuum.

Air is drawn into the carburetor air horn by manifold vacuum. As the air passes through the carburetor on its way to enter the cylinders, low pressure is created at the fuel discharge outlets of the carburetor. The fuel bowl is vented to atmospheric and to carburetor air inlet pressure through a vent hole in the upper body assembly. The high air pressure exerted on the fuel in the bowl forces the fuel to travel up through the fuel discharge channels and out into the air stream passing through the carburetor. The fuel and air is mixed

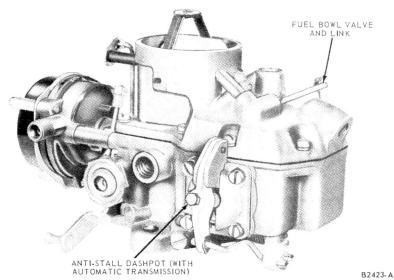

FIG. 1—Carburetor—Right Front ¾ View

at this point and distributed into the engine cylinders for burning.

FUEL INLET SYSTEM

The fuel inlet system (Fig. 3) of the carburetor maintains a predetermined fuel level in the fuel bowl. **The fuel level in the bowl is extremely important to carburetor calibration.** If the level of the fuel in the bowl is below the specified setting, a lean fuel-air mixture will result. A rich fuel-air mixture will occur from a higher than specified fuel level. The entire calibration of the carburetor is disturbed if the fuel level is not set as specified.

Fuel enters the fuel bowl through the fuel inlet needle valve and seat assembly. The amount of fuel entering is regulated by the distance the

needle valve is moved off the seat and by fuel pump pressure. **Correct fuel pump pressure is required to maintain the carburetor fuel level within the specified limits.**

The fuel level is maintained at a predetermined level by the float and lever assembly which controls the movement of the needle valve. The needle valve, riding on the tab of the float and lever assembly, reacts to any change in height of the float and the fuel level in the fuel bowl.

IDLE FUEL SYSTEM

The idle system (Fig. 4) functions when the engine is operating at low rpm. It supplies the fuel-air mixture when the air flow past the carburetor venturi is insufficient to operate the main metering system.

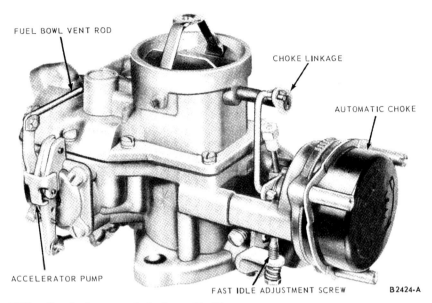

FIG. 2—Carburetor—Left Rear ¾ View

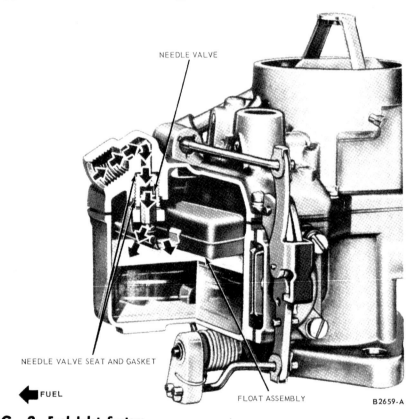

FIG. 3—Fuel Inlet System

The range of the idle system will extend into the operation of the main metering system. Fuel flows from the main well, up the idle well and through the calibrated idle jet. Filtered air from the carburetor air horn enters the idle air bleed restriction and mixes with the fuel. The air bleed restriction also serves as a vent to prevent syphoning of fuel at high speeds or when the engine is shut off. The fuel-air mixture then passes down through an idle channel restriction and is transferred to the idle channel in the lower body assembly.

The fuel air mixture passes down the idle channel, past two idle transfer holes, to the idle mixture adjusting screw (needle). The idle transfer holes act as additional air bleeds at normal idle. The fuel air mixture flows past the idle adjusting screw needle and seat and is discharged below the throttle plate. The amount of mixture to be discharged is determined by the position of the idle screw needle in relation to the seat in the lower body passage.

During off-idle operation, when the throttle plate is moved past the idle transfer holes, each hole begins discharging fuel as it is exposed to the lower air pressure (manifold vacuum). Continued opening of the throttle plate increases engine rpm and air flow through the carburetor. The greater air flow past the booster venturi causes a pressure drop in the venturi great enough to bring the main fuel metering system into operation as the idle fuel metering system tapers off.

MAIN FUEL METERING SYSTEM

The main fuel metering system (Fig. 5) supplies the fuel required for engine operation during the cruise or part-throttle range. The system begins to function when the air flow through the carburetor venturi creates sufficient vacuum to start fuel flowing in the main system. The vacuum at the discharge nozzle will increase as the air flow increases. The faster the engine operates, the more fuel will flow through the main fuel system.

Fuel entering the main jet, located at the bottom of the main well, flows up toward the main nozzle. A main well tube is inserted within the main well. Air from the high speed bleed channel enters the main well tube through a calibrated restriction at the top of the tube. The air passes through holes spaced along the tube, mixing with the fuel flowing up the main well. The fuel and air mixture being lighter than solid fuel, responds faster to changes in venturi pressures. The mixture continues flowing up the main well to the anti-syphon bleed. More air is introduced at the anti-syphon bleed to the fuel and air mixture which is then discharged from the main nozzle. The fuel is mixed with the filtered air moving past and through the booster venturi.

The anti-syphon bleed also acts as a vent to prevent syphoning of fuel at low engine speeds.

ACCELERATING PUMP SYSTEM

Smooth acceleration requires a momentary increase in the supply of

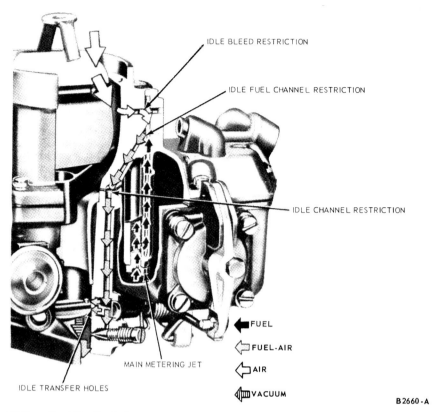

IDLE BLEED RESTRICTION

IDLE FUEL CHANNEL RESTRICTION

IDLE CHANNEL RESTRICTION

FUEL

FUEL-AIR

AIR

VACUUM

MAIN METERING JET

IDLE TRANSFER HOLES

B 2660-A

FIG. 4—Idle Fuel System

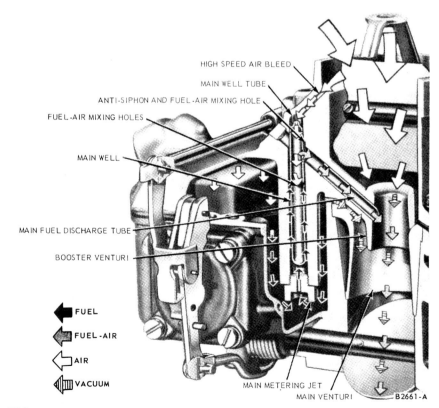

HIGH SPEED AIR BLEED

MAIN WELL TUBE

ANTI-SIPHON AND FUEL-AIR MIXING HOLE

FUEL-AIR MIXING HOLES

MAIN WELL

MAIN FUEL DISCHARGE TUBE

BOOSTER VENTURI

FUEL

FUEL-AIR

AIR

VACUUM

MAIN METERING JET

MAIN VENTURI

B 2661-A

FIG. 5—Main Metering System

fuel. The air flow through the carburetor responds almost immediately

to any increase in carburetor throttle valve opening. The fuel within the

metering passages will lag momentarily in its response to the pressure difference created by this increased air flow. This lag in fuel response will cause a temporary leanness in the fuel-air mixture that results in a hesitation in engine acceleration. A mechanically operated accelerating pump system (Fig. 6) supplies added fuel to provide a richer fuel-air mixture for this brief period of time.

The accelerating pump, located on the side of the lower body assembly, is actuated by linkage connected to the throttle shaft. When the throttle is opened on acceleration, the diaphragm forces fuel from the accelerating pump chamber into the discharge channel. The inlet ball check closes to prevent a reverse flow of fuel. Fuel under pressure forces the outlet ball check valve and the weight off its seat, allowing fuel to pass up to the discharge nozzle. The fuel is sprayed from the nozzle into the air stream above the main venturi.

When the throttle plate is closed on deceleration, a return spring forces the diaphragm back, drawing fuel through the inlet channel. The inlet ball check opens, allowing fuel to pass into the chamber while the outlet ball check closes preventing entry of air. A bleed hole is located in the body casting to allow vapor and excess pressure to escape from the diaphragm chamber.

POWER FUEL SYSTEM

When the engine is required to deliver more power to meet an increased road load demand or wide-open throttle operation, the carburetor must deliver a richer fuel-air mixture than supplied during the operation of the main fuel system at cruise or part throttle operation. When the engine is running under a high power demand, intake manifold vacuum is low. The vacuum below the carburetor throttle plate approximates intake manifold vacuum. The carburetor power valve (Fig. 7) will open when the manifold vacuum drops below a predetermined value. The fuel-air mixture is thus automatically enriched to meet the increased engine power demands.

Manifold vacuum is transmitted from an opening below the throttle plate, through a channel to the upper body assembly and to the top of the power valve piston. At idle and normal engine speeds, the manifold vacuum is great enough to hold the power valve piston up.

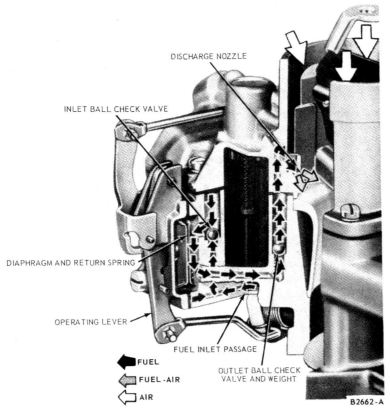

FIG. 6—Accelerating Pump System

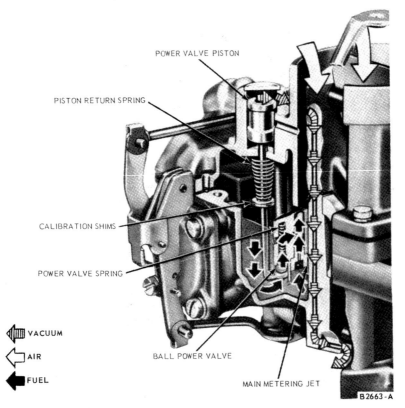

FIG. 7—Power Valve and Fuel Enrichment System

The power valve rod is connected to the piston. The foot of the rod controls the spring-loaded power valve ball check. With the piston

held up by manifold vacuum, the ball check closes the power jet inlet channel.

A power valve spring is located on the rod. The spring is shim calibrated to overcome the vacuum above the piston when manifold vacuum drops below a predetermined level. Upon demand for more power, the manifold vacuum drops below this level. The spring tension moves the rod down and allows the power valve ball check to open. Air pressure above the fuel bowl forces fuel to flow through the power jet, adding to fuel in the main fuel system, enriching the fuel-air mixture.

As the demand for power de-decreases and manifold vacuum increases, the vacuum above the piston overcomes the spring tension. The piston and rod move up and the ball check closes the power jet channel.

Automatic Choke System

The automatic choke system (Fig. 8) provides the proper choking action required to enrich the fuel-air mixture during the engine warm up period. This is accomplished primarily through the use of a bimetal thermostatic coil spring. The automatic choke control assembly is mounted on the lower body assembly and linked to the choke shaft lever by the choke control rod.

The bimetal thermostatic spring winds up when cold and unwinds when warm. When the engine is cold, the thermostatic spring, through attaching linkage, holds the choke plate in a closed position. A cold engine is started by opening the throttle fully to permit the pressure exerted by the bimetal spring to close the choke plate when the engine is cold. A fast idle cam is also rotated into position by the automatic choke lever and through a torsion spring to contact the fast idle adjusting screw.

The throttle is returned to a partially opened position and the engine is cranked. When the engine starts running, the spring action of the bimetal spring will permit partial opening of the choke plate. As the throttle is returned to the idle position, the pulldown rod opens the choke plate mechanically to a calibrated setting. The fast idle screw, attached to the throttle lever, increases the engine idle speed for smoother running when the engine is cold.

A cold engine is started by opening the throttle fully to permit the

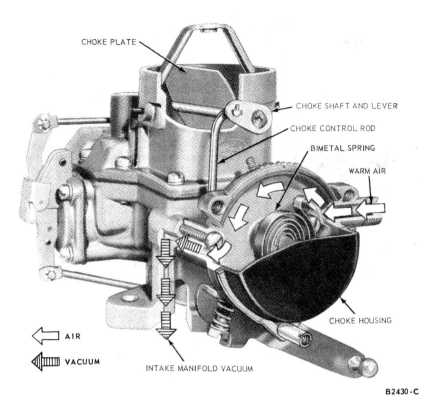

CHOKE PLATE

CHOKE SHAFT AND LEVER

CHOKE CONTROL ROD

BIMETAL SPRING

WARM AIR

CHOKE HOUSING

⇐ AIR

⇐ VACUUM

INTAKE MANIFOLD VACUUM

B2430-C

FIG. 8—Automatic Choke System

pressure exerted by the bi-metal spring to close the choke plate. A fast idle cam is also rotated into position by the automatic choke lever and torsion spring to contact the fast idle adjusting screw. The throttle is then returned to a partially opened position and the engine is cranked. When the engine starts running, the spring action of the bimetal spring will permit partial opening of the choke plate.

As the throttle is returned to the idle position, the pull-down rod opens the choke plate mechanically to a calibrated setting and the fast idle screw, attached to the throttle lever, increases the engine idle speed for smoother running when the engine is cold.

During driveaway, increased air flow will result in increased pressure on the choke plate, causing the choke plate to partially open against the force of the bimetal spring, thereby controlling fuel-air mixture in response to engine demand.

As the engine continues to run, manifold vacuum, channeled through a passage on the bottom of the lower body to the choke housing, draws heated air from the exhaust manifold heat chamber through the thermostatic choke control outlet line

housing is controlled by restriction of air channels in the carburetor.

The warmed air from the heat chamber enters the choke housing and heats the thermostatic spring, causing it to warm up. Tension of the thermostatic spring gradually decreases as the temperature of the air from the heat chamber rises, allowing the choke plate to open. The air in the choke housing is exhausted into the intake manifold.

When the engine reaches its normal operating temperature, the spring exerts full tension on the choke plate, forcing it to the full open position.

When the choke plate is partially or fully closed, a fast idle cam is rotated into position to contact the fast idle adjustment screw. The screw, attached to the throttle lever, permits a faster engine idle speed for smoother running when the engine is cold. The thermostatic choke lever and torsion spring rotate the fast idle cam to lower the engine idle speed when the engine temperature rises and choking is reduced.

The throttle lever and pull-down rod partially opens the choke plate when the accelerator pedal is fully

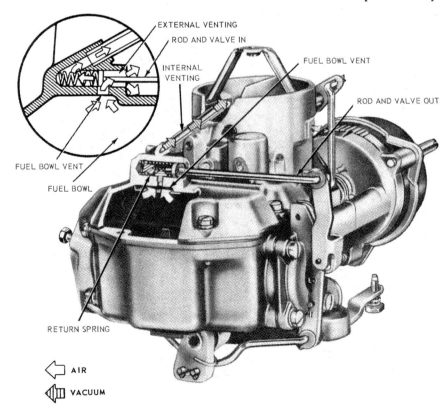

EXTERNAL VENTING

ROD AND VALVE IN

INTERNAL VENTING

FUEL BOWL VENT

ROD AND VALVE OUT

FUEL BOWL VENT

FUEL BOWL

RETURN SPRING

⇐ AIR

⇐ VACUUM

B2431-A

FIG. 9—Fuel Bowl Venting System

connected to the choke housing. The amount of air entering the choke

depressed. This permits unloading a flooded engine.

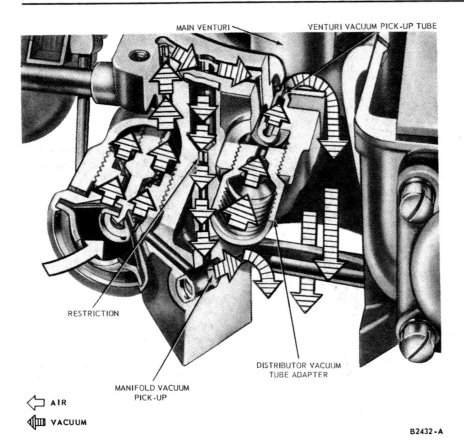

FIG. 10—Spark (Distributor Vacuum) Control System

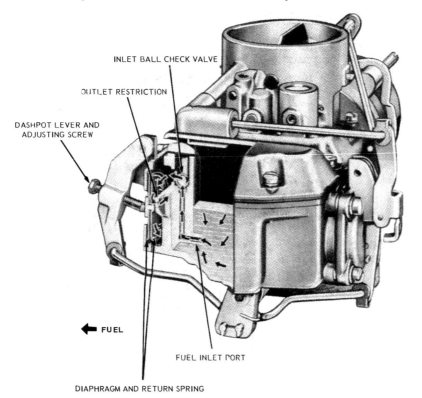

FIG. 11—Anti-Stall Dashpot

FUEL BOWL VENT SYSTEM

The fuel bowl requires venting (Fig. 9) to provide proper operation for the various systems. Fuel vapors may form in the fuel bowl when a hot engine is stopped, idling, or operating at very low speeds. By venting the fuel bowl to the atmosphere by means of a vent control valve, engine performance is improved. At higher engine speeds, venting to the carburetor air horn prevents calibration changes due to normal air cleaner contamination.

The restriction of air due to air cleaner contamination causes a pressure drop in the carburetor air horn, and a richer air-fuel mixture. The pressure drop will increase as demand for air (engine speed) is increased.

The vent control valve, connected through linkage to the throttle shaft and located in a bore over the fuel bowl, is at the inward position during closed or part throttle operation. In this position, the valve allows venting only to the atmosphere. At normal or wide-open throttle operation the valve moves outward, sealing the external vent and opening the vent to the carburetor throat.

SPARK (DISTRIBUTOR VACUUM) CONTROL SYSTEM

The degree of spark advance in the distributor is determined by the strength of the vacuum acting on the distributor diaphragm. A high vacuum will increase spark advance. The carburetor is calibrated to provide the required vacuum to the distributor through an interaction of venturi vacuum and manifold vacuum. Venturi vacuum is obtained through the pickup tube in the main venturi and is supplied to the distributor only when it exceeds manifold vacuum (Fig. 10).

Manifold vacuum supplied to the distributor, is obtained from a pickup hole at the throttle plate edge (when the throttle is closed) and metered to the distributor. An additional passage is always open to manifold vacuum. The purpose of the additional passage is to provide a higher spark advance at closed throttle during deceleration to promote complete burning of the fuel and greater efficiency.

Metering of the manifold vacuum to the distributor is accomplished through the use of the spark valve and restrictors in the vacuum channels. *The spark valve is held open* through the combination of vacuum and atmospheric pressure acting on the spark valve diaphragm to overcome the tension of a calibrated spring in the spark valve.

Calibrated restrictors in the manifold vacuum channels limit the flow of manifold vacuum to the distributor. Also, during low manifold vacuum periods, the bypass restrictor controls the reduction of venturi vacuum caused by bleed back.

At off-idle engine speeds, vacuum at the throttle edge is high due to a venturi effect created by the position of the throttle plate in the throttle bore. The high vacuum in this area is supplied to the distributor through the manifold vacuum channels for the required increase in distributor spark advance.

Upon acceleration and under wide-open throttle operation, manifold vacuum drops. When the manifold vacuum falls below a predetermined point, the spark valve closes, shutting off the manifold vacuum to the distributor. The drop in distributor vacuum retards the spark advance. Venturi vacuum, now greater than manifold vacuum, supplies vacuum to the distributor, thus preventing a full spark retard.

As the engine load demands decrease, the increase in manifold vacuum will become greater than venturi vacuum. The increased manifold vacuum opens the spark valve and the higher vacuum now supplied to the distributor increases the spark advance for more efficient engine operation.

DASHPOT SYSTEM

The low idle rpm setting on automatic transmission equipped units requires a means of control to prevent engine stall upon sudden closing of the throttle plate. This is accomplished by hydraulic dampening of the throttle closing rate.

The dashpot, located on the side of the fuel bowl, is actuated by linkage connected to the throttle shaft (Fig. 11). When the throttle is opened a return spring forces the diaphragm back, drawing fuel through the inlet channel. The inlet ball check opens, allowing fuel to flow into the dashpot chamber.

When the throttle plate is closed, the dashpot actuating lever and adjusting screw moves the diaphragm inward. The diaphragm moving inward seats the inlet ball check, closes the inlet channel and forces fuel through a restriction into the fuel outlet channel into the bowl. The discharge restriction limits the flow of fuel and slows the closing of the throttle plate.

---

2 REMOVAL AND INSTALLATION

REMOVAL

Flooding, stumble on acceleration and other performance complaints are, in many instances, caused by the presence of dirt, water, or other foreign matter in the carburetor. To aid in diagnosing the complaint, the carburetor should be carefully removed from the engine without removing the fuel from the bowl. The contents of the bowl may then be examined for contamination as the carburetor is disassembled.

1. Remove the air cleaner from the air horn of the carburetor (Part 10-5, Section 2).

2. Disconnect the clean air tube, accelerator return spring, accelerator linkage, automatic choke heat tube, in-line fuel filter and the distributor vacuum line.

3. Remove the carburetor to intake manifold retaining nuts. Remove the carburetor, spacer and the upper and lower spacer gaskets. Discard the gaskets.

INSTALLATION

1. Clean the gasket surfaces of the carburetor, intake manifold and spacer. Position the spacer between 2 new gaskets and position them on the intake manifold.

2. Install the carburetor and tighten the retaining nuts, evenly and alternately, to specification.

3. Connect the distributor vacuum line, in-line fuel filter, automatic choke heat tube, clean air tube, accelerator linkage and the accelerator return spring.

4. Adjust the idle fuel mixture and engine idle speed, and the anti-stall dashpot (automatic transmission), if so equipped. Refer to Common Adjustments and Repairs (Part 10-1, Section 2) for the proper procedures.

---

3 MAJOR REPAIR OPERATIONS

DISASSEMBLY

Use a separate container for the component parts of the various assemblies to facilitate cleaning, inspection and assembly.

The following is a step-by-step sequence of operations for completely overhauling the carburetor; however, certain components of the carburetor may be serviced without a complete disassembly of the entire unit.

A disassembled view of the carburetor is shown in Fig. 12.

AUTOMATIC CHOKE

1. Remove the choke pull-down rod to throttle lever retainer (Fig. 12). Remove the rod from the lever.

2. Remove the choke thermostatic spring housing to choke housing retaining screws. Remove the thermostat spring housing clamp, housing and the gasket.

3. Remove the choke housing to lower the body retaining screws. Rotate the choke housing to disconnect the choke control rod and remove the choke housing and the gasket.

4. Remove the choke control lever to thermostatic choke shaft screw. Remove the choke control lever assembly and the spring. Slide the choke shaft out of the choke housing.

5. Remove the choke control rod from the lever.

6. Remove the choke pulldown rod adjusting nut from the rod. Slide the rod out of the swivel.

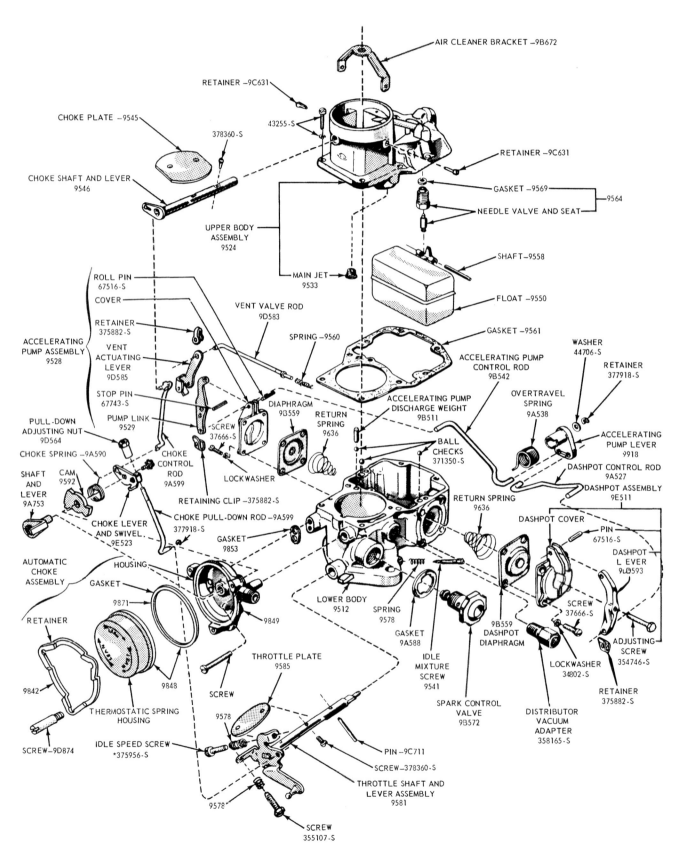

AIR CLEANER BRACKET –9B672

RETAINER –9C631

CHOKE PLATE –9545

378360 -S

43255-S

RETAINER –9C631

CHOKE SHAFT AND LEVER
9546

GASKET –9569

NEEDLE VALVE AND SEAT

9564

UPPER BODY
ASSEMBLY
9524

SHAFT –9558

MAIN JET
9533

FLOAT –9550

ROLL PIN
67516-S

COVER

VENT VALVE ROD
9D583

GASKET –9561

RETAINER
375882-S

SPRING –9560

WASHER
44706-S

RETAINER
377918-S

ACCELERATING
PUMP ASSEMBLY
9528

VENT
ACTUATING
LEVER
9D585

ACCELERATING PUMP
CONTROL ROD
9B542

STOP PIN
67743-S

DIAPHRAGM
9B559

RETURN
SPRING
9636

ACCELERATING PUMP
DISCHARGE WEIGHT
9B511

OVERTRAVEL
SPRING
9A538

ACCELERATING
PUMP LEVER
9918

PULL-DOWN
ADJUSTING NUT
9D564

PUMP LINK
9529

SCREW
37666-S

BALL
CHECKS
371350-S

DASHPOT CONTROL ROD
9A527

CHOKE SPRING –9A590

LOCKWASHER

DASHPOT ASSEMBLY
9E511

SHAFT
AND
LEVER
9A753

CAM
9592

CHOKE
CONTROL
ROD
9A599

RETAINING CLIP –375882-S

RETURN SPRING
9636

DASHPOT COVER

PIN
67516-S

CHOKE LEVER
AND SWIVEL
9E523

CHOKE PULL-DOWN ROD –9A599

377918-S

GASKET
9853

DASHPOT
L EVER
9LD593

AUTOMATIC
CHOKE
ASSEMBLY

HOUSING

GASKET

9871

LOWER BODY
9512

SPRING
9578

9B559
DASHPOT
DIAPHRAGM

SCREW
37666-S

RETAINER

9849

GASKET
9A588

LOCKWASHER
34802-S

ADJUSTING
SCREW
354746-S

9842

9848

THERMOSTATIC SPRING
HOUSING

9578

IDLE
MIXTURE
SCREW
9541

RETAINER
375882-S

SCREW –9D874

IDLE SPEED SCREW
*375956-S

THROTTLE PLATE
9585

SCREW

SPARK CONTROL
VALVE
9B572

DISTRIBUTOR
VACUUM
ADAPTER
358165-S

PIN –9C711

9578

SCREW –378360-S

THROTTLE SHAFT AND
LEVER ASSEMBLY
9581

9578

SCREW
355107-S

B2433-B

FIG. 12—Single-Barrel Carburetor—Disassembled

**UPPER AIR HORN AND
LOWER BODY**

1. Depress the tang on the fuel bowl vent rod to accelerating pump actuating lever retainer (Fig. 12), and disconnect the vent rod from the lever. Remove the fuel bowl vent rod to accelerating pump actuating lever retainer (Fig. 12).

2. Remove the upper to lower body retaining screws and the carburetor identification tag. Separate the upper body assembly, gasket and lower body assembly (Fig. 12). Discard the gasket.

3. Invert the lower body assembly and allow the accelerating pump discharge weight and ball check, the accelerating pump inlet ball check, and the dashpot ball check, if so equipped, to fall into the hand.

UPPER BODY (AIR HORN)

1. Remove the float retaining pin and the float assembly (Fig. 12).

2. Remove the fuel inlet needle valve. Remove the needle valve seat and gasket. Discard the gasket.

3. Remove the main jet.

4. Remove the air cleaner bracket retaining roll pins with pliers. Turn them in a direction that will coil the pins to a smaller diameter. If they offer resistance to turning, turn them in the opposite direction. Pull the bracket out of the retaining channels.

5. If it is necessary to remove the choke plate and shaft, lightly scribe the choke along the choke shaft so that the choke plate can be installed in the same position during installation.

Remove the choke plate screws. The retaining screws are staked in the choke shaft. If the tips of the screws are flared excessively, file off the flared portion to avoid damage to the threads in the choke shaft. Be careful not to damage the choke shaft or venturi while filing the screws. Remove the choke plate from the top of the air horn by sliding the plate out of the shaft. Slide the shaft out of the body.

FUEL VENT VALVE ROD

1. Remove the stake marks at the vent rod opening with a scraper or file.

2. Remove the vent rod assembly and spring by pulling the vent rod outward.

LOWER BODY

1. Depress the tab on the accel-

erating pump lever to control rod retaining clip and slide the rod out of the lever (Fig. 12). Remove the clip from the lever.

2. Remove the accelerating pump cover retaining screws. Remove the cover assembly from the lower body. Separate the pump diaphragm and spring from the cover or lower body.

If necessary, remove the fuel vent rod actuating lever to cover retaining pin and the accelerating pump lever to cover retaining pin with pliers. Turn them in a direction that will coil the pins to a smaller diameter. If the pins offer resistance to turning, turn them in the opposite direction. Remove the levers from the cover.

3. If the carburetor is equipped with a dashpot, depress the tab on the dashpot lever and control rod retaining clip, and slide the rod out of the dashpot lever. Remove the dashpot cover retaining screws and remove the cover assembly. Separate the diaphragm and spring from the cover or body.

If necessary, remove the lever to cover retaining pin with pliers. Turn the pin in a direction that will coil the pin to a smaller diameter. If the pin offers resistance to turning, turn it in the opposite direction and remove the lever from the cover.

4. Remove the throttle shaft lever and retaining ring and washer. Remove the lever and overtravel spring from the throttle shaft. Remove the accelerator pump and dashpot control rods from the lever.

5. Remove the distributor vacuum outlet adapter.

6. Remove the spark valve and gasket.

7. Remove the idle mixture adjusting screw and spring.

8. If it is necessary to remove the throttle plate and shaft, lightly scribe the throttle plate along the throttle shaft so that the throttle plates can be installed in the same position during installation.

Remove the throttle plate retaining screws and slide the plate out of the shaft. For assembly purposes, note that the dimple in the throttle plate is located below the throttle shaft. **The retaining screws are staked in the throttle shaft.** If the tips of the screws are flared excessively, file off the flared portion to avoid damage to the threads in the throttle shaft. **Be careful not to damage the throttle shaft or venturi while filing the screws.**

9. Remove the overtravel spring tension pin from the throttle shaft and slide the shaft out of the body.

CLEANING AND INSPECTION

Clean and inspect the carburetor component parts. Refer to Part 10-1, Section 3, for the proper procedure. Replace all worn or damaged parts.

ASSEMBLY

Make sure all holes in the new gaskets have been properly punched and that no foreign material has adhered to the gaskets.

During assembly of the carburetor, certain adjustments are required. The details of these adjustments are covered in Part 10-1, Section 2, under Common Adjustments and Repairs.

A disassembled view of the carburetor is shown in Fig. 12.

FUEL VENT VALVE ROD

1. Insert the fuel vent valve return spring in the fuel vent passage in the upper body (Fig. 12). Insert the piston end of the fuel vent rod in the passage.

2. Punch three indentations in the vent valve passage opening with a center punch and a hammer. The indentations must distort the inside edge of the opening sufficiently to act as a stop for the piston end of the vent rod. Perform a Vent Valve Adjustment after the carburetor is assembled and installed on the car (Part 10-2, Section 2).

UPPER BODY (AIR HORN)

1. If the choke plate and the shaft were removed, insert the choke shaft assembly into the air horn with the lever pointing toward the accelerating pump side of the carburetor (Fig. 12).

Refer to the line previously scribed on the choke plate and insert the choke plate into its original position with the plate indentation facing upward and toward the accelerating pump side of the carburetor. Install the choke plate retaining screws snug, but not tight.

Check for proper plate fit, binding in the air horn and free rotation of the shaft by moving the plate from the closed position to the open position. If it moves freely, tighten the choke plate retaining screws while holding the plate in the fully-closed position. Stake the screws. **When staking the screws, support the shaft and plate on a block of wood or a**

metal bar to prevent bending of the shaft.

2. Install the main jet in the main fuel well.

3. Install the needle valve seat gasket and the seat within the tapped seat hole. Tighten the needle valve seat firmly. Insert the needle valve into the needle valve seat, with the viton tip toward the seat.

4. Position the float assembly in the body, with the tab on the arm located over the needle valve and the hinge of the arm lined up between the hinge bracket holes in the upper body casting. Insert the float hinge pin through the holes in the upper body and float assembly.

5. Check the float setting. Refer to Common Adjustments and Repairs (Part 10-1, Section 2) for the proper procedure.

6. Insert the air cleaner bracket in the channels of the air horn and install the bracket retaining pins.

LOWER BODY

1. If the throttle plate and shaft were removed, slide the throttle shaft into the lower body, with the lever on the throttle shaft located opposite the fuel bowl and the fast idle adjusting screw facing upward (Fig. 12).

Refer to the line previously scribed on the throttle plate and insert the plate through the slot in the throttle shaft. The plate indentation must face the bottom of the body and point toward the accelerator pump side of the lower body. Install the throttle plate screws snug, but not right.

Rotate the throttle shaft while lightly tapping the throttle plate within the throttle bore. Check for free rotation of the throttle shaft. Hold the lower body up to the light. **Little or no light should show between the throttle plate and throttle bore.** When the plate is properly located, hold the throttle plate closed; then, tighten and stake the retaining screws. **When staking the screws, support the shaft and plate on a block of wood or a metal bar to prevent bending of the shaft.**

2. Install the distributor vacuum outlet fitting.

3. If the lever was removed from the accelerating pump cover, position the top hole of the lever between the top bracket holes in the cover; then, install the retaining roll pin.

Position the vent rod lever over

the accelerating pump cover bracket. Line up the hole in the lever with the holes in the bracket and install the retaining roll pin.

Install the roll pin in the HI (lower) stop hole in the lever.

Position the small diameter end of the diaphragm return spring in the boss in the accelerating pump chamber. Position the diaphragm assembly in the accelerating pump cover, with the diaphragm plunger facing the lever, and line up the holes. Position the cover and diaphragm over the return spring and onto the body. Install the cover retaining screws finger-tight. Push the diaphragm assembly inward with the lever and tighten the cover screws.

4. If the carburetor is equipped with a dashpot (Fig. 12), proceed with the following steps:

If the lever was removed from the dashpot cover, position the hole in the lever between the holes in the bracket on the cover. Install the lever retaining roll pin. Install the adjusting screw in the lever, if necessary.

Position the small diameter of the diaphragm return spring on the boss in the dashpot chamber. Position the diaphragm in the dashpot cover with the diaphragm plunger facing the lever, and line up the holes. Position the cover and the diaphragm over the return spring and onto the body. Install the cover retaining screws finger tight. Push the diaphragm assembly inward with the lever and tighten the cover screws.

5. Position the overtravel spring (Fig. 12) on the accelerating pump lever and hook the tang of the spring on the lever. Position the accelerating pump lever and spring on the throttle shaft and insert the accelerating pump actuating rod and dashpot actuating rod, if so equipped, into the two holes in the lever.

6. Install the overtravel tension spring retaining pin in the throttle shaft. Pull the arm of the spring over the retaining pin to apply spring tension to the overtravel lever. Install the washer and retaining clip on the throttle shaft. Insert the keyed end of the accelerating pump actuating and the dashpot actuating rod (if so equipped) into the inboard side of the slotted holes in the accelerating pump lever.

7. Position the accelerating pump actuating rod retaining clip over the hole in the accelerating lever, with the tab side of the clip toward the carburetor barrel (Fig. 12). Depress

the tab and insert the shorter end of the rod through the lever and clip. Release the tab when the rod is inserted. Perform the Accelerating Pump Adjustments (Part 10-1, Section 2) after the carburetor is assembled.

8. If the carburetor is equipped with a dashpot, position the dashpot actuating rod retaining clip over the hole in the dashpot lever, with the tab side of the clip facing toward the carburetor barrel (Fig. 12). Depress the tab and insert the shorter end of the rod through the lever and clip, then release the tab when the rod is inserted. Perform an Anti-Stall Dashpot Adjustment (Part 10-1, Section 2); after the carburetor is assembled.

9. Position the new spark valve gasket over the spark valve and screw the valve into the lower body (Fig 12). Tighten the valve securely. **A loose valve will cause poor engine operation.**

10. Install the idle mixture adjusting screw and spring in the lower body (Fig. 12). Perform the Preliminary Idle Mixture Setting (Part 10-1, Section 2) after the carburetor is assembled.

UPPER (AIR HORN) TO LOWER BODY ASSEMBLY

1. Place the ball check and the accelerating pump weight into the lower body accelerating pump outlet passage (Fig. 12). Insert a ball check in the accelerating pump inlet passage.

2. If the carburetor is equipped with a dashpot, insert a ball check in the dashpot inlet passage (Fig. 12).

3. Install the new upper to lower body gasket onto the lower body. **Make certain the word "TOP"** (inscribed on the gasket) is facing upward. Position the upper body on the lower body and gasket. **During the installation, observe the float shaft to make certain it does not dislodge.** Install the upper to lower body retaining screws and the carburetor identification tag. Tighten the screws.

4. Position the fuel vent valve rod retaining clip over the hole in the actuating lever, with the tab side of the clip toward the carburetor air horn. Depress the tab on the clip and connect the rod to the actuating lever. Release the tab.

AUTOMATIC CHOKE

1. When facing the cam side of the choke housing (Figs. 12 and 13),

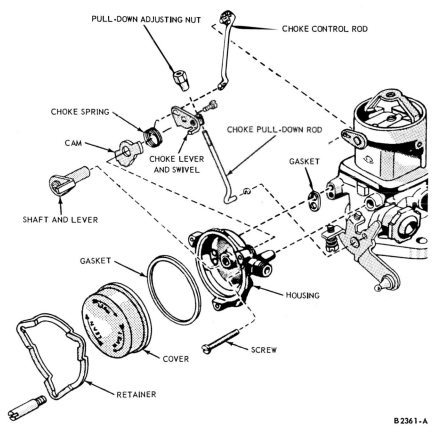

PULL-DOWN ADJUSTING NUT

CHOKE CONTROL ROD

CHOKE SPRING

CAM

CHOKE PULL-DOWN ROD

CHOKE LEVER AND SWIVEL

GASKET

SHAFT AND LEVER

GASKET

HOUSING

COVER

SCREW

RETAINER

B 2361-A

FIG. 13—Automatic Choke Linkage

position the choke shaft spring over the bushing hub with the hook of the spring on the fast idle cam finger (spring windup will rotate the cam counterclockwise).

2. Hold the cam finger clockwise and against the stop of the housing, then rotate the spring counterclockwise until the spring straight end passes the cam finger. Position the choke control lever over the fast idle cam, with the pulldown swivel away from the housing and the short tang between the cam finger and the spring straight end.

3. Insert the thermostatic choke shaft assembly into the choke hous-

ing from the bimetal spring side of the housing and into the choke control lever (the pull-down swivel and the thermostatic spring arm should be aligned and not opposite), and install the retaining screw.

4. Insert the threaded end of the choke pull-down rod through the swivel (from the bottom) and install the adjusting nut.

5. Position the short end of the choke control rod into the keyhole in the choke housing choke lever.

6. Insert the choke assembly retaining screws into the choke housing. Position the choke housing to main body gasket and the choke

housing onto the lower body, connecting the control rod to the choke plate shaft. Start the retaining screws into the body

7. Insert the end of the choke pull down rod into the front of the throttle shaft lever hole and install the retainer.

8. Check the position of the choke housing to main body gasket and tighten the retaining screws

9. Position the thermostatic spring, housing, gasket and cover to the choke housing, making sure the loop at the end of the thermostatic spring is on the choke lever (Fig. 14). The spring must wind clockwise toward the center when viewed from the choke housing side of the carburetor. Loosely install the spring housing clamp and the retaining screws. Rotate the spring housing in a counterclockwise (rich) direction and align the index mark on the spring housing with the specified index mark (Part 10-1, Section 2) on the choke housing. Tighten the thermostatic spring housing clamp retaining screws.

10. Perform the Automatic Choke Plate Clearance (Pull-Down) and Fast Idle Cam Linkage Adjustment (Part 10-1, Section 2).

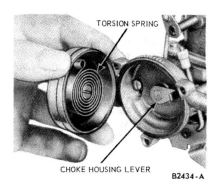

TORSION SPRING

CHOKE HOUSING LEVER

B2434-A

FIG. 14—Correct Position of Automatic Choke Torsion Spring

PART 10-3 FORD 2-V CARBURETORS

Section	Page
1 Description and Operation	10-36
Description	10-36
Operation	10-36
Fuel Inlet System	10-36
Automatic Choke System	10-37
Idle Fuel System	10-38
Accelerating System	10-39
Main Fuel System	10-39
Power Fuel System	10-40
2 Removal and Installation	10-40
Removal	10-40

Section	Page
Installation	10-40
3 Major Repair Operations	10-41
Disassembly	10-41
Air Horn	10-41
Vacuum Piston Choke	10-41
Main Body	10-41
Parts Repair or Replacement	10-42
Assembly	10-42
Main Body	10-42
Vacuum Piston Choke	10-44
Air Horn	10-44

1 DESCRIPTION AND OPERATION

DESCRIPTION

The carburetors (Figs. 1 and 2) have two main assemblies, the air horn and the main body.

The air horn assembly, which serves as the main body cover, contains the choke plate and the vents for the fuel bowl.

The throttle plate, accelerating pump assembly, power valve assembly and the fuel bowl are in the main body. The automatic choke housing is attached to the main body.

The two barrels each contain a main and booster venturi, main fuel discharge, accelerating pump discharge, idle fuel discharge and a throttle plate.

OPERATION
FUEL INLET SYSTEM

The amount of fuel entering the fuel bowl (Fig. 3) is regulated by the distance the fuel inlet needle is raised off its seat and by fuel pump pressure. Movement of the fuel inlet needle in relation to the seat is controlled by the float and lever assembly which rises and falls with the fuel level. When the fuel in the fuel bowl reaches a pre-set level, the float lowers the fuel inlet needle to a position where it restricts the flow of fuel, admitting only enough fuel to replace that being used.

An integral retaining clip is attached to the fuel inlet needle assem-

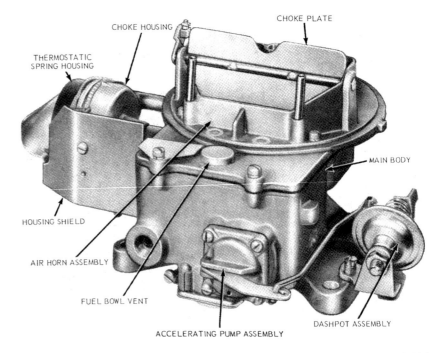

FIG. 1—¾ Left Front View

bly. The clip hooks over the tab on the end of the lever of the float assembly. This clip assures reaction of the fuel inlet needle to any downward movement of the float.

A wire-type retainer prevents movement of the float shaft within the guides on each side of the fuel bowl. The retainer fits into a groove on the outside of the fuel inlet nee-

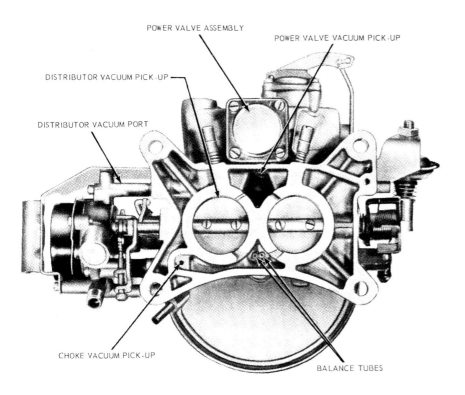

POWER VALVE ASSEMBLY
POWER VALVE VACUUM PICK-UP
DISTRIBUTOR VACUUM PICK-UP
DISTRIBUTOR VACUUM PORT
CHOKE VACUUM PICK-UP
BALANCE TUBES

B2665-A

FIG. 2—Bottom View

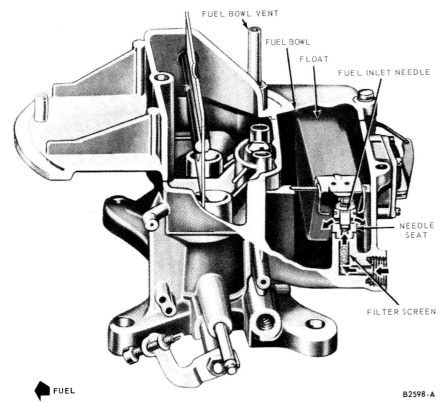

FUEL BOWL VENT
FUEL BOWL
FLOAT
FUEL INLET NEEDLE
NEEDLE SEAT
FILTER SCREEN

FUEL

B2598-A

FIG. 3—Fuel Inlet System

dle seat. The ends of the retainer are hooked over grooves on opposite ends of the float shaft.

The fuel bowl is internally vented

into the air cleaner. It is also externally vented to the atmosphere.

AUTOMATIC CHOKE SYSTEM

The choke plate, located in the air horn above the barrels, when closed, provides a high vacuum above as well as below the throttle plates. With a vacuum above the throttle plates, fuel will flow from the main fuel system as well as from the idle fuel system. This provides the extremely rich fuel mixture necessary for cold engine operation.

The carburetor choke shaft is linked to a thermostatic choke control mechanism mounted on the main body (Fig. 4).

The linkage between the choke lever and the throttle shaft is designed so that the choke plate will partially open when the accelerator pedal is fully depressed. This permits unloading of a flooded engine.

The automatic choke is equipped with a bimetal thermostatic spring and a vacuum piston (Fig. 4). The bimetal thermostatic spring mechanism winds up when cold and unwinds when warm. When the engine is cold, the thermostatic spring, through attaching linkage, holds the choke piston upward and the choke plate in a closed position prior to engine start. Manifold vacuum channeled through a passage in the choke control housing draws the choke vacuum piston downward, exerting an opening force on the choke plate.

When the engine is started, manifold vacuum, acting directly on the piston located in the choke housing, immediately moves the choke plate against the tension of the thermostatic spring to a partially open position to prevent stalling.

As the engine continues to operate, manifold vacuum draws heated air from the exhaust manifold heat chamber. The amount of air entering the choke housing is controlled by restrictions in the air passages in the carburetor.

The warmed air enters the choke housing and heats the thermostatic spring, causing it to unwind. The tension of the thermostatic spring gradually decreases as the temperature of the air from the heat chamber rises, allowing the choke plate to open. The air is exhausted into the intake manifold.

When the engine reaches its normal operating temperature, the thermostatic spring exerts tension on the choke plate forcing it to the full open position. In this position, the

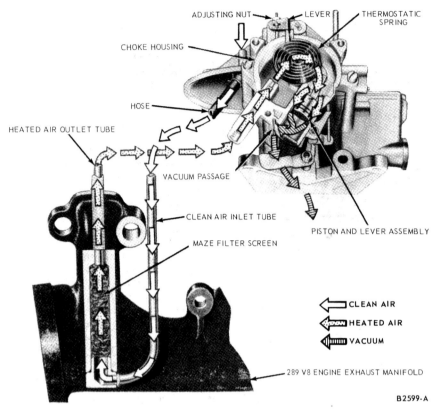

CLEAN AIR
HEATED AIR
VACUUM

289 V8 ENGINE EXHAUST MANIFOLD

B2599-A

FIG. 4—Automatic Choke System

choke piston is at its lowest point in the cylinder. Slots in the piston chamber wall allow sufficient air to bleed past the piston and into the intake manifold, causing a continual flow of warm air to pass through the thermostatic spring housing. The spring remains heated and the choke plate remains fully open until the engine is stopped and allowed to cool.

The choke rod actuates the fast idle cam during choking. Steps on the edge of the fast idle cam contact the fast idle adjusting screw. This permits a faster engine idle speed for smoother running when the engine is cold. As the choke plate is moved through its range of travel from the closed to the open position, the choke rod rotates the fast idle cam. Each step on the fast idle cam permits a slower idle rpm as engine temperature rises and choking is reduced.

During the warm-up period, if the engine should reach the stall point due to a lean mixture, manifold vacuum will drop considerably. The tension of the thermostatic spring then overcomes the lowered vacuum acting on the choke piston and the choke plate is moved toward the closed position, providing a richer mixture to help prevent stalling.

The linkage between the choke lever and the throttle shaft is designed

so that the choke plate will partially open when the accelerator pedal is

fully depressed. This permits unloading of a flooded engine.

IDLE FUEL SYSTEM

The difference in pressure between the fuel bowl and the idle discharge port forces fuel through the idle fuel system. Fuel flows from the fuel bowl through the main jet and into the bottom of the main well (Fig. 5).

From the main well, the fuel flows up through the idle tube and through a short diagonal passage in the booster venturi assembly into the idle passage in the main body. A calibrated restriction, at the upper tip of the idle tube, meters the flow of fuel.

Air enters the idle system from the air bleed, located directly above the idle tube. The air bleed also acts as a vent to prevent siphoning at off idle or high speeds and when the engine is stopped. Additional air is bled into the system through an air bleed located at the bottom of the diagonal passage in the booster venturi where the fuel enters the idle passage in the main body.

Fuel flows down the idle passage in the main body past three idle transfer holes. The idle transfer holes act as additional air bleeds at curb idle. The fuel then flows past the pointed tip of the adjusting needle which controls

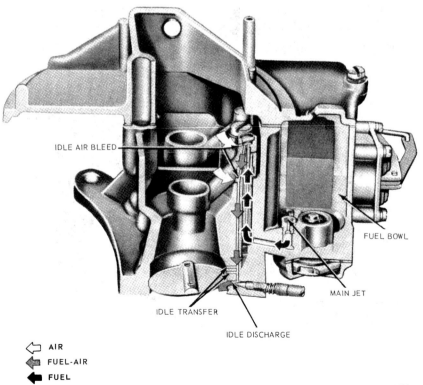

AIR
FUEL-AIR
FUEL

B2600-A

FIG. 5—Idle Fuel System

the idle fuel discharge. From the adjusting needle chamber, the fuel flows through a short horizontal passage and is discharged below the throttle plates.

During off idle when the throttle plate is moved slightly past the idle transfer holes, each hole begins discharging fuel as it is exposed to manifold vacuum. As the throttle plate is opened still wider and engine speed increases, the air flow through the carburetor is also increased. This creates a vacuum in the booster venturi strong enough to bring the main fuel system into operation. Fuel flow from the idle fuel system tapers off as the main fuel system begins discharging fuel.

ACCELERATING SYSTEM

Upon acceleration, the air flow through the carburetor responds almost immediately to the increased throttle opening. There is, however, a brief interval before the flowing fuel, which is heavier than air, can gain the required flow speed to maintain the desired balace of fuel and air. During the interval, the accelerating system (Fig. 6) supplies fuel until the other systems can once again provide the proper mixture.

When the throttle is closed, the diaphragm return spring forces the diaphragm toward the cover, drawing fuel into the chamber through the inlet. The inlet has an Elastomer valve which uncovers the inlet hole to admit fuel from the fuel bowl. The valve covers the inlet hole when the accelerating pump is operated to prevent the fuel from returning to the bowl. A discharge weight and ball check prevents air from entering the discharge nozzle when fuel is drawn into the diaphragm chamber.

When the throttle is opened, the diaphragm rod is forced inward, forcing fuel from the chamber into the discharge passage. Fuel under pressure forces the pump discharge weight and ball off their seat and fuel passes through the accelerating pump discharge screw and is sprayed into each main venturi through discharge ports.

An air bleed in the wall of the accelerating pump fuel chamber prevents vapor entrapment and pressure build-up in the diaphragm chamber.

MAIN FUEL SYSTEM

As engine speed increases, the air passing through the booster venturi creates a vacuum. The amount of

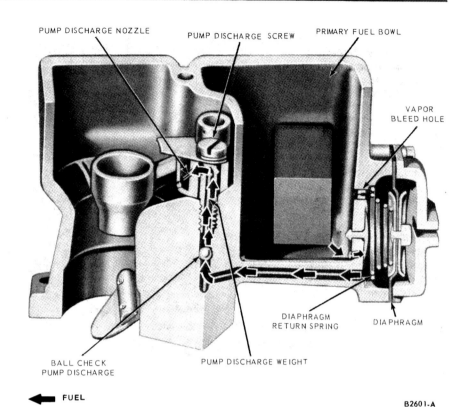

FIG. 6—Accelerating Pump System

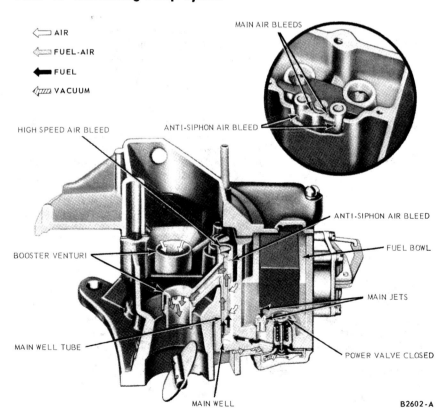

FIG. 7—Main Fuel System

vacuum is determined by the air flow through the venturi, which in turn is

regulated by the speed of the engine. The difference in pressure between the main discharge port and the fuel bowl causes fuel to flow through the main fuel system (Fig. 7).

At a predetermined venturi vacuum, fuel flows from the fuel bowl, through the main jets, and into the bottom of the main well. The fuel moves up the main well tube past air bleed holes. Filtered air from the high speed air bleed enters the fuel flow in the main well tube through holes in the side of the tube. The high speed air bleed meters an increasing amount of air to the fuel as venturi vacuum increases, maintaining the required fuel-air ratio. The mixture of fuel and air is lighter than raw fuel and responds faster to changes in venturi vacuum. It also atomizes more readily than raw fuel. The fuel and air continue up the main well tube past another air bleed which also acts as a vent to prevent siphoning when the engine is shut down. The fuel is discharged into the booster venturi where it is atomized and mixed with air flowing through the carburetor.

The throttle plate controls the amount of the fuel-air mixture admitted to the intake manifold, regulating the speed and power output of the engine.

A balance tube is located in each barrel directly below the booster venturi. When decelerating, the balance tube siphons off any excess fuel droplets remaining around the edge of the booster venturi and discharges the droplets into the equalizing slots in the base of the carburetor where they are mixed with the idle fuel. The balance tube also acts as an additional air bleed during the idle fuel system operation.

POWER FUEL SYSTEM

During periods of increased road loads or high speed operation, the

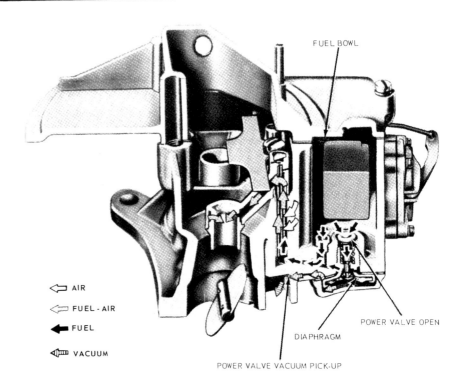

AIR
FUEL - AIR
FUEL
VACUUM

B2603-A

FIG. 8—Power Fuel System

fuel-air ratio must be increased for added power. The added fuel required during this period is supplied by the power fuel system (Fig. 8).

The power fuel system is controlled by the intake manifold vacuum.

Manifold vacuum is transmitted from an opening in the base of the main body, through a passage in the main body and power valve chamber to the power valve diaphragm. The manifold vacuum, acting on the power valve at idle speed or normal road load conditions, is great enough to hold the power valve diaphragm down, overcoming the tension of the

spring on the valve stem and holding the valve closed. When high power operation places a greater load on the engine and manifold vacuum drops below a predetermined value, the spring opens the power valve. Fuel from the fuel bowl flows through the power valve and into passages leading to the main fuel well. Here the fuel is added to the fuel from the main fuel system, enriching the mixture.

As engine power demands are reduced, manifold vacuum increases. The increased vacuum overcomes the tension of the valve stem spring and closes the power valve.

2 REMOVAL AND INSTALLATION

REMOVAL

Flooding, stumble on acceleration and other performance complaints are, in many instances, caused by the presence of dirt, water or other foreign matter in the carburetor. To aid in diagnosing the cause of complaint, the carburetor should be carefully removed from the engine without removing the fuel from the bowls. The contents of the bowls may then be examined for contamination as the carburetor is disassembled.

1. Remove the air cleaner (Part 10-5, Section 2). Remove the choke shield retaining screws and remove the hose and shield from the carburetor assembly.

2. Remove the accelerator linkage from the carburetor throttle lever. Disconnect the distributor vacuum line, in-line fuel filter and the choke heat tube at the carburetor.

3. Disconnect the choke clean air tube from the air horn.

4. Remove the carburetor retain-

ing nuts and lockwashers; then remove the carburetor. Remove the spacer and gaskets from the intake manifold. Discard the gaskets.

INSTALLATION

1. Clean the gasket surface of the intake manifold, spacer and carburetor. Place the spacer between two new gaskets and position them on the intake manifold. Position the carburetor on the spacer.

2. Connect the in-line fuel filter,

accelerator linkage, choke heat tube and distributor vacuum line. Install the carburetor retaining nuts. Tighten the carburetor retaining nuts. Position the heater hose on the choke

shield and install the shield and retaining screws.

3. Connect the choke clean air tube to the air horn.

4. Refer to Part 10-1, Section 2,

Common Adjustments and Repairs, and adjust the engine idle speed, the idle fuel mixture, anti-stall dashpot (if so equipped) and the accelerating pump stroke (if required). Install the air cleaner (Part 10-5, Section 2).

3 MAJOR REPAIR OPERATIONS

DISASSEMBLY

To facilitate working on the carburetor, and to prevent damage to the throttle plates, install carburetor legs on the base. If legs are unavailable, install four bolts (about 2¼ inches long of the correct diameter) and 8 nuts on the carburetor base.

Use a separate container for the component parts of the various assemblies to facilitate cleaning, inspection and assembly.

The following is a step-by-step sequence of operations for completely overhauling the carburetor. However, certain components of the carburetor may be serviced without a complete disassembly of the entire unit. For a complete carburetor overhaul, follow all of the steps. To partially overhaul the carburetor or to install a new gasket kit, follow only the applicable steps.

Refer to Fig. 21 for parts identification.

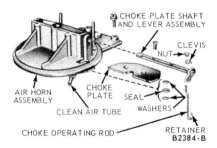

FIG. 9—Air Horn Assembly—Typical

AIR HORN

1. Remove the air cleaner anchor screw.

2. Remove the automatic choke control rod retainer.

3. Remove the air horn retaining screws, lock washers and the carburetor identification tag. Remove the air horn and air horn gasket (Fig. 9).

4. Remove the choke control rod by loosening and turning the choke shaft lever clevis nut counterclockwise. Remove the rod from the air horn. Slide the felt seal and two washers out of the air horn.

If it is necessary to remove the choke plate, remove the staking

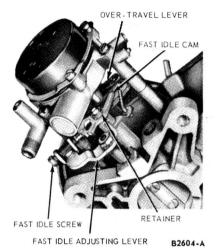

FIG. 10—Fast Idle Cam and Fast Idle Lever

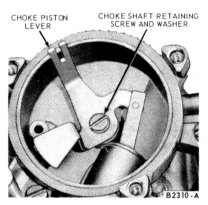

FIG. 11—Choke Shaft and Lever

marks on the choke plate retaining screws and remove the screws. Remove the choke plate by sliding it out of the shaft from the top of the air horn. Slide the choke shaft out of the air horn.

If the tips of the screws are flared excessively, file off the flared portion to prevent damage to the threads in the shaft.

VACUUM PISTON CHOKE

1. Remove the fast idle cam retainer (Fig. 10).

2. Remove the thermostatic choke spring housing retaining screws and remove the clamp, housing and gasket.

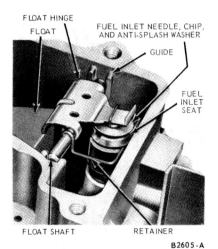

FIG. 12—Float Assembly

3. Remove the choke housing assembly retaining screws. If the air horn was not previously removed, remove the choke control rod retainer. Remove the choke housing assembly, gasket and the fast idle cam. Remove the fast idle cam and rod from the choke fast idle cam lever.

4. Remove the choke lever retaining screw and washer (Fig. 11). Remove the choke piston lever from the housing. If necessary, remove the pin securing the choke piston to the choke lever link. Remove the choke lever and fast idle cam lever from the choke housing.

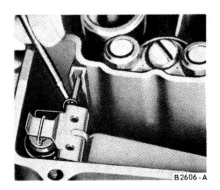

FIG. 13—Float Shaft Retainer Removal or Installation

MAIN BODY

1. With the use of a screwdriver, pry the float shaft retainer from the fuel inlet seat (Figs. 12 and 13). Remove the float, float shaft retainer

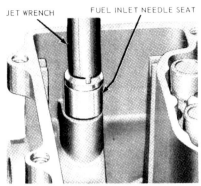

FIG. 14—Fuel Inlet Needle Seat Removal or Installation

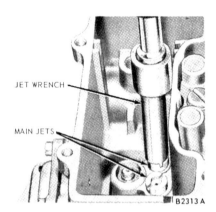

FIG. 15—Main Jet Removal or Installation

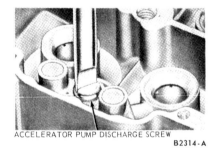

FIG. 16—Booster Venturi Removal or Installation

and fuel inlet needle assembly. Remove the retainer and float shaft from the float lever.

2. Remove the fuel inlet needle, seat, filter screen, and the main jets with a jet wrench (Figs. 14 and 15).

3. Remove the accelerator pump discharge screw, air distribution plate (*if so equipped*), booster venturi and gasket (Fig. 16). Invert the main body and let the accelerating pump discharge weight and ball fall into the hand. Remove the fuel inlet fitting.

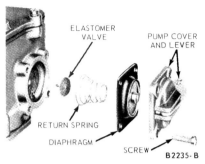

FIG. 17—Accelerating Pump Assembly

4. Remove the accelerator pump operating rod from the over-travel lever and the retainer. **To release the operating rod from the over-travel lever retainer, press the ends of the retainer together; then, at the same time, press the rod away from the retainer until it is disengaged.** Remove the rod and retainer.

5. Remove the accelerating pump cover retaining screws. Remove the accelerating pump cover, diaphragm assembly and spring (Fig. 17).

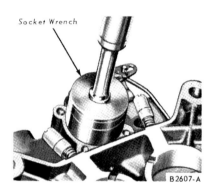

FIG. 18—Power Valve Removal or Installation

6. If it is necessary to remove the Elastomer valve, grasp it firmly and pull it out. If the Elastomer valve tip broke off during removal, be sure to remove the tip from the fuel bowl. **An Elastomer valve must be replaced whenever it has been removed from the carburetor.**

7. Invert the main body and remove the power valve cover and the gasket. Remove the power valve with a box wrench or socket wrench (Fig. 18). Remove the power valve gasket. Discard the gasket.

8. Remove the idle fuel mixture adjusting screws (needles) and the springs.

9. If necessary remove the nut and washer securing the fast idle adjusting lever assembly to the throttle shaft,

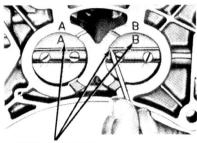

FIG. 19—Throttle Plate Removal

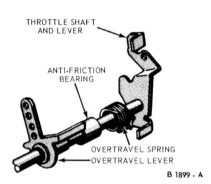

FIG. 20—Throttle Shaft Assembly

and remove the lever assembly (Fig. 10). If necessary, remove the idle screw and the retainer from the fast idle adjusting lever.

10. Remove the anti-stall dashpot, if so equipped.

11. If it is necessary to remove the throttle plates, lightly scribe the throttle plates along the throttle shaft, and mark each plate and its corresponding bore with a number or letter for proper installation (Fig. 19).

12. Slide the throttle shaft out of the main body. Remove the accelerating pump over-travel lever retainer. Slide the anti-friction bearing (bushing), spring and the lever off the throttle shaft (Fig. 20).

PARTS REPAIR OR REPLACEMENT

Clean and inspect the carburetor component parts. Refer to Part 10-1, Section 3 for the proper procedure. Replace all worn or damaged parts.

ASSEMBLY

Make sure all holes in the new gaskets have been properly punched and that no foreign material has adhered to the gaskets. Make sure the accelerating pump diaphragm is not torn or cut.

B2666-A

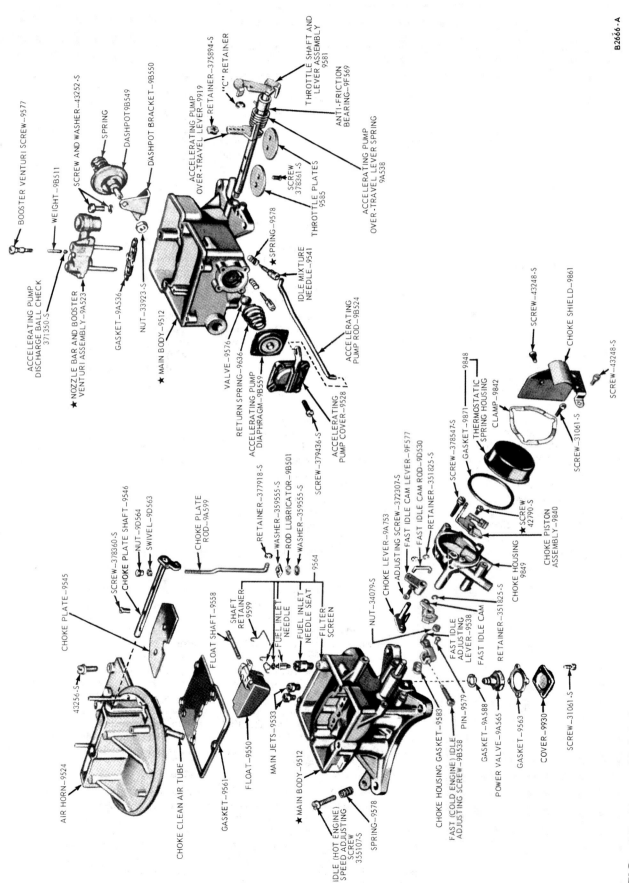

FIG. 21—Disassembled Carburetor

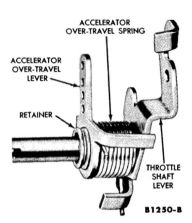

FIG. 22—Accelerator Over-Travel Spring and Lever Installation

The carburetor assembly is shown in Fig. 21.

MAIN BODY

1. If the throttle plates were removed, install the over-travel anti-friction bushing over the boss on the over-travel lever. Place the over-travel spring, with the shortest tang end first, over the bushing and boss on the over-travel lever. Place the short tang of the spring under the lug on the accelerator over-travel lever.

2. Slide the over-travel lever and spring assembly on the throttle shaft and bushing. Hook the longest tang of the spring under the closed throttle lug of the throttle lever (Fig. 22). Install the over-travel lever retainer. Slide the throttle shaft assembly into the main body.

3. Refer to the lines scribed on the throttle plates and install the throttle plates in their proper location with the screws snug, but not tight. Close the throttle plates. Invert the main body, and hold it up to the light. Little or no light should show between the throttle plates and the throttle bores. Tap the plates lightly with a screwdriver handle to seat them. Hold the throttle plates closed and tighten and stake the retaining screws. **When staking the screws, support the shaft and plate on a block of wood or a metal bar to prevent bending of the shaft.**

4. If necessary, install the fast idle screw pin and the screw on the fast idle adjusting lever.

5. Install the anti-stall dashpot, if so equipped.

6. If the fast idle lever was removed place the fast idle lever assembly on the throttle shaft and install the retaining washer and nut (Fig. 10).

7. If the Elastomer valve was removed, lubricate the tip of a new Elastomer valve and insert the tip into the accelerator pump cavity center hole. Using a pair of needle nosed pliers, reach into the fuel bowl and grasp the valve tip. Pull the valve in until it seats in the pump cavity wall and cut off the tip forward of the retaining shoulder. Remove the tip from the bowl.

8. Install the accelerating pump diaphragm return spring on the boss on the chamber (Fig. 17). Insert the diaphragm assembly in the cover and place the cover and diaphragm assembly into position on the main body. Install the cover screws.

9. Insert the accelerating pump operating rod into the inboard hole of the accelerating pump actuating lever. Position the accelerating pump operating rod retainer over the specified hole (Part 10-8) in the over-travel lever to suit the operating and climatic conditions under which the car is to be operated. Press the ends of the retainer together; then, at the same time, insert the operating rod through the retainer and the hole in the over-travel lever. Release the ends of the retainer to secure the rod.

10. Invert the main body. Install the power valve (economizer valve) and new gasket with a wrench (Fig. 18). **Tighten the valve securely.** Install the power valve cover and new gasket.

11. Install the idle mixture adjusting screws (needles) and springs (Fig. 21). Turn the needles in gently with the fingers until they just touch the seat, then back them off the specified (Part 10-8) turns for a preliminary idle fuel mixture adjustment.

12. Install the main jets and the fuel inlet seat, filter screen, and new gasket, using a jet wrench (Figs. 14 and 15). **Be sure the correct jets are installed.**

13. Install the fuel inlet needle assembly in the fuel inlet seat. The fuel inlet needle and seat are matched assemblies. **Be sure the correct needle and seat are assembled together.**

14. Slide the float shaft into the float lever (Fig. 12). Position the float shaft retainer on the float shaft.

15. Insert the float assembly into the fuel bowl and hook the float lever tab under the fuel inlet needle assembly. Insert the float shaft into its guides at the sides of the fuel bowl.

16. With the use of a screwdriver, position the float shaft retainer in the groove on the fuel inlet needle seat (Fig. 13). Refer to Part 10-1, Section 2 and check the dry float setting.

17. Drop the accelerating pump discharge ball into its passage in the main body. Seat the ball with a brass drift and a light hammer. **Make sure the ball is free in the bore.** Drop the accelerating pump discharge weight on top of the ball. Position the new booster venturi gasket and the booster venturi in the main body. Position the air distribution plate, if so equipped, and install the accelerator pump discharge screw (Fig. 16). Tighten the screw.

VACUUM PISTON CHOKE

1. If the choke piston and link was disassembled install the choke piston on the choke thermostatic spring lever link and install the retaining pin (Fig. 23).

2. Position the fast idle cam lever on the thermostatic choke shaft and lever assembly (Fig. 23). **The bottom of the fast idle cam lever adjusting screw must rest against the tang on the choke lever.** Insert the choke shaft assembly into the rear of the choke housing. Position the choke shaft lever so that the hole in the lever is to the left side of the choke housing.

3. Insert the choke piston into the choke housing, and install the choke piston lever on the flange of the choke lever. Install the choke piston lever to choke lever retaining screw and washer (Fig. 11).

4. Install the fast idle cam rod on the fast idle cam lever. Place the fast idle cam on the fast idle cam rod and install the retainer. Place the choke housing vacuum pick-up port to main body gasket on the choke housing flange. Position the choke housing on the main body and, at the same time, install the fast idle cam on the hub on the main body. Position the gasket, and install the choke housing retaining screws. Install the fast idle cam retainer. **The thermostatic spring housing is installed after the choke plate clearance (pull-down) has been adjusted to specification.**

AIR HORN

Refer to Fig. 9 for the correct location of the parts.

1. If the choke plate shaft was removed, position the choke plate shaft in the air horn. Place the choke plate rod seal between the two brass washers and slide them into position on the choke plate rod seal retainer.

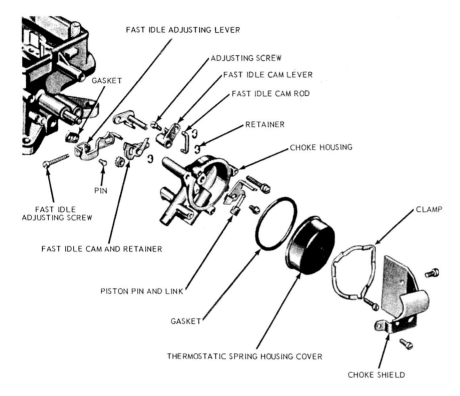

FAST IDLE ADJUSTING LEVER

ADJUSTING SCREW

FAST IDLE CAM LEVER

GASKET

FAST IDLE CAM ROD

RETAINER

CHOKE HOUSING

PIN

CLAMP

FAST IDLE ADJUSTING SCREW

FAST IDLE CAM AND RETAINER

PISTON PIN AND LINK

GASKET

THERMOSTATIC SPRING HOUSING COVER

CHOKE SHIELD

B2608-A

FIG. 23—Choke Housing Assembly

Insert the choke plate rod through the rod seal and the air horn. Insert choke rod into the choke shaft lever clevis and nut, and turn the nut clockwise to thread the rod onto the nut.

2. If the choke plate was removed, insert the choke plate into the choke plate shaft. Install the choke plate screws snug, but not tight. Check for proper plate fit, binding in the air horn and free rotation of the shaft by moving the plate from the closed position to the open position. If necessary, remove the choke plate and grind or file the plate edge where it is binding or scraping on the air horn wall. If the choke plate and shaft moves freely, tighten the choke plate screws while holding the choke in the fully-closed position. Stake the screws. **When staking the screws, support the shaft and plate on a block of wood or a metal bar to prevent bending of the shaft.**

3. Position the air horn gasket on the main body, with the fuel bowl vent hole in the gasket located opposite the fuel inlet.

4. Position the air horn over the main body and insert the end of the choke plate rod into the automatic choke lever. Install the air horn retaining screws and the carburetor identification tag. Tighten the retaining screws. Install the choke plate rod retainer. Install the air cleaner anchor screw.

5. Refer to Part 10-1, Section 2 Common Adjustments and Repairs and perform the automatic choke plate clearance (pull-down) and fast idle cam linkage adjustment. Perform a fuel level float adjustment (wet) after the carburetor has been installed on the car.

PART 10-4

FORD 4-V CARBURETORS

Section	Page
1 Description and Operation	10-46
Description	10-46
Operation	10-46
Fuel Inlet System	10-46
Automatic Choke System	10-47
Manual Choke System	10-49
Idle Fuel System	10-49
Accelerating System	10-50
Primary Stage Main Fuel System	10-50
Power Fuel System	10-51
Secondary Throttle Operation and Main Fuel System	10-51
2 Removal and Installation	10-52

Section	Page
Removal	10-52
Installation	10-53
3 Major Repair Operations	10-53
Disassembly	10-53
Air Horn	10-53
Vacuum Piston Choke	10-54
Main Body	10-54
Parts Repair or Replacement	10-55
Assembly	10-55
Main Body	10-55
Vacuum Piston Choke	10-57
Air Horn	10-58

1 DESCRIPTION AND OPERATION

DESCRIPTION

The Ford 4-V (Venturi) carburetors (Figs. 1, 2, 3, 4, 5) have two main assemblies: the air horn, and the main body.

The air horn assembly, which serves as the main body cover, contains the choke plate, vents for the fuel bowls, secondary throttle control vacuum tube(s) and the automatic choke (if so equipped) clean air pick-up tube. A rubber hose and steel tube connects the clean air pick-up tube to the automatic choke heat chamber in the right exhaust manifold.

The primary and secondary throttle plates, accelerating pump assembly, power valve assembly, secondary operating diaphragm assembly and the fuel bowls are in the main body. On an automatic choke equipped carburetor, the choke housing is attached to the main body. On a manual choke equipped carburetor, the choke cable bracket and the choke cam and lever are attached to the main body.

The two primary (front) barrels each contain a main and booster venturi, main fuel discharge, accelerating pump discharge, idle fuel discharge and a primary throttle plate.

The two secondary (rear) barrels each have a main fuel discharge, and a vacuum operated throttle plate.

OPERATION

FUEL INLET SYSTEM

A separate fuel bowl is provided for the primary and secondary stages (Fig. 6). The fuel enters the primary fuel bowl through the fuel inlet. A drilled passage through the right side of the main body connects the fuel bowls. The pressure in the two fuel bowls is balanced by means of a pressure equalizing chamber built into the left side of the main body. Two baffles in the internal fuel equalizer passages be-

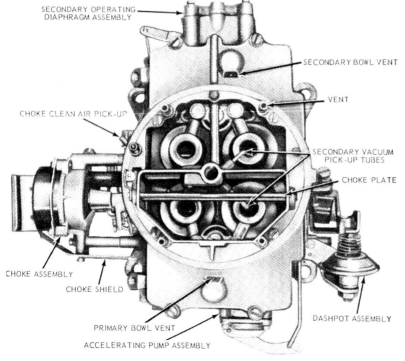

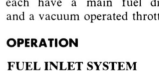

B2667-A

FIG. 1—Top View—Air Horn Installed (Automatic Choke)

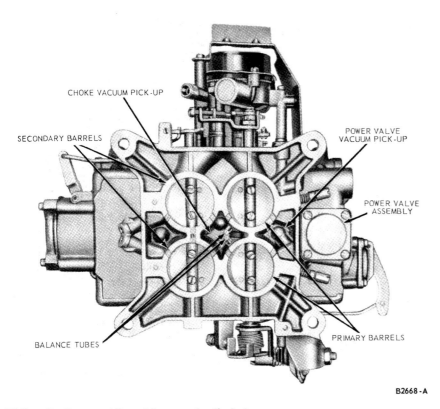

FIG. 2—Bottom View (Automatic Choke)

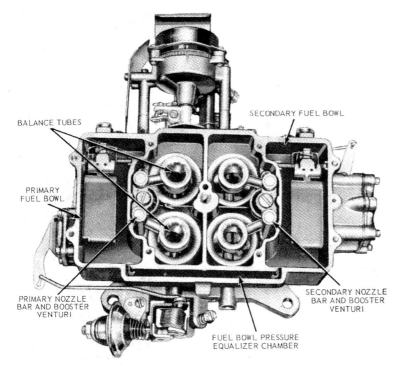

FIG. 3—Top View—Air Horn Removed (Automatic Choke)

tween the primary and secondary fuel bowls permit proper control and

balance of the metering forces within each fuel bowl.

The amount of fuel entering a fuel bowl is regulated by the distance the fuel inlet needle is raised off its seat and by fuel pump pressure. Movement of the fuel inlet needle in relation to the seat is controlled by the float and lever assembly which rises and falls with the fuel level. When the fuel in the fuel bowl reaches a pre-set level, the float lowers the fuel inlet needle to a position where it restricts the flow of fuel, admitting only enough fuel thru the filter screen to replace that being used.

A retracting clip is attached to the fuel inlet needle and hooks over the tab on the end of the lever of the float assembly. This clip assures reaction of the fuel inlet needle to any movement of the float.

A wire-type retainer prevents movement of the float shaft within the guides on each side of the fuel bowl. The retainer fits into a groove on the inlet needle seat. The ends of the retainer are hooked over grooves on opposite end of the float shaft.

The fuel filter screen, located below the inlet needle seat, prevents the entrance of foreign matter.

The primary and secondary fuel bowls are vented externally at all times. In addition, both the primary and secondary fuel bowls are internally vented into the air cleaner. The standpipe pitot tubes in the primary and secondary internal vent tube openings raise the level of the internal vent openings above the external vent openings. This provides the necessary pressure differential for proper evacuation of the gaseous vapors through the external vent during a hot soak period.

An integral anti-splash washer is located on top of each fuel inlet needle.

AUTOMATIC CHOKE SYSTEM

The choke plate, located in the air horn above the primary barrels, when closed, provides a high vacuum above as well as below the throttle plates. With a vacuum above the throttle plates, fuel will flow from the main fuel system as well as from the idle fuel system. This provides the extremely rich fuel mixture necessary for cold engine operation.

The carburetor choke shaft is linked to a thermostatic choke control mechanism mounted on the main body (Fig. 7).

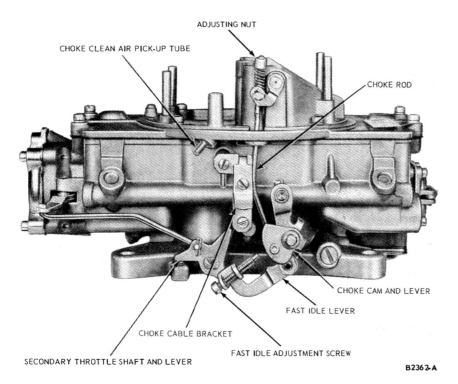

CHOKE CLEAN AIR PICK-UP TUBE
ADJUSTING NUT
CHOKE ROD
CHOKE CAM AND LEVER
FAST IDLE LEVER
CHOKE CABLE BRACKET
FAST IDLE ADJUSTMENT SCREW
SECONDARY THROTTLE SHAFT AND LEVER

B2362-A

FIG. 4—Side View (Manual Choke)

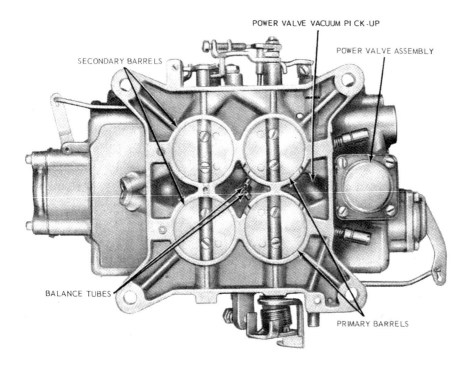

POWER VALVE VACUUM PICK-UP
POWER VALVE ASSEMBLY
SECONDARY BARRELS
BALANCE TUBES
PRIMARY BARRELS

B2670-A

FIG. 5—Bottom View (Manual Choke)

The linkage between the choke lever and the throttle shaft is designed so that the choke plate will partially open when the accelerator pedal is fully depressed. This permits unloading of a flooded engine.

The automatic choke is equipped with a bimetal thermostatic spring and a vacuum piston (Fig. 7). The bimetal thermostatic spring mecha-

nism winds up when cold and unwinds when warm. When the engine is cold, the thermostatic spring, through attaching linkage, holds the choke piston upward and the choke plate in a closed position prior to engine start. Manifold vacuum channeled through a passage in the choke control housing draws the choke vacuum piston downward, exerting an opening force on the choke plate.

When the engine is started, manifold vacuum, acting directly on the piston located in the choke housing, immediately moves the choke plate against the tension of the thermostatic spring to a partially open position to prevent stalling.

As the engine continues to operate, manifold vacuum draws heated air from the exhaust manifold heat chamber. The amount of air entering the choke housing is controlled by restrictions in the air passages in the carburetor.

The warmed air enters the choke housing and heats the thermostatic spring, causing it to unwind. The tension of the thermostatic spring gradually decreases as the temperature of the air from the heat chamber rises, allowing the choke plate to open. The air is exhausted into the intake manifold.

When the engine reaches its normal operating temperature, the thermostatic spring exerts tension on the choke plate forcing it to the full open position. In this position, the choke piston is at its lowest point in the cylinder. Slots in the piston chamber wall allow sufficient air to bleed past the piston and into the intake manifold, causing a continual flow of warm air to pass through the thermostatic spring housing. The spring remains heated and the choke plate remains fully open until the engine is stopped and allowed to cool.

The choke rod actuates the fast idle cam during choking. Steps on the edge of the fast idle cam contact the fast idle adjusting screw. This permits a faster engine idle speed for smoother running when the engine is cold. As the choke plate is moved through its range of travel from the closed to the open position, the choke rod rotates the fast idle cam. Each step on the fast idle cam permits a slower idle rpm as engine temperature rises and choking is reduced.

During the warm-up period, if the engine should reach the stall point due to a lean mixture, manifold vacuum will drop considerably. The ten-

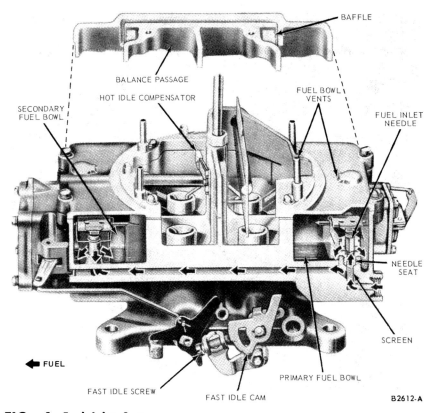

FIG. 6—Fuel Inlet System

Labels on figure:
BAFFLE
BALANCE PASSAGE
HOT IDLE COMPENSATOR
FUEL BOWL VENTS
SECONDARY FUEL BOWL
FUEL INLET NEEDLE
NEEDLE SEAT
FUEL
SCREEN
FAST IDLE SCREW
FAST IDLE CAM
PRIMARY FUEL BOWL
B2612-A

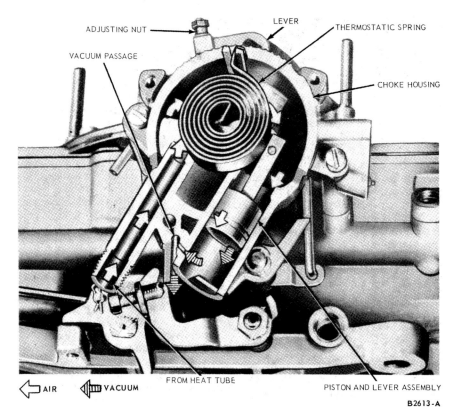

FIG. 7—Automatic Choke System

Labels on figure:
ADJUSTING NUT
LEVER
THERMOSTATIC SPRING
VACUUM PASSAGE
CHOKE HOUSING
AIR
VACUUM
FROM HEAT TUBE
PISTON AND LEVER ASSEMBLY
B2613-A

sion of the thermostatic spring then overcomes the lowered vacuum act-ing on the choke piston and the choke plate is moved toward the

closed position, providing a richer mixture to help prevent stalling.

The linkage between the choke lever and the throttle shaft is designed so that the choke plate will partially open when the accelerator pedal is fully depressed. This permits unloading of a flooded engine.

MANUAL CHOKE SYSTEM

The choke plate, located in the air horn above the primary barrels, when closed, provides a high vacuum above as well below the throttle plates. With a vacuum above the throttle plates, fuel will flow from the main fuel system as well as from the idle fuel system. This provides the extremely rich fuel mixture necessary for cold engine operation.

A rod connects the choke cam and lever to the choke shaft through a swivel, spring and spring tension adjusting nut (Fig. 4).

When the choke cam and lever is pulled to a full choke position by the choke cable, the choke (pull-down) rod actuates the choke shaft and plate through the spring and adjusting nut and rotates the choke shaft and plate to the closed position.

As soon as the engine starts, engine vacuum will open the choke plate, against pull-down spring tension, to the pre-determined setting (pull-down clearance) that was present with a gauge during the initial adjustment. This prevents engine stalls and flooding.

The fast idle speed adjusting screw bears against the bottom of the choke cam during idle or closed throttle conditions. The fast idle speed screw is adjusted to a pre-determined setting (fast idle rpm) which opens the throttle slightly for smoother engine running when the engine is cold and as the manual choke position is selected.

IDLE FUEL SYSTEM

The difference in pressure between the fuel bowls and the idle discharge ports forces fuel through the primary and secondary stage idle fuel systems.

Primary Stage

Fuel flows from the primary stage fuel bowl through the main jet and into the bottom of the main well (Fig. 8).

From the main well, the fuel flows up through the idle tube and through a short diagonal passage in the booster venturi assembly into the idle passage in the main body. A calibrated restriction, at the upper tip of the idle tube, meters the flow of fuel.

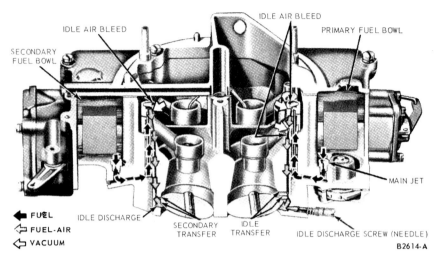

FIG. 8—Idle Fuel System

Air enters the idle system from the air bleed, located directly above the idle tube. The air bleed also acts as a vent to prevent siphoning at off-idle or high speeds and when the engine is stopped. The fuel and air pass down a diagonal passage in the booster venturi and through a calibrated restrictor. Additional air is bled into the system through an air bleed, located at the bottom of the diagonal passage where the fuel enters the idle passage in the main body.

Fuel flows down the idle passage in the main body past two idle transfer holes. The idle transfer holes act as additional air bleeds at curb idle. The fuel then flows past the pointed tip of the adjusting needle which controls the idle fuel discharge in the primary stage. From the adjusting needle chamber, the fuel flows through a short horizontal passage and is discharged below the primary throttle plates.

During off-idle when the primary throttle plate is moved slightly past the idle transfer holes, each hole begins discharging fuel as it is exposed to manifold vacuum. As the primary throttle plate is opened still wider and engine speed increases, the air flow through the carburetor is also increased. This creates a vacuum in the booster venturi strong enough to bring the primary stage main fuel system into operation. Fuel flow from the primary idle fuel system *begins* tapering off as the main fuel system begins discharging fuel.

Hot Idle Compensator System

On a 289-V8 engine with a Thermactor exhaust emission system and the 352 and 390-V8 engines, a thermostatically controlled hot idle com-

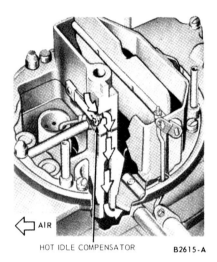

FIG. 9—Hot Idle Compensator System

pensator is located on the air horn above the secondary booster venturis (Fig. 9). At carburetor high inlet air temperatures, the hot idle compensator will open and allow air to bypass the throttle plates through a passage in the air horn and main body and enter the intake manifold. This improves idle stability and minimizes the effect of fuel vaporization which results in excessively rich idle mixtures.

Secondary Stage

Fuel flows from the secondary stage fuel bowl through the main jet and into the bottom of the main well (Fig. 8).

From the main well, the fuel flows up through the idle tube and through a short diagonal passage in the booster venturi assembly and then into the idle passage in the main body. A calibrated restriction,

at the upper tip of the tube, meters the flow of fuel.

Fuel flows down the idle passage in the main body, past two transfer holes above the closed throttle plate, and flows through a metered restriction into a short horizontal passage where it is discharged into the secondary barrel below the closed throttle plate. The transfer holes act as air bleeds at idle. The secondary idle fuel system continues discharging fuel until the secondary main fuel system comes into operation.

Air is introduced into the secondary stage idle fuel system from the idle air bleed, located directly above the idle tube. The air bleed also acts as a vent to prevent siphoning in the idle fuel system at high speeds and when the engine is stopped.

ACCELERATING SYSTEM

Upon acceleration, the air flow through the carburetor responds almost immediately to the increased throttle opening. There is, however, a brief interval before the flowing fuel, which is heavier than air, can gain speed to maintain the desired balance of fuel and air. During this interval, the accelerating system (Fig. 10) supplies fuel until the other systems can once again provide the proper mixture.

When the throttle is closed, the diaphragm return spring forces the diaphragm toward the cover, drawing fuel into the chamber through the inlet. The inlet has an Elastomer valve which uncovers the inlet hole to admit fuel from the fuel bowl. The valve covers the inlet hole when the accelerating pump is operated to prevent the fuel from returning to the bowl. A discharge weight and ball check prevents air from entering from the discharge nozzle when fuel is drawn into the diaphragm chamber.

When the throttle is opened, the diaphragm rod is forced inward, forcing fuel from the chamber into the discharge passage. Fuel under pressure forces the pump discharge weight and ball off their seat and fuel passes through the accelerating pump discharge screw and is sprayed into each main venturi through discharge ports.

An air bleed in the wall of the accelerating pump fuel chamber prevents vapor entrapment and pressure build-up in the diaphragm chamber.

PRIMARY STAGE MAIN FUEL SYSTEM

As engine speed increases, the air

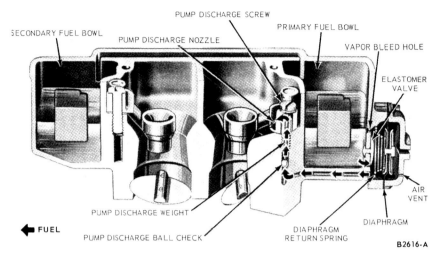

SECONDARY FUEL BOWL
PUMP DISCHARGE NOZZLE
PUMP DISCHARGE SCREW
PRIMARY FUEL BOWL
VAPOR BLEED HOLE
ELASTOMER VALVE
AIR VENT
DIAPHRAGM
DIAPHRAGM RETURN SPRING
PUMP DISCHARGE BALL CHECK
PUMP DISCHARGE WEIGHT
FUEL
B 2616-A

FIG. 10—Accelerating System

passing through the booster venturi creates a vacuum. The amount of vacuum is determined by the air flow through the venturi, which in turn is regulated by the speed of the engine. The difference in pressure between the main discharge port and the fuel bowl causes fuel to flow through main fuel system (Fig. 11).

At a predetermined venturi vacuum, fuel flows from the primary fuel bowl, through the main jets, and into the bottom of the main well.

The fuel moves up the main well tube past air bleed holes. Filtered air from the high speed air bleed enters the fuel flow in the main well tube through holes in the side of the tube. The high speed air bleed meters an increasing amount of air to the fuel as venturi vacuum increases, maintaining the required fuel-air ratio. The mixture of fuel and air is lighter than raw fuel and responds faster to changes in venturi vacuum. It also atomizes more readily than raw

fuel. The fuel and air continue up the main well tube past another air bleed which also acts as a vent to prevent siphoning when the engine is shut down. The fuel is discharged into the booster venturi where it is atomized and mixed with the air flowing through the carburetor.

The throttle plate controls the amount of the fuel-air mixture admitted to the intake manifold, regulating the speed and power output of the engine.

A balance tube is located in each primary barrel directly below the booster venturi. When decelerating, the balance tube siphons off any excess fuel droplets remaining around the edge of the booster venturi and discharges the droplets into the equalizing slots in the base of the carburetor where they are mixed with the idle fuel. The balance tube also acts as an additional air bleed during the idle fuel system operation.

POWER FUEL SYSTEM

During periods of increased road loads or high speed operation, the fuel-air ratio must be increased for added power. The added fuel required during this period is supplied by the power fuel system (Fig. 12).

The power fuel system is controlled by manifold vacuum.

Manifold vacuum is transmitted from an opening in the base of the main body, through a passage in the main body and power valve chamber to the power valve diaphragm. The manifold vacuum, acting on the power valve at idle speed or normal road load conditions, is great enough to hold the power valve diaphragm down, overcoming the tension of the spring on the valve stem and holding the valve closed. When high power operation places a greater load on the engine and manifold vacuum drops below a predetermined value, the spring opens the power valve. Fuel from the primary fuel bowl flows through the power valve and into passages leading to both primary stage main fuel wells. Here the fuel is added to the fuel from the primary stage main fuel system, enriching the mixture.

As engine power demands are reduced, manifold vacuum increases. The increased vacuum overcomes the tension of the valve stem spring and closes the power valve.

SECONDARY THROTTLE OPERATION AND MAIN FUEL SYSTEM

To provide sufficient fuel-air mix-

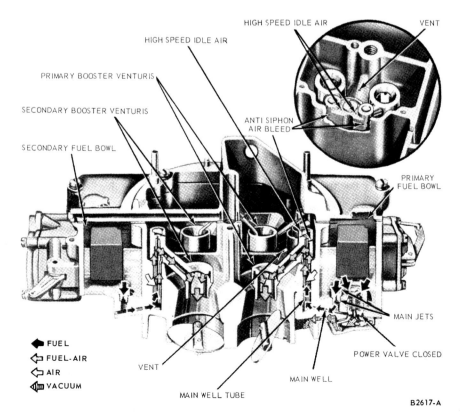

HIGH SPEED IDLE AIR
VENT
HIGH SPEED IDLE AIR
PRIMARY BOOSTER VENTURIS
SECONDARY BOOSTER VENTURIS
ANTI SIPHON AIR BLEED
SECONDARY FUEL BOWL
PRIMARY FUEL BOWL
FUEL
FUEL-AIR
AIR
VACUUM
VENT
MAIN JETS
POWER VALVE CLOSED
MAIN WELL
MAIN WELL TUBE
B2617-A

FIG. 11—Primary Stage Main Fuel System

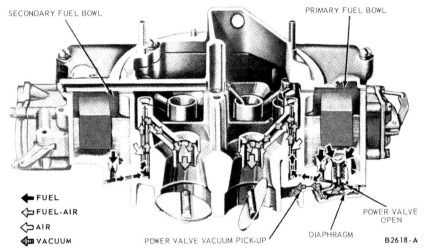

FIG. 12—Power Fuel System

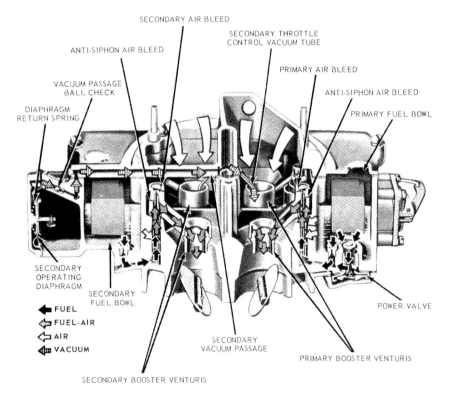

FIG. 13—Secondary Stage Main Fuel System

ture to operate the engine at maximum power, the mixture supplied by the primary stage is supplemented by an additional quantity of fuel-air mixture from the secondary stage (Fig. 13).

This additional supply of fuel-air mixture is delivered through the two secondary (rear) barrels of the carburetor. The secondary stage throttle plates are operated by a spring-loaded vacuum diaphragm assembly attached to the main body and linked to the secondary throttle shaft.

Opening of the secondary throttle plates is controlled by vacuum from the booster venturi. The vacuum is transmitted from the secondary throttle control vacuum tube(s) through passages in the air horn, main body, and behind the secondary operating diaphragm. **A single secondary throttle control vacuum tube, located in the primary booster venturi, is used on the carburetor for Fairlane and Comet 390 V-8 engines.**

As the primary throttle plates are opened, primary venturi vacuum increases. When the vacuum reaches a predetermined amount, it starts to act on the secondary stage operating diaphragm, which in turn starts to open the secondary throttle plates.

A ball check, located in the vacuum passage in the diaphragm housing, controls the rate at which the secondary throttle plates are allowed to open. Any rapid increase in vacuum which would tend to open the secondary throttle plates too suddenly holds the ball check against its seat. The opening of the secondary throttle plates is slowed to a rate governed by the amount of vacuum passing through a bleed in the ball seat.

As the secondary throttle plates begin to open, fuel flows from the secondary fuel bowl through the secondary main jets into the bottom of the main well and up the main well tube past air bleed holes. Air is introduced through an air bleed at the top of the tube. When the secondary throttle plates are moved slightly past the secondary transfer holes, each hole begins discharging fuel as it is exposed to manifold vacuum. As secondary venturi vacuum is increased, the fuel is discharged into the secondary booster venturi. Fuel from the transfer holes tapers off and the holes act as additional air bleeds.

When decelerating, vacuum in the primary venturi decreases and the secondary throttle plates begin to close. The ball check in the diaphragm housing passage will unseat when the throttle is closed quickly, allowing the low pressure on the vacuum side of the diaphragm to rapidly return to atmospheric pressure. As the vacuum acting on the diaphragm is lessened, the load on the diaphragm spring will start closing the secondary plates.

2 REMOVAL AND INSTALLATION

REMOVAL

Flooding, stumble on acceleration, and other performance complaints are, in many instances, caused by the presence of dirt, water, or other foreign matter in the carburetor. To aid in diagnosing the cause of a complaint, the carburetor should be carefully removed from the engine without removing the fuel from the bowls. The contents of the bowls may then be examined for contamination as the carburetor is disassembled.

1. Remove the air cleaner assembly (Part 10-5, Section 2).

2. Disconnect the throttle rod, in-line fuel filter and the distributor vacuum line (if so equipped) from the carburetor.

3. On an automatic choke equipped carburetor, disconnect the choke clean air tube and the choke heat tube from the carburetor. Remove the bracket that secures the heater hose to the automatic choke.

On a manual choke equipped carburetor, loosen the retaining clip securing the choke cable housing to the carburetor. Loosen the retaining screw securing the choke cable to the clevis on the fast idle cam lever. Remove the choke cable assembly from the carburetor.

4. Remove the carburetor retaining nuts and lock washers; then remove the carburetor. Remove the spacer gasket from the spacer and discard the gasket. **Whenever the carburetor is removed from the engine, care must be exercised to prevent damage to the throttle plates. The lower edges of the throttle plates project below the carburetor body whenever they are open.**

5. Disconnect the crankcase ventilation system hose from the carburetor spacer, if required. Remove the spacer and gaskets. Discard the gaskets.

INSTALLATION

1. Clean the gasket surface of the intake manifold, spacer and carburetor. Place a new gasket above and below the spacer and install the spacer. Connect the crankcase ventilation system hose to the spacer, if required. Position the carburetor on the spacer.

2. Connect the throttle rod, in-line fuel filter and the distributor vacuum line (if so equipped) to the carburetor. To prevent leakage, distortion or damage to the carburetor body flange, snug the nuts; then, alternately tighten each nut in a crisscross pattern to the specified torque. Connect the throttle conrol rod.

3. On an automatic choke equipped carburetor, connect the choke clean air tube and the choke heat tube to the carburetor.

On a manual choke equipped carburetor, install the manual choke cable assembly on the retaining clip on the carburetor. Connect the choke cable to the clevis on the choke lever clevis. Refer to Common Adjustments and Repairs (Part 10-1, Section 2) and adjust the choke cable linkage.

4. Start the engine and check for leaks. Refer to Common Adjustments and Repairs (Part 10-1, Section 2) and adjust the accelerating pump stroke (if necessary), the idle fuel mixture and idle speed, and the anti-stall dashpot (if so equipped). Install the air cleaner (Part 10-5, Section 2).

3 MAJOR REPAIR OPERATIONS

DISASSEMBLY

To facilitate working on the carburetor and to prevent damage to the throttle plates, install carburetor legs on the base. If legs are unavailable, install 4 bolts (about 2¼ inches long of the correct diameter) and 8 nuts on the carburetor base.

Use a separate container for the component parts of the various assemblies to facilitate cleaning, inspection and assembly.

For a complete carburetor overhaul, follow all the steps. To partially overhaul the carburetor or to install a new gasket kit, follow only the applicable steps. Refer to Fig. 27 for parts identification.

AIR HORN

1. Remove the air cleaner anchor screw.

2. On an automatic choke equipped carburetor, remove the choke plate operating rod to choke lever retainer (Fig. 14).

On a manual choke equipped carburetor, remove the retainer securing the choke cam and lever to the choke lever shaft on the main body. Remove the flat washer and the choke cam and lever from the car-

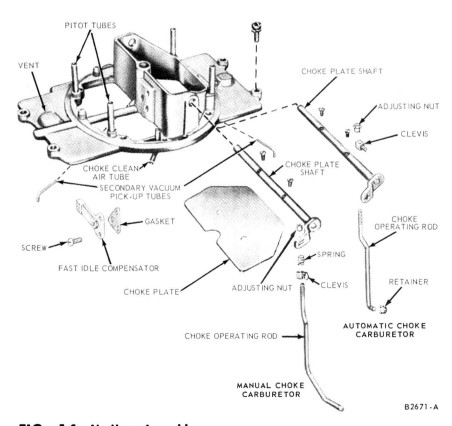

FIG. 14—Air Horn Assembly

buretor.

3. Remove the air horn retaining screws and lock washers and the identification tag. Remove the air horn and air horn gasket.

4. If necessary, remove the choke plate actuating rod, seal and washers as follows:

On an automatic choke equipped carburetor, remove the choke plate rod by loosening and turning the choke shaft lever clevis nut counterclockwise. Remove the choke rod. Remove the upper and lower seal washers and the seal from the choke rod seal retainer in the air horn.

On a manual choke equipped carburetor, unscrew the plastic nut from the choke rod and remove the choke rod spring (Fig. 14). Remove the swivel from the choke lever. Remove the choke rod. Remove the upper and lower seal washers and the seal from the choke rod seal retainer in the air horn.

5. If it is necessary to remove the choke plate or choke shaft, remove the staking marks on the choke plate retaining screws and remove the screws. **If the tips of the screws are flared excessively, file off the flared portion to prevent damage to the threads of the shaft.** Remove the choke plate by sliding it out of the shaft, from the top of the air horn. Slide the choke shaft out of the air horn.

6. If it necessary to remove the secondary throttle control vacuum tube(s), pry them out with needle nose pliers. Discard the tube(s) after removal.

VACUUM PISTON CHOKE

1. Remove the fast idle cam retainer (Fig. 15).

2. Remove the thermostatic choke spring housing retaining screws, and remove the clamp, housing and gasket (Fig. 15).

3. Remove the choke housing assembly retaining screws. If the air horn was not previously removed, remove the choke control rod retainer. Remove the choke housing assembly, gasket and the fast idle cam. Remove the fast idle cam and rod from the fast idle cam lever.

4. Remove the choke lever retaining screw and washer (Fig. 16). Remove the choke piston lever from the housing. If necessary, remove the pin securing the choke piston to the choke lever link. Remove the choke lever and fast idle cam lever from the choke housing.

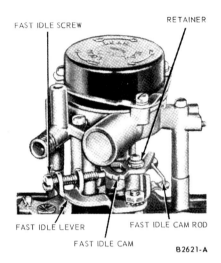

FIG. 15—Fast Idle Cam and Fast Idle Lever

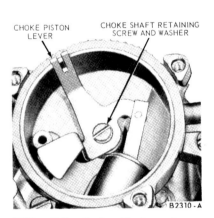

FIG. 16—Choke Shaft and Piston Lever

MAIN BODY

1. With the use of a screwdriver, pry the float shaft retainer from the fuel inlet seat in each fuel bowl (Figs. 17 and 18). Remove the floats, float shaft retainers and fuel inlet needle assemblies. Remove the retainer and float shaft from each float lever.

2. Using a jet wrench, remove the fuel inlet needle seat, gasket and filter screen from each fuel bowl (Fig. 19).

3. Remove the primary stage and secondary stage main jets (Fig. 20).

4. Remove the air distribution plate (if so equipped) primary stage booster venturi assembly and gasket (Fig. 21). Invert the main body and let the accelerating pump discharge weight and ball fall into the hand.

5. Remove the secondary stage booster venturi assembly and gasket.

6. Remove the accelerating pump

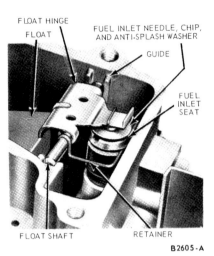

FIG. 17—Float Assembly

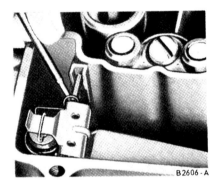

FIG. 18—Float Shaft Retainer Removal or Installation

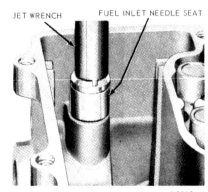

FIG. 19—Fuel Inlet Needle Seat Removal or Installation

operating rod retainer. To release the rod from the retainer clip, press the tab ends of the clip together; then, at the same time, press the rod away from the clip until it is disengaged. Remove the rod. Remove the accelerating pump cover, diaphragm assembly and spring (Fig. 22).

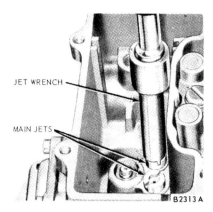

FIG. 20—Main Jet Removal or Installation

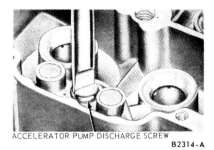

FIG. 21—Booster Venturi Removal or Installation

If it is necessary to remove the Elastomer valve, grasp it firmly and pull it out. If the Elastomer valve tip broke off during removal, be sure to remove the tip from the fuel bowl. **An Elastomer valve must be replaced whenever it is removed from the main body.**

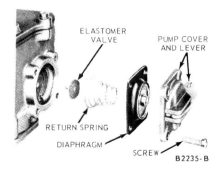

FIG. 22—Accelerating Pump Assembly

7. Remove the secondary diaphragm operating rod retainer and remove the rod. Remove the diaphragm cover, return spring, and diaphragm (Fig. 23). Invert the main body and let the secondary ball check fall into the hand.

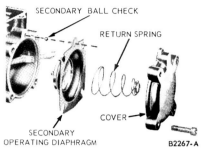

FIG. 23—Secondary Diaphragm Assembly

8. Invert the main body and remove the power valve cover and gasket. Using a socket wrench or box wrench, remove the power valve and gasket (Fig. 24).

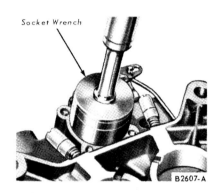

FIG. 24—Power Valve Removal or Installation

9. Remove the idle fuel mixture adjusting screws (needles) and springs.
10. Remove the anti-stall dashpot, if so equipped.
11. If necessary, remove the idle (hot engine) adjusting screw and spring, and the nut and washer securing the fast idle adjusting lever assembly to the primary throttle shaft (Fig. 13). Remove the lever assembly.
12. If it is necessary to remove the throttle plates, lightly scribe the primary and secondary throttle plates along the throttle shafts, and mark each plate and its corresponding bore with a number or letter for proper installation (Fig. 25). Remove the staking marks on the throttle plate retaining screws and remove the screws. **If the tips of the screws are flared excessively, file off the flared portion to prevent damage to the threads of the shaft(s). Do not scratch the edge of the plates or walls of the barrels.** Remove the screws and the throttle plates.
Slide the primary and secondary

FIG. 25—Throttle Plate Removal

throttle shafts out of the main body.
Remove the accelerating pump over-travel lever retainer (Fig. 26) and slide the anti-friction bearing, spring and level off the primary throttle shaft.

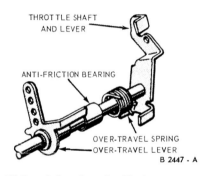

FIG. 26—Throttle Shaft Assembly

PARTS REPAIR OR REPLACEMENT

Clean and inspect the carburetor component parts. Refer to Cleaning and Inspection (Part 10-1, Section 3) for the proper procedure. Replace all worn or damaged parts.

ASSEMBLY

Make sure all holes in the new gaskets have been properly punched and that no foreign material has adhered to the gaskets. Make sure the accelerating pump diaphragm and secondary operating diaphragm are not torn or cut. The carburetor assembly is shown in Fig. 27.

MAIN BODY

1. If the throttle plates were removed, install the accelerator over-travel spring anti-friction bearing on the accelerator over-travel lever boss. Place the accelerator over-travel

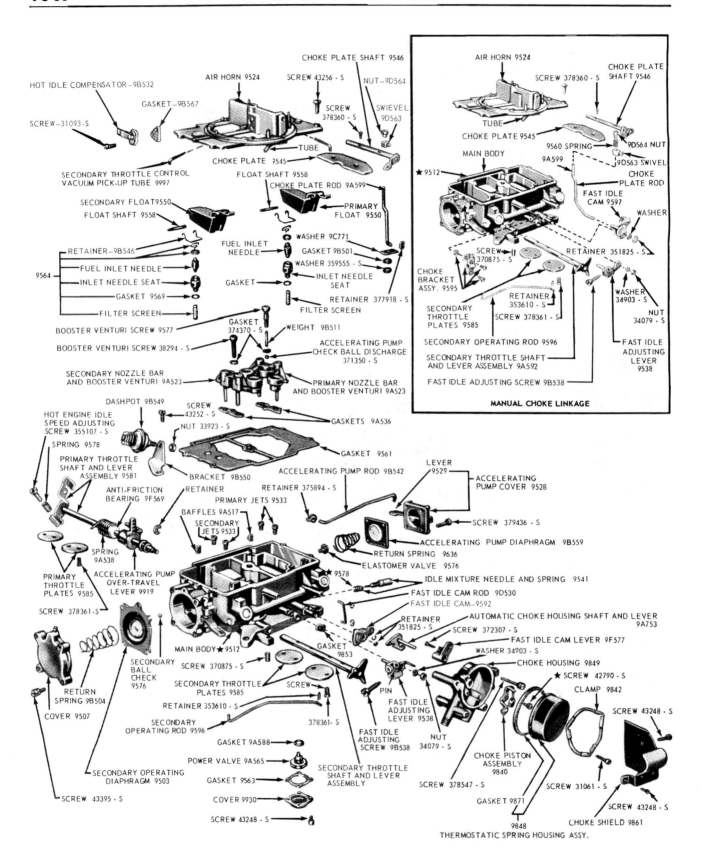

FIG. 27—Carburetor Assemblies

spring, with the shortest tang end first, over the bearing on the over-travel lever (Figs. 26 and 28). Place the short tang of the spring under the lug on the over-travel lever. Slide the over-travel lever spring and bearing assembly on the primary throttle shaft. Hook the longest tang of the spring under the closed throttle lug of the throttle lever. Install the over-travel lever retainer. Slide the primary throttle shaft assembly into the main body.

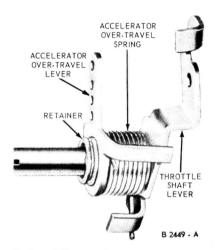

FIG. 28—Accelerator Over-Travel Spring and Lever Installation

Refer to the lines and identification marks scribed on the throttle plates (Fig. 25), and install the primary throttle plates in their proper location with the screws snug, but not tight. Invert the main body and hold it up to the light. Little or no light should show between the throttle plates and the throttle bores. Tap the plates lightly with a screwdriver handle to seat them. Tighten and stake the screws.

Slide the secondary throttle shaft into the main body. Refer to the lines scribed on the secondary throttle plates and install the throttle plates in their proper location. To install the plates, follow the procedure given for the primary throttle plates.

Adjust the secondary throttle plates. Refer to Secondary Throttle Plate Adjustment (Part 10-1, Section 2) for the proper procedure.

2. Install the idle (hot engine) adjusting screw and spring.

3. If the fast idle lever was removed, place the fast idle lever assembly on the primary throttle shaft, and install the retaining washer and

nut (Fig. 15). On an automatic choke equipped carburetor, do not install the fast idle cam or retainer at this time.

4. Install the anti-stall dashpot, if so equipped.

5. If the Elastomer valve was removed, lubricate the tip of a new Elastomer valve and insert the tip into the accelerator pump cavity center hole (Fig. 22). Using a pair of needle nosed pliers, reach into the fuel bowl and grasp the valve tip. Pull the valve in until it seats and cut off the tip forward of the retaining shoulder. Remove the tip from the bowl. Position the diaphragm return spring on the boss in the chamber.

6. Position the accelerator pump diaphragm assembly to the cover and place the cover and diaphragm assembly in position on the return spring and main body. Install the cover screws finger-tight. Push the accelerating pump plunger the full distance of its travel and tighten the cover screws.

7. Install the accelerating pump operating rod. Refer to Accelerating Pump Adjustments (Part 10-1, Section 2) and adjust the accelerating pump stroke.

8. Invert the main body. Using a socket wrench or box wrench, install the power valve and new gasket (Fig. 24). **Tighten the power valve securely.** Install the cover and new gasket.

9. Install the idle mixture adjusting screws (needles) and springs. Turn the needles in gently with the fingers until they just touch the seat; then back them off the specified number of turns (Part 10-8) for a preliminary idle adjustment.

10. Drop the secondary discharge ball check into the passage in the main body (Fig. 23).

11. Install the secondary operating diaphragm and Palnut (if so equipped) on the secondary operating lever. Install the diaphragm return spring on the cover. Install the cover with the screws finger-tight. With the diaphragm in the extended position, tighten the cover screws. Install the secondary operating rod in the operating lever, and secure the rod to the secondary throttle shaft with the retaining clip.

Check the operation and seal of the secondary vacuum system by opening the primary and secondary throttle plates. Hold the secondary throttle plates open. Place a finger

over the secondary vacuum inlet hole in the main body and release the secondary throttle plates. This is a check for vacuum leakage at the diaphragm. The throttle plates should not close fully. They will move slightly when released, but they must stop and should not move toward the closed position after the initial movement. Replace the diaphragm or tighten the cover screws as necessary to correct the vacuum leakage.

12. Using a jet wrench, install the primary and secondary main jets (Fig. 20). **Be sure the correct jets are installed for the primary and secondary systems (Part 10-8).**

13. Install the primary and secondary fuel inlet filters in the inlet valve seat mounting bores. Install the valve seats and gaskets (Fig. 19). Install the fuel inlet needle valves (Fig. 15).

14. Slide the primary float shaft into the float lever (Fig. 17). Position the float shaft retainer on the float shaft.

Insert the float assembly into the fuel bowl and hook the float lever tab under the fuel inlet needle clip. Insert the float shaft into its guides at the sides of the fuel bowl.

With the use of a screwdriver, position the float shaft retainer on the goove of the fuel inlet needle seat (Figs. 17 and 18).

15. Repeat step 14 on the secondary stage fuel bowl.

16. Refer to Part 10-1, Section 2, Float Adjustment (Dry) and perform a dry float fuel level adjustment on the primary and secondary floats.

17. Drop the accelerating pump discharge ball into its passage in the primary side of the main body. Seat the ball with a brass drift and a light hammer. **Make sure the ball is free.** Drop the accelerating pump discharge weight on top of the ball. Position the primary booster venturi assembly and gasket in the main body. Install the air distribution plate (if so equipped) and retaining screw. Tighten the retaining screw securely (Fig. 21). **The primary booster screw is hollow.**

18. Position the secondary booster venturi assembly and gasket in the main body, and install the gasket and retaining screw.

VACUUM PISTON CHOKE

1. If the choke piston and link was disassembled, install the choke piston on the choke thermostatic spring lever link and install the retaining pin (Fig. 29).

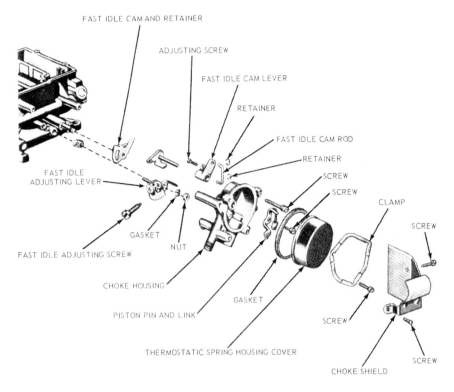

FIG. 29—Choke Housing Assembly

2. Position the fast idle cam lever on the thermostatic choke shaft and lever assembly (Figs. 29 and 30). **The bottom of the fast idle lever adjusting screw must rest against the tang on the choke shaft lever.** Insert the choke shaft assembly into the rear of the choke housing. Position the choke shaft lever so that the hole in the lever is to the left side of the choke housing (Fig. 30).

3. Insert the choke piston into the choke housing. Position the choke thermostatic spring lever on the flange of the choke shaft, and install the retaining screw and washer (Fig. 14).

4. Install the fast idle cam rod on the fast idle cam lever (Fig. 30). Place the fast idle cam on the fast idle cam rod and install the retainer.

Place the choke housing vacuum pick-up port to main body gasket on the choke housing flange. Position the choke housing on the main body, and, at the same time, install the fast idle cam on the hub of the main body. Position the gasket and install the choke housing retaining screws. Install the fast idle cam retainer. **The thermostatic spring housing is installed after the choke plate clearance (pull-down) has been adjusted to specification.**

AIR HORN

Refer to Fig. 14 for the correct location of the parts.

1. If the choke plate and shaft was removed, position the choke plate shaft in the air horn.

On an automatic choke equipped carburetor, insert the plastic choke pulldown adjusting nut and swivel into the keyed hole in the choke shaft lever. Position the felt washer

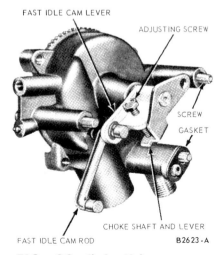

FIG. 30—Choke Linkage Installation

between the two brass washers and slide them into place on the choke control rod seal retainer on the bottom of the air horn.

Insert the choke plate rod through the plate rod seal and the air horn. Insert the choke control rod into the choke shaft lever clevis nut, and turn the nut clockwise to thread the rod onto the nut.

On a manual choke equipped carburetor, insert the plastic swivel into the keyed hole in the choke shaft lever (Fig. 14). Position the felt washer between the two brass washers and slide them into place on the choke control rod seal retainer on the bottom of the air horn.

Insert the choke control rod thru the control rod seal, air horn and the swivel. Install the control rod spring, and screw the control rod adjusting nut clockwise to thread the nut onto the control rod.

2. If the choke plate and shaft was removed, insert the choke plate into the choke plate shaft. Install the choke plate screws snug, but not tight.

Check for proper plate fit, binding in the air horn, and free rotation of the shaft by moving the plate from the closed position to the open position. If necessary, remove the choke plate and grind or file the plate edge where it is binding or scraping on the air horn wall. If the choke plate and shaft moves freely, tighten the choke plate screws while holding the choke in the fully-closed position. Stake the screws. **When staking the screws, support the shaft and plate on a block of wood or a metal bar to prevent bending of the shaft.**

3. If necessary, start new secondary throttle control vacuum tubes into the air horn. **Make certain the tubes are installed in a manner that will insure that the pick-up end will face downward toward the booster venturi when the air horn is installed.** Drive each tube into the air horn by grasping it lightly below the shoulder with pliers and striking the pliers with a hammer. Drive each tube in until its stops against its shoulder. **Do not crush or bend the tubes. The tube should not touch the booster venturi wall when the air horn is installed on the main body. The correct position of each tube is 0.020-0.060 inch from the wall.**

4. Position the main body gasket on the main body (Fig. 31).

On an automatic choke equipped carburetor, position the air horn on the main body and gasket so that

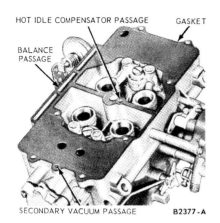

HOT IDLE COMPENSATOR PASSAGE   GASKET

BALANCE PASSAGE

SECONDARY VACUUM PASSAGE   B2377-A

FIG. 31—Main Body Gasket Installation

the choke plate rod fits into the opening in the choke housing lever. Install the choke plate rod retainer.

On a manual choke equipped carburetor, position the air horn on the main body and gasket. Position the choke cam and lever on the choke control rod and the shaft on the main body. Install the flat washer and the choke cam and lever retainer on the shaft.

Use care to prevent damage to the secondary throttle control vacuum tubes during the air horn installation.

5. Install the air horn retaining screws, lock washers and the carburetor identification tag.

6. Refer to Part 10-1, Section 2, Common Adjustments and Repairs

and perform the fast idle cam linkage and automatic choke plate clearance (pull-down) adjustment.

7. On an automatic choke equipped carburetor, position the thermostatic choke spring housing gasket on the choke housing. Install the spring housing on the choke housing and gasket, with the slot in the arm of the thermostatic spring lever inserted into the loop of the thermostatic spring. Position the spring housing retainer (clamp) over the spring housing and loosely install the retaining screws.

8. Refer to Part 10-1, Section 2, Common Adjustments and Repairs and perform the automatic choke spring housing adjustment.

PART 10-5   AIR CLEANER

1 Description and Operation 10-60
Conventional Air Cleaner 10-60
Hot and Cold Air Intake Air Cleaner 10-60
Closed Crankcase Ventilation System
Air Cleaners 10-60

2 Removal and Installation 10-60
Air Cleaners and Filter Elements 10-60
Hot and Cold Air Intake Duct and
Valve Assembly 10-61

1 DESCRIPTION AND OPERATION

CONVENTIONAL AIR CLEANER

All engines except the standard 289 V-8 engines are equipped with a conventional dry-type air cleaner that has a replaceable filtering element. The air cleaner body is mounted on a sealing gasket, located on the carburetor air horn. The air cleaner assembly is retained on the engine by a stud on the carburetor body and a wing nut above the filter cover. The filter element has integral plastic gaskets, located on the top and bottom of the element. The gaskets prevent entry of dirt and unfiltered air into the engine.

The air from the engine compartment enters the air cleaner assembly through the opening (horn) on the side of the body, into a silencing chamber and passes through the filter element. Dust particles are trapped in the filter element as the air passes through it. After leaving the filter element, the air is deflected down into the carburetor.

HOT AND COLD AIR INTAKE AIR CLEANER

The standard 289 V-8 engines are equipped with a thermostatically controlled carburetor air inlet duct assembly.

The air cleaner body is mounted on a sealing gasket, located on the carburetor air horn. The air cleaner assembly is retained on the engine by a stud in the carburetor body and

a wing nut above the filter cover. The replaceable filter element assembly has integral plastic gaskets located on the top and bottom of the element. The gaskets prevent entry of dirt and unfiltered air into the engine.

The thermostatically controlled air inlet duct and shroud assembly is attached to the air cleaner body with two wing screws. The shroud is positioned on the left exhaust manifold. The air inlet duct control mechanism consists of a valve plate, thermostat, adjustable thermostat rod, two springs and a retaining clip.

The air received from the air duct passes through a silencing chamber in the air cleaner body and then through the filter element. After leaving the filter element, the air is deflected down into the carburetor. Dust particles and other foreign materials are trapped in the filter element as the air rushes through it.

The temperature of the air entering the air cleaner is thermostatically controlled by the carburetor air duct assembly. Air from the engine compartment, or heated air from a shroud around the exhaust manifold, is available to the engine.

A thermostatic bulb in the air duct is exposed to the incoming air. A spring-loaded valve plate is connected to the thermostatic bulb through linkage. The valve plate spring holds the valve in the closed position

(heat on) until the thermostatic bulb overcomes the valve tension.

During the engine warm-up period when the air temperature entering the air duct is less than 75°F, the thermostat is in the retracted position and the valve plate is held in the up position (heat on) by the valve plate spring, thus shutting off the air from the engine compartment. All air is then drawn from the shroud around the exhaust manifold.

As the temperature of the air passing the thermostatic bulb approaches 85°F, the thermostat starts to expand, and pulls the valve plate down. This allows cooler air from the engine compartment to enter the air cleaner. When the temperature of the air reaches approximately 105°F, the valve plate will be in the down position (heat off) so that only engine compartment air is allowed to enter the air cleaner.

CLOSED CRANKCASE VENTILATION SYSTEM AIR CLEANERS

On the closed crankcase ventilation system engine models, air is drawn into the crankcase ventilation system at the integral air inlet tube, located on the air cleaner body, and passes through the connecting rubber hose into the crankcase ventilation system.

2 REMOVAL AND INSTALLATION

AIR CLEANER MAINTENANCE

Refer to Group 19 for the air cleaner assembly recommended maintenance mileage interval.

AIR CLEANERS AND FILTER ELEMENTS
REMOVAL
1. Disconnect the crankcase ven-

tilation system hose, if so equipped, from the air cleaner body.

2. Remove the wing nut retaining the air cleaner assembly to the car-

buretor. On cars equipped with a hot and cold air intake duct, remove the 2 wing-type screws that secure the air duct and thermostat assembly to the air cleaner.

3. Remove the air cleaner assembly, then remove the cover and lift the filter element out of the air cleaner body.

CLEANING AND INSPECTION

Refer to Part 10-1, Section 3 for the carburetor air cleaner and filter element cleaning and inspection procedure.

INSTALLATION

1. Install a new air cleaner mounting gasket on the carburetor, if required.

2. Position the air cleaner body on the carburetor, and make certain the body is properly seated on the gasket.

3. Connect the air inlet duct and valve assembly, if so equipped, to the air cleaner with the wing-type retaining screws. Tighten the screws.

4. Place the filter element on the air cleaner body. **Make sure the filter is properly seated. If the word TOP is indicated on the filter element, make sure the word TOP faces up.** Install the cover and tighten the retaining wing nut.

5. Connect the crankcase vent hose, if so equipped, to the air cleaner and tighten the retaining clamp.

HOT AND COLD AIR INTAKE DUCT AND VALVE ASSEMBLY

The air intake duct thermostatic valve can be adjusted to change the air temperature at which the valve opens. Increasing the rod length will move the valve toward the heat-OFF position. Decreasing the rod length will move the valve toward the heat-ON position. Adjustments must be verified by removing the duct and valve assembly, and testing the opening temperature as detailed in Part 10-1, Section 1.

REMOVAL

1. Remove the air duct and shroud retaining nut and washer from the exhaust manifold.

2. Remove the two wing-type screws that secure the air duct and thermostat assembly to the air cleaner. Carefully lift the air duct, shroud and tube as an assembly from the engine.

DIAGNOSIS AND TESTING

Refer to Part 10-1, Section 1 for the air intake duct and valve testing procedures.

INSTALLATION

1. Install the air inlet duct and valve assembly and shroud on the exhaust manifold as a unit. Install the shroud retaining nut and washer. Tighten the nut.

2. Connect the air inlet duct and valve assembly to the air cleaner and tighten the wing-type retaining screws.

DISASSEMBLY

1. Loosen the retaining screw and separate the air inlet duct and valve assembly from the shroud and tube assembly.

2. If the duct and valve assembly was removed because of a suspected malfunction, check the operation of the thermostat and air duct assembly. Refer to the Air Intake Duct Test (Part 10-1, Section 1) for the proper procedure.

3. If inspection reveals that the valve plate is sticking or the thermostat is malfunctioning, remove the thermostat and valve plate as follows:

Detach the valve plate tension spring from the valve plate with the use of long-nose pliers. Loosen the thermostat lock nut and unscrew the thermostat from the mounting bracket. Remove the lock nut. Grasp the valve plate and withdraw it from the duct.

ASSEMBLY

1. If it was necessary to disassemble the thermostat and air duct and valve, assemble the unit as follows:

Install the valve plate. Install the lock nut on the thermostat, and screw the thermostat into the mounting bracket. Install the valve plate tension spring on the valve plate and duct.

Check the operation of the thermostat and air duct assembly. Refer to the Air Intake Duct Test (Part 10-1, Section 1) for the proper procedure. Adjust the thermostat, as required.

2. Connect the duct and valve assembly to the shroud and tube assembly. Tighten the retaining screw.

PART 10-6
FUEL PUMP AND FUEL FILTER

Section	Page
1 Description and Operation	10-62
2 Removal and Installation	10-63
Fuel Filter Replacement	10-63
Fuel Pump Removal	10-63
Fuel Pump Installation	10-63

Section	Page
3 Major Repair Operations	10-63
AC Fuel Pump—6-Cylinder Engines	10-63
Carter Permanently Sealed Fuel	
Pumps	10-64

1 DESCRIPTION AND OPERATION

Single action fuel pumps are standard equipment for all car models.

The fuel pumps on the 6-cylinder engines are mounted on the lower, left-center of the engine cylinder block.

On all V-8 engines, the fuel pumps are mounted on the left-side of the cylinder front cover.

An AC design fuel pump (Fig. 1) is used on the 170 and 200 Six engines.

A Carter permanently-sealed fuel pump is used on the 289 and 390 V-8 engines (Fig. 2).

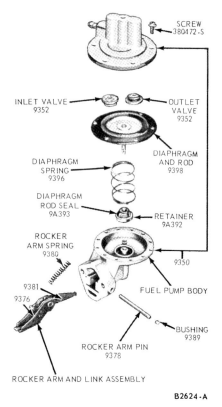

FIG. 1—AC Fuel Pump Assembly

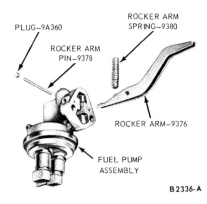

FIG. 2—Typical Carter Sealed Design Fuel Pump

A separate in-line fuel filter (Fig. 3) is used on all engines. **The filter is of one-piece construction and does not contain a cleanable filter element.**

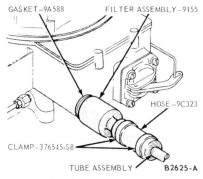

FIG. 3—Typical In-Line Fuel Filter Assembly

The fuel pumps are mechanically actuated by means of the fuel pump rocker arm and an eccentric on the camshaft.

A flexible fuel pump diaphragm is operated by a combination of rocker arm action and calibrated spring tension.

On the fuel intake stroke, the cam-

shaft eccentric causes the rocker arm to lift the fuel pump diaphragm against the diaphragm spring pressure. This action draws fuel through the intake valve into the pump inlet chamber and closes the outlet valve. At the same time, fuel is drawn from the fuel tank through the fuel intake line to replace the fuel drawn into the chamber.

As the camshaft eccentric continues to rotate, the rocker arm relieves the pressure on the diaphragm spring and allows the spring to move the diaphragm toward the inlet and outlet valves, exerting pressure on the fuel inlet chamber. This pressure causes the pump inlet valve to close and the ensuing pressure build-up opens the outlet valve. The fuel is then forced through the pump outlet to the fuel filter where it is cleansed before entering the carburetor. **Fuel is delivered to the carburetor only when the fuel inlet valve in the carburetor is open. The carburetor inlet valve is closed by fuel pressure on the float when the specified fuel level in the carburetor float chamber is reached.**

When there is no demand for fuel from the carburetor, the diaphragm spring tension is not strong enough to force the diaphragm against the fuel pressure built up in the inlet chamber of the pump. Thus, the up and down rocker arm action continues, but the diaphragm remains stationary until pressure against the carburetor float is relieved by a demand for fuel at the carburetor.

The Carter permanently-sealed pumps contain pressure relief orifices in the inlet and outlet valve cages to prevent pressure build-up in the line to the carburetor during hot soak periods.

An air vent is located in the fuel

pump bodies to relieve air pressure build-up on the spring side of the diaphragm.

The fuel pumps contain a diaphragm rod seal to prevent the entrance of engine oil into the fuel pump.

2 REMOVAL AND INSTALLATION

FUEL FILTER REPLACEMENT

The in-line fuel filter used on all engines (Fig. 3) is of one-piece construction and cannot be cleaned. **Replace the filter if it becomes clogged or restricted.**

1. Remove the air cleaner (Part 10-5, Section 2).

2. Loosen the retaining clamp securing the fuel inlet hose to the fuel filter (Fig. 3).

3. Unscrew the fuel filter from the carburetor and discard the gasket. Disconnect the fuel filter from the hose and discard the retaining clamp.

4. Install a new clamp on the inlet hose and connect the hose to the filter. Place a new gasket on the new fuel filter and screw the filter into the carburetor inlet port. Tighten the filter.

5. Position the fuel line hose clamp and crimp the clamp securely.

6. Start the engine and check for fuel leaks.

7. Install the air cleaner (Part 10-5, Section 2).

FUEL PUMP REMOVAL

1. Disconnect the inlet line and the outlet line at the fuel pump.

2. Remove the fuel pump retaining screws and remove the pump and the gasket. Discard the gasket.

FUEL PUMP INSTALLATION

1. If the fuel pump on a 170 or 200 Six engine is to be replaced, transfer the fuel pump fitting(s) to the new fuel pump.

2. Remove all the gasket material from the mounting pad and pump. Apply oil-resistant sealer to both sides of a new gasket. Position the new gasket on the pump flange and hold the pump in position against the mounting pad. **Make sure the rocker arm is riding on the camshaft eccentric.**

3. Press the pump tight against the pad, install the retaining screws, and alternately torque them to specifications.

4. Connect the fuel inlet line or hose (use a new clamp on the hose) and the outlet line. If a hose is used at the fuel pump connection, crimp the retaining clamp securely.

5. Operate the engine and check for fuel leaks.

3 MAJOR REPAIR OPERATIONS

AC FUEL PUMP—
6-CYLINDER ENGINES

DISASSEMBLY

The fuel pump assembly is shown in Fig. 1.

1. Scribe a line on the flanges of the pump body and valve housing to identify their original position.

2. Remove the valve housing from the fuel pump body.

3. Remove the staking marks from around the valves, remove both valves from the valve housing. **Carefully note the position of the valves in the valve housing cover so that new valves can be correctly installed.**

4. Using a blunt punch or tool T56L-9350-A, Detail 3, drive the rocker arm pin out of the pump body (Fig. 4).

5. Press the pump diaphragm into the fuel pump body and pull the rocker arm outward to unhook the diaphragm actuating rod from the rocker arm and link assembly (Fig. 5).

6. Remove the diaphragm and diaphragm return spring, rocker arm and link assembly, and the rocker arm return spring from the pump body.

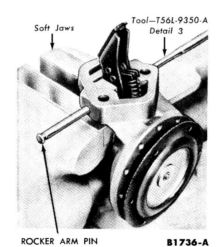

FIG. 4—Rocker Arm Pin Removal

7. Remove the diaphragm actuating rod oil seal retainer and the oil seal from the pump body (Fig. 1).

CLEANING AND INSPECTION

Refer to Part 10-1, Section 3 for the cleaning and inspection procedures.

ASSEMBLY

1. Immerse the new oil seal in

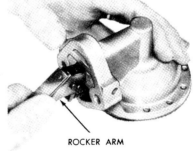

FIG. 5—Fuel Pump Diaphragm Removal

clean engine oil for 2 minutes prior to installation. Install the diaphragm actuating rod oil seal and retainer so that the seal protrudes towards the diaphragm mounting flange (Fig. 1).

2. Seat the oil seal retainer, using tool 9350-C or T56L-9350-A, Detail 1 (Fig. 6). Stake the oil seal retainer in at least 3 places to secure the installation.

3. Install the valves in the valve body so that the valve positions are as shown in Fig. 1.

4. Seat the valves firmly in the valve body, using tool 9350-D or T56L-9350-A. Detail 2. Stake the valves in place.

Tool—9350-C or
Tool—T56L-9350-A, Detail 1

B2627-A

FIG. 6—Seating the Oil Seal

5. Lubricate the diaphragm actuating rod.

6. Position the fuel pump diaphragm and spring assembly into the pump body as shown in Fig. 7.

DIAPHRAGM

OIL SEAL

DIAPHRAGM RETURN SPRING   B2628-A

FIG. 7—Diaphragm Installation

7. Hold the diaphragm assembly in the pump body; position the pump body so that the mounting flange faces up. Apply slightly more pressure to the lower edge of the diaphragm, and insert the rocker arm link assembly with the cam shoe facing away from the diaphragm. Hook the rocker arm link to the diaphragm actuating rod.

8. Lift one edge of the diaphragm and observe the positioning of the oil seal. **Make sure the oil seal is fully extended as shown in Fig. 8.** If the oil seal is not properly positioned, push the diaphragm into the pump body as far as possible with a slight twisting motion to the diaphragm. This will assist the oil seal to position itself properly on the diaphragm rod. **Do not twist the diaphragm too severely or the rod may be unhooked from the link.**

9. Install the rocker arm return spring and hold it in place by cocking the rocker arm slightly.

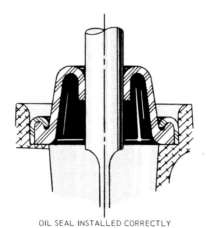

OIL SEAL INSTALLED CORRECTLY

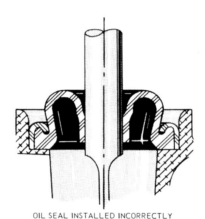

OIL SEAL INSTALLED INCORRECTLY

B2366-A

FIG. 8—Fuel Pump Oil Seal Installation

10. Install the rocker arm pin in the pump body.

11. Position the valve body and pump body so that the previously scribed marks are aligned.

12. Install all the screws and the lockwashers until the screws just engage the fuel pump body. **Make sure that all of the screws pass through the holes in the diaphragm without tearing the fabric.**

13. Alternately and evenly tighten all of the screws.

14. Cover all but one vent hole in the pump lower body, using masking tape or a similar material.

15. Using a suitable vacuum source, apply 15 inches of vacuum (Hg) to the underside of the pump diaphragm at the open vent hole. **Use a suitable rubber tipped probe or hose to assure proper sealing at the vent hole.** Apply vacuum to the diaphragm 2 times for a minimum of one minute each time. This will position the oil seal properly on the diaphragm rod. Remove the sealing tape from the vents.

CARTER PERMANENTLY SEALED FUEL PUMPS

DISASSEMBLY

The fuel pump assembly is shown in Fig. 2.

1. Scrape away the staking mark and remove the rocker arm pin seal plug as shown in Fig. 9.

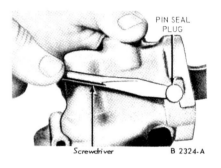

PIN SEAL PLUG

Screwdriver   B 2324-A

FIG. 9—Rocker Arm Pin Seal Plug Removal

2. Release the tension on the rocker arm spring pressure and allow the rocker arm pin to fall out. If the pin does not come out freely, tap the fuel pump assembly lightly on the bench until the pin sticks out of the bore; then, remove the pin with pliers. Remove the rocker arm and spring(s).

CLEANING AND INSPECTION

Clean and inspect the fuel pump component parts. Refer to Cleaning and Inspection (Part 10-1, Section 3) for the proper procedure. Replace all worn or damaged parts.

ASSEMBLY

The fuel pump assembly is shown in Fig. 2.

1. Insert the rocker arm spring into the spring guide bore in the dome of the fuel pump rocker arm cavity.

2. Insert the rocker arm into the cavity and hook it onto the diaphragm rod, directly below the rod flange. Position the rocker arm spring(s) over the spring locater(s) on the rocker arm. Align the rocker arm pin holes and install the rocker arm pin. **Make certain the rocker arm spring(s) is properly positioned on the spring locater on the rocker arm.**

3. Install a new rocker arm pin plug. Stake the plug into position.

PART 10-7 FUEL TANK AND LINES

Section	Page	Section	Page
1 Description and Operation	10-65	Fuel Tank	10-68
2 Removal and Installation	10-67	Fuel Lines	10-69
Filler Pipe	10-67		

1 DESCRIPTION AND OPERATION

The Falcons (except ranchero and station wagon models) and the Mustangs have a 16 gallon fuel tank. The Comets (all models), the Falcons (ranchero and station wagon models) and the Fairlanes (all models) have a 20 gallon fuel tank.

The fuel systems are shown in Figs. 1-4.

The fuel tank used on the Comet (except station wagon models), Falcon (except ranchero and station wagon models), Fairlane (except station wagon models) and Mustang is located in the center of the luggage compartment floor and is retained

to the floor by screws. The fuel tank used on the Falcon ranchero and station wagon models is basically the same but is inverted and retained by two steel support straps. The fuel tank used on the Comet station wagon models and the Fairlane station wagon models is located behind the wheel opening in the left rear quarter panel and is held in position by one steel support strap.

The fuel tank sender unit is located on the front side of the tank and is accessible from underneath the car. On Comet station wagon models and Fairlane station wagon models, a

fuel tank guard in the wheel well must be removed to gain access to the fuel sender unit.

The fuel outlet line is fastened to a connecting hose that is attached to a line which enters the fuel tank through the sender unit assembly. A filter is located in the tank on the fuel line pick-up tube. **This filter does not require servicing.**

The Fairlane (except station wagon models) fuel tank filler pipe is located behind the rear license plate. The Mustang fuel tank filler pipe is located in the center of the lower back panel. On all other models, the fuel

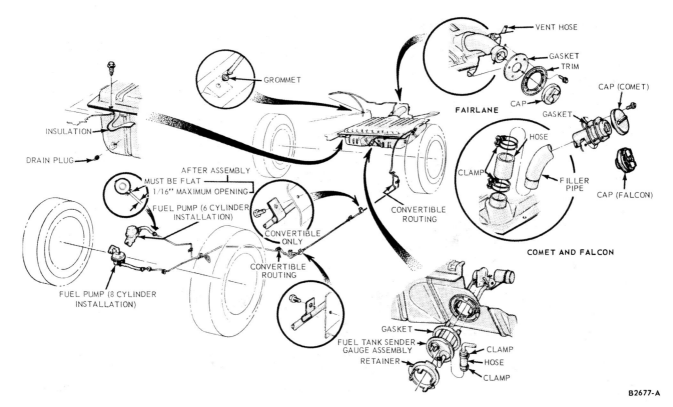

FIG. 1—Fuel System—Comet, Falcon and Fairlane (Except Ranchero and Station Wagon Models)

B2677-A

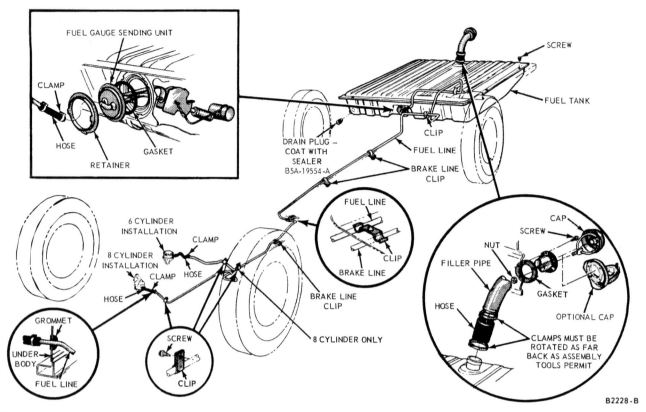

FIG. 2—Fuel System—Mustang

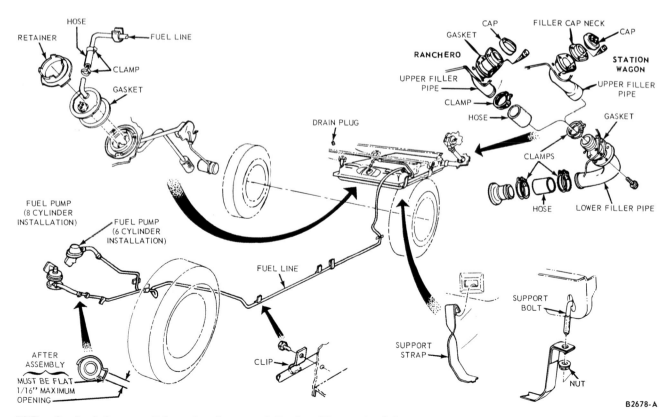

FIG. 3—Fuel System—Falcon Ranchero and Station Wagon Models

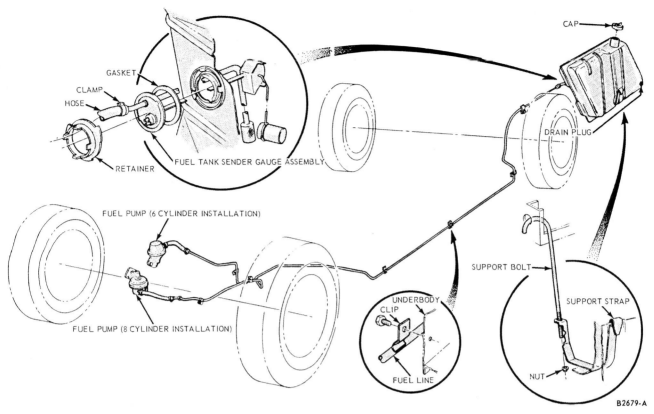

FIG. 4—Fuel System—Comet and Fairlane Station Wagon Models

tank filler pipe is located in the left rear quarter panel.

On Fairlanes (except station wagon models), the fuel tank is vented by a vent tube. On all other models, the fuel tank is vented through the fuel filler cap.

The fuel tank filler pipe used on Comets (station wagon models) and Fairlanes (all models) is a part of the fuel tank. The fuel tank filler pipe used on Falcons and Comets (except ranchero and station wagon models) and Mustangs is attached to the tank with a hose and hose clamps. The fuel tank filler pipe used on Falcons (ranchero models) has an upper filler pipe connected with a hose and clamps to the lower filler pipe which is connected with a hose and clamps to the fuel tank opening. The fuel tank filler pipe used on Falcons station wagon models) has an upper filler pipe connected with a clamp to the lower filler pipe which is connected with a hose and clamps to the fuel tank opening.

The fuel line is routed from the fuel tank, passing beneath the left side of the underbody; then, under the left fender and through the forward part of the fender apron. The complete fuel line is not normally replaced as a unit, only the damaged segments are usually replaced.

2 REMOVAL AND INSTALLATION

FILLER PIPE

FAIRLANE (ALL MODELS) AND COMET (STATION WAGON MODELS ONLY)

The fuel tank filler pipe is a part of the fuel tank on these models and cannot be replaced separately.

FALCON (EXCEPT RANCHERO AND STATION WAGON MODELS), COMET (EXCEPT STATION WAGON) AND MUSTANG

Removal

1. Drain the fuel tank with a si-phon to a level below the filler pipe opening in the tank. The gas should be drained into a suitable clean container.

2. Remove the retaining screws securing the filler pipe to the body panel.

3. Loosen the hose clamp and loosen the hose from the filler pipe.

4. Rotate the filler pipe and pull it outward to remove it from the fuel tank.

Installation

1. If necessary install new hose clamps on the filler pipe hose.

2. Place the gasket on the filler pipe.

3. Position the filler pipe in the body panel and slide the hose onto the filler pipe.

4. Install and tighten the filler pipe retaining screws.

5. Tighten the hose clamp and install the siphoned gas back in the fuel tank.

FALCON RANCHERO AND STATION WAGON MODELS

Removal

1. Drain the fuel tank with a si-phon to a level below the filler pipe

opening in the fuel tank. The gas should be drained into a suitable clean container.

2. Working from inside the rear quarter panel, loosen the hose clamp(s).

3. Working from underneath the car, loosen the hose clamps and remove the retaining screws securing the lower filler pipe to the body.

4. Remove the retaining screws securing the upper filler pipe to the body panel.

5. Pull the lower filler pipe down and remove it from the car.

6. Pull the upper filler pipe out through the body panel. The end of the upper filler pipe will have to be folded over for removal through the body panel.

Installation

1. If necessary, install new hose clamps on the filler pipe hose(s).

2. Place the gasket on the lower filler pipe and slide it into the body panel and hose from the fuel tank. Install the retaining screws and tighten the hose clamps.

3. On ranchero models, slide the hose onto the lower filler pipe. Place the gasket on the upper filler pipe and slide the upper filler pipe through the opening in the body side panel and into the hose. Install the upper filler pipe retaining screws and tighten the hose clamps.

4. On station wagon models, fold over the end of the upper filler pipe and slide it through the body side panel and over the lower filler pipe. Install the filler pipe neck retaining screws and tighten the hose clamp.

5. Place the siphoned fuel back in the fuel tank.

FUEL TANK

The fuel tank installations are shown in Figs. 1 thru 4.

ALL EXCEPT STATION WAGON AND RANCHERO MODELS

Removal

1. Raise the rear of the car and position safety stands.

2. Remove the fuel tank drain plug and drain the fuel into a suitable container.

3. Disconnect the fuel gauge sending unit wire at the sending unit.

4. Loosen the hose clamp, slide the clamp forward and disconnect the fuel line at the fuel gauge sending unit.

5. Disconnect the fuel tank vent hose at the tank, if so equipped.

If the fuel gauge sending unit is to be removed, turn the unit retaining ring counterclockwise and remove the sending unit retaining ring and gasket.

6. Remove the spare tire from the luggage compartment. Pull the compartment floor mat out of the way for access to the fuel tank.

7. Remove the fuel tank filler neck retaining screws.

8. Loosen the filler neck to tank hose clamps. Remove the filler neck, mounting gasket, and filler neck to tank hose.

9. Remove the fuel tank to luggage compartment floor pan retaining screws and remove the fuel tank.

Installation

1. Make sure all the old sealer has been removed from the fuel tank mounting flange and mounting surface at the luggage compartment floor pan. Apply caulking cord to the fuel tank mounting surface at the luggage compartment floor pan.

2. Position the fuel tank to the luggage compartment floor pan and install the retaining screws.

3. Position the hose and filler neck assembly and gasket to the body back panel. Position the hose to the fuel tank neck.

4. Install the filler neck to body back panel retaining screws and tighten the hose clamps.

5. If the fuel gauge sending unit was removed, make sure all the old gasket material has been removed from the unit mounting surface on the fuel tank. Using a new gasket, position the fuel gauge to the fuel tank and secure with the retaining ring.

6. Position the luggage compartment floor mat and install the spare tire.

7. Connect the fuel gauge sending unit wire to the sending unit.

8. Connect the fuel line at the fuel gauge sending unit and tighten the hose clamps securely. Install the drain plug.

9. Connect the fuel tank vent hose, if so equipped.

10. Remove the safety stands and lower the car.

11. Fill the tank and check all connections for leaks.

FALCON STATION WAGON AND RANCHERO MODELS

Removal

1. Siphon the fuel from the fuel tank into a suitable container.

2. Loosen the filler hose clamp at the tank and disconnect the hose.

3. Disconnect the fuel gauge sending unit wire at the sending unit.

4. Loosen the clamps and disconnect the flexible fuel line at the sending unit.

5. Remove the two nuts retaining the fuel tank support straps to the underbody. Remove the straps and lower the tank.

6. Remove the fuel gauge sending unit.

Installation

1. Using a new gasket, install the fuel gauge sending unit.

2. Hold the tank in position against the underbody. Hook the support straps to the retainers in the underbody. Position the straps over the studs, then install the nuts retaining the straps to the underbody.

3. Connect the fuel line and filler hose.

4. Connect the fuel gauge sending unit wire.

5. Fill the tank and check all connections for leaks.

FAIRLANE AND COMET STATION WAGONS

Removal

1. Remove the filler cap. Using necessary precautions, siphon the fuel into a suitable clean container.

2. Raise the car on a hoist.

3. Remove the left rear wheel assembly.

4. Remove the wheel well splash shield.

5. Disconnect the fuel gauge sending unit wire and fuel line at the sending unit.

6. Remove the nut retaining the tank support strap to the body. Remove the strap and remove the tank.

7. Remove the sending unit from the old tank if a new tank is to be installed.

Installation

1. If a new tank is to be installed, install the fuel gauge sending unit and a new mounting gasket in the fuel tank.

2. Hold the tank in position and install the retaining strap.

3. Connect the fuel line and sending unit wire to the sending unit.

4. Install the wheel well splash shield.

5. Install the left rear wheel and lower the car.

6. Fill the fuel tank and install the filler cap.

7. Check all connections for leaks.

FUEL LINES

The various fuel lines (Figs. 1 thru 4) are not serviced as assemblies. They must be cut, squared and formed out of rolls of fuel system service tubing and hose material available at dealerships.

A damaged section of **tubing** longer than 12 inches can be cut out of the existing line and replaced by a comparable service **tubing section,** spliced into the line by means of connecting hoses and retaining clamps.

A damaged section of tubing shorter than 12 inches can be cut out of the line and replaced by a length of service hose and two retaining clamps. **All replacement hoses must be cut to a length that will insure proper clamp retention beyond the flared ends of the connecting tubing.**

REMOVAL

1. Drain the fuel from the tank.

2. Disconnect the line at the fuel gauge sender unit and the fuel pump. Remove the lines from the holding clips along the underbody. Remove all damaged hose sections and tube sections.

INSTALLATION

1. Cut a new section of tubing to approximately the same length as the section to be replaced. **Allow extra length for flaring the ends of the tubing.** Square the ends of the cut tubing with a file.

2. Ream the inside edges of the cut tubing with the reamer blade on the tube cutter. **Be sure metal chips are removed from inside the tube(s).** Flare the ends of the cut tubing, as required, with a standard tube flaring kit and tool (Fig. 5).

3. Bend the tube section to conform to the contour of the original tube. Cut an ample length of hose to form a coupling between the flared ends of the fuel lines. Connect the

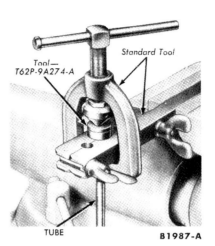

FIG. 5—Fuel Line Tube Die

hose couplings to the tubing and install the retaining clamps.

4. Position the lines in the underbody clips and tighten the clips. Connect the line to the fuel gauge sender unit and the fuel pump. Fill the tank and check for leaks.

PART 10-8

SPECIFICATIONS

NOTE: All specifications are given in inches unless otherwise noted.

CARBURETORS

The basic part number of all the carburetors is 9510.

The part number prefix and suffix appears on the identification tag mounted on the carburetor.

Always refer to the Master Parts Catalog for parts usage and interchangeability before replacing a carburetor, or a component part for a carburetor.

CARBURETOR APPLICATION AND GENERAL INFORMATION

Engine and Trans.	Carb. Part Number (9510)	Carb. Model	Throttle Bore Dia.		Venturi Diameter		Main Metering Jet Normal		Altitude		Booster Venturi		Power Valve Color		Spark Valve Color	Choke Cover Spring
			Pri.	Sec.	Pri.	Sec.	Pri.	Sec.	Pri.	Sec.	Pri.	Sec.	Normal	Altitude		
170-1V Std.	C5DF-L	Ford 1100-A	1.437	—	1.100	—	64F	—	62F	—	—	—	—	—	Plain⑤	TM
170-1V Std.①	C6DF-C	Ford 1100-A	1.437	—	1.100	—	65F	—	63F	—	—	—	—	—	—	TS
170-1V Auto.	C5DF-M	Ford 1100-A	1.437	—	1.100	—	62F	—	60F	—	—	—	—	—	Plain⑤	TM
170-1V Auto.①	C6DF-D	Ford 1100-A	1.437	—	1.100	—	62F	—	60F	—	—	—	—	—	—	TP
200-1V Std.	C5OF-Y	Ford 1100-A	1.437	—	1.200	—	69F	—	67F	—	—	—	—	—	Plain⑤	TS
200-1V Std.③	C5OF-AC	Ford 1100-A	1.437	—	1.100	—	62F	—	60F	—	—	—	—	—	Plain⑤	TS
200-1V Std.①	C6DF-C	Ford 1100-A	1.437	—	1.100	—	65F	—	63F	—	—	—	—	—	—	TS
200-1V Auto.	C5OF-Z	Ford 1100-A	1.437	—	1.200	—	67F	—	65F	—	—	—	—	—	Plain⑤	TP
200-1V Auto.①	C6OF-G	Ford 1100-A	1.147	—	1.200	—	67F	—	65F	—	—	—	—	—	—	TP
289-2V Std.	C6OF-A	Ford 2100-A	1.437	—	1.145	—	51F	—	49F	—	CG	—	Red	Plain	—	TW
289-2V Std.①	C6DF-E	Ford 2100-A	1.437	—	1.145	—	50F	—	48F	—	P	—	Plain	Green	—	TW
289-2V Auto.	C6DF-B	Ford 2100-A	1.437	—	1.145	—	50F	—	48F	—	CE	—	Green	Yellow	—	TO
289-2V Auto.①	C6DF-F	Ford 2100-A	1.437	—	1.145	—	49F	—	47F	—	P	—	Plain	Green	—	TO
289-4V Std.	C6ZF-A	Ford 4100-A	1.437	1.437	1.080	1.189	49F	58F	47F	56F	CF	H	Plain	Green	—	TN
289-4V Std.①	C6ZF-D	Ford 4100-A	1.437	1.437	1.080	1.189	47F	58F	45F	56F	DA	FA	Plain	Green	—	TN
289-4V Std.④	C6ZF-C	Ford 4100-A	1.562	1.562	1.125	1.189	52F	68F	50F	66F	M	BA	Plain	Green	—	—
289-4V Auto.	C6ZF-B	Ford 4100-A	1.437	1.437	1.080	1.189	48F	57F	46F	55F	CH	H	Plain	Green	—	TO
289-4V Auto.①	C6ZF-E	Ford 4100-A	1.437	1.437	1.080	1.189	46F	58F	44F	56F	DA	FA	Plain	Green	—	TO
390-2V Std.	C6OF-B	Ford 2100-A	1.564	—	1.231	—	57F	—	55F	—	D	—	Plain	Green	—	TN
390-2V Std.①	C6OF-K	Ford 2100-A	1.564	—	1.231	—	56F	—	54F	—	P	—	Plain	Green	—	TN
390-2V Auto.	C6OF-C	Ford 2100-A	1.687	—	1.330	—	60F	—	58F	—	D	—	Plain	Green	—	TN
390-2V Auto.①	C6OF-L	Ford 2100-A	1.687	—	1.330	—	60F	—	58F	—	P	—	Plain	Green	—	TN
390-4V Std.	C6OF-D	Ford 4100-A	1.437	1.437	1.080	1.189	49F	67F	47F	65F	D	F	Plain	Green	—	TN
390-4V Std.①	C6OF-H	Ford 4100-A	1.437	1.437	1.080	1.189	48F	46F	67F	65F	D	F	Plain	Green	—	TN
390-4V Auto.	C6OF-E	Ford 4100-A	1.437	1.437	1.080	1.190	48F	67F	46F	65F	D	F	Plain	Green	—	TO
390-4V Auto.①	C6OF-J	Ford 4100-A	1.437	1.437	1.080	1.189	47F	67F	45F	65F	D	F	Plain	Green	—	TO

① Thermactor Exhaust Emission Control System ③ Police ③ Taxi ④ High Performance ⑤ Spark Valve Closes @ 8.500 Inches of Mercury

CARBURETOR SETTINGS AND ADJUSTMENTS

Refer to Group 10, Part 10-1, Section 2 of the shop manual for the carburetor adjustment procedures

Carb. Part No. (9510)	Choke Spring Housing Setting	Choke Plate Clearance (Pull-Down)— 0.036 Inch Gauge⑥	Accelerator Pump Setting		Dry Float Setting		Fuel Level (Wet)		Fast Idle RPM	Curb Idle RPM③④	Anti-Stall Dashpot (If So Equipped) Clearance at Curb Idle	Secondary Throttle Plate Setting
			Pump Lever	Throttle Lever	Pri.	Sec.	Pri.	Sec.				
C5DF-L	2 Lean	0.100-0.120	0.190②	②	1.090	—	—	—	1400	575-600	3½ Turns	—
C6DF-C	1 Lean	0.120-0.130	0.190②	②	1.090	—	—	—	1300	625-650	—	—
C5DF-M	Index	0.140-0.160	0.190②	②	1.090	—	—	—	1500	500-525	3½ Turns	—
C6DF-D	Index	0.140-0.160	0.190②	②	1.090	—	—	—	1500	550-575	3½ Turns	—
C5OF-Y	1 Lean	0.130-0.150	0.190②	②	1.090	—	—	—	1400	575-600		—
C5OF-AC	1 Lean	0.130-0.150	0.190②	②	1.090	—	—	—	1400	575-600		—
C5OF-Z	Index	0.140-0.160	0.190②	②	1.090	—	—	—	1500 High Cam	500-525	3½ Turns	—
C6OF-G	Index	0.140-0.160	0.190②	②	1.090	—	—	—	1500	550-575	3½ Turns	—
C6DF-A	Index	0.130-0.150	Inboard	4	0.491	—	0.875	—	1400	575-600	—	—
C6DF-E	Index	0.130-0.150	Inboard	3	0.371	—	0.750	—	1400	610-635	—	—
C6DF-B	2 Rich	0.110-0.130	Inboard	3	0.491	—	0.875	—	1600	475-500	0.060-0.090	—
C6DF-F	2 Rich	0.110-0.130	Inboard	3	0.371	—	0.750	—	1600	525-550	0.060-0.090	—
C6ZF-A	2 Rich	0.100-0.120	Inboard	3	0.531	0.531	0.910	0.910	1400	575-600	—	1 Turn⑥
C6ZF-D	2 Rich	0.110-0.130	Inboard	3	0.491	0.621	0.880	1.000	1400	610-635	—	1 Turn⑥
C6ZF-C	—	0.210-0.250	Inboard	3	0.491	0.621	0.875	1.000	—	750-775	—	1 Turn⑥
C6ZF-B	2 Rich	0.110-0.130	Inboard	3	0.571	0.531	0.940	0.910	1600	475-500	0.060-0.090	1 Turn⑥
C6ZF-E	2 Rich	0.110-0.130	Inboard	3	0.491	0.621	0.880	1.000	1600	525-550	0.060-0.090	1 Turn⑥
C6OF-B	Index	0.190-0.210	Inboard	3	0.491	—	0.880	—	1300⑦	575-600	—	—
C6OF-K	Index	0.190-0.210	Inboard	3	0.431	—	0.810	—	1300	610-635	—	—
C6OF-C	Index	0.170-0.190	Inboard	3	0.491	—	0.880	—	1400⑦	475-500	0.060-0.090	—
C6OF-L	Index	0.170-0.190	Inboard	3	0.431	—	0.810	—	1500	525-550	0.060-0.090	—
C6ZF-C	—	0.210-0.250	Inboard	3	0.491	0.621	0.875	1.000	—	750-775	—	1 Turn⑥
C6ZF-B	2 Rich	0.110-0.130	Inboard	3	—	0.531	0.940	0.910	1600	475-500	0.060-0.090	1 Turn⑥
C6ZF-E	2 Rich	0.110-0.130	Inboard	3	0.491	0.621	0.880	1.000	1600	525-550	0.060-0.090	1 Turn⑥
C6OF-B	Index	0.190-0.210	Inboard	3	0.491	—	0.880	—	1300⑦	575-600	—	—
C6OF-K	Index	0.190-0.210	Inboard	3	0.431	—	0.810	—	1300	610-635	—	—
C6OF-C	Index	0.170-0.190	Inboard	3	0.491	—	0.880	—	1400⑦	475-500	0.060-0.090	—
C6OF-L	Index	0.170-0.190	Inboard	3	0.431	—	0.810	—	1500	525-550	0.060-0.090	—
C6OF-D	2 Rich	0.150-0.170	Inboard	3	0.531	0.681	0.910	1.060	1200⑦	575-600	—	1 Turn⑥
C6OF-H	2 Rich	0.150-0.170	Inboard	3	0.491	0.621	0.880	1.000	1300	610-635	—	1 Turn⑥
C6OF-E	1 Rich	0.130-0.150	Inboard	3	0.531	0.681	0.910	1.060	1300⑦	475-500	0.060-0.090	1 Turn⑥
C6OF-J	1 Rich	0.130-0.150	Inboard	3	0.491	0.621	0.880	1.000	1500	525-550	0.060-0.090	1 Turn⑥

① DECHOKE CLEARANCE—Choke Plate to Air Horn
Ford 1-V...1/16
Ford 2-V and 4-V..1/16

② ACCELERATOR PUMP ADJUSTMENTS—FORD 1-V
Accelerator Pump Lever Clearance—Inches Pin in HI position, throttle plate seated

Accelerator Pump Lever Adjustment—Pin Placement

50° F. or below..HI
Above 50° F. and/or above 5,000 ft.........................LO

③ IDLE FUEL MIXTURE ADJUSTMENT—Initial Setting
All Carburetors...............................1 to 1½ Turns Open

④ IDLE SPEED ADJUSTMENT—Initial Setting
All Carburetors..................................1½ Turns Open

⑤ ANTI-STALL DASHPOT CLEARANCE—FORD 1-V
Turns In After Initial Contact of Adjusting Screw With Diaphragm Assembly

⑥ SECONDARY THROTTLE PLATE SETTING
Turns After Screw Contacts Lever

⑦ COLD OPERATION AT 0° F. OR LOWER
Increase the Fast Idle Speed 200 rpm

CARBURETOR AIR CLEANERS

CAR MODEL	ENGINE APPLICATION	COLOR	TYPE
Falcon	170, 200 Six	Red	Dry
Falcon	289 V-8	Gold	Dry
Fairlane	200 Six	Red	Dry
Fairlane	289, 390 V-8 (Except 390 4-V Open Emission System)	Gold Bronze	Dry
Fairlane	390 4 V, V 8—Open Emission System	Gold	Dry
Mustang	200 Six	Red	Dry
Mustang	289 4-V, V-8— High Performance	Gold and Chrome	Dry
Mustang	289 V-8—Except High Performance	Gold	Dry
Comet	200 Six	Yellow	Dry
Comet	289 and 390 2-V, V-8	Yellow	Dry
Comet	390 4-V, V-8	Chrome and Red	Dry

MECHANICAL FUEL PUMPS

FUEL PUMP STATIC PRESSURE—Psi @ 500 Engine rpm	
All..4.0 to 6.0	
MINIMUM FUEL PUMP VOLUME—Flow @ 500 Engine rpm	
All 6-Cyl.............................1 pint in 30 seconds	
All 8-Cyl.............................1 pint in 20 seconds	
MINIMUM INTAKE STATIC VACUUM—Inches of Mercury @ 500 Engine rpm	
All...6.0	
ECCENTRIC TOTAL LIFT	
All 6-Cyl.....................................0.290—0.310	
All 8-Cyl.....................................0.690—0.710	

FUEL TANK CAPACITIES

FALCON (Except Ranchero, Sedan Delivery and Station Wagon)
U. S. Measure..16 gallons
Imperial Measure (Approximate)....................13¼ gallons

FALCON RANCHERO, SEDAN DELIVERY AND STATION WAGON
U. S. Measure..20 gallons
Imperial Measure (Approximate)....................16¾ gallons

COMET
U. S. Measure..20 gallons
Imperial Measure (Approximate)....................16¾ gallons

MUSTANG
U. S. Measure..16 gallons
Imperial Measure (Approximate)....................13¼ gallons

FAIRLANE
U. S. Measure..20 gallons
Imperial Measure (Approximate)....................16¾ gallons

SPECIAL TOOLS

DESCRIPTION	TOOL NUMBER
Choke Plate Staking Pliers	9586
Power Valve Test Fixture	T57L-9904-A
Float Bending Tool	9564-A
Choke Plate Clearance (Pull-Down) Piston Slot Wire Gauge	0.036 inch
Wire Gauges—Specified Clearance Sizes	As Required
Fuel Line Tube Die	T62P-9A274-A

COOLING SYSTEM

GROUP 11

PART 11-1   **PAGE**
GENERAL COOLING SYSTEM
SERVICE 11-1

PART 11-2
WATER PUMP 11-6

PART 11-3
RADIATOR 11-8

PART 11-4   **PAGE**
FAN DRIVE CLUTCH 11-9

PART 11-5
SPECIFICATIONS 11-10

PART 11-1   GENERAL COOLING SYSTEM SERVICE

Section	Page
1 Diagnosis and Testing	11-1
Diagnosis Guide	11-1
Cooling System Pressure Test	11-2
Thermostat Tests	11-2
Fan Drive Clutch Test	11-3
2 Maintenance	11-3
Coolant	11-3
Draining and Filling the Cooling System	11-3
Fan Drive Belts	11-3

Section	Page
3 Common Adjustments and Repairs	11-3
Drive Belts	11-3
Fan Replacement	11-4
Fan Drive Belt Replacement	11-4
Radiator Hose Replacement	11-4
Thermostat Replacement	11-4
4 Cleaning and Inspection	11-5
Cleaning Cooling System	11-5
Water Pump	11-5

This part covers general cooling system service. For cooling system component removal, disassembly, assembly, installation, major repair procedures and specifications, refer to the pertinent part of this group.

Radiator identification on the downflow units can be found on the left hand side bracket, as viewed from the drivers seat. On the crossflow type the identification is marked on the top bracket. The radiator chart can be found in the specification section (Part 11-5). Note that the identification number found on the radiator bracket should be cross ref-erenced to the service part number. Use the service part number to order a new part. As a double check, the number of fins per inch should be checked. However, for accuracy the total fins over at least four inches should be counted; then divided by the number of inches.

1   DIAGNOSIS AND TESTING

DIAGNOSIS

Engine overheating and slow engine warm-up are the two engine troubles most commonly attributed to the cooling system.

Loss of coolant, thermostat stuck in the closed position, restricted air flow through the radiator, or accumulation of rust and scale in the system are the main causes of overheating. Coolant loss may be due to external leakage at the radiator, radiator pressure cap, water pump, hose connections, heater, or core plugs. Coolant loss may also be caused by internal leakage due to a defective cylinder head gasket, improper tightening of the cylinder head bolts, or warped cylinder head or block gasket surfaces.

Internal leakage can be detected by operating the engine at fast idle and looking for the formation of bubbles in the radiator. Oil in the radiator may indicate leakage in the engine block or a leak in the automatic transmission oil cooler. Water formation on the oil level dipstick could also be an indication of internal leakage.

Rust and scale that form in the engine water passages are carried into the radiator passages by the circulation of the coolant. This clogs the radiator passages and causes overheating. Rust can be detected by the appearance of the coolant. If the coolant has a rusty or muddy appearance, rust is present.

A defective thermostat that remains open will cause slow engine warm-up.

DIAGNOSIS GUIDE

ENGINE OVERHEATS	Exhaust control valve sticking (except 170 and 200 engine). Belt tension incorrect. Radiator fins obstructed. Thermostat stuck closed, or otherwise defective. Cooling system passages blocked	by rust, scale or other foreign matter. Water pump inoperative. Faulty fan drive clutch. Ignition initial timing incorrect. Distributor advance incorrect.
ENGINE FAILS TO REACH NORMAL OPERATING TEMPERATURE OR HAS WRONG INDICATED TEMPERATURE	Thermostat stuck open or of incorrect heat range. Temperature sending unit defective (causing gauge to indicate low engine temperature).	Temperature gauge defective (not indicating true engine temperature) or incorrectly installed. Incorrect temperature gauge indication.
LOSS OF COOLANT	Leaking radiator, radiator supply tank, or transmission oil cooler. Loose or damaged hose connections. Water pump leaking. Cylinder head gasket defective. Improper tightening of cylinder	head bolts. Cylinder block core plugs leaking. Cracked cylinder head or block, or warped cylinder head or block gasket surface. Radiator pressure cap defective or wrong type.

TESTING

COOLING SYSTEM PRESSURE TEST

It is recommended that a cooling system pressure test gauge be used to properly test the system for:

1. Blown or leaking cooling system sealing gaskets.
2. Internal or external coolant leakage.
3. Pressure cap malfunction.

Many types of pressure gauges are available for use. Therefore, it is recommended that the gauge manufacturer's instructions be followed when performing the test. **Never exceed the rated pressure indicated on the pressure cap when performing the pressure test.**

THERMOSTAT TEST— THERMOSTAT INSTALLED

The thermostat can be tested without removing it from the engine, by using the Rotunda Thermostat Tester. The engine should be cool (below 115°F.) when starting to perform this test.

1. Loosen the radiator cap to release any pressure; then re-tighten it.
2. Remove the temperature sending unit from the engine. A small amount of coolant may run out of the threaded opening but it should stop almost immediately. **If it does not stop running out, the pressure cap may be defective and should be tested. Replace it if defective.**
3. Calibrate the Rotunda Thermostat Tester by pressing the control

button to the ADJUST position. While holding the control button in the ADJUST position, turn the adjusting knob until the indicator on the upper meter points to the SET position. Push the control switch to the ON position.

4. Screw the engine test probe into the threaded opening from which the temperature sending unit was removed (the dual fitting arrangement provides for use on any engine).
5. Attach the single connector from the Rotunda Thermostat Tester to the engine test probe and ground the tester by attaching the ground wire clip to any convenient place on the engine which will provide a good ground.
6. Remove the radiator cap, attach the double connector, and place the radiator test probe in the filler opening making certain that the probe is well immersed in the coolant.
7. Turn the heater temperature control to the OFF position, start the engine, and allow it to idle.
8. Watch the **lower meter** to read the warmup rate. The needle should move through the RED area into the GREEN (normal) area. This indicates that the thermostat is remaining closed allowing proper warmup. **If the needle remains in the RED area it means that the thermostat is stuck in the open position, is defective, and should be replaced.**
9. When the lower meter needle

reaches the GREEN area, the upper meter needle will move toward the opening temperature of the thermostat. When this (upper metering) needle reaches the approximate opening temperature of the thermostat, the lower meter needle should move back through the RED area. When this happens, you can, by observing the upper meter needle, know that the thermostat is functioning and know at what temperature it is opening.

On six cylinder engines, the upper meter will momentarily drop somewhat below the thermostat opening temperature. This is normal and is due to the sending unit being located at the rear of the cylinder head.

THERMOSTAT TEST— THERMOSTAT REMOVED

It is good practice to test new thermostats before installing them in the engine.

Remove the thermostat and immerse it in boiling water. Replace the thermostat if it does not open more than ¼ inch.

If the problem being investigated is insufficient heat, the thermostat should be checked for leakage. This may be done by holding the thermostat up to a lighted background. Light leakage around the thermostat valve (thermostat at room temperature) is unacceptable and the thermostat should be replaced. It is possible, on some thermostats, that a slight leakage of light at one or two locations on the perimeter of the valve may be detected. This should be considered normal.

FAN DRIVE CLUTCH TEST

1. Run the engine at approximately 1000 rpm until normal operating temperature is reached. This process can be speeded up by blocking off the front of the radiator with cardboard. Regardless of temperatures, the unit must be operated for at least five minutes immediately before being tested.

2. Stop the engine and, using a cloth to protect the hand, immediately check the effort required to turn the fan. If considerable effort is required, it can be assumed that the coupling is operating satisfactorily. If very little effort is required to turn the fan, it is an indication that the coupling is not operating properly, and it should be replaced.

2 MAINTENANCE

COOLANT

Correct coolant level is essential for maximum circulation and adequate cooling. In addition, for the cooling system to perform its function, it must receive proper care. This includes keeping the radiator fins clean and a periodic inspection of the cooling system for leakage.

Use care when removing the radiator cap to avoid injury from escaping steam or hot water.

In production, the cooling system is filled with a long-life coolant mixture which prevents corrosion, keeps the cooling system clean, provides anti-freeze protection to −35°F in winter and provides for summer operation at system temperatures up to 250°F without boiling.

For the most effective cooling system operation, this mixture strength should be maintained all year round and in all climates.

All coolant added should be a 50-50 mixture of Rotunda permanent anti-freeze and water.

To avoid possible overheating in very hot weather, do not use mixtures with more than 50% anti-freeze except in areas where anti-freeze protection below −35° is required. In this case, refer to the coolant mixture chart on the Rotunda permanent anti-freeze container.

Whenever the system is completely refilled, add a can of Rotunda Radiator Rust Inhibitor.

A standard ethylene glycol hydrometer can be used to check the protection level of the long-life coolant.

Refer to Group 19 for the recommended cooling system drain interval.

DRAINING AND FILLING THE COOLING SYSTEM

To prevent loss of anti-freeze when draining the radiator, attach a hose on the radiator drain cock and drain the anti-freeze from the radiator into a clean container.

To drain the radiator, open the drain cock located at the bottom of the radiator. The 6-cylinder engine block has one drain plug located at the right rear of the cylinder block, ahead of the starter (Fig. 1). The V-8 engines have a drain plug on each side of the cylinder block.

To fill the cooling system, close the drain cock. Install the block drain plug(s). Disconnect the heater outlet hose at the water pump to bleed or release trapped air in the system. When the coolant begins to escape, connect the heater outlet hose.

Operate the engine until normal operating temperature is reached, and add more coolant, if necessary, to fill the radiator to the proper level, one inch below bottom of filler neck.

FIG. 1—Typical Cylinder Block Drain Plug

After the initial fill the coolant level may drop approximately one quart after the engine has been operated about 20 minutes at 2000 rpm. This is due to the displacement of entrapped air. Refill to the proper level.

FAN DRIVE BELTS

If the fan drive belt(s) are noisy, check the tension of the belts to make certain they are within specifications. Also, check for misaligned pulleys. If the drive belts are worn or frayed, replace them following the procedures in Part 11-1, Section 3.

3 COMMON ADJUSTMENTS AND REPAIRS

ADJUSTMENTS

DRIVE BELTS

The fan drive belt(s) should be properly adjusted at all times. A loose drive belt(s) causes improper alternator, fan and water pump operation. A belt(s) that is too tight places a severe strain on the water pump and the alternator bearings.

Properly tensioned drive belts minimize noise and also prolong service life of the belt. Therefore, it is recommended that a belt tension gauge be used to check and adjust the belt tension. **Any belt that has operated for a minimum of 10 minutes is considered a used belt, and** when adjusted, it must be adjusted to the reset tension shown in the specifications.

Belt Tension

1. Install the belt tension tool on the drive belt (Fig. 2) and check the tension following the instructions of the tool manufacturer.

Tool—T63L-8620-A

B1573-B

FIG. 2—Checking Drive Belt Tension

2. If adjustment is necessary, loosen the alternator mounting and adjusting arm bolts. Move the alternator toward or away from the engine until the correct tension is obtained. Tighten the alternator adjusting arm and the mounting bolts. Check the belt tension.

REPAIRS

FAN REPLACEMENT

6-Cylinder Engines

1. Loosen the fan belt. Remove the capscrews and lock washers retaining the fan to the water pump hub. Remove the fan.

2. Position the fan on the water pump hub. Install the lock washers and capscrews and torque the capscrews to specifications. Adjust the fan belt.

V-8 Engines

On a car with an air conditioner or extra-cooling radiator, a fan drive clutch may be used. Cars without air conditioning utilize a pulley-to-fan spacer.

1. Remove the radiator upper support and fan guard. Loosen the fan belt. Remove the capscrews and lock washers retaining the fan and spacer (or fan drive clutch) to the water pump hub. Remove the fan and spacer (or fan drive clutch).

2. If equipped with a fan drive clutch, remove the retaining capscrews and lock washers and separate the fan from the drive coupling. Position the replacement fan on the drive clutch and install the lock washers and capscrews.

3. Position the fan and spacer (or drive clutch) on the water pump hub and install the lock washers and capscrews. Torque the capscrews

evenly and alternately to specifications. Adjust the fan belt tension to specifications. Install the radiator upper support and fan guard.

FAN DRIVE BELT REPLACEMENT

1. On a car with power steering, loosen the power steering pump bracket at the water pump and remove the drive belt.

On a car with an air conditioner, remove the compressor drive belt.

2. Loosen the alternator mounting and adjusting arm bolts. Move the alternator toward the engine. Remove the belt(s) from the alternator and crankcase pulleys, and lift them over the fan.

3. Place the belt(s) over the fan. Insert the belt(s) in the water pump pulley, crankshaft pulley and alternator pulley grooves. Adjust the belt tension to specifications.

4. On a car with an air conditioner, install and adjust the compressor drive belt to specifications.

5. On a car with power steering, install the power steering pump drive belt and tighten the pump bracket to the water pump. Adjust the drive belt tension to specifications.

RADIATOR HOSE REPLACEMENT

Radiator hoses should be replaced whenever they become cracked, rotted or have a tendency to collapse.

1. Drain the radiator; then loosen the clamps at each end of the hose to be removed. Slide the hose off the radiator connection and the radiator supply tank connection (upper hose) or the water pump connection (lower hose).

2. Position the clamps at least ⅛" from each end of the hose. Slide the hose on the connections. **Make sure the clamps are beyond the bead and placed in the center of the clamping surface of the connections.** Tighten the clamps. Fill the radiator with coolant. Operate the engine for several minutes; then check the hoses and connections for leaks. Check for proper coolant level after the engine has reached normal operating temperature.

THERMOSTAT REPLACEMENT

A poppet-type thermostat is mounted in a recess in the coolant outlet passage at the front of the intake manifold on the V-8 engines. On 6-cylinder engines, the thermostat is located in the coolant outlet

passage at the front of the cylinder head. When the thermostat is closed, coolant flows to the water pump through a bypass passage at the front of the engine. When the thermostat is open, coolant flows through the coolant outlet elbow (thermostat housing) to the radiator.

The thermostat used in production is for use with water or permanent-type anti-freeze. A thermostat is also available for use with non-permanent-type anti-freeze or water. For operating temperatures, refer to specifications.

Check the thermostat before installing it following the procedure under "Thermostat Test", Part 11-1.

Do not attempt to repair the thermostat. It should be replaced if it is not operating properly.

Removal

1. Drain the cooling system below the level of the coolant outlet housing.

2. Remove the coolant outlet housing retaining bolts and slide the housing (with the hose attached) to one side.

3. Remove the thermostat and gasket.

Installation

1. Clean the coolant outlet housing and cylinder head surface. Coat a new coolant outlet housing gasket with sealer. Position the gasket on the cylinder head or intake manifold (289 V-8). **The gasket must be positioned on the cylinder head or intake manifold before the thermostat is installed.**

2. Coat the edge of the thermostat with grease for thermostat adhesion. Position the thermostat in the recess of the coolant outlet housing so that the copper pellet or heat element will be in the cylinder head or intake manifold (289 V-8). Install the thermostat with the word TOP toward the top of the engine and the valve end of the thermostat facing outward. **If the thermostat is improperly positioned, it will cause the engine to overheat.**

3. Position the coolant outlet housing and install the retaining screws. Torque the screws to specifications.

4. Fill the radiator. Operate the engine and check for coolant leaks and proper coolant level after the engine reaches normal operating temperature.

4 CLEANING AND INSPECTION

CLEANING COOLING SYSTEM

To remove rust, sludge and other foreign material from the cooling system, use Rotunda Cooling System Cleanser. Removal of such material restores cooling efficiency and avoids over-heating.

In severe cases where cleaning solvents will not properly clean the cooling system for efficient operation, it will be necessary to use the pressure flushing method.

Various types of flushing equipment are available. If pressure flushing is used, make sure the cylinder head bolts are properly tightened to prevent possible water leakage into the cylinders.

Always remove the thermostat prior to pressure flushing.

A pulsating or reversed direction of flushing water flow will loosen sediment more quickly than a steady flow in the normal direction of coolant flow.

WATER PUMP

1. Clean the gasket mounting surfaces of the water pump and cylinder block.

2. Clean and inspect the seal seating surface of the water pump.

3. Clean the pump housing and inspect it for cracks, sand holes, improper machining, and damaged surfaces. If the water pump housing is damaged beyond repair, replace the complete water pump.

PART 11-2   WATER PUMP

Section	Page
1 Description and Operation	11-6
2 Removal and Installation	11-6
170 Six and 200 Six Engines	11-6

Section	Page
289 V-8	11-6
390 V-8	11-7

1 DESCRIPTION AND OPERATION

On 6-cylinder engines, a centrifugal-type water pump is mounted on the front of the cylinder block. On the 289 V-8, the centrifugal-type water pump is mounted on the cylinder front cover. On the 390 V-8 the centrifugal-type water pump is mounted at two points on the cylinder block. The water pump inlet port is connected to the radiator bottom tank to draw coolant from the radiator when the thermostat is open. On the V-8 engines, a bypass port on the water pump is connected to the coolant outlet housing to permit coolant circulation within the engine when the thermostat is closed, bypassing the radiator. On the 6-cylinder engines, the water pump bypass passage is aligned with a bypass passage in the cylinder block for coolant circulation in the engine when the thermostat is closed.

A vane-type, impeller supplies coolant through centrifugal action to the water pump outlet port on 6-cylinder engines. On the V-8 engines, the water pump has two outlet ports, one for each cylinder bank, to provide uniform coolant circulation in both banks of the engine.

The water pumps have a sealed bearing integral with the water pump shaft. The bearing requires no lubrication. A bleed hole in the water pump housing allows water that may leak past the seal to be thrown out by the slinger. **This is not a lubrication hole.**

The cooling fan hub is pressed a specified distance onto the water pump shaft.

2 REMOVAL AND INSTALLATION

170 SIX AND 200 SIX

REMOVAL

1. Drain the cooling system.

On a car with power steering, remove the power steering drive belt.

On a car with air conditioning, remove the compressor drive belt.

2. Disconnect the radiator lower hose at the water pump. Remove the drive belt, fan, or fan and drive clutch, and water pump pulley.

3. Disconnect the heater hose at the water pump.

4. Remove the water pump.

INSTALLATION

Before a water pump is re-installed, check it for damage. If it is damaged and requires repair, replace it *with a new pump* or *install a rebuilt pump* obtained from a Ford-Authorized Reconditioner.

1. If a new water pump is to be installed, remove the heater hose fitting from the old pump and install it on the new pump. Clean the gasket surfaces on the water pump and cylinder block.

2. Coat a new gasket on both sides with water-resistant sealer and position it on the cylinder block.

3. Position the water pump in place and install the lock washers and retaining bolts (the alternator adjusting arm is retained by one water pump bolt). Torque the bolts to specifications.

4. Connect the radiator lower hose and the heater hose to the water pump.

5. Install the water pump pulley and fan or fan and drive clutch. Torque the bolts evenly and alternately to specifications.

6. Install the drive belt and adjust the tension to specifications.

On a car with power steering, install the drive belt and adjust the tension to specifications.

On a car with air conditioner, install the compressor drive belt and adjust the tension to specifications.

7. Fill and bleed the cooling system. Operate the engine until normal operating temperature is reached. Check for leaks and check the coolant level.

289 V-8

REMOVAL

1. Drain the cooling system.

On a car with power steering, re- move the power steering drive belt. Remove the power steering pump and bracket, as an assembly, and position to one side.

On a car with an air conditioner, remove the compressor drive belt.

2. Disconnect the radiator lower hose and heater hose at the water pump. Loosen and remove the drive belt. Remove the fan, fan spacer or fan drive clutch and pulley.

3. Loosen the bypass hose clamp at the water pump.

4. Remove the bolts retaining the pump to the cylinder front cover. Remove the pump and gasket. Discard the gasket.

INSTALLATION

Before a water pump is re-installed, check it for damage. If it is damaged and requires repair, replace it with a new pump or install a rebuilt pump obtained from a Ford-Authorized Reconditioner.

1. Remove all gasket material from the mounting surfaces of the cylinder front cover and water pump.

2. Position a new gasket, coated on both sides with water-resistant sealer, on the cylinder front cover; then install the pump.

3. Install the retaining bolts and torque them to specifications.

On a car with power steering, install the power steering pump and the drive belt and adjust the tension to specifications.

On a car with an air conditioner, install the compressor drive belt and adjust the tension to specifications.

4. Install the pulley, spacer or fan drive clutch and fan. Install and adjust the drive belt to the specified belt tension. Connect the radiator hose and heater hose.

5. Fill and bleed the cooling system. Operate the engine until normal operating temperatures have been reached and check for leaks.

390 V-8

REMOVAL

1. Drain the cooling system.

On a car with power steering remove the power steering drive belt; then remove the power steering pump and bracket as an assembly, and po-

sition to one side. If so equipped, remove the air conditioner drive belt.

2. Disconnect the lower radiator hose, and the heater hose at the water pump.

3. Loosen and remove the fan belt. Remove the fan, the spacer, and the water pump pulley.

4. Loosen the bypass hose clamp at the water pump.

5. Remove the alternator and position it to one side.

6. Remove the retaining bolts, and remove the water pump.

INSTALLATION

Before a water pump is re-installed, check it for damage. If it is damaged and requires repair, replace it with a new pump or install a rebuilt pump obtained from a Ford-Authorized Reconditioner.

1. Remove all gasket material from the mounting surfaces of the block and the water pump.

2. Coat new gaskets on both sides with water resistant sealer. Position

them on the block.

3. Apply water resistant sealer to the bypass fitting and, sliding the bypass hose into position, install the pump and the retaining bolts, and torque them to specifications.

4. Install the alternator.

5. Tighten the bypass hose clamp at the water pump.

6. Install the water pump pulley, the spacer, and the fan. Install the retaining screws, and torque them to specifications. Install and adjust the fan belt.

7. Connect the lower radiator hose and the heater hose at the water pump.

On a car with power steering install the power steering pump and bracket assembly, and install and adjust the drive belt. If so equipped, install and adjust the air conditioner drive belt.

8. Fill and bleed the cooling system. Operate the engine until normal operating temperatures have been reached, and check for leaks.

PART 11-3   RADIATOR

Section   **Page**
1 Description and Operation 11-8

Section   **Page**
2 Removal and Installation 11-8

1 DESCRIPTION AND OPERATION

The radiators are of the tube and corrugated-fin-core type with the tubes arranged for vertical flow of the coolant. Two header tanks, one on the top and one on the bottom of the radiator provide uniform distribution of the coolant to the tubes. The radiator outlet port (lower header tank) is connected to the water pump inlet port. The radiator inlet port (upper header tank) is connected to the coolant outlet housing of the engine, thereby permitting coolant circulation through the radiator when the thermostat is open.

2 REMOVAL AND INSTALLATION

REMOVAL

1. Drain the cooling system. Disconnect the radiator upper and lower hoses at the radiator.

2. On a car with automatic transmission, disconnect the oil cooler lines at the radiator.

3. Remove the radiator support bolts and remove the radiator.

INSTALLATION

1. If a new radiator is to be installed, remove the drain cock from the old radiator and install it in the new radiator. On a car with automatic transmission, remove the oil cooler line fittings from the old radiator, and install them in the new radiator, using oil-resistant sealer.

2. Position the radiator assembly and install the support bolts.

3. Connect the radiator upper and lower hoses.

On a car with automatic transmission, connect the oil cooler lines.

4. Close the drain cock. Fill and bleed the cooling system.

5. Operate the engine and check for leaks at the hose connections and the automatic transmission oil cooler lines. Check the automatic transmission fluid level.

PART 11-4   FAN DRIVE CLUTCH

Section	Page	Section	Page
1 Description and Operation	11-9	2 Removal and Installation	11-9

1   DESCRIPTION AND OPERATION

The fan drive clutch (Fig. 3) is a fluid coupling containing silicone oil. Fan speed is regulated by the torque-carrying capacity of the sili-

FIG. 3—Typical Fan Drive Clutch Installation

cone oil. The more silicone oil in the coupling the greater the fan speed, and the less silicone oil the slower the fan speed.

Two types of fan drive clutches are available. On one (Fig. 4) a bimetallic strip and control piston on the front of the fluid coupling regulates the amount of silicone oil entering the coupling. The bi-metallic

strip bows outward with a decrease in surrounding temperature and allows a piston to move outward. The

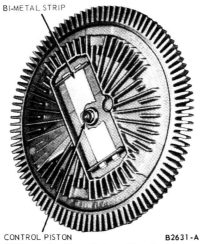

FIG. 4—Fan Drive Clutch With Flat Bi-Metal Spring

piston opens a valve regulating the flow of silicone oil into the coupling from a reserve chamber. The silicone oil is returned to the reserve chamber through a bleed hole when the valve is closed.

On the other type of fan drive clutch (Fig. 5) a heat-sensitive, bi-metal spring connected to an

opening plate brings about a similar result. Both units cause the fan speed to increase with a rise in tempera-

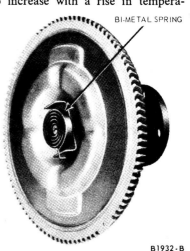

FIG. 5—Fan Drive Clutch With Flat Coil Bi-Metal Spring

ture and to decrease as the temperature goes down.

In some cases a Flex-Fan is used instead of a Fan Drive Clutch. Flexible blades vary the volume of air being drawn through the radiator, automatically increasing the pitch at low engine speeds.

2   REMOVAL AND INSTALLATION

REMOVAL

1. Loosen the fan belt. Remove the capscrews retaining the fan drive clutch to water pump hub (Fig. 4). Remove the fan drive clutch and fan as an assembly.
2. Remove the retaining capscrews

and separate the fan from the drive clutch.

INSTALLATION

1. Position the fan on the drive clutch and install and tighten the retaining capscrews evenly and alternately to specifications.

2. Position the fan drive clutch and fan assembly to the water pump hub (Fig. 4). Install and tighten the retaining capscrews evenly and alternately to specifications. Check the fan clutch mounting face for proper alignment.
3. Adjust the fan belt.

PART 11-5 SPECIFICATIONS

COOLING SYSTEM CAPACITY

	Approximate Capacity① (Quarts)	
	U.S. Measure	Imperial Measure
STANDARD COOLING SYSTEM		
170 and 200....................	9½	8
289..........................	15	12½

① Includes heater. If deleted, subtract one quart.

THERMOSTATS

LOW TEMPERATURE	
OPENS °F	
170 and 200........................	157°-164°
289.............................	155°-162°
FULLY OPEN	
170 and 200........................	184°-186°
289.............................	182°
HIGH TEMPERATURE	
OPENS °F	
170 and 200........................	185°-192°
289.............................	188°-195°
FULLY OPEN	
170 and 200........................	211°-214°
289.............................	210°-212°

WATER PUMP

WATER PUMP DRIVE ARRANGEMENT
Water pump, fan and alternator drive belt from crankshaft damper.

WATER PUMP PULLEY TO ENGINE RATIO
Standard Cooling and Air Conditioner—Equipped
170...1.04:1
200...1.18:1
289...1.04:1
289 (With Thermactor)...................1.13:1

WATER PUMP ASSEMBLY DIMENSIONS
Front Face of Pulley Hub to Pump Housing Face
170 and 200................................3.94
289...5.426
Impeller to Housing Cover Mounting Surface Clearance
170 and 200.........................0.011-0.045
289.................................0.030-0.050

DRIVE BELT TENSION

ALL BELTS	LBS.
New...110-140
Used (any belt operated over 10 minutes).................80-110

TORQUE VALUES

NOTE: All specifications are given in Ft-Lbs. unless otherwise noted.

Water Pump to Cylinder Block (or Cylinder Front Cover)	
All Engines.................................12-15
Water Outlet Housing	
All Engines.................................12-15
Fan and Spacer to Pulley Hub	
All Engines.................................10-15
Fan to Fan Clutch (with a/c)	
All Engines.................................10-15
Radiator to Front End Sheet Metal	
All Engines.................................8-13
Radiator to Engine Hose Clamps	
All Engines.................................1.0-2.5
Transmission Oil Cooler Tube Hose to Radiator	
Fairlane....................................8-12
Transmission Oil Cooler Tube Nut to Bottom of Radiator	
All Except Fairlane.........................10-15
Radiator Inlet and Outlet Hose Clamps	
All Engines.................................1.0-2.5

SPECIAL SERVICE TOOLS

FORD TOOL NO.	FORMER TOOL NO.	DESCRIPTION
T63-8620-A	8620-A	Belt Tension Gauge

RADIATOR AND COOLING FAN IDENTIFICATION

Radiator dimensions are given for the core only; do not measure the mounting flanges or header tanks.

CAR, ENGINE AND COOLING	RADIATOR IDENTIFICATION Dimensions—Inches				TRANSMISSION		THERMACTOR EQUIPPED		RADIATOR SERVICE PART NUMBER	FANS—DIAMETER X BLADE WIDTH AND NO. BLADES (4)	
	Depth	Height	Width	Fins/Inch	Std.	Auto.	No	Yes		W/O Thermactor	W/Thermactor
COMET 200 Six											
Std. Cool.	1.27	17.38	17.24	8	X		X	X	C60Z-E	15.50 x 1.40(4)	15.50 x 1.40(4)
Std. Cool.	1.27	17.38	17.24	10		X	X	X	C60Z-E	15.50 x 1.40(4)	15.50 x 1.40(4)
Ext. Cool.	1.27	17.38	20.24	11	X	X	X	X	C30Z-F	17.00 x 2.00(5)	17.00 x 2.00(5)
Air. Cond.	1.27	17.38	20.24	11	X	X	X	X	C30Z-F	①17.00 x 1.75(6)	17.00 x 1.75(6)
298 V-8 Std. Cool.	1.27	17.38	17.24	11	X	X	X	X	C50Z-D	17.50 x 2.00(4)	17.00 x 1.75(4)
Ext. Cool.	1.27	17.38	20.24	15	X	X	X	X	C50Z-C	17.00 x 2.00(5)	17.00 x 2.00(5)
Air. Cond.	1.27	17.38	20.24	15	X	X	X	X	C50Z-C	①17.50 x 2.00(7)	17.50 x 2.00(7)
390 V-8 Std. Cool.	1.27	17.38	23.24	10	X		X	X	C60Z-B	18.50 x 2.00(4)	18.50 x 2.00(4)
Std. Cool.	1.95	17.38	23.24	9		X	X	X	C60Z-D	18.50 x 2.00(4)	18.50 x 2.00(4)
Ext. Cool.	1.95	17.38	23.24	14	X	X	X	X	C60Z-A	18.00 x 2.00(7)	18.00 x 2.00(7)
Air. Cond.	1.95	17.38	23.24	14	X	X	X	X	C60Z-A	①18.00 x 2.00(7)	18.00 x 2.00(7)
FALCON 170 Six											
Std. Cool.	1.27	16.44	17.24	8	X		X	X	C6DZ-A	15.50 x 1.40(4)	16.00 x 1.40(4)
Std. Cool.	1.27	16.44	17.24	10		X	X	X	C6DZ-A	15.50 x 1.40(4)	16.00 x 1.40(4)
Std. Cool.	1.27	17.38	17.24	8	X		X	X	C60Z-E	15.50 x 1.40(4)	16.00 x 1.40(4)
Std. Cool.	1.27	17.38	17.24	10		X	X	X	C60Z-E	15.50 x 1.40(4)	16.00 x 1.40(4)
Ext. Cool.	1.27	17.38	20.24	11	X	X	X	X	C30Z-F	15.50 x 1.40(4)	16.00 x 1.40(4)
Air Cond.	1.27	17.38	20.24	11	X	X	X	X	C30Z-F	①17.00 x 1.75(6)	17.00 x 1.75(6)
200 Six Std. Cool.	1.27	16.44	17.24	10	X		X	X	C6DZ-C	15.50 x 1.40(4)	16.00 x 1.40(4)
Std. Cool.	1.27	16.44	17.24	12		X	X	X	C6DZ-C	15.50 x 1.40(4)	16.00 x 1.40(4)
Std. Cool.	1.27	17.38	17.24	8	X		X	X	C60Z-E	15.50 x 1.40(4)	16.00 x 1.40(4)
Std. Cool.	1.27	17.38	17.24	10		X	X	X	C60Z-E	15.50 x 1.40(4)	16.00 x 1.40(4)
Ext. Cool.	1.27	17.38	20.24	11	X	X	X	X	C30Z-F	15.50 x 1.40(4)	16.00 x 1.40(4)
Air. Cond.	1.27	17.38	20.24	11	X	X	X	X	C30Z-F	①17.00 x 1.75(6)	17.00 x 1.75(6)
289 V-8 Std. Cool.	1.27	16.44	17.24	10	X		X	X	C6DZ-B	17.50 x 2.00(4)	17.50 x 2.00(4)
Std. Cool.	1.27	16.44	17.24	12		X	X	X	C6DZ-B	17.50 x 2.00(4)	17.50 x 2.00(4)
Std. Cool.	1.27	17.38	17.24	11	X	X	X	X	C50Z-D	17.50 x 2.00(4)	17.50 x 2.00(4)
Ext. Cool.	1.27	17.38	20.24	15	X	X	X	X	C50Z-C	17.00 x 2.00(5)	17.00 x 2.00(5)
Air. Cond.	1.27	17.38	20.24	15	X	X	X	X	C50Z-C	①17.50 x 2.00(7)	17.50 x 2.00(7)
FAIRLANE 200 Six											
Std. Cool.	1.27	17.38	17.24	8	X		X	X	C60Z-E	15.50 x 1.40(4)	15.50 x 1.40(4)
Std. Cool.	1.27	17.38	17.24	10		X	X	X	C60Z-E	15.50 x 1.40(4)	15.50 x 1.40(4)
Ext. Cool.	1.27	17.38	20.24	11	X	X	X	X	C30Z-F	17.00 x 2.00(5)	17.00 x 2.00(5)
Air Cond.	1.27	17.38	20.24	11	X	X	X	X	C30Z-F	①17.00 x 1.75(6)	17.00 x 1.75(6)
289 V-8 Std. Cool.	1.27	17.38	17.24	11	X	X	X	X	C50Z-D	17.50 x 2.00(4)	17.00 x 1.75(4)
Ext. Cool.	1.27	17.38	20.24	15	X	X	X	X	C50Z-C	17.00 x 2.00(5)	17.00 x 2.00(5)
Air Cond.	1.27	17.38	20.24	15	X	X	X	X	C50Z-C	①17.50 x 2.00(7)	17.50 x 2.00(7)

RADIATOR AND COOLING FAN IDENTIFICATION (Continued)

CAR, ENGINE AND COOLING	RADIATOR IDENTIFICATION Dimensions—Inches				TRANSMISSION		THERMACTOR EQUIPPED		RADIATOR SERVICE PART NUMBER	FANS—DIAMETER X BLADE WIDTH AND NO. BLADES (4)	
	Depth	Height	Width	Fins/Inch	Std.	Auto.	No	Yes		W/O Thermactor	W/Thermactor
FAIRLANE (Cont'd) 390 V-8											
Std. Cool.	1.27	17.38	23.24	10	X		X	X	C6OZ-B	18.50 x 2.00(4)	18.50 x 2.00(4)
Std. Cool.	1.95	17.38	23.24	9		X	X	X	C6OZ-D	18.50 x 2.00(4)	18.50 x 2.00(4)
Ext. Cool.	1.95	17.38	23.24	14	X	X	X	X	C6OZ-A	18.00 x 2.00(7)	18.00 x 2.00(7)
Air Cond.	1.95	17.38	23.24	14	X	X	X	X	C6OZ-A	①18.00 x 2.00(7)	18.00 x 2.00(7)
MUSTANG 200 Six											
Std. Cool.	1.27	16.44	17.24	9	X		X		C5ZZ-C	15.50 x 1.40(4)	
Std. Cool.	1.27	16.44	17.24	10	X			X	C5ZZ-C		16.00 x 1.40(4)
Std. Cool.	1.27	16.44	17.24	11		X	X		C5ZZ-C	15.50 x 1.40(4)	
Std. Cool.	1.27	16.44	17.24	12		X		X	C5ZZ-C		16.00 x 1.40(4)
Ext. Cool.	1.27	16.44	17.24	13	X		X	X	C5ZZ-C	15.50 x 1.40(4)	16.00 x 1.40(4)
Ext. Cool.	1.27	16.44	17.24	15		X	X	X	C5ZZ-C	15.50 x 1.40(4)	16.00 x 1.40(4)
Air Cond.	1.27	16.44	17.24	13	X		X	X	C5ZZ-C	②15.00 x 2.00(6)	15.00 x 2.00(6)
Air Cond.	1.27	16.44	17.24	15		X	X	X	C5ZZ-C	15.00 x 2.00(6)	15.00 x 2.00(6)
289 V-8 Std. Cool.	1.27	16.44	17.24	10	X		X	X	C3DZ-K	17.50 x 2.00(4)	17.00 x 2.00(5)
Std. Cool.	1.27	16.44	17.24	12		X	X	X	C3DZ-K	17.50 x 2.00(4)	17.00 x 2.00(5)
Ext. Cool.	1.27	16.44	17.24	12	X		X	X	C3DZ-K	17.50 x 2.00(4)	17.00 x 2.00(5)
Ext. Cool.	1.27	16.44	17.24	15		X	X	X	C3DZ-K	17.50 x 2.00(4)	17.00 x 2.00(5)
Air Cond.	2.20	16.00	17.24	11½	X	X	X	X	C6ZZ-A	③17.50 x 2.00(7)	17.50 x 2.25(7)

① Selectaire ② Economy

EXHAUST SYSTEM

GROUP 12

PART 12-1   **PAGE**
GENERAL EXHAUST SYSTEM SERVICE .. 12-1

PART 12-2
EXHAUST PIPES, MUFFLERS AND
CONTROL VALVE 12-5

PART 12-3   **PAGE**
THERMACTOR EXHAUST EMISSION
CONTROL SYSTEM 12-16

PART 12-4
SPECIFICATIONS 12-23

PART 12-1 GENERAL EXHAUST SYSTEM SERVICE

Section   **Page**
1 Diagnosis and Testing 12-1
  Exhaust System Diagnosis 12-1
  Thermactor Exhaust Emission Control
    System Diagnosis 12-2
  Exhaust Control Valve Test 12-2
  Check Valve Test 12-3
  Anti-Backfire Valve Test 12-3
  Air Supply Pump Test 12-3
2 Common Adjustments and Repairs 12-3
  Exhaust System Alignment 12-3

Section   **Page**
  Exhaust Control Valve Maintenance 12-4
  Mufflers, Inlet Pipes and Outlet
    Pipes 12-4
  Thermactor Exhaust Emission Control
    System 12-4
3 Cleaning and Inspection 12-4
  Exhaust System 12-4
  Thermactor Exhaust Emission Control
    System 12-4

This part covers general exhaust system diagnosis, tests, adjustment and repair procedures. In addition, the cleaning and inspection procedures are covered.

For exhaust system component removal, disassembly, assembly, installation, major repair procedures and specifications, refer to the pertinent part of this group.

Always refer to the Master Parts Catalog for parts usage and interchangeability before replacing a component part of the exhaust system.

1 DIAGNOSIS AND TESTING

DIAGNOSIS

EXHAUST SYSTEM

Exhaust system performance complaints, such as excessive back pressure or a sticking exhaust control valve, are usually noticeable by their effect on engine performance.

An exhaust control valve that is stuck in the open position will result in poor engine performance during initial warm-up, because the heat passing through the intake manifold heat riser is insufficient for proper fuel atomization.

On V-8 engines, if the valve is stuck in the closed position, the intake manifold will be supplied with excessive heat after the initial warm-up period. This will cause poor acceleration, a lack of power, and poor high speed performance.

However, other defective, malfunctioning, or improperly adjusted components have similar effects on engine performance and are characterized by the same symptom or complaint. Thus, for diagnosis of exhaust system problems that affect engine performance, refer to Part 8-1, Section 1.

External leaks in the exhaust system are often accompanied by noises or greyish-white smoke emitted from under the car. Small leaks are usually inaudible and not visible. A visual inspection of the exhaust system usually will show the location of a leak. Look for holes, ruptured joints and eroded areas in the muffler(s), resonator(s), inlet pipe(s) and outlet pipe(s). Examine joints and connections for greyish white deposits that would be caused by exhaust gas leakage.

A misaligned exhaust system is usually indicated by vibration, grounding, rattling, or binding of the components. Often the associated noise is hard to distinguish from other chassis noises. Look for broken or loose clamps and brackets and replace or tighten as necessary. The exhaust system components should be inspected for proper alignment, and the necessary adjustments should be made to maintain the installation clearances shown in Part 12-3. If this does not eliminate the noise (symptom or complaint), examine the chassis for possible location of the problem. Be sure the noise is isolated to and caused by the exhaust system before replacing any of the components.

DIAGNOSIS GUIDE

THERMACTOR EXHAUST EMISSION CONTROL SYSTEM

A preliminary "Diagnosis Guide" is included below as an aid in trouble shooting the Thermactor exhaust emission control system.

Prior to performing any extensive diagnosis of the Thermactor system, **it must be determined that the engine as a unit is functioning properly.** Disconnect the anti-backfire valve vacuum sensing and air supply lines at the intake manifold connections. Plug the manifold connections to preclude leakage. Normal engine diagnosis procedures (Part 8-1) can then be performed.

EXCESSIVE BACKFIRE IN EXHAUST SYSTEM	Anti-backfire valve vacuum line collapsed, plugged, disconnected or leaking. Defective or malfunctioning anti-	backfire valve resulting in insufficient air delivery to the intake manifold or air delivery not timed to engine requirement.
EXCESSIVE HESITATION ON ACCELERATION AFTER SUDDEN THROTTLE PLATE CLOSURE (ABOVE 20 MPH)	Intake vacuum leak at anti-backfire valve vacuum line or air outlet line (to intake manifold).	Defective or malfunctioning anti-backfire valve.
AIR SUPPLY HOSE(S) BAKED OR BURNED	Defective check valve on air supply manifold(s).	
NOISY AIR PUMP DRIVE BELT	Drive belt improperly adjusted. Seized or failing air pump.	Misaligned or defective pulleys.
ROUGH ENGINE IDLE	Improper carburetor adjustment —idle speed, idle fuel mixture, automatic choke, etc., (Group 10). Improper initial ignition timing. Intake vacuum leak at the anti-	backfire valve vacuum line or air inlet hose. Anti-backfire valve defective or stuck open.
ENGINE SURGES AT ALL SPEEDS	Anti-backfire valve defective or stuck open. Improper carburetor adjustment—	idle speed, idle fuel mixture, automatic choke, etc., (Group 10).

TESTING

EXHAUST CONTROL VALVE

Check the thermostatic spring of the valve to make sure it is hooked on the stop pin. To check the exhaust control valve on the car, make sure the spring holds the valve closed. Actuate the counterweight by hand to make sure it moves freely through approximately 90° of rotation without binding.

The closed and open positions of the exhaust control valve for the 390 V-8 are shown in Fig. 1.

The valve is closed when the engine is cold. However, a properly operating valve will open when very light finger pressure is applied to the counterweight. Rapidly accelerate

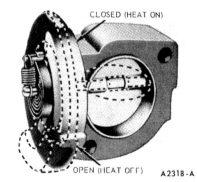

FIG. 1—390 V-8 Engine Exhaust Control Valve

the engine to make sure the valve momentarily opens. The valve is de-

signed to open when the engine is at normal operating temperature and is operated at high rpm.

THERMACTOR EXHAUST EMISSION CONTROL SYSTEM

The following procedures are recommended for checking and/or verifying that the various components of the Thermactor exhaust emission control system are operating properly. **The engine and all components must be at normal operating temperatures when the tests are performed.**

Prior to performing any extensive *diagnosis of the* Thermactor system, it must be determined that the engine **as a unit** is functioning properly. Disconnect the anti-backfire valve vacuum sensing and air supply lines at the intake manifold connections. Plug the manifold connections to preclude leakage. Normal engine diagnosis procedures (Part 8-1) can then be performed.

Check Valve Test

This test can be performed at the same time as the Air Pump Test.

1. Operate the engine until it reaches normal operating temperature.

2. Inspect all hoses and hose connections for obvious leaks and correct as necessary before checking the check valve operation.

3. Disconnect the air supply hose(s) at the check valve on the air manifold(s).

4. Visually inspect the position of the valve plate inside the valve body. It should be lightly positioned against the valve seat—away from the air manifold.

5. Insert a probe into the hose connection on the check valve and depress the valve plate. It should freely return to the original position, against the valve seat, when released.

If equipped with two air manifold and check valve assemblies, check both valves for free operation.

6. Leave the hose(s) disconnected and start the engine. Slowly increase the engine speed to 1500 rpm and watch for exhaust gas leakage at the check valve(s). **There should not be any exhaust leakage.** The valve may flutter or vibrate at idle speeds, but this is normal due to the exhaust pulsations in the manifold.

7. If the check valve(s) does not meet the recommended conditions (steps 4, 5 and 6), replace it.

Anti-Backfire Valve Test

1. Operate the engine until it reaches normal operating temperature.

2. Inspect all hoses and hose connections for obvious leaks, and correct as necessary before checking the anti-backfire valve operation.

3. Disconnect the pressure air hose (from air pump) at the anti-backfire valve. Insert a suitable plug in the hose and fasten it securely with a hose clamp **to prevent air pressure from blowing out the plug.**

4. Connect a vacuum gauge to the air pressure (hose) connection on the anti-backfire valve.

5. Operate the engine at normal idle speed with the transmission in neutral.

6. The vacuum gauge should indicate zero vacuum. If a vacuum is indicated, the anti-backfire valve is not seating properly and it should be replaced.

7. Open and close the throttle rapidly. The vacuum gauge indicator should move up scale rapidly and slowly settle back to zero. Repeat several times. If the gauge fails to respond, the valve is not functioning properly and should be replaced.

Air Supply Pump Test

1. Assemble a test gauge adapter as shown in Fig. 2, and install a fuel pump test gauge on the adapter. **The test gauge used must be accurate and readable in ¼ psi increments.**

2. Operate the engine until it reaches normal operating temperature.

3. Inspect all hoses and hose connections for leaks and correct as necessary before checking the air supply pump.

4. Check the air pump belt tension and adjust to specifications.

5. Disconnect the air supply hose(s) at the air manifold check valve(s). If there are two check valves, close off one hose by inserting a suitable plug in the end of the hose. **Use a hose clamp and secure the plug so it will not blow out.**

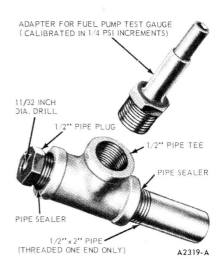

FIG. 2—Air Supply Pump Test Gauge Adapter

6. Insert the open pipe end of the test gauge adapter in the other air supply hose. **Clamp the hose securely to the adapter to prevent it from blowing out.**

Position the adapter and test gauge so that the air blast emitted through the drilled pipe plug will be harmlessly dissipated.

7. Install a tachometer on the engine. Start the engine and slowly increase the engine speed to 1500 rpm. Observe the pressure produced at the test gauge. The air pressure should be one (1) psi or more.

8. If the air pressure does not meet or surpass the above pressures, disconnect and plug the air supply hose to the anti-backfire valve. Clamp the plug in place, and repeat the pressure test.

If the air pump pressure still doesn't meet the minimum requirement, install a new air pump filter element and repeat the pump test. Replace the air pump filter element and/or air pump as determined by the result of this test.

---

2 COMMON ADJUSTMENTS AND REPAIRS

ADJUSTMENTS

The exhaust system must be free of leaks, binds, grounding and excessive vibration.

Exhaust system vibration, grounding or binds are usually caused by: loose, broken or improperly aligned clamps, or brackets, or improperly connected pipes. Any of the aforementioned conditions may cause changes to clearances of the exhaust system components. If any of these conditions exist, the exhaust system components must be checked, adjusted or replaced to make certain the specified clearances (refer to the illustrations in Part 12-2) are maintained.

EXHAUST SYSTEM ALIGNMENT

Refer to the pertinent illustration in Part 12-2 for the clearance specifications and location of components.

Perform the following procedure to adjust the exhaust system components:

1. Loosen the pipe connection clamps and the pipe support bracket clamp(s). Loosen the inlet pipe to exhaust manifold retaining nuts.

2. Torque the exhaust manifold to inlet pipe retaining nuts evenly and alternately to specification to insure uniform pressure on the seal and inlet pipe flange.

3. Work from the front of the car toward the rear and progressively adjust the exhaust system components and clamps at the various pipe connections to relieve binds and improper pipe connections. **Be sure the inlet and outlet pipes and mufflers are aligned so that all clearances are within the limits shown on the illustrations in Part 12-2.** Then torque the clamps to specification.

4. Check the exhaust system for leaks.

REPAIRS

EXHAUST CONTROL VALVE MAINTENANCE

Refer to Group 19 for the recommended maintenance mileage interval.

The exhaust control valve, if the car is so equipped, should be periodically checked to make certain it is operating properly. A valve that is struck in the open position will result in poor engine performance during initial warm-up, because the heat passing through the intake manifold heat riser is insufficient for proper fuel atomization.

On V-8 engines, if the valve is stuck in the closed position, the intake manifold will be supplied with excessive heat after the initial warm-up period. This will cause poor acceleration, a lack of power, and will cause poor high speed performance in general.

Lubricate the valve with FoMoCo Exhaust Control Valve Solvent (COAZ-19A501-A).

MUFFLERS, INLET PIPES AND OUTLET PIPES

Brackets, clamps and insulators should be replaced if they are defective or become badly corroded. Do not attempt repair of these parts.

THERMACTOR EXHAUST EMISSION CONTROL SYSTEM

Air Nozzles

For cleaning and inspection of the air nozzles, refer to Section 3.

Air Pump Air Cleaner

Replace the air cleaner filter element at the recommended maintenance interval. Refer to the maintenance chart in Group 19.

---

3 CLEANING AND INSPECTION

EXHAUST SYSTEM

INSPECTION

Inspect the inlet pipe(s), outlet pipe(s), resonator(s) and muffler(s) for cracked joints, broken welds and corrosion damage (holes) that would result in a leaking exhaust system. Inspect the clamps, brackets and insulators for cracks and stripped or badly corroded bolt threads. When pipe clamp(s) are loosened and/or removed to replace a pipe, muffler or resonator, replace the clamp(s), if there is reasonable doubt that its service life is limited.

Check the exhaust control valve. Be sure the thermostatic spring is hooked on the stop pin. Move the counterweight by hand to make sure it moves freely throughout its normal travel range (approximately 90° of rotation).

THERMACTOR EXHAUST EMISSION CONTROL SYSTEM

CLEANING AND INSPECTION

Anti-Backfire Valve

Do not attempt to clean the anti-backfire valve.

Air Pump Air Cleaner

When replacing the air cleaner element, clean the air cleaner body

with a low-volatility, petroleum-base solvent, and wipe it dry with a clean, lint-free cloth.

Hoses, Lines And Air Manifolds

Normally, the air hoses, vacuum line and air manifolds should be cleaned only during major engine overhaul. If malfunctions or restrictions occur in the system, these components may require cleaning. Use a low-volatility, petroleum-base solvent and a suitable stiff bristle brush. Dry the cleaned parts, except the check valve, with compressed air. **Do not blow compressed air through the check valve in either direction. Shake it dry.**

Air Nozzles

With the air nozzles removed, clean the nozzle tips with a wire brush. Clean the nozzle air hole with a $5/16$-inch-diameter stiff wire brush. Inspect the air nozzles for eroded, burned or damaged tips that would restrict the normal air flow. Inspect the connections for stripped or damaged threads and damaged tube nut seats.

Air Supply Pump

The air supply pump is protected against the entrance of foreign ma-

terial by the air cleaner. Thus, it should require cleaning only when it is being overhauled.

Do not immerse the rotor and housing assembly in solvent as the bearing is permanently lubricated.

Clean the vane and bearing assemblies and rotor ring and rear bearing assembly in a clean petroleum-base solvent. **Do not use compressed air to dry the bearings. Shake the bearings to remove excess solvent, and let them drain dry.**

Inspect the bearings for discoloration, uneven rotation or looseness, and replace as required.

Wipe the rotor, housing and cover assembly with a cloth dampened in cleaning solvent. Wipe the parts dry with a clean cloth. Use compressed air to blow all carbon dust out of the rotor and housing assembly.

Clean the carbon shoes and shoe springs by wiping with a clean, dry cloth.

Inspect the vanes and carbon shoes for grooves or scores that would permit air leakage. Place each vane on the shaft (cover assembly) and check it for loose or worn bearings. Inspect the shaft for grooves and worn areas that might cause early wear on the vane and bearing assemblies.

Replace all worn, defective or broken parts.

PART 12-2 EXHAUST PIPES, MUFFLERS AND CONTROL VALVE

Section	Page
1 Description	12-5
Single Exhaust Systems	12-5
Dual Exhaust Systems	12-5
2 Removal and Installation	12-5

Section	Page
Exhaust Control Valve Replacement—	
390 V-8	12-5
Single Exhaust Systems	12-6
Dual Exhaust Systems	12-6

1 DESCRIPTION

The exhaust systems for the various car models are shown in Figs. 1 through 7.

SINGLE EXHAUST SYSTEMS

The single exhaust system on cars with a six cylinder engine (Figs. 1 through 4) consists of a muffler inlet pipe and muffler with integral outlet pipe assembly.

The single exhaust system on cars with a 289 V-8 engine (Figs. 1 through 4) consists of a Y-type muffler inlet pipe and muffler inlet pipe extension, muffler with integral outlet pipe assembly.

The single exhaust system for the Fairlane and Comet with a 390 V-8 engine (Fig. 5) consists of a Y-type muffler inlet pipe, inlet pipe extension with integral resonator and a muffler with integral outlet pipe.

DUAL EXHAUST SYSTEMS

The dual exhaust system for the Fairlane and Comet with a 390 V-8 engine (Fig. 6) consists of an H-type muffler inlet pipe and an integral inlet pipe extension and muffler and outlet pipe assembly for each side.

The dual exhaust system for the Mustang with a 289 4-V high performance engine (Fig. 7) consists of a H-type muffler inlet pipe, resonator, muffler and inlet pipe extension assemblies, and outlet pipe extensions.

The location and type of exhaust system gaskets, retaining clamps and loop-type support brackets are shown in the respective exhaust system illustrations. The loop-type support brackets eliminate tension on the supports due to thermal expansion of the system.

2 REMOVAL AND INSTALLATION

The replacement procedures given apply to all car models and to right and left assemblies on dual and single exhaust systems unless otherwise noted. Typical exhaust systems for the various car models are shown in Figs. 1 through 7.

EXHAUST CONTROL VALVE REPLACEMENT—390 V-8
SEDANS AND STATION WAGONS
Removal

1. Remove the retaining bolts or clamps securing the muffler(s) and outlet pipes to the support bracket and insulator assemblies (Figs. 5 and 6).

2. Temporarily support the muffler, inlet pipe and outlet pipe assembly(ies) with soft wire.

3. Remove the nuts securing the inlet pipe to both exhaust manifolds.

4. Pull the inlet pipe rearward and remove the exhaust control valve and all mounting gaskets. Discard the gaskets.

5. Clean the exhaust control valve and the flanges of the exhaust manifolds and inlet pipe. Replace all defective or damaged parts.

Installation

1. Place a new gasket on the exhaust control valve and position it over the studs of the right exhaust manifold (Figs. 5 and 6). Place new gasket(s) on the inlet pipe flange(s).

2. Install the muffler inlet pipe on the exhaust manifolds. Install the retaining nuts and torque them to specifications.

3. Attach the mufflers and outlet pipes to the support bracket and insulator assembly(ies). Tighten the bolts or clamp to specifications.

4. Remove the temporary support wire.

5. Adjust the exhaust system components to conform to the clearance specifications (Figs. 5 and 6). Properly position the respective clamps and brackets. Working from the front of the exhaust system toward the rear, progressively torque the retaining bolts, nuts and clamps to specifications.

6. Check the exhaust system for leaks.

CONVERTIBLES
Removal

1. Remove the nuts securing the inlet pipe to the right exhaust manifold (Fig. 6).

2. Remove the choke heat tubes from the manifold. Remove the right exhaust manifold retaining bolts and remove the exhaust manifold from the cylinder head along with the exhaust control valve. Discard the gaskets.

3. Clean the exhaust control valve and the flanges of the exhaust manifold and inlet pipe. Replace all damaged or defective parts.

Installation

1. Place a new gasket on the exhaust control valve, and position it over the studs of the right exhaust manifold (Fig. 6). Place a new

gasket on the inlet pipe flange.

2. Install the right exhaust manifold with the exhaust control valve to the engine and inlet pipe. Install the exhaust manifold bolts and inlet pipe retaining nuts, and torque to specifications.

3. Install the choke heat tubes to the right exhaust manifold.

4. Check the exhaust system for leaks.

SINGLE EXHAUST SYSTEMS

MUFFLER AND OUTLET PIPE ASSEMBLY

The single exhaust systems for the various car models are shown in (Figs. 1 through 5).

Removal

1. Loosen the inlet pipe clamp at the muffler, and slide the clamp forward onto the inlet pipe.

2. Remove the clamp attaching the outlet pipe to the rear support bracket. Remove the bolts that retain the muffler assembly to the rear support bracket (if so equipped).

3. Support the inlet pipe with soft wire. Separate the muffler from the inlet pipe and remove the muffler and outlet pipe assembly.

4. Replace any damaged parts.

Installation

1. Slide the muffler and outlet pipe assembly onto the inlet pipe, and position the inlet pipe to muffler clamp.

2. Install the bolts or clamp that retain the muffler assembly to the rear support bracket snug, but not tight.

3. Adjust the exhaust system and torque the retaining bolts and clamps to specifications. Remove the temporary support wire.

4. Start the engine and check the exhaust system for leaks.

RESONATOR AND INLET PIPE EXTENSION

Removal

1. Loosen the inlet pipe extension clamp at the muffler (Fig. 5) and slide it forward.

2. Loosen the inlet pipe extension clamp at the Y-inlet pipe. Support the inlet pipe with soft wire. Remove the clamp attaching the resonator support to resonator outlet pipe.

3. Separate the inlet pipe extension from the muffler and from the Y-inlet pipe, and remove the inlet

pipe extension and resonator assembly.

4. Replace any damaged parts.

Installation

1. Position the inlet pipe extension and resonator assembly to the Y-inlet pipe and to the muffler (Fig. 5). Position the retaining clamps the specified distance from the end of of the pipe, and tighten them snug, but not tight.

2. Adjust the exhaust system and torque the clamps to specifications.

3. Remove the temporary support wire. Start the engine and check the exhaust system for leaks.

INLET PIPE—6-CYLINDER ENGINES

Removal

1. Loosen the inlet pipe to muffler clamp (Figs. 1 through 4). Remove the clamp attaching the inlet pipe to intermediate support bracket (if so equipped). Temporarily support the muffler with soft wire. Remove the clamp securing the inlet pipe to engine bracket.

2. On Mustang convertibles, remove the front floor lower crossmember plate.

3. Remove the nuts that secure the inlet pipe to the exhaust manifold. Remove the inlet pipe.

4. Clean the gasket surface of the exhaust manifold.

5. Discard the gasket and replace any damaged parts.

Installation

1. Install a new gasket on the inlet pipe flange (Figs. 1 through 4).

2. Install the inlet pipe to the muffler and exhaust manifold and install the retaining nuts on the studs of the manifold snug, but not tight. Position the inlet pipe to muffler retaining clamp.

3. Position the inlet pipe to engine bracket retaining clamp. Connect the inlet pipe to the muffler and position the inlet pipe to muffler clamp. Position the inlet pipe to the intermediate support bracket (if so equipped) and loosely install the retaining clamp. Remove the temporary support wire.

4. Adjust the exhaust system components to conform to the clearance specifications. Working from the front of the car toward the rear, progressively torque the retaining nuts and clamps to specifications. On Mustang convertibles, install the front floor lower crossmember plate.

5. Start the engine and check the exhaust system for leaks.

INLET PIPE—V-8 ENGINES

Removal

1. Loosen the clamp at the inlet pipe to inlet pipe extension and slide it rearward (Figs. 1 through 5).

2. Remove the clamp attaching the inlet pipe to intermediate support bracket (if so equipped). Loosen the inlet pipe extension to muffler clamp and separate the inlet pipe extension from the muffler. Temporarily support the inlet pipe extension in position with soft wire.

3. Remove the retaining nuts securing the inlet pipe to exhaust manifolds. Slide the inlet pipe out of the inlet pipe extension and remove the inlet pipe from the exhaust manifolds.

On sedans and station wagons with a 390 V-8, remove the exhaust control valve from the right exhaust manifold.

On a convertible with a 390 V-8, remove the right exhaust manifold and exhaust control valve.

4. Clean the gasket surfaces of the exhaust manifolds, inlet pipe and exhaust control valve (if so equipped). Discard the gaskets and replace any damaged parts.

Installation

1. Install new gaskets on the inlet pipe flanges (Figs. 1 through 5).

On sedans and station wagons with a 390 V-8, place a new gasket on the exhaust control valve, and install it on the right exhaust manifold.

On a convertible with a 390 V-8, place a new gasket on the studs of the exhaust manifold and install the exhaust control valve. Install the exhaust manifold with exhaust control valve to the engine. Torque the manifold bolts to specifications.

2. Install the inlet pipe on the exhaust manifolds, and install the retaining nuts on the manifold studs snug, but not tight.

3. Connect the inlet pipe to the inlet pipe extension and position the clamp. Place the inlet pipe extension and clamp on the muffler. Position the inlet pipe to the intermediate support bracket (if so equipped) and install the retaining clamp. Tighten all clamps snug, but not tight. Remove the soft wire used to temporarily support the inlet pipe extension.

4. Adjust the exhaust system components to conform to the clearance

specifications. Working from the front of the car toward the rear, progressively torque the nuts and retaining clamps to specifications.

5. Start the engine and check the exhaust system for leaks.

DUAL EXHAUST SYSTEMS

OUTLET PIPES—FAIRLANE AND COMET

Removal

1. Loosen the outlet pipe clamp at the muffler(s) and slide the clamp(s) forward onto the muffler (Fig. 6). Temporarily support the muffler with soft wire.
2. Loosen the clamp on the outlet pipe(s) and slide the clamp off the support bracket.
3. Separate the outlet pipe(s) from the muffler(s) and remove the outlet pipe(s) from the car.
4. Replace any damaged parts.

Installation

1. Slide the outlet pipe(s) onto the muffler(s) (Fig. 6). Position the muffler(s) to the support bracket assembly and position the clamp the proper distance from the end of the outlet pipe(s). Tighten the clamp(s) snug, but not tight.
2. Position the outlet pipe(s) to the support bracket(s) and install the clamp. Tighten the clamp snug, but not tight.
3. Adjust the exhaust system and torque the clamps to specification. Remove the temporary support wire.
4. Start the engine and check the exhaust system for leaks.

OUTLET PIPE EXTENSION(S)—MUSTANG

Removal

1. Loosen the outlet pipe extension to muffler clamp and slide it forward (Fig. 7).
2. Loosen the outlet pipe extension to support bracket clamp and slide it forward.
3. Remove the outlet pipe extension from the muffler.
4. Replace any damaged or defective parts.

Installation

1. Place the clamps on the outlet pipe extension and install it on the muffler.
2. Position the outlet pipe extension to muffler clamp and outlet pipe extension to support bracket clamp, and tighten the clamps snug, but not tight.

3. Adjust the exhaust system and torque the clamps to specifications.
4. Start the engine and check the exhaust system for leaks.

MUFFLER AND INLET PIPE EXTENSION ASSEMBLY—FAIRLANE AND COMET

Removal

1. Remove the outlet pipe(s) (Fig. 6).
2. Loosen the clamp(s) at the H-pipe (muffler inlet pipe) and inlet pipe extension assembly and slide the clamp(s) forward.
3. Remove the muffler and inlet pipe extension assembly(ies) from the vehicle.
4. Replace any damaged parts.

Installation

1. Slide the muffler and inlet pipe extension assembly(ies) onto the H-pipe (Fig. 6). Support the rear of the muffler(s) with the support bracket(s).
2. Position the clamp on the connection between the H-pipe and the muffler and inlet pipe extension assembly. Tighten the clamp snug, but not tight.
3. Install the outlet pipe(s).
4. Adjust the exhaust system to specifications. Starting from the front of the car, progressively torque the retaining clamps to specifications.
5. Start the engine and check the exhaust system for leaks.

MUFFLER AND INLET PIPE EXTENSION ASSEMBLY—MUSTANG

Removal

1. Remove the outlet pipe extension(s) (Fig. 7). Support the muffler outlet pipe(s) with soft wire.
2. Loosen the H-pipe (muffler inlet pipe) clamp(s) at the muffler inlet pipe extension(s). Slide the clamp(s) forward onto the H-pipe. Support the H-pipe with soft wire.
On convertible models, remove the front floor lower crossmember plate.
3. Remove the bolts or clamps attaching the muffler(s) to the intermediate support bracket(s).
4. Remove the muffler assembly(ies) from the H-pipe, and remove the muffler and inlet pipe extension assembly(ies) from the car.
5. Replace all damaged or defective parts.

Installation

1. Position the muffler assembly

(ies) in the vehicle (Fig. 7). Support the muffler outlet pipe(s) with soft wire.
2. Slide the muffler assembly(ies) into the H-pipe. Position the H-pipe clamp(s) and tighten it snug, but not tight.
3. Install, but do not tighten, the muffler to intermediate support bracket bolts or clamp(s).
4. Install the outlet pipe extension(s). **Adjust the exhaust system components to conform to the clearance specifications,** and torque all clamps and bolts to specifications. Remove the temporary support wire.
On convertible models, install the front floor lower crossmember plate.
5. Start the engine and check the exhaust system for leaks.

H-PIPE (MUFFLER INLET PIPE)—FAIRLANE AND COMET

Removal

1. Loosen the clamps (Fig. 6) attaching the muffler and inlet pipe extension assemblies to the H-pipe (muffler inlet pipe) and slide them rearward.
2. Loosen the clamps attaching the intermediate support brackets to the mufflers and slide them off the brackets.
3. Remove the bolts attaching the outlet pipes to the rear support brackets. Temporarily support the outlet pipes with soft wire.
4. Slide the muffler and inlet pipe extension assemblies from the H-pipe. Temporarily support the muffler and inlet pipe extension assemblies with soft wire.
5. Remove the retaining nuts securing the H-pipe to the exhaust manifolds, and remove the H-pipe from the vehicle.
On sedans and station wagons, remove the exhaust control valve from the right exhaust manifold.
On convertibles, remove the right exhaust manifold and exhaust control valve.
6. Clean the gasket surfaces of the exhaust manifolds, H-pipe and exhaust control valve.
7. Discard the gaskets and replace any worn or damaged parts.

Installation

1. On convertibles only, place a new gasket on the studs of the right exhaust manifold and install the exhaust control valve. Install the exhaust manifold with control valve on the engine.
On sedans and station wagons,

place a new gasket on the exhaust control valve, and install it on the right exhaust manifold.

2. Install new gaskets on the H-pipe flanges (Fig. 6). Install the H-pipe on the exhaust manifolds and tighten the retaining nuts snug, but not tight.

3. Slide the muffler and inlet pipe extension assemblies onto the H-pipe and position the clamps on the connections to specifications. Tighten the clamps snug, but not tight.

4. Position the mufflers to the support brackets and install the clamps. Tighten the clamps snug, but not tight.

5. Position the outlet pipes to the support brackets and install the clamps. Tighten the clamps snug, but not tight.

6. Adjust the exhaust system components to conform to the clearance specifications shown in Fig. 6. Working from the front of the car toward the rear, progressively torque the clamps and retaining nuts to specifications. Remove the soft wire used to temporarily support the exhaust system.

7. Start the engine and check the exhaust system for leaks.

H-PIPE (MUFFLER INLET PIPE)—MUSTANG

Removal

1. Loosen the H-pipe (muffler inlet pipe) clamp(s) at the muffler inlet pipe) extension(s) (Fig. 7), and slide the clamps rearward onto the inlet pipe extensions.

On convertible models, remove the front floor lower crossmember plate.

2. Support the outlet pipe extensions with soft wire. Loosen both outlet pipe extension to support bracket clamps. Slide the clamps forward onto the outlet pipe extensions. **On models with the outlet pipe extension protruding through the modesty panel, be sure the pipe is properly supported to avoid damage to the chrome bell and bezel.**

3. Remove the bolts or clamps attaching the mufflers to the intermediate support brackets. Support the muffler assemblies with soft wire.

4. Remove the retaining nuts securing the H-pipe to the exhaust manifolds.

5. Separate the H-pipe from the muffler inlet pipe extensions and remove the H-pipe from the car. Temporarily support the inlet pipe extensions with soft wire.

6. Clean the gasket surfaces of the H-pipe and exhaust manifolds. Discard the gaskets. Replace any damaged or defective parts.

Installation

1. Install new gaskets on the H-pipe flanges and install the H-pipe in the car (Fig. 7). With the H-pipe held in position, tighten the retaining nuts snug, but not tight.

2. Slide the muffler inlet pipe extensions onto the H-pipe. Position the clamps and tighten them snug, but not tight.

3. Install the bolts or clamps attaching the mufflers to the intermediate support brackets. Tighten the bolts or clamps snug, but not tight.

4. Position the outlet pipe extension clamps and tighten them snug, but not tight. **Adjust the exhaust system components to conform to the clearance specifications.** Working from the front of the car towards the rear, progressively torque the bolts and clamps to specifications. Remove the temporary support wires.

On convertible models, install the front floor lower crossmember plate.

5. Start the engine and check the exhaust system for leaks.

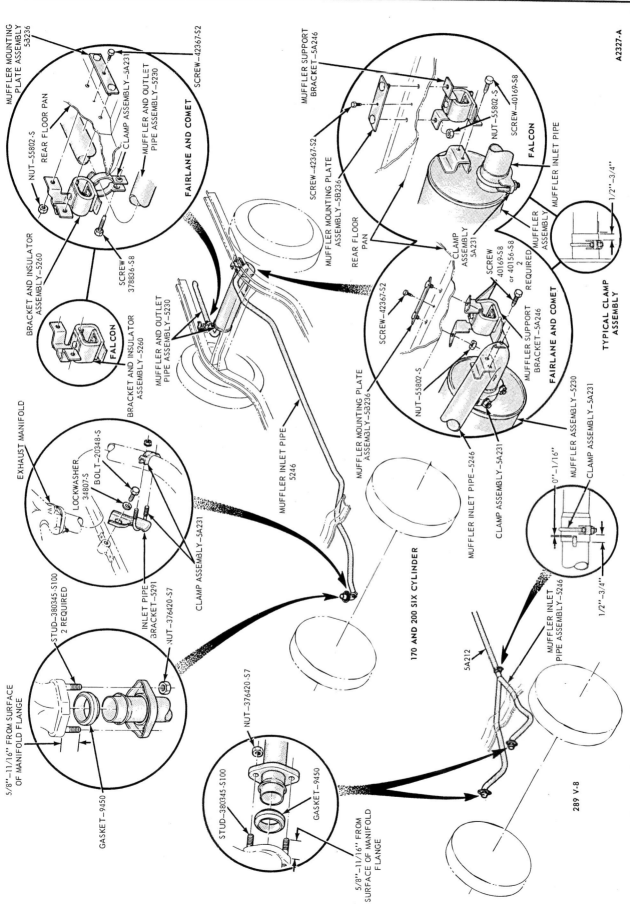

A2327-A

FIG. 1—Fairlane, Falcon and Comet Single Exhaust System—Sedan and Convertible (170, 200 and 289 Engines)

A2328-A

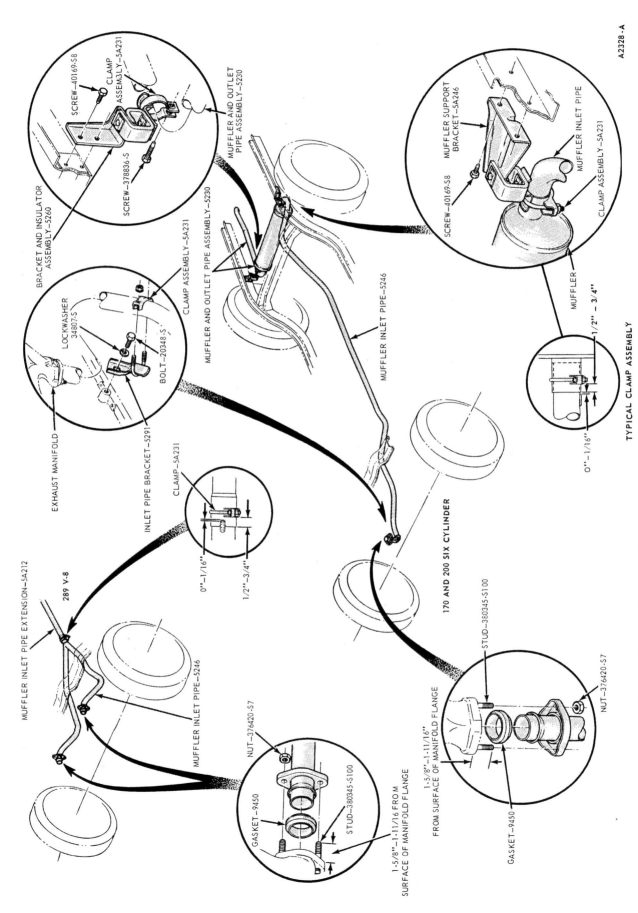

FIG. 2—Falcon Single Exhaust System—Station Wagon (170, 200 and 289 Engines)

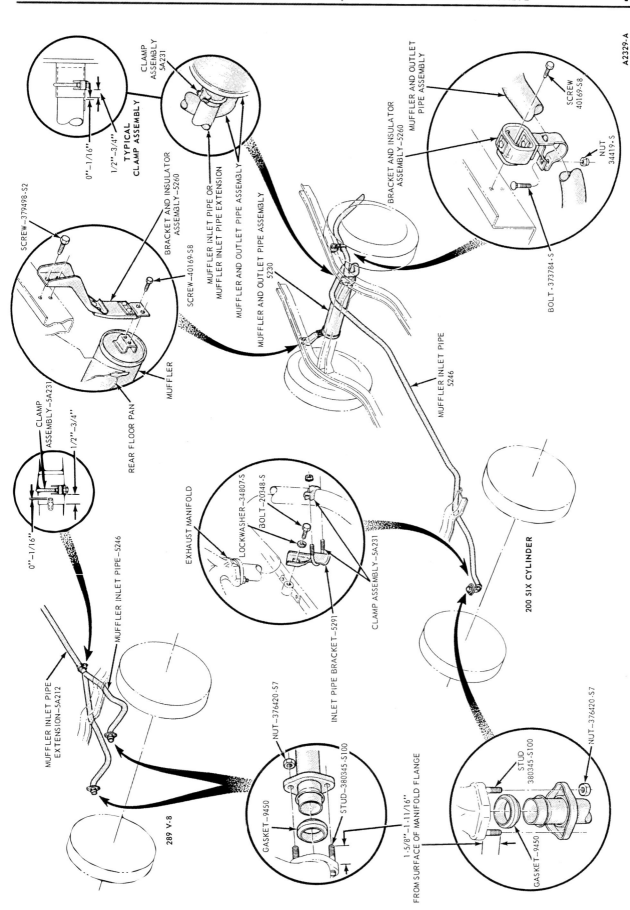

A2329-A

FIG. 3—Fairlane and Comet Single Exhaust System—Station Wagon (170, 200 and 289 Engines)

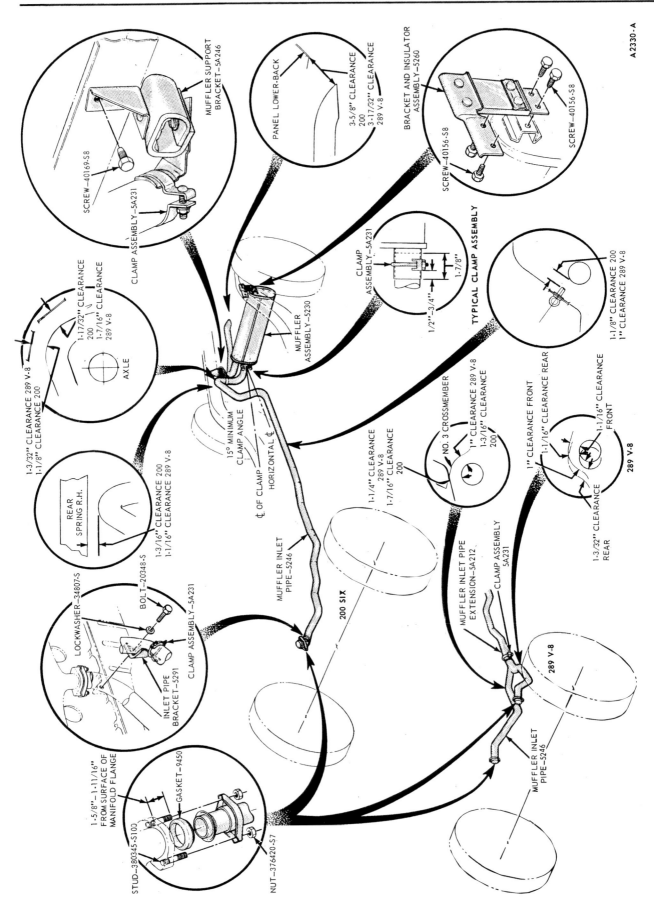

A2330-A

SCREW-40169-S8

MUFFLER SUPPORT BRACKET-5A246

CLAMP ASSEMBLY-5A231

PANEL LOWER-BACK

3-5/8" CLEARANCE 200
3-17/32" CLEARANCE 289 V-8

BRACKET AND INSULATOR ASSEMBLY-5260

SCREW-40156-S8

SCREW-40156-S8

CLAMP ASSEMBLY-5A231

MUFFLER ASSEMBLY-5230

TYPICAL CLAMP ASSEMBLY

1/2"-3/4"

1-7/8"

1-1/8" CLEARANCE 200
1" CLEARANCE 289 V-8

1-17/32" CLEARANCE 200
1-7/16" CLEARANCE 289 V-8

AXLE

1-3/32" CLEARANCE 289 V-8
1-1/8" CLEARANCE 200

15° MINIMUM CLAMP ANGLE

¢ OF CLAMP HORIZONTAL ¢

REAR SPRING R.H.

1-3/16" CLEARANCE 200
1-1/16" CLEARANCE 289 V-8

NO. 3 CROSSMEMBER

1" CLEARANCE 289 V-8
1-3/16" CLEARANCE 200

1-1/4" CLEARANCE 289 V-8
1-7/16" CLEARANCE 200

1" CLEARANCE FRONT

1-1/16" CLEARANCE REAR

1-1/16" CLEARANCE FRONT

289 V-8

1-3/32" CLEARANCE REAR

MUFFLER INLET PIPE-5246

200 SIX

LOCKWASHER-34807-S

BOLT-20348-S

CLAMP ASSEMBLY-5A231

INLET PIPE BRACKET-5291

MUFFLER INLET PIPE EXTENSION-5A212

CLAMP ASSEMBLY 5A231

289 V-8

MUFFLER INLET PIPE-5246

1-5/8"-1-11/16" FROM SURFACE OF MANIFOLD FLANGE

GASKET-9450

STUD-380345-S100

NUT-376420-S7

FIG. 4—Mustang Single Exhaust System (170, 200 and 289 Engines)

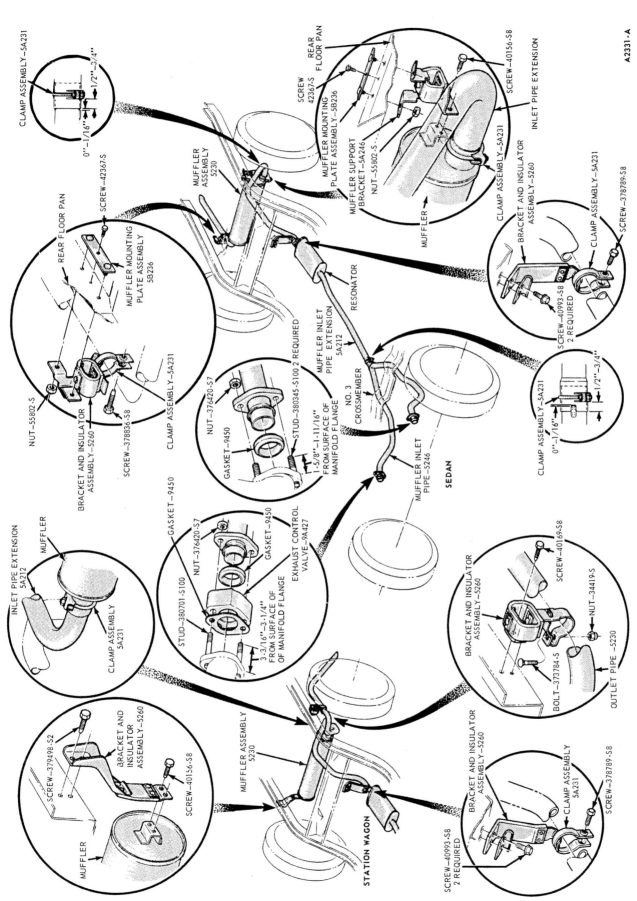

FIG. 5—Fairlane and Comet Single Exhaust System—Sedan and Station Wagon (390 V-8)

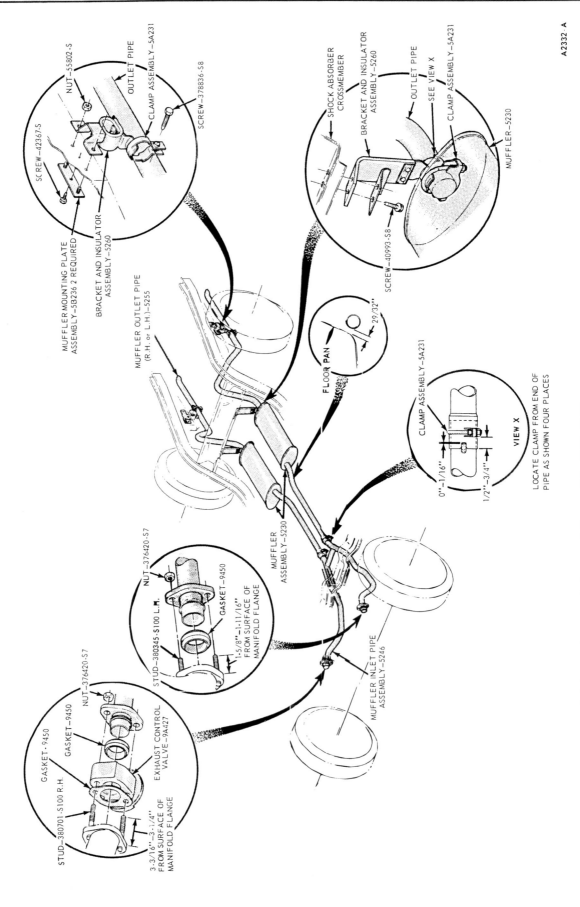

A2332-A

FIG. 6—Fairlane and Comet Dual Exhaust System—Sedan and Convertible (390 V-8)

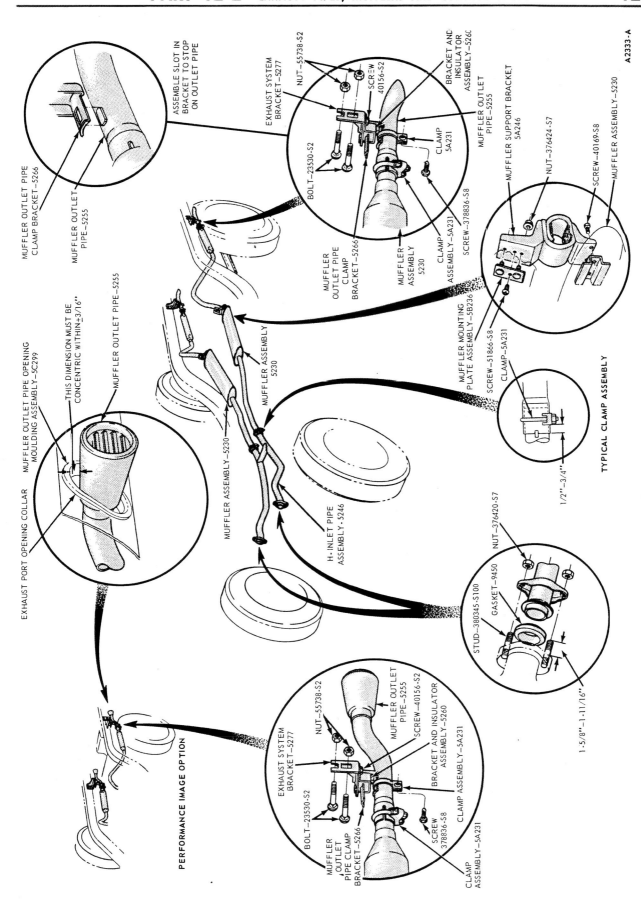

FIG. 7—Mustang Dual Exhaust System (High Performance 289 V-8)

PART 12-3 THERMACTOR EXHAUST EMISSION CONTROL SYSTEM

Section	Page
1 Description and Operation	12-16
2 In-Car Adjustments and Repairs	12-19
Drive Belt Adjustment	12-19
3 Removal and Installation	12-19
Air Pump Air Cleaner Element Replacement	12-19
Air Cleaner	12-19
Drive Belt Replacement	12-20
Anti-Backfire Valve	12-20

Section	Page
Check Valve Replacement	12-20
Air Manifold	12-20
Air Nozzle Replacement	12-20
Drive Pulley Replacement	12-20
Air Supply Pump	12-20
4 Major Repair Operations	12-21
Air Supply Pump	12-21
Relief Valve Replacement	12-22

1 DESCRIPTION AND OPERATION

The Thermactor exhaust emission control system is designed to reduce the hydrocarbon and carbon monoxide content of gasoline engine exhaust gases. By controlling the amount of contaminants emitted through the exhaust system to an acceptable minimum, air pollution is reduced.

Control of exhaust-emitted gases by the Thermactor system is achieved by burning the hydrocarbon and carbon monoxide concentrations in the exhaust ports of the cylinder head(s). To accomplish this burning of the contaminants, air under pressure is injected into the exhaust ports near each exhaust valve. The oxygen in the air plus the heat of the exhaust gases in each exhaust outlet port induces combustion during the exhaust stroke of the piston. The burned gases then flow out the exhaust manifold into the exhaust system.

The Thermactor system consists of: an air supply pump; an air manifold for each cylinder head; an anti-backfire valve; an air cleaner; a check valve on each air manifold; an air nozzle for the exhaust port of each engine cylinder; and the connecting air supply hoses and vacuum sensing line. On some engines, the ignition distributor and carburetor are specially calibrated.

A schematic of the Thermactor system is shown in Fig. 1, and the anti-backfire valve is shown in Fig. 2. Installation drawings for each engine series are included (Figs. 3, 4 and 5).

Air under pressure from the pump flows through a hose(s) to the air manifold(s) that distributes the air to the air nozzle in each exhaust port.

A check valve is incorporated in the inlet air side of the air manifold. The check valve prevents a backflow of exhaust gases into the air pump during operating periods when the exhaust back pressure exceeds the air pump delivery pressure.

The anti-backfire valve operates only during periods of sudden decreases in intake manifold pressure. The valve is necessary, because, immediately following the closing of the throttle after a period of acceleration, a rich fuel mixture is present in the intake manifold. The rich mixture is due to the momentary continuation of fuel flow from the carburetor, or from the boiling of residual fuel in the manifold as a result of the sudden reduction in manifold pressure.

This overly-rich mixture does not burn completely during the normal combustion period, and it is discharged through the engine into the exhaust system. The secondary air being injected into the exhaust ports reduces the rich mixture to a combustible mixture, causing an explosion or backfire in the exhaust system. To prevent this condition and provide a combustible mixture, the anti-backfire valve allows additional fresh air to enter the induction system, whenever intake manifold pressure decreases.

The anti-backfire valve is controlled and operated by intake manifold vacuum as follows:

Assume the vehicle is accelerating at a rate to produce 3 inches of Mercury (in. Hg) vacuum in the intake manifold. Then, there must also be 3 in. Hg manifold vacuum in

chambers A and B (Fig. 2) since they are both connected to the intake manifold. The vacuum in chamber C is also 3 in. Hg, because it connects to chamber A through a balance restriction in the diaphragm assembly.

Since the vacuum on both sides of the diaphragm assembly is the same, the forces cancel and the diaphragm spring holds the air valve on its seat. Thus, with a steady intake manifold vacuum, the anti-backfire valve remains inoperative (or closed).

When the carburetor throttle plate is closed, or during vehicle deceleration, manifold vacuum rises to about 23 in. Hg. Now, there is 23 in. Hg vacuum in chambers A and B, but for the moment still 3 in. Hg in chamber C. There is more vacuum on the A chamber side of the diaphragm assembly than on the C chamber side; therefore, the diaphragm moves toward the air valve, compressing the diaphragm spring and lifting the air valve from its seat to an open position. This allows the air pump to force air through the open valve into chamber B and into the intake manifold as a gulp of air.

However, since the balance restriction connects chambers A and C, the vacuum pressures are soon equalized. When this occurs, the spring returns the diaphragm and air valve to its original closed position.

Suppose that during pumping of air into the intake manifold, it is required to accelerate the vehicle. At the moment of acceleration the valve must close fast, or an unsatisfactory acceleration results, due to the excess air being pumped into the intake manifold. For this reason, a

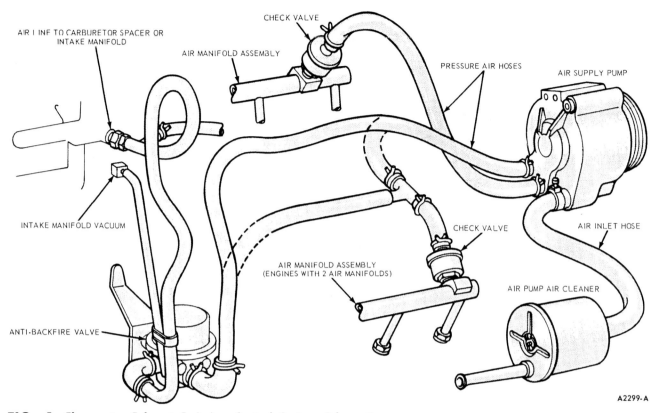

FIG. 1—Thermactor Exhaust Emission Control System Schematic

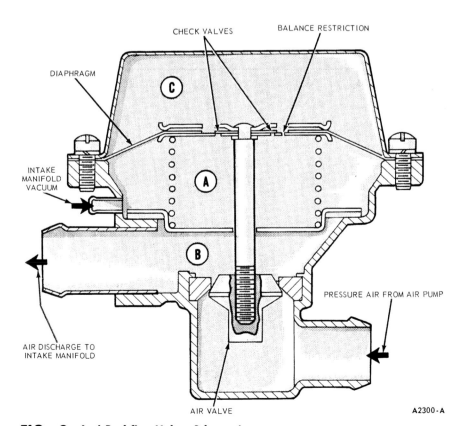

FIG. 2—Anti-Backfire Valve Schematic

quick return feature has been designed into the valve.

Assume that the gulp is about ½ completed and the vacuum in chamber C has reached an intermediate value between 23 in. and 3 in. Hg (about 10 in. Hg). If at this moment the car is suddenly accelerated and the manifold vacuum in chamber A drops to 3 in. Hg, there is more vacuum in chamber C than in chamber A. Then, the check valves in the diaphragm assembly open immediately, equalizing the vacuum in chambers A and C, and the spring instantly moves the diaphragm closing the air valve.

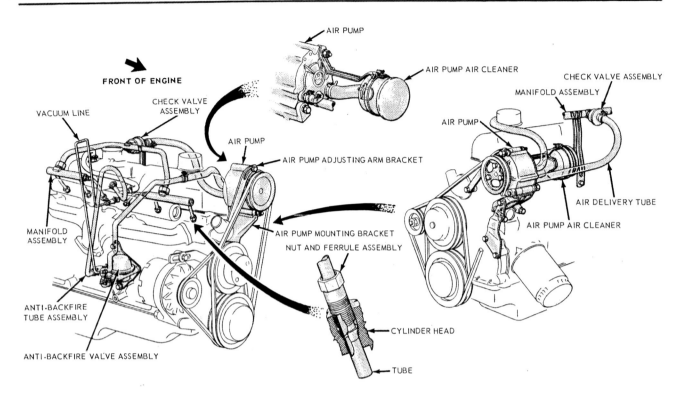

FIG. 3—170 and 200 Six Engine—Typical Thermactor Exhaust Emission System

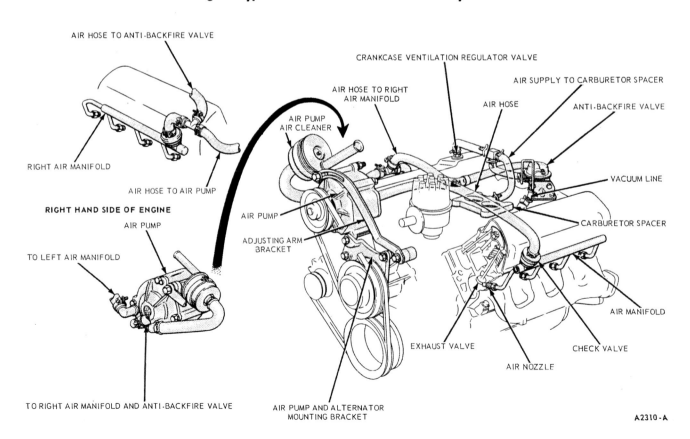

FIG. 4—289 V-8 Engine With Thermactor Exhaust Emission System

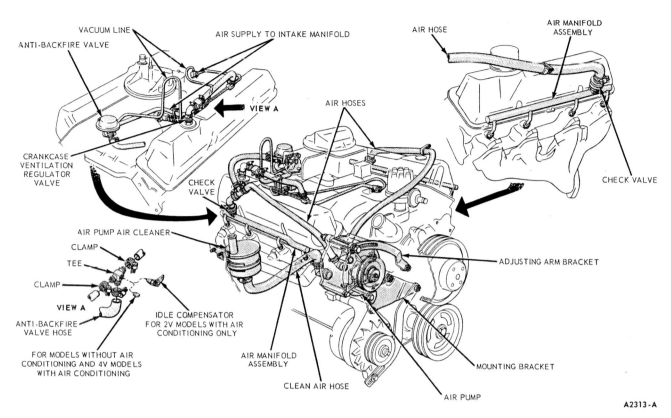

FIG. 5—390 V-8 Engine With Thermactor Exhaust Emission System

2 IN-CAR ADJUSTMENTS AND REPAIRS

DRIVE BELT ADJUSTMENT

The air supply pump drive belt should be properly adjusted at all times. A loose drive belt causes improper air pump operation. A belt that is too tight places a severe strain on the air pump bearings.

Properly tensioned drive belts minimize noise and also prolong service life of the belt. Therefore, it is recommended that a belt tension gauge be used to check and adjust the belt tension. **Any belt that has operated for a minimum of 10 min-** utes is considered a used belt, and, **when adjusted, it must be adjusted to the reset tension shown in the specifications.**

BELT TENSION

1. Install the belt tension tool (T63L-8620-A) on the drive belt and check the tension following the instructions of the tool manufacturer. Compare the belt tension to the specified belt tension (Part 12-4) and adjust as necessary.

2. If adjustment is necessary, loosen the air pump mounting and adjusting arm bolts (Figs. 3, 4 or 5). Move the air pump toward or away from the engine until the correct tension is obtained. **Use a suitable bar and pry against the pump rear cover to hold belt tension while tightening the mounting bolts. Do not pry against the pump housing.** Remove the gauge. Tighten the air pump adjusting arm and mounting bolts. Install the tension gauge and check the belt tension.

3 REMOVAL AND INSTALLATION

AIR PUMP CLEANER ELEMENT REPLACEMENT

1. Remove the wing nut (Fig. 6) and air horn assembly. Remove the filter element from the air horn assembly.

2. Wipe the air horn assembly and air cleaner with a clean, lint-free cloth to remove any accumulated dirt or foreign matter. Under ex- tremely dirty conditions it may be necessary to wash both the air horn and body in low-volatility mineral spirits. Be sure the parts are dry before installing them.

3. **The filter element is not cleanable. Refer to Group 19 for the recommended replacement interval.** Place a new filter element on the air horn assembly. Position the assembled air horn and filter element in the air cleaner body. **Be sure the tang is fitted in the slot (Fig. 6).** Install the wing nut.

AIR CLEANER

REMOVAL

1. Note the position of the air horn with respect to the car (or engine) and with respect to the air cleaner mounting bracket.

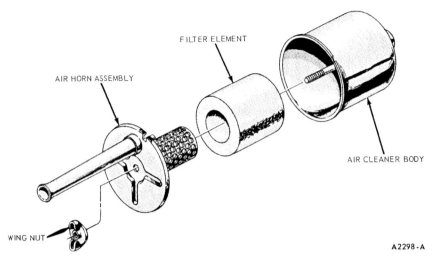

AIR HORN ASSEMBLY

FILTER ELEMENT

AIR CLEANER BODY

WING NUT

A2298-A

FIG. 6—Thermactor Exhaust Emission System Air Cleaner

2. Disconnect the air hose from the air cleaner body. Remove the air cleaner mounting bracket screws and remove the air cleaner.

INSTALLATION

1. Position the air cleaner and mounting bracket assembly in the same way that it was previously installed, and install the mounting bracket screws.

2. Connect the air hose to the air cleaner body.

DRIVE BELT REPLACEMENT

1. Loosen the air supply pump adjusting arm nut and bolt (Fig. 3, 4 and 5). Loosen the air supply pump to mounting bracket nut and bolt, and push the air pump towards the cylinder block. Remove the drive belt.

2. Install a new drive belt. With a suitable bar, **pry against the rear cover of the air pump** to obtain the specified belt tension (refer to Part 12-4), and tighten the adjusting arm bolt and nut. **Do not pry against the pump housing.** Adjust the belt tension (refer to Section 3) as necessary. **Always use a belt tension gauge (Tool T63L-8620-A) to check belt tension.**

3. Tighten the air supply pump to mounting bracket bolt and nut.

ANTI-BACKFIRE VALVE

REMOVAL

Disconnect the air and vacuum hoses at the anti-backfire valve body (Figs. 3, 4 and 5). Remove the valve to mounting bracket bolts and separate the valve from the mounting bracket.

INSTALLATION

Position the anti-backfire valve on the mounting bracket, and install the attaching bolts. Be sure the valve is positioned properly (Fig. 3, 4 and 5), and connect the air and vacuum hoses.

CHECK VALVE REPLACEMENT

1. Disconnect the air supply hose at the valve. Use a 1¼ inch crowfoot wrench to unscrew the check valve assembly (the valve has a standard, right-hand pipe thread).

2. Clean the threads on the air manifold adapter with a wire brush. Install the check valve and torque it to specifications. Connect the air supply hose.

AIR MANIFOLD

REMOVAL

1. Disconnect the air supply hose at the check valve and position the hose out of the way.

2. Loosen all of the air manifold to cylinder head tube coupling nuts (compression fittings). Then unscrew each one until it is free of the cylinder head. Grasp the air manifold at each end and pull it away from the cylinder head. Follow the same procedure to remove the other air manifold, if the engine is so equipped.

INSTALLATION

1. Position the air manifold(s) on the cylinder head. Be sure all the tube coupling nuts are aligned with the cylinder head. Screw each *coupling* nut into the cylinder head 1 to 2 threads. Tighten the tube coupling nuts.

2. Connect the air supply hose to the air manifold.

AIR NOZZLE REPLACEMENT

Normally, air nozzles would be replaced as necessary during cylinder head overhaul. A nozzle may be replaced without removing the cylinder head by removing the air manifold and using a hooked tool to pull the nozzle.

For cleaning and inspection of the air nozzles, refer to Part 12-1, Section 3. Additionally, the air nozzles could be inspected for badly eroded tips with the aid of a mirror, when the exhaust manifold(s) is removed.

DRIVE PULLEY REPLACEMENT

1. Loosen the air supply pump adjusting arm and mounting bolts and nuts to relieve the belt tension.

2. Remove the drive pulley attaching bolts and pull the drive pulley off the air pump shaft.

3. Position the drive pulley on the air supply pump shaft, and install the retaining bolts. Torque the bolts in sequence, across from each other, to specifications.

4. Position the drive belt and adjust the belt tension (Section 3) to specifications. Tighten the adjusting arm and mounting bolts and nuts.

AIR SUPPLY PUMP

REMOVAL

1. Disconnect the air inlet and outlet hoses at the air pump.

2. Loosen the adjusting arm to air pump and air pump to mounting bracket bolts to relieve the drive belt tension.

3. Disengage the drive belt. Remove the mounting bolts and air pump.

REPAIR

For disassembly and repair procedures, refer to Section 4 of this part.

INSTALLATION

1. Position the air pump on the mounting bracket and install the mounting bolt and nut.

2. Place the drive belt in the pulleys and attach the adjusting arm to the air pump. Adjust the drive belt tension to specifications and *tighten the adjusting arm and* mounting bolts.

3. Connect the air inlet and outlet hoses to the air pump.

4 MAJOR REPAIR OPERATIONS

AIR SUPPLY PUMP

The air supply pump and component parts are shown in Fig. 7.

DISASSEMBLY

1. Position the air supply pump

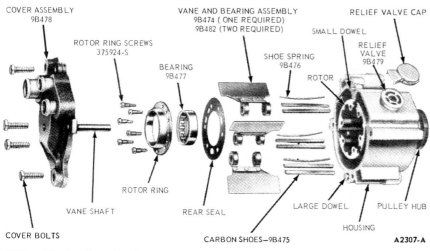

COVER ASSEMBLY 9B478

ROTOR RING SCREWS 375924-S

BEARING 9B477

VANE AND BEARING ASSEMBLY 9B474 (ONE REQUIRED) 9B482 (TWO REQUIRED)

SHOE SPRING 9B476

ROTOR

RELIEF VALVE CAP

SMALL DOWEL

RELIEF VALVE 9B479

VANE SHAFT

ROTOR RING

REAR SEAL

LARGE DOWEL

PULLEY HUB

HOUSING

COVER BOLTS

CARBON SHOES—9B475

A2307-A

FIG. 7—Air Supply Pump

in a vise with the pulley hub between the vise jaws and the pump assembly above the vise. **Do not mount the pump housing in a vise.**

2. Remove the cover bolts. Use a plastic (or rawhide) hammer to tap the cover assembly off the dowel pins. Then pull the cover assembly off the pump by hand.

3. Remove the rotor ring screws and remove the rotor ring and bearing assembly. Remove the rear seal. This is a carbon seal and it should be replaced whenever the pump is disassembled.

4. Locate the vane (Fig. 8) that is attached to the bearing nearest the cover assembly (rear of pump). Grasp it with the fingers and pull it as far as possible out of the rotor. Then pull the other vanes out as far as possible. Alternately pull each vane until they are free of the rotor. If the carbon shoes and shoe springs move out of the rotor as the vanes are being removed, push down on the carbon shoe next to the shoe spring. Then remove the shoe spring. This will aid in removal of the vanes.

5. Use a pair of tweezers to remove the carbon shoes. If needle-nosed pliers are used to remove the carbon shoes, **do not pinch the shoes with the pliers too tightly as the carbon is easily crushed.**

6. If the bearing in the rotor ring requires replacement, position the

rotor ring on Tool T66L-9A486-AB with the bearing part number facing upwards. Place Tool T66L-9A486-AA on the bearing and use an arbor press to remove the bearing.

Further disassembly of the rotor

from the housing is not recommended. If any components of the housing assembly require replacement, the entire housing must be replaced.

CLEANING AND INSPECTION

Refer to Part 12-1, Section 3 for the cleaning and inspection procedures.

ASSEMBLY

1. **The rotor ring is a matched assembly with the housing and rotor assembly, thus these parts are replaceable as a unit only.** If the rotor ring bearing was removed, use Tools T66L-9A486-AA and T66L-9A486-AB and press a new bearing into the rotor ring. **The part number side of the bearing should be on the same side of the rotor ring as the flat surface (side towards rotor),** and the bearing should be flush to $1/32$ inch below the surface of the ring.

2. Place the rotor and housing assembly in a vise with the vise jaws gripping the pulley hub. **Do not clamp the housing assembly in a vise.**

3. Lubricate the vane assembly bearings with only the special air pump bearing lubricant (refer to Part 12-4 for the lube specification) as follows:

Hold each vane assembly bearing over the vane assembly pin (Tool-

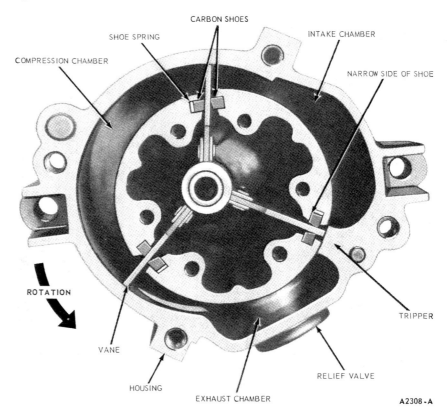

CARBON SHOES

SHOE SPRING

INTAKE CHAMBER

COMPRESSION CHAMBER

NARROW SIDE OF SHOE

ROTATION

TRIPPER

VANE

RELIEF VALVE

HOUSING

EXHAUST CHAMBER

A2308-A

FIG. 8—Vanes, Carbon Shoes and Springs Installed in Rotor

T66L-9A486-C) with the pin just engaged in the bearing. Fill the inside of the bearing with bearing lubricant. Cover the open end of the bearing with the thumb or finger, and press the bearing onto the assembly pin. This will force the lubricant into and around the needle rollers of the bearing. Wipe off the excess grease. Repeat the procedure for the other vane bearings.

4. Mesh the bearings of the vane assemblies so that the ends of the vanes are even, and install the vanes in the rotor (Fig. 8).

5. Install the carbon shoes in the rotor. **One side of each shoe is not square with the other sides.** The shoes must be installed with the narrow edge towards the vane bearings as shown in Fig. 8 and the slant side against the vane.

6. Install the shoe springs between the rotor and shoe in front of the leading (counterclockwise rotation from rear of pump) face of each vane. **The springs must be installed with the tension at the ends of the spring against the rotor and the tension at the center of the spring against the shoe.**

Position the vanes with one vane against the stripper part of the housing as shown in Fig. 8.

7. **Lubricate the rotor rear bearing (in the rotor ring) with air pump lubricant (refer to Part 12-4 for the specification).** Coat the bearing surfaces with lubricant and work it into the bearing with the thumb or finger. Wipe the excess lubricant from the bearing and rotor ring assembly.

8. Position a new rear seal and the rotor ring and bearing assembly on the rotor. The rotor ring bolt holes are unevenly spaced to ensure the rotor ring being properly aligned with the rotor. Apply a thin coating of Loctite thread locking compound to the rotor ring attaching screws, and install the ring screws and torque to specifications.

9. Using the vane assembly pin (T66L-9A486-C), align the vane bearings. Remove the alignment tool.

10. Carefully align the cover assembly with the rotor and insert the vane shaft into the vane bearings. **Do not force the shaft into place, or the vanes will become misaligned.** It may be necessary to rotate the cover and shaft and/or wiggle it slightly from side to side while pushing inward.

Rotate the cover to align with the housing dowels, and push it onto the dowels.

11. Install the cover bolts and torque evenly and alternately in sequence to specifications.

RELIEF VALVE REPLACEMENT

Do not disassemble the air pump to replace the relief valve, but remove it from the engine.

1. Position Tool T66L-9A486-D on the air pump and remove the relief valve with the aid of a slide hammer (T59L-100-B).

2. Position the relief valve on the pump housing and hold Tool T66L-9A486-B on the relief valve. Use a hammer to **tap the tool lightly** until the relief valve is seated.

PART 12-4   SPECIFICATIONS

TORQUE LIMITS

EXHAUST SYSTEM	Ft-lbs
Inlet pipe(s) To Exhaust Manifold(s)	25-35
Inlet Pipe To Inlet Pipe Extension Clamp	14-22
Inlet Pipe To Muffler Clamp	14-22
Inlet Pipe To Frame Bracket Nut and Bolt	17-22
Inlet Pipe To Frame Bracket Clamp	14-22
Outlet Pipe Extension To Muffler Clamp	14-22
Outlet Pipe To Support Bracket Clamp—Fairlane, Falcon and Comet Single Exhaust System Sedans and Convertibles **ONLY**	14-22
Outlet Pipe Extension Support Bracket To Frame Nuts (Mustang ONLY)	18-22
Support Bracket and Insulator to Frame Nuts	14-22

THERMACTOR EXHAUST EMISSION SYSTEM	
Check Valve To Air Manifold	16-19
Air Pump Mounting Bolts	23-28

LUBRICANTS

	Ford Part No.
Exhaust Control Valve Lubricant	COAZ-19A501-A, R-149-A

SEALERS

	Ford Part No.
Loctite (thread locking compound)	C3AZ-19554-A

SPECIAL TOOLS

Description	Ford Tool No.	Kent-Moore Tool No.
Rotor Ring Bearing Remover and Installer		T66L-9A486-AA
Rotor Ring Support		T66L-9A486-AB
Relief Valve Installer		T66L-9A486-B
Vane Assembly Pin		T66L-9A486-C
Relief Valve Remover (Use With T59L-100-B)		T66L-9A486-D
Handle Adapter (Use With T66P-9A486-B)	T62L-201-A	
Slide Hammer	T59L-100-B	
Belt Tension Gauge	T63L-8620-A	
Crowfoot Wrench—1¼ inch (Check Valve Removal)	Commercial Tool	

CHARGING SYSTEM GROUP 13

PART 13-1   **PAGE**
GENERAL CHARGING SYSTEM
    SERVICE **13-1**

PART 13-2
AUTOLITE ALTERNATORS **13-13**

PART 13-3
AUTOLITE ALTERNATOR REGULATORS **13-16**

PART 13-4
53-AMPERE LEECE NEVILLE
    ALTERNATOR **13-21**

PART 13-5   **PAGE**
LEECE NEVILLE ALTERNATOR
    REGULATORS **13-23**

PART 13-6
SPECIFICATIONS **13-25**

PART 13-1 GENERAL CHARGING SYSTEM SERVICE

Section   **Page**
1 Diagnosis 13-1
  Battery Low In Charge, Headlights Dim
    at Idle 13-2
  Charge Indicator Gauge—No Reading or
    Gauge Operates in Reverse 13-2
  Charge Indicator Light Stays On 13-2
  Charge Indicator Gauge Indicates Constant
    Discharge 13-2
  Battery Will Not Hold Charge 13-2
  Alternator Has No Output 13-2
  Alternator Has Low Output 13-2
  Lights and Fuses, Fail Prematurely, Short
    Battery Life 13-4
  Battery Uses Excessive Amount of Water 13-4

Section   **Page**
  Burning of Distributor Points, Ignition
    Resistor Wire, or Coil 13-4
  High Battery Charging Rate 13-4
  Alternator Noisy 13-4
  Charge Indicator Gauge Fluctuates or
    Warning Light Flickers 13-5
2 Testing 13-5
  Alternator Test 13-5
  Alternator Regular and Circuit
    Tests 13-7
  Battery Tests and Conclusions 13-8
3 Common Adjustments and Repairs 13-12
  Belt Adjustment 13-12
4 Cleaning and Inspection 13-12

1 DIAGNOSIS

The charging system consists of an alternator, alternator regulator, battery, charge indicator light or gauge, and the necessary wiring to connect the components (Figs. 1 and 2).

Battery discharge is not always due to charging system defects. Excessive use of lights and accessories while the engine is either off or running at low idle; corroded battery cables and connectors; low water level in the battery; or prolonged disuse of the battery, which would permit self-discharge; are all possi-

ble reasons which should be considered when a battery is run down or low in charge.

Charging system troubles such as low alternator output, no alternator output (indicated by the indicator light being on or the indicator gauge showing discharge while the engine is running), or alternator output voltage too high, require testing of both the alternator and the alternator regulator.

Alternator regulator failures are usually not recognized except by the direct effect on the alternator output

and, of course, eventual battery discharge. As the regulator is the control valve for the alternator, it acts to protect the battery by preventing excessive voltage output. Discharge of the battery to ground through the alternator is prevented by the diodes of the alternator which permit current flow in one direction (to 'the battery) only. Proper adjustment of the two units in the alternator regulator (field relay and voltage limiter), is very important.

The road map type of procedures which follow will assist in a logical

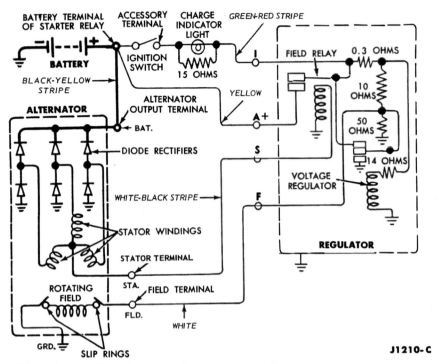

FIG. 1—Autolite Alternator System With Indicator Light

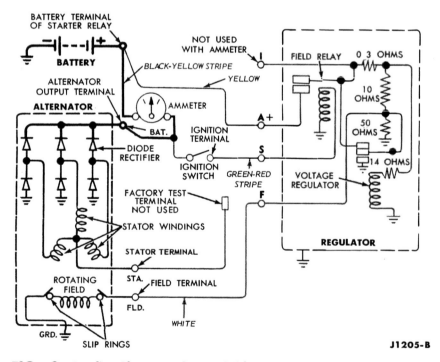

FIG. 2—Autolite Alternator System With Ammeter

sequence of pinpointing specific troubles. **Always determine the cause of failure as well as making the repair.**

BATTERY LOW IN CHARGE, HEADLIGHTS DIM AT IDLE

Refer to Fig. 3 for these symptoms.

CHARGE INDICATOR GAUGE— NO READING OR GAUGE OPERATES IN REVERSE

Either of two different type indicator gauges may be encountered. One type of gauge has external loops on the back of the gauge. The gauge wire is routed through these loops

with no physical connection to the gauge. The other type gauge uses external terminal post connections. In this case, the gauge wire is connected to the terminal posts.

To test the charge indicator gauge, turn the headlights ON with the engine off. The indicator pointer should move toward the D or discharge portion of the scale. The test for indication in the charge direction is made by first turning on the lights for about two minutes and then running the engine at about 1500 rpm. Turn the lights off and observe the pointer travel. If charge is indicated, the indicator is satisfactory.

If no movement of the needle is obtained, check the loop (or connections) on the rear of the gauge to see if the battery to alternator wire passes inside the loop (or the connections are tight). If the wire is in the loop (or the connections are tight) and the gauge does not indicate a charge or discharge, the gauge is inoperative.

If the pointer moves toward the C or charge portion of the scale when the headlights are first turned ON, the wire passes through the loop in the wrong direction (or the wire connections are reversed). Feed the wire through the loop in the opposite direction (or reverse the wires on the terminals), observing the precaution of disconnecting the battery before working under the instrument panel.

CHARGE INDICATOR LIGHT STAYS ON

Refer to Fig 4 for this symptom. Other symptoms covered under this heading are: charge indicator gauge indicates constant discharge; battery will not hold charge; alternator has no output; alternator has low output.

NOTE 1

If the owner has had previous difficulty with the battery running down and past history does not indicate that the problem is due to excessive night driving, excessive use of accessories, short trips or extended periods of idle, then it is suggested that the complete charging system be checked.

NOTE 2

Test the alternator output at the battery. With the ammeter in series between the battery cable and battery post, it is necessary to add 2 amperes to the output reading obtained to cover the current draw of

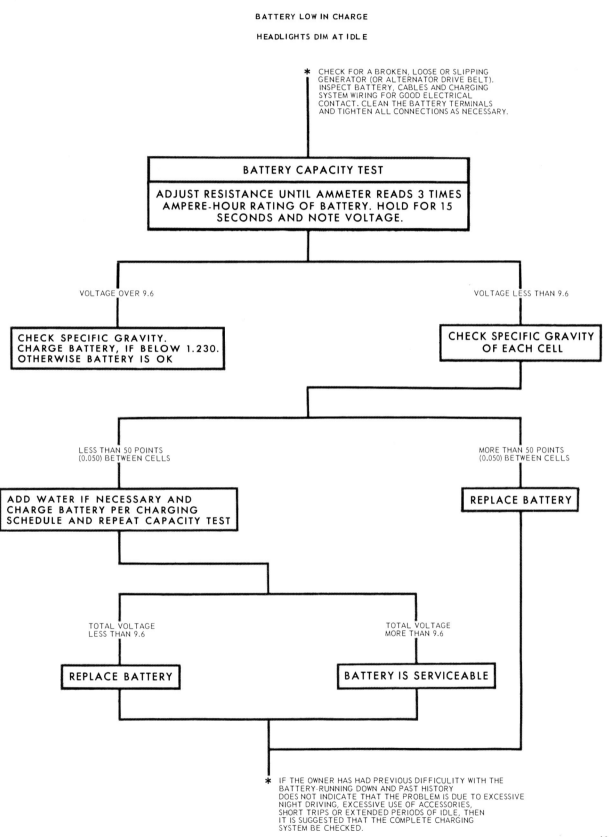

FIG. 3—Battery Low in Charge, Headlights Dim at Idle—Road Map

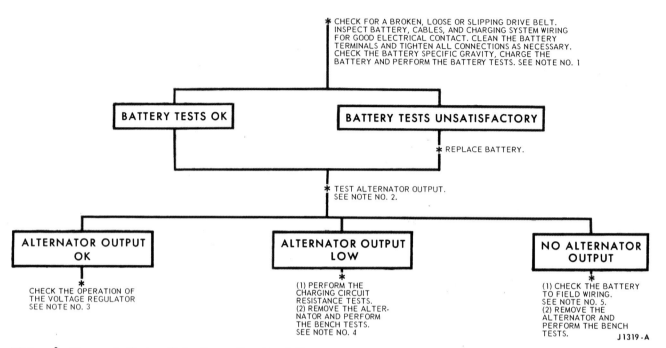

FIG. 4—Charge Indicator Light Stays On—Road Map

the standard ignition system and 6 amperes for the transistor ignition system.

NOTE 3

Check the voltage limiter setting, and check the closing voltage of the field relay (the voltage at which the field relay contacts just make contact). Adjust the voltage limiter if necessary. Adjust the field relay if its setting is out of specification.

On some cars the location of the regulator may prevent adjustment on the car. Remove the regulator to an alternator-regulator test stand if adjustment is necessary.

The field relay used with the transistorized voltage regulator is a sealed unit and is not to be adjusted. To determine *its closing voltage*, follow the procedure given in Section 2 Testing, under Autolite Regulator and Circuit Tests.

If the regulator was adjusted properly, check the green-red wire from the accessory terminal of the ignition switch through the charge indicator light and 15-ohm resistor to the voltage regulator, and the white-black wire from the voltage regulator to the alternator. Repair or replace as necessary.

With the engine at 1000 rpm, the

voltage produced at the STA terminal of the alternator should be 6 volts or more. A voltage less than 6 volts may be caused by an open negative diode.

NOTE 4

An output of 2 to 5 amperes less than that specified usually indicates an open diode. An output of approximately 10 amperes less than that specified usually indicates a shorted diode.

NOTE 5

To check the battery to field wiring, connect the field rheostat between the battery positive terminal and the alternator FLD terminal and repeat the alternator output test. If the alternator now has good output the wire from the battery terminal of the starter relay to the FLD terminal of the alternator is defective. If the alternator still has no output it is defective. Remove the alternator and perform the bench tests. Replace defective parts.

LIGHTS AND FUSES FAIL PREMATURELY, SHORT BATTERY LIFE

Refer to Fig. 5 for these symptoms. Other symptoms covered un-

der this heading are: battery uses excessive amount of water; burning of distributor points, ignition resistor wire, or coil; high battery charging rate.

ALTERNATOR NOISY

When investigating the complaint of alternator noise, first try to localize the noise area to make sure that the alternator is a fault rather than the alternator belt, water pump, or another part of the vehicle. Start the engine and use a stethoscope or similar sound detector instrument to localize the noise. An alternator bearing, water pump bearing or belt noise is usually evidenced by a squealing sound.

An alternator with a shorted diode will normally whine (magnetic noise) and will be most noticeable at idle speeds. Perform the alternator output test. If the output is approximately 10 amperes less than that specified, a shorted diode is usually indicated.

To eliminate the belt(s) as the cause of noise, check the belt(s) for bumps, apply a light amount of belt dressing to the belt(s). If the alternator belt is at fault, adjust the belt to specification, or replace the belt if necessary.

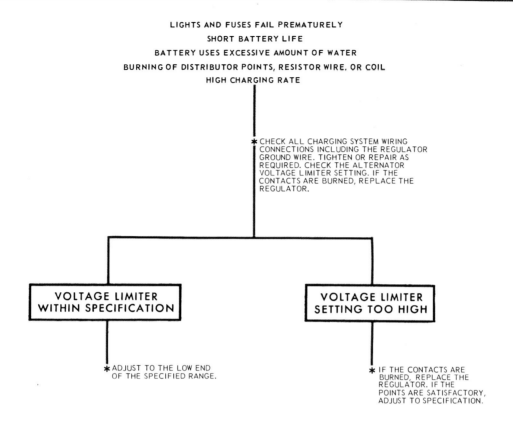

FIG. 5—Lights and Fuses Fail Prematurely—Road Map

If the belt(s) is satisfactory and the noise is believed to be in the alterminator or water pump, remove the alternator belt. Start the engine and listen for the noise as a double check to be sure that the noise is not caused by another component. Use this test and the sound detector test to isolate the offending unit. If the noise is traced to the alternator, remove it and inspect the bearings for wear, shaft scoring, or an out-of-round condition.

CHARGE INDICATOR GAUGE FLUCTUATES OR WARNING LIGHT FLICKERS

This condition may be caused by dirty or oxidized regulator contacts loose or damaged connections in the charging system wiring harness, worn brushes, or improper brush tension.

At certain engine speeds the ammeter needle will fluctuate to some degree when voltage regulation is just starting, and when the turn signals are in operation, which is normal.

2 TESTING

ALTERNATOR TESTS

Refer to Wiring Diagram Manual Form 7795P-66 for locations of wiring harnesses. Schematics are shown in Group 22 of this manual. **Use care when connecting any test equipment to the alternator system, as the alternator output terminal is connected to the battery at all times.**

ALTERNATOR OUTPUT TEST—ON ENGINE

When the alternator output test is conducted off the car, a test bench must be used. Follow the procedure given by the test bench equipment manufacturer. **When the alternator is removed from the car for this purpose always disconnect a battery cable as the alternator output connector is connected to the battery at all times.**

To test the output of the alternator on the car, proceed as follows:

1. Place the transmission in neutral or park **and apply the parking brake.** Make the connections as shown in Fig. 6 or 7. Be sure that the field resistance control is at the OFF position at the start of this test.

2. Close the battery adapter switch. Start the engine, then open the battery adapter switch.

3. Increase the engine speed to approximately 2000 rpm. Turn off all lights and electrical accessories.

4. Turn the field rheostat clockwise until 15 volts is indicated on the voltmeter. Turn the master control clockwise until the voltmeter indicates between 11 and 12 volts. Holding the master control in this position turn the field rheostat clockwise to its maximum rotation. Turn the master control counterclockwise until the voltmeter indicates 15 volts. Observe the ammeter reading. Add 2 amperes to this reading when the car is equipped with standard ignition or 6 amperes with the transistor ignition system, to obtain total alternator output. If rated output cannot be obtained increase the engine speed to 2900 rpm and repeat this step.

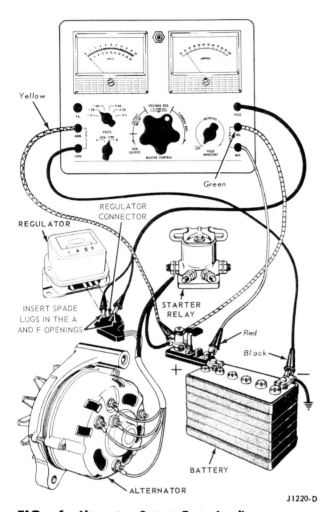

J1220-D

FIG. 6—Alternator Output Test—Autolite

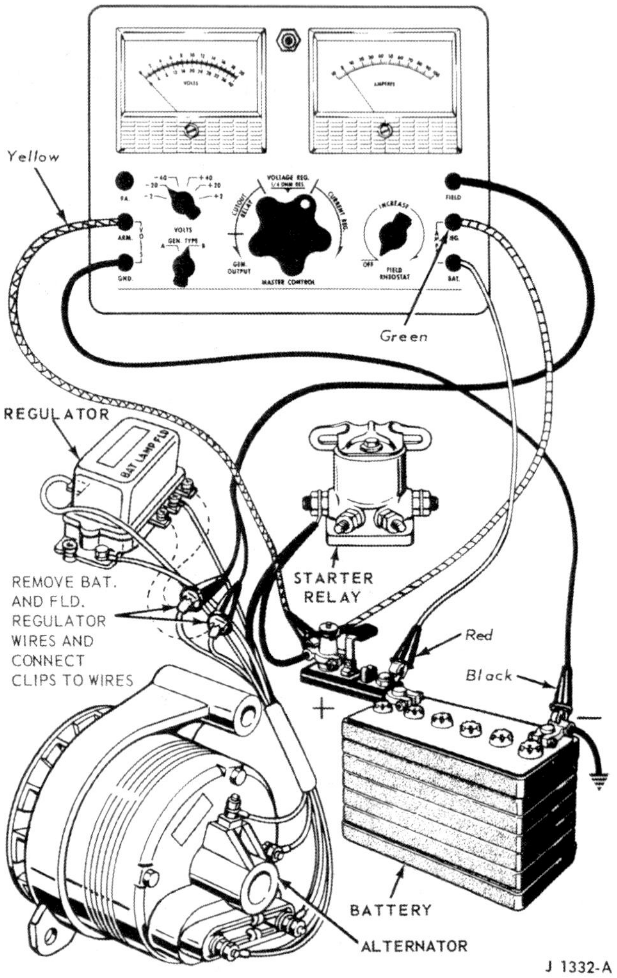

J 1332-A

FIG. 7—Alternator Output Test—Leece Neville

5. Return the field resistance control to the maximum counterclockwise position, release the master control, and stop the engine. Disconnect the test equipment, if no further tests are to be made.

An output of 2 to 8 amperes below specifications usually indicates an open diode rectifier. An output of approximately 10 to 15 amperes below specifications usually indicates a shorted diode rectifier. An alternator with a shorted diode will usually whine, which will be most noticeable at idle speed.

AUTOLITE STATOR NEUTRAL VOLTAGE TEST—ON ENGINE

The Autolite alternator STA terminal is connected to the stator coil neutral or center point (see Figs. 1 and 2). The voltage generated at this point is used to close the field relay in the charge indicator light system.

To test for the stator neutral voltage, connect the voltmeter positive lead to the STA terminal and con-

nect the negative lead to ground. Start the engine and run it at 1000 rpm. Turn off all lights and accessories. The voltage indicated on the meter should be 6 volts or more.

FIELD OPEN OR SHORT CIRCUIT TEST—ON BENCH

Make the connection as shown in Fig. 8. The current draw, as indicated by the ammeter, should be to specifications. If there is little or no current flow, the field or brushes have a high resistance or are open. A current flow considerably higher than that specified above, indicates shorted or grounded turns or brush leads touching. If the test shows that the field is shorted or open and the field brush assembly or slip rings are not at fault, the entire rotor must be replaced.

If the alternator has output at low rpm and no output at high rpm, centrifugal force may be causing the rotor windings to short to ground. Put the alternator on a test stand

and repeat the preceding test. Run the alternator at high speed during the test.

DIODE TEST—ON BENCH

Disassemble the alternator and disconnect the diode assembly from the stator and make the test connections as shown in Figs. 10 or 11.

To test the negative diodes contact one probe to the diode plate as shown and contact each of the three stator lead terminals with the other probe. Reverse the probes and repeat the test. Test the positive diodes in the same way.

All of the diodes should show a low reading of approximately 60 ohms in one direction and infinite reading (no needle movement) with the probes reversed. **Be sure to use the Rotunda ohmmeter with the multiply-by knob at 10.**

OPEN OR GROUNDED STATOR COIL TESTS—ON BENCH

These tests are made to verify

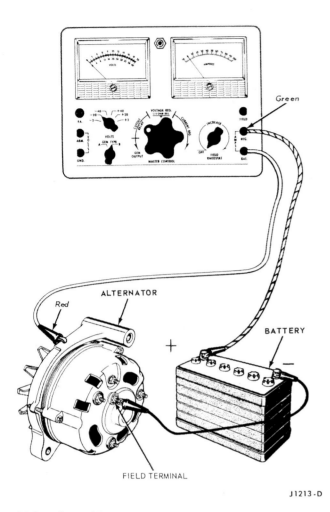

J1213-D

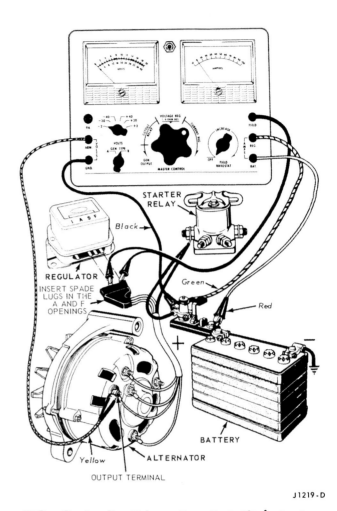

J1219-D

FIG. 8—Field Open or Short Circuit Test— Typical

FIG. 9—Autolite Voltage Drop Test Alternator to Battery Positive Terminal

that the stator coil is defective. Disassemble the stator from the alternator and rectifier assembly for these tests.

Open Stator Test—On Bench. Set the Rotunda ohmmeter multiply-by knob at 1. Connect the ohmmeter between each pair of stator leads. If the ohmmeter does not show equal readings between each pair of stator leads, the stator is open and must be replaced.

Grounded Stator Test—On Bench. Set the Rotunda ohmmeter multiply-by knob at 1000. Connect the ohmmeter between one of the stator leads and the stator core. Be sure that the test lead makes a good electrical connection to the core. The ohmmeter should not show any continuity, if it does, the stator winding is grounded and must be replaced.

ALTERNATOR REGULATOR AND CIRCUIT TESTS

Circuit Resistance Tests. For the purpose of this test, the resistance values of the circuits have been converted to voltage drop readings for a current flow of 20 amperes.

Alternator to Battery Positive Terminal. To check the alternator to battery ground terminal voltage drop, make the connections as shown in Fig. 9 or 12. Turn off all electrical accessories and lights. Close the battery adapter switch, start the engine, then open the battery adapter switch. Increase the engine speed to 2000 rpm. Adjust the field rheostat until the ammeter indicates 20 amperes. Note the voltmeter reading at this point. The voltage reading should be no greater than 0.3 volt on a car with a charge indicator light and 0.5 volt on a car with an ammeter.

These voltage drops have been computed for a standard car. The

current used by any auxiliary, continuously operating, heavy-duty equipment will not show on the ammeter and will have to be taken into account when making this test.

Alternator to Battery Ground Terminal. To check the alternator to battery positive terminal voltage drop, make the connections as shown in Fig. 13 or 14. Close the battery adapter switch, start the engine and open the adapter switch. Maintain the engine speed at 2000 rpm. Adjust the field rheostat until the ammeter indicates 20 amperes. The voltage indicated on the voltmeter should be less than 0.1.

REGULATOR TESTS

Voltage Limiter Test. Voltage limiter calibration tests must be made with the regulator cover in place and the regulator at normal operating temperature (equivalent to the temperature after 20 minutes

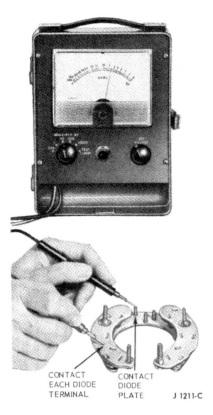

CONTACT   CONTACT
EACH DIODE   DIODE
TERMINAL   PLATE   J 1211-C

FIG. 10—Autolite Diode Test

CONTACT   CONTACT EACH
HEAT SINK   DIODE TERMINAL   J 1262-D

FIG. 11—53-Ampere Leece Neville Diode Test

of operation on the car with the hood down).

For accurate voltage limiter testing, the battery specific gravity must be at least 1.225. If the battery is low in charge, either charge it to 1.225 specific gravity or substitute a fully charged battery, before making a voltage limiter test.

To test the voltage regulator on the car, make the test connections to the battery as shown in Fig. 15. Turn all accessories off, including door operated dome lights. Close the battery adapter switch, start the engine, then open the adapter switch. Attach a voltage regulator thermometer to the regulator cover. Operate the engine at approximately 2000 rpm for 5 minutes.

When the battery is charged, and the voltage regulator has been temperature stabilized, the ammeter should indicate less than 10 amperes with the master control set at the ¼-OHM position.

Cycle the regulator as follows (mechanical regulators only): turn the ignition key to OFF to stop the engine, close the adapter switch, start the engine, and open the adapter switch. Allow the battery to normalize for a few seconds, then read the voltmeter. Read the thermometer, and compare the voltmeter reading with the voltage given in Table 1 for the ambient temperature indicated on the thermometer. If the regulated voltage is not within specifications, make a voltage limiter adjustment. After each adjustment, be sure to cycle the regulator before each reading (mechanical regulator only). **The readings must be made with the cover in place (mechanical regulator only).**

On some cars the location of the regulator may prevent adjustment on the car. Remove the regulator to an alternator-regulator test stand if adjustment is necessary.

TABLE 1—Voltage Limiter Setting Versus Ambient Air Temperature (Mechanical or Transistor Regulator)

Ambient Air Temperature °F	Voltage Limiter Setting (Volts)
50	14.3-15.1
75	14.1-14.9
100	13.9-14.7
125	13.8-14.6

Field Relay Test—Mechanical Regulator. Remove the regulator from the car, and remove the regulator cover. Make the connections as shown in Fig. 16, 18 or 19. Slowly rotate the field rheostat control clockwise from the maximum counterclockwise position until the field relay contacts close. Observe the voltmeter reading at the moment that the relay contacts close. This is the relay closing voltage. If the relay closes immediately, even with the field rheostat close to the maximum counterclockwise position, push the red button between the two meters, and repeat the test. If the closing voltage is not to specifications, adjust the relay (Part 13-3).

Field Relay Test—Transistor Regulator. Disconnect the relay connector plug. Make the connections as shown in Fig. 18. Slowly rotate the field rheostat control clockwise from the maximum counterclockwise position until the test light comes on. Observe the voltmeter reading at the moment that the light comes on. This is the relay closing voltage. If the relay closes immediately, even with the field rheostat close to the maximum counterclockwise position, push the red button between the two meters, and repeat the test. If the closing voltage is not to specification, replace the relay.

BATTERY TESTS AND CONCLUSIONS

Tests are made on a battery to determine the state of charge and also the condition. The ultimate result of these tests is to show that the battery is good, needs recharging, or must be replaced.

If a battery has failed, is low in charge, or requires water frequently, good service demands that the reason for this condition be found. It may be necessary to follow trouble shooting procedures to locate the cause of the trouble (Section 1 in this part).

Hydrogen and oxygen gases are produced during normal battery operation. This gas mixture can explode if flames or sparks are brought near the vent openings of the battery. The sulphuric acid in the battery electrolyte can cause a serious burn if spilled on the skin or spattered in the eyes. It should be flushed away with large quantities of clear water.

Before attempting to test a battery, it is important that it be given

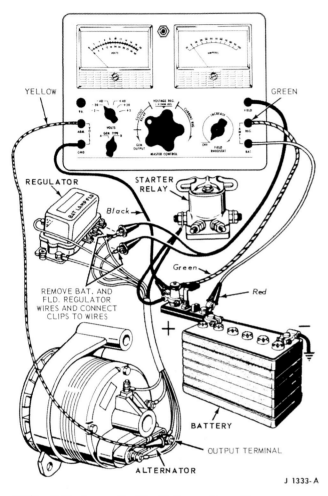

YELLOW

REGULATOR

STARTER RELAY

Black

Green

REMOVE BAT. AND FLD. REGULATOR WIRES AND CONNECT CLIPS TO WIRES

Red

BATTERY

OUTPUT TERMINAL

ALTERNATOR

J 1333-A

FIG. 12—Leece Neville Voltage Drop Test—Alternator to Battery Positive Terminal

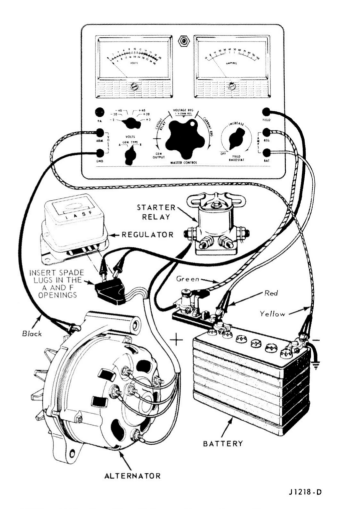

GREEN

STARTER RELAY

REGULATOR

INSERT SPADE LUGS IN THE A AND F OPENINGS

Green

Red

Yellow

Black

BATTERY

ALTERNATOR

J1218-D

FIG. 13—Autolite Voltage Drop Test—Alternator to Battery Ground Terminal

a thorough visual examination to determine if it has been damaged. The presence of moisture on the outside of the case and/or low electrolyte level in one or more of the cells are indications of possible battery damage.

The Ford and Mercury batteries incorporate a single one-piece cover which completely seals the top of the battery and the individual cell connectors. This cover must not be pierced with test probes to perform individual cell tests.

A battery can be tested by determining its ability to deliver current. This may be determined by conducting a Battery Capacity Test. Fig. 20 shows the battery capacity test in outline form.

BATTERY CAPACITY TEST

A high rate discharge tester (Battery-Starter Tester) in conjunction with a voltmeter is used for this test.

1. Turn the control knob on the

Battery-Starter Tester to the OFF position.

2. Turn the voltmeter selector switch to the 16 or 20-volt position.

3. Connect both positive test leads to the positive battery post and both negative test leads to the negative battery post. **The voltmeter clips must contact the battery posts and not the high rate discharge tester clips. Unless this is done the actual battery terminal voltage will not be indicated.**

4. Turn the load control knob in a clockwise direction until the ammeter reads three times the ampere hour rating of the battery. (A 45 ampere-hour battery should be tested at 135 amperes load.)

5. With the ammeter reading the required load for 15 seconds, note the voltmeter reading. **Avoid leaving the high discharge load on the battery for periods longer than 15 seconds.**

6. If the voltmeter reading is 9.6

volts or more, the battery has good output capacity and will readily accept a charge, if required. Check the specific gravity. If the specific gravity reading is 1.230 or below, add water if necessary and charge the battery until it is fully charged.

The battery is fully charged when the cells are all gassing freely and the specific gravity ceases to rise for three successive readings taken at hourly intervals. Additional battery testing will not be necessary after the battery has been properly charged.

7. If the voltage reading obtained during the capacity test is below 9.6 volts, check the specific gravity of each cell.

8. If the difference between any two cells is more than 50 points (0.050), the battery is not satisfactory for service and should be replaced.

9. If the difference between cells is less than 50 points (0.050) the battery should be charged according

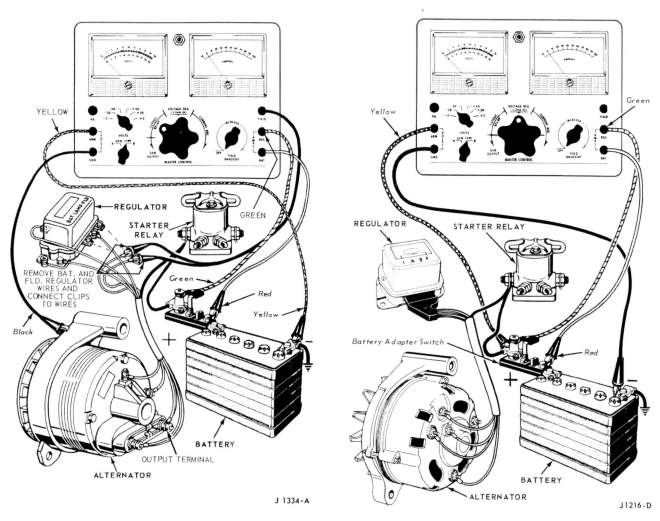

FIG. 14—Leece Neville Voltage Drop Test—Alternator to Battery Ground Terminal

FIG. 15—Voltage Limiter Test—Typical

to the charging schedule in Table 2. In some cases the electrolyte level may be too low to obtain a specific gravity reading. In such cases water should be added until the electrolyte level just covers the ring in the filler well, then charge the battery at 35 amperes for the maximum charging time indicated in Table 2, for capacity of the battery being tested.

10. After the battery has been charged, repeat the capacity test. If the capacity test battery voltage is still less than 9.6 volts, replace the battery. If the voltage is 9.6 volts or more, the battery is satisfactory for service.

11. If the battery is found to be discharged only, check for a loose fan belt, loose electrical connections, charging system performance, and make a battery drain test (in this section).

BATTERY DRAIN TEST

This test will determine if there is

TABLE 2—Allowable Battery High Rate Charge Time Schedule

Specific Gravity Reading	Charge Rate Amperes	Battery Capacity—Ampere Hours			
		45	55	70	80
1.125-1.150[1]	35	65 min.	80 min.	100 min.	115 min.
1.150-1.175	35	50 min.	65 min.	80 min.	95 min.
1.175-1.200	35	40 min.	50 min.	60 min.	70 min.
1.200-1.225	35	30 min.	35 min.	45 min.	50 min.
Above 1.225	5	[2]	[2]	[2]	[2]

[1]If the specific gravity is below 1.125, use the indicated high rate of charge for the 1.125 specific gravity, then charge at 5 amperes until the specific gravity reaches 1.250 at 80° F.

[2]Charge at 5 ampere rate **only** until the specific gravity reaches 1.250 at 80° F. **At no time during the charging operation should the electrolyte temperature exceed 130° F.**

any external load that would cause unwanted battery discharge.

Disconnect the battery ground cable and connect the positive lead of a voltmeter to the cable. Connect

the negative lead of the voltmeter to *the battery negative post.*

With all circuits off, the meter should read zero. Any battery external load will cause the voltmeter to

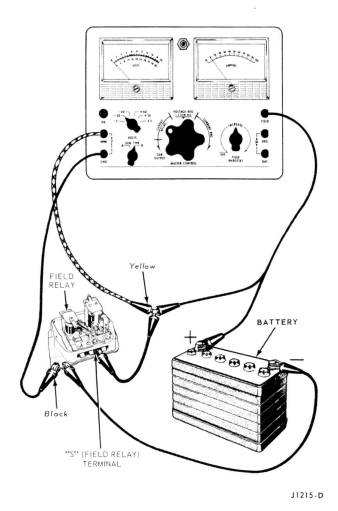

J1215-D

FIG. 16—Autolite Field Relay Test—Mechanical
Regulator

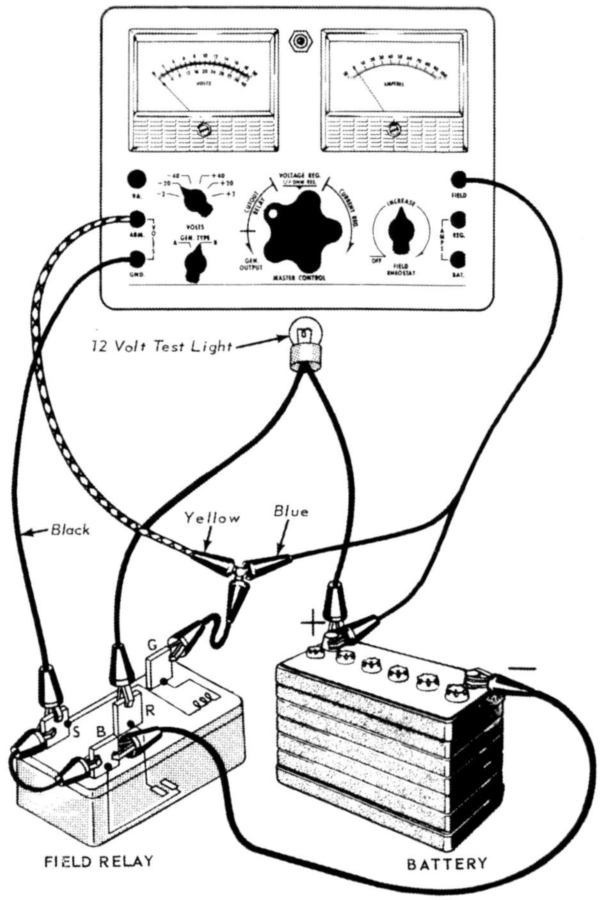

J1329-A

FIG. 17—Autolite Field Relay Test—Transistor
Regulator

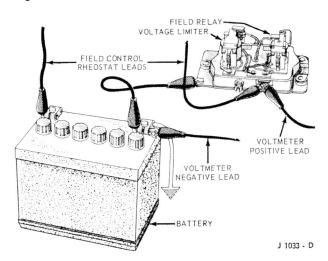

J 1033 - D

FIG. 18—Leece Neville Field Relay Test—Light
Circuit

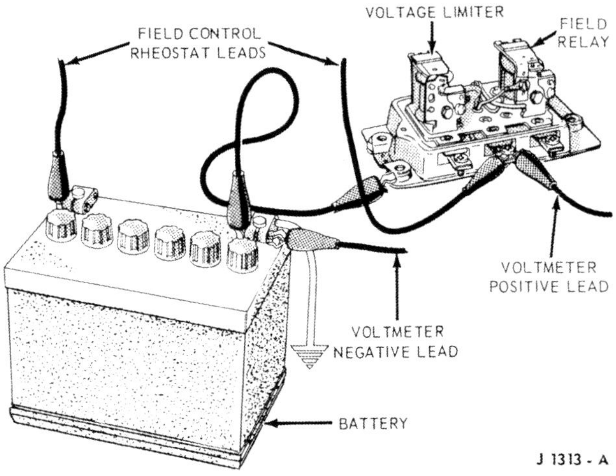

J 1313 - A

FIG. 19—Leece Neville Field Relay Test—Ammeter
Circuit

read full battery voltage.

If the car is equipped with an
electric clock, momentarily connect

the battery ground cable to the battery negative post to make certain
that the clock is wound. When the

clock runs down at the end of approximately 2 minutes the voltmeter
will show full battery voltage.

3 COMMON ADJUSTMENTS AND REPAIRS

BELT ADJUSTMENT—ALTERNATOR

1. Loosen the alternator mounting bolt and the adjusting arm bolts.

2. **Apply pressure on the alternator front housing only** and tighten the adjusting arm to alternator bolt.

3. Check the belt tension using tool T63L-8620-A. Adjust the belt for specified tension.

4. Tighten all mounting bolts.

4 CLEANING AND INSPECTION

1. The rotor, stator, and bearings must not be cleaned with solvent. Wipe these parts off with a clean cloth.

2. Rotate the front bearing on the drive end of the rotor drive shaft. Check for any scraping noise, looseness or roughness that will indicate that the bearing is excessively worn. Look for excessive lubricant leakage.

If any of these conditions exist, replace the bearing.

3. Inspect the rotor shaft at the rear bearing surface for roughness or severe chatter marks. Replace the rotor assembly if the shaft is not smooth.

4. Place the rear end bearing on the slip-ring end of the shaft and rotate the bearing on the shaft. Make the same check for noise, looseness or roughness as was made for the front bearing. Inspect the rollers and cage for damage. Replace the bearing if these conditions exist, or if the lubricant is lost or contaminated.

5. Check the pulley and fan for excessive looseness on the rotor shaft. Replace any pulley or fan that is loose or bent out of shape. Check the rotor shaft for stripped or damaged threads. Inspect the hex hole in the end of the shaft for damage.

6. Check both the front and rear housings for cracks. Check the front housings for stripped threads in the mounting ear. Replace defective housings.

7. Check all wire leads on both the stator and rotor assemblies for loose soldered connections, and for burned insulation. Resolder poor connections. Replace parts that show burned insulation.

8. Check the slip rings for nicks and surface roughness. Nicks and scratches may be removed by turning down the slip rings. Do not go beyond the minimum diameter limit of 1.22 inches. If the slip rings are badly damaged, the entire rotor will have to be replaced, as it is serviced as a complete assembly.

9. Replace any parts that are burned or cracked. Replace brushes and brush springs that are not to specification.

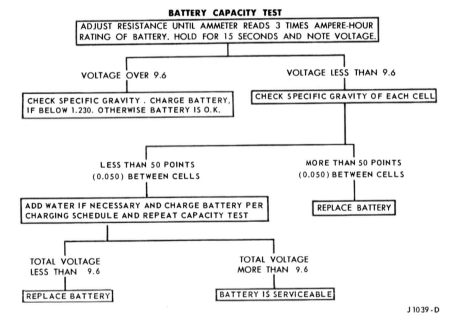

FIG. 20—Battery Capacity Test Outline

PART 13-2
AUTOLITE ALTERNATORS

Section	Page	Section	Page
1 Description and Operation	13-13	3 Major Repair Operations	13-14
2 Removal and Installation	13-13		

1 DESCRIPTION AND OPERATION

The alternator charging system is a negative (—) ground system, and consists of an alternator, a regulator, a charge indicator, a storage battery and associated wiring. Refer to Wiring Diagram Manual Form 7795P-66 for locations of wiring harnesses. Schematics are shown in Group 22 of this manual.

ALTERNATOR

The alternator is belt driven from the engine. The mechanical construction of the alternator differs from a generator in that the field rotates, and the generating windings are stationary. Energy is supplied from the alternator-regulator system to the rotating field through two brushes to two slip rings. The slip rings are mounted on the rotor shaft (Fig. 2), and are connected to the field coil.

The alternator produces power in the form of alternating current. The alternating current is rectified to direct current by six diodes (Fig. 6) for use in charging the battery and supplying power to the electrical system.

2 REMOVAL AND INSTALLATION

REMOVAL

1. Disconnect the battery ground cable, then raise the car on a hoist.
2. Loosen the alternator mounting bolts and remove the adjustment arm to alternator bolt.
3. Disengage the alternator belt. Remove the alternator mounting bolt, disconnect the alternator wiring harness and remove the alternator.

INSTALLATION

1. Attach the alternator wiring harness (Fig. 1). Position the alternator to the engine, and install the alternator mounting bolt finger-tight.
2. Install the adjustment arm to alternator bolt.
3. Adjust the belt tension using tool T63L-8620-A. **Apply pressure on the alternator front housing only, when tightening the belt.** Tighten the adjusting arm bolts and the mounting bolt.
4. Lower the car and connect the battery ground cable.

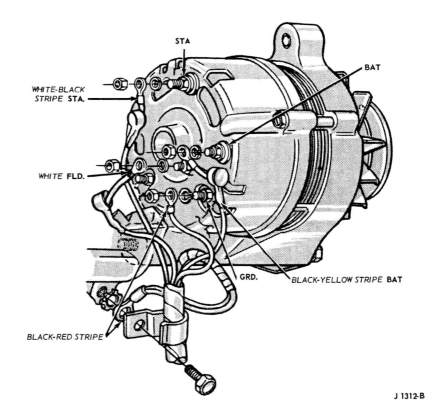

FIG. 1—Wiring Harness Connections—Typical

3 MAJOR REPAIR OPERATIONS

DISASSEMBLY

Fig. 2 shows a disassembled view of the Ford alternator.

discard the roll pins from the diode plates.

9. Remove the drive pulley nut,

field open or short circuit test (Part 13-1).

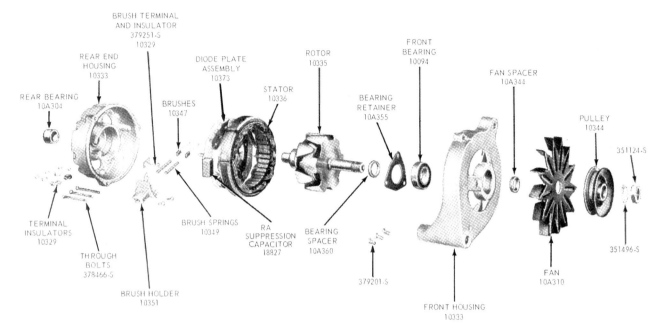

FIG. 2—Disassembled Alternator

1. Mark both end housings and the stator with a scribe mark for assembly.

2. Remove the three housing through bolts.

3. Separate the front end housing and rotor from the stator and rear end housing.

4. Remove all the nuts and washers from the rear end housing and remove the rear end housing from the stator and diode plate assembly.

5. Remove the brush holder mounting screws and remove the holder, brushes, brush springs, insulator and terminal.

6. If replacement is necessary, press the *bearing from the rear* end housing, supporting the housing on the inner boss.

7. If the diode plate assembly is being replaced, unsolder the stator leads from the printed-circuit board terminals, and separate the stator from the diode plate assembly. Use a 100-watt soldering iron.

8. If the printed-circuit board is being replaced, cut the printed-circuit board into six separate pieces and unsolder each piece from the diode it is attached to. Remove and

lockwasher, pulley, fan, fan spacer, rotor and rotor stop (Fig. 3).

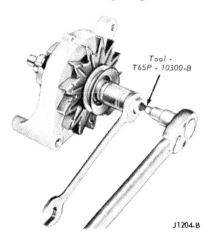

FIG. 3—Pulley Removal

10. Remove the three screws that hold the front end bearing retainer, and remove the retainer. Support the housing close to the bearing boss, and press out the old bearing from the housing, only if the bearing is defective or has lost its lubricant.

11. Perform a diode test and a

PARTS REPAIR OR REPLACEMENT

Nicks and scratches may be removed from the rotor slip rings by turning down the slip rings. Do not go beyond the minimum diameter limit of 1.22 inches. If the slip rings are badly damaged, the entire rotor must be replaced as it is serviced as an assembly. The diode plate assembly is serviced as an assembly. However the printed circuit board is serviced separately.

ASSEMBLY

1. Press the front end bearing in the bearing boss and install the bearing retainer.

2. If the stop-ring on the rotor drive shaft was damaged, install a new stop-ring. Push the new ring on the shaft and into the groove. **Do not open the ring with snap ring pliers as permanent damage will result.**

3. Position the rotor stop on the drive shaft with the recessed side against *the stop-ring.*

4. Position the front end housing, fan spacer, fan, pulley and lock washer on the drive shaft and install the retaining nut (Fig. 3), to specified torque.

5. If the rear end housing bearing was removed, support the housing on the inner boss and press in a new bearing flush with the outer end surface.

6. Place the brush springs, brushes, brush terminal and terminal insulator in the brush holder and hold the brushes in position by inserting a piece of stiff wire in the brush holder as shown in Fig. 4.

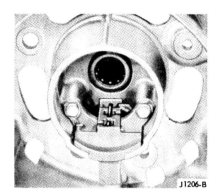

FIG. 5—Brush Lead Positions

each diode lead and solder the diode leads to the printed-circuit board. Use a 100-watt iron. Avoid excess heat on the printed-circuit board so as not to loosen the printed-circuit wiring from the board.

9. Wrap the three stator winding leads around the printed-circuit board terminals and solder them. Use a 100-watt soldering iron and rosin-core solder. Position the stator neutral lead eyelet on the stator terminal insulators (Fig. 6). Position the diode assembly (Fig. 6).

10. Install the STA and BAT terminal insulators (Fig. 6). Position the stator and diode plate assembly in the rear end housing. Position the STA (black), BAT (red) and FLD (white) insulators, on the terminal bolts, and install five retaining nuts (Fig. 7).

11. Wipe the rear end bearing surface of the rotor shaft with a clean lint-free rag.

12. Position the rear end housing and stator assembly over the rotor and align the scribe marks made during disassembly. Seat the machined portion of the stator core into the step in both end housings. Install the housing through bolts. Remove the brush retracting rod, and put a daub of waterproof cement over the hole to seal it.

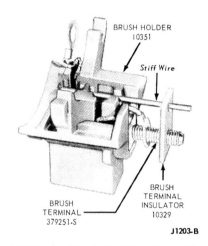

FIG. 4—Brush Holder Assembly

7. Position the brush holder assembly in the rear end housing and install the mounting screws. Position the brush leads in the brush holder as shown in Fig. 5.

8. If a new diode plate or printed-circuit board is being installed, position the diode plate so that the diode leads go through the three holes in the printed-circuit board. Install the terminal bolt and insulator. Install new roll pins to maintain the ½-inch insulator spacing between the printed-circuit board and the diode plate. Install a small tinned washer and a solder ring on

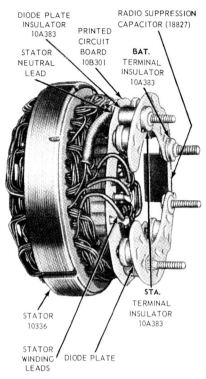

FIG. 6—Stator Lead Connections

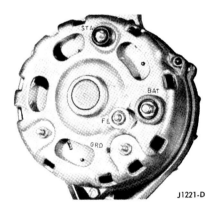

FIG. 7—Alternator Terminal Locations

PART 13-3 AUTOLITE ALTERNATOR REGULATORS

Section	Page	Section	Page
1 Description and Operation	13-16	Mechanical Regulator Adjustments	13-17
Mechanical Voltage Regulator	13-16	Transistorized Regulator Adjustments	13-20
Transistorized Voltage Regulator	13-16	3 Removal and Installation	13-20
2 In-Car Adjustments and Repairs	13-17		

1 DESCRIPTION AND OPERATION

MECHANICAL VOLTAGE REGULATOR

The alternator regulator is composed of two control units, a field relay and a voltage limiter, mounted as an assembly (Fig. 1). Because the reverse current through the rectifier is small, a reverse current cutout relay is not needed. The alternator is self current limiting, thus a current limiter is not needed. Refer to Wiring Diagram Manual Form 7795P-66 for locations of wiring harnesses. Schematics are shown in Group 22 of this manual.

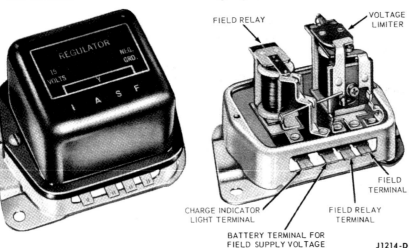

FIG. 1—Alternator Regulator

FIELD RELAY

The field relay serves to connect charging system voltage to the field circuit when the engine is running.

CHARGE INDICATOR CIRCUIT—LIGHT

When the ignition switch is closed, battery current flows through the charge indicator light and 15-ohm parallel resistor, and through the regulator voltage limiter contacts to the field coil. This small current is enough to allow the alternator to start generating, and is necessary, as residual magnetism in the alternator is usually too small to start voltage build-up. The charge indicator light is shunted with a 15-ohm resistor to supply adequate starting field current.

When the alternator builds up enough voltage to close the field relay contacts, full voltage is applied to the field, and the charge indicator light goes out.

CHARGE INDICATOR CIRCUIT —AMMETER

When the ignition switch is closed, the field relay is energized. Closing of the relay contacts connects the battery and alternator output to the field through the voltage limiter contacts.

VOLTAGE LIMITER

The temperature compensated voltage limiter is a double contact unit. Limiting is accomplished by controlling the amount of current supplied to the rotating field.

When the upper contacts are closed, full system voltage is applied to the field and maximum field current will flow. When the limiter armature floats between the contacts, field current is reduced by flowing through the field resistor. When the limiter lower contacts are closed, zero current flows to the field. At low engine speed and with a load applied, the armature vibrates on the upper contact. At high engine speed and light or no load the armature vibrates on the lower contact.

A 50-ohm resistor is connected from the field terminal to ground to absorb electrical surges in the alternator circuits as the voltage limiter armature vibrates on the contacts.

TRANSISTORIZED VOLTAGE REGULATOR

The transistorized voltage regulator (Fig. 2), controls the alternator voltage output in a similar manner to a mechanical voltage regulator, by regulating the alternator field current. The regulation is accomplished electronically with the use of transistors and diodes rather than by a vibrating armature relay. The voltage sensing element is a zener diode which has the characteristic of suddenly changing its resistance when a specified voltage is reached. The field relay (Fig. 3) is still used, but it is mounted separately from the voltage regulator.

Figs. 4 and 5 show schematics of the transistorized voltage regulator system. When the engine is started, battery current is supplied to the field through the field relay, field current supply diode, and the power transistor.

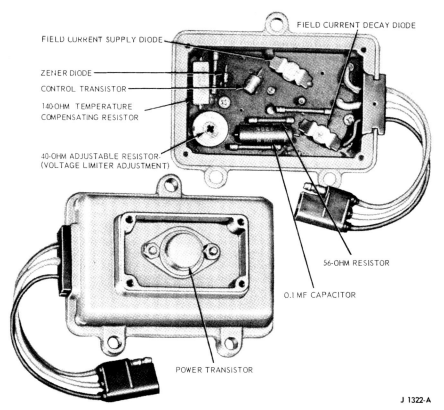

FIELD CURRENT DECAY DIODE

FIELD CURRENT SUPPLY DIODE

ZENER DIODE

CONTROL TRANSISTOR

140-OHM TEMPERATURE
COMPENSATING RESISTOR

40-OHM ADJUSTABLE RESISTOR
(VOLTAGE LIMITER ADJUSTMENT)

56-OHM RESISTOR

0.1 MF CAPACITOR

POWER TRANSISTOR

J 1322-A

FIG. 2—Transistorized Voltage Regulator

J 1323-A

FIG. 3—Field Relay

As the alternator begins to supply current, the battery voltage will increase. When the battery voltage reaches approximately 14.5 volts, the zener diode (Figs. 4 and 5), due *to its* characteristics, suddenly reduces its resistance and lowers the voltage at point B on the control transistor. The control transistor then acting as a switch applies battery voltage to point B on the power transistor. The power transistor also acting as a switch then opens, cutting off battery current to the field.

The battery voltage drops slightly, the zener diode increases its resistance, opening the control transistor, which in turn closes the power transistor and battery current again flows to the alternator field.

This sequence of events repeats itself at an approximate rate of 2000 times per second, which is faster than the rate that a mechanical regulator interrupts the field current.

The field current supply diode is used to protect the power transistor.

The field current decay diode per-

forms the same function as the resistors in a mechanical regulator, providing a path to ground for the energy from the field when the field current is interrupted.

The 140-ohm resistor is made of a special material that changes its resistance with temperature in such a manner that during cold weather the battery charging voltage is increased. This resistor performs the same function as the bimetal hinge on the voltage limiter armature of a mechanical regulator.

The alternator output voltage is adjusted by varying the 40-ohm adjustable resistor (Fig. 2). Varying the adjustable resistor performs the same function as adjusting the voltage limiter armature spring tension on a mechanical regulator.

The 0.1 microfarad capacitor in series with the 56-ohm resistor causes the control transistor and the power transistor to switch on and off faster providing better control of the field current.

The remaining resistors in the unit provide proper operating voltages for the zener diode and the two transistors.

2 IN-CAR ADJUSTMENTS AND REPAIRS

MECHANICAL REGULATOR ADJUSTMENTS

Erratic operation of the regulator, indicated by erratic movement of the voltmeter pointer during a voltage limiter test, may be caused by dirty or pitted regulator contacts. **Vehicle ammeter pointer waver at certain critical engine speeds and electrical loads, is normal.** Use a very fine abrasive paper such as silicon carbide, 400 grade, to clean the field

relay and the voltage limiter contacts. Wear off the sharp edges of the abrasive by rubbing it against another piece of abrasive paper. Fold the abrasive paper over and pull the paper through the contacts to clean them. Keep all oil or grease from contacting the points. Do not use compressed air to clean the regulator. When adjusting the gap spacing use only hospital clean feeler gauges.

REGULATOR GAP ADJUSTMENTS

Voltage Limiter. The difference between the upper stage and lower stage regulation (0.3 volt), is determined by the voltage limiter contact and core gaps. Make the gap adjustment with the regulator removed from the car.

Bend the lower contact bracket to obtain 0.017 to 0.022-inch gap at the lower contacts with the upper

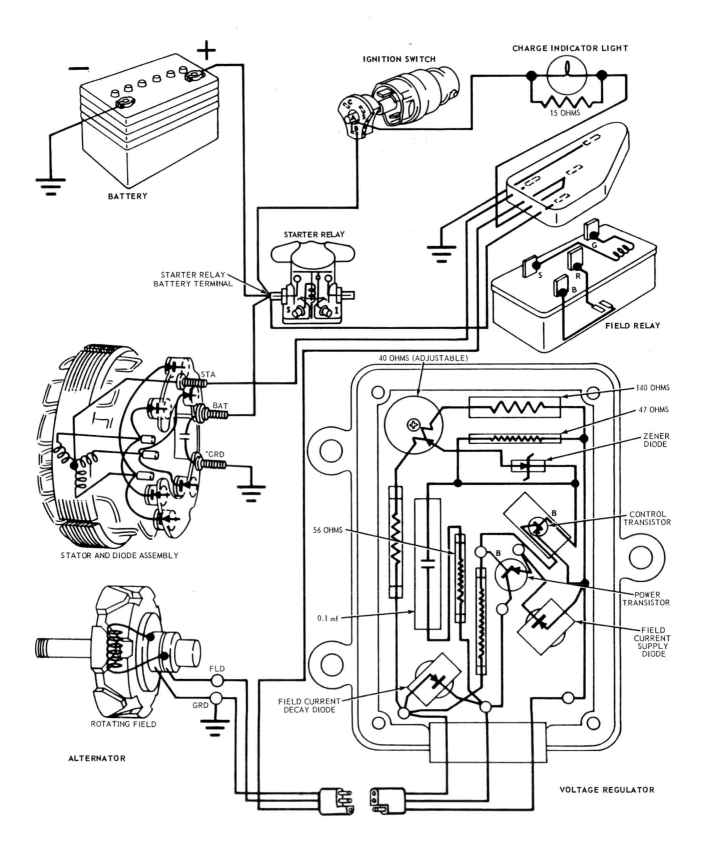

FIG. 4—Alternator System With Transistor Voltage Regulator and Charge Indicator Light

J1326-A

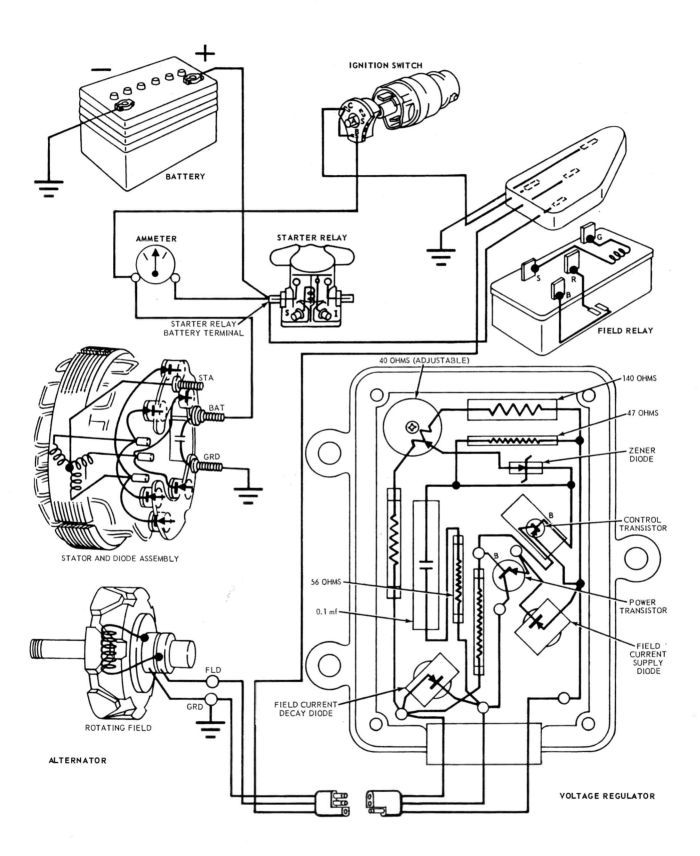

J1321-A

FIG. 5—Alternator System With Transistor Voltage Regulator and Ammeter

contacts closed. Maintain the contacts in alignment.

Adjust the core gap with the upper contacts closed. Loosen the center lock screw ¼ turn. Use a screwdriver blade in the adjustment slot under the lock screw. Adjust the core gap for 0.049 to 0.056-inch clearance between the armature and the core at the edge of the core closest to the contact points. Tighten the lock screw and recheck the core gap.

Field Relay. Place a 0.010 to 0.018-inch feeler gauge on top of the coil core closest to the contact points. Hold the armature down on the gauge. Do not push down on the contact spring arm. Bend the contact post arm (Fig. 6) until the bottom contact just touches the upper contact.

REGULATOR VOLTAGE LIMITER ADJUSTMENTS

Final adjustment of the regulator must be made with the regulator at normal operating temperature.

The field relay closing voltage is adjusted by bending the relay frame (Fig. 6). To increase the closing voltage, bend the armature frame down. To decrease the closing voltage, bend the frame up.

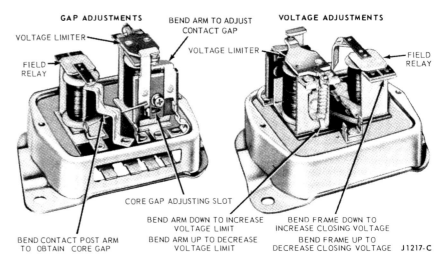

FIG. 6—Regulator Adjustments

The voltage limiter is adjusted by bending the voltage limiter spring arm (Fig. 6). To increase the voltage setting, bend the adjusting arm downward. To decrease the voltage setting, bend the adjusting arm upward.

Before setting the voltage and before making a final voltage test, the alternator speed must be reduced to zero and the ignition switch opened momentarily, to cycle the regulator.

On some cars the location of the regulator may prevent adjustment on the car. Remove the regulator to an alternator-regulator test stand if adjustment is necessary.

TRANSISTORIZED REGULATOR ADJUSTMENTS

REGULATOR VOLTAGE LIMITER ADJUSTMENTS

The only adjustment on the transistorized alternator regulator is the voltage limiter adjustment.

Adjustment of the transistor voltage limiter must be made with the regulator at normal operating temperature. Remove the regulator mounting screws and remove the bottom cover from the regulator. The voltage setting may be moved up or down by adjusting the 40-ohm adjustable resistor (Fig. 2).

---

3 REMOVAL AND INSTALLATION

1. Remove the battery ground cable.
2. Remove the regulator mounting screws.
3. Disconnect the regulator from the wiring harness.

4. Connect the new regulator to the wiring harness.
5. Mount the regulator to the regulator mounting plate. The radio suppression condenser mounts under one mounting screw. The ground

lead mounts under the other mounting screw.
6. Connect the battery ground cable, and test the system for proper voltage regulation.

PART 13-4

53-AMPERE LEECE NEVILLE ALTERNATOR

Section	Page	Section	Page
1 Description and Operation 13-21		3 Major Repair Operations 13-21	
2 Removal and Installation 13-21			

1 DESCRIPTION AND OPERATION

The operation and general electrical description of the Leece Neville 53-ampere alternator is similar to that of the Autolite alternators, (Part 13-2). The field brushes are mounted in an insulated brush holder which is mounted in the brush end housing (Fig. 2).

The drive end bearing is a sealed ball bearing. The brush end bearing is a needle type bearing and is not sealed. The alternator mountings are shown in Fig. 1.

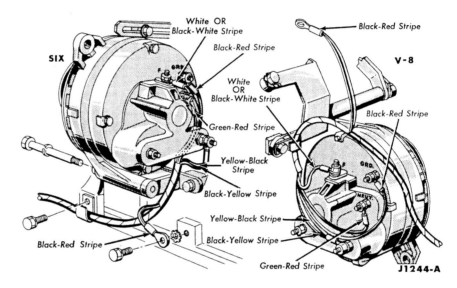

FIG. 1—Alternator Mounting—Typical

2 REMOVAL AND INSTALLATION

REMOVAL

1. Disconnect the battery ground cable.
2. Loosen the alternator mounting bolts and remove the adjustment arm to alternator bolt.
3. Disengage the alternator belt. Remove the alternator mounting bolt, disconnect the alternator wiring and remove the alternator.

INSTALLATION

1. Attach the alternator wiring. Position the alternator to the engine, and install the alternator mounting bolt finger-tight (Fig. 1).

2. Install the adjustment arm to alternator bolt.
3. Adjust the belt tension using tool T63L-8620-A. Apply pressure on the alternator drive end housing only. Tighten the adjusting arm bolts and the mounting bolt.
4. Connect the battery ground cable.

3 MAJOR REPAIR OPERATIONS

DISASSEMBLY

1. Remove the brush holder and the brushes (Fig. 2). Scribe the end housings for reference in assembly.
2. Remove the alternator housing through bolts, and separate the drive end housing and rotor from the stator and brush end housing.

3. Press the rotor shaft out of the drive end housing only if the rotor or bearing are being replaced. Remove the bearing spacer.
4. Remove the bearing retainer, support the housing around the bearing pocket to prevent damage to the housing, and press the bearing from

the drive end housing. Remove the bearing only if replacement is required.
5. Remove the BT, Neut., and ground terminal nuts and washers, and remove the brush end housing from the stator and diode rectifier assembly.

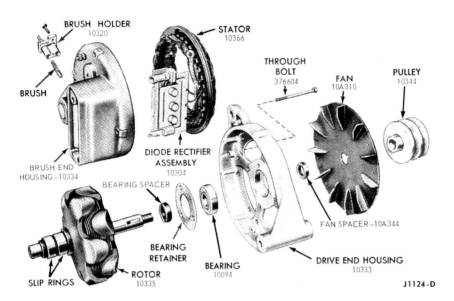

FIG. 2—Disassembled 53-Ampere Leece Neville Alternator

6. If the diode plates or stator are being replaced, carefully unsolder the three stator leads from the diode connector eyelets, and separate the leads from each other. Clean the solder from the eyelets.

7. Press the brush end housing bearing from the housing only if it is being replaced.

**PARTS REPAIR
OR REPLACEMENT**

Nicks and scratches may be re-moved from the rotor slip rings by turning down the slip rings. Remove only enough to clean up the surface. If the slip rings are badly damaged, they should be replaced. Repair any broken lead wires.

ASSEMBLY

1. If the drive end bearing was removed, press the new bearing into the drive end housing putting pressure on the outer race only. Install the bearing retainer.

2. Place the bearing spacer on the drive end shaft and press the drive end bearing on the shaft tight against the spacer. Put pressure on the inner race only.

3. If the brush end housing bearing was removed, press a new bearing into the housing flush with the outer surface of the housing.

4. Position the two diode plate assemblies together with the insulators and terminal bolts as shown in Fig. 3. The positive diode plate is positioned closest to the outside.

5. Position the eyelets over the diode leads, insert the three stator leads in the eyelets and solder them in position.

6. Position the brush end housing over the diode plate assembly and install the insulators, washers and terminal nuts. The condenser ground lug is mounted under the ground terminal nut. Make certain that the stator leads are positioned out of the way of the rotor (Fig. 4).

7. Position the rotor and drive end housing and the stator and brush end housing together. Align the housing scribe marks and install the housing through bolts.

8. Install the slip rings brushes and brush holder.

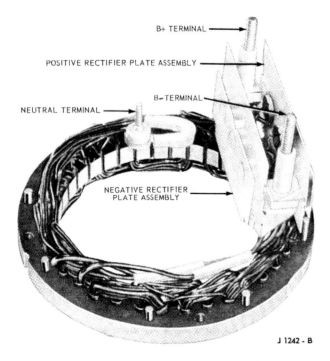

FIG. 3—Diode Plate and Stator Assembly

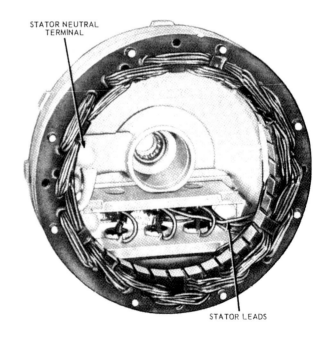

FIG. 4—Stator Lead Dress

PART 13-5

LEECE NEVILLE ALTERNATOR REGULATORS

Section	Page
1 Description and Operation	13-23
2 In-Car Adjustments and Repairs	13-23

Section	Page
3 Removal and Installation	13-24

1 DESCRIPTION AND OPERATION

The alternator regulators are composed of two control units mounted as an assembly (Fig. 1). The units are similar in operation to those used on the standard alternator regulator and consist of a double-contact voltage limiter and a field relay.

Two regulators are used. The regulator used with an ammeter charge indicator has three terminals, battery (BAT), ignition (IGN), and field (FLD). The regulator used with the charge indicator light has four terminals; three on the front, battery (BAT), light (LAMP), and field (FLD); one on the back, neutral (NEUT). The replacement regula-

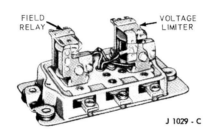

FIG. 1—Leece-Neville Alternator Regulator

tor has five terminals including an ignition terminal (IGN).

Refer to Wiring Diagram Manual Form 7795P-66 for locations of wiring harnesses. Schematics are shown

in Group 22 of this manual.

FIELD RELAY

The field relay (Fig. 1) is controlled by the ignition switch, on cars with an ammeter, and by alternator neutral junction voltage on cars with a charge indicator light. The field relay connects the battery to the alternator field through the voltage limiter contacts.

VOLTAGE LIMITER

The voltage limiter holds the alternator voltage within a predetermined range by controlling the amount of current supplied to the rotating field.

2 IN-CAR ADJUSTMENTS AND REPAIRS

REGULATOR ADJUSTMENTS

Final checking of the regulator must be made with the regulator at normal operating temperature and the cover in place. For any of the adjustments given below, remove the cover by removing the two mounting screws.

REGULATOR GAP ADJUSTMENTS

Make the regulator gap adjustments with the regulator removed from the car.

Voltage Limiter. Adjust the contact gap first. Loosen the contact-gap adjusting arm lock screw (Fig. 2), and adjust the contact gap to specification (Part 13-7). Tighten the lock screw. Adjust the core gap with the lower contacts closed. Loosen the core gap lock screw and move the contact insulator up or down until the specified core gap is arrived at between the coil core and

the armature. Tighten lock screw.

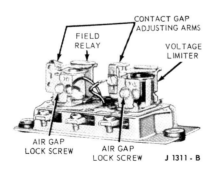

FIG. 2—Regulator Gap Adjustments

Field Relay. Adjust the core gap first. Loosen the field relay air gap lock screw and move the contact insulator up or down until the specified core air gap is arrived at between the coil core and the armature. Tighten the lock screw. Put the blade of a small screw driver in the field relay adjusting arm slot (Fig.

2), and bend the arm to obtain the specified contact gap (Part 13-7).

REGULATOR VOLTAGE ADJUSTMENTS

Voltage Limiter. To increase the voltage setting, bend the adjusting arm downward (Fig. 3). To decrease the voltage setting, bend the adjusting arm upward (Fig. 3). **Before adjusting the voltage, and before making a final voltage reading**

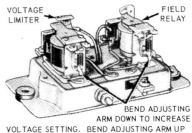

FIG. 3—Alternator Regulator Adjustments—Typical

with the cover in place, cycle the alternator. Reduce the alternator speed to zero and turn the ignition switch to OFF momentarily. This

procedure must be repeated each time an adjustment is made.

Field Relay. The field relay cut-in voltage is increased by bending the

adjusting arm downward, or decreased by bending the adjusting arm upward (Fig. 3).

---

3 REMOVAL AND INSTALLATION

1. Disconnect the battery ground cable.

2. Remove the wires from the regulator.

3. Remove the regulator mounting screws and the regulator.

4. Position the regulator and install the mounting screws. Mount the black-red stripe ground wire lug under the mounting screw at the ground strap end of the regulator. (Fig. 4 or 5).

5. Connect the remaining regulator wires (Fig. 4 or 5).

6. Connect the battery ground cable and check the regulator operation.

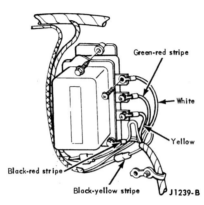

FIG. 4—Regulator Mounting—Ammeter Circuit

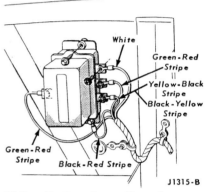

FIG. 5—Regulator Mounting—Indicator Light Circuit

PART 13-6 SPECIFICATIONS

ALTERNATOR

Supplier	Stamp Color	Rating		Field Current Amps @ 12V	Cut-In Speed (Engine r.p.m.)	Rated Output Speed (Engine r.p.m.)	Slip-Ring Turning (Inches)		Brush Length (Inches)		Pulley Nut Torque (ft.-lbs.)	Belt Tension (lbs.)	
		Amperes @ 15V	Watts @ 15V				Min. Dia.	Max. Runout	New	Wear Limit		6 Cyl.	8 Cyl. ①
Autolite	Purple	38	570	2.5	400	1500 Cold 2900 Hot	1.22	0.0005	½	⁵/₁₆	60-100	60-90	80-110
Autolite	Orange	42	630	2.9	400	1600 Cold 2900 Hot	1.22	0.0005	½	⁵/₁₆	60-100	60-90	80-110
Autolite	Black	45	675	2.9	400	1700 Cold 2900 Hot	1.22	0.0005	½	⁵/₁₆	60-100	60-90	80-110
Autolite	Red	55	825	2.9	400	1400 Cold 2900 Hot	1.22	0.0005	½	⁵/₁₆	60-100	60-90	80-110
Leece-Neville	—	53	795	2.9	400	1700 Cold 2100 Hot	Light Cut	0.002	⅝	⅜	30-50	60-90	80-110

①Used Belt. New Belt 110-140. A used belt is one that has been in operation more than 10 minutes. Ford Alternator Pulley nut Torque 60-100 foot pounds.

VOLTAGE REGULATION SETTING

Ambient Temperature °F.	All Alternator Regulators
50	14.3-15.1
75	14.1-14.9
100	13.9-14.7
125	13.8-14.6
150	13.6-14.4
175	13.5-14.3

BATTERY FREEZING TEMPERATURES

Specific Gravity	Freezing Temp.
1.280	−90°F.
1.250	−62°F.
1.200	−16°F.
1.150	+ 5°F.
1.100	+19°F.

BATTERY

Filler Cap Color	Number of Plates	Amp. Hours
Yellow	54	45
Red	66	55
Gray	66	70
Black	78	80
Black	90	85

ALLOWABLE BATTERY HIGH RATE CHARGE TIME SCHEDULE

Specific Gravity Reading	Charge Rate Amperes	BATTERY CAPACITY AMPERE HOURS			
		45	55	70	80
1.125-1.150*	35	65 min.	80 min.	100 min.	115 min.
1.150-1.175	35	50 min.	65 min.	80 min.	95 min.
1.175-1.200	35	40 min.	50 min.	60 min.	70 min.
1.200-1.225	35	30 min.	35 min.	45 min.	50 min.
Above 1.225	5	**	**	**	**

*If the specific gravity is below 1.125, use the indicated high rate of charge for the 1.125 specific gravity, then charge at 5 amperes until the specific gravity reaches 1.250 at 80°F.
**Charge at 5 ampere rate only until the specific gravity reaches 1.250 at 80°F.
At no time during the charging operation should the electrolyte temperature exceed 130°F.

TOOLS

Ford Tool No.	Former No.	Description
Tool T63L-8620-A	8620 BT-33-73-F	Belt Tension Gauge

REGULATOR

Vendor	Current Reading	Lower Stage Voltage Regulation @75°F.①	VOLTAGE LIMITER		FIELD RELAY		
			Contact Gap (Inches)	Core Air Gap (Inches)	Contact Gap (Inches)	Core Air Gap (Inches)	Closing Volts
Autolite	Used With Ford Alternators②	14.1-14.9	0.017-0.022	0.049-0.056	—	0.010-0.018	2.5-4
Autolite	Transistor Regulator Used With 38, 42, 45, and 55 Ampere Alternators	14.1-14.9	—	—	—	—	2.5-4
Leece-Neville Indicator Light Circuit	Used With 53 Ampere Leece-Neville Alternator	14.1-14.9	0.018-0.020 With Lower Contacts Closed	0.042-0.052 With Lower Contacts Closed	0.018-0.020	0.009-0.011 With Contacts Touching	1.6-2.6
Leece-Neville Ammeter Circuit	Used With 53-Ampere Leece-Neville Alternator	14.1-14.9	0.018-0.020 With Lower Contacts Closed	0.042-0.052 With Lower Contacts Closed	0.024-0.026	0.011-0.013 With Contacts Touching	6.2-7.2

①See table on this page for voltage settings at other temperatures.
②Silver stamp color is used with 38 and 42-ampere alternators.
  Yellow stamp color is used with 45 and 55-ampere alternators.

STARTING SYSTEM

GROUP 14

PART 14-1   **PAGE**
GENERAL STARTING SYSTEM SERVICE . 14-1

PART 14-2
STARTER 14-8

PART 14-3   **PAGE**
SPECIFICATIONS 14-10

PART 14-1   GENERAL STARTING SYSTEM SERVICE

Section   **Page**
1 Diagnosis and Testing 14-1
    Road Service 14-1
    Starter Will Not Crank the Engine 14-1
    Starter Cranks Engine Slowly 14-3
    Engine Will Crank at Normal Speed
        But Will Not Start 14-3
    Starter Load Test 14-3
    Starter No-Load Test 14-3

Section   **Page**
    Armature and Field Grounded Circuit
        Test-On Test Bench 14-3
    Starter Cranking Circuit Test 14-5
2 Common Adjustments and Repairs 14-6
    Brush Replacement 14-6
    Armature Replacement 14-6
3 Cleaning and Inspection 14-6

1 DIAGNOSIS AND TESTING

The starting system includes the starting motor and drive, the battery, the starter relay, the starter (ignition) switch, and the necessary cables and wiring to connect the components. Vehicles equipped with an automatic transmission employ a neutral-start switch in the system which prevents operation of the starter in all selector positions except N (neutral) and P (park).

A schematic diagram of the starting circuit is shown in Fig. 1.

The majority of starting problems usually fall into one of the following situations: the starter will not crank the engine; the engine will crank at normal speed but will not start; and the starter cranks the engine very slowly.

If the engine will crank but will not start, the trouble is usually in the engine, fuel system or ignition system rather than in the starting system.

Following are road map type charts which may be followed to determine the cause of the difficulty and the corrective action.

ROAD SERVICE

On road service calls, connect a

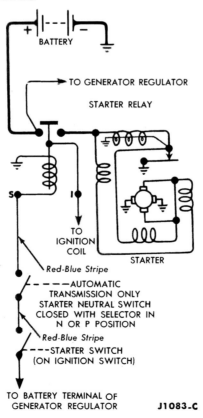

FIG. 1—Starting Circuit   J1083-C

booster battery to the system for cases of a starter that will not crank the engine or a starter that cranks the engine very slowly. If the starter turns the engine over, but the engine still will not start, even with the booster battery attached, refer to the following charts. **Be certain that correct battery polarity is observed when using a booster battery; positive to positive, and negative to negative connection of the auxiliary cables.**

STARTER WILL NOT CRANK THE ENGINE

Refer to Fig. 2 for this symptom.

NOTE 1—NEUTRAL START SWITCH TEST

On vehicles equipped with an automatic transmission, apply the brakes and attempt to start the engine while moving the selector lever through all ranges. This may determine if the problem is caused by a maladjusted or defective neutral-start switch. Refer to Group 7 Part 3 for the adjustment of this switch.

NOTE 2

Connect a heavy jumper cable

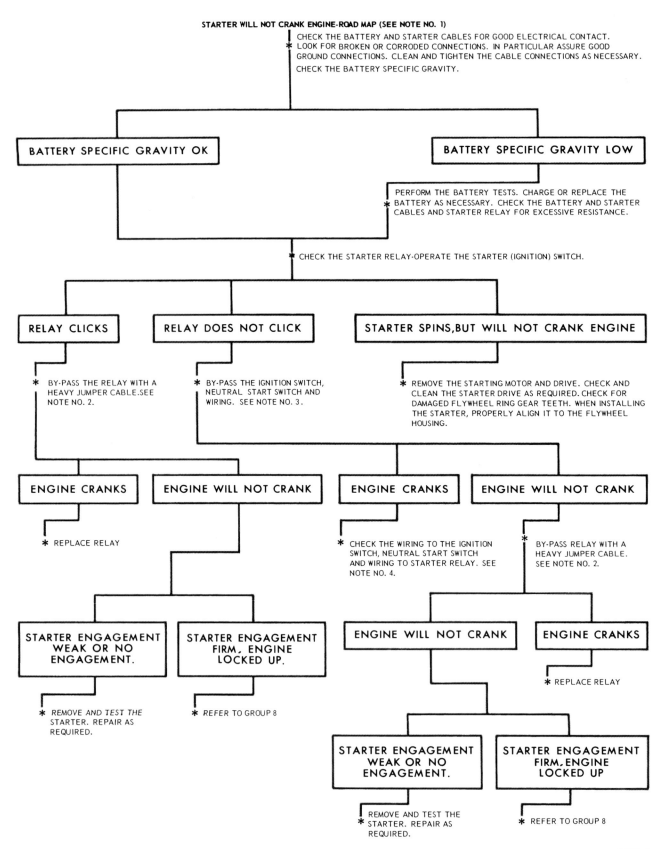

STARTER WILL NOT CRANK ENGINE-ROAD MAP (SEE NOTE NO. 1)

* CHECK THE BATTERY AND STARTER CABLES FOR GOOD ELECTRICAL CONTACT. LOOK FOR BROKEN OR CORRODED CONNECTIONS. IN PARTICULAR ASSURE GOOD GROUND CONNECTIONS. CLEAN AND TIGHTEN THE CABLE CONNECTIONS AS NECESSARY. CHECK THE BATTERY SPECIFIC GRAVITY.

BATTERY SPECIFIC GRAVITY OK

BATTERY SPECIFIC GRAVITY LOW

* PERFORM THE BATTERY TESTS. CHARGE OR REPLACE THE BATTERY AS NECESSARY. CHECK THE BATTERY AND STARTER CABLES AND STARTER RELAY FOR EXCESSIVE RESISTANCE.

* CHECK THE STARTER RELAY-OPERATE THE STARTER (IGNITION) SWITCH.

RELAY CLICKS

RELAY DOES NOT CLICK

STARTER SPINS, BUT WILL NOT CRANK ENGINE

* BY-PASS THE RELAY WITH A HEAVY JUMPER CABLE. SEE NOTE NO. 2.

* BY-PASS THE IGNITION SWITCH, NEUTRAL START SWITCH AND WIRING. SEE NOTE NO. 3.

* REMOVE THE STARTING MOTOR AND DRIVE. CHECK AND CLEAN THE STARTER DRIVE AS REQUIRED. CHECK FOR DAMAGED FLYWHEEL RING GEAR TEETH. WHEN INSTALLING THE STARTER, PROPERLY ALIGN IT TO THE FLYWHEEL HOUSING.

ENGINE CRANKS

ENGINE WILL NOT CRANK

ENGINE CRANKS

ENGINE WILL NOT CRANK

* REPLACE RELAY

* CHECK THE WIRING TO THE IGNITION SWITCH, NEUTRAL START SWITCH AND WIRING TO STARTER RELAY. SEE NOTE NO. 4.

* BY-PASS RELAY WITH A HEAVY JUMPER CABLE. SEE NOTE NO. 2.

STARTER ENGAGEMENT WEAK OR NO ENGAGEMENT.

STARTER ENGAGEMENT FIRM, ENGINE LOCKED UP.

ENGINE WILL NOT CRANK

ENGINE CRANKS

* REPLACE RELAY

* REMOVE AND TEST THE STARTER. REPAIR AS REQUIRED.

* REFER TO GROUP 8

STARTER ENGAGEMENT WEAK OR NO ENGAGEMENT.

STARTER ENGAGEMENT FIRM, ENGINE LOCKED UP

* REMOVE AND TEST THE STARTER. REPAIR AS REQUIRED.

* REFER TO GROUP 8

J 1316—A

FIG. 2—Starter Will Not Crank Engine—Road Map

from the battery terminal of the re-lay to the starter terminal of the relay (Fig. 3, connection No. 1).

NOTE 3—STARTER RELAY TEST

Connect a jumper from the bat-tery terminal of the relay to the starter (ignition) switch terminal of the relay (Fig. 3, connection No. 2). If the engine does not crank, the *starter* relay probably is at fault.

NOTE 4—STARTER CONTROL CIRCUIT TEST

On vehicles equipped with an au-tomatic transmission, if the engine cranks, connect a jumper from the relay side of the neutral-start switch battery terminal of the relay to the (Fig. 3, connection No. 3). If the engine does not crank, the wiring be-tween the neutral-start switch and the relay is at fault. If the engine cranks, relay side of the neutral-start switch connect a jumper from the battery terminal of the relay to the starter (ignition) switch side of the neutral-start switch (Fig. 3, connection No. 4). If the engine does not crank, the neutral-start switch is out of adjust-ment or defective. If the engine cranks, check for voltage at the bat-tery terminal of the starter (ignition) switch wiring harness connector with a test light or a voltmeter. If voltage is not available, the wiring between the battery terminal of the starter re-lay and the battery terminal of the starter (ignition) switch is at fault. If voltage is available, substitute an ignition switch from stock. If the en-gine cranks, replace the ignition switch. If the engine still will not crank, the trouble is in the wiring or connections between the ignition switch and the starter-neutral switch.

STARTER CRANKS ENGINE SLOWLY

Refer to Fig. 4 for this symptom.

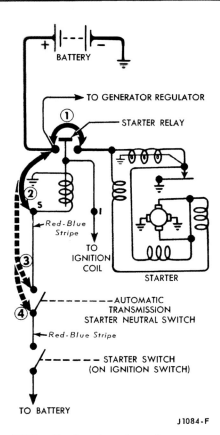

J1084-F

FIG. 3—Starting Control Circuit Tests

ENGINE WILL CRANK AT NORMAL SPEED BUT WILL NOT START

Refer to Group 8 for this symp-tom.

STARTER LOAD TEST

Connect the test equipment as shown in Fig. 5. Be sure that no cur-rent is flowing through the ammeter and heavy-duty carbon pile rheo-stat portion of the circuit (rheostat at maximum counterclockwise posi-tion).

Crank the engine with the ignition OFF, and determine the exact read-ing on the voltmeter. This test is ac-complished by disconnecting and grounding the high tension lead from the spark coil, and by connecting a jumper from the battery terminal of the starter relay to the ignition switch terminal of the relay.

Stop cranking the engine, and re-duce the resistance of the carbon pile until the voltmeter indicates the same reading as that obtained while the starter cranked the engine. The am-

meter will indicate the starter current draw under load.

STARTER NO-LOAD TEST

The starter no-load test will un-cover such faults as open or shorted windings, rubbing armature, and bent armature shaft. The starter can be tested, at no-load, on the test bench only.

Make the test connections as shown in Fig. 6. The starter will run at no-load. Be sure that no current is flowing through the ammeter (rheo-stat at maximum counterclockwise position). Determine the exact read-ing on the voltmeter.

Disconnect the starter from the battery, and reduce the resistance of the rheostat until the voltmeter indi-cates the same reading as that ob-tained while the starter was running. The ammeter will indicate the starter no-load current draw.

ARMATURE OPEN CIRCUIT TEST—ON TEST BENCH

An open circuit armature may sometimes be detected by examining the commutator for evidence of burning. The spot burned on the commutator is caused by an arc formed every time the commutator segment, connected to the open cir-cuit winding, passes under a brush.

ARMATURE AND FIELD GROUNDED CIRCUIT TEST—ON TEST BENCH

This test will determine if the winding insulation has failed, permit-ting a conductor to touch the frame or armature core.

To determine if the armature windings are grounded, make the connections as shown in Fig. 7. If the voltmeter indicates any voltage, the windings are grounded.

Grounded field windings can be detected by making the connections as shown in Fig. 8. If the voltmeter indicates any voltage, the field wind-ings are grounded.

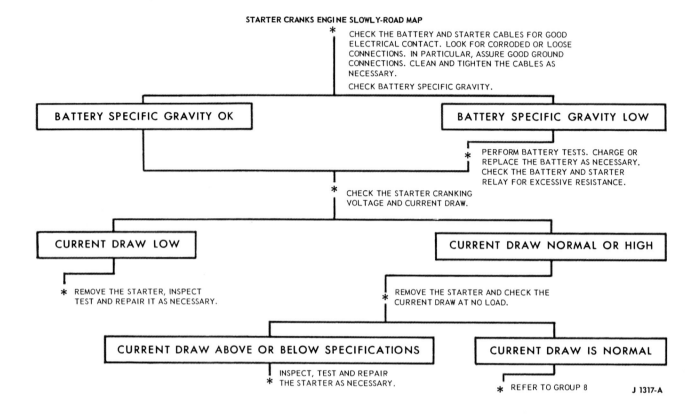

STARTER CRANKS ENGINE SLOWLY-ROAD MAP

* CHECK THE BATTERY AND STARTER CABLES FOR GOOD
ELECTRICAL CONTACT. LOOK FOR CORRODED OR LOOSE
CONNECTIONS. IN PARTICULAR, ASSURE GOOD GROUND
CONNECTIONS. CLEAN AND TIGHTEN THE CABLES AS
NECESSARY.

CHECK BATTERY SPECIFIC GRAVITY.

| BATTERY SPECIFIC GRAVITY OK | BATTERY SPECIFIC GRAVITY LOW |

* PERFORM BATTERY TESTS. CHARGE OR
REPLACE THE BATTERY AS NECESSARY.
CHECK THE BATTERY AND STARTER
RELAY FOR EXCESSIVE RESISTANCE.

* CHECK THE STARTER CRANKING
VOLTAGE AND CURRENT DRAW.

| CURRENT DRAW LOW | CURRENT DRAW NORMAL OR HIGH |

* REMOVE THE STARTER, INSPECT
TEST AND REPAIR IT AS NECESSARY.

* REMOVE THE STARTER AND CHECK THE
CURRENT DRAW AT NO LOAD.

| CURRENT DRAW ABOVE OR BELOW SPECIFICATIONS | CURRENT DRAW IS NORMAL |

* INSPECT, TEST AND REPAIR
THE STARTER AS NECESSARY.

* REFER TO GROUP 8   J 1317-A

FIG. 4—Starter Cranks Engine Slowly—Road Map

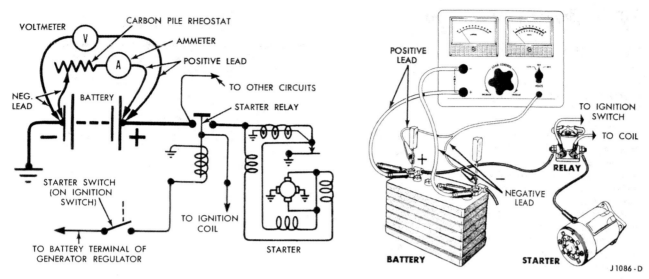

FIG. 5—Starter Load Test

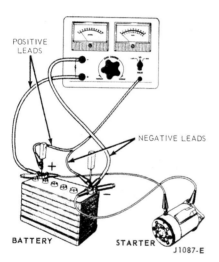

FIG. 6—Starter No-Load Test on Test Bench

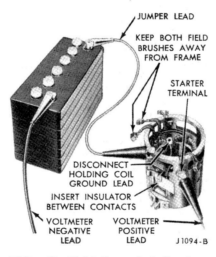

FIG. 8—Field Grounded Circuit Test

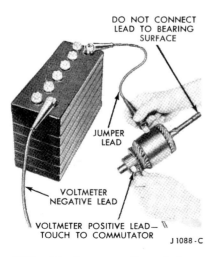

FIG. 7—Armature Grounded Circuit Test

STARTER CRANKING CIRCUIT TEST

Excessive resistance in the starter circuit can be determined from the results of this test. Make the test connections as shown in Fig. 9. Crank the engine with the ignition OFF. This is accomplished by disconnecting and grounding the high tension lead from the spark coil and by connecting a jumper from the battery terminal of the starter relay to the ignition switch terminal(s), of the relay.

The voltage drop in the circuit will be indicated by the voltmeter (o to 2 volt range). Maximum allowable voltage drop should be:

1. With the voltmeter negative lead connected to the starter terminal and the positive lead connected to the battery positive terminal (Fig. 9, connection ①) .... 0.5 volt.

2. With the voltmeter negative lead connected to the battery terminal of the starter relay and the positive lead connected to the positive terminal of the battery (Fig. 9, connection ②) .... 0.1 volt.

3. With the voltmeter negative lead connected to the starter terminal of the starter relay and the positive lead connected to the positive terminal of the battery (Fig. 9, connection ③) ....0.3 volt.

4. With the voltmeter negative lead connected to the negative terminal of the battery and the positive lead connected to the engine ground (Fig. 9, connection ④) .... 0.1 volt.

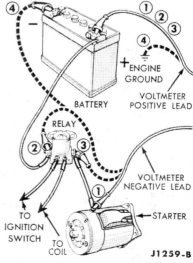

FIG. 9—Starter Cranking Circuit Test

2 COMMON ADJUSTMENTS AND REPAIRS

STARTER DRIVE REPLACEMENT CIRCUIT TEST

1. Loosen and remove the brush cover band and the starter drive plunger lever cover.

2. Loosen the through bolts enough to allow removal of the rear end housing and the starter drive plunger lever return spring.

3. Remove the pivot pin retaining the starter drive plunger lever and remove the lever.

4. Remove the drive gear stop ring retainer and stop ring from the end of the armature shaft and remove the drive gear assembly.

5. Apply a thin coating of Lubriplate 777 on the armature shaft splines. Install the drive gear assembly on the armature shaft and install a new stop ring.

6. Position the starter gear plunger lever on the starter frame and install the pivot pin. **Be sure that the plunger lever properly engages the starter drive assembly.**

7. Install a new stop-ring retainer. Position the starter drive plunger lever return spring and rear end housing to the starter frame, and then tighten the through bolts to specifications (55-75 inch pounds).

8. Position the starter drive plunger lever cover and the brush cover band, with its gasket, on the starter. Tighten the brush cover band retaining screw.

BRUSH REPLACEMENT

Replace the starter brushes when they are worn to ¼ inch. Always install a complete set of new brushes.

1. Loosen and remove the brush cover band, gasket, and starter drive plunger lever cover. Remove the brushes from their holders.

2. Remove the two through bolts from the starter frame.

3. Remove the rear end housing, and the plunger lever return spring.

4. Remove the starter drive plunger lever pivot pin and lever, and remove the armature.

5. Remove the front end plate.

6. Remove the ground brush retaining screws from the frame and remove the brushes (cut the ground brush nearest the starter terminal from the brush terminal block, as close to the brush lead terminal as possible).

7. Cut (or unsolder) the insulated brush leads from the field coils, as close to the field connection point as possible.

8. Clean and inspect the starter motor.

9. Replace the front end plate if the insulator between the field brush holder and the end plate is cracked or broken.

10. Position the new insulated field brushes lead on the field coil terminal. Install the clip provided with the brushes to hold the brush lead to the terminal. Solder the lead, clip, and terminal together, using rosin core solder (Fig. 4, Part 14-2). Use a 300-watt iron.

11. Install the ground brush leads to the frame with the retaining screws.

12. Clean the commutator with #00 or #000 sandpaper.

13. Position the front end plate to the starter frame, with the end plate boss in the frame slot.

14. Position the fiber washer on the commutator end of the armature shaft and install the armature in the starter frame.

15. Install the starter drive gear plunger lever to the frame and starter drive assembly, and install the pivot pin.

16. Position the return spring on the plunger lever, and the rear end housing to the starter frame. Install the through bolts and tighten to specified torque (55-75 inch pounds). Be sure that the stop ring retainer is seated properly in the rear end housing.

17. Install the commutator brushes in the brush holders. Center the brush springs on the brushes.

18. Position the plunger lever cover and the brush cover band, with its gasket, on the starter. Tighten the band retaining screw.

19. Connect the starter to a battery to check its operation.

ARMATURE REPLACEMENT

1. Loosen the brush cover band retaining screw and remove the brush cover band, gasket, and the starter drive plunger lever cover. Remove the brushes from their holders.

2. Remove the through bolts, the rear end housing, and the drive plunger lever return spring.

3. Remove the pivot pin retaining the starter gear plunger lever, and remove the lever.

4. Remove the armature. If the starter drive gear assembly is being reused, remove the stop ring retainer and the stop ring from the end of the armature shaft, and remove the assembly.

5. Place the drive gear assembly on the new armature with a new stop ring.

6. Install the fiber thrust washer on the commutator end of the armature shaft and install the armature.

7. Position the drive gear plunger lever to the frame and drive gear assembly and install the pivot pin.

8. Position the drive plunger lever return spring, the rear end housing, and the front end plate to the starter frame, and then install and tighten the through bolts to specification. Be sure that the stop ring retainer is seated properly in the drive gear housing. If the starter has needle bearings apply a small amount of grease to the needles before installing the starter ends.

9. Place the brushes in their holders, and center the brush springs on the brushes.

10. Position the plunger lever cover and the brush cover band, with its gasket, and then tighten the retaining screw.

11. Connect the starter to a battery to check its operation.

3 CLEANING AND INSPECTION

1. Use a brush or air to clean the field coils, armature, commutator, armature shaft, front end plate, and rear end housing. Wash all other parts in solvent and dry the parts.

2. Inspect the armature windings for broken or burned insulation and unsoldered connections.

3. Check the armature for open circuits and grounds.

4. Check the commutator for run-out (Fig. 10). Inspect the armature shaft and the two bearings for scoring and excessive wear. On a starter with needle bearings apply a small

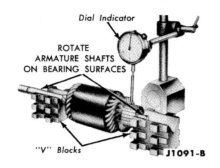

Dial Indicator

ROTATE
ARMATURE SHAFTS
ON BEARING SURFACES

"V" Blocks   J1091-B

FIG. 10—Commutator Runout Check

amount of grease to the needles. If the commutator is rough, or more than 0.005 inch out-of-round, turn it down.

5. Check the brush holders for broken springs and the insulated brush holders for shorts to ground. Tighten any rivets that may be loose. Replace the brushes if worn to ¼ inch in length.

6. Check the brush spring tension. Replace the springs if the tension is not within specified limits (40 ounces minimum).

7. Inspect the field coils for burned or broken insulation and continuity. Check the field brush connections and lead insulation.

PART 14-2

STARTER

Section	Page
1 Description and Operation	14-8
2 Removal and Installation	14-8
3 Major Repair Operation	14-8

Section	Page
Disassembly	14-8
Parts Repair or Replacement	14-9
Assembly	14-9

1 DESCRIPTION AND OPERATION

The function of the starting system is to crank the engine at high enough speed to permit it to start. The system includes the starter motor and drive, the battery, a remote control starter switch (part of the ignition switch), the neutral-start switch, the starter relay, and heavy circuit wiring. The starter mounting is shown in Fig. 1.

Turning of the ignition key to the START position actuates the starter relay, through the starter control circuit. The starter relay then connects the battery to the starter.

Cars equipped with an automatic transmission have a neutral-start switch, in the starter control circuit, which prevents operation of the

FIG. 1—Starter Mounting

starter if the selector lever is not in the N (neutral) or P (park) position.

The starter utilizes an integral positive-engagement drive (Fig. 2).

When the starter is not in use, one of the field coils is connected directly to ground through a set of contacts. When the starter is first connected to the battery a large current flows through the grounded field coil, actuating a movable pole shoe. The pole shoe is attached to the starter drive plunger lever and thus the drive is forced into engagement with the flywheel.

When the movable pole shoe is fully seated, it opens the field coil grounding contacts and the starter is then in normal operation. A holding coil is used to maintain the movable pole shoe in the fully seated position, during the time that the starter is turning the engine.

2 REMOVAL AND INSTALLATION

1. Raise the car on a hoist. (8-cyl. engine only).
2. Disconnect the starter cable at the starter terminal.
3. On a Comet with power steering (8-cyl. engine), disconnect and lower the idler arm from the frame.

Push the bolts back through the frame.
4. Remove the starter mounting bolts. Remove the starter assembly.
5. Position the starter assembly to the flywheel housing, and start the mounting bolts.

6. Snug all bolts, then torque them to specification.
7. Connect the starter cable.
8. Install the idler arm (if removed), and lower the car.

3 MAJOR REPAIR OPERATIONS

Use the following procedure when it becomes necessary to completely overhaul the starter. Fig. 2 illustrates a partially disassembled starter.

DISASSEMBLY

1. Loosen the brush cover band retaining screw and remove the brush cover band and the starter drive plunger lever cover. Observe the lead positions for assembly and then re-

move the commutator brushes from the brush holders.
2. Remove the through bolts, starter rear end housing, and the starter drive plunger lever return spring.
3. Remove the pivot pin retaining the starter gear plunger lever and remove the lever and the armature.
4. Remove the stop ring retainer. Remove and discard the stop ring re-

taining the starter drive gear to the end of the armature shaft, and remove the starter drive gear assembly.
5. Remove the front end plate.
6. Remove the two screws retaining the ground brushes to the frame.
7. On the field coil that operates the starter drive gear actuating lever, bend the tab up on the field retainer and remove the coil retainer.
8. Remove the three coil retaining

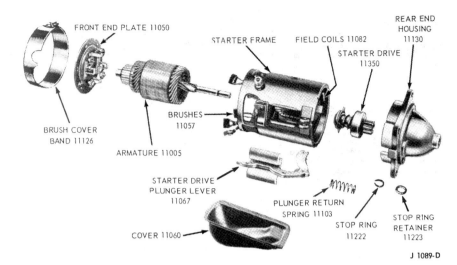

FIG. 2—Starter Disassembled

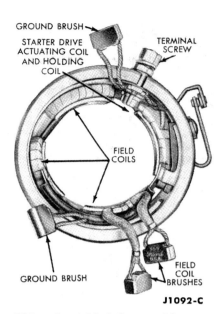

FIG. 4—Field Coil Assembly

screws, using tool 10044-A and an arbor press (Fig. 3). The arbor press prevents the wrench from slipping out of the screw. Unsolder the field coil leads from the terminal screw, and remove the pole shoes and coils from the frame (use a 300-watt iron).

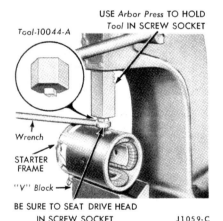

FIG. 3—Pole Shoe Screw Removal

9. Cut (or unsolder) the insulated brush leads from the field coils, as close to the field connection point as possible.

10. Remove the starter terminal nut, washer, insulator and terminal from the starter frame. Remove any excess solder from the terminal slot.

PARTS REPAIR OR REPLACEMENT

Nicks and scratches may be removed from the commutator by

turning it down. A brush kit and a contact kit are available. All other assemblies are to be replaced rather than repaired. If the starter has needle bearings, apply a small amount of grease to the needles before assembly.

ASSEMBLY

1. Install the starter terminal, insulator, washers, and retaining nut in the frame (Fig. 4). Be sure to position the slot in the screw perpendicular to the frame end surface.

2. Position the coils and pole pieces, with the coil leads in the terminal screw slot, and then install the retaining screws (Fig. 3). As the pole shoe screws are tightened, strike the frame several sharp blows with a soft-faced hammer to seat and align the pole shoes, then stake the screws.

3. Install the solenoid coil and retainer and bend the tabs to retain the coils to the frame.

4. Solder the field coils and solenoid wire to the starter terminal using rosin core solder. Use a 300-watt iron.

5. Check for continuity and grounds in the assembled coils.

6. Position the new insulated field brushes lead on the field coil terminal. Install the clip provided with the brushes to hold the brush lead to the terminal. Solder the lead, clip, and terminal together, using rosin core solder (Fig. 4). Use a 300-watt iron.

7. Position the solenoid coil ground terminal over the nearest ground screw hole.

8. Position the ground brushes to

the starter frame and install the retaining screws (Fig. 4).

9. Position the starter brush end plate to the frame, with the end plate boss in the frame slot.

10. Apply a thin coating of Lubriplate 777 on the armature shaft splines. Install the starter motor drive gear assembly to the armature shaft and install a new retaining stop ring. Install a new stop ring retainer.

11. Position the fiber thrust washer on the commutator end of the armature shaft and position the armature in the starter frame.

12. Position the starter drive gear plunger lever to the frame and starter drive assembly, and install the pivot pin.

13. Position the starter drive plunger lever return spring and the rear end housing to the frame and install and tighten the through bolts to specification (55-75 inch pounds). **Do not pinch the brush leads between the brush plate and the frame.** Be sure that the stop ring retainer is seated properly in the drive housing.

14. Install the brushes in the brush holders. **Be sure to center the brush springs on the brushes.**

15. Position the drive gear plunger lever cover on the starter and install the brush cover band with a gasket. Tighten the band retaining screw.

16. Check the starter no-load amperage draw.

PART
14-3
SPECIFICATIONS

Vendor	Current Draw Under Normal Load (Amperes)	Normal Engine Cranking Speed (rpm)	Minimum Stall Torque @ 5 Volts (Foot Pounds)	Maximum Load (Amperes)	No-Load (Amperes)	Brushes		
						Mfg. Length (Inches)	Wear Limit (Inches)	Brush Spring Tension (Ounces)
Ford Positive Engagement 4 1/2-Inch Diameter	250	250-290	15.5	670	70	0.5	0.25	40
Ford Positive Engagement—4-inch Diameter	100-150	250-290	9	460	70	0.5	0.25	40

Maximum commutator runout in inches is 0.005.
Maximum starting circuit voltage drop (battery + terminal to starter terminal @ normal engine temperature) 0.5 volt.
Starter through-bolt torque 55-75 inch pounds.
Starter mounting-bolt torque 3/8 inch bolt two-hole mounting 15-20 foot pounds, 5/16 inch bolt three-hole mounting 12-15 foot pounds.

SPECIAL TOOLS

Tool Number	Description
Tool 10044-A	Generator Pole Screw Wrench

LIGHTING SYSTEM, HORNS AND INSTRUMENTS

GROUP 15

PART 15-1   **PAGE**
GENERAL LIGHTING SYSTEM,
HORNS AND INSTRUMENTS
SERVICE **15-1**

PART 15-2
LIGHTING SYSTEM AND HORNS **15-6**

PART 15-3   **PAGE**
SWITCHES, CIRCUIT BREAKERS
AND FUSES **15-9**
PART 15-4
INSTRUMENTS **15-12**
PART 15-5
SPECIFICATIONS **15-24**

PART 15-1   GENERAL LIGHTING SYSTEM, HORNS AND INSTRUMENT SERVICE

Section	Page
1 Diagnosis and Testing 15-1	
Light Trouble Diagnosis Guide 15-1	
Instrument Trouble Diagnosis Guide 15-2	
Horn Trouble Diagnosis Guide 15-2	
Turn Indicator Trouble Diagnosis Guide 15-3	
Windshield Wiper Trouble Diagnosis Guide ...15-3	
Horn Test 15-3	
Headlight Switch and Beam Selector Switch Test ...15-3	
Constant Voltage Regulator Test 15-3	
Fuel Gauge and Fuel Level Sending Unit Test ...15-3	

Section	Page
Temperature Gauge Test 15-4	
Oil Pressure Indicator Light Test 15-4	
Oil Pressure Indicator Gauge Test— Comet ...15-4	
Charge Indicator Light Test 15-4	
Ammeter Test—Comet, Falcon, Mustang 15-4	
Speedometer Tests 15-4	
2 Common Adjustments and Repairs 15-4	
Horn Adjustment 15-4	
3 Cleaning and Inspection 15-4	
Single Speed Wiper Motor 15-4	
Two Speed Wiper Motor 15-5	

1 DIAGNOSIS AND TESTING

LIGHT TROUBLE DIAGNOSIS GUIDE

ALL HEADLIGHTS DO NOT LIGHT	1. Loose battery cable. 2. Loose quick disconnect or broken wire from the battery to the headlight switch. 3. Defective headlight switch. 4. Disconnected or broken wire from the headlight switch to the beam selector switch.	5. Loose or broken wire to the bulbs. 6. Defective beam selector switch. 7. All headlight bulbs burned out. This may be caused by a defective or improperly adjusted alternator voltage regulator (Group 13).
INDIVIDUAL LIGHTS DO NOT LIGHT	1. Burned out bulb. 2. Loose or broken wires to the bulb.	3. Poor ground.
LIGHTS BURN OUT REPEATEDLY	1. Loose or corroded electrical connections. 2. Excessive vibration.	3. Improperly adjusted or defective alternator voltage regulator (Group 13).

CONTINUED ON NEXT PAGE

INSTRUMENT TROUBLE DIAGNOSIS GUIDE

OIL PRESSURE INDICATOR LIGHT INOPERATIVE	1. Indicator bulb burned out. 2. Loose or broken wire from the light to the indicator switch.	3. Defective oil pressure sender unit (in this part).
CHARGE INDICATOR LIGHT INOPERATIVE	1. Burned out bulb.	2. Loose or broken wires.
CHARGE INDICATOR LIGHT STAYS ON AT IDLE	1. Idle speed too low. 2. Parallel resistance wire burned out.	3. Loose fan belt.
OIL PRESSURE INDICATOR GAUGE INOPERATIVE—COMET	1. Loose or broken wire from the constant voltage regulator to the oil pressure gauge. 2. Grounded or broken wire from	the engine oil pressure sending unit. 3. Defective gauge. 4. Defective oil pressure sending unit.
AMMETER GAUGE INOPERATIVE—COMET	1. Defective gauge (in this part). 2. Loose or broken wires.	3. Charging system malfunction.
FUEL GAUGE ERRATIC OR INOPERATIVE	1. Loose or broken wire from the constant voltage regulator to the fuel gauge. 2. Defective fuel gauge. 3. Loose, broken, or shorted wire from fuel gauge to the fuel tank sending unit.	4. Defective constant voltage regulator. 5. Defective fuel tank sending unit. 6. Poor ground between fuel tank and body.
TEMPERATURE GAUGE ERRATIC OR INOPERATIVE	1. Loose or broken wire from constant voltage regulator to the temperature gauge. 2. Defective temperature gauge. 3. Loose or broken wire from the temperature sending unit to the tem-	perature gauge. 4. Defective temperature sending unit. 5. Defective constant voltage regulator.
FUEL, TEMPERATURE, AND OIL PRESSURE GAUGES ERRATIC	1. Loose or corroded constant voltage regulator ground. 2. Defective constant voltage regulator.	3. Broken or loose wire from or to the constant voltage regulator. 4. Defective ignition switch.

HORN TROUBLE DIAGNOSIS GUIDE

HORNS DO NOT SOUND	1. Loose connections at horn button contact. 2. Open wire (yellow-green stripe) from horn to horn button. 3. Open wire (yellow) from head-	light switch to horn button. 4. Horns defective or out of adjustment. 5. Defective circuit breaker in headlight switch.
ONE HORN FAILS TO OPERATE	1. Broken or loose wire to the horn (black wire).	2. Horn defective or out of adjustment.
HORNS OPERATE CONTINUOUSLY	1. Horn button defective.	

CONTINUED ON NEXT PAGE

TURN INDICATOR TROUBLE DIAGNOSIS GUIDE

TURN INDICATOR LIGHTS INOPERATIVE	**1.** Burned out bulbs, or loose sockets. **2.** Loose or broken wire from ignition switch to flasher. **3.** Defective flasher.	**4.** Loose or broken wire from flasher to turn indicator switch. **5.** Defective turn indicator switch. **6.** Broken, shorted, or loose wires from switch to lights.
TURN INDICATOR LIGHTS OPERATE INCORRECTLY	**1.** Burned out bulb. **2.** Loose, broken, or shorted wires from switch to lights.	**3.** Defective indicator switch. **4.** Defective flasher.
TURN INDICATOR CANCELS IMPROPERLY	**1.** Cam improperly positioned on steering wheel hub.	**2.** Coil spring on switch plate assembly loose or weak.

WINDSHIELD WIPER TROUBLE DIAGNOSIS GUIDE

INOPERATIVE OR SLOW WIPER	**1.** Binding linkage. **2.** Defective switch. **3.** Defective wiper motor(s).	**4.** Defective wiring or circuit breaker.
CONTINUOUS WIPER ACTION WITH SELECTOR AT INTERMITTENT POSITION— COMET	**1.** Loose, broken, or plugged vacuum hose from engine to control to governor. **2.** Ruptured governor or governor	switch diaphragm. **3.** Defective control selector switch.
EXCESSIVE DWELL TIME DURING INTERMITTENT OPERATION—COMET	**1.** Pinched hose from lower governor fitting to control switch rear fitting.	**2.** Plugged orifice in control selector dwell regulator.

TESTING

Refer to Wiring Diagram Manual Form 7795P-66 for schematics and locations of wiring harnesses.

HORN TEST

The only test necessary on the horn is for current draw.

Current Draw Test

Connect a voltmeter and ammeter to the horn and to a voltage supply as shown in Fig. 1. The normal current draw for the horns at 12 volts is 3.5-5.5 amperes.

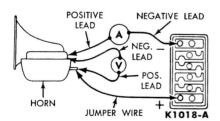

FIG. 1—Horn Current Draw Test

HEADLIGHT SWITCH AND BEAM SELECTOR SWITCH TESTS

The following tests may be made to determine whether a headlight

switch or a beam selector switch is defective:

Turn on the headlights, and operate the beam selector switch. If none of the headlights turn on when the beam selector switch is operated, yet the instrument panel lights operate, the headlight switch or the red-yellow stripe wire from the headlight switch to the beam control switch is probably defective. Substitute a known good switch for the suspected switch to determine whether the switch or the wiring is at fault.

If the headlights operate only with the beam selector switch in one position, the selector switch or the wiring from the switch to the headlight is defective. Substitute a known good selector switch for the suspected switch to determine whether the switch or the wiring is at fault.

CONSTANT VOLTAGE REGULATOR TEST

Turn the ignition switch on, check for voltage at the gauge feed wire (black with green stripe) at one of the gauges. The voltage should oscillate between zero and about 10 volts. If it does not, the constant voltage regulator is defective, or

there is a short to ground between the voltage regulator and the gauges.

If a gauge unit is inaccurate or does not indicate, replace it with a new unit. If the gauge unit still is erratic in its operation, the sending unit or wiring to the sending unit is faulty.

If both the fuel gauge and the temperature gauge indicate improperly and in the same direction, the constant voltage regulator could be defective, as it supplies both gauges.

FUEL GAUGE AND FUEL LEVEL SENDING UNIT TEST

Disconnect the wire from the fuel level sending unit and connect it to a known good sending unit. Using a jumper for a ground, connect it to the sending unit mounting plate and car frame. Raise the float arm to the upper stop, the instrument panel gauge should read full. Lower the float arm to the bottom stop, the gauge should read empty.

If the gauge reads properly, the sending unit in the gas tank is defective.

If the gauge unit still indicates improperly or is erratic in its operation, the gauge unit or the wiring to the gauge unit is faulty. Repair the wire or replace the gauge unit.

TEMPERATURE GAUGE TEST

Start the engine and allow it to run at 1200 rpm for 30 minutes. Place a thermometer in the coolant at the radiator filler cap. The temperature should read a minimum of 180°F., and the gauge in the instrument panel should indicate within the normal band.

If the gauge does not indicate, short the temperature sender unit terminal wire to ground (ignition switch on). **Do not leave the sender wire grounded longer than necessary to make the test, as the gauge may be damaged.** If the gauge now indicates, the sender unit is defective or not properly sealed to the engine. **Be sure to use an electrically conductive sealer C3AZ-19554-B.** If the gauge does not indicate, the gauge, the wires leading to the gauge, or the constant voltage regulator are at fault.

OIL PRESSURE INDICATOR LIGHT TEST

To test the indicator light, turn on the ignition switch. Do not start the engine. The light should come on. Start the engine. The light should go out, indicating that the oil pressure has built up a safe value.

To test the oil pressure switch on the engine, turn the ignition switch on, engine not running, the indicator light should come on. If the indicator light does not come on, short the terminal of the oil pressure switch unit to ground. If the light now comes on, the oil pressure switch is defective or not properly sealed to the engine. **Be sure to use electrically conductive sealer C3AZ-19554-B.** If the light still does not come on, the bulb is burned out or the wires from the bulb to the ignition switch

and oil pressure switch are defective.

OIL PRESSURE INDICATOR GAUGE TEST—COMET

Remove the oil pressure sender unit and temporarily attach an oil pressure gauge in its place. Operate the engine to determine the oil pressure. If the oil pressure is normal, the gauge should indicate within the normal band.

If the gauge did not indicate, **momentarily short the oil pressure sender wire to ground. Do not leave the sender wire grounded longer than necessary to make the test, as the gauge may be damaged.** If the gauge now indicates, the sender unit is defective or not properly sealed to the engine. **Be sure to use electrically conductive sealer C3AZ-19554-B.** If the gauge does not indicate, the gauge, the wires leading to the gauge or the constant voltage regulator are at fault.

CHARGE INDICATOR LIGHT TEST

To test the charge indicator light, turn the ignition switch on with the engine stopped. The light should come on. If it does not, the bulb is burned out, or the wiring to the light is defective.

An open resistor wire in the Ford alternator charging system wiring harness will usually cause the charge indicator light to stay on until the engine speed is increased to several thousand rpm. This effect will be noticed each time the engine is started. In some cases the light will not go out at all.

The charge indicator light may be tested with the use of a test light containing a trade number 67 or 1155 bulb.

Disconnect the regulator plug from the regulator. Turn the ignition switch to ACC position. Touch one test probe from test light to the igni-

tion terminal and the other to the regulator base. The test light will come on if the circuit is in proper working order. If the 15 ohm resistor or circuit is open, the indicator light will operate at full brightness and the test light will be out.

AMMETER TEST—COMET, FALCON, MUSTANG

To test the ammeter, turn the headlights on with the engine stopped. The meter pointer should move toward the D or discharge scale. If no movement of the needle is observed, check the rear of the meter housing to see if the battery to circuit breaker wire connections are loose. If the connections are tight, and the meter does not indicate a discharge, the meter is inoperative. **If the meter pointer moves toward the C or charge scale when the headlights are turned ON, the wire connections at the meter are reversed. When the headlights are turned on, the battery is reversed, or the wire passes through the loop in the wrong direction. Feed the wire through in the opposite direction to correct this condition, after checking first to make sure that the battery is not reversed.**

SPEEDOMETER TESTS

To test the odometer accuracy, drive the car over a measured mile. Speedometer accuracy can be checked by comparing the speedometer in question against one known to be accurate, while two cars are moving at the same speed, or by timing the car on a measured mile. The Ford Car Master Parts Catalog or the Lincoln-Mercury Parts and Accessories Catalog show the proper combination of gears to use for various rear axle and tire size combinations.

2 COMMON ADJUSTMENTS AND REPAIRS

HORN ADJUSTMENT

Horn current can be adjusted by changing the contact tension. Con-

nect the horn as shown in Fig. 1. Turn the self-locking adjusting nut

until the current is within the limits for the horn being adjusted.

3 CLEANING AND INSPECTION

SINGLE-SPEED WIPER MOTOR

1. Clean the gear housing of all old grease. **Do not allow any clean-

ing fluid to contact the armature shaft and output shaft bearings.**

2. Wipe all other parts with a clean cloth.
3. Cover the motor housing bear-

ing, and blow out any dust from the housing with compressed air.

4. Inspect the armature for burned commutator bars and loose connections. Check all shafts, bushings, and gears for scored surfaces. Check the thrust ball for pitting or discoloration due to heat. Make sure that the output gear is not loose on the output shaft, and that the cam surface is not worn. Replace any defective parts.

5. Check the armature for grounds with a test light. Replace the armature if it is grounded.

6. Inspect the brush plate assembly for cracks or distortion. The brush holders should be securely fastened to the brush plate. Inspect the contact points for burned or pitted surfaces. Replace defective parts.

7. Inspect the motor housing and magnet assembly. Replace the assembly if it has a cracked magnet, or if the thrust button is hollowed out to a diameter greater than $1/32$ inch.

8. Replace the brushes if they are worn to $5/16$ inch. Replace distorted or burned brush springs.

9. Add new grease to the housing and gears.

TWO-SPEED WIPER MOTOR

1. Clean the gear housing of all old grease. **Do not allow any cleaning fluid to contact the armature shaft and output shaft bearings.**

2. Wipe all other parts with a clean cloth.

3. Inspect the gear housing for cracks or distortion. Replace a cracked or distorted housing.

4. Check all shafts, bushings, and gears for scored surfaces. Replace defective parts and add new grease to the housing and gears.

PART 15-2 LIGHTING SYSTEM AND HORNS

Section	Page
1 Description and Operation	15-6
Headlights	15-6
Horns	15-6
2 In-Car Adjustments and Repairs	15-6
Headlight Alignment	15-6
No. 1 Headlight High Beam Adjustment— Lower Lights	15-7
No. 2 Headlight Low Beam Adjustment— Upper Lights	15-7
3 Removal and Installation	15-8

Section	Page
Headlights	15-8
Parking Light	15-8
Tail, Stop, and Back-Up Light Bulbs	15-8
Tachometer Light Bulbs	15-8
License Plate Light	15-8
Dome Light	15-8
Instrument Lights	15-8
Horns	15-8
Horn Button	15-8

1 DESCRIPTION AND OPERATION

Refer to Wiring Diagram Manual Form 7795P-66 for locations of wiring harnesses. Schematics are shown in Group 22 of this manual.

HEADLIGHTS

The Falcon and Mustang use two No. 2 type sealed-beam headlights. Each light has low-beam and high-beam filaments.

The Comet and Fairlane use four sealed-beam headlights. The No. 1 light is in the lower position and the No. 2 light is in the upper position.

A conventional beam selector switch is located on the floorboard at the left of the driver.

Quick disconnect terminals are also provided at the left and right of the radiator support assembly. The terminals are color coded. Like colored terminals are connected together.

HORNS

A pair of tuned horns are used. The horn button closes the circuit to the horns. One of the horns has a high-pitched tone; the other has a low-pitched tone.

2 IN-CAR ADJUSTMENTS AND REPAIRS

HEADLIGHT ALIGNMENT

All headlight adjustments should be made with a half-full fuel tank plus or minus one gallon, with a person seated in the driver's seat and a person in the passenger seat, the car unloaded and the trunk empty except for the spare tire and jacking equipment, and recommended pressure in all tires. Before each adjustment, bounce the car by pushing on the center of both the front and rear bumpers, to level the car.

To align the No. 1 headlights by means of a wall screen, select a level

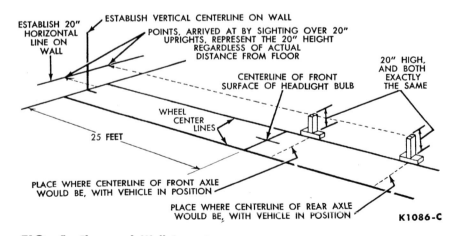

FIG. 1—Floor and Wall Layout

portion of the shop floor. Lay out the floor and wall as shown in Fig. 1.

Establish the headlight horizontal centerline by subtracting 20 inches

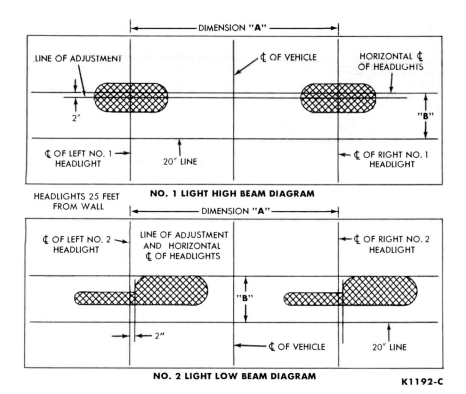

FIG. 2—Headlight Wall Screens

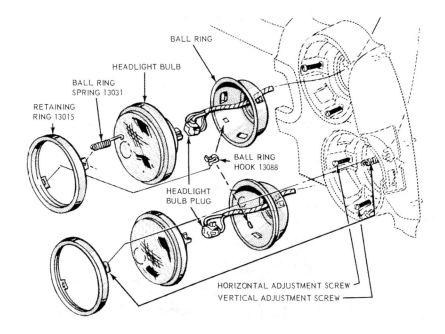

FIG. 3—Headlight Adjustment—Comet

from the actual measured height of the headlight lens center from the floor and adding this difference to the 20-inch reference line obtained by sighting over the uprights to obtain dimension B (upper diagram Fig. 2). Draw a horizontal line 2 inches below, and parallel to the headlight horizontal centerline. Then draw the headlight vertical centerlines on the screen as measured on the car (dimension A, upper diagram Fig. 2).

NO. 1 HEADLIGHT HIGH BEAM ADJUSTMENT—LOWER LIGHTS

Adjust each No. 1 headlight beam as shown in Fig. 2 upper diagram. **Cover the No. 2 lights when making this adjustment.**

Some states may not approve of the 2-inch dimension for the No. 1 headlights. Check the applicable state law, as a 3-inch dimension may be required.

NO. 2 HEADLIGHT LOW BEAM ADJUSTMENT—UPPER LIGHTS

To align the No. 2 headlights (upper lights), a new wall chart is used. Dimension B for the No. 2 lights will be different than B for the No. 1 lights, but dimension A which is measured on the car will be the same as for the No. 1 lights. **Note that the line of adjustment of the No. 2 lights is the horizontal centerline of the No. 2 lights.** Turn the headlights to low beam and adjust each No. 2 light as shown in Fig. 2.

Each headlight can be adjusted by means of two screws located under the headlight trim ring. Always bring each beam into final position by turning the adjusting screws clockwise so that the headlights will be held against the tension springs when the operation is completed (Fig. 3).

3 REMOVAL AND INSTALLATION

HEADLIGHTS

1. Remove the screws and remove the headlight trim ring (Fig. 3).

2. Place a hand over the headlight assembly and unhook the spring from the retaining ring.

3. Remove the retaining ring by unhooking the ring from the clip located directly across the bulb from the spring hook.

4. Pull the headlight bulb forward and disconnect the wiring assembly plug.

5. Plug in the new bulb and place it in position, locating the bulb glass tabs in the positioning slots.

6. Hook the retaining ring over the clip, then over the bulb and secure it with the existing ball-ring spring.

7. Align the bulb with the wall screen.

8. Install the trim ring in position and install the retaining screws.

PARKING LIGHT

The parking light is shown in Fig. 4. To replace the bulb, remove the lens retaining screws and the lens.

TAIL, STOP, AND BACK-UP LIGHT BULBS

To replace the tail, stop, and/or the back-up lights, remove the retaining screws and remove the lens,

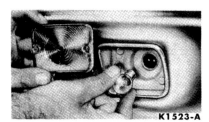

FIG. 4—Parking Light—Typical

then remove the bulb.

TACHOMETER LIGHT BULBS

To replace the light bulb in either the Sun, or the Sprint tachometer, it is necessary to remove the tachometer from its mounting. In the case of the Sprint tachometer it is also necessary to remove the tachometer from its outside housing. The snap-in bulb socket is then pulled out for replacement of the bulb.

On the Rotunda tachometer the bulb is not serviceable.

LICENSE PLATE LIGHT

To replace the bulb, remove the bezel retaining screw, bezel, and lens.

DOME LIGHT

Remove the two screws retaining the dome light lens. Remove the lens and then replace the bulb.

INSTRUMENT LIGHTS

The instrument panel light bulbs can be replaced by pulling out the individual light sockets from the rear of the instrument panel.

HORNS

Disconnect the horn wire from the terminal. Remove the horn mounting bracket to horn retaining screws and remove the horn.

To install, mount the horn in position, then connect the horn wire to the horn terminal.

HORN BUTTON

1. Disconnect the horn wire connector, that has a yellow and a yellow-green wire in it, under the instrument panel, to the left of the steering column.

2. Press down evenly on the horn button and turn counter-clockwise until it lifts out from the steering wheel.

3. Remove the horn button and spring.

4. The horn button contacts are integral with the turn signal switch and are removed with the switch.

5. Install the horn button spring and button.

6. Connect the horn wire connector under the instrument panel.

PART 15-3 SWITCHES, CIRCUIT BREAKERS, AND FUSES

Section	Page
1 Description and Operation	15-9
Headlight Switch	15-9
Fuse Panel	15-9
Mechanical Stop Light Switch	15-9
2 Removal and Installation	15-10
Headlight Switch	15-10
Headlight Beam Selector Switch	15-10

Section	Page
Stop Light Switch	15-10
Dome Light Switch	15-10
Ignition Switch and Lock Cylinder	15-10
Windshield Wiper Switch	15-11
Neutral Start Switch	15-11
Back-Up Light Switch	15-11

1 DESCRIPTION AND OPERATION

Refer to Wiring Diagram Manual Form 7795P-66 for locations of wiring harnesses. Schematics are shown in Group 22 of this manual.

HEADLIGHT SWITCH

A combination headlight switch and two circuit breakers is used (Fig. 1). The headlight circuit is protected by an 18 ampere circuit breaker for the Comet and Fairlane, a 12 ampere circuit breaker for the Falcon and the Mustang. The tail, parking, license plate light and horn circuits are protected by a 15 ampere circuit breaker.

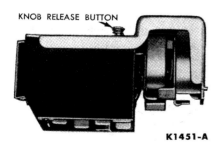

FIG. 1—Headlight Switch

FUSE PANEL

The fuse panel is mounted on the left side cowl panel except that on Fairlane cars it is mounted on the brake pedal support. Fig. 2 shows the fuses, their values and locations.

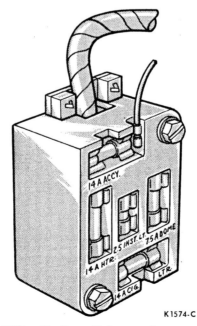

FIG. 2—Fuse Valves and Locations—Typical

MECHANICAL STOP LIGHT SWITCH

The mechanical stoplight switch differs from the hydraulic switch formerly used. The switch assembly is installed on the pin of the brake pedal arm so that it straddles the master cylinder push rod. The switch assembly is a slip fit on the pedal arm pin and thus the switch assembly moves with the pedal arm whenever the brake pedal is depressed.

The brake pedal arm pin has a designed-in clearance with the eye of the master cylinder push rod (Fig. 3). Because of this clearance, whenever the brake pedal is pushed forward, the stop light switch contacts, moving with the pedal arm, are actually pushed against the end of the master cylinder push rod, through the switch actuating pin. It is this movement of the switch with respect to the actuating pin and master cylinder push rod that closes the switch contacts completing the circuit to the stoplights.

When the brake pedal is released, the spring in the stop light switch returns the actuating pin to its normal position and the circuit to the stop lights opens.

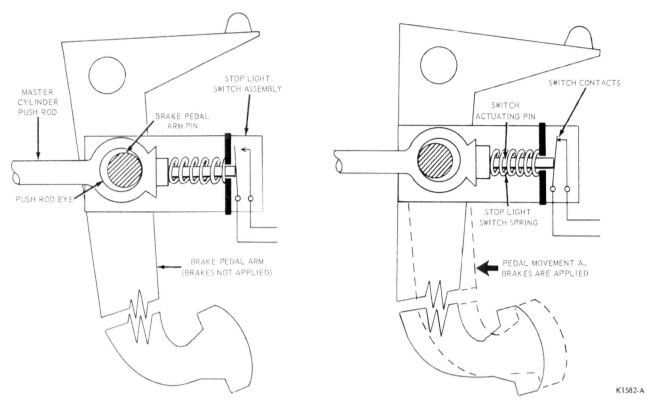

FIG. 3—Mechanical Stoplight Switch Operation

② REMOVAL AND INSTALLATION

HEADLIGHT SWITCH

1. Disconnect the battery ground cable.

2. Remove the control knob and shaft by pressing the knob release button on the switch housing (Fig. 1), with the knob in the full ON position. Pull the knob out of the switch.

3. Unscrew the mounting nut, remove the switch, then remove the junction block from the switch.

4. To install the switch, connect the junction block to the headlight switch, position the switch in the instrument panel, and install the mounting nut.

5. Install the knob and shaft assembly by inserting it all the way into the switch until a distinct click is heard. In some instances it may be necessary to rotate the shaft slightly until it engages the switch-contact carrier.

6. Connect the battery ground cable.

HEADLIGHT BEAM SELECTOR SWITCH

Lay the floor mat back from the area of the switch, and remove the

mounting screws (Fig. 4). Disconnect the wire terminal block from the switch.

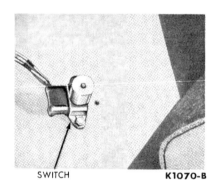

SWITCH   K1070-B

FIG. 4—Headlight Beam Selector Switch

To install the switch, connect the terminal block to the switch and install the switch to the floor. Replace the floor mat.

STOP LIGHT SWITCH

1. Disconnect the wires at the connector.

2. Remove the hairpin retainer, slide the stop light switch, the push

rod and the nylon washers and bushing away from the pedal, and remove the switch (Fig. 5).

3. Position the switch, push rod, and bushing and washers on the brake pedal pin, in the order shown in Fig. 5, and install the hairpin retainer.

4. Connect the wires at the connector, and install the wires in the retaining clip (Fig. 5).

DOME LIGHT SWITCH

The dome light switch is part of the headlight switch. It is actuated by rotating the switch control knob to the maximum counterclockwise position. The dome light and headlight switch is replaced as a unit (Fig. 1).

IGNITION SWITCH AND LOCK CYLINDER

1. Disconnect the negative cable from the battery.

2. Turn the ignition key to the accessory position. Slightly depress the pin shown in Fig. 6, turn the key counterclockwise, *and pull the key and lock cylinder* out of the switch assembly. If only the lock cylinder is

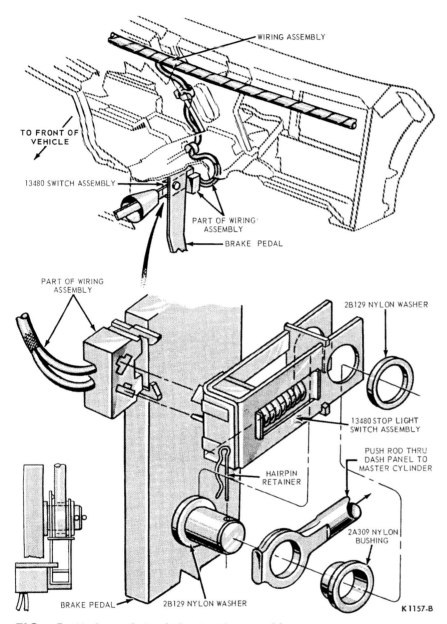

FIG. 5—Mechanical Stoplight Switch Assembly

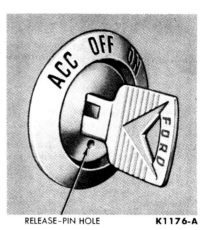

FIG. 6—Typical Ignition Switch Removal

to be replaced, proceed to Step 9.

3. Press in on the rear of the switch and rotate the switch ⅛ turn counterclockwise (as viewed from the terminal end). Remove the bezel, switch, and spacer.

4. Remove the nut from the back of the ignition switch. Remove the accessory and gauge feed wires from the accessory terminal of the switch. Pull the insulated plug from the rear of the switch.

5. If a new ignition switch is to be installed, insert a screwdriver into the lock opening of the ignition

switch and turn the slot in the switch to a full counterclockwise position.

6. Connect the insulated plug with wires to the back of the ignition switch. Position the accessory and gauge wires on the ignition switch stud and install the retaining nut.

7. Position the spacer on the switch with the open face away from the switch.

8. Place the bezel, switch, and spacer in the switch opening, press the switch toward the instrument panel and rotate it ⅛ turn to lock it in position.

9. If a new lock cylinder is to be installed, insert the key in the cylinder and turn the key to the accessory position. Place the lock and key in the ignition switch, depress the pin slightly (Fig. 6) and turn the key counterclockwise. Push the lock cylinder into the switch. Turn the key to check the lock cylinder operation.

10. Connect the battery cable and check the ignition switch.

WINDSHIELD WIPER SWITCH

1. Disconnect the battery cable.

2. Remove the wiper switch knob, bezel nut, and bezel.

3. Pull out the switch from under the instrument panel. Disconnect the plug connector from the switch and remove the switch.

4. Position the switch and connect the plug connector.

5. Position the switch in the instrument panel and install the bezel, bezel nut, and knob.

6. Connect the battery cable and check the operation of the switch.

NEUTRAL START SWITCH

See Part 7-2 for replacement of the neutral start switch on cars equipped with automatic transmissions.

BACK-UP LIGHT SWITCH

On cars equipped with the steering column standard shift, the switch is located on the lower end of the steering column.

On cars equipped with a shift lever directly over either the standard or automatic transmissions, the back-up light switch is located on the transmission.

PART 15-4
INSTRUMENTS

Section	Page
1 Description and Operation	15-12
Gauges	15-12
Constant Voltage Regulator	15-12
Fuel Gauge	15-13
Temperature Gauge	15-13
Charge Indicator Light—Except Comet	15-13
Charge Indicator Gauge—Comet	15-13
Oil Pressure Indicator Light—Except Comet	15-13
Oil Pressure Indicator Gauge—Comet	15-13
Turn Indicator	15-13
Emergency Warning Flasher	15-13
Speedometer	15-13
Windshield Wiper—Comet	15-13
2 In-Car Adjustments and Repairs	15-15
Windshield Wiper Blade Adjustment	15-15
3 Removal and Installation	15-15
Instrument Cluster—Except Fairlane	15-15
Instrument Panel Control Identification Lens—Fairlane	15-15
Auxiliary Instrument Cluster— Mustang Rally Pac	15-16
Constant Voltage Regulator—Comet	15-16
Constant Voltage Regulator—Fairlane	15-16
Fuel Gauge—Falcon, Mustang	15-16
Fuel Gauge—Comet	15-16
Fuel Gauge—Fairlane	15-17
Fuel Sending Unit	15-17
Temperature Gauge—Except Comet	15-17
Temperature Gauge—Comet	15-17
Temperature Sending Unit	15-17
Oil Pressure Indicator Gauge—Comet	15-17
Oil Pressure Sending Unit or Oil Pressure Switch	15-18

Section	Page
Charge Indicator Gauge—Comet	15-18
Electric Clock—Fairlane	15-18
Turn Indicator Switch	15-18
Turn Indicator Flasher	15-18
Emergency Warning Flasher	15-18
Speedometer—Fairlane	15-18
Speedometer—Comet	15-18
Speedometer—Falcon, Mustang	15-19
Speedometer Cable	15-19
Windshield Wiper Switch—Fairlane	15-19
Windshield Wiper Motor—Except Fairlane	15-19
Windshield Wiper Motor—Fairlane	15-19
Wiper Pivot Shaft and Link	15-20
4 Major Repair Operations	15-20
Disassembly—Permanent Magnet Type Single or Two-Speed Electric Wiper Motor	15-20
Parts Repair or Replacement	15-21
Assembly—Permanent Magnet Type Single or Two-Speed Electric Wiper Motor	15-21
Windshield Wiper Motor Park Switch Test and Adjustment—Single and Two-Speed Permanent Magnet Type	15-21
Disassembly—Oscillating Type Two-Speed Electric Wiper Motor	15-21
Parts Repair or Replacement	15-22
Assembly—Oscillating Type Two-Speed Electric Wiper Motor	15-22
Electro-Pneumatic Governor and Control Selector Switch—Comet	15-23
Speedometer Diagnostic Procedures	15-23
Speedometer Repair Procedures	15-23

1 DESCRIPTION AND OPERATION

Refer to Wiring Diagram Manual Form 7795P-66 for locations of wiring harnesses. Schematics are shown in Group 22 of this manual.

All of the instruments are electrically operated except the speedometer. Brightness of the instrument panel lights is controlled by a rheostat on the lighting switch.

GAUGES

The instrument cluster for the Falcon, Fairlane and Mustang includes a fuel gauge, temperature gauge, charge indicator light, oil pressure indicator light, speedometer, high-beam indicator light, and a left and right-hand turn signal indicator light. The instrument cluster for the

Comet includes the same components except that an oil pressure indicator gauge and a charge indicator gauge are used instead of indicator lights. There are also separate left-and-right-hand turn signal indicator lights in the instrument panel.

CONSTANT VOLTAGE REGULATOR

The constant voltage regulator (Fig. 1) used with the fuel, temperature, and oil gauges maintains an average value of 5.0 volts at the gauge terminals.

The regulator operates by means of a bimetallic arm and a heating coil. When the ignition switch is turned on, the heating coil (Fig. 1)

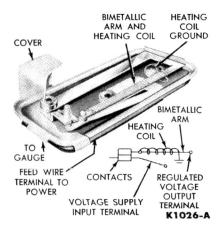

FIG. 1—Constant Voltage Regulator

heats the bimetallic arm causing it to bend and break the contacts, disconnecting the voltage supply from the heating coil. The bimetallic arm then cools and brings the contacts together again. The making and breaking of the contacts, causes a pulsating voltage, with an effective average value of 5.0 volts to be supplied to the gauges. Although these pulsations are quite rapid, there is in each gauge a bimetallic arm which changes temperature quite slowly, and this assures steady average readings.

As the pulsating voltage would normally cause radio interference, a radio interference suppression choke is connected in series with the constant voltage regulator supply wire.

FUEL GAUGE

The fuel gauge consists of a sending unit, located on the gas tank, and a remote register unit (fuel gauge) mounted in the instrument cluster. The remote register unit pointer is controlled by a bimetallic arm and heating coil. The sending unit is a rheostat that varies its resistance depending on the amount of fuel in the tank. The rheostat is operated by a float control. As the fuel level rises or falls the float control arm moved by the float, varies the resistance.

TEMPERATURE GAUGE

The temperature gauge consists of a sending unit mounted in the cylinder head at the top front on the V-8 (Fig. 2 or 3), left rear on the six, and a remote register unit, (temperature gauge) mounted in the instrument cluster.

Changes of engine temperature vary the resistance of the sending unit which in turn operates the temperature gauge.

CHARGE INDICATOR LIGHT—EXCEPT COMET

A red alternator charge indicator light is used. This light flashes on if the battery is discharging and the alternator is not supplying current.

When the ignition switch is closed, battery current flows through the charge indicator light and 15-ohm parallel resistor, and through the regulator voltage limiter contacts to the field.

When the alternator builds up enough voltage to close the field relay contacts, full voltage is applied to the field, and the charge indicator light goes out.

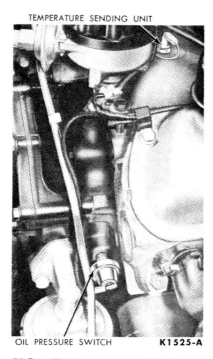

FIG. 2—Temperature Sender and Oil Pressure Switch—Falcon and Comet V-8

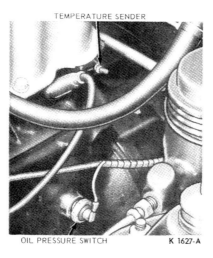

FIG. 3—Temperature and Oil Pressure Sender—Fairlane 6

CHARGE INDICATOR GAUGE—COMET

The charge indicator gauge is an ammeter, which indicates whether the battery is being charged or discharged. The ammeter is non-adjustable and should be replaced if proved to be defective.

OIL PRESSURE INDICATOR LIGHT—EXCEPT COMET

A red indicator light flashes on when the oil pressure is below a safe value. The light should come on when

the ignition switch is first turned on, and it should go out when the engine comes up to speed. The light is connected between the oil pressure switch unit mounted on the engine at the left rear on the six, above the oil filter on the V-8 (Fig. 2), and the coil terminal of the ignition switch.

OIL PRESSURE INDICATOR GAUGE—COMET

The meter-type oil pressure gauge consists of a sending unit on the engine above the oil filter on the V-8 (Fig. 3), at the left rear on the six, and a remote register unit in the instrument cluster.

The sending unit operates by varying resistance according to actual oil pressure against it, which in turn operates the oil pressure gauge.

TURN INDICATOR

The turn indicator uses the dual filament parking lights as indicator lights.

The turn indicator flasher is located in the back of the instrument panel, on the steering column brace.

On the Mustang the flasher is mounted on the front side of the air duct.

EMERGENCY WARNING FLASHER

The emergency flasher warning system is controlled by a combination switch and flasher assembly. All turn signal lights can be made to flash at the same time by closing the switch of the switch-flasher assembly.

SPEEDOMETER

The speedometer is connected to the output shaft of the transmission by means of a flexible shaft, and a drive gear located inside the transmission. The flexible shaft drives the speedometer which registers speed in miles per hour and also drives an odometer which records distance traveled in miles and tenths of a mile.

WINDSHIELD WIPER—COMET

The Comet wiper provides high speed (65 to 75 cycles per minute) constant wiping action, and also intermittent low speed (5-30 cycles per minute), intermittent wiping action. This low speed operation is based not on a low speed wiping stroke but on an adjustable dwell period in the park position.

The intermittent wiper is operated through the use of a dual knob. The outer or large knob, when in the cen-

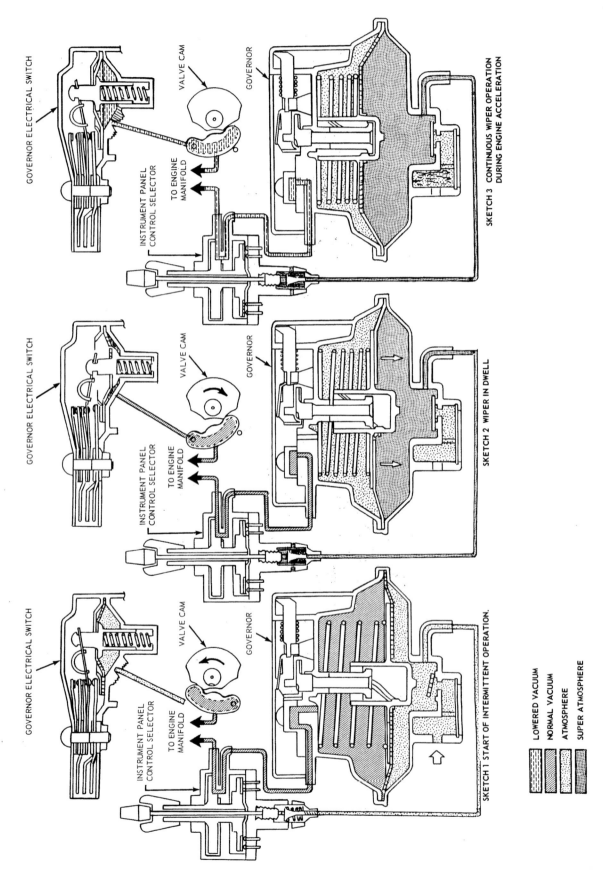

K 1633-A

FIG. 4—Electro-Pneumatic Governor For Intermittent Windshield Wiper

ter position, turns the system off. When turned fully clockwise, the wiper is in the constant high speed setting. When turned fully counterclockwise, the wiper goes on the intermittent lower speed range. The intermittent wiper action is controlled by the inner, or small knob.

The intermittent wiper control is an electro-pneumatic system, a governor located in the engine compartment, that allows selection of either varying dwell between wipe cycles or continuous wiper action thru application of variable opposing vacuum and pressure within the system.

With the control selector in the instrument panel turned to intermittent wiper control, engine manifold vacuum is applied to the upper chamber of the governor (Sketch I, Fig. 4). Atmospheric pressure in the lower chamber then moves the diaphragm upward. Simultaneous rotation of the governor valve cam thru the spiral action of the follower applies manifold vacuum to the diaphragm of the normally closed electrical switch. The switch diaphragm is moved down-

ward compressing the diaphragm spring and moving the switch into the park position. The wiper blades then move to the park position and remain there. (Sketch II, Fig. 4).

Rotation of the governor valve cam that applied vacuum to the governor switch also opened the upper governor chamber to atmosphere. The compressed diaphragm spring applies downward pressure to the diaphragm creating super atmosphere in the lower chamber. This is allowed to bleed off thru a variable orifice in the control selector. The size of this orifice is determined by the position of the intermittent selector (inner knob) and establishes the length of wiper cycle dwell (Sketch II, Fig. 4).

As the diaphragm moves downward, the governor valve cam is rotated thru the spiral action of the cam follower, opening the lower chamber of the electrical switch diaphragm to atmosphere. The compressed diaphragm spring moves the switch into the closed position, actuating the wiper motor. Simultane-

ously, the rotational movement of the valve cam applies manifold vacuum to the upper chamber of the governor, thus beginning a new cycle.

If the engine is subjected to sudden acceleration as in passing, the available manifold vacuum will be greatly reduced. When the vacuum loss becomes sufficient to allow the electrical switch diaphragm spring to overcome the vacuum, the switch will be moved to the closed position providing continuous wiper operation. This will continue until the engine has returned to an operating condition that will provide normal manifold vacuum. The wipers will then return to whatever wiper cycle dwell had been previously selected.

In the same manner as above, under engine acceleration, if any loss of vacuum or pressure in the intermittent control system occurs due to a mechanical failure or malfunction, the wipers will automatically shift to continuous operation, thereby rendering the system fail safe (Sketch III, Fig. 4).

2 IN-CAR ADJUSTMENTS AND REPAIRS

WINDSHIELD WIPER BLADE ADJUSTMENT

Turn the ignition switch to the ac-

cessory position momentarily, with the wiper switch off. After bringing the pivot shafts to their park posi-

tions, install the wiper blades so that they lie flat against the lower edge of the windshield.

3 REMOVAL AND INSTALLATION

INSTRUMENT CLUSTER — EXCEPT FAIRLANE

1. Disconnect the battery cable.
2. Disconnect the speedometer cable from the speedometer head.
3. Remove the six screws retaining the instrument cluster assembly to the instrument panel and tilt the cluster forward.
4. Disconnect the wiring and the bulb sockets and remove the cluster assembly.
5. Position the cluster and connect the wiring and the bulb sockets.
6. Install the instrument cluster assembly to the instrument panel with the six retaining screws.
7. Connect the speedometer cable and the battery cable.
8. Check the operation of all gauges, lights, and signals.

To replace the fuel gauge, temperature gauge, oil pressure gauge,

charge indicator gauge, and speedometer, it is necessary to remove the instrument cluster assembly.

INSTRUMENT PANEL CONTROL IDENTIFICATION LENS— FAIRLANE

1. Disconnect the battery ground cable.
2. Remove the radio, knobs and nuts.
3. Disconnect the speedometer cable.
4. Remove the screws from the cluster assembly and position it outward.
5. Disconnect the bulbs, constant voltage regulator and ground wire, clock and the fuel gauge. Move the cluster assembly to a bench.
6. Remove the clock knob and the screws retaining the rear cluster cover which retains the speedometer,

clock, fuel gauge, and bulbs for the alternator, oil pressure, and hot and cold water temperature.
7. Remove the screws from the right side front of the cluster. Remove the mask and the lens.
8. Insert and position the new lens and retaining screws.
9. Position the rear cover assembly to the front of the cluster and install the retaining screws. Install the clock knob and screw.
10. Position the cluster assembly and connect all leads and bulbs.
11. Position the cluster assembly to the instrument panel and install the retaining screws.
12. Position the radio to the cluster and install the nuts and bulbs.
13. Connect the speedometer cable.
14. Connect the battery and check the operation of all disconnected parts.

AUXILIARY INSTRUMENT CLUSTER—MUSTANG RALLY PAC

REMOVAL

1. Disconnect the battery ground cable.

2. Disconnect the wiring. Note the color code relationships (for correct assembly later).

3. Remove the mounting clamp assembly screws below the steering column and remove the clamp.

4. Remove the RALLY PAC cluster assembly from the steering column.

INSTALLATION

1. Position the RALLY PAC cluster assembly to the steering column.

2. Position the mounting clamp and install the retaining screws.

3. Connect the wiring (Fig. 5).

4. Connect the battery ground cable.

6. Install the constant voltage regulator in place with the ground wire and retaining screw and connect the electrical leads to the regulator.

7. Install the instrument cluster assembly to the instrument panel and secure it with screws.

8. Connect the speedometer cable.

9. Check the operation of all disconnected parts.

CONSTANT VOLTAGE REGULATOR—FAIRLANE

1. Disconnect the battery ground cable.

2. Remove the radio knobs, mounting nuts and radio.

3. Disconnect the speedometer cable.

4. Remove the screws retaining the cluster assembly to the instrument panel. Position the cluster outward.

5. Disconnect the wire leads and remove the mounting screw from the

FUEL GAUGE—FALCON, MUSTANG

1. Remove the instrument cluster assembly.

2. Remove the six screws retaining the instrument cluster back plate assembly, and remove the back plate assembly.

3. Remove the two screws retaining the fuel gauge to the back plate and remove the gauge.

4. Position the fuel gauge and install the two retaining screws.

5. Position the back plate assembly and install the six retaining screws.

6. Install the instrument cluster assembly in the instrument panel.

FUEL GAUGE—COMET

1. Disconnect the battery.

2. Disconnect the speedometer cable.

3. Remove the screws retaining the cluster assembly to the instru-

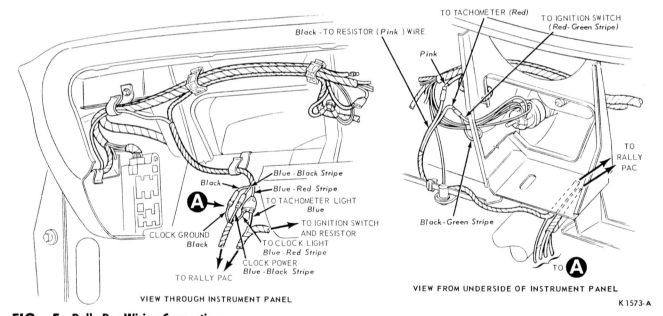

FIG. 5—Rally Pac Wiring Connections

CONSTANT VOLTAGE REGULATOR—COMET

1. Disconnect the battery ground cable.

2. Disconnect the speedometer cable.

3. Remove the instrument cluster assembly from the instrument panel and tilt the cluster outward.

4. Disconnect the wires from the constant voltage regulator.

5. Remove the constant voltage regulator retaining screw and remove the regulator and ground wire from under the same screw.

constant voltage regulator and remove the regulator.

6. Position the new constant voltage regulator, install the mounting screw and connect the wire leads.

7. Position the cluster assembly to the instrument panel and install the retaining screws.

8. Position the radio to the cluster and install the nuts and knobs.

9. Connect the speedometer cable.

10. Connect the battery and check the operation of all disconnected parts.

ment panel and position it outward.

4. Disconnect the bulbs, temperature gauge, fuel gauge, constant voltage regulator, and charge indicator and remove the assembly to a bench.

5. Remove the screws retaining the back cover of the cluster to the front of the cluster. There is no clock in this cluster. The light for the oil pressure indicator is in the charge indicator gauge.

6. Remove the nuts retaining the fuel gauge.

7. Position the new fuel gauge and

install the retaining nuts.

8. Position the rear cover to the front of the cluster with retaining screws. The rear cover retains all gauges and the speedometer head.

9. Position the cluster assembly and connect all leads and bulbs.

10. Install the cluster assembly to the instrument panel and secure it with screws.

11. Connect the speedometer cable.

12. Connect the battery and check the operation of all disconnected parts.

FUEL GAUGE—FAIRLANE

1. Disconnect the battery ground cable.

2. Remove the radio knobs, mounting nuts and radio.

3. Disconnect the speedometer cable.

4. Remove the screws retaining the cluster assembly to the instrument panel. Position the cluster assembly outward.

5. Disconnect the bulbs, constant voltage regulator, the clock and fuel gauge. Remove the cluster assembly to a bench.

6. Remove the clock knob and the screws retaining the rear cluster cover.

The cover retains the speedometer, clock and fuel gauge, also the bulbs for the alternator charge indicator, oil pressure gauge and the hot-cold engine temperature indicator.

7. Remove the screws retaining the speedometer head to the cover and four rubber insulators. Remove the head.

8. Remove the nuts retaining the fuel gauge, and remove the gauge.

9. Install the new fuel gauge with mounting nuts.

10. Position the speedometer and install the retaining screws at the rear. Install the four rubber insulators in the front.

11. Position the rear cover assembly to the front of the cluster and install the retaining screws. Install the clock knob and screw.

12. Position the cluster assembly. Connect all of the wire leads and bulbs.

13. Position the cluster assembly to the instrument panel and install the retaining screws.

14. Position the radio to the cluster and install the mounting nuts and knobs.

15. Connect the speedometer cable.

16. Connect the battery and check the operation of all disconnected parts.

FUEL SENDING UNIT

1. Remove the fuel from the fuel tank.

2. Disconnect the fuel gauge sending unit wire from the sending unit.

3. Loosen the hose clamp and disconnect the tank line at the sending unit.

4. Remove any dirt that has accumulated around the sending unit so that it will not enter the tank.

5. Turn the sending unit retaining ring counterclockwise and remove the unit, retaining ring, and mounting gasket.

6. Clean the fuel gauge sending unit mounting surface at the fuel tank.

7. Position the sending unit and mounting gasket on the fuel tank and secure with the retaining ring.

8. Connect the sending unit wire and the fuel tank line.

9. Fill the tank with the fuel removed.

10. Check the fuel gauge operation and check for leaks.

TEMPERATURE GAUGE

1. Remove the instrument cluster assembly.

2. Remove the six screws retaining the instrument cluster back plate assembly and remove the back plate assembly.

3. Remove the two screws retaining the temperature gauge to the back plate and remove the gauge.

4. Position the temperature gauge and install the two retaining screws.

5. Position the back plate assembly and install the six retaining screws.

6. Install the instrument cluster assembly in the instrument panel.

TEMPERATURE GAUGE —COMET

1. Disconnect the battery.

2. Disconnect the speedometer cable.

3. Remove the screws retaining the cluster assembly to the instrument panel and position it outward.

4. Disconnect the bulbs, temperature gauge, fuel gauge, constant voltage regulator, and ammeter and remove the assembly to a bench.

5. Remove the screws retaining the back cover of the cluster to the front of the cluster. There is no clock

in this cluster. The light for the oil pressure indicator is in the ammeter.

6. Remove the nuts retaining the temperature gauge.

7. Position the new gauge and install the retaining nuts.

8. Position the rear cover to the front of the cluster with retaining screws. The rear cover retains all gauges and the speedometer head.

9. Position the cluster assembly and connect all leads and bulbs.

10. Install the cluster assembly to the instrument panel and secure it with screws.

11. Connect the speedometer cable.

12. Connect the battery and check the operation of all disconnected parts.

TEMPERATURE SENDING UNIT

1. Disconnect the temperature sending unit wire from the sending unit.

2. Prepare the new temperature sending unit for installation by applying a small amount of conductive water resistant sealer C3AZ-19554-B, to the threads.

3. Remove the temperature sending unit from the cylinder head and immediately install the new temperature sending unit.

4. Connect the wire to the temperature sending unit.

5. Start the engine and check the sending unit operation.

OIL PRESSURE INDICATOR GAUGE—COMET

1. Remove the instrument cluster assembly.

2. Remove the six screws retaining the instrument cluster back plate assembly and remove the back plate assembly.

3. Remove the two screws retaining the speedometer, the two screws retaining the speedometer dial to the back plate, and remove the speedometer assembly.

4. Remove the two nuts retaining the oil pressure gauge and remove the gauge.

5. Position the oil pressure gauge and install the two retaining nuts.

6. Position the speedometer assembly and install the two speedometer dial retaining screws and the two speedometer retaining screws.

7. Position the back plate assembly and install the six retaining screws.

8. Install the instrument cluster assembly to the instrument panel.

OIL PRESSURE SENDING UNIT OR OIL PRESSURE SWITCH

To replace the unit, disconnect the wire from the terminal. Remove the unit from the engine. Apply conductive sealer C3AZ-19554-B to the threads of the new unit and install the unit. Connect the wire to the terminal and check the operation of the unit.

CHARGE INDICATOR GAUGE—COMET

1. Disconnect the battery.
2. Disconnect the speedometer cable.
3. Remove the screws retaining the cluster assembly to the instrument panel and position it outward.
4. Disconnect the bulbs, temperature gauge, fuel gauge, constant voltage regulator, and charge indicator and remove the assembly to a bench.
5. Remove the screws retaining the back cover of the cluster to the front of the cluster. There is no clock in this cluster. The light for the oil pressure indicator is in the charge indicator gauge.
6. Remove the nuts retaining the charge indicator gauge.
7. Position the new gauge and install the retaining nuts.
8. Position the rear cover to the front of the cluster and install the retaining screws. The rear cover retains all the gauges and the speedometer head.
9. Position the cluster assembly and connect all leads and bulbs.
10. Install the cluster assembly to the instrument panel and secure it with screws.
11. Connect the speedometer cable.
12. Connect the battery and check the operation of all disconnected parts.

ELECTRIC CLOCK—FAIRLANE

1. Disconnect the battery ground cable.
2. Remove the clock setting knob.
3. Remove the clock push-on connector.
4. Remove the clock screws and the clock from under the instrument panel. **Handle the clock with care, as the clock hands are not protected.**
5. Position the clock from the underside of the instrument panel and install the retaining screws.
6. Push on the clock wire connector.
7. Install the clock setting knob.
8. Connect the battery ground ca-

ble and set the clock hands to the exact time.

TURN INDICATOR SWITCH

REMOVAL

1. Disconnect the negative (ground) cable from the battery.
2. Remove the steering wheel hub and steering wheel retaining nut.
3. Remove the steering wheel from the shaft.
4. Disconnect the two wire-connector blocks at the dash panel above the steering column.
5. Remove the wires and terminals from the connector blocks. This can be done by depressing the tab on the wire terminal with an awl, or by inserting a ball point pen (refill plastic type) over the bullet pin and pull the wire and terminal from the connector block. **Record the color code and location of each wire before removing it from the connector block.** Tape the wires together and attach a piece of heavy cord to the wires to help pull the wires through the steering column during installation.
6. Remove the turn indicator handle from the side of the steering column.
7. Remove 3 bearing retainer attaching screws and remove the bearing retainer and turn indicator switch and wires from the steering column. Disconnect the heavy cord from the switch wires.

INSTALLATION

1. Tape the ends of the switch wires together and attach the cord to the wires.
2. Pull the wires down through the steering column with the cord, and position the switch to the steering column hub.
3. Install the bearing retainer and attaching screws.
4. Install the turn indicator switch lever.
5. Press the switch wires into the connector blocks in their correct location recorded during removal. Plug the connector blocks together with the mating connector blocks at the dash panel.
6. Install the steering wheel on the shaft.
7. Install the steering wheel retaining nut and hub.
8. Connect the battery ground cable and check the operation of the turn signal switch and horns.

TURN INDICATOR FLASHER

Disconnect the wires from the

flasher unit terminals and pull the flasher from its retaining clip. Observe the color code and number on the cover of the flasher. **Be certain to replace it with a new flasher with the same color code and number on the cover.**

EMERGENCY WARNING FLASHER

Pull the flasher from the retaining clip, and disconnect the wires (Fig. 6).

SPEEDOMETER—FAIRLANE

1. Disconnect the battery ground cable.
2. Remove the radio knobs, mounting nuts, and radio.
3. Disconnect the speedometer cable.
4. Remove the screws retaining the cluster assembly to the instrument panel. Position the cluster assembly outward.
5. Disconnect the bulbs, constant voltage regulator and its ground wire, the clock and the fuel gauge.
6. Remove the cluster assembly to a bench.
7. Remove the clock knob and the screws retaining the rear cluster cover. The cover retains the speedometer, clock, fuel gauge, the bulbs for the alternator charge indicator, oil pressure, and the hot and cold engine temperature indicators.
8. Remove the screws retaining the speedometer *head* to the *cover* and the four rubber insulators. Remove the speedometer head.
9. Position the speedometer and install the retaining screws at the rear. Install the four rubber insulators.
10. Position the rear cover assembly to the front of the cluster. Install the retaining screws. Install the clock knob.
11. Position the cluster assembly. Connect all leads and bulbs.
12. Position the cluster assembly to the instrument panel. Install the retaining screws.
13. Position the radio to the cluster and install the mounting nuts and knobs.
14. Connect the speedometer cable.
15. Connect the battery ground cable and check the operation of the disconnected parts.

SPEEDOMETER—COMET

1. Disconnect the battery ground cable.
2. Disconnect the speedometer ca-

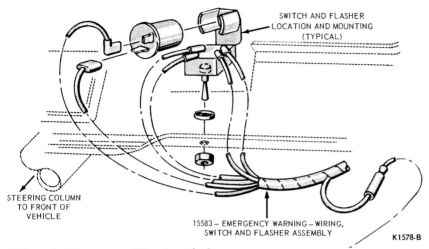

SWITCH AND FLASHER
LOCATION AND MOUNTING
(TYPICAL)

STEERING COLUMN
TO FRONT OF
VEHICLE

15583 — EMERGENCY WARNING — WIRING,
SWITCH AND FLASHER ASSEMBLY

K1578-B

FIG. 6—Emergency Warning Flasher

ble.

3. Remove the screws retaining the cluster assembly to the instrument panel. Position the cluster assembly outward.

4. Disconnect the bulbs, and wiring from the temperature gauge, fuel gauge, constant voltage regulator and charge indicator. Remove the assembly to a bench.

5. Remove the screws from the cover retaining the back portion of the cluster assembly and separate it from the front portion.

6. Remove the screws retaining the speedometer and remove the speedometer head.

7. Position the new speedometer head and install the retaining screws.

8. Position the back cover of the cluster to the forward portion and install the retaining screws. The back cover houses all of the gauges and the speedometer head.

9. Connect all wire leads and bulbs in the cluster assembly.

10. Position the cluster assembly to the instrument panel and install the retaining screws.

11. Connect the speedometer cable.

12. Connect the battery ground cable and check the operation of all disconnected parts.

SPEEDOMETER—FALCON, MUSTANG

1. Disconnect the battery ground cable.

2. Disconnect the speedometer cable.

3. Remove the instrument cluster assembly.

4. Remove the six screws retaining the instrument cluster back plate

assembly and remove the back plate assembly.

5. Remove the two screws retaining the speedometer, the two screws retaining the speedometer dial to the back plate, and remove the speedometer assembly.

6. Position the speedometer and install the two speedometer dial retaining screws and the two speedometer retaining screws.

7. Position the back plate assembly and install the six retaining screws.

8. Install the instrument cluster assembly to the instrument panel.

9. Connect the speedometer cable, avoiding sharp bends.

10. Connect the battery ground cable.

SPEEDOMETER CABLE

To replace the speedometer drive cable, disconnect the cable housing from the speedometer, and pull the cable out of the housing. Wipe off all of the old lubricant. Lubricate the new cable with cable lubricant B5A-19581-A (do not over lubricate), insert it all the way into the housing, and twist it slightly to make sure that the squared drive is engaged in the speedometer driven gear. **If a speedometer cable is broken, it will be necessary to disconnect both ends of the cable housing in order to remove the broken sections. Tighten the mounting bolt to 3-4½ foot-pounds torque (Fig. 7).**

The speedometer driven gear is held on to the speedometer cable housing by a retainer clip. When replacing the driven gear, make certain that the gear is secure by placing the gear in position before inserting

the retainer clip through the gear slots.

WINDSHIELD WIPER SWITCH —FAIRLANE

1. Disconnect the battery ground cable.

2. Remove both control knobs and disconnect the washer.

3. From the lower edge of the cluster remove the retaining screws from the switches. Disconnect the electrical leads and remove the switch assembly from the instrument panel.

4. Remove a screw and separate the wiper and washer switches from each other including the plastic bar between the switches.

5. Assemble the wiper and washer switches to each other including the plastic bar so that when the washer switch is turned on the wipers will start.

6. Connect the electrical leads to the assembly and install it to the instrument panel.

7. Install the control knobs and connect the wiper washer.

8. Connect the battery ground cable.

WINDSHIELD WIPER MOTOR —EXCEPT FAIRLANE

1. Disconnect the harness connector from the wiper motor.

2. Remove the three bolts retaining the wiper motor and mounting bracket assembly to the dash panel. Lower the assembly and disconnect the wiper links at the motor. Remove the motor and bracket assembly.

3. Transfer the mounting bracket with grommets to the new motor.

4. Position the motor and bracket assembly and connect the wiper links to the motor.

5. Position the motor and bracket assembly to the dash panel and install the three retaining bolts.

6. Connect the harness connector to the wiper motor.

7. Connect the battery and check the operation of the wiper motor and the park position of the wiper blades.

WINDSHIELD WIPER MOTOR —FAIRLANE

1. Disconnect the wiper links drive arm from the wiper motor drive shaft (under the instrument panel).

2. Disconnect the wiring leads from the motor.

3. Remove the wiper motor mounting bolts and remove the motor.

4. Apply sealer around the edge of the new motor mounting bracket and

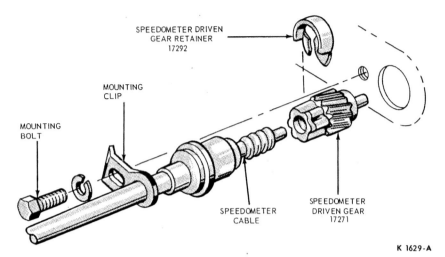

FIG. 7—Speedometer Driven Gear Retainer and Mounting

around each bracket bolt hole. Position the motor to the dash and install the mounting bolts.

5. Attach the wiring leads to the motor.

6. Position the wiper links drive arm on the motor driveshaft and install the mounting nut.

7. Check the operation of the wiper and adjust the park position if necessary.

WIPER PIVOT SHAFT AND LINK

1. Remove the windshield wiper blade and arm assembly.

2. Remove the pivot shaft retaining nut, bezel and gasket.

3. Disconnect the wiper link from the motor and remove the link and pivot shaft assembly.

4. Position the link and pivot shaft assembly on the cowl and wiper motor. Connect the link to the motor.

5. Install the pivot shaft to the cowl and install the gasket, bezel, and retaining nut.

6. Install the wiper blade and arm assembly.

7. Check the pivot shaft and link operation.

---

4 MAJOR REPAIR OPERATIONS

DISASSEMBLY—PERMANENT MAGNET TYPE SINGLE OR TWO-SPEED ELECTRIC WIPER MOTOR

1. Remove the gear cover retaining screws, ground terminal and cover (Fig. 8).

2. Remove the gear and pinion re-

tainer.

3. Remove the idler gear and pinion and thrust washer.

4. Remove the motor through

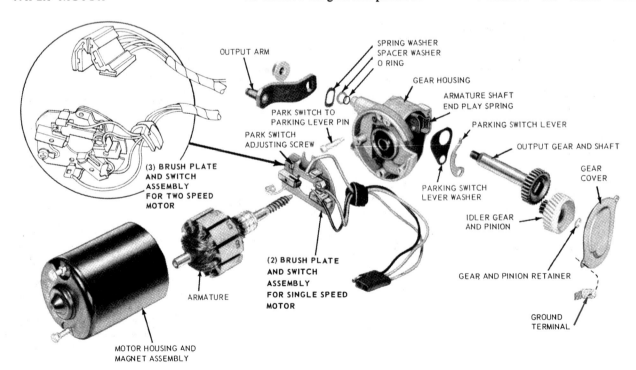

FIG. 8—Disassembled Single or Two-Speed Wiper Motor—Permanent Magnet Type

bolts, motor housing, switch terminal insulator sleeve, and armature. **Do not pound the motor housing magnet assembly as the ceramic magnets may be damaged.**

5. Mark the position of the output arm with respect to the output shaft, for assembly. Remove the output arm retaining nut, output arm, spring washer, flat washer, output gearshaft assembly, thrust washer, and parking switch lever and parking switch lever washer.

6. Remove the brushes and brush springs.

7. Remove the brush plate and switch assembly, and remove the switch contact to parking lever pin from the gear housing.

PARTS REPAIR OR REPLACEMENT

All parts on both the single-speed and two-speed wiper are replaced and not repaired.

ASSEMBLY—PERMANENT MAGNET TYPE SINGLE OR TWO-SPEED ELECTRIC WIPER MOTOR

1. Install the parking switch lever washer.

2. Install the parking switch lever on the gear and pinion shaft with the cam rider pointing toward the gear housing output shaft hole. Make certain that the lever bottoms against the casting.

3. Apply a film of Sun Prestige grease to the output gear teeth and shaft bearing surface. Insert the shaft in the bearing. Make certain that the parking switch lever is clear of the cam and gear assembly.

4. Place the spacer washer and spring washer on the shaft, position the output arm on the shaft in the marked position from which it was removed, and install the mounting nut.

5. Position the brush springs and brushes in the holders and wrap wire around them to hold them in the fully retracted position. Push the insulated brush connector onto the switch terminal.

6. Place the switch-contact to parking-lever pin in the gear housing. Position the brush plate assembly to the housing and install the mounting screws. Make the park switch contact points adjustment covered under **Windshield Wiper Motor Park Switch Test and Adjustment—Single and Two-Speed Permanent Magnet Type** in this section.

7. Apply Sun Prestige grease to the ball bearing in the end of the armature shaft. Position the armature shaft in the gear housing and remove the brush retracting wires.

8. Holding the armature in position, install the terminal insulating sleeve, motor housing and magnet assembly, and through bolts. Seal the area where the terminal insulator sleeve seats against the motor and gear housings.

9. Apply Sun Prestige grease to the worm gear and idler gear, and install the idler gear, thrust washer and retainer.

10. Apply a generous amount of Sun Prestige grease to the area around the end of the armature shaft. Install the gear housing cover and ground terminal.

WINDSHIELD WIPER MOTOR PARK SWITCH TEST AND ADJUSTMENT—SINGLE AND TWO-SPEED PERMANENT MAGNET TYPE

With jumper wires connected as shown in Fig 9, the motor should move to the park position. If it does, the motor is all right and the fault lies in the panel switch or wiring. If the motor does not park, proceed with the following park switch ad-

justment (Figs. 8 and 10).

Remove the motor thru bolts and remove the motor cup and armature.

Rotate the output shaft until the park switch lower contacts are firmly closed as shown.

Rotate the adjusting screw clockwise until the park switch lower contacts just open.

Rotate the adjusting screw counterclockwise one full turn.

Check the bridge to assure that the legs are contacting the brush plate when the lower contacts are closed.

Install the armature, motor cup and thru bolts.

DISASSEMBLY—OSCILLATING TYPE TWO-SPEED ELECTRIC WIPER MOTOR

The two-speed electric motor may be disassembled for service of the drive mechanism parts.

1. Remove the gear housing cover plate and gasket (Fig. 11).

2. Remove the output shaft retainer and spacer washer.

3. Remove the crankpin bearing retainer and remove the spacer washer and cam return spring assembly.

4. Remove the arm and link assembly.

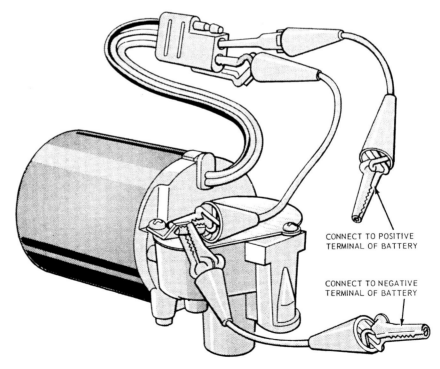

CONNECT TO POSITIVE TERMINAL OF BATTERY

CONNECT TO NEGATIVE TERMINAL OF BATTERY

K 1630 A

FIG. 9—Windshield Wiper Motor Park Switch Test—Single-Speed

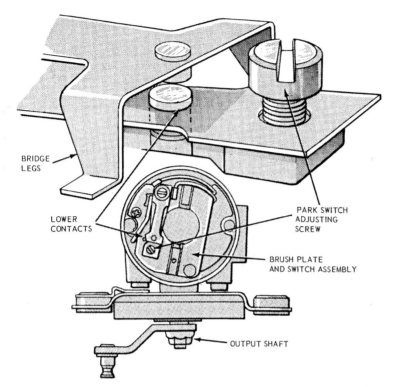

K 1631 - A

FIG. 10—Windshield Wiper Motor Park Switch Adjustment

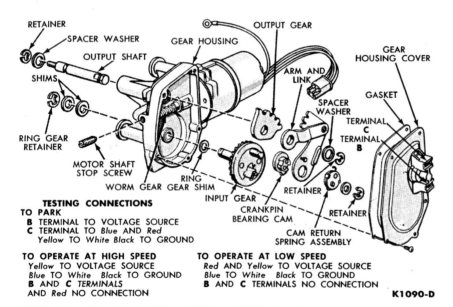

TESTING CONNECTIONS
TO PARK
B TERMINAL TO VOLTAGE SOURCE
C TERMINAL TO *Blue* AND *Red*
   Yellow TO *White Black* TO GROUND

TO OPERATE AT HIGH SPEED
Yellow TO VOLTAGE SOURCE
Blue TO *White Black* TO GROUND
B AND **C** TERMINALS
AND *Red* NO CONNECTION

TO OPERATE AT LOW SPEED
Red AND *Yellow* TO VOLTAGE SOURCE
Blue TO *White Black* TO GROUND
B AND **C** TERMINALS NO CONNECTION

K1090-D

FIG. 11—Two-Speed Wiper Motor—Oscillating Type

5. Remove the crankpin bearing cam.

6. Remove the input gear retainer and outer spacer shim, and remove the input gear and inner spacer shim.

7. Remove the wiper arm lever nut and lock washer.

8. Remove the wiper arm lever

and spacer, and remove the output shaft and gear assembly from the housing.

9. The output gear may be removed from its shaft by tapping with a fiber hammer. Be careful not to damage the end of the shaft.

The worm drive gear and armature assembly is not serviced.

PARTS REPAIR OR REPLACEMENT

All parts on both the single-speed and the two-speed electric wipers are replaced and not repaired.

ASSEMBLY—OSCILLATING TYPE TWO-SPEED ELECTRIC WIPER MOTOR

1. Tighten the motor cover. Adjust the motor shaft end play to 0.000-0.005 inch by turning the shaft stop screw. Measure with a feeler gauge between the stop screw and the motor shaft.

2. Install the input gear shim on the input gear shaft and install the gear in the housing. Adjust the end play to 0.005 to 0.010 inch by adding or removing shims under the input gear retainer. Install the retainer.

3. Install the output gear on the output shaft. Make sure that the gear is bottomed on the shaft.

4. Install the output shaft and gear assembly into the housing with the gear teeth facing the motor. Install one spacer washer to the outside end of the output shaft and assemble the wiper arm lever to the output shaft, with the linkage studs facing away from and above the shaft. Secure the lever with a lock washer and nut.

5. Place the bearing cam on the crankpin with the small diameter portion of the cam facing outward.

6. Install the arm and link assembly to the bearing cam. As the arm is placed on the shaft, the gears must be meshed and the link which is riveted to the arm must be installed to the output shaft at the same time. Proper gear indexing is obtained when the bottom tooth of the arm and gear segment will be in mesh with the bottom valley of the output shaft gear.

7. Install the output shaft spacer washer and retainer. Check the end play of the output shaft (0.005-0.010 inch). Remove or install spacer washers under the shaft retainer to adjust the end play.

8. Install the cam return spring assembly.

9. Install the bearing spacer and retainer. If the retainer cannot be installed, one or more coils of the spring clutch are probably out of place. If the bearing has excessive end play on the crankpin, the projection of the bearing may ride out of the semi-circular slot in the end plate. Add spacer washers under the retainer if necessary.

10. Apply generous amounts of Sun Prestige grease to all moving parts. Install the gear housing cover plate.

When operating the unit on the bench, do not place hands or fingers between the wiper lever and the case, or inside the gear housing, as considerable power is developed by the gear reduction.

ELECTRO-PNEUMATIC GOVERNOR AND CONTROL SELECTOR SWITCH—COMET

The electro-pneumatic governor and the control selector switch are serviced as assemblies only. Should any internal component become defective the complete assembly must be replaced.

In the event of suspected partial or total blockage of internal passages, light air pressure may be applied in an attempt to remove the cause of blockage.

Although the vacuum hoses are an integral part of the wiring harness assembly, individual hoses may be replaced if required.

SPEEDOMETER DIAGNOSTIC PROCEDURES

Speedometer system complaints are generally the result of a visible or audible defect in the system. It is imperative that the specific defect be determined prior to attempting any physical repairs to preclude unnecessarily disassembling system components. The following suggestions are intended to aid in quick and accurate system problem diagnosis.

VISIBLE DEFECTS

Slight Needle Waver or Severe Needle Fluctuation (No Noise)

1. Loose cable nut.
2. Defective speedometer head.

3. Bent cable core at attaching nut.
4. Kinked or pinched cable housing.
5. Excessive grease in speedometer head.
6. Defective speed control regulator.

Inoperative

1. Broken cable core.
2. Defective drive and/or driven gear.
3. Defective speedometer head.

AUDIBLE DEFECTS

Clicking or Ticking (With Needle Waver), Grinding or Ringing

1. Loose cable nut.
2. Defective drive and/or driven gear.
3. Defective speedometer head.
4. No lube on cable.

SPEEDOMETER REPAIR PROCEDURES
LOOSE CABLE ATTACHING NUTS

1. Cable nuts should be tightened with pliers to approximately 18 to 25 in-lbs.
2. Cable nuts should start and run up freely by hand for at least three to four turns.
3. A loose cable nut can cause a bent cable core. Tightening will not always correct the problem.

DEFECTIVE SPEEDOMETER HEAD

Before removing a speedometer head, disconnect the cable at the head and insert a short section of cable core in the head. Rotate the section of core to check for any dragging or noise. The speedometer shaft should turn freely and evenly.

DEFECTIVE CABLE CORE AND HOUSING

1. To check for a kinked cable core remove and wipe dry. Lay the core out straight on a flat surface and roll it back and forth. Any kinks or damage will be seen. Then take an end in each hand, allowing core to hang in approximately a 9-inch loop. Rotate both ends to be sure core turns evenly.
2. Routing of the cable housing is particularly important where the cable leaves the speedometer head. The optimum routing would provide that the cable and housing take virtually no change of direction for at least a length of 8 inches from the speedometer head.
3. When installing a new cable and housing it is necessary that the new assembly be guided and routed properly to eliminate any kinks.
4. Proper lubrication of the cable core is accomplished by a light application of B5A-19581-A lubricant after the cable has been wiped clean. A light film is all that is required.

DEFECTIVE DRIVE AND DRIVEN GEARS

1. A score nicked or gouged driven gear is usually indicative of a defective drive gear on those vehicles that have the drive gear integral with the transmission output shaft. The output shaft should be carefully inspected for imperfections and replaced if necessary.
2. A driven gear with two or three adjoining teeth badly scored is indicative of improper assembly procedure. The gear should be inserted in the transmission while simultaneously turning the drive shaft. This will insure initial gear engagement and prevent gear damage. Force should never be used.
3. Whenever a drive gear is replaced, a new driven gear should also be installed, regardless of its apparent condition.

PART
15-5
SPECIFICATIONS

BULB CHART

Unit	Candela① or Wattage		Trade Number
Headlight No. 1 (Inner or Lower)	37.5 W.		4001
Headlight No. 2 (Outer or Upper)	37.5/50 W.		4002
Headlight (Falcon-Mustang)	40/50 W.		6012
Fog Light (Mustang)	35 W.		4415
Front Turn Signal/Parking	32 C.		1157
Rear Turn Signal and Stop/Tail	32 C.		1157
License Plate	4 C.		1155
Back-Up Lights (Falcon Sdn)	32 C.		1156
Back-Up Lights (Falcon Sta. Wag.)	32 C.		1076
Back-Up Lights (Mustang)	21 C.		1142
Spot Light	30 W.		4405
Luggage Compartment	6 C.		631
Luggage Compartment (Fairlane)	15 C.		93
Cargo Light (Wagon—Comet)	15 C.		1003
Engine Compartment (Comet)	15 C.		93
Dome Light	15 C.		1003
Warning Lights			
Oil and Generator	2 C.		1895
Park Brake (Comet—Mustang)	1 C.		257
Park Brake	2 C.		1895
Seat Belt (Fairlane)	1.6 C.		257
Seat Belt (Comet—Falcon)	2 C.		1895
Emergency Flasher	2 C.		1895
Alternator	2 C.		1895
Turn Signal (Inst. Panel)	2 C.		1895
Illumination			
Instruments	2 C.		1895
Clock	2 C.		1895
Heater Control	2 C.		1895
Hi-Beam Indicator	2 C.		1895
Speedometer	2 C.		1895
Glove Compartment	2 C.		1895
Glove Compartment (Mustang Console)	1.5 C.		1445
Courtesy Light (Ins. Panel)	6 C.		631
Radio Pilot Light (Fairlane)	2 C.		1892
Radio Pilot Light (Mustang)	1.9 C.		1891
Radio Pilot Light (Falcon)	2 C.		1891
Radio Dial (Comet)	2 C.		1895
Arm Rest Courtesy (Fairlane)	6 C.		631
Courtesy Light (Front Door—Comet)	4 C.		1155
Courtesy Light (Fast Back—Mustang)	15 C.		1003
Courtesy Light (Falcon Conv.)	6 C.		631
Ash Receptacle (Fairlane)	1.5 C.		1445
Courtesy Light (Mustang Console)	3 C.		1816
Clock (Mustang Rally Pac)	3 C.		1816
Tachometer (Mustang—Rally Pac)	2 C.		1895
Automatic Transmission Control	2 C.		1895
Map Light	6 C.		631

①Candela is the new international term for candlepower

CIRCUIT PROTECTION

FUNCTION	LOCATION	Falcon Comet RATING TYPE	Fairlane RATING TYPE	Mustang RATING TYPE
Dome Courtesy-Map Cargo	Fuse Panel	7½ SFE	7½ SFE	7½ SFE
Tail-Park License	Light Switch	15 C.B.	15 C.B.	15 C.B.
Stop Light	Light Switch	15 C.B.	15 C.B.	15 C.B.
Clock	Fuse Panel	7½ SFE	7½ SFE	7½ SFE
Back-up	Fuse Panel	14 SFE	14 SFE	14 SFE
Turn Signals (act as a circuit breaker)				
Radio	Fuse Panel (Acc. Socket)	14 SFE	14 SFE	14 SFE
Heater	Fuse Panel	14 SFE	14 SFE	14 SFE
Heater and PRNDL dial	Fuse Panel Heater Socket			14 SFE
Cigar Lighter	Fuse Panel	14 SFE	14 SFE	14 SFE
Cigar Lighter and Emergency Warning Flasher	Fuse Panel Cigar Lighter Socket	20 SFE	20 SFE	20 SFE
Tachometer	Fuse Panel (Dome Socket)	7½ SFE	7½ SFE	7½ SFE
Convertible Top	Between starter relay & Junction Block	Safety Link	Safety Link	Safety Link
Power Window—Power Seat	On Starter Relay	20 C.B.	20 C.B.	20 C.B.
Overdrive	Clips to overdrive relay	20 SFE	20 SFE	20 SFE
Seat Belt Warning	Fuse	14 SFE	14 SFE	14 SFE
Windshield Washer (Two speed wiper)	Panel Acc.	14 SFE	14 SFE	
Windshield Washer (Single speed wiper)	Socket	14 SFE	14 SFE	14 SFE
Windshield Washer (Two speed wiper)	Wiper Switch			12 C.B.
Windshield Wiper	Wiper Switch	6 (S. Sp.) C.B. 7 (2 Sp.) C.B. (Falcon) 7 Intermittent	6 (S. Sp.) C.B. 7 (2 Sp.) C.B.	5 (S. Sp.) C.B. 12 (2 Sp.) C.B.
Light-Instrument Panel	Fuse Panel	2½ AGA	2½ AGA	2½ AGA
Light-Instrument Cluster	Instrument	2½ AGA	2½ AGA	2½ AGA
Light-Clock	LP Socket	2½ AGA	2½ AGA	2½ AGA
Light-Tachometer	Connected into	2½ AGA	2½ AGA	2½ AGA
Light-Ash Receptacle	15 C.B.	2½ AGA	2½ AGA	2½ AGA
Light-PRNDL Dial	Light Switch	2½ AGA	2½ AGA	
Light-PRNDL Dial (Console Only)	Fuse Panel Acc. Socket	14 SFE	14 SFE	
Light-Luggage Compartment	Fuse Panel	7½ SFE	7½ SFE	7½ SFE
Light-Door Open Warning	Fuse Panel		7½ SFE	
Light-Glove Box	Fuse Panel	7½ SFE	7½ SFE	7½ SFE
Light-Spotlight	In Line	7½ SFE	7½ SFE	7½ SFE
Light-Headlights	Light Switch	18 Comet C.B. 12 Falcon C.B.		
Emergency Warning Flasher	Fuse Panel	14 SFE	14 SFE	14 SFE
Horns	Light Switch	15 C.B.	15 C.B.	15 C.B.
Air Conditioner (Integrated)	On Ign. Switch	25 C.B.	25 C.B.	25 C.B.
Back Light Control	At Starter Relay	20 C.B.	20 C.B.	
Economy Air Conditioner	In Line	15 AGC	15 AGC	15 AGC
Motor Windshield Wiper	Circuit Breaker Integral With Motor	C.B.	C.B.	C.B.
Motor Convertible Top		C.B.	C.B.	C.B.
Motor Power Window		C.B.	C.B.	C.B.
Motor Power Seat		C.B.	C.B.	C.B.

SPEEDOMETER CABLE

Mounting Clip bolt Torque	3-4½ ft. lbs.

VENTILATING, HEATING, AND ACCESSORIES | GROUP 16

PART 16-1   **PAGE**
VENTILATING SYSTEM AND
HEATER 16-1
PART 16-2
AIR CONDITIONING—FORD 16-10

PART 16-3   **PAGE**
AIR CONDITIONING—SELECTAIRE ...16-20
PART 16-4
RADIO 16-26
PART 16-5
SPECIFICATIONS 16-29

PART 16-1   VENTILATING SYSTEM AND HEATER

Section   **Page**
1 Description and Operation 16-1
  Ventilating and Heating System—Comet,
    Falcon and Fairlane 16-1
  Ventilating and Heating System—Mustang 16-2
2 Diagnosis and Testing 16-6
  Ventilating and Heating Trouble Diagnosis
    Guide 16-6
  Heater Current Draw Test 16-6
  Loose Motor Fan Test 16-6
  Blower Switch Test 16-6
  Plugged Heater Core Test 16-6
3 Common Adjustments and Repairs 16-6
  Ventilating System 16-6
  Heating System 16-6
    Control Adjustments—Mustang 16-6
    Bowden Cable Adjustments—Comet,
      Falcon and Fairlane 16-7
    Blower Motor Electrical Circuit—
      Comet, Falcon and Fairlane 16-7

    Heater Hose Routing 16-7
    Heater Hose Replacement 16-7
    Bleeding Air From Heater Core 16-7
4 Removal and Installation 16-7
  Heater—Mustang 16-7
  Heater Core—Mustang 16-8
  Heater Control Assembly—Fairlane 16-8
  Heater Control Assembly—Falcon 16-8
  Heater Control Assembly—Comet 16-8
  Discharge Air Registers 16-8
  Defroster Nozzles—Comet, Falcon and
    Fairlane 16-8
  Heater Core Assembly—Comet,
    Falcon and Fairlane 16-8
  Blower Motor and Wheel Assembly—
    Comet, Falcon and Fairlane 16-8
  Heater Blower—Mustang 16-8
  Defroster Nozzles—Mustang 16-9
  Blower Switch—Mustang 16-9

1 DESCRIPTION AND OPERATION

VENTILATING AND HEATING SYSTEM—COMET, FALCON AND FAIRLANE

The 1966 heater is a blend air system connected to an opening in the right vent air duct. The entire heater assembly is located under the instrument panel and it is necessary to remove the right air vent duct and heater case assembly to service major components of the heater assembly (Fig. 1).

Outside air is drawn into the vehicle from the cowl through the right air duct, into the blower housing, forced through and/or around the heater core, mixed, and then discharged through the outlets in the

discharge air register or defroster outlets (Fig. 2).

The air temperature is controlled by the position of the temperature air valve, or door, located between the blower and heater core in the heater housing. As the temperature lever is moved from LOW to HIGH; a Bowden cable moves the temperature door in the heater housing from minimum heat to full heat position to modulate the air flow through and/or around the heater core. The air through the core and the air through the bypass chamber is then mixed as it enters the plenum chamber.

A heater air valve, referred to as

the heat-defrost door, is located in the plenum chamber to control the discharge air between heat and defrost, and close off all air in the OFF position. The heat-defrost lever actuates a Bowden cable connected to the heater air valve in the plenum chamber. Air flow through the plenum is directed, as required by the operator, through the discharge air outlets in the plenum, in the heat position; or up to the windshield in the defrost position. The air flow can also be modulated by setting the controls in any position between heat and defrost.

A single defroster nozzle leads to

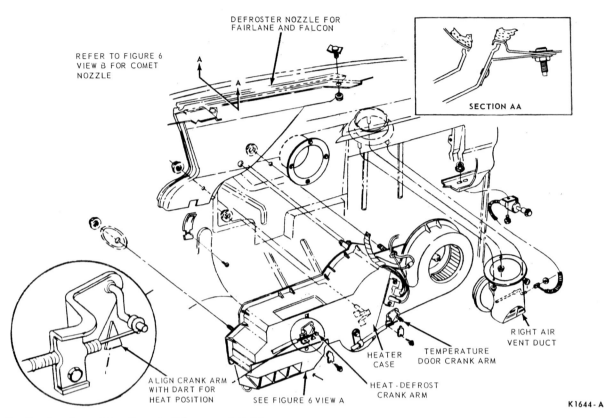

FIG. 1—Heater Assembly—Comet, Falcon and Fairlane

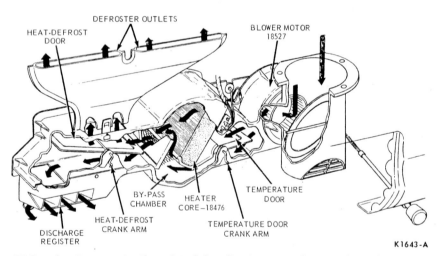

FIG. 2—Heater Air Flow (Modulated)—Comet, Falcon and Fairlane

two slots in the forward instrument panel crash pad.

Three speeds are provided for the blower fan with a four position switch in the control assembly and a resistor assembly located to the right of the heater core in the heater housing. The resistor in the blower motor circuit controls the low and medium blower speeds.

The nomenclature for the Fairlane heater controls is located on the lower right side of the instrument cluster, and the horizontal control levers are directly below on the lower lip of the instrument panel (Fig. 3).

The Falcon control, located on the right side of the cluster assembly, contains two vertical slide le-

vers and the blower switch (Fig. 4).

The Comet heater controls are located to the left of the steering column in the lower instrument panel area. The dial for the Caliente and Cyclone models are illuminated with one bulb; the Capri and 202 model does not have an illuminated dial (Fig. 5).

In order to provide adequate air distribution on all vehicles, two air distribution register assemblies are provided. All vehicles equipped with consoles or economy air conditioning is equipped with a register that distributes the air to the left and right of the tunnel area. The register for standard vehicles has air outlets across the face of the register and a small outlet on the lower left end (View A, Fig. 9).

VENTILATING AND HEATING SYSTEM—MUSTANG

VENTILATING SYSTEM

Two manually operated doors lo-

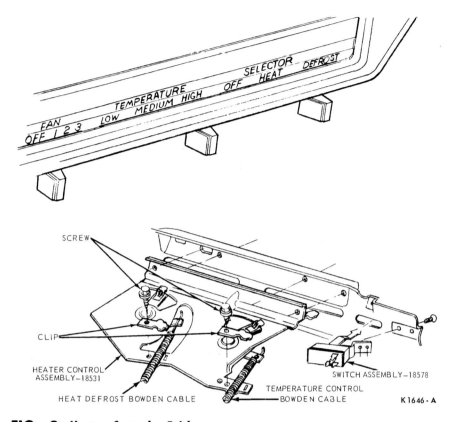

FIG. 3—Heater Controls—Fairlane

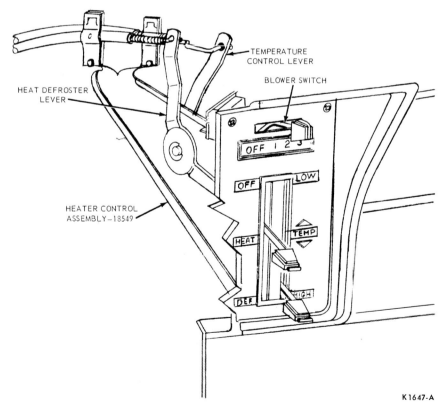

FIG. 4—Heater Controls—Falcon

only when the HEAT lever is in the up position. The position of the fresh air doors deflects the air as desired.

HEATING SYSTEM

The fresh air heater is designed to function in conjunction with the right duct of the fresh air ventilating system. The heater assembly couples to an outlet provided in the right cowl assembly. A door in the duct and two doors in the heater housing are operated by controls located on the instrument panel, allowing the selection of outside air for ventilation or heating (Figs. 6 and 7).

The defroster control lever operates a valve in the heater plenum chamber. Push the lever downward for proportionately more air to the defroster registers.

The PUSH FOR TEMP lever operates the blend-air valve in the heater blower housing. The blend-air door controls the amount of air flow through the heater core. Any intermediate position of the blend-air door allows both cool and heated air to be mixed in the plenum chamber for lower than maximum temperatures.

The PUSH FOR HTR lever operates a door in the right incoming air duct. When the lever is in the up position air from the cowl grille enters the passenger compartment through an opening under the right side of the instrument panel. A manually operated door closes the opening, or deflects air as desired. Pushing the lever downward allows air to enter the heater blower inlet duct.

To operate the blower motor, move the top lever from the center OFF position. Moving the lever to the left will give high speed operation, and moving it to the right will give low speed operation (Fig. 8).

cated under each end of the instrument panel allow fresh air to enter

the passenger compartment. The right door is open to the cowl inlet

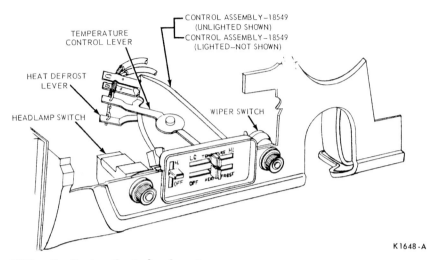

FIG. 5—Heater Controls—Comet

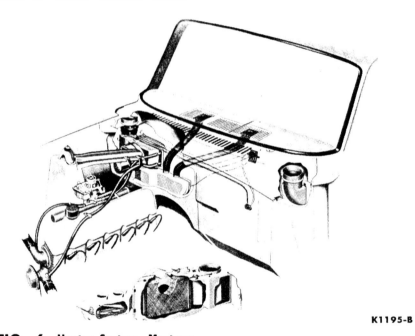

FIG. 6—Heater System—Mustang

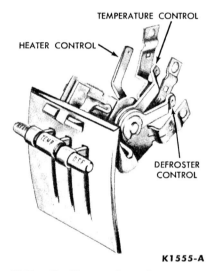

FIG. 8—Heater Controls—Mustang

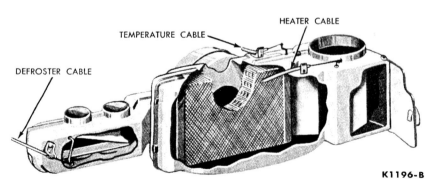

FIG. 7—Heater Control Cables—Mustang

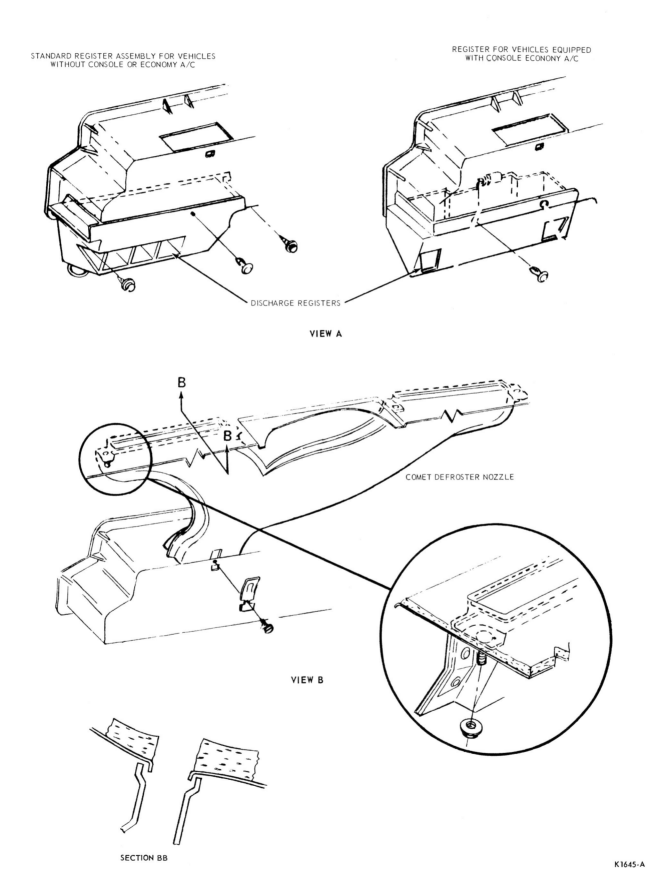

STANDARD REGISTER ASSEMBLY FOR VEHICLES
WITHOUT CONSOLE OR ECONOMY A/C

REGISTER FOR VEHICLES EQUIPPED
WITH CONSOLE ECONOMY A/C

DISCHARGE REGISTERS

VIEW A

B

B

COMET DEFROSTER NOZZLE

VIEW B

SECTION BB

K1645-A

FIG. 9—Air Distribution Registers—Types

2 DIAGNOSIS AND TESTING

VENTILATING AND HEATING TROUBLE DIAGNOSIS GUIDE

INSUFFICIENT OR NO HEAT	**1.** Burned out fuse or loose wires to the heater blower. **2.** Defective motor ground, or defective blower motor. **3.** Fan loose on motor shaft, or motor stalled. **4.** Defective heater blower switch. **5.** A kinked, clogged, or collapsed water hose.	**6.** Improperly connected heater hoses. **7.** Plugged heater core, or air outlet. **8.** Improperly installed or defective engine thermostat. **9.** Incorrectly installed and adjusted control cables. **10.** Air leaks in the body.
INSUFFICIENT OR NO DEFROSTING	**1.** Improperly adjusted defroster control cable, or disconnected defroster hose. **2.** Binding defroster valve. **3.** Plugged or loose defroster noz-	zle, or obstructed defroster openings at windshield. **4.** Defroster hoses not properly attached at plenum.
TOO MUCH HEAT	**1.** Incorrectly adjusted blend-air valve.	

TESTING

Refer to Wiring Diagram Manual Form 7795P-66 for locations of wiring harnesses. Schematics are shown in Group 2 of this manual.

The following tests may be made on the heater: Burned out fuses, loose wire connections, defective wires, collapsed hoses, loose defroster hoses and air leaks in the body may be determined by visual inspection of the parts.

HEATER CURRENT DRAW TEST

This test will determine if the blower motor is defective. Connect a 0-50 ammeter as shown in Fig. 10. The blower motor will operate independently of the control switch, and the current drawn by the motor will be indicated on the ammeter.

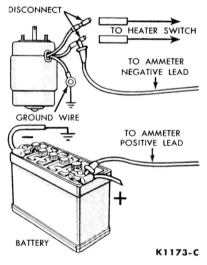

FIG. 10—Heater Motor Current Draw Test

Current draw should be to specification.

LOOSE MOTOR FAN TEST

Turn on the heater switch, and listen for the sound of the motor. If only a hum is heard, the fan is loose on the motor shaft.

BLOWER SWITCH TEST

Substitute a known good blower switch for the suspected switch.

PLUGGED HEATER CORE TEST

Start the engine and temporarily remove the outlet hose from the heater core (the hose that leads to the water pump). Very little or no flow of water from the core outlet indicates that the core is plugged. Make certain that water is being supplied to the core inlet.

3 COMMON ADJUSTMENTS AND REPAIRS

VENTILATING SYSTEM

Bowden cable operated vents and air inlets are adjusted so that the vents are tightly closed when the control knobs are all the way in. Loosen the Bowden cable retaining screw at the vent control arm, move the cable housing back and forth until the vent is closed when the knob is $1/16$ to $1/8$ inch from the in position, then tighten the retaining screw.

HEATING SYSTEM

CONTROL ADJUSTMENTS— MUSTANG

To assure maximum temperature the following temperature control adjustments should be used.

1. Insert a ⅛-inch spacer between the temperature control lever (center lever) and the bottom of the slot. Move the lever down until it is

seated against the spacer.

2. Loosen the control cable retaining clip (at either end of the cable).

3. With the temperature control damper crank (heater assembly) held tightly in the full heat position, tighten the control cable retaining clip screw.

4. Remove the spacer from the control head and check the lever

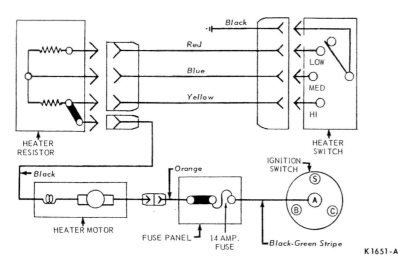

FIG. 11—Blower Motor Circuit—Comet, Falcon and Fairlane

travel. All overtravel (springback) should appear at the bottom of the lever travel.

BOWDEN CABLE ADJUSTMENTS—COMET, FALCON AND FAIRLANE

Temperature

Adjust the temperature Bowden cable at the heater case (Figs. 1 or 2), with the temperature door crank arm in the far left position and the temperature control lever on HI. Provide approximately ⅛ inch clearance between the lever and edge of the slot for proper adjustment.

Heat and Defrost

Adjust the heat-defrost Bowden cable at the heater case by aligning the crank arm (Figs. 1 or 2), with

the locating dart directly below the crank arm on the case. With the crank arm in this position, the heat-defrost door is in a horizontal position for maximum heat.

The Bowden cables can also be adjusted at the control assembly (Figs. 4, 5 and 9).

BLOWER MOTOR ELECTRICAL CIRCUIT—COMET, FALCON AND FAIRLANE

For the blower motor circuit wiring diagram refer to Figure 11 or the Wiring Diagram Manual Form 7795P-66.

HEATER HOSE ROUTING

Care must be taken when servicing the hoses to insure a smooth kink free installation for maximum heating (Fig. 12).

HEATER HOSE REPLACEMENT

To replace a heater hose, drain the coolant, remove the hose, cut a new hose to the same length as the old hose, install the hose, and replace the coolant. **Make certain that the heater hoses do not come in contact with any part of the exhaust system.**

After the coolant has been replaced, bleed the air from the heater core.

BLEEDING AIR FROM HEATER CORE

Remove the hose at the outlet connection of the heater core (hose that leads to the water pump). Allow any trapped air to flow out. When a continuous flow of coolant is obtained, connect the hose to the core.

4 REMOVAL AND INSTALLATION

HEATER—MUSTANG

Most of the heater repairs can be performed with the heater assembly lying on the car floor. Therefore, the following procedure will not remove the heater assembly from the car. The heater core or plenum replacement procedures contain the additional required steps to remove the heater assembly from the car.

REMOVAL

1. Drain the cooling system.
2. Remove the glove box.
3. Disconnect the three control cables.
4. Disconnect the defroster hoses at the heater plenum.

5. Disconnect the heater hoses at the water pump and the carburetor heater. Remove the heater hoses from the retaining clips. On 8-cylinder models remove the hose from the choke clip (Fig. 12).
6. Disconnect the wires at the heater motor and remove the ground-wire-to-dash panel retaining screw.
7. Remove the heater and motor assembly retaining nuts from the dash panel.
8. Disconnect the fresh air inlet rubber boot, pull the heater assembly from the dash panel and lay the heater assembly on the floor.

INSTALLATION

1. Position the heater assembly to the dash panel and install the retaining nuts.
2. Connect the heater motor wires to the wiring harness, and connect the heater motor ground wire to the dash panel with the retaining screw.
3. Connect the heater hoses and install the hose retaining clips.
4. Connect the fresh air inlet boot.
5. Connect the defroster hoses to the heater plenum.
6. Connect and adjust the three cables to the heater, and install the glove box.

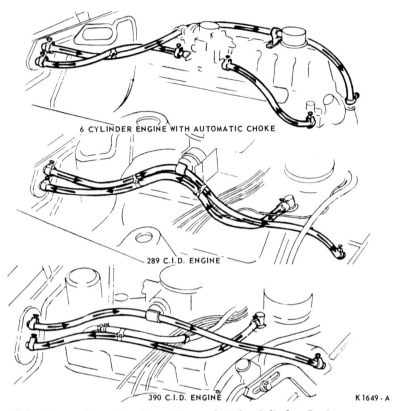

6 CYLINDER ENGINE WITH AUTOMATIC CHOKE

289 C.I.D. ENGINE

390 C.I.D. ENGINE   K 1649 - A

FIG. 12—Heater Hose Routings—Six and Eight Cylinder Engines

7. Fill the cooling system, and check the system for leaks.

8. Bleed the system.

HEATER CORE—MUSTANG

1. Remove the heater assembly and lay the assembly on the car floor.

2. Remove the clips retaining the heater housing halves together and separate the halves.

3. Lift the heater core from the heater housing chamber. On console equipped cars it may be necessary to remove the heater from the car.

4. Position the heater core in the forward half of the heater housing, assemble the housing, and install the retaining clips. If a 2-inch core is used, transfer the adapter from the old core to the new core.

5. Position the assembly on the car floor.

6. Install the heater assembly.

7. Refill and bleed the cooling system and check for leaks.

HEATER CONTROL ASSEMBLY —FAIRLANE

To remove the control assembly, remove the three control knobs and remove two control mounting screws from the face of the instrument pan-

el, then lower the control from under the panel and disconnect the Bowden cables.

The blower switch is located to the left of the two control levers and retained with one screw in the face of the lower instrument panel (Fig. 4).

HEATER CONTROL ASSEMBLY —FALCON

To service the controls, remove the three knobs, remove two upper screws in the control bezel and two lower mounting nuts behind the instrument cluster. Lower the control assembly and disconnect the two Bowden cables and blower switch wiring (Fig. 5).

HEATER CONTROL ASSEMBLY —COMET

To remove the control assembly, remove the knobs and spanner nuts from the headlight and wiper switches and lower the control assembly from under the instrument panel, then disconnect the Bowden cables, light bulb, and wiring.

DISCHARGE AIR REGISTERS

The discharge air registers can be

removed from the heater assembly if necessary (View A, Fig. 9).

DEFROSTER NOZZLES—COMET, FALCON AND FAIRLANE

The Fairlane and Falcon have a common type nozzle; the nozzle for the Comet is unique due to the wider space between the two openings in the instrument panel.

1. Remove the glove box.

2. Remove the defroster nozzle retaining clip screw (Figs. 2 and 3).

3. Remove the defroster nozzle retaining nuts; two on the Fairlane and Falcon, and four on the Comet.

4. Lower the nozzle down and out from under the panel on the Fairlane and Falcon; remove the Comet nozzle through the glove box opening.

HEATER CORE ASSEMBLY— COMET, FALCON AND FAIRLANE

The heater core is mounted in the heater case in a diagonal position in the center of the case and is serviced through an opening in the back plate. With the heater assembly out of the vehicle, simply remove four screws from the cover plate and pull the core from the housing (Fig. 13). The core is mounted in the heater housing with butyl rubber pads on each end to insure a snug fit.

BLOWER MOTOR AND WHEEL ASSEMBLY—COMET, FALCON AND FAIRLANE

To remove the blower motor and wheel assembly, it is necessary to remove the right air vent duct and the heater case assembly. The blower motor and wheel assembly is mounted to the forward right side of the heater case in the blower scroll and attached with four screws to the back plate (Fig. 13).

HEATER BLOWER MOTOR— MUSTANG

1. Remove the heater assembly and lay the assembly on the car floor.

2. Remove the blower motor and bracket to the blower housing retaining screws and remove the blower assembly.

3. Loosen the blower cage set screw and remove the blower cage from the motor.

4. Remove the blower motor mounting plate from the motor.

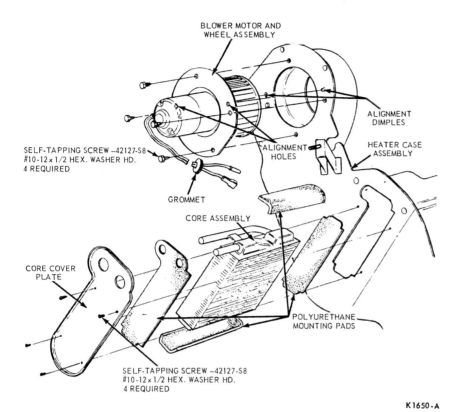

FIG. 13—Heater Blower Motor and Core Assemblies—Comet, Falcon and Fairlane

5. Install the blower motor mounting plate to the new motor.

6. Install the blower cage and tighten the set screw.

7. Install the heater motor and bracket to the blower housing.

8. Install the heater assembly.

DEFROSTER NOZZLES— MUSTANG

1. Remove the defroster outlet register retaining screws and remove the register.

2. Disconnect the defroster hose at the plenum.

3. Remove the defroster nozzle retaining clips and remove the nozzle assembly.

4. Transfer the retaining clips to the new defroster nozzle assembly.

5. Install the defroster nozzle to the instrument panel.

6. Install the defroster outlet register.

7. Connect the hoses to plenum.

BLOWER SWITCH— MUSTANG

1. Loosen the screw in the knob.

2. Disconnect the wiring.

3. Remove one screw holding the blower switch to the control head assembly, and remove the switch.

PART 16-2 AIR CONDITIONING—FORD

Section	Page
1 Description and Operation	16-10
Receiver Unit	16-10
Evaporator Unit	16-10
Expansion Valve	16-11
Compressor Unit	16-11
Liquid Sight Glass	16-11
Magnetic Clutch	16-11
Thermostatic Switch	16-11
Service Valves	16-11
2 Diagnosis and Testing	16-12
Air Conditioning Diagnosis Guide	16-12
Checking For Leaks	16-12
Use of Sight Glass	16-13
Checking System Pressures	16-13
Interpreting Abnormal System Pressures	16-13
Thermostatic Switch Test	16-14
Magnetic Clutch	16-14
Blower Motor	16-14
Expansion Valve	16-14
Compressor Volumetric Efficiency Test	16-14
3 Common Adjustments and Repairs	16-14
Safety Precautions	16-14

Section	Page
Discharging the System	16-15
Evacuating the System	16-15
Making a Partial Charge	16-15
Making a Complete Charge	16-16
Charging From Small Containers	16-16
Compressor Oil Level Check	16-16
Isolating The Compressor	16-16
4 Removal and Installation	16-17
Evaporator	16-17
Condenser	16-17
Compressor	16-17
Compressor Components	16-17
Valve Plate	16-17
Crankshaft Seal	16-18
Expansion Valve	16-18
Thermostatic Switch	16-18
Air Conditioner Blower Motor	16-19
Belt	16-19
Clutch	16-19
5 Cleaning and Inspection	16-19
Compressor	16-19

1 DESCRIPTION AND OPERATION

Refer to Wiring Diagram Manual Form 7795P-66 for locations of wiring harnesses. Schematics are shown in Group 22 of this manual.

The Ford air conditioner is used on the Falcon and Fairlane (Fig. 1).

FIG. 1—Ford Air Conditioner

The Mercury air conditioner is used on the Comet. The Selectaire is available on the Fairlane. All units use a receiver, an expansion valve, an evaporator, a compressor, and a condenser. These parts are the standard units which are used in any air

cooling system. Besides these major cooling components there is a liquid sight glass, an oil separator (integral with the compressor), a cooling unit thermostatic switch, and a blower assembly.

Fig. 2 shows an air conditioning system in schematic form. Arrows indicate the direction of refrigerant flow.

RECEIVER UNIT

The air cooling system stores the

liquid Refrigerant-12 under pressure in a combination receiver and dehydrator (Fig. 2). The pressure in the receiver normally varies from about 80 to 300 psi, depending on the surrounding air temperature and compressor speed.

The dehydrator serves the purpose of removing any traces of moisture that may have accumulated in the system. Even small amounts of moisture will cause an air cooling unit to malfunction. A fusible plug is screwed into the receiver. This will release the refrigerant before the refrigerant temperature exceeds 212°F.

EVAPORATOR UNIT

When the cooling system is in operation, the liquid Refrigerant-12 flows from the combination receiver and dehydrator unit through a flexible hose to the evaporator (Fig. 2) where it is allowed to evaporate at a reduced pressure, to cool the evaporator.

Passenger compartment air is blown through the evaporator fins and is thus cooled by the evaporator.

K1559-A

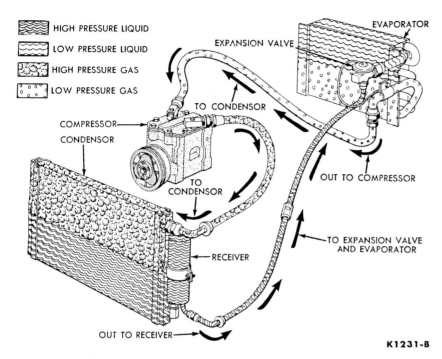

HIGH PRESSURE LIQUID
LOW PRESSURE LIQUID
HIGH PRESSURE GAS
LOW PRESSURE GAS

K1231-B

FIG. 2—Air Conditioning System

EXPANSION VALVE

The rate of refrigerant evaporation is controlled by an expansion valve (Fig. 2) which allows only enough refrigerant to flow into the evaporator to keep the evaporator operating efficiently, depending on its heat load.

The expansion valve consists of the valve and a temperature sensing capillary tube and bulb. The bulb is clamped to the outlet pipe of the evaporator. Thus the valve is controlled by evaporator outlet temperature.

The restricting effect of the expansion valve at the evaporator causes a low pressure on the low pressure side of the system of 12 to 50 psi, depending on the surrounding air temperature and compressor speed.

COMPRESSOR UNIT

The evaporated refrigerant leaving the evaporator (now in the form of a gas) at a pressure of 12 to 50 psi is pumped by the compressor, located on the engine (Fig. 3), into the top of the condenser, located in front of the radiator.

The compressor maintains a pressure on its high pressure side of from 80 to 300 psi, depending on the surrounding air temperature and compressor speed.

As the now heated and compressed refrigerant gas flows down

K1561-A

FIG. 3—Compressor Installed

through the condenser, it is cooled by air passing between the sections of the condenser. The cooled, compressed refrigerant gas condenses to liquid refrigerant which then flows into the receiver.

LIQUID SIGHT GLASS

A liquid sight glass is mounted in the high pressure refrigerant line between the receiver and the expansion valve (Fig. 2). The sight glass is used to check whether there is enough liquid refrigerant in the system.

MAGNETIC CLUTCH

It is necessary to control the amount of cooling that the system produces. To accomplish this, the

compressor is electrically cut in and out of operation by the use of a magnetic clutch pulley mounted on the compressor crankshaft (Fig. 2). The magnetic clutch is controlled by a thermostatic switch which has its temperature sensing tube inserted in the fins of the evaporator core.

THERMOSTATIC SWITCH

The thermostatic switch controls the operation of the compressor by controlling the compressor magnetic clutch. The temperature sensing tube of the switch is placed in contact with the evaporator fins. When the temperature of the evaporator becomes too cold, the thermostatic switch opens the magnetic clutch electrical circuit, disconnecting the compressor from the engine. When the temperature of the evaporator rises to the upper limit at which the thermostatic switch is set, the thermostatic switch closes and energizes the magnetic clutch. This connects the compressor to the engine, and cooling action begins again.

When the ignition switch is off or the cooling control thermostatic switch is in the off position, the magnetic clutch is not energized, and the compressor can not operate.

When the ignition switch is on (engine running), and the cooling control is in the cooling range, the magnetic clutch is energized, the compressor is connected to the engine and the cooling system is in operation.

The thermostatic switch may be adjusted to maintain an average evaporator temperature of from 30°-60°F. The thermostatic switch operating differential temperature at any one setting is 6°F.

SERVICE VALVES

The service valves on the compressor are used to test and service the cooling system (Figs. 4 and 5). The high pressure service valve, mounted at the outlet to the compressor, allows access to the high pressure side of the system for attaching a pressure gauge, or a servicing hose.

The low pressure valve, mounted at the inlet to the compressor, allows access to the low pressure side of the system for attaching a pressure gauge or a servicing hose.

Both service valves may be used to shut off the rest of the system from the compressor during compressor service.

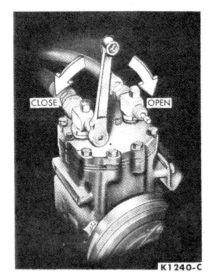

FIG. 4—Low Pressure Service Valve Gauge Port

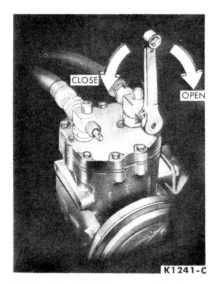

FIG. 5—High Pressure Service Valve Gauge Port

2 DIAGNOSIS AND TESTING

AIR CONDITIONING—DIAGNOSIS GUIDE

INSUFFICIENT OR NO COOLING	1. Inoperative magnetic clutch. 2. Inoperative blower, motor, or switch. 3. Obstructed air passages. 4. Complete loss of charge (No foam in sight glass at system start-up). 5. Partial loss of charge (Continuous foam in sight glass after start-up). 6. Service valves improperly set (should be maximum counterclockwise).	7. Compressor defective, or loose or broken compressor belt. 8. A/C thermostat defective. 9. Clutch lead disconnected or broken. 10. Expansion valve inoperative —stays open or closed. 11. Plugs left in compressor under service valve (both gauges indicate the same pressure). 12. Moisture in system.
NOISY COMPRESSOR	1. Loose, torn or misaligned belt. 2. Loose or slipping clutch. 3. Foreign material or damaged	parts in compressor. 4. Compressor loose on bracket.
COMPRESSOR VIBRATION	1. Broken or loose mounting bracket.	2. Loose clutch. 3. Loose belt.

TESTING

Obstructed air passages, broken belts, disconnected or broken wires, loose clutch, loose or broken mounting brackets may be determined by visual inspection of the parts.

CHECKING FOR LEAKS

Attach the manifold gauge set (Fig. 6). Leave both manifold gauge valves at the maximum clockwise position. Set both service valves at the center position. Both gauges should now show approximately 60 to 80 pounds pressure at 75°F. If very little or no pressure is indicated, leave the vacuum pump valve closed, open the Refrigerant-12 tank valve, and set the low pressure manifold gauge valve to the counterclockwise position. This opens the system to tank pressure.

Check all connections, and the compressor shaft seal for leaks, using a flame type leak detector (Fig. 7). Follow the directions with the leak detector. The smaller the flame the more sensitive it is to leaks. Therefore, to insure accurate leak indication keep the flame as small as possible. The copper element must be red hot. If it is burned away, replace the element. Hold the open end of the hose at each suspected leak point for two or three seconds (Fig. 8). The flame will normally be almost color-

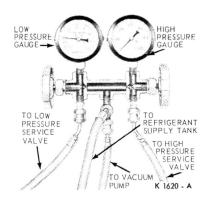

FIG. 6—Manifold Gauge Set

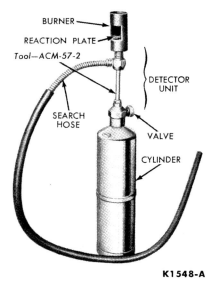

FIG. 7—Flame Type Leak Detector

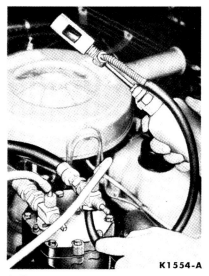

FIG. 8—Checking for Leaks

less. The slightest leak will be indicated by a bright color to the flame. Be sure to check the manifold gauge set and hoses for leaks as well as the rest of the system.

If the surrounding air is contaminated with refrigerant gas the leak detector will indicate this gas all the time. Good ventilation is necessary to prevent this situation. A fan, even in a well ventilated area, is very helpful in removing small traces of refrigerant vapor.

USE OF SIGHT GLASS

When observing the sight glass for foam, run the engine at 1500 rpm with the thermostatic switch control lever set for maximum cooling, and the blower on high. Foam in the sight glass indicates an undercharge of refrigerant. Check the system for leaks, repair if necessary and charge the system with the proper amount of Refrigerant-12.

No foam in the sight glass will indicate either a full charge or a complete loss of refrigerant. Clean the sight glass. If the system is fully charged, the sight glass will be perfectly clear. If the system is completely empty of refrigerant, the sight glass will look oily and will not be as clear as when refrigerant is flowing through it.

When the compressor is not operating and when the system is completely charged, an occasional large bubble of Refrigerant-12 vapor will normally be seen in the sight glass.

Under conditions of extremely high temperatures occasional foam or bubbles may appear.

CHECKING SYSTEM PRESSURES

The pressures developed on the high pressure and low pressure side of the compressor indicate whether the system is operating properly.

Attach the manifold gauge set (Fig. 6). It will not be necessary to attach the Refrigerant-12 tank unless refrigerant is to be added to the system. Set both manifold gauge valves at the maximum clockwise or closed position. Set both service valves at the center position.

Check the system pressures with the engine running at 1500 rpm, all controls set for maximum cooling, and the front of the car at least five feet from any wall.

The actual pressures indicated on the gauge will depend on the temperature of the surrounding air and the humidity. High air temperatures along with low humidity, will give higher system pressures. The lowest figures given are for an ambient (surrounding air) temperature of 75°F., 50% relative humidity.

The low pressure gauge should indicate a pressure of from 12 to 50 pounds. The high pressure gauge should indicate a pressure of six or seven times the low pressure or 80 to 300 pounds.

At idle speed and a surrounding air temperature of 100° to 110°F., the high pressure may go as high as 300 pounds or more. If it becomes necessary to operate the air conditioner under these conditions, keep the high pressure down with a fan directed at the condenser and radiator.

INTERPRETING ABNORMAL SYSTEM PRESSURES

Low Pressure Below Normal, High Pressure Normal

These pressures indicate a restriction between the receiver and the expansion valve or between the expansion valve and the low pressure service valve. If the low pressure is actually a vacuum, the expansion valve is probably closed tightly. Shut the system down and allow it to warm to room temperature. Start the engine and if the evaporator will now become cool, the expansion valve was frozen because of moisture in the system. Release the refrigerant, replace the dryer-receiver assembly, check for leaks, then evacuate and charge the system.

Whenever the system has been opened three times the receiver dryer should be replaced as a precaution against internal icing of the expansion valve.

Check the system between the receiver outlet and the low pressure service valve for restrictions, by feeling all of the connections and components. Any portion that is cold to the touch or that frosts up, with the pressures as indicated here, is restricting the refrigerant flow.

Low Pressure Above Normal, High Pressure Normal

Observe both pressure gauges. If the low pressure is above normal (12 to 50 pounds) and the high pressure is at or near normal (80 to 300 pounds), the expansion valve is not operating properly. This condition may cause the compressor to receive slugs of liquid and thus to be very noisy. Also, the suction side of the compressor and the crankcase and head will be colder than normal and will frost up.

The expansion valve will allow too much liquid refrigerant to flow to the compressor if it is defective or, if the temperature sensing element is not making close contact with the evaporator outlet pipe. Make sure that the element is securely clamped to the outlet pipe, and properly covered.

High Pressure Below Normal, Low Pressure Above Normal

If the two pressures are equal or within 30 pounds of each other, the compressor may be defective. Perform a compressor volumetric efficiency test. Repair or replace the compressor as needed.

High Pressure Above Normal

High compressor head pressures are caused by an overcharge of refrigerant, condenser air passages clogged, a restriction between the condenser inlet and the receiver, or high surrounding air temperatures. High head pressures are generally evidenced by a noisy compressor.

Discharge excess refrigerant until foam is seen in the sight glass (system operating at 1500 engine rpm), then add ½ pound of refrigerant.

THERMOSTATIC SWITCH TEST

The switch must be removed for this test. Move the switch arm to the coldest temperature setting by holding the arm against the stop nearest

or an ohmmeter connected to the switch leads to check whether or not the switch is closed. Release the switch arm. The switch should be open.

MAGNETIC CLUTCH

Disconnect the magnetic clutch wire at the bullet connector, and connect it to the negative lead of an ammeter. Connect the positive lead of the ammeter to the battery positive terminal. The magnetic clutch should pull in with a distinct click and the current reading on the ammeter should be to specification. Make certain that the brushes and brush slip rings are clean and free of oil or grease.

BLOWER MOTOR

Disconnect the blower motor wire at the bullet connector, and connect it to the negative lead of an ammeter. Connect the positive lead of the ammeter to the battery positive terminal. The motor should operate and the reading on the ammeter should be to specification.

EXPANSION VALVE

Remove the expansion valve from the evaporator. Connect the Refrigerant-12 supply hose to the expansion valve inlet with a suitable adapter. Open the refrigerant supply valve slightly. Refrigerant gas should come

out of the expansion valve outlet. If no gas comes out of the outlet, the temperature sensing element has lost

its charge and the expansion valve must be replaced.

COMPRESSOR VOLUMETRIC EFFICIENCY TEST

Malfunction of the compressor can be isolated by checking the compressor volumetric efficiency with a special tool. Make the test with the car in a clean dry atmosphere.

Run the engine at 1500 rpm with all controls at maximum cooling for at least 10 minutes. Adjust the engine idle with a tachometer to exactly 515 rpm with the compressor clutch engaged. Turn the engine off and set the cooling control to the OFF position. Isolate the compressor, then remove both high and low pressure service valve gauge port caps, allowing the gas in the compressor to escape.

Attach the special tool (calibrated orifice with gauge attached) to the high pressure service valve gauge port (Fig. 9). Start the engine. Engage the magnetic clutch for 15 second intervals, by moving the cooling control from the OFF position to the maximum cooling position, and observe the maximum gauge pressure at the end of each 15 second interval. **Be sure to allow the gauge pressure to drop to zero between the 15 second intervals.** Stop the engine.

A good compressor will bring the pressure to 200 psi in 15 seconds. If the pressure does not come up to 200 psi, in 15 seconds, clean the compressor intake screen. If the intake screen is clean, remove and inspect the valve plate. Most of the failures to come up to the 200 psi specification will be caused by small foreign particles under the valve plate leaves or a defective valve plate. Clean the valve plate and assemble it to the compressor using new gaskets. If this does not effect a cure, replace the valve plate or the compressor as required.

If no further work is to be done on the system after making the volumetric efficiency test, disconnect the orifice tool and gauge, evacuate the compressor and connect it back into the system.

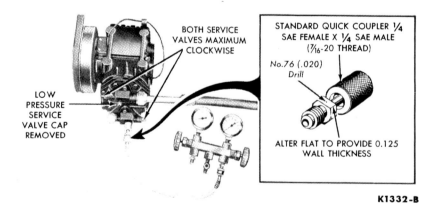

FIG. 9—Voltmetric Efficiency Test

to the vacuum actuator. At room temperature the switch should be closed. Use a self powered test light

3 COMMON ADJUSTMENTS AND REPAIRS

SAFETY PRECAUTIONS

The refrigerant used in the air

conditioner system is Refrigerant-12. Refrigerant-12 is nonexplosive, non-

inflammable, noncorrosive, has practically no odor, and is heavier than air. Although it is classified as a safe refrigerant, certain precautions must be observed to protect the parts involved and the person who is working on the unit. **Use only Refrigerant-12.**

Liquid Refrigerant-12, at normal atmospheric pressure and temperatures, evaporates so quickly that it tends to freeze anything that it contacts. For this reason, extreme care must be taken to prevent any liquid refrigerant from coming in contact with the skin and especially the eyes.

Refrigerant-12 is readily absorbed by most types of oil. It is therefore recommended that a bottle of sterile mineral oil and a quantity of weak boric acid solution be kept nearby when servicing the air conditioning system. Should any liquid refrigerant get into the eyes, use a few drops of mineral oil to wash them out, then wash the eyes clean with the weak boric acid solution. Seek a doctor's aid immediately even though irritation may have ceased.

Always wear safety goggles when servicing any part of the refrigerating system.

The Refrigerant-12 in the system is always under pressure. Because the system is tightly sealed, heat applied to any part would cause this pressure to build up excessively.

To avoid a dangerous explosion, never weld, use a blow torch, solder, steam clean, bake body finishes, or use any excessive amount of heat on, or in the immediate area of, any part of the air cooling system or refrigerant supply tank, while they are closed to the atmosphere whether filled with refrigerant or not.

The liquid refrigerant evaporates so rapidly that the resulting refrigerant gas will displace the air surrounding the area where the refrigerant is released. To prevent possible suffocation in enclosed areas, always discharge the refrigerant from an air cooling system into the garage exhaust collector. Always maintain good ventilation surrounding the work area. **If the car is to be undercoated, make certain that the undercoating does not plug the evaporator drain tubes.**

Although Refrigerant-12 gas, under normal conditions, is non-poisonous, the discharge of refrigerant gas near an open flame can produce a very poisonous gas. This gas will also attack all bright metal surfaces. This poisonous gas is generated in small quantities when the flame-type leak detector is used. Avoid inhaling the

fumes from the leak detector. **Make certain that Refrigerant-12 is both stored and installed in accordance with all state and local ordinances.**

When admitting Refrigerant-12 gas into the cooling unit, always keep the tank in an upright position. If the tank is on its side or upside down, liquid Refrigerant-12 will enter the system and damage the compressor. **In surrounding air temperatures above 90°F., prolonged engine idle will result in excessively high compressor pressures.**

DISCHARGING THE SYSTEM

Discharge the refrigerant from the system before replacing any part of the system, except the compressor.

To discharge the system, connect the manifold gauge set to the system (Fig. 10). Do not connect the manifold center connection hoses to the

sor will be forced out along with it.

EVACUATING THE SYSTEM

Attach the manifold gauge set, a tank of Refrigerant-12 and a vacuum pump to the system (Fig. 10). Make certain that the Refrigerant-12 tank valve is tightly closed. Set both service valves to the mid-position. Open both manifold valves. Release any pressure in the system. Open the vacuum pump valve and run the pump until the low pressure gauge reads at least 25 inches, and as close to 30 inches of vacuum as possible. Continue vacuum pump operation for 20 to 30 minutes to boil any moisture out of the system. Close the pump valve. Turn off the pump.

MAKING A PARTIAL CHARGE

Attach the manifold gauge set

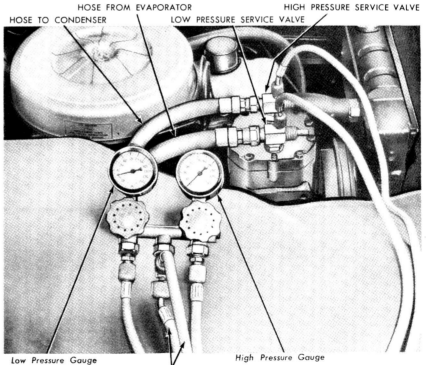

HOSE FROM EVAPORATOR

HOSE TO CONDENSER LOW PRESSURE SERVICE VALVE

HIGH PRESSURE SERVICE VALVE

Low Pressure Gauge   *High Pressure Gauge*

TO REFRIGERANT SUPPLY AND VACUUM PUMP

K1557-A

FIG. 10—Charging the Air Conditioning System

Refrigerant-12 tank, or vacuum pump. Place the open end of these hoses in a garage exhaust outlet. Set the high pressure manifold gauge valve at the maximum counterclockwise or open position. Open the high pressure service valve a slight amount (Fig. 5), and allow the refrigerant to discharge slowly from the system.

Do not allow the refrigerant to rush out, as the oil in the compres-

(Fig. 10). Open both manifold valves. Close the vacuum pump valve. Open the Refrigerant-12 tank valve. Purge the air from the high pressure hose by loosening the high pressure hose at the service valve, for a few seconds. Tighten the connection and set the high pressure manifold gauge valve at the maximum clockwise position. Loosen the low pressure gauge hose slightly at the low pressure service valve, for a few seconds, to purge the air from the hose. Tighten the connection. Set both service valves at the center position (Fig. 10).

Run the engine at 1500 rpm with all controls at the maximum cold position. Charge the system until all foam disappears from the sight glass, and then add ¼ pound of Refrigerant-12. Shut the Refrigerant-12 tank valve.

It may be necessary to place the Refrigerant-12 tank in a container of hot water at about 150°F. to force the gas from the tank during charging.

Never heat the Refrigerant-12 tank with a torch. A dangerous explosion may result.

Set both service valves at the maximum counterclockwise position. Remove the gauge set, and cap the service valve gauge ports and valve stems.

MAKING A COMPLETE CHARGE

Check for leaks first, release the pressure, then evacuate the system. Leave both service valves at the mid-position and the vacuum pump valve closed. Leave the low pressure manifold gauge valve at the maximum counterclockwise or open position. Set the high pressure manifold gauge valve at the maximum clockwise or closed position. Set all controls to the maximum cold position.

Open the Refrigerant-12 tank valve. Run the engine at 1500 rpm. Charge the system until the sight glass is clear of foam, then add an additional ¼ pound of refrigerant.

During the charging, the high pressure may build up to an excessive value. This can be caused by an overcharge of refrigerant, or an overheated engine, in combination with high surrounding temperatures. Never allow the high pressure to exceed 240 pounds while charging. Stop the engine, determine the cause, and correct it.

After the *proper charge* has been made, close the Refrigerant-12 tank valve, and check the system pressures for proper operation. Set both service valves at the maximum counterclockwise position. Remove the gauge set, and cap the service valve gauge ports and valve stems.

CHARGING FROM SMALL CONTAINERS

Refrigerant-12 is available in one-pound cans. A scale is not necessary if these small containers are used instead of a tank.

Attach the hose, that would normally attach to the large tank (Fig. 10), to the special valve that is provided for the small cans. Close the valve (maximum clockwise position) and follow the procedure for leak testing, evacuating and charging the system as previously given.

For charging, attach a one-pound can of Refrigerant-12 to the special valve, and open the valve. Keep the can in an upright position. When the can is empty (no frost showing), close the valve, remove the empty can, attach a new one, and open the valve again.

Charge the system until the sight glass clears of foam then add an additional ¼ pound of refrigerant. Estimate the ¼ pound weight by observing the frost line on the one-pound can.

Check the system pressures, set both service valves at the maximum counterclockwise position. **Remove the gauge set, and cap the service valve gauge ports and valve stems.**

COMPRESSOR OIL LEVEL CHECK

Under normal conditions when the air cooling system is operating satisfactorily the compressor oil level need not be checked. There is no place for the oil to go except inside the sealed system. When the car is first started some of the oil will be pumped into the rest of the system. After 15 minutes of operation, most of the oil is returned to the compressor crankcase.

Check the compressor oil level only if a portion of the refrigerant system is being replaced or if there was a leak in the system and the refrigerant is being replaced.

Check the oil after the system has been charged and has been operating at an engine speed of 1500 rpm for 15 minutes in 60°F. surrounding air temperature or above. Turn off the engine, and isolate the compressor. Remove the oil filler plug from the compressor, insert a flattened ⅛-inch diameter rod (Fig. 11), in the oil filler hole until it bottoms. The rod should show ⅞ inch of oil on Tecumseh compressors and ¾ inch of oil on York compressors. This is equivalent to 11 ounces on Tecumseh and 10 ounces on York. It may be necessary to rotate the compressor crankshaft slightly (by hand) so that the dip rod will clear the crank-

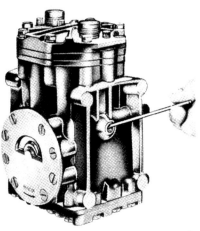

K1544-A

FIG. 11—Oil Level Check

shaft. If additional oil is needed in the compressor, add Suniso 5 or Capella E refrigerator compressor oil, or equivalent.

If more than ⅞ inch of oil is indicated, as might happen if a new compressor is installed and oil already in the system is pumped back to the compressor, draw out the excess oil until the proper quantity is indicated.

Replace the oil filler plug, then evacuate and connect the compressor back into the system. Be sure to check the compressor filler opening for leaks.

ISOLATING THE COMPRESSOR

This procedure is used when checking the compressor oil level and when it is desired to replace the compressor without losing the refrigerant charge.

To isolate the compressor from the system, turn both the high and the low pressure service valves to the extreme clockwise position. Loosen the cap on the high pressure service valve gauge port, and allow the gas to escape until the compressor is relieved of refrigerant pressure.

Loosen the cap a small amount only, and do not remove it until the pressure is completely relieved.

To connect the compressor back into the system, evacuate the compressor at the high pressure service valve gauge port, close the vacuum pump valve, turn both service valves to the maximum counterclockwise position, and cap the high pressure service valve gauge port and service valve stems.

4 REMOVAL AND INSTALLATION

EVAPORATOR

REMOVAL

1. Discharge the refrigerant from the system.
2. Disconnect the two wires from the unit, demount the evaporator assembly, and set the unit on the car floor.
3. Disconnect the refrigerant hoses. On some models it may be necessary to remove the assembly from the car before going further.
4. Remove the front panel, covers and the expansion valve from the unit. (See Expansion Valve Removal and Installation.)
5. Remove the thermostatic switch temperature sensing tube from between the evaporator fins, remove the evaporator-to-base mounting screws and remove the evaporator from the base.

INSTALLATION

1. Attach the old expansion valve to the new evaporator and leak test the connection by capping the outlet of the evaporator and using a suitable reducing connector from the valve inlet to a tank of Refrigerant-12.
2. Position the evaporator on the base and install the two evaporator-to-base mounting screws.
3. Push the thermostatic switch sensing tube into the same relative position at about the center of the evaporator, but if the same core is being used position the sensing tube between the next two fins for good temperature conduction. Install the covers and front panel.
4. Attach the refrigerant lines and leak test the connections.
5. Mount the assembly, connect the two wires, leak test, evacuate and charge the system.

CONDENSER

1. Discharge the refrigerant from the system.
2. Remove the front grille to radiator support bracket, and the hood latch.
3. Disconnect the refrigerant lines from the condenser and receiver. Remove the condenser mounting screws and remove the condenser receiver assembly. On the Mustang a special arrangement is used where the radiator retaining studs are part of the condenser.
4. Position and mount the new condenser, remove the protective

plugs, attach the refrigerant lines and install the grille to radiator support bracket and hood latch.
5. Check for leaks, evacuate and charge the system.

COMPRESSOR

REMOVAL

1. Isolate the compressor (see Common Adjustments and Repairs in this part). Disconnect the two service valves and hoses from the compressor (Fig. 12). Energize the clutch and loosen and remove the clutch mounting bolt.
2. Install a ⅝-11 bolt in the clutch drive shaft hole. With the clutch still energized, tighten the bolt to loosen the clutch from the shaft. Disconnect

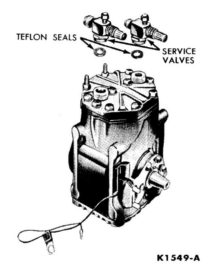

FIG. 12—Compressor—Service Valves Removed

the clutch wire at the bullet connector.
3. Loosen the belt, remove the belt and the clutch, and then remove the mounting bolts and the compressor.
4. With the compressor on the work bench, remove the key from the shaft.

INSTALLATION

Before installing the compressor, see Cleaning and Inspection in this part.
1. Mount the clutch on the shaft and install the mounting screw and washer finger-tight. Place the compressor on the mounting bracket and install the four mounting bolts.
2. Connect the clutch wire, ener-

gize the clutch and torque the clutch mounting bolt to specification. **If the new compressor was shipped with a bolt and washer in the end of the crankshaft, remove and discard the bolt and use a bolt with a nylon insert in it.** Install and adjust the drive belt.
3. Making sure that the protective rubber plugs have been removed, install the service valves on the compressor using new seals. Tighten the service valve nuts to specification. **Do not over-tighten the nuts.** The ROTO-LOK service valves can be rotated slightly on their seat without breaking the high pressure seal. This is not an indication of a loose valve. Leak test the compressor, then evacuate it and connect it back into the system.
4. Check the oil level in the compressor and add or remove oil if necessary.

COMPRESSOR COMPONENTS

All compressor removal and installation operations, except belt replacement, can be performed only after the unit has been isolated from the rest of the system. (See Common Adjustments and Repairs in this part.)

VALVE PLATE

Removal

1. Isolate the compressor and disconnect the service valves. Remove the 12 head bolts.
2. Remove the cylinder head and valve plate from the top of the compressor body (Fig. 13). Do not tap or hit the head with any hard tool, as damage could result (York compressors are made of aluminum).
3. Remove and discard all gaskets, and be sure to clean gasket shreds from all gasket surfaces. Examine the cylinders and top of the pistons, particularly in case of valve breakage. If there are score marks, replace the compressor assembly.
4. If the cylinders and pistons are in good condition, check the valve plate and valve reeds for damage. If the valve assembly is in good condition, it can be used again. If the valve plate is damaged, install the entire replacement kit which includes the valve plate, valve reeds, and the two gaskets (Fig. 13).
5. When the valve plate assembly is re-used, wash it in clean solvent and dry in dry air. Check the oil for dirt. If the system is not clean, replace the oil.

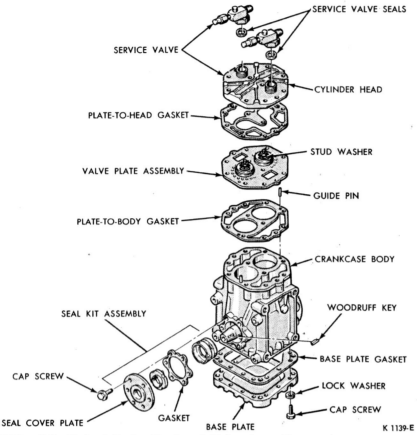

FIG. 13—York Cylinder Head and Valve Assembly

Installation

1. Starting with the valve plate gasket, assemble the parts in the order shown in Fig. 13. Insert the cylinder head bolts carefully to avoid damaging the gaskets. Before assembly apply a film of new refrigeration oil to both sides of both gaskets.

2. Tighten all bolts finger-tight, then torque the bolts ¼ turn at a time to specification. Then tighten the remaining bolts in a sequence so that those diagonally opposite are evenly tightened to the required torque.

3. Connect the compressor into the system. Check the oil level in the compressor, and add or remove oil if necessary. (See Cleaning and Inspection.)

CRANKSHAFT SEAL

REMOVAL

1. Isolate the compressor, loosen and remove the belt.

2. Remove the clutch and remove the Woodruff key (on some six cylinder engine installations it will be necessary to loosen the compressor mounting bolts and slide the compressor back slightly).

3. Carefully remove all accumulated dirt and foreign material from the seal plate and surrounding area of the compressor, and position a small drain pan beneath the seal plate.

4. Remove the seal plate bolts, and remove the plate and gasket. Do not mar the sealing surfaces, or the polished shaft surface.

5. Remove the carbon seal ring and seal housing assembly from the crankshaft. A disassembled view of the crankshaft seal assembly is included in Fig. 13.

6. Clean all old gasket material from the seal plate and the compressor. Make certain that the shaft, the seal plate and the compressor gasket surfaces are completely clean before installing the new seal.

INSTALLATION

1. Lubricate the new shaft seal parts in clean compressor oil, and position the seal assembly on the crankshaft, with the carbon ring toward the seal plate.

2. Position the new gasket on the compressor, center the crankshaft in the seal plate and install the seal plate.

3. Torque the bolts to specification.

4. Make certain that there are no burrs or dirt on the compressor shaft. Then install the key, and the clutch.

5. If the compressor was moved, reposition it and tighten the mounting bolts, then install the belt and adjust the tension.

6. Check the oil level (see Common Adjustments and Repairs).

EXPANSION VALVE

REMOVAL

1. Discharge the refrigerant from the system. Disconnect the two wires from the unit, demount the evaporator assembly, and set the unit on the car floor. Disconnect the refrigerant hoses. On some models, it may be necessary to remove the assembly from the car before going further.

2. Remove the expansion valve protection shield.

3. Carefully slit the insulation covering the temperature bulb and remove the temperature bulb clamp. Then disconnect the valve from the inlet pipe and remove the valve.

INSTALLATION

1. Connect the new valve to the inlet pipe, and leak test the connection by capping the outlet end of the evaporator and using a suitable reducing connector from the valve inlet to a tank of Refrigerant-12. Position the temperature bulb to the outlet pipe, and install the bulb clamp. Be sure that the bulb, pipe, and clamp are clean and that the clamp is tight. Go over these parts with fine sandpaper to assure this.

2. Wrap the insulating material around the temperature bulb, pipe, and valve, and position the rubber seal over the pipe connections.

3. Install the expansion valve protection shield.

4. Connect the refrigerant hoses and leak test the connections.

5. Mount the assembly, connect the wires, leak test, evacuate and charge the system.

THERMOSTATIC SWITCH

The thermostatic switch is mounted to the air conditioner front register. Remove the three register to evaporator case screws. Pull the register from the case and pull the sensing tube from the evaporator fins. Remove the wires and the knob from the switch and remove the switch.

AIR CONDITIONER BLOWER MOTOR

REMOVAL

1. Disconnect the battery ground cable.

2. Remove one screw and the shield from the right hand lower side of the evaporator case.

3. Remove the cover plate mounting screw and the cover plate at the left hand side of the evaporator case.

4. Remove the mounting screws from the register panel, and remove the panel from the evaporator case. **Care should be taken not to damage the temperature sensing tube when drawing it from between the fins of the evaporator.**

5. Remove the bolts which retain the evaporator case to the lower instrument panel, and lower the evaporator to the floor.

6. Remove the mounting bracket from each side of the evaporator, and remove the ground wire from the left hand side.

7. Remove the clips which connect the upper and lower halves of the evaporator case, and lift off the upper half of the case.

8. Disconnect the blower wire at the connector.

9. Remove the blower retaining screws and remove the blower motor assembly from the evaporator case. (It will be necessary to lift the evaporator core slightly to allow removal of the blower motor wire.)

10. Remove the blower cages, mounting bracket, and the insulator pad.

INSTALLATION

1. Install the blower cages, mounting bracket and insulator pad.

2. Lift the evaporator core slightly to allow positioning of the blower motor wire, and position the blower in the evaporator case.

3. Connect the blower wire at the connector.

4. Position the two halves of the evaporator case, and install the connecting clips.

5. Install the mounting bracket to each side of the evaporator, and install the ground wire on the left hand side.

6. Position the evaporator to the lower instrument panel and install the mounting bolts.

7. Position the register panel near the evaporator and insert the sensing tube between the fins of the evaporator. **For best results the sensing tube should be inserted in between the next two fins from where it was originally withdrawn. This assures a more positive contact and more exact transfer of temperature changes. Install the mounting screws.**

8. Position the cover plate to the left hand side of the evaporator case and install the mounting screw.

9. Position the shield to the lower right hand side of the evaporator case and install the retaining screw.

10. Connect the battery ground cable.

It may be necessary in the case of console equipped cars to remove the evaporator assembly from the car in order to remove the blower motor.

BELT

8-CYLINDER

1. Loosen the idler pulley, then remove the belt.

2. Place the new belt in position, and slide the compressor toward the outside of the car and carefully align the belt. Then tighten the four mounting bolts.

3. Adjust the belt tension to specification, using the idler pulley.

6-CYLINDER

1. Loosen the alternator mounting and adjusting screws, and swing the alternator toward the center of the car until the old belt can be removed.

2. Install the new belt and adjust to specification.

3. Tighten the alternator mounting and adjusting screws. Some engines have a means of adjusting the belt with a vertical lock screw.

CLUTCH

1. Loosen the belt.

2. Energize the clutch and loosen and remove the clutch mounting bolt.

3. Install a ⅝-11 bolt in the clutch drive shaft hole. With the clutch still energized, tighten the bolt to loosen the clutch from the shaft, then remove the magnetic clutch. For clearance on some installations, it is necessary to loosen the compressor mounting bolts and slide the compressor back slightly.

4. Install the clutch, the clutch mounting bolt, and the washer.

5. Energize the clutch, and torque the bolt to specification.

5 CLEANING AND INSPECTION

COMPRESSOR

On compressor clutch installations, carefully remove any burrs or dirt that may be on the compressor shaft. The shaft must be dry and brightly polished. Then install the key in the shaft.

When the compressor is disassembled, completely clean all surfaces of gasket shreds and foreign objects.

If the compressor shaft seal is being replaced, inspect the compressor internally and clean out dirt or chips as required.

When installing a new control assembly or parts, inspect for dirt and foreign objects.

PART 16-3

AIR CONDITIONING—SELECTAIRE

Section	Page
1 Description and Operation	16-20
Comet, Falcon and Fairlane SelectAire Air Conditioning and Heating System	16-20
Controls	16-21
Air Velocity	16-21
Discharge Air	16-22
A/C-Heater Electrical System	16-22
2 Removal and Installation	16-24

Section	Page
Heater Air Conditioner Assembly	16-24
Evaporator Core	16-24
Heater Core	16-24
Expansion Valve	16-24
Blower Motor Switch	16-25
Blower Motor	16-25
A/C-Heat Door Vacuum Actuator	16-25
Heat-Defrost Door Vacuum Actuator	16-25

1 DESCRIPTION AND OPERATION

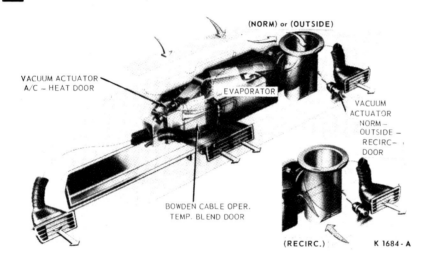

FIG. 1—Comet, Falcon and Fairlane A/C-Heater Air Flow—NORM—OUTSIDE—RECIRC

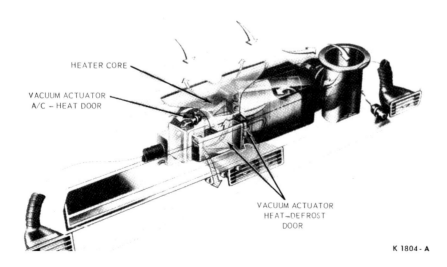

FIG. 2—Comet, Falcon and Fairlane A/C-Heater Air Flow—HEAT

COMET, FALCON AND FAIRLANE SELECTAIRE AIR CONDITIONING AND HEATING SYSTEM

The SelectAire air conditioning and heating assembly is contained entirely in one case under the instrument panel.

Outside air is drawn in from the cowl through the outside air door into the right vent duct, into the blower scroll, forced through the evaporator core, through and/or around the heater core then mixed and discharged through either the A/C air duct or through the heat-defrost plenum air outlet, depending on the position on the control setting (Figs. 1 and 2).

The temperature door is located to the left of the evaporator core and to the rear of the heater core in the left side of the case.

The A/C-heat door is located in the left rear corner of the case, and the heat-defrost door is in the plenum chamber attached to the rear face of the case assembly.

A single defroster nozzle leading to two openings in the instrument panel is attached directly in the plenum chamber with a clip. The Comet defroster nozzle is unique in design; the Fairlane and Falcon are the same.

The A/C registers located in the lower instrument panel are located; one to the far left; one to the far right; and a double register in the center.

The Fairlane and Falcon registers are *barrel type registers that can be* moved up and down and the vertical vanes are positioned by moving a

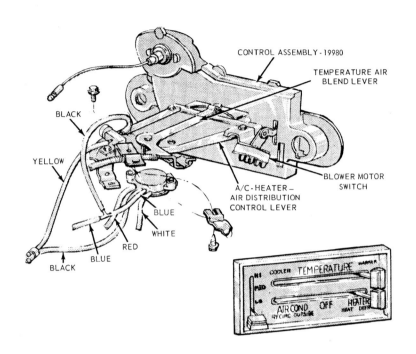

FIG. 3—Comet A/C-Heater Control Assembly

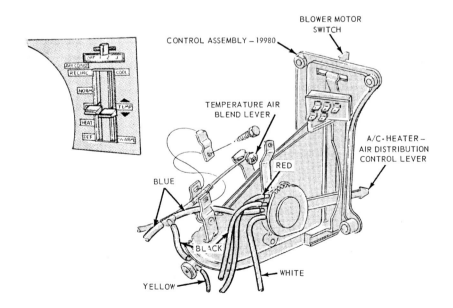

FIG. 4—Falcon A/C-Heater Controls

horizontal wheel within the assembly. The Comet registers are positioned by moving a swivel knob or lever in the center of the registers that control both horizontal and vertical vanes in the assembly.

The blower motor and wheel assembly is located in the blower scroll immediately forward of the right vent duct assembly. The evaporator core is located in a diagonal position in the center of the case; and the heater core in a diagonal position in the left side of the case.

Vacuum actuators that operate the normal-recirc door in the right vent, and the A/C-heat door, are controlled by a vacuum selector on the control head assembly.

CONTROLS

The air temperature is controlled by the location of the temperature air blend lever in the control assembly (Figs. 3, 4 and 5). As the lever is moved from **cool** to **warm**, a Bowden cable moves the (temperature blend door) from maximum cooling position to minimum cooling position. A vacuum switch on the control assembly is actuated to supply vacuum to close the water valve when the temperature lever is in the maximum cool setting and the A/C-heater, air distribution control lever is in either A/C position. See the A/C-Heater Control Setting Chart, Table 1, and the Vacuum Schematic in Fig. 6.

Air distribution is controlled by the A/C-heater lever in the control panel assembly and the blower switch setting. The lever actuates a vacuum selector switch on the control assembly which in turn operates vacuum actuators at the outside or recirculating air door in the right vent duct; the A/C-heat air-blend door in the case, and the heat-defrost door in the plenum chamber.

The blower switch must be on to engage the compressor clutch for air conditioning. With the A/C-heater control lever in either air conditioning position, the air conditioner heat door is in the air conditioning position (vacuum) and pressure is applied to the compressor clutch switch to close the circuit and engage the clutch.

AIR VELOCITY

Three speeds are provided for the blower fan with a four position switch in the control assembly and a resistor assembly located in the blow-

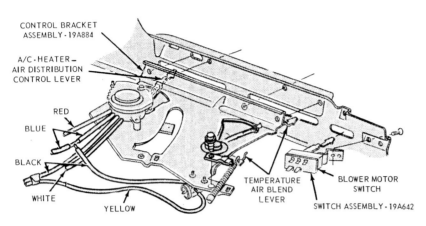

CONTROL BRACKET
ASSEMBLY - 19A884

A/C - HEATER —
AIR DISTRIBUTION
CONTROL LEVER

RED

BLUE

BLACK

WHITE

YELLOW

TEMPERATURE
AIR BLEND
LEVER

BLOWER MOTOR
SWITCH

SWITCH ASSEMBLY - 19A642

K 1851 - A

FIG. 5—Fairlane A/C-Heater Controls

over the tunnel or to the windshield defroster nozzle, depending on the location on the heat-defrost door within the plenum.

A/C—HEATER ELECTRICAL SYSTEM

The A/C heater electrical circuit is protected by a 25 ampere circuit breaker and consists of the blower switch on the control assembly, blower motor, blower motor resistor, A/C thermostatic switch, clutch switch and compressor clutch solenoid (Fig. 7).

er housing. The resistor in the blower motor circuit controls the low and medium blower motor speeds.

DISCHARGE AIR

An A/C floor cooler tube located at the lower rear corner of the duct is used to discharge cold air to the center of the left front floor area. A deflector on the tube can be positioned manually for driver comfort.

The two outboard registers can be closed by a push-pull knob and lever that actuates the balanced door behind the registers. On the Fairlane and Falcon the knob is located below the registers on the lower lip of the instrument panel. The Comet control knob is located in the instrument panel at the inboard side of each outboard register.

The plenum chamber located on the left rear face of the case assembly distributes heated air to the floor

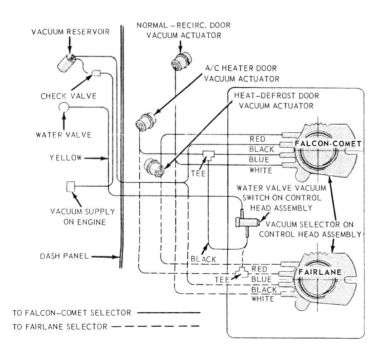

VACUUM RESERVOIR

NORMAL — RECIRC. DOOR
VACUUM ACTUATOR

A/C HEATER DOOR
VACUUM ACTUATOR

CHECK VALVE

HEAT–DEFROST DOOR
VACUUM ACTUATOR

WATER VALVE

RED
BLACK
BLUE
WHITE

FALCON-COMET

YELLOW

TEE

WATER VALVE VACUUM
SWITCH ON CONTROL
HEAD ASSEMBLY

VACUUM SUPPLY
ON ENGINE

VACUUM SELECTOR ON
CONTROL HEAD ASSEMBLY

DASH PANEL

BLACK

TEE

RED
BLUE
BLACK
WHITE

FAIRLANE

TO FALCON-COMET SELECTOR ————

TO FAIRLANE SELECTOR — — — — —

K 1852 - A

FIG. 6—Comet, Falcon and Fairlane A/C-Heater Vacuum Schematic

TABLE 1—SELECTAIRE CONTROL SETTING CHART

		FUNCTIONAL CONTROL LEVER POSITION				
		A/C		OFF	HEAT	
		RECIRC	NORM OR OUTSIDE		NORM OR HEAT	DEF OR DEFROST
AIR DOOR	OUTSIDE RECIRC	OPEN TO RECIRC V	OPEN TO OUTSIDE NV	OPEN TO RECIRC V	OPEN TO OUTSIDE NV	
	A/C HEAT	A/C POSITION V		HEAT POSITION NV	NV	
	HEAT DEFROST	NV				DEFROST POSITION V
CLUTCH SWITCH		ON SEE WIRING DIAGRAM		OFF		
BLOWER SWITCH		ON-L-M-H	ON-L-M-H OFF-RAM AIR	OFF ON-RECIRC CONDITION	ON-L-M-H OFF-RAM AIR	
WATER VALVE VACUUM SWITCH	COOL	OPEN		VACUUM SWITCH BY-PASSED BY SELECTOR SWITCH CIRCUIT NV		
	MOD	CLOSED				
	WARM					
WATER VALVE	COOL	CLOSED	V	SELECTOR SWITCH CIRCUIT OPENS WATER VALVE BY CLOSING OFF VACUUM NV		
	MOD	OPEN	NV			
	WARM					
TEMP DOOR	COOL	ALL COLD AIR BY-PASSES HEATER CORE		OUTSIDE AIR BY-PASSES HEATER CORE		
	MOD	COLD AIR PASSES THRU AND AROUND HEATER CORE THEN MIXED		OUTSIDE AIR PASSES THRU AND AROUND HEATER CORE THEN MIXED		
	WARM	ALL COLD AIR PASSES THRU HEATER CORE		OUTSIDE AIR PASSES THRU HEATER CORE		

L—LOW   V—VACUUM
M—MEDIUM   NV—NO VACUUM
H—HIGH   MOD—MODULATED

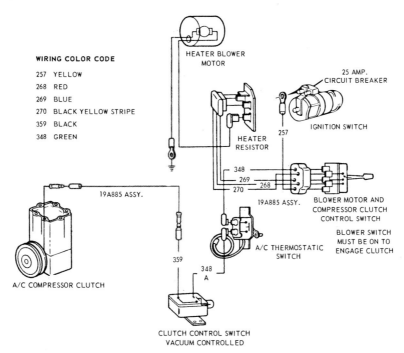

WIRING COLOR CODE

257 YELLOW
268 RED
269 BLUE
270 BLACK YELLOW STRIPE
359 BLACK
348 GREEN

K 1853- A

FIG. 7—Comet, Falcon and Fairlane A/C-Heater Wiring Diagram

2 REMOVAL AND INSTALLATION

HEATER AIR CONDITIONER ASSEMBLY

REMOVAL

1. Partially drain the cooling system.

2. Discharge the air conditioning system.

3. Disconnect the heater hoses at the dash and remove the weather seal pads.

4. Unwrap the insulation from the sensing bulb and unclamp the bulb. Disconnect the receiver to evaporator hose at the dash panel. Leave the expansion valve attached to the hose. Remove the weatherseal at the dash.

5. Disconnect the evaporator to compressor hose at the dash panel.

6. Remove the glove box liner.

7. Remove the right hand fresh air duct from the cowl upper panel. Remove the vacuum line from the vacuum actuator and remove the actuator.

8. Disconnect the wires from the resistor block and thermostatic switch.

9. Disconnect the three plenum to instrument panel air ducts from the plenum and position them out of the way.

10. Disconnect the vacuum line from the heat-defrost door vacuum actuator.

11. Remove the defroster plenum and vacuum actuator as an assembly.

12. Remove the instrument panel upper and lower support and remove the speaker grille.

13. Remove the speaker retaining screws and position the speaker out of the way.

14. Remove the defroster nozzle.

15. Remove the evaporator case drain hose clamp and drain hose at the dash.

16. Cover the floor mats and remove the 4 nuts retaining the heater air conditioner assembly to the dash. Pull the assembly from the dash and rest it on the car floor.

17. Disconnect the wire from the thermostatic switch.

18. Disconnect the temperature-blend door actuating Bowden cable and the vacuum line at the A/C-heat door vacuum actuator.

19. Position the front seat all the way back, turn the bottom of the assembly toward the rear of the car and remove the assembly from the car.

INSTALLATION

1. Position the assembly under the instrument panel resting it on the floor.

2. Connect the thermostatic switch wire (left top of plenum).

3. Connect and adjust (as shown in Fig. 8), the temperature-blend door Bowden cable.

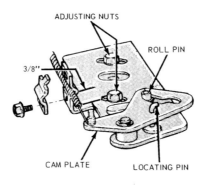

ADJUSTING NUTS

ROLL PIN

3/8"

CAM PLATE   LOCATING PIN

K 1805 - A

FIG. 8—Temperature-Blend Door Bowden Cable Adjustment—Except Mustang

4. Connect the vacuum line at the A/C-heat door vacuum actuator.

5. Position the heater-air conditioner assembly to the dash and install the mounting nuts.

6. Install the defroster nozzle, the speaker and speaker grille.

7. Install the instrument panel upper and lower supports.

8. Install the defroster plenum and connect the red vacuum line to the heat-defrost door vacuum actuator.

9. Connect the wires to the resistor block and thermostatic switch.

10. Install the right hand fresh air duct and the vacuum actuator and install the white vacuum line to the actuator.

11. Install the glove box liner and install the 3 plenum to instrument panel air ducts.

12. Position the rubber seals and connect the heater hoses.

13. Install the evaporator case drain hose.

14. Connect the compressor-to-evaporator hose at the dash and in-

stall the expansion valve temperature sensing bulb.

15. Connect the receiver to evaporator hose at the dash and install the seal and temperature bulb insulation.

16. Fill the cooling system.

17. Leak test, evacuate and charge the air conditioning system.

18. Check the operation of the system.

EVAPORATOR CORE

1. Remove the heater air-conditioner assembly (in this section), and place it on a bench.

2. Remove the thermostatic switch from the evaporator.

3. Separate the heater housing from the plenum.

4. Remove the evaporator core from the housing.

5. Transfer the mounting bracket and rubber pad to the new evaporator.

6. Install the evaporator in the plenum.

7. Position the plenum to the housing and install the mounting screws, clips, resistor block wires and seal and retainer.

8. Install the heater-air conditioner assembly (in this section).

HEATER CORE

1. Remove the heater air conditioner assembly (in this section), and place it on a bench.

2. Separate the heater housing from the plenum.

3. Slip the heater core out of the plenum.

4. Transfer the heater core seal from the old core to the new core.

5. Slip the new core with seal into the plenum.

6. Install the plenum to the heater housing. Connect the wires at the resistor block, and install the seal and retainer at the evaporator tubes.

7. Install the heater-air conditioner assembly (in this section).

EXPANSION VALVE

1. Discharge the air conditioning system.

2. Remove the insulation and remove the sensing bulb from the compressor to evaporator line.

3. Disconnect the expansion valve from the evaporator and disconnect the valve from the valve to condenser line.

4. Position and connect the new valve to the evaporator.

5. Connect the condenser to valve line to the valve.

6. Install and insulate the sensing bulb.

7. Leak test, evacuate and charge the system. Check the system operation.

BLOWER MOTOR SWITCH

1. Remove the air conditioning plenum to center register air duct. Disconnect the plenum to right register air duct at the plenum and position it out of the way.

2. Remove the switch knob. Remove the switch mounting screw retaining the switch to the control assembly and lower the switch.

3. Disconnect the wires from the switch and remove the switch.

4. Connect the wires to the new switch and install it in the control assembly.

5. Install the two air ducts.

6. Install the switch knob and check the operation of the switch.

BLOWER MOTOR

1. Remove the glove box.

2. Remove the right hand fresh air duct and vacuum actuator assembly. Disconnect the vacuum line from the actuator and position it out of the way.

3. Disconnect the plug from the resistor block and remove the resistor block.

4. Remove the blower motor cover and remove the motor and blower wheel.

5. Remove the blower wheel and install it on the new motor.

6. Install the motor and wheel and ground wire in the heater case. Install the blower cover.

7. Install the resistor block to the plenum and connect the wires. Check the blower operation.

8. Install the fresh air duct and vacuum actuator.

9. Install the glove box.

A/C—HEAT DOOR VACUUM ACTUATOR

1. Remove the glove box liner.

2. Remove the vacuum line at the actuator, and remove the defroster plenum chamber.

3. Remove the instrument panel lower and upper support.

4. Remove the speaker grille, the speaker mounting screws, and position the speaker out of the way.

5. Remove the defroster nozzle.

6. Disconnect the A/C plenum to right hand register air duct at the plenum and position it out of the way.

7. Disconnect the vacuum line from the actuator, remove the actuator mounting screws, disconnect the actuator to door lever arm at the lever and remove the actuator.

8. Install the new vacuum actuator and connect the actuator arm and vacuum line.

9. Connect the right hand register air duct.

10. Position and install the defroster nozzle.

11. Install the speaker and speaker grille.

12. Install the instrument panel upper and lower support.

13. Connect the red vacuum line to heat-defrost door vacuum actuator.

14. Install the glove box liner.

HEAT—DEFROST DOOR VACUUM ACTUATOR

The defrost door vacuum actuator may be replaced after first removing the defroster plenum from the heater assembly.

After installing the new actuator, check its operation for full travel of the air door.

PART 16-4 RADIO

Section	Page
1 Description and Operation	16-26
Cars and Radio Types	16-26
2 Diagnosis and Testing	16-26
Radio Diagnosis Guide	16-26
3 Common Adjustments and Repairs	16-27
Push Button Adjustment—Comet, Falcon and Fairlane	16-27

Section	Page
4 Removal and Installation	16-27
Radio Receiver	16-27
Antenna—Comet, Falcon, and Fairlane	16-27
Front Speaker—Falcon and Fairlane	16-28
Rear Speaker	16-28
Interference Suppression	16-28

1 DESCRIPTION AND OPERATION

CARS AND RADIO TYPES

Car	Manufacturer and Type	Model No.
Comet	Philco AM / Bendix AM-FM	6TPE / F6TBG
Falcon	Philco AM	6TPD
Fairlane	Philco AM	6TPO
Mustang	Philco AM	6TPZ

The antenna is mounted on the right fender. A rear seat speaker is available. The radios have push button tuning as well as manual tuning.

On all cars except the Comet the push buttons on the AM-FM radio may be divided between AM and FM stations.

On the Comet and Mustang, a band selector switch is provided for selection of either the AM or the FM broadcast band. The five push buttons can be preset to select five AM stations or five FM stations or any combination thereof, however, the push buttons cannot be used to change from one broadcast band to the other. The band selector switch must first be positioned to the desired band before selecting stations with the push buttons. When selecting stations with the manual tuning control, the band (AM or FM) in use is controlled by the band selector switch, if the band selector switch is set to AM, the manual tuning control (right hand knob) will select AM stations.

2 DIAGNOSIS AND TESTING

RADIO DIAGNOSIS GUIDE

NO RECEPTION	1. Burned out fuse. 2. Defective antenna. 3. Shorted speaker lead or defective speaker. 4. Reversed battery polarity. Make certain that voltage is available at the A lead (12 volts), then	substitute a known good antenna and speaker. **Be sure to turn off the radio receiver before removing or installing the speaker.** If the radio still will not play, remove the receiver for a major repair.
NOISY OR ERRATIC RECEPTION	**NOISY RECEPTION—ENGINE NOT RUNNING** 1. Loose connections. **NOISY RECEPTION—ENGINE RUNNING** 1. Defective suppression equipment. 2. Suppression condensers not properly grounded.	3. Receiver not properly grounded to the instrument panel. **NOISY RECEPTION—CAR IN MOTION** 1. Loose or broken lead-in cable. 2. Loose or defective radio antenna. 3. Defective wheel static collector.

CONTINUED ON NEXT PAGE

RADIO DIAGNOSIS GUIDE—(Continued)

DISTORTED OR GARBLED SOUND	1. Voice coil rubbing on center pole piece of speaker magnet. 2. Torn speaker cone. 3. Foreign material on cone.	4. Bent or twisted speaker mounting. **Be sure to turn off the radio receiver before removing or installing the speaker.**
WEAK RECEPTION	1. Poor adjustment of the antenna trimmer (AM only). 2. Beyond normal reception distance from station (FM only).	3. Defective antenna. If FM reception is poor, be sure that the antenna is at 30 to 32 inch height before trying a new antenna.
NO SOUND FROM ONE SPEAKER	1. One speaker defective. 2. Wiring to dead speaker defec-	tive. Operate the fader to determine the speaker at fault.

TESTING

Tests for any of the components in the radio system may be made by substituting known good parts. In the case of an antenna or speaker, it will not be necessary to remove the suspected antenna or speaker. Disconnect the antenna or speaker at the radio and plug in the known good unit. Check the antenna with the car outside of the garage. Plug the antenna lead into the antenna socket in the radio, and extend the antenna wand through the open window of the car.

3   COMMON ADJUSTMENTS AND REPAIRS

PUSH BUTTON ADJUSTMENT— COMET, FALCON AND FAIRLANE

Turn the radio on, and allow it to warm up for 15 minutes. Extend the antenna to a height of approximately 33 inches.

AM PUSH BUTTONS

Place the band selector switch to the AM position. Pull out the push button to be set to unlock the push button mechanism. The letters AM must appear at the top of the push button face. If the letters FM appear, pull the push button out approximately $1/10$ inch further until the push button is free to rotate and rotate the push button 180° to the AM position. Carefully tune in the desired AM station with the manual tuning knob. After the station is clearly tuned in, push the button straight in until it stops and then release it. Repeat this procedure for the remaining buttons.

FM PUSH BUTTONS

Place the band selector switch to the FM position. Pull out the push button to be set to unlock the push button mechanism. The letters FM must appear at the top of the push button face. If the letters AM appear, pull the push button out approximately $1/10$ inch further until the push button is free to rotate and rotate the push button 180° to the FM position. Carefully tune in the desired FM station with the manual tuning knob. After the station is clearly tuned in, push the button straight in until it stops and then release it. Repeat this procedure for the remaining buttons.

4   REMOVAL AND INSTALLATION

RADIO RECEIVER

REMOVAL

To remove the radio receiver, proceed as follows:

1. Pull the radio control knobs off and remove the nuts and washers retaining the radio to the instrument panel.
2. Disconnect the antenna lead at the right side of the radio (at the back of the AM-FM radio).
3. Disconnect the speaker lead.
4. Disconnect the radio lead wire and the pilot light wire from the quick disconnects.
5. Remove the radio support bracket to radio retaining nut.
6. Remove the radio assembly from the instrument panel.

INSTALLATION

1. Position the radio to the instrument panel, and then install the washers and retaining nuts at the knob shafts. Be sure that the radio mounting stud enters the support bracket.
2. Install the radio support bracket retaining nut. Torque all mounting nuts to specification.
3. Connect the antenna lead to the radio.
4. Connect the radio speaker lead.
5. Connect the radio power lead and the pilot light lead.
6. Install the radio control knobs.
7. Check the radio operation.

ANTENNA—COMET, FALCON AND FAIRLANE

1. Disconnect the antenna lead from the side of the radio receiver (at the back of the AM-FM radio). Tie a string to the end of the antenna lead.

2. Remove the antenna cap, four screws, and remove the antenna assembly.

3. Tie the string to the new antenna lead.

4. Position the antenna assembly

in the opening, put the spacer in position on the antenna and install the antenna.

5. Pull the antenna lead through the opening and route the lead under the glove box and connect the lead to the radio.

FRONT SPEAKER—FALCON AND FAIRLANE

1. Disconnect the speaker wires from the radio receiver.
2. Remove the glove box.
3. Remove the speaker retaining nuts and remove the speaker through the glove box opening.
4. Install the new speaker through the glove box to the instrument panel and secure it with retaining nuts.
5. Connect the speaker leads to the radio and check the radio operation.
6. Install the glove box.

REAR SPEAKER

The rear seat speaker is accessible for replacement from the luggage compartment. On the station wagon the speaker is mounted on the left rear trim panel. Remove the trim panel to replace the speaker.

INTERFERENCE SUPPRESSION

Interference suppression items are shown in Fig. 1. An alternator condenser is an internal part of the alterference suppression items used on denser, and wheel static collectors are also used. A constant voltage regulator choke and a hood bonding clip are used on the Comet only. Interference suppression items used on the Fairlane are shown in Fig. 2.

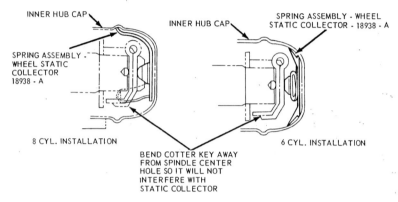

K 1494 -C

FIG. 1—Radio Interference Suppression—Except Fairlane

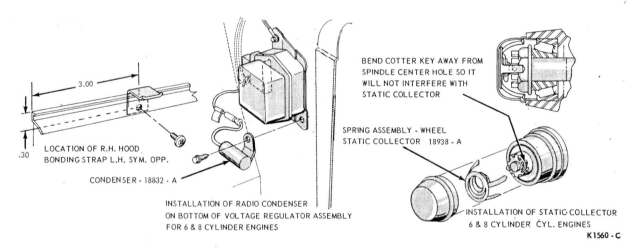

K 1560 - C

FIG. 2—Fairlane Radio Interference Suppression

PART 16-5

SPECIFICATIONS

Blower Motor Current Draw at 12 Volts	Heater	Air Conditioner
High Speed	6-8 Amps	6.5-7.5 Amps
Medium Speed	4-6 Amps	4.5-5.5 Amps
Low Speed	2-4 Amps	3.0-4.0 Amps

CIRCUIT PROTECTION	SFE 14 Fuse	3AG 15 Fuse
Location	Fuse Panel	In Line

RADIO CURRENT DRAW

1 Amp Max. at 12 Volts

MOUNTING TORQUE (in-lbs)

Radio to Instrument Panel	30
Support Bracket Screw and Nut	30
Antenna Mounting Nut	15

MAGNETIC CLUTCH CURRENT DRAW

1-2 Amperes at 12 Volts

AIR CONDITIONER COMPRESSOR

Location	Torque (ft-lbs) York
Cylinder Head	14-18
Front Seal Plate	13-17
Service Valves (Rotolock)	35-Max.
Mounting Bolts	14-17
Oil Filler Plug	18-22
Clutch Mounting Bolt	15-22
Base Plate	7-11
Back Plate	7-10
Oil Capacity—¾ inch (10 ounces) Use Suniso #5, or Capella E	

DRIVEN BELT TENSION

Between Fan Pulley and Air Conditioner Compressor All Engines ....New 120-150 / Used① 90-120
①Belt operated for a minimum of 10 minutes is considered a used belt.

<table>
<tr><td colspan="4">BODY, DOORS AND WINDOWS</td><td colspan="2">GROUP 17</td></tr>
</table>

PART 17-1 **PAGE**

GENERAL BODY SERVICE **17-1**

PART 17-2

FRONT SHEETMETAL, BUMPERS, EXTERIOR MOULDINGS **17-11**

PART 17-3 **PAGE**

DOORS, WINDOWS, TAILGATE AND DECK LID **17-30**

PART 17-1 GENERAL BODY SERVICE

Section	Page	Section	Page
1 Diagnosis and Testing. 17-1		Paint Refinishing. 17-4	
Dust and Water Leaks. 17-1		3 Cleaning and Inspection. 17-8	
2 Common Adjustments and Repairs. 17-1		Care of Wood Grain Paneling. 17-9	
Types of Sealer and Application 17-1		4 Hoisting. 17-10	
Body Alignment. 17-3			

1 DIAGNOSIS AND TESTING

DUST AND WATER LEAKS

Sealer locations should be considered when checking for dust or water leaks. The forward motion of the car creates a slight vacuum within the body, particularly if a window or ventilator is partially open. Any unsealed small opening in the lower section of the body will permit air to be drawn into the body. If dust is present in the air, it will follow any path taken by the air from the point of entry into the passenger and luggage compartments. Opening the ventilator air ducts will equalize these pressures. Dust accumulates in the rocker panel, and may eventually work its way to the kick-up or the rear body pillar, and follow the contour of the wheelhouse into the luggage compartment.

To eliminate dust leakage, determine the exact point at which the dust enters. The point of entry is often deceptive in that the dust may enter at one point, then follow the passages formed by interior trim to another point.

Under certain conditions, water can enter the body at any point where dust can enter. Any consideration of water leakage must take into account all points covered under dust leaks.

To determine the exact location of a dust leak, it may be necessary to remove the following trim from the car:

1. Cowl trim panel.
2. Quarter trim panel.
3. Rear seat back and seat cushion.
4. Luggage compartment floor mats, spare wheel, and side trim panel.

5. Center pillar trim on 4-door models.
6. Scuff plates.

After removing the trim, the location of most leaks will be readily evident. The entrance of dust is usually indicated by a pointed shaft of dust or silt. Seal these leaks, and road test the car on a dusty road to make sure that all leaks are sealed.

After the road tests, check for indications of a dust pattern around the door openings, cowl panel, lower part of the quarter panel, and in the luggage compartment.

Sometimes leaks can be located by putting bright lights under the car, with the above components removed, and checking the interior of the body joints and weld lines. The light will show through where leaks exist.

2 COMMON ADJUSTMENTS AND REPAIRS

TYPES OF SEALER AND APPLICATION

The all-purpose sealers described below have been selected for service use. The method and points of application are given under each sealer type.

CAULKING CORD AB19560-A

This sealer has a plastic base with an asbestos filler, is heavy bodied, and is commonly known as permagum. It is used on spotweld holes, around moulding clips, or between two surfaces not properly sealed by a gasket. Apply the sealer with a putty knife.

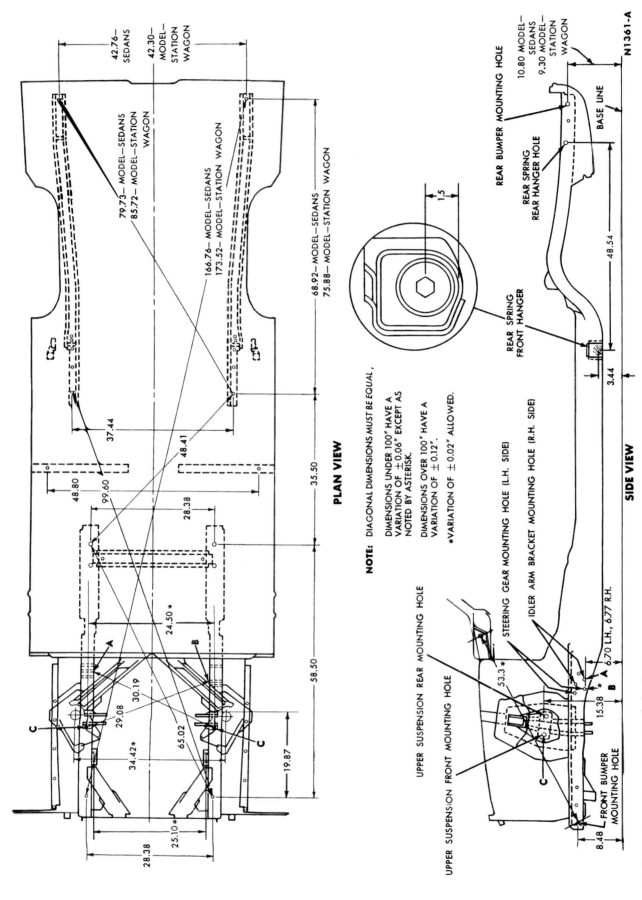

FIG. 1—Comet and Falcon Underbody Dimensions

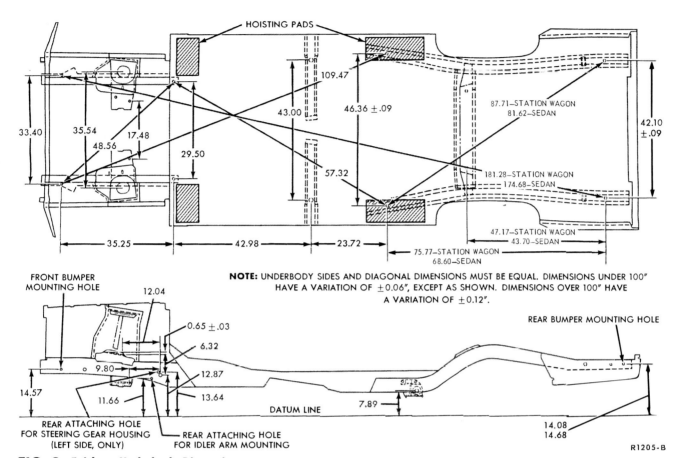

FIG. 2—Fairlane Underbody Dimensions

TRIM CEMENT C2AZ-19C525-A

This cement is recommended for instrument panel safety cover and body panel plastic water shield installation. It is also useful for repair or replacement of other vinyl and rubber trim.

RUBBER CEMENT 8A-19552-B

This quick-drying, strong adhesive material is designed to hold weatherstripping on doors, bodies, deck lids, cowl ventilators, and the surrounding metal. Windows and windshields which are set in rubber can be effectively sealed against leakage by flowing cement into the affected areas.

Clean all grease, dirt, and old sealer from the surfaces to be cemented. For best results, apply a medium coat of cement to both surfaces, allow it to dry until tacky, and press both surfaces firmly together.

**SILICON LUBRICANT
COAZ-19553-A (JELLY) AND
COAZ-19553-C (SPRAY)**

This lubricant is to be used on the door window weatherstrips. It is rec-

ommended that silicone lubricant be applied to the upper weatherstrips at every regular lubrication period. Its use makes the doors easier to close, avoids weatherstrip squeaks, retards excess weatherstrip wear from chafing between the door glass upper frame and the weatherstrip, and helps to retain door window alignment by reducing friction between the glass frame and rubber weatherstrip.

BODY ALIGNMENT

Servicing the unitized body should present no unusual difficulties or necessitate additional equipment other than that required for the conventional frame and body repair. The application of heat and the use of heavy-duty jacks must be carefully controlled because of the difference in the gauge of the metal in the sub-frame of a unitized body and the stress points developed in a single welded unit construction. It is possible to pull damaged areas back into alignment with the use of light-weight jacks and hydraulic equipment without heating the metal.

Rough out badly damaged areas before taking measurements for squaring up a body. If necessary, remove the glass from the damaged area to prevent damage. In severe cases reinforcement brackets and other inner construction may have to be removed or cut to permit restoration of the outer shell and pillars without excessive strain on the parts. Straighten, install, and secure all such parts in place before attempting to align the body.

In cases of severe or sharp bends, it may be necessary to use heat. Any attempt to cold-straighten a severely bent bracket may cause ruptures of the welds and may also cause cracks in the bent part. Never heat the area more than a dull red.

CHECKING BODY FOR MISALIGNMENT

To align or square up a body, take two opposite diagonal measurements between pillars. Use a measuring tram for these measurements. Take the measurements between reference points such as crease lines or weld joints which are diagonally opposite each other on the two pillars being measured. Since all measurements should be made from the bare metal, remove all interior trim from the checking points.

In some cases, it is difficult to obtain proper body alignment when repairing a body that is damaged on both sides. In these cases, horizontal and vertical measurements can be taken from a body of the same body style. Once these basic dimensions are taken and established on the damaged body, alignment can be made by diagonal measurements taken from points on the two pillars.

Do not attempt to correct any serious misalignment with one jacking operation. This is particularly true if other sections of the body also require aligning. Align each section proportionately until the proper dimensions are obtained.

Door openings are checked in the same manner as the body. Horizontal, vertical, and diagonal checking points are established on all four sides of the door opening that is being measured.

CHECKING UNDERBODY FOR MISALIGNMENT

The dimensions of the underbody must be restored in the repair of major body damage, to provide correct front and rear wheel geometry (Figs. 1, 2 and 3). All the dimensions are detailed to the center line of existing holes in the underbody assembly. Once the frame and suspension members are aligned, the balance of the repair can be performed.

PAINT REFINISHING
PAINT DAMAGES AND PROCEDURES FOR REPAIR

Paint Repairs on Galvanized Metals. If for any reason it becomes necessary to perform paint repairs on galvanized rocker panels or any other galvanized steel surfaces, care must be exercised in preparing the bare galvanized surface to properly accept paint, and the best possible paint products must be employed to insure satisfactory adhesion to the metal and to give a good color match with acceptable durability. Most of the approved paint suppliers for refinishing materials agree on the procedure for metal preparation but use different primer recommendations. The methods involving the use of DuPont Preparakote and Ditzler Zinc Dust Primer are indicated here and it is important that either one be

employed exactly as directed. No short cuts nor any inter-mixing should be attempted.

METAL PREPARATION FOR GALVANIZED STEEL

1. Strip, sand-off or otherwise remove all paint from the affected galvanized steel panel.

2. Wire-brush or steel-wool the entire metal surface and remove all grease or oil by wiping with a clean solvent.

3. Wipe the panel using a clean cloth or sponge with Lithoform No. 2 (Distributed by the Neilson Chemical Division of Amchem Products, Inc.) or Bonderite No. 34 (Distributed by Parker Rustproof). The work should be kept completely wet for at least three minutes and the metal should be thoroughly etched. If any bright metal remains the treatment should be repeated.

4. Rinse the area with clean water and blow off with compressed air.

5. The dried surface must be primed immediately. Then succeeding coats and color as required must be applied according to vendor's directions. Examples such as the Du-Pont and Ditzler systems are given as follows:

SYSTEM FOR USING DUPONT PREPARAKOTE

1. Spray Preparakote over properly prepared metal. Force-dry with radiant heat or air-dry overnight. This primer must be dried hard enough to sand wet or dry.

2. Sand the Preparakote very carefully, preferably with No. 400 paper so as to avoid cutting through to bare metal. Blow off and tack clean.

3. Spray two coats of No. 22 clear sealer and allow to air-dry for thirty minutes.

4. Spray on matching Acrylic Lacquer as directed. Then air-dry or force-dry until the lacquer is hard enough to be polished.

5. Polish the lacquer as recommended by supplier.

SYSTEM FOR USING DITZLER ZINC DUST PRIMER

1. Prime the galvanized area with DPE659 Zinc Dust Primer. This is a two-component product and the zinc must be carefully mixed with the vehicle as directed. A recommended film thickness of one mil may be recoated with a lacquer base primer surfacer such as DZL3200 in

about twenty minutes. Do not sand DPE659.

2. Spray primer surfacer DZL3200 reduced as directed to a film thickness of about two mils.

3. After drying the primer surfacer about thirty minutes, carefully sand with No. 360 or No. 400 silicon carbide paper, wet or dry, so as not to cut through the zinc dust primer coat. Blow off and tack clean.

4. Spray matching Duracryl lacquers as directed and after drying rub and polish as required.

All material coatings may be force-dried. Careful manipulation is recommended.

Acrylic Enamels. Acrylic enamels exhibit better hardness, mar resistance and gloss retention in metallic colors than the ordinary enamels. Acrylic enamels also possess the property of good polishability.

Following are recommended repair procedures for acrylic enamels:

Repair By Polishing. Repair of minor dirt or fallout, sags, mars, scratches, dry spray, overspray, and orange peel can be accomplished by machine or hand polishing or by both sanding and polishing without the necessity of repainting. Repairs of this type should apply to an entire panel while spot repairs should be attemped only in isolated areas.

The suggested polish repair procedure consists of:

1. Remove the defect by oil sanding with 600 grit paper, using water or mineral spirits as a lubricant.

2. Apply a white or light colored medium grit machine polishing compound (Sno-Flake No. 16 or equivalent) to the painted surface with a brush.

3. Polish the entire panel surface using an 1850 rpm wheel and a carpet pad (approximately ⅝-inch nap) or lambswool pad.

4. Buff the surface with a clean lambswool pad.

Normally, acrylic enamels do not need polishing to improve their gloss; however, the foregoing procedure can be used to restore the original luster to the film after weathering, or to improve the surface smoothness of the finish on the entire car.

Repair By Repainting. Acrylic enamels can be repaired by repainting with either conventional air drying or low bake enamels, or with acrylic lacquers. When repainting metallic colors, it is recommended that acrylic lacquer be used since a better color match can be obtained;

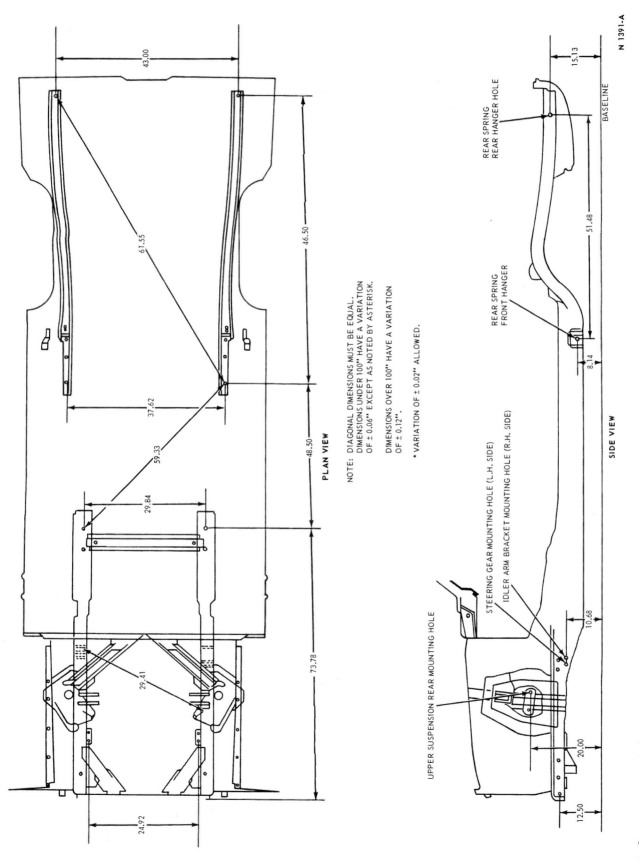

NOTE: DIAGONAL DIMENSIONS MUST BE EQUAL. DIMENSIONS UNDER 100" HAVE A VARIATION OF ± 0.06" EXCEPT AS NOTED BY ASTERISK.

DIMENSIONS OVER 100" HAVE A VARIATION OF ± 0.12".

* VARIATION OF ± 0.02" ALLOWED.

N 1391-A

FIG. 3—Mustang Underbody Dimensions

both the original finish and the repair can be polished to provide the same luster, and the air dry acrylic repair lacquer will provide better durability in service than air dry enamels. **Do not use Nitrocellulose lacquers for exterior repairs.**

When using any one of the three types of repair materials over acrylic enamel, remove all traces of wax, polish or grease with a good silicone remover such as DL-60-3721-A. It is extremely important that a thorough sanding of the original finish be accomplished using No. 400 grit paper. Care should be exercised to insure that all surfaces, including edges and areas adjacent to applied mouldings, are thoroughly sanded in order to provide adhesion of the repair top coat. Areas sanded to the base metal (cut through) should be treated with an acid cleaner such as Metalprep (distributed by Amchem Products Inc.). Follow the directions of the supplier as stated on the container.

After sanding, proceed with the application of a primer surfacer reduced according to the supplier's recommendations to any bare metal spots that have been exposed. After the recommended air dry time, sand the primer surfacer with No. 400 grit paper before application of the repair material. The lacquer or enamel used should be reduced as recommended by its supplier.

PAINT DEFECTS AND REPAIR PROCEDURES

Listed here are some of the abnormal paint conditions that may be encountered (Fig. 4). It is very important to identify the paint condition correctly so that the proper repair procedure may be followed. For each of the following paint conditions described, the recommended repair procedure will be indicated.

BLISTERING

Blistering is the formation of bubbles or pin points on the surface of the finished work. Unless inspected by a magnifying glass, this condition is very hard to identify. In some instances, this complaint may be confused with dirt in the paint. To verify blistering, prick the suspected areas, and note whether a hole exists under the bubble. This condition is caused by rust, moisture, or oil between the coats, metal not properly cleaned, or uneven temperatures between the metal and the paint being sprayed.

Acrylic Enamel. Repair by repainting (color coat). Priming procedure must first be followed if defect is due to poor metal preparation.

CHECKING

Line checking has the appearance of thin, straight lines criss-crossing each other. These lines may be from one-half inch to four inches or longer, increasing in length as the finish ages.

Acrylic Enamel. Refinish panel. (Color coat–primer if damaged.)

CHIPPING AND STONE BRUISES

Chipping occurs when the surface of the finish coat of paint has been broken by a sharp blow, and small particles of paint have flaked off. Frequently, stone bruises result in chipping.

Acrylic Enamel. Refinish panel. Paint may be spotted if in isolated areas. (Prime to be bare metal.)

CRACKING

Cracking is evidenced by the paint curling. Frequently, cracking starts at the edge of the panel. This is caused by poor mixing of paint or by temperature changes during the various painting stages.

Acrylic Enamel. Refinish panel. (Prime if both color and primer cracking.)

CROW FOOTING

Crow footing may be described as small lines branching off from a point in all directions and giving the appearance of a crow's foot. Crow footing is usually caused by spraying a second coat before the first coat is dry, by spraying an excessively thick coat, or by thinners which evaporate too fast.

Acrylic Enamel. Refinish panel. (Color coat.)

DIRT IN PAINT

Patches where dirt appears are sometimes confused with blistering. To vertify the condition, prick the suspected areas, and note whether there is foreign material under the surface.

Acrylic Enamel. Refinish panel. procedure will be effective in most cases. (Color coat.)

MILDEW

Mildew growth which occurs along radial lines is most commonly found in a very dark gray or black color.

Acrylic Enamel. Repair by polishing.

OFF-COLOR

The term off-color is applied to adjacent areas on which the colors do not match. It may also appear when making spot repairs.

Acrylic Enamel. Refinish panel if polishing does not correct condition (Color coat.)

ORANGE PEEL

Orange peel is a term used to describe an uneven, mottled appearance on the paint surface. This is usually caused by improper thinning of the paint.

Acrylic Enamel. Refinish panel if polishing does not correct condition. (Color coat.)

OVERSPRAY

Overspray is evidenced by a rough, dull finish in the area surrounding the paint repair.

PEELING

Peeling occurs when large areas of the finish or primer coat separate from the metal or prime coat. This is usually caused by wax, grease, rust or oil under the paint. Do not confuse with orange peel.

PITS AND POP-UPS

Pits and craters may be identified by the appearance of small round depressions in the paint. These may be caused by not allowing the first coat ot dry sufficiently before applying the second coat or from failure to remove silicone polishes before repainting.

Acrylic Enamel. First use polish repair procedure refinish panel if necessary. (Color coat.)

THIN PAINT

The primer will show through the finish coat as a result of an excessively thin color coat, or application of the color coat before the surface is dry.

Acrylic Enamel. Refinish panel. (Color coat.)

RUNS AND SAGS

The uneven collections of paint on the finish surface are referred to as runs and sags. The collections may appear in the form of tear drops or sagging lines. Usually these lines are quite soft and sometimes they may be wrinkled. This is usually

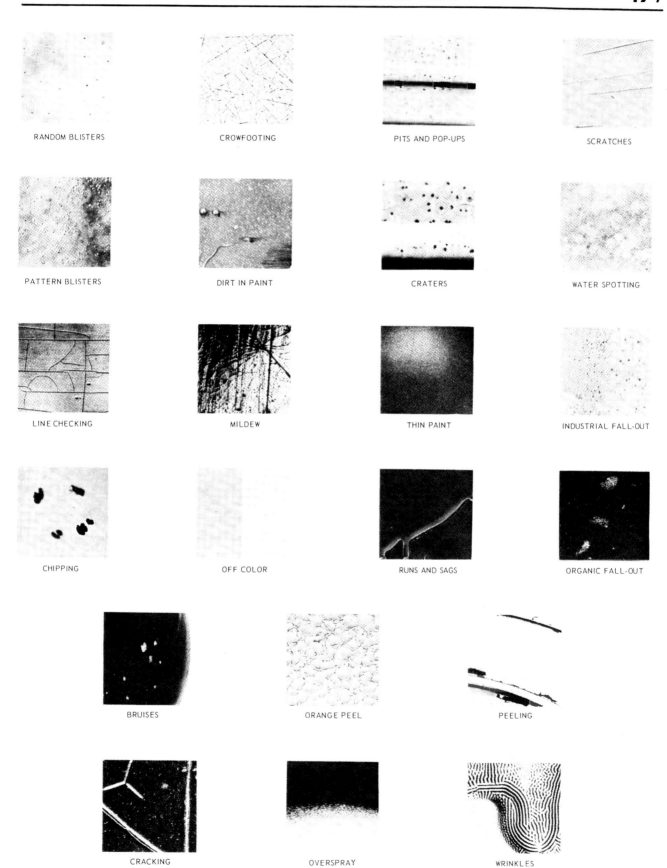

RANDOM BLISTERS   CROWFOOTING   PITS AND POP-UPS   SCRATCHES

PATTERN BLISTERS   DIRT IN PAINT   CRATERS   WATER SPOTTING

LINE CHECKING   MILDEW   THIN PAINT   INDUSTRIAL FALL-OUT

CHIPPING   OFF COLOR   RUNS AND SAGS   ORGANIC FALL-OUT

BRUISES   ORANGE PEEL   PEELING

CRACKING   OVERSPRAY   WRINKLES

N–1471-A

FIG. 4—Paint Defects

caused by over-application of paint or hesitation in the stroke of the gun.

Acrylic Enamel. Use polish repair procedure.

SCRATCHES

Scratches are thin marks or tears that may partially or completely penetrate the surface of the finish coat of paint.

Acrylic Enamel. Use polish repair procedure for shallow penetration. Refinish panels to correct conditions of deep penetration.

SPOT DISCOLORATION

This is evidenced by brown spots or stains on the surface. Stains or spots can be caused by road tar, acid or alkali-bearing water from the streets.

Acrylic Enamel. Use polish repair procedure.

WATER SPOTTING

Water spotting is evidenced by a milky pattern where water drops have fallen.

Acrylic Enamel. Use polish repair procedure.

INDUSTRIAL FALL-OUT

Industrial fall-out is the result of particles being exhausted into the air by the various processes of heavy industry, or in areas where there is a concentration of industry.

Industrial fall-out particles appear to the eye as tiny rust-colored dots on the paint film and the surface will feel rough to the touch. Some of the particles have excellent adhesion and are difficult to remove. However, the following procedure has proven effective in the removal of this fall-out.

1. Wash the car with car wash compound (COAA-19B521-A) to remove loose soil. Rinse well and examine the painted surfaces for iron base fall-out particles. If there

is a significant quantity of fall-out not removed by ordinary washing, the oxalic treatment should then be used. All cracks, ledges, grooves, etc., where fall-out has accumulated should be cleaned by wiping or by air blow-off.

2. Dissolve six to eight ounces of oxalic acid (dry) in one gallon of warm water and add one or two tablespoonsful of a non-alkaline detergent such as car wash compound (COAA-19B521-A). This acid detergent solution must be prepared and kept in a clean **NON-METALLIC** container.

Apply this solution liberally to all affected surfaces of the car with a large sponge. Use a broad wiping stroke and keep the work completely wet for about 15 minutes, or until the operator can no longer feel any surface roughness or isolated gritty particles with bare or gloved finger tip. If this is not done thoroughly, rust staining may soon redevelop. Be sure that the entire acid cleaning procedure is performed in a sheltered area so that the work will be kept as cool as possible to prevent rapid evaporation of water and consequent surface drying. Do not work in the sun.

3. Rinse with clear water. This must be done very thoroughly to prevent possible corrosion.

No traces of acid should be left on any surface. Bright trim parts, particularly anodized aluminum and stainless steel, may be stained by prolonged contact with the cleaning solution. Painted areas also can be spotted by prolonged exposure. It is also important to keep the oxalic acid cleaner solution from leaking to the inside of the car because some fabrics might be bleached or discolored by the solution.

If the fall-out is not completely removed or is deeply imbedded in the paint film, cleaning with the acid detergent mixture must be

repeated. This may be aided by using a fine scrub brush, possibly a nylon bristle type. Make sure that the light scrubbing required does not scratch the paint. It is sometimes helpful to briskly rub the work with a mixture of equal parts of oxalic acid cleaner and FoMoCo cleaner wax polish (8A-19519-A) using a piece of heavy toweling. Again, a thorough water rinsing is extremely important.

Sometimes small black spots remain after the oxalic cleaning has removed all iron based fall-out. Such deposits might be asphaltic or they might be over-spray. These usually can be removed by rubbing vigorously with a cloth saturated with a mixture of kerosene and Actusol (about five parts of kerosene to one part of Actusol). Any residue of this solvent mixture may be readily flushed off with water.

ORGANIC FALL-OUT

Organic fall-out may result from parking cars under trees or from the air under certain atmospheric conditions.

Acrylic Enamel. Refinish damaged panels. (Color coat and primer.)

INTERIOR PAINT REPAIRS

The proper matching of colors can be obtained if the following procedures are carefully adhered to:

1. Clean the surface to be painted with wax and silicone remover.

2. Feather-edge the damaged area with 400 grit wet or dry sandpaper. (Prime all areas of bare metal with M-6J-12S Primer.)

3. Mix the paint per instructions on the can and spray several light coats.

Allow the paint to become tacky between coats.

4. Spray the entire area sparingly with B7A-645-S Lacquer Leveler which will blend the repaired area with existing painted surfaces.

---

3 CLEANING AND INSPECTION

FLOOR PAN PLUGS AND GROMMETS

The floor-pan plugs seal the various access holes. If any plugs are missing or improperly installed, a dust or water leak may result. This also applies to the grommets used on the dash panel. When dust or

water leaks are evident, these plugs and grommets should be checked for proper installation.

DRAIN HOLES

Drain holes or valves located on the underside of each rocker panel, quarter panel, and door should be

cleared periodically.

BODY MAINTENANCE

Regular body maintenance preserves *the car's appearance and re*duces the cost of maintenance during the life of the car. The following steps are suggested as a guide for regular body maintenance:

1. Vacuum the interior thoroughly and wash the car.

2. Check all openings for water leaks, and seal where necessary.

3. Cement all loose weatherstrips which are still usable.

4. Replace all door and deck lid weatherstrips which are unfit for service.

5. Apply silicone lubricant to the weatherstripping.

6. Replace all cracked, fogged, or chipped glass.

7. Align the hood, doors, and deck lid if necessary.

8. Inspect the windshield wiper blades and replace them if necessary.

9. Tighten the sill plate and garnish moulding screws.

10. Clean the seats, door trim panels, and headlining.

11. Touch up or paint chipped or scratched areas.

12. Drain holes located on the underside of each rocker panel, quarter panel, and door, should be cleared periodically.

RATTLE ELIMINATION

Most rattles are caused by a loose bolt or screw. Foreign objects such as nuts, bolts, or small pieces of body deadener in the door wells, pillars and quarter panels are often the source of rattles. Door wells can be checked by carefully striking the underside of the door with a rubber mallet. The impact made by the mallet will indicate if loose objects are in the door well.

In the event that tightening the bolts and screws, located on such assemblies as the doors, hood, and deck lid does not eliminate the rattles, the trouble is probably caused by misalignment. If this is the case, follow the adjustment and alignment procedures for these assemblies.

Rattles and squeaks are sometimes caused by weatherstripping and antisqueak material that has slipped out of position. Apply additional cement or other adhesive, and install the material in the proper location to eliminate this difficulty.

EXTERIOR CLEANING

The outside finish should be frequently washed. Never wipe the painted surface with a dry cloth. Dusting the finish when it is dry tends to rub the dust and dirt into the baked enamel, and leaves a sandpaper effect on the surface. To keep the finish bright and attractive

and eliminate the necessity of using polish, wash the car whenever it has accumulated a moderate amount of dirt and road salt.

The bright metal parts of the car require no special care. Periodic cleaning will preserve the beauty and life of these finishes. Wash with clear water or if the parts are very dirty use FoMoCo COAA-19B521-A compound. Using a clean soft cloth or a sponge and water, rinse and wipe the parts dry. FoMoCo Chrome Cleaner may be used sparingly to remove rust or salt corrosion from chrome plated parts. Do not scour aluminum or chrome finished parts with steel wool or polish them with products containing abrasives. A FoMoCo Polish will provide excellent protection for all bright metal parts.

INTERIOR CLEANING

Use a vacuum cleaner to remove dust and dirt from the upholstery or floor covering. Vinyl and woven plastic trim that is dusty can usually be cleaned with a damp cloth. **Do not use cleaning materials containing kerosene, naptha, toluol, xylol 10°, lacquer thinners, cellulose acetate, butyl cellosolve, carbon tetrachloride, body polish, battery acid, antifreeze, gasoline, motor oils or other type lubricants.**

Approved cleaners B8A-19523 -A, or -B, B5A-19525-A, COAZ-19526-A or -B (soft trim cleaners), BAF-19521-A (leather and vinyl upholstery cleaner), and CIAZ-19C507 -A (convertible back window cleaner) are available for service. Instructions for the use of these cleaners are indicated with their containers.

CARE OF WOOD GRAIN PANELING
WASHING

Never wipe the panels or trim rails with a dry cloth. This method of cleaning tends to rub dust particles into the finished surface and leave fine scratches. Flush off all loose dirt and other elements, and wipe the body panels and rails with a sponge and plenty of cold water. If desired, a mild soap may be used. Rinse thoroughly with clear water and wipe dry.

GLASS FIBER TRIM RAIL REMOVAL AND INSTALLATION

The glass fiber trim rails are serviced with the wood-grain already

applied. To remove the body side trim rails, remove the cap over each trim rail screw to gain access to the screws. Remove the screws and the trim rail assembly.

When installing the body side trim rail, apply sealer (AB-19560-A) around each mounting hole. Install the cap retainer, screw and cap.

APPLICATION OF WOOD-GRAIN TRANSFERS

Wood grain transfers are available for application to the panels. The materials necessary to apply the transfers are a bonding coat (M-4584), 20% transfer solution of M-5412-A, and clear spar varnish.

If the surface on which the transfer is to be applied is damaged, repair and metal finish first.

1. Mask off the area where the transfer is to be applied.

2. Prime-coat all bare metal areas, and wet-sand.

3. Spray the surface with transfer bonding coat (M-4584). This coat is the binder for the transfer adhesive.

4. Allow the binding coat to air-dry for one hour, or heat-dry (160°F) for 20 minutes.

5. Lightly wet-sand the binding coat, and wipe it dry.

6. Make a paper template of the damaged area, and cut the new transfer to size, using the template as a guide. Leave about ½ inch of extra material around the edge of the transfer to allow for matching and trimming.

7. Mix a solution of 20% transfer solution M-5412-A and 80% water. This solution permits shifting of the transfer after it has been applied, so that the graining can be matched. **Try a sample of the transfer and solution on an old piece of metal or fender. If the transfer cannot be pulled off after two minutes, the solution is too strong and must be diluted with more water.**

8. Soak the transfer in lukewarm water for one minute to loosen the paper backing. **Do not remove the backing until the transfer is applied.**

9. Using a cheese cloth pad, apply a 20% M-5412-A transfer solution to the panel. **Any excess solution that runs down on adjacent panels must be wiped off immediately.**

10. Place the wet transfer on the panel, paper side out. Adjust the transfer to match the graining on adjoining panels, and carefully remove the paper backing.

11. Sponge the transfer with clean water to remove all traces of the paper backing adhesive.

12. Remove all air bubbles and wrinkles with a squeegee.

13. Wash the transfer with clear water and dry with a chamois.

14. Pierce any blisters or small air bubbles as they appear, and press down the area with a finger to remove the air and excess solution.

15. Allow the panel to air-dry for one hour, or heat dry (160°F.) for 20 minutes.

16. When the panel is dry, spray two coats of clear spar varnish over the transfer. **Do not use clear lacquer or shellac.**

---

4   HOISTING VEHICLE

The unitized body-frame construction requires special precautions and procedures when the car is jacked up or hoisted. In some cases, special hoist adapters must be used as recommended by specific hoist manufacturers.

Refer to the Owner's Manuals when using the jack supplied with the car.

DRIVE-ON TYPE HOIST

To prevent possible damages to the underbody, do not drive the car onto the drive-on type hoist without first checking for possible interference between the upright flanges of the hoist rails and the underbody. Should there be interference, the hoist flanges should be modified as necessary and/or the approach ramps built up to provide the needed clearance.

RAIL TYPE—FREE WHEELING HOIST
FRONT

The front adapters or hoist plates must be carefully positioned in contact with the lower suspension arms to assure safe, accurate lifting.

REAR

The hoist adapters must be positioned carefully under the rear axle to prevent damage to the shock absorbers when the car is raised. The hoist rails should be raised slowly and the position of the adapters checked.

FORK LIFT—TWIN POST HOIST
FRONT

To assure safe hoisting, the front post adapters must be positioned carefully to contact the center of the lower suspension arms (Figs. 5 and 6).

REAR

To prevent damage to the shock absorbers, the rear forks must contact the axle at points not farther out board than one inch from the circumference welds near the differential housing. Carefully raise the rear post and check the position of the fork (Figs. 5 and 6).

FRAME CONTACT HOIST

Frame contact hoist adapters are necessary to lift the car. The hoist adapter pads should each cover at least 12 square inches of underbody area. Figs. 5 and 6 show recommended contact points for the hoist pads.

FLOOR JACK

When a stationary floor jack or a roll jack is to be used, there are several specific recommended points of contact. Either side of the car may be raised at the front by jack contact at the lower arm strut connection. Either side of the front end of the car may also be raised by jack pressure on the front crossmember, or on the crossmember to which the stabilizer is connected. **Do not attempt to use jack pressure on either front or rear Mustang bumpers.**

FRONT RAIL TYPE, FORK LIFT
OR FLOOR JACK CONTACT AREA

FRONT FRAME CONTACT AREA   M1111-A

FIG. 5—Front Hoist Contact Areas

REAR FRAME CONTACT AREA

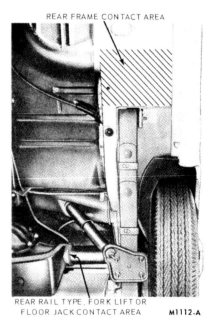

REAR RAIL TYPE, FORK LIFT OR
FLOOR JACK CONTACT AREA   M1112-A

FIG. 6—Rear Hoist Contact Areas

PART 17-2 FRONT SHEET METAL, BUMPERS, EXTERIOR MOULDINGS

Section	Page
1 In-Car Adjustments and Repairs............17-11	
Hood Adjustments....................17-11	
Hood Lock Adjustments—Mustang........17-11	
Hood Lock Adjustment—Comet, Falcon, Fairlane............................17-11	
2 Removal and Installation..............17-12	
Hood Hinge.........................17-12	
Radiator Grille—Comet................17-12	
Radiator Grille—Falcon................17-12	

Section	Page
Radiator Grille—Fairlane................17-12	
Radiator Grille—Mustang................17-14	
Front Bumper—Comet, Falcon, Fairlane.....17-14	
Front Bumper—Mustang................17-15	
Rear Bumper—Falcon..................17-16	
Rear Bumper—Comet, Fairlane............17-16	
Rear Bumper—Mustang..................17-16	
Rear Bumper Guard—Mustang............17-17	
Exterior Mouldings....................17-17	

1 IN-CAR ADJUSTMENTS AND REPAIRS

HOOD ADJUSTMENTS

The hood is provided with fore and aft, vertical, and side-to-side adjustments (Fig. 1). These directions refer to the position of the hood when it is fully lowered. The elongated bolt slots in the hinge at the hood provide the side-to-side adjustment. The enlarged holes in the hinge at the fender apron provide both vertical and fore and aft adjustments.

Hood bumpers, located on the top left and the top right surface of the radiator support, can be adjusted up and down to provide a level surface alignment of the hood panel with the front fenders

HOOD LOCK ADJUSTMENTS MUSTANG

Before adjusting the hood lock mechanism, make certain that the hood is properly aligned. The hood lock (Fig. 2) can be moved fore or aft and side to side to align it with the lock dowel. The safety catch can be adjusted to engage the hood lock catch.

1. Loosen the hood lock attaching bolts. Move the lock assembly as required to align it with the lock dowel on the hood.

2. Tighten the attaching bolts.

3. Loosen the lock nut on the hood lock dowel and turn the dowel inward to adjust the hood tighter, or outward to loosen the adjustment. **Do not bend the hood lock dowel.**

4. The lock dowel is adjusted correctly when the top of the hood is flush with the fenders, when locked.

5. Tighten the dowel lock nut after adjusting the lock dowel.

6. To adjust the safety catch striker, loosen the two attaching screws and position the catch correctly. Tighten the screws and lower the hood to make certain the safety catch striker engages the hood lock safety catch.

7. Open and close the hood several times to be certain that the lock mechanism is secure.

COMET, FALCON AND FAIRLANE

1. With the hood open loosen the hood lock retaining screws (Figs. 3, 4 and 5).

2. Move the hood lock mechanism as required to align it with the lock striker.

3. Tighten the lock retaining screws. Open and close the hood several times to be sure that it latches securely.

FIG. 1—Hood Hinge Installation —Typical

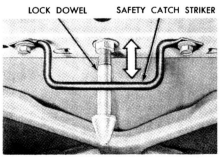

LOCK DOWEL   SAFETY CATCH STRIKER

N1071-B

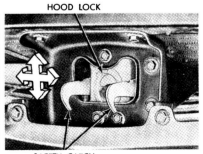

HOOD LOCK

SAFETY CATCH

N1184-B

FIG. 2—Hood Lock Mechanism—Mustang

2 REMOVAL AND INSTALLATION

HOOD HINGE

1. Prop the front of the hood in the open position and cover the fender and cowl panel.

2. Remove the hinge-to-hood retaining bolts, the retaining bolts at the fender apron and cowl (Fig. 1), and remove the hinge.

3. Position the hood hinge on the body and install the hinge retaining bolts.

4. Adjust the hood for proper fit.

RADIATOR GRILLE—COMET
REMOVAL

1. Remove one screw and two bolts retaining the grille assembly to the center lock support and the right and left sides at the stone deflector (Fig. 3).

2. Remove the four screws retaining the grille assembly to the upper support; remove the grille assembly from the grille opening and place it on a bench.

3. Remove the eight screws retaining the grille center panel to the grille assembly and remove the panel.

4. Remove the nut and washer retaining the grille ornament to the grille and remove the grille ornament.

INSTALLATION

1. Position the grille ornament on the left grille and install the retaining nuts and washers.

2. Position the grille center panel to the grille assembly and install the retaining screws.

3. Position the grille assembly in the grille opening.

4. Install the grille top retaining screws, the grille-to-center lock support retaining screw and the right and left side grille retaining bolts.

RADIATOR GRILLE—FALCON
REMOVAL

1. Remove the headlight door retaining screws and remove the headlight doors.

2. Remove one retaining screw from each side of the grille at the headlight housing (Fig. 4).

3. Remove the lower grille to center retaining screw (Fig. 4).

4. Remove the upper grille to support bracket retaining screws (Fig. 4) and remove the grille assembly.

INSTALLATION

1. Position the grille assembly in the grille opening and loosely install the upper retaining bolts.

2. Loosely install the lower grille-to-center support bracket retaining screw.

3. Install the end grille retaining screw at each headlight housing and tighten all bolts and screws.

4. Install the headlight doors.

RADIATOR GRILLE—FAIRLANE
REMOVAL

1. Remove the headlight door retaining screws and remove the headlight doors.

2. Remove the screws retaining the grille assembly to the hood lock support, the screws retaining the grille to the upper grille support brackets, and the three retaining screws from each end of the grille (Fig. 5).

3. Remove the grille assembly from the car.

4. Remove the three nuts retaining the grille ornament and remove the ornament.

5. Remove the screws retaining the upper and lower grille mould-

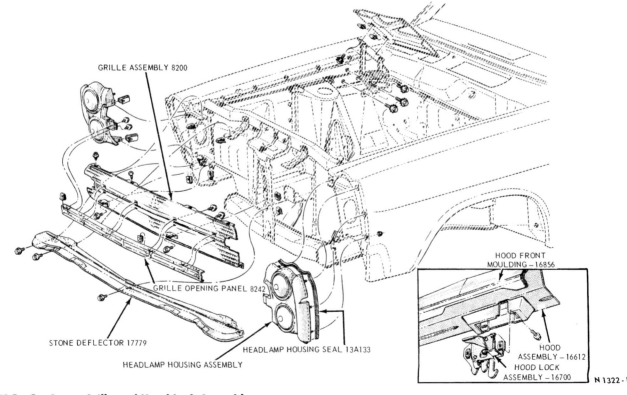

FIG. 3—Comet Grille and Hood Lock Assembly

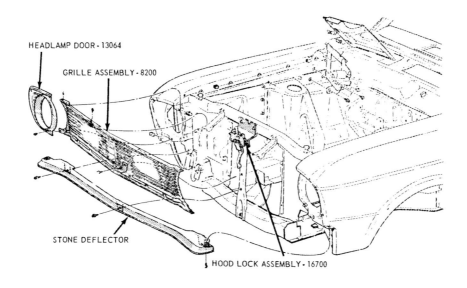

HEADLAMP DOOR - 13064

GRILLE ASSEMBLY - 8200

STONE DEFLECTOR

HOOD LOCK ASSEMBLY - 16700

N 1185 - E

FIG. 4—Falcon Grille and Hood Lock Assembly

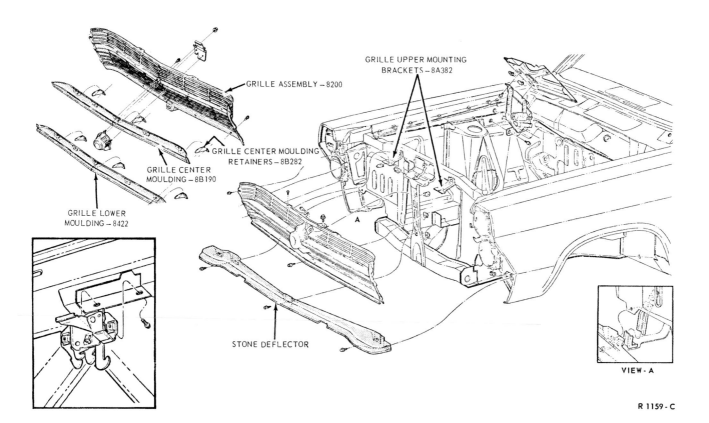

GRILLE ASSEMBLY - 8200

GRILLE UPPER MOUNTING
BRACKETS - 8A382

GRILLE CENTER MOULDING
RETAINERS - 8B282

GRILLE CENTER
MOULDING - 8B190

GRILLE LOWER
MOULDING - 8422

STONE DEFLECTOR

A

VIEW - A

R 1159 - C

FIG. 5—Fairlane Grille and Hood Lock Assembly

ings to the grille assembly and remove the grille mouldings and grille
moulding retainers.

INSTALLATION

1. Install the upper and lower
grille moulding retainers on the
grille mouldings, position the grille
mouldings on the grille and install
the grille moulding retaining screws.

2. Position the grille ornament
on the grille and install the ornament retainer and retaining nuts.

3. Position the grille assembly on
the car and grille assembly retaining screws

4. Install the headlight doors.

GRILLE—MUSTANG
REMOVAL

1. Open the hood.

2. Remove the four grille retaining screws from the lower inner
flange of the grille.

3. Remove the four grille retaining screws from the upper flange of
the grille upper center support
bracket to the hood lock hook support.

4. Remove the grille assembly.

INSTALLATION

1. Transfer the upper center support bracket, the grille bars and
ornament, and the spring nuts to the
new grille assembly.

2. Position the grille assembly on
the car and install the grille retaining screws.

3. Close the hood.

FRONT BUMPER—COMET,
FALCON, FAIRLANE
REMOVAL

1. Disconnect the parking light
wiring connectors and push the wires
through their routing holes in the
fender aprons.

2. Remove the bumper left and
right inner and outer arm-to-frame
side rail retaining bolts and remove
the bumper assembly. (Figs. 6, 7,
and 8).

3. Remove the bumper inner and
outer arms from the bumper.

4. Remove the license plate.

5. Remove the parking light assembly retaining nuts and remove
the parking light assemblies.

INSTALLATION

1. Install the license plate on the
new bumper.

2. Install the parking light assemblies in the new bumper.

3. Install the bumper inner and
outer arms on the new bumper using

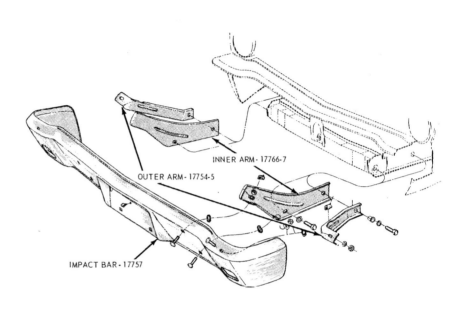

N 1365 - C

FIG. 6—Comet Front Bumper Installation

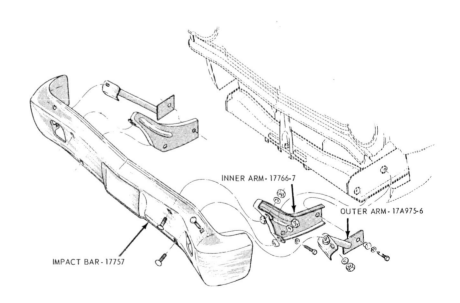

N 1366 - B

FIG. 7—Falcon Front Bumper Installation

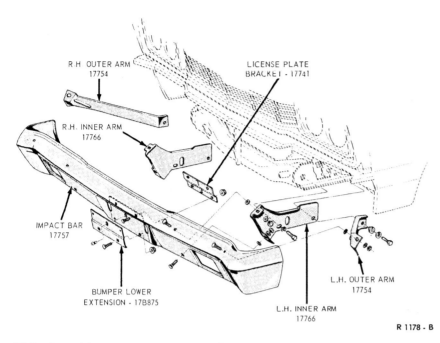

FIG. 8—Fairlane Front Bumper Installation

spacers and washers as shown in Figs. 6, 7 and 8.

4. Position the bumper assembly to the car and loosely install the bumper arm-to-frame side rail retaining bolts.

5. Align the bumper assembly and tighten the bumper arm-to-frame side rail retaining bolts.

6. Route the parking light wiring through the fender aprons and connect the wiring connectors.

FRONT BUMPER—MUSTANG
REMOVAL

1. Raise the car to provide working access.

2. Tape the stone deflector to prevent scratching the paint finish.

3. Remove the left and right bumper-to-fender bracket bolts from the fenders.

4. Remove the bumper bar-to-inner arm and the bumper bar-to-outer arm retaining bolts from each side of the bumper (Fig. 9). Remove the bumper and bumper-to-fender bracket as an assembly.

INSTALLATION

1. Transfer the bumper-to-fender bracket to the new bumper.

2. Position the bumper on the car. Install the bumper bar-to-inner arm and the bumper bar-to-outer arm retaining bolts.

3. Install the bumper-to-fender bracket retaining bolts.

4. Remove the protective tape from the stone deflector and lower the car.

FRONT BUMPER GUARD—MUSTANG

1. Remove the screw and washer retaining the bumper guard to the

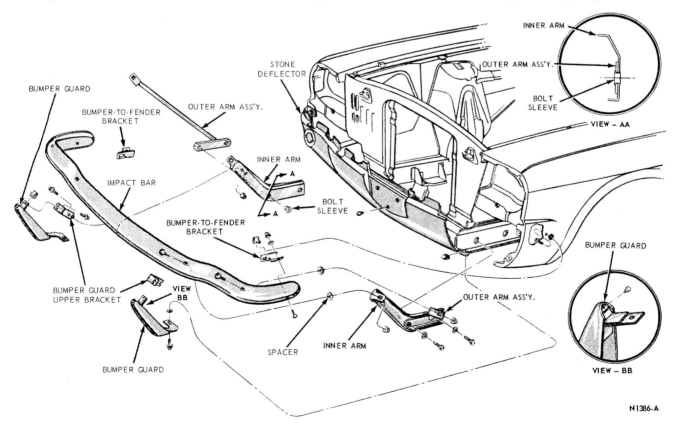

FIG. 9—Mustang Front Bumper Installation

lower frame side rail (Fig. 9).

2. Remove the screw and washer retaining the bumper-guard-to-guard upper bracket and remove the guard assembly.

3. Transfer the nut and retainer assembly and the rubber spacer to the new bumper guard (Fig. 9, View "BB").

4. Position the bumper guard assembly on the car.

5. Install the two retaining screws and washers.

REAR BUMPER—FALCON
REMOVAL

1. Remove the screws retaining the license plate lamp assembly to the rear bumper.

2. Remove the rear license plate.

3. Remove the four bumper arm-to-frame retaining bolts (Fig. 10), and remove the bumper assembly.

INSTALLATION

1. Transfer the rear bumper arms and rubber bumper to the new bumper.

2. Position the bumper assembly on the car and install the bumper arm-to-frame retaining bolts.

3. Position the license plate lamp assembly to the bumper and install the retaining bolts.

4. Install the license plate.

REAR BUMPER IMPACT BAR— COMET, FAIRLANE
REMOVAL

1. Open the luggage compartment. Disconnect the license light wiring connector and push the license light wire out of its routing grommet.

2. Remove the spare tire and wheel assembly.

3. From beneath the car, remove the access covers from the lower bumper arm-to-lower back panel retaining screw and washer assemblies.

4. Remove the lower inner arm-to-lower back panel retaining screw and washer assemblies (Fig. 11).

5. From inside the luggage compartment, remove the upper inner arm-to-lower back panel retaining screw and washer assemblies (Fig. 11). Remove the bumper assembly from the car and place it on a bench.

6. FAIRLANE ONLY: Remove the screw and washer assemblies retaining the license plate support bracket to the impact bar (Fig. 11), and remove the license plate support bracket assembly from the impact bar.

7. Remove the rubber license sup-

port bracket-to-impact bar bumpers (Fig. 11).

8. Remove the bumper outer and inner arm-to-impact bar retaining bolts and spacers (Fig. 11). Remove the outer and inner arms from the impact bar.

INSTALLATION

1. Insert the bumper inner and outer arm-to-impact bar retaining bolts in the impact bar. Install the spacers and the inner and outer arms on the impact bar. Torque the retaining nuts to 17 to 23 ft-lbs.

2. Install the license plate support rubber bumpers on the impact bar.

3. FAIRLANE ONLY: Install the license plate support on the impact bar.

4. Position the bumper assembly on the car. Feed the license plate light wire through its routing grommet in the lower back panel and start one upper arm-to-body retaining screw on each side.

5. Shift the bumper assembly as necessary for proper alignment and install the remaining bumper arm-to-body retaining screws. Torque the retaining screws to 25 to 38 ft-lbs specification.

6. Install the lower bumper arm-to-lower back panel retaining screw access covers.

7. Install the spare tire and wheel assembly. Connect the license plate light wiring connector.

REAR BUMPER—MUSTANG
REMOVAL

1. Open the luggage compartment. Remove the spare wheel and disconnect the license light wiring connector.

2. Remove the four bumper mounting bracket-to-body retaining bolts and remove the bumper assembly (Fig. 12).

3. Remove the four bumper-to-mounting bracket retaining bolts and remove the brackets (Fig. 12).

4. Remove the two license plate light and bracket retaining screws and remove the light and bracket.

INSTALLATION

1. Position the license plate light and bracket on the bumper and install the two retaining screws.

2. Position the bumper mounting brackets on the bumper and install the bumper-to-mounting bracket retaining bolts.

3. Connect the license light wiring and install the spare wheel.

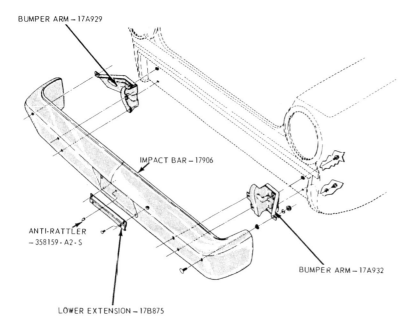

BUMPER ARM – 17A929

IMPACT BAR – 17906

ANTI-RATTLER –358159-A2-S

BUMPER ARM – 17A932

LOWER EXTENSION – 17B875

N 1367 - B

FIG. 10—Falcon Rear Bumper Installation

REAR BUMPER GUARD—MUSTANG

REMOVAL

1. Open the luggage compartment door and remove the spare tire assembly to provide access to the upper guard retaining screw and washer.

2. From inside the luggage compartment, remove the upper guard retaining screw and washer (Fig. 12).

3. From beneath the car, remove the lower guard retaining screw and washer (Fig. 12). Remove the bumper guard.

INSTALLATION

1. Transfer the two nuts and retainers to the new bumper guard. Transfer the rubber spacers to the new bumper guard.

2. Position the bumper guard on the car and install the two retaining screws and washers.

3. Install the spare tire assembly.

EXTERIOR MOULDINGS

Before removing the exterior mouldings, it should be determined by the type of retainer used whether a respective door, quarter or luggage compartment trim panel must first be removed to provide access (Figs. 13 through 31).

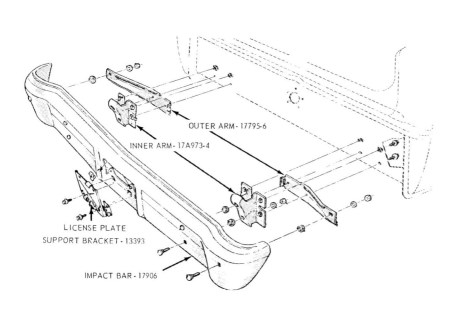

N 1417-B

FIG. 11—Comet, Fairlane Rear Bumper Installation

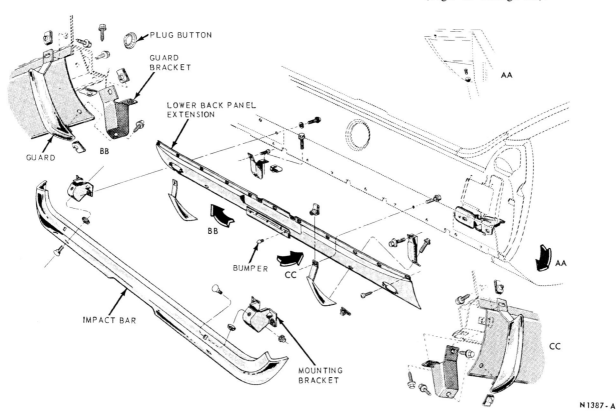

N 1387-A

FIG. 12—Mustang Rear Bumper Installation

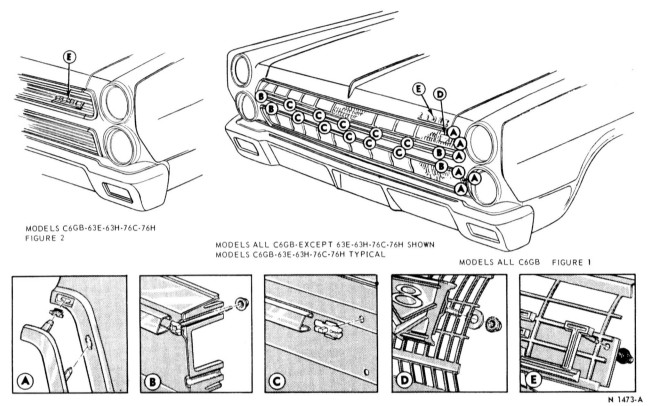

MODELS C6GB-63E-63H-76C-76H
FIGURE 2

MODELS ALL C6GB-EXCEPT 63E-63H-76C-76H SHOWN
MODELS C6GB-63E-63H-76C-76H TYPICAL

MODELS ALL C6GB   FIGURE 1

N 1473-A

FIG. 13—Exterior Front Mouldings—Comet Models (ALL)

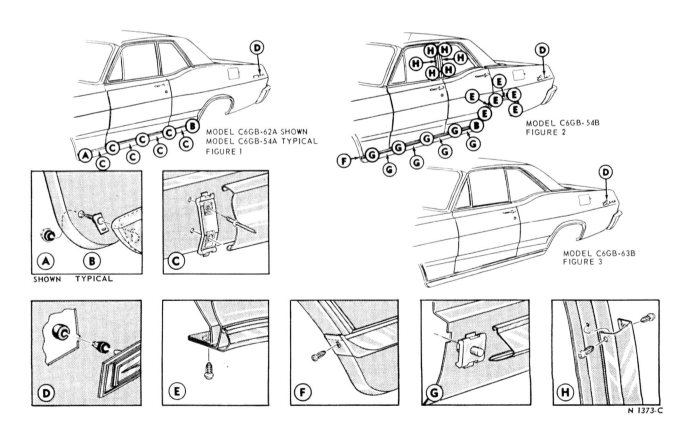

MODEL C6GB-62A SHOWN
MODEL C6GB-54A TYPICAL
FIGURE 1

MODEL C6GB-54B
FIGURE 2

MODEL C6GB-63B
FIGURE 3

SHOWN   TYPICAL

N 1373-C

FIG. 14—Exterior Mouldings—Comet Models 54A, 62A, 63B

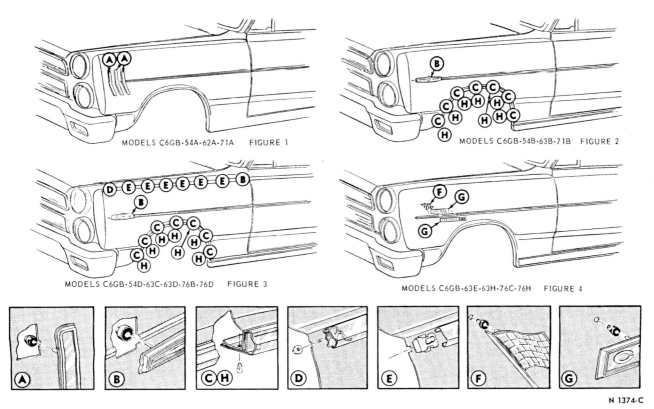

FIG. 15—Exterior Front Mouldings—Comet (Except Models 71C)

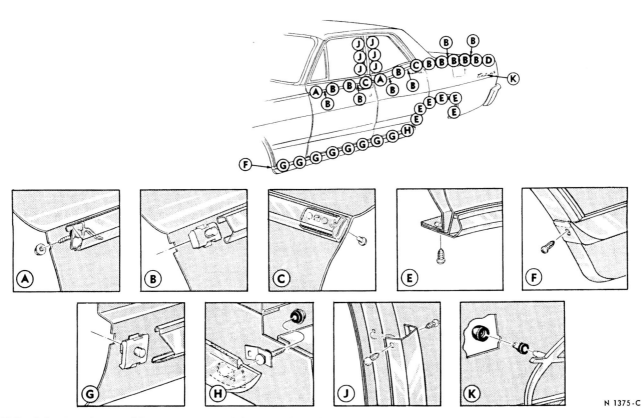

FIG. 16—Exterior Mouldings—Comet Models 54D, 63C, 63D, 76B, 76D

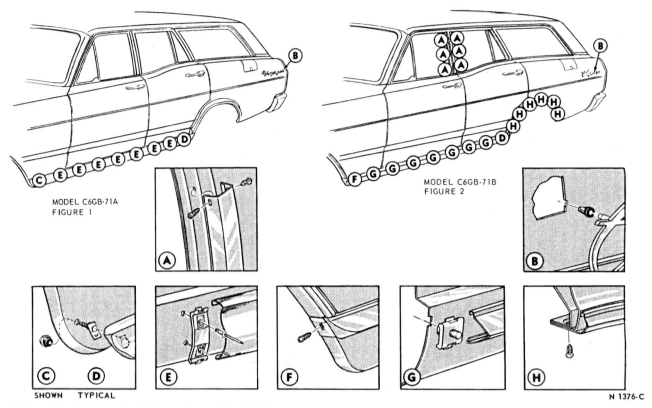

FIG. 17—Exterior Mouldings—Comet Model 71

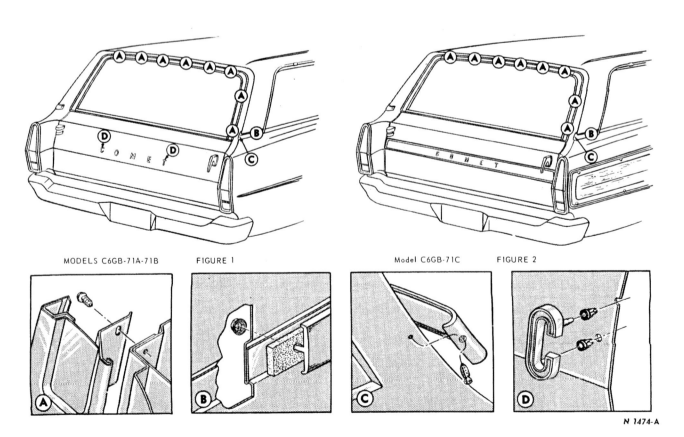

FIG. 18—Exterior Rear Mouldings—Comet Model 71

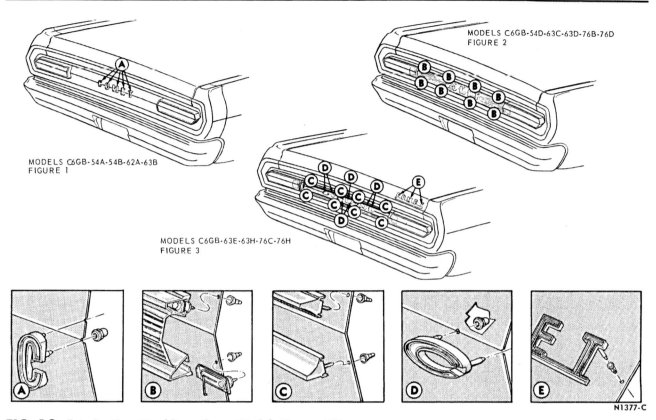

MODELS C6GB-54A-54B-62A-63B
FIGURE 1

MODELS C6GB-54D-63C-63D-76B-76D
FIGURE 2

MODELS C6GB-63E-63H-76C-76H
FIGURE 3

N1377-C

FIG. 19—Exterior Rear Moulding—Comet Models (Except 71)

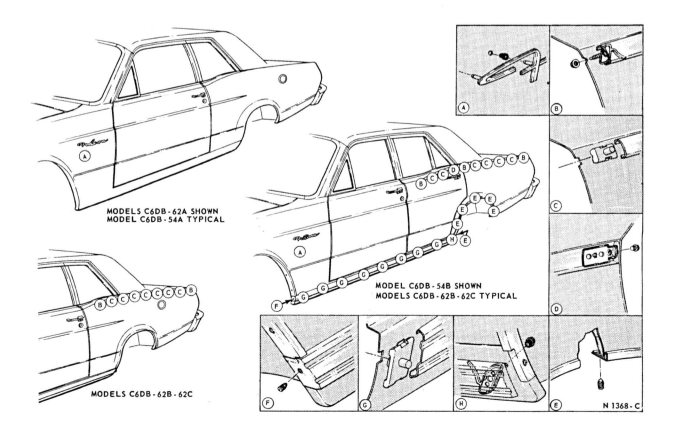

MODELS C6DB-62A SHOWN
MODEL C6DB-54A TYPICAL

MODELS C6DB-62B-62C

MODEL C6DB-54B SHOWN
MODELS C6DB-62B-62C TYPICAL

N 1368-C

FIG. 20—Exterior Mouldings—Falcon Models 54A, 54B, 62A, 62B, 62C

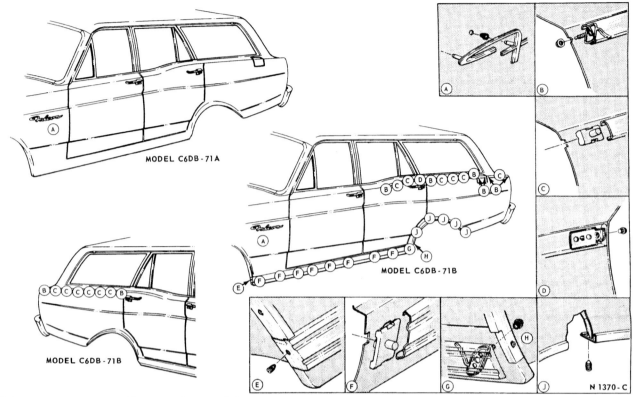

FIG. 21—Exterior Mouldings—Falcon Models 71A, 71B

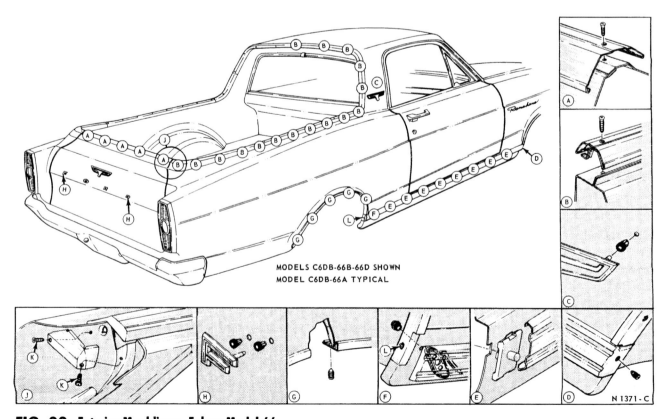

FIG. 22—Exterior Mouldings—Falcon Model 66

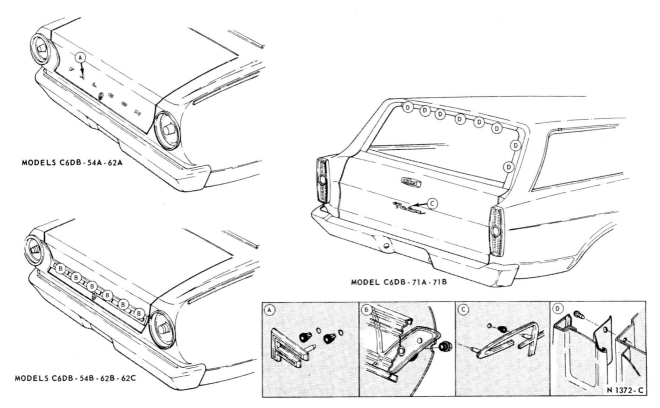

MODELS C6DB - 54A - 62A

MODELS C6DB - 54B - 62B - 62C

MODEL C6DB - 71A - 71B

N 1372 - C

FIG. 23—Exterior Rear Mouldings—Falcon Models 54, 62, 71

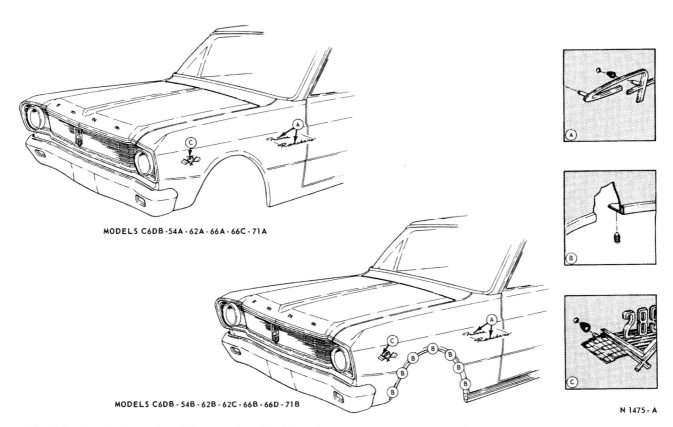

MODELS C6DB - 54A - 62A - 66A - 66C - 71A

MODELS C6DB - 54B - 62B - 62C - 66B - 66D - 71B

N 1475 - A

FIG. 24—Exterior Front Mouldings—Falcon Models (ALL)

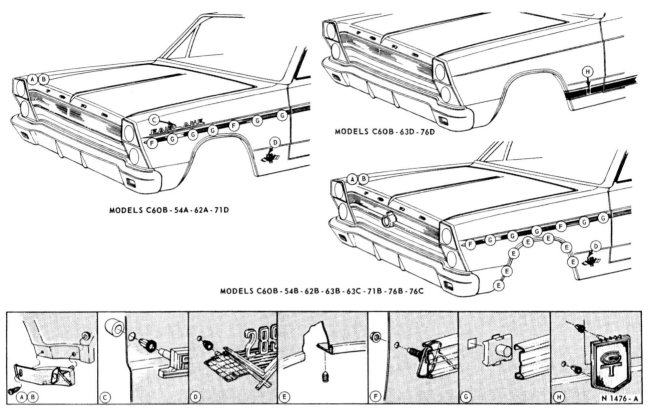

MODELS C60B - 54A - 62A - 71D

MODELS C60B - 63D - 76D

MODELS C60B - 54B - 62B - 63B - 63C - 71B - 76B - 76C

N 1476 - A

FIG. 25—Exterior Front Mouldings—Fairlane

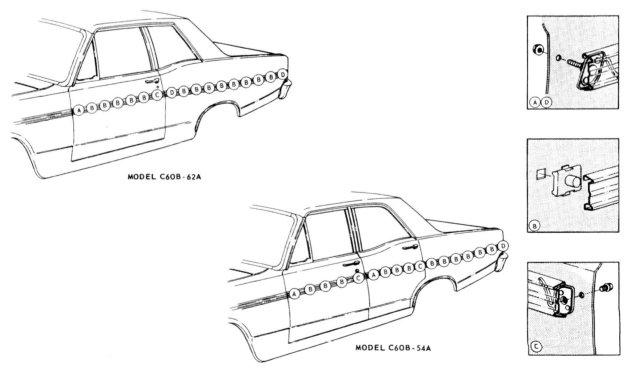

MODEL C60B - 62A

MODEL C60B - 54A

N 1381-C

FIG. 26—Exterior Mouldings—Fairlane Models 54A, 62A

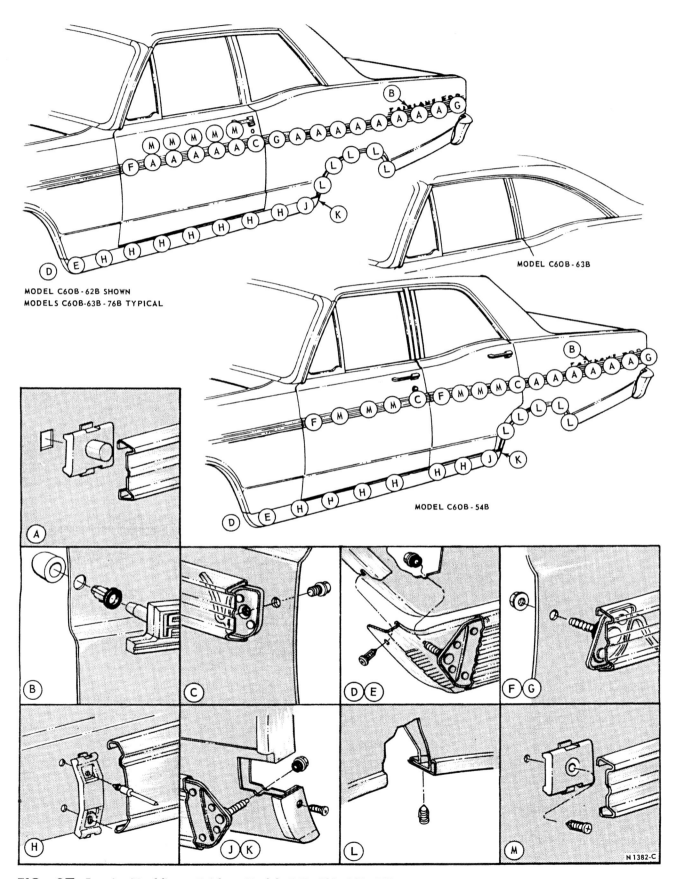

MODEL C60B-63B

MODEL C60B-62B SHOWN
MODELS C60B-63B-76B TYPICAL

MODEL C60B-54B

FIG. 27—Exterior Mouldings—Fairlane Models 54B, 62B, 63B, 76B

N 1382-C

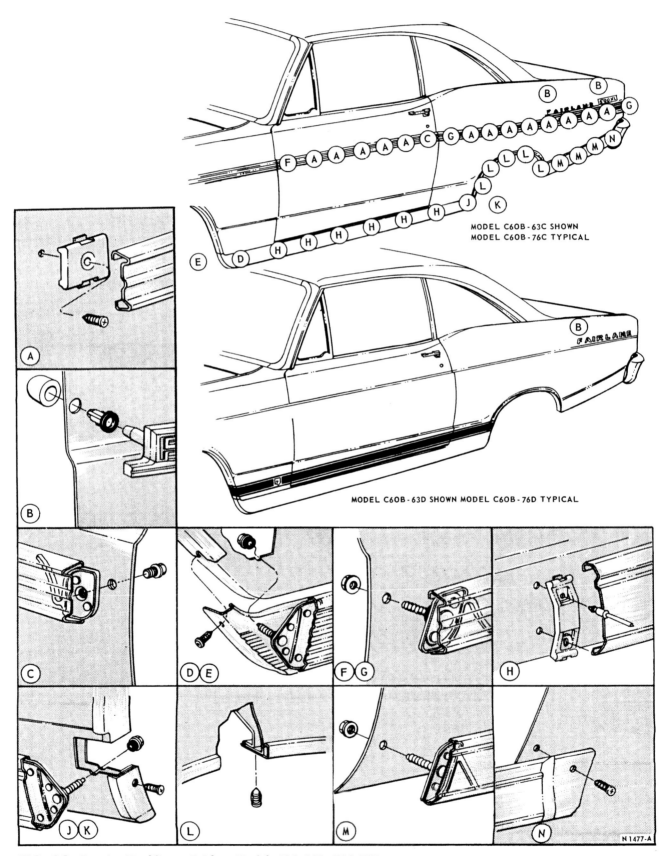

MODEL C60B - 63C SHOWN
MODEL C60B - 76C TYPICAL

MODEL C60B - 63D SHOWN MODEL C60B - 76D TYPICAL

N 1477-A

FIG. 28—Exterior Mouldings—Fairlane Models 63C, 63D, 76C, 76D

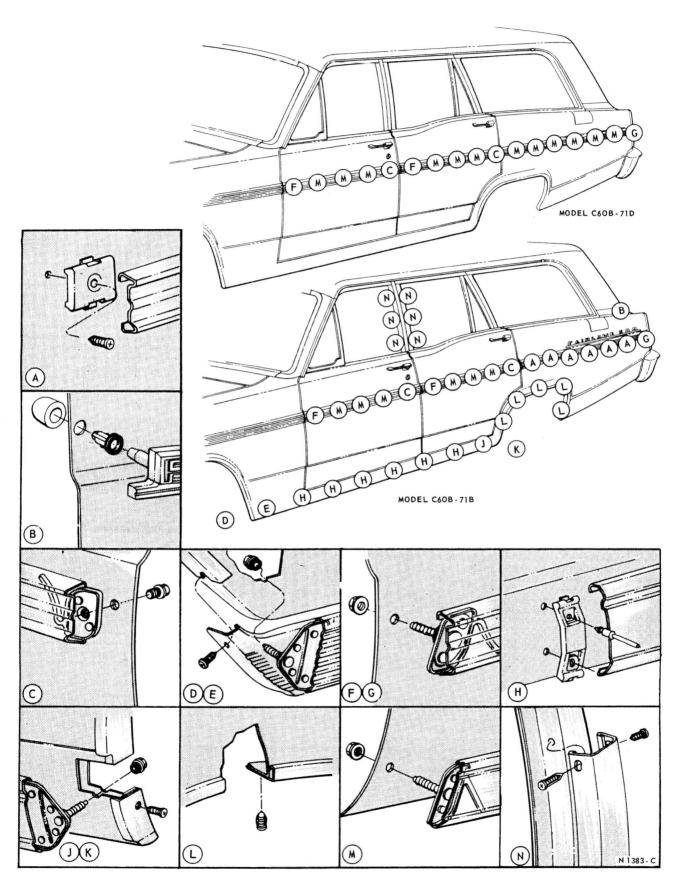

FIG. 29—Exterior Mouldings—Fairlane Models 71

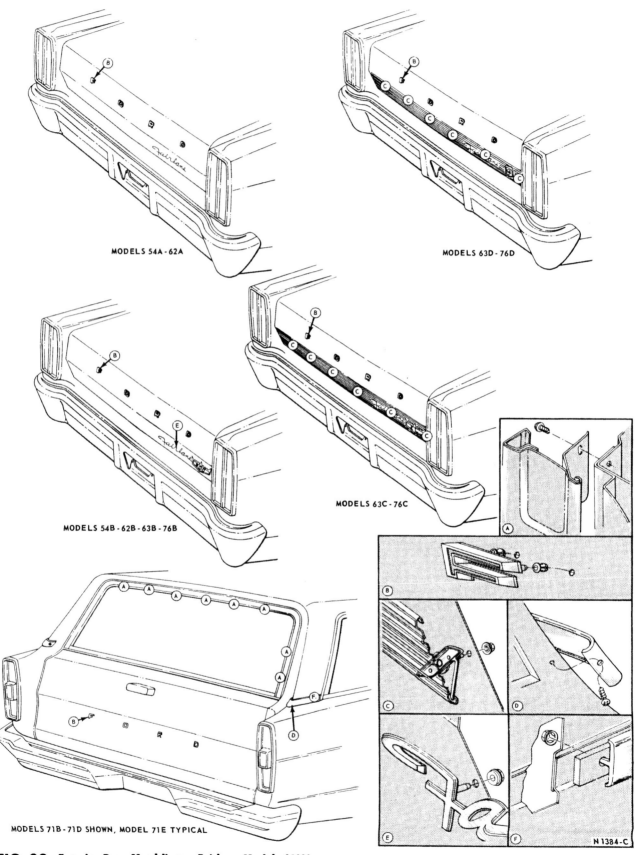

MODELS 54A - 62A

MODELS 63D - 76D

MODELS 54B - 62B - 63B - 76B

MODELS 63C - 76C

MODELS 71B - 71D SHOWN, MODEL 71E TYPICAL

N 1384-C

FIG. 30—Exterior Rear Mouldings—Fairlane Models (ALL)

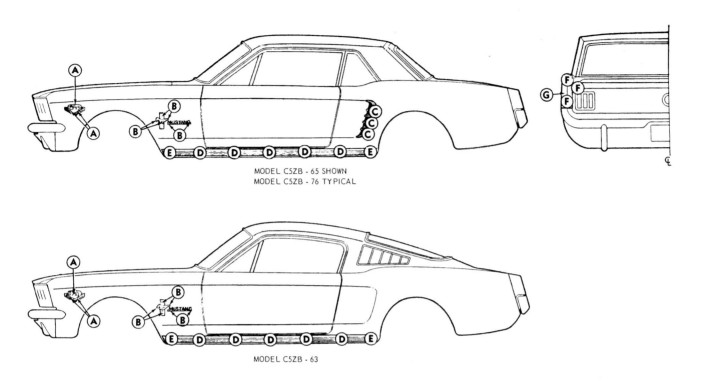

MODEL C5ZB - 65 SHOWN
MODEL C5ZB - 76 TYPICAL

MODEL C5ZB - 63

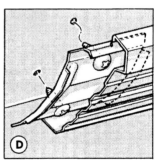

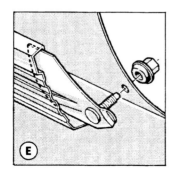

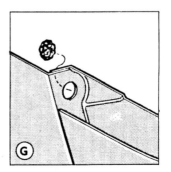

N 1416 - A

FIG. 31—Exterior Mouldings—Mustang Models (ALL)

PART 17-3

DOORS, WINDOWS, TAILGATE AND DECK LID

Section   **Page**

1 In-Car Adjustments and Repairs..............17-30
   Door Alignment.........................17-30
   Lock Striker Adjustment...................17-30
   Vent Window Adjustment—Comet, Falcon
     Except Models 63, 76...................17-31
   Door Glass Adjustment—Comet, Fairlane
     Models 63, 76......................17-31
   Front Door Glass Adjustment—Comet,
     Falcon, Fairlane Models 54, 71..........17-32
   Door Glass Adjustment—Comet, Falcon,
     Fairlane Models 62....................17-32
   Door Window Adjustment—Mustang.......17-32
   Rear Door Window Adjustment—Comet,
     Falcon, Fairlane......................17-33
   Quarter Window Adjustment—Comet,
     Falcon, Fairlane Model 62...............17-36
   Quarter Window Adjustment—Comet,
     Fairlane Model 63....................17-36
   Quarter Window Adjustment—Comet,
     Fairlane Model 76....................17-36
   Quarter Window Adjustment—Mustang......17-36
   Tailgate Emergency Opening Procedure.......17-36
   Dual-Action Tailgate Adjustments..........17-37
   Standard Tailgate Hinge Adjustment........17-37
   Deck Lock Adjustment..................17-37
   Deck Lid Alignment....................17-37
2 Removal and Installation....................17-39
   Doors................................17-39
   Front Door Lock—Except Models 63, 76.....17-39
   Front Door Lock—Models 63, 76...........17-39
   Rear Door Lock........................17-39
   Door Lock Cylinder.....................17-39
   Door Handle or Push Button..............17-39
   Door Vent Window Frame—Except
     Models 63, 76......................17-39
   Vent Window or Weatherstrip—Models
     63, 76...........................17-41
   Front Door Glass—Except Models 63, 76.....17-41

Section   **Page**

   Front Door Glass—Comet, Fairlane
     Model 63, 76.......................17-41
   Front Door Window Regulator—Manual—
     Comet, Fairlane—Model 63, 76...........17-42
   Front Door Window Regulator—Except
     Models 63, 76......................17-42
   Front Door Rear Glass Run—Models 63, 76..17-42
   Rear Door Glass—Comet, Falcon—
     Model 54..........................17-42
   Rear Door Window Regulator..............17-42
   Quarter Glass—Model 62................17-43
   Quarter Window Regulator—Model 62.......17-43
   Quarter Window Regulator—Model 63.......17-43
   Quarter Window Front Guide—Model 63.....17-43
   Quarter Window Rear Guide—Model 63.....17-43
   Rear Quarter Window Glass—Fairlane,
     Comet—Model 76...................17-43
   Rear Quarter Window and/or Weatherstrip—
     Model 71..........................17-44
   Windshield—Comet, Falcon, Fairlane........17-44
   Windshield—Mustang Model 63, 65.........17-47
   Windshield—Mustang Model 76...........17-48
   Back Window and/or Weatherstrip—
     Comet, Falcon, Fairlane................17-49
   Back Window—Mustang Model 65.........17-49
   Back Window—Mustang Model 63.........17-50
   Inside Rear View Mirror (Bonded to
     Windshield)........................17-51
   Tailgate Glass.........................17-52
   Tailgate Window Regulator...............17-53
   Tailgate Switch and Lock Cylinder—Power...17-54
   Tailgate Window Handle and Lock Cylinder—
     Manual...........................17-54
   Dual-Action Tailgate Hinges...............17-55
   Dual-Action Tailgate Locks................17-55
   Dual-Action Tailgate Torsion Bar...........17-55
   Deck Lid Hinge or Torsion/Bar.............17-55
   Deck Lid Lock........................17-55

1 IN-CAR ADJUSTMENTS AND REPAIRS

DOOR ALIGNMENT

The door hinges provide sufficient adjustment to correct most misalignment conditions. Loosen the door hinge attaching bolts and adjust the door so that it is centered in the door opening when closed. Then, tighten the hinge attaching bolts.

After adjustment at the hinge attaching points, check the alignment between the door lock and

striker plate for proper door closing. **Do not cover up poor door adjustment with striker plate adjustment.**

LOCK STRIKER ADJUSTMENT

The striker pin can be adjusted laterally and vertically as well as fore and aft. **The lock striker should not be adjusted to correct door sag.** The lock striker should be shimmed to get the clearance shown in Fig. 1

between the lock striker and the lock. To check this clearance, clean the lock jaws and the striker area, and then apply a thin layer of dark grease to the lock striker. As the door is closed and opened, a measurable pattern will result. Move the striker assembly laterally to provide a flush fit at the door and the pillar or quarter panel.

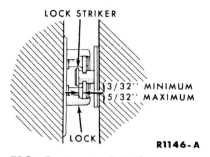

FIG. 1—Door Lock Striker Adjustment

VENT WINDOW ADJUSTMENTS—COMET, FALCON EXCEPT MODELS 63, 76

The vent glass and/or the vent window frame may be adjusted in various ways. With the vent glass installed, the lower pivot spring tension may be adjusted with a socket, extension, and ratchet used through the access hole in the door inner panel. Adjust so that the glass will stay open at highway speeds. The door frame mounting holes are elongated to provide a tight fit for the vent window frame in the door frame. The upper pivot mounting holes are slotted to help provide a weather-proof fit of the glass frame within the vent window frame.

DOOR GLASS ADJUSTMENT— COMET, FAIRLANE MODELS 63, 76

The door must be properly aligned in the body opening before glass adjustments are made.

1. Remove the door trim panel and peel back the watershield to provide access.
2. Loosen screw and washer assemblies A, J, Z and AB, also nuts C, E and L (Fig. 2).
3. Cycle the window to its up position and manually position the window assembly inboard or outboard, as required, for proper alignment to the outside belt weatherstrip and tighten the screw and washer assemblies J.
4. Tilt the window assembly fore or aft as required, to obtain a parallel relationship between the top of the window and the roof rail weatherstrip. This will position the rear guide assembly in correct fore and aft alignment. Tighten nut L temporarily. Turn screw G clockwise or counter-clockwise, as required, to maintain position of the guide assembly and tighten nut and washer assembly H securely. At this point, adjust the door window stop assemblies up or down as required, for correct engagement.

Tighten the screw and washer assemblies, Y and AB securely.

5. Position the vent window assembly and vent window division bar glass run rearward, into a position relative to the door window glass and tilt fore and aft, as required, to maintain a parallel relationship to the front body pillar. Tighten the screw and washer assemblies A securely. The adjusted position of the vent window assembly should be such as to provide window travel free of binding.
6. To provide a proper interference relationship of the vent window and the door window assemblies to the top roof rail weatherstrip, tilt these assemblies inboard or outboard as required, by turning the screws, B, D and K clockwise or counterclockwise, to the desired setting and then tighten the nuts C, E and L securely. At this point, secure the vent window regulator assembly door vent window, by tightening the screw and the washer assemblies A securely.
7. When the above steps are completed, cycle the window down until the top of the window is flush with the belt and position the down stop assembly to the bumper door window stop and secure it with the

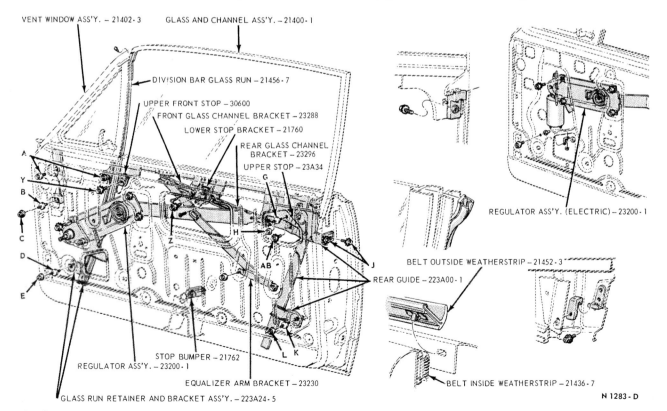

FIG. 2—Door Window Mechanism—Comet, Fairlane Models 63, 76

screw and washer assemblies Z.

8. Install the watershield and the door trim panel.

FRONT DOOR GLASS ADJUSTMENTS—COMET, FALCON FAIRLANE MODELS 54, 71

The door trim panel must be removed to make any of the following adjustments.

Fore-and-aft adjustment for snug glass fit within the runs may be made by using suitable shim stock between the front run and the vent window division bar. The front and/or the rear run may also be shimmed at the lower attaching point(s).

Vertical adjustment is possible by means of the single stop (Fig. 3). When the glass is fully lowered, the upper edge should be even with the belt line.

Lateral adjustment for smooth movement of the glass within the runs can be made by moving the lower attaching points of the run (Fig. 3).

DOOR GLASS ADJUSTMENT—COMET, FALCON, FAIRLANE MODELS 62

1. Remove the door trim panel and peel back the watershield to pro-

vide access. Refer to Fig. 4 for the following adjustments.

2. To obtain proper alignment of the lockside glass run retainer assembly to the door window frame and vent window division bar with the retainer, loosen nut and washer assembly D and screw and washer assembly E. Drop the top edge of the glass and channel assembly to approximately four inches above the door outer panel belt line. Turn screw C clockwise or counterclockwise as required. Tighten items D and E securely.

3. To obtain a flush condition between the top edge of the glass and channel assembly and the belt line when the window is in the down position, the stop assembly is adjusted up or down at screw and washer assemblies U. After adjustment, tighten the screw and washer assemblies U securely.

DOOR WINDOW ADJUSTMENT—MUSTANG

1. Remove the door trim panel and watershield.

2. With the glass and channel assembly in the up position, the vent window assembly is adjusted forward or backward and up or down at

points A to obtain a parallel clearance between the windshield side moulding and the forward edge of the front door vent window frame, typical of Fig. 5. Adjustment fore and aft is to be made so that the glass and channel assembly will operate freely with no binding in the door glass lockside run and retainer assembly, but still have adequate engagement of sliding glass with the vent window division bar run and bracket assembly. Tighten the screw and washer assemblies at point A sufficiently to hold the vent window in position.

3. To obtain proper alignment with the windshield outside side moulding and to obtain the proper interference between the roof rail weatherstrip and the top edge of the vent window frame, the vent window assembly may be tilted toward the inside or outside of the body by rotating the adjusting screw at point B clockwise or counterclockwise. Tighten the jam nut at point B. Then, adjust the set screw at point C until the shoulder of the screw is against the door vent window division bar lower support. Do not create any bind or distort the glass run. After adjustment, tighten the jam nut at point C. Tighten the

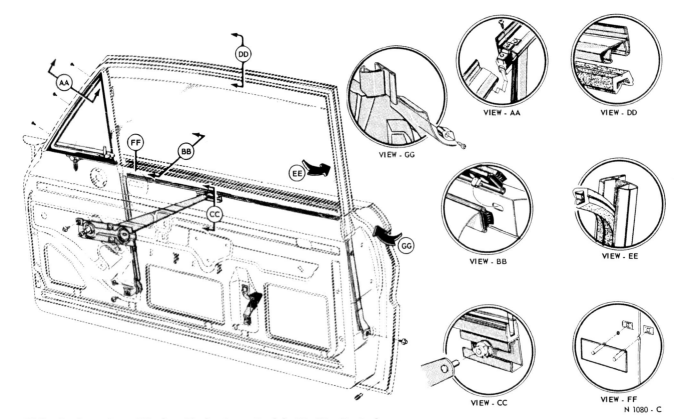

FIG. 3—Front Door Window Mechanism—Models 54, 71—Typical

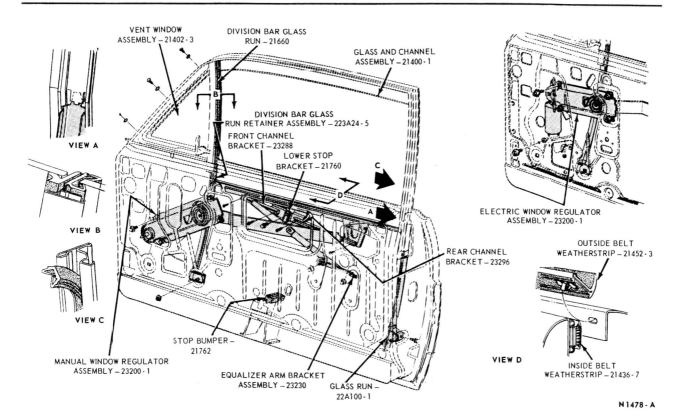

FIG. 4—Door Window Mechanism—Falcon, Comet, Fairlane—Model 62

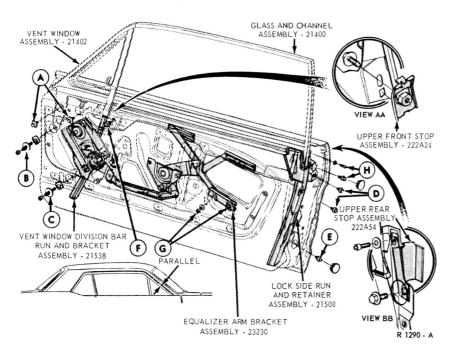

FIG. 5—Door Window Mechanism—Mustang

screw and washer assemblies at point A.

4. To obtain the proper interference of the glass assembly against the outside belt rail weatherstrip and the roof rail weatherstrip, the glass assembly may be adjusted to tilt toward the inside or outside of the body at points D and E. After adjustment, tighten the screw and washer assemblies at points D and E.

5. To obtain a flush condition between the top edge of the glass and channel assembly and the top edge of the vent window frame, the front stop assembly is adjusted up or down at point F; after adjustment, tighten the screw and washer assembly at point F securely. (See View AA, Fig. 5).

6. To make the top edge of the glass assembly parallel to the roof rail weatherstrip, the equalizer arm bracket and the rear stop assembly may be adjusted up or down as required at points G and H. After adjustment, tighten the nuts at points G and the screw and washer assembly, point H securely.

REAR DOOR WINDOW ADJUSTMENT—COMET, FALCON, FAIRLANE

1. Remove the door trim panel and watershield.

2. To obtain proper alignment of retainer and division bar assembly-to-door- window frame, loosen nut and washer assembly C. Drop the glass and channel assembly to its down position and turn screw B clockwise or counterclockwise as required. Tighten nut and washer assembly C securely (Fig. 6).

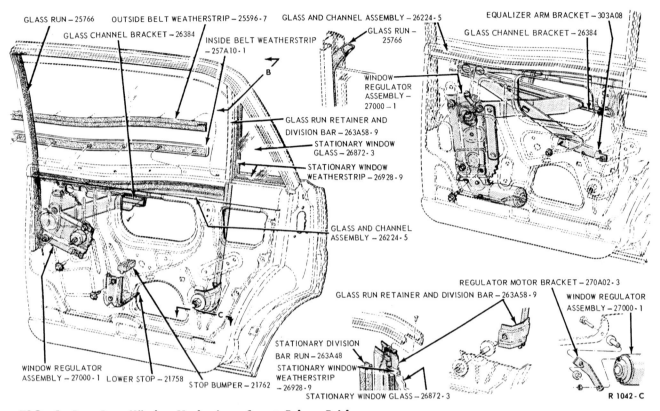

FIG. 6—Rear Door Window Mechanism—Comet, Falcon, Fairlane

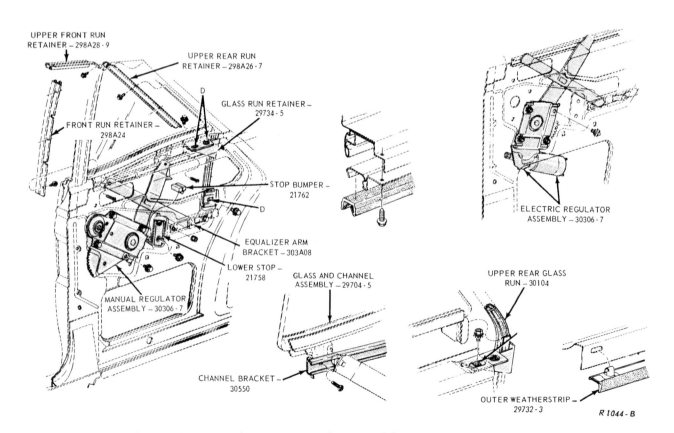

FIG. 7—Quarter Window Mechanism—Falcon, Comet, Fairlane—Model 62

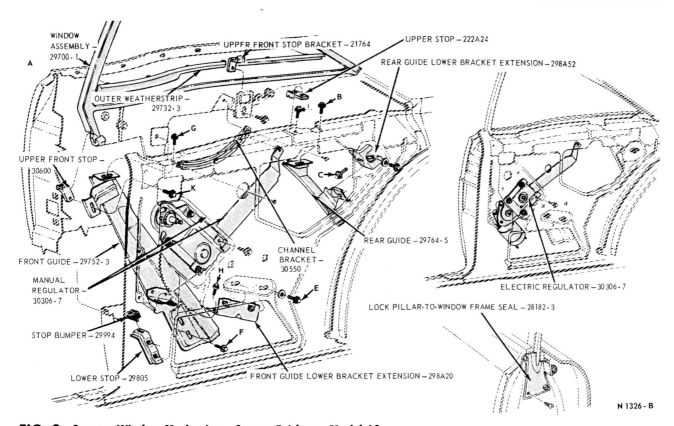

FIG. 8—Quarter Window Mechanism—Comet, Fairlane—Model 63

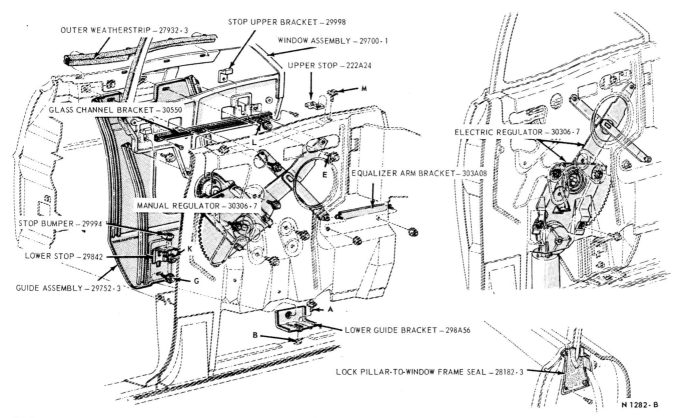

FIG. 9—Quarter Window Mechanism—Comet, Fairlane—Model 76

3. Install the watershield and door trim panel.

QUARTER WINDOW ADJUST-MENT—COMET, FALCON, FAIRLANE—MODEL 62

1. Remove the quarter trim panel and watershield.

2. To obtain proper clearance between the quarter window assembly and the quarter window glass run retainer assembly, operate the window to its full down position, loosen screw and washer assembly D, and adjust the retainer assembly forward. After adjustment, tighten the screw and washer assembly finger tight (Fig. 7).

3. To obtain proper clearance between the quarter window assembly and the quarter window glass run retainer assembly, operate the window to its full up position. Loosen screw and washer assemblies D and adjust the retainer assembly forward. After adjustment, tighten screw and washer assemblies D securely.

4. Install the watershield and quarter trim panel.

QUARTER WINDOW ADJUST-MENT—COMET, FAIRLANE MODEL 63

1. Remove the quarter trim panel and watershield to provide access. Refer to Fig. 8 for the following procedure.

2. Temporarily loosen screw and washer assemblies A, B, C, E, F, G, H, K, and L (Fig. 8).

3. It is necessary to obtain a 0.26 to 0.30 inch parallel dimension between the front edge of the quarter window frame and the rear edge of the door window frame as shown in view B, the 0.26 inch parallel dimension as shown in view C, and maintain height relationship of the quarter window to the door window frame and roof rail weatherstrip. To do this, set the quarter window assembly into position and temporarily secure the front guide assembly and *the rear guide* assembly, by tightening screw and washer assemblies G and B finger tight. Also secure the upper stop assemblies and the door window stop bracket, by tightening the screw and washer assemblies K, L and M securely. The extension assembly, quarter window front guide lower bracket, is secured by tightening screw and washer assemblies E.

4. To obtain proper alignment of the quarter window assembly with

the door window glass and channel assembly and proper interference with the roof rail weatherstrip, tilt the front guide assembly inboard or outboard at the bottom as required. When adjustment is complete, tighten screw and washer assemblies H securely.

5. Cycle the quarter window assembly to its down position, flush with the top of the quarter panel. This will locate the rear guide assembly and quarter window rear guide lower extension assembly in its proper position.

6. Tighten screw and washer assemblies A and C securely. Position the quarter window lower stop assembly firmly against the bottom edge of the quarter window assembly and tighten screw and washer assemblies F securely.

7. Cycle the quarter window assembly to its down position and secure the front and rear guide assemblies by tightening screw and washer assemblies B and G securely.

8. Install the watershield and quarter trim panel.

QUARTER WINDOW ADJUST-MENT—COMET, FAIRLANE MODEL 76

1. Remove the quarter trim panel and watershield.

2. Loosen the screw and washer assemblies A, B, E, G, K, L and M (Fig. 9).

3. Position the window fore and aft and tilt it fore and aft as required for alignment to the front door window and roof rail. This will properly position the quarter window guide panel assembly. Tighten screw and washer assemblies E securely.

4. Position the upper stop assemblies (Fig. 9) and the quarter upper stop brackets and tighten the retaining screw and washer assemblies L and M.

5. Secure the window guide lower bracket to the guide assembly by tightening screw and washer assembly G.

6. To provide alignment with the front door window and an interference fit with the roof rail weatherstrip, tilt the guide assembly inboard or outboard as required. Tighten screw and washer assemblies A and B.

7. Cycle the window to its down position so that the top of the window is flush with the belt line. Position the lower stop assembly

against the window channel and tighten the lower stop assembly retaining screw K (Fig. 9).

8. Cycle the window up and down to recheck alignment. Then, install the watershield and quarter trim panel.

QUARTER WINDOW ADJUST-MENT—MUSTANG

1. Remove the rear seat cushion and seat back.

2. Remove the quarter trim panel and watershield.

3. To obtain the 0.28-inch parallel dimension between the front edge of the quarter window frame and the rear edge of the door window frame as shown in sectional view AA (Fig. 10) and to maintain a parallel alignment and interference between the top edge of the quarter window assembly and the roof rail weatherstrip, the quarter window guide assembly is adjusted forward or backward and up or down at the screw and washer assembly items A. See sectional views BB and CC (Fig. 10). Tighten the screw and washer assembly at items A, finger tight.

4. To obtain the proper alignment and interference between the top edges of the quarter window assembly and the roof rail weatherstrip, the guide assembly may be tilted toward the inside or outside of body at the screw and washer assembly at items A and B. After adjustment, tighten the screw and washer assemblies, items A and B securely.

5. To obtain the proper level between the quarter panel at the belt line and top edge of the glass and channel assembly, the quarter window stop may be adjusted up or down as required at the screw and washer assembly, item C. This adjustment is made with the window in the down position. After adjustment, tighten the screw and washer assembly, item C securely.

TAILGATE EMERGENCY OPENING PROCEDURE

Should failure occur on the power operated tailgate window in the up position, entry can be accomplished by disconnecting the window regulator arms from the glass assembly. Use the following procedure:

Carefully insert a hooked tool or wire between the outer weatherstrip and the tailgate window. Locate the window regulator arm *rollers. Insert* the hooked tool into the roller retaining spring clip and remove the

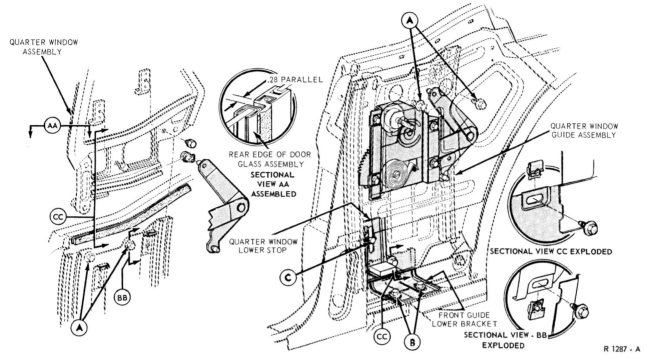

FIG. 10—Quarter Window Mechanism—Mustang Model 65, 76

clip from the roller. Hold the tailgate window firmly and pry the regulator arms off of the two rollers, carefully lower the window into the tailgate, then open the tailgate.

DUAL-ACTION TAILGATE ADJUSTMENTS

While full adjustments are provided for the dual action tailgate, no unique methods are employed. The following information will assist in locating and performing the adjustments.

The fore and aft and up and down adjustment of the tailgate is accomplished at the hinge side by means of square holes in the body pillar, backed by floating tapping plates, at the upper and lower hinge attachments (Fig. 11 and 12).

Lateral adjustment of the tailgate is accomplished at the upper hinge by adding or removing spacer shims between the hinge on the body and the pillar. Lateral adjustment at the lower hinge is accomplished by means of oversize holes in the tailgate at the hinge on the gate attachment (Figs. 11 and 12).

Fore and aft and up and down adjustment of the strikers is accomplished by means of square holes in the pillar backed by floating tapping plates. Lateral adjustment is accomplished by adding or removing shims (Fig. 13).

STANDARD TAILGATE HINGE ADJUSTMENT

The tailgate can be adjusted fore or aft and up or down at the hinge to body mounting bolts.

To adjust the tailgate from side

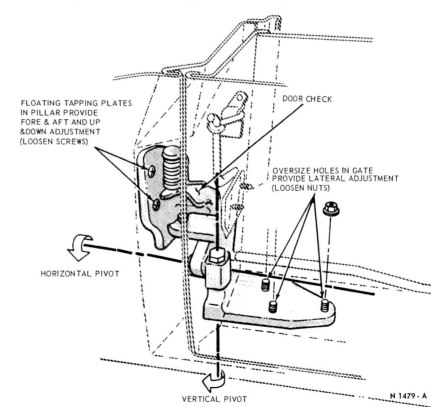

FIG. 11—Lower Left Hinge Assembly

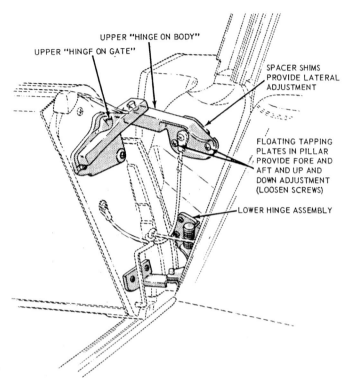

FIG. 12—Upper Left Hinge Assembly

to side in the tailgate opening, remove the trim panel, loosen the hinge to tailgate bolts and shift the tailgate as required.

DECK LOCK ADJUSTMENT

The striker plate can be adjusted laterally and vertically and the lock can be adjusted laterally. Before adjusting the deck lid lock, make sure that the deck lid is properly aligned. To adjust the lock, loosen the attaching screws, move the lock as required to make good contact and tighten the attaching screws. Move the striker plate up or down as necessary to increase or decrease the clearance between the deck lid and the lower back panel.

DECK LID ALIGNMENT

The deck lid can be shifted fore and aft, up and down, and from side to side. Slotted holes in the lid provide fore and aft movement. Slotted hinge bolt holes in the mounting bracket provide up and down movement. Enlarged hinge mounting bolt holes in the lid inner panel provide limited lateral movement.

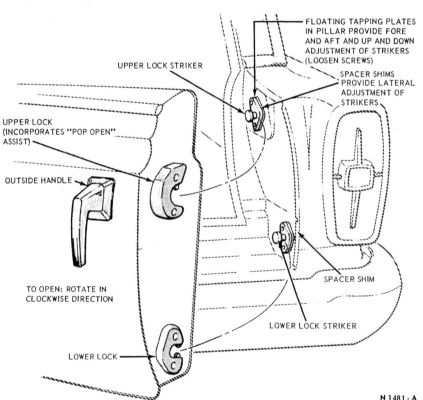

FIG. 13—Tailgate Lock Striker Adjustment

2 REMOVAL AND INSTALLATION

DOORS
REMOVAL

1. Remove the door hinge-to-door attaching bolts, and remove the door.

2. If a hinge is damaged, remove the pillar attaching bolts and remove the hinge.

3. If the door is damaged, a replacement door is furnished as a sheet metal shell in prime paint. It has no hinges, trim, glass, runs, or hardware. When a door is replaced, make any needed minor repairs to the new shell, drill holes necessary for mouldings, paint the door, and transfer all usable parts. Cement the weatherstrip properly.

If only a door outer panel is seriously damaged, the whole door need not be replaced. A replacement outer panel is available.

INSTALLATION

1. If the hinge was removed, install it to the pillar.

2. Position the door to the hinges. Partially tighten the bolts, align the door, and tighten the bolts securely.

3. Align the door glass, glass runs, stops, regulator, and remote control.

4. Install the door water shield and the door trim.

FRONT DOOR LOCK— EXCEPT MODELS 63, 76
REMOVAL

1. Remove the trim panel and position the water shield away from the access holes.

2. Disconnect the door lock remote control link, the lock actuating rod and the lock control to cylinder at the lock (Fig. 14). Remove the knob from the push button rod.

3. Remove the glass rear run lower retaining bolt and position the run away from the door lock.

4. Remove the lock assembly from the door. Remove the push button rod from the lock.

INSTALLATION

1. Connect the push button rod to the lock.

2. Position the lock in the door, and install the retaining screws. Connect the lock control to cylinder rod, the lock actuating rod, and the remote control link at the lock. Install the push button.

3. Position the glass rear run in the door. Install the retaining bolt, adjust the rear run, and tighten the

retaining bolt.

4. Check the operation of the lock. If necessary, adjust the lock striker.

5. Carefully position the water shield to the inner panel; and install the trim panel.

FRONT DOOR LOCK— MODELS, 63, 76
REMOVAL

1. Remove the door trim panel and watershield.

2. Remove the door window glass channel bracket retaining screws. Prop the window in its up position and cycle the regulator arms to the down position.

3. Disconnect the control rods from the lock assembly (Fig. 14).

4. Remove the three screws retaining the lock assembly and remove the lock assembly from the door.

INSTALLATION

1. Position the lock assembly in the door and install the three lock assembly-to-door retaining screws.

2. Connect the control rods to the lock assembly.

3. Raise the window regulator arms and bracket and install the regulator arm bracket-to-window channel retaining screws. Remove the prop used to temporarily hold the window in its up position.

4. Install the door trim watershield and the door trim panel.

REAR DOOR LOCK
REMOVAL

1. Remove the trim panel and position the water shield away from the access holes.

2. Disconnect the door lock remote control rod and door lock control rod at the door lock assembly.

3. Remove the three screws retaining the lock assembly to the door and remove the lock assembly from the door (Fig. 14).

INSTALLATION

1. Position the lock assembly in the door, and install the retaining screws.

2. Connect the door lock remote control rod and the door lock control rod at the door lock assembly.

3. Check the operation of the lock. If necessary, adjust the lock striker.

4. Carefully position the water

shield to the inner panel, and install the trim panel.

DOOR LOCK CYLINDER

The key code is stamped on the lock cylinder to assist in replacing lost keys.

When a lock cylinder is replaced, both door lock cylinders and the ignition lock cylinder should be replaced in a set. This will avoid carrying an extra key which will fit only one lock.

1. Remove the trim panel and position the water shield away from the access holes.

2. Disconnect the lock control to door lock cylinder rod at the lock cylinder.

3. Pull the door lock cylinder retainer rearward to release the cylinder, and remove the lock cylinder from the door.

4. Transfer the lock cylinder arm to the new lock cylinder.

5. Position the lock cylinder in the door, and install the lock cylinder retainer (Fig. 14).

6. Connect the lock control to door lock cylinder rod at the lock cylinder.

7. Carefully position the water shield to the inner panel and install the trim panel.

DOOR HANDLE AND/OR PUSH BUTTON

1. Remove the door trim panel, and position the water shield away from the access holes.

2. Remove the handle retaining screw and nut, and remove the handle (Fig. 14). To remove the front door handle, it will be necessary to disconnect the lock actuating link.

3. To replace the push button remove the retaining plate screw, retaining plate, spring, push button, and rubber seal from the handle.

4. Install the push button assembly if it was removed, and install the handle assembly. Connect the lock actuating link to the door handle.

5. Carefully position the water shield to the inner panel, and install the trim panel.

DOOR VENT WINDOW FRAME —EXCEPT MODELS 63, 76

1. Remove the door trim panel, trim panel lower retainer and the watershield.

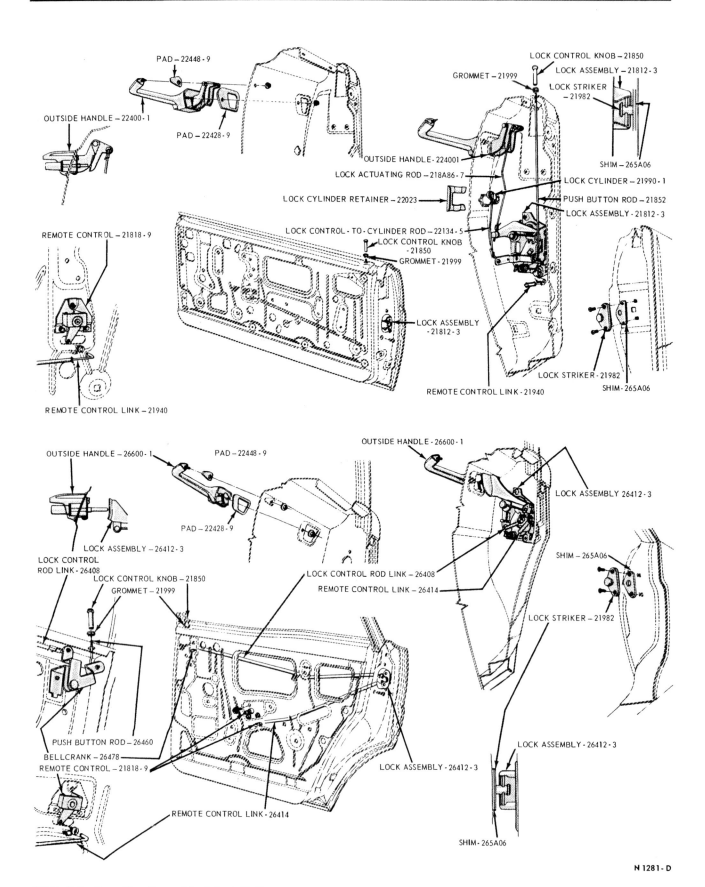

FIG. 14—Door Handle and Lock Installation

N 1281-D

2. Remove the inner and outer door belt line weatherstrips (view D, Fig. 4) by prying them loose from the door.

3. Remove the window lower stop and completely lower the door window.

4. Remove the front glass run adjusting bolt, lock nut and washer.

5. Remove the front glass run from the division bar retainer at the vent frame by sliding the run down and removing it from the door through the inner panel access hole.

6. Remove the three screws retaining the vent frame to the door frame. Remove the vent window assembly and place it on a bench.

7. Remove the screws retaining the upper vent pivot to the vent frame assembly. Remove the nut retaining the lower pivot bolt and remove the spring nylon bushings, washer and stop washer.

8. Remove two screws from the top of the assembly and remove the four rivets retaining the vent frame and division bar weatherstrip. Separate the frame and division bar.

9. Using a tool such as shown in Fig. 15, remove the glass. Remove the weatherseal.

INSTALLATION

1. Position new weatherseal to the vent glass.

2. Lubricate the weatherseal with Ru-Glyde and seat the glass assembly in its channel.

3. Position the division bar to the vent frame. Position the vent frame and division bar weatherstrip and install the four rivets and two screws at the top of the frame.

4. Assemble the vent tension spring to the lower pivot and adjust the pivot spring tension so that the window will stay open at highway speeds.

GLASS AND CHANNEL REMOVAL TOOL (NO. 2900) AVAILABLE FROM SOMMER AND MALA GLASS MACHINE COMPANY, 5501 W. OGDEN AVENUE, CHICAGO 50, ILLINOIS

FIG. 15—Glass Channel Replacement

5. Position the frame assembly on the door and install the three retaining screws.

6. Position the glass front run in the door and slide it into the vent frame retainer.

7. Loosely install the front run adjusting bolt and nut.

8. Raise the window halfway and loosely install the lower glass stop.

9. Adjust the front run and tighten the retaining nut.

10. Lower the window so that the top of the glass is level with the window opening belt line.

11. Install the belt line weatherstrips.

12. Install the door watershield and trim panel.

VENT WINDOW OR WEATHER-STRIP—MODELS 63, 76
REMOVAL

The vent window glass may be removed and/or installed by using the tool shown in Fig. 15. When installing new glass, use new glass tape, and apply sealer to the frame horizontal channel and to the other channel in the area of the upper pivot.

1. Remove the door trim panel and position the water shield away from the access holes.

2. Remove the front run bracket retaining bolt, and position the run out of the vent window division bar (Fig. 2).

3. Remove the door vent window assembly retaining bolts and retaining nut, and remove the vent window assembly.

4. Remove the upper pivot from the frame and remove the lower pivot spring assembly, then remove the vent window and frame.

5. Remove the weatherstrip.

INSTALLATION

1. Install the weatherstrip.

2. Position the vent window and frame into the vent assembly.

3. Install the pivot and the pivot spring assembly. Adjust the spring tension so that the vent glass will stay open when the car is driven at highway speeds.

4. Position the vent window assembly in the door and install the retaining bolts and retaining nut snugly.

5. Position the front run in the vent window division bar and install the retaining bolt snugly.

6. Align the vent window and front run and tighten the retaining bolts and retaining nut.

7. Carefully position the water shield to the inner panel and install the trim panel.

FRONT DOOR GLASS—
EXCEPT MODELS 63, 76
REMOVAL

1. Remove the trim panel and position the water shield away from the access holes.

2. After removing the stop (Fig. 4), lower the glass until the regulator arm roller is out of the glass channel.

3. Unsnap and remove the belt weatherstrips, loosen the front run attaching bolt at the mounting bracket, and remove the bracket attaching bolt from the inner panel.

4. Remove the front run from the division bar by pulling rearward on the edges of the run.

5. Remove the glass.

INSTALLATION

1. Using the tool shown in Fig. 15, remove the channel from the glass.

2. Install the channel, using new glass tape.

3. Simultaneously, position the glass and run in the door, and install the belt weatherstrips.

4. Position the regulator arm roller in the channel, and finally position the run in the division bar.

5. Connect the run and bracket, making necessary lateral adjustment.

6. Install the stop, making necessary adjustment.

7. Carefully position the water shield, the inner panel, and install the trim panel.

FRONT DOOR GLASS—COMET, FAIRLANE—MODEL 63, 76
REMOVAL

1. Remove the door trim panel and watershield.

2. Remove the door trim panel upper retainer from the door. This provides access to the window upper stop retaining screws.

3. Remove the window upper stops (Fig. 2).

4. Remove the vent window and division bar retaining screws and nuts (Fig. 1).

5. Remove the rear guide retaining screws and nuts. Remove the rear guide from the door.

6. Remove the glass channel roller brackets from the lower window channel.

7. Lower the window assembly into the door.

8. Remove the door belt inner

weatherstrip by unsnapping the weatherstrip retainer clips from the door inner panel.

9. Remove the run assembly from the vent division bar.

10. Remove the vent window assembly from the door.

11. Lift the door glass assembly up and out of the door.

12. Remove the frame from the glass.

INSTALLATION

1. Position the frame on new glass.

2. Position the door glass assembly in the door.

3. Position the vent window assembly in the door.

4. Install the front run assembly in the Vent division bar.

5. Snap the door belt inner weatherstrip and retaining clips into place on the door inner panel.

6. Raise the door glass and install the regulator channel brackets on the lower window frame.

7. Position the rear guide assembly in the door and install, but do not tighten, the retaining nuts and screws snug.

8. Position the window upper stops and install, but do not tighten, the stop retaining screws.

9. Adjust the vent window assembly to the front pillar and tighten the division bar retaining screws and nuts.

10. Adjust the rear guide and tighten the retaining nuts and screws.

11. Adjust the window upper stops and tighten the stop retaining screws.

12. Install the door trim panel upper retainer.

13. Install the door trim panel watershield and the door trim panel.

FRONT DOOR WINDOW REGULATOR—MANUAL— COMET, FAIRLANE—MODEL 63, 76
REMOVAL

1. Remove the front door trim panel and watershield.

2. Remove the four regulator assembly retaining screws.

3. Prop the window in its up position and remove the front channel bracket from the window frame.

4. Loosen the front run retaining nut and remove the regulator from the door. The regulator arm rollers will slide out of the rear channel bracket and the equalizer arm bracket to permit removal of the regulator assembly from the door.

INSTALLATION

1. Position the regulator assembly in the door and install the regulator arm rollers in the channel brackets.

2. Align the regulator retaining screw holes with the retaining screw holes in the door panel and install the four regulator assembly retaining screws.

3. Install the front run lower retaining nut.

4. Install the front channel bracket on the window frame.

5. Install the watershield and door trim panel.

FRONT DOOR WINDOW REGULATOR—EXCEPT MODELS 63, 76
REMOVAL

1. Remove the trim panel and position the water shield away from the access holes.

2. Disconnect the regulator from the glass channel roller.

3. Raise the glass by hand and secure it in the raised position.

4. Remove the regulator retaining bolts (Fig. 3) and remove the regulator through the door access hole.

INSTALLATION

1. Position the regulator inside the door and install the retaining bolts snugly.

2. Lower the glass and connect the regulator.

3. Check the operation of the glass, adjust it if necessary, and tighten the retaining bolts.

4. Carefully position the water shield to the inner panel and install the trim panel.

FRONT DOOR REAR GLASS RUN—MODELS 63, 76
REMOVAL

1. Remove the trim panel and position the water shield away from the access holes.

2. Remove both window upper stop brackets from the glass lower channel.

3. Disconnect both regulator arms from the glass lower channel, and remove the rollers. Remove the glass assembly.

4. Remove the glass rear run lower retaining bolt. Remove the run upper adjusting screw lock nut. **Do not disturb the position of the adjusting screw.** Remove the run from the door.

INSTALLATION

1. Position the rear run in the

door and install the lower retaining bolt and upper adjusting screw lock nut snugly.

2. Position the glass assembly in the door. Install the rollers in the glass lower channel, and connect both regulator arms.

3. Attach the window upper stop brackets to the lower channel.

4. Adjust the rear run and tighten the retaining bolt and nut.

5. Carefully position the water shield to the inner panel and install the trim panel.

REAR DOOR GLASS—COMET, FALCON—MODEL 54
REMOVAL

1. Remove the door trim panel and watershield.

2. Remove the two screws retaining the regulator roller channel bracket to the lower window channel (Fig. 3).

3. Remove the lower stop assembly.

4. Remove the screw and nut retaining the rear run retainer and stationary glass. Move the run retainer and glass back and down in the door.

5. Remove the door belt, outside weatherstrip.

6. Tilt the door window down and then lift it out of the door.

7. Using a tool such as shown in Fig. 15, remove the glass from the lower channel.

INSTALLATION

1. Position new glass tape on the glass and, using a tool such as shown in Fig. 15, install the lower channel on the glass.

2. Position the glass and channel assembly in the door.

3. Position the rear run retainer and stationary glass assembly and install the retainer screw and nut.

4. Install the regulator roller channel bracket on the window channel.

5. Install the lower window stop.

6. Install the door trim watershield and the door trim panel.

7. Install the window outside belt weatherstrip.

REAR DOOR WINDOW REGULATOR
REMOVAL

1. Remove the trim panel and position the water shield away from the access holes.

2. Disconnect the regulator from the glass channel roller.

3. Raise the glass by hand and secure it in the raised position.

4. Remove the regulator retaining screws and remove the regulator through the door access hole.

INSTALLATION

1. Position the regulator inside the door and install the retaining screws snugly.
2. Lower the glass and connect the regulator.
3. Check the operation of the glass, adjust it if necessary, and tighten the retaining bolts.
4. Carefully position the water shield to the inner panel and install the trim panel.

QUARTER GLASS—MODEL 62
REMOVAL

1. Remove the rear seat cushion and back.
2. Remove the trim panel and position the water shield away from the access hole.
3. Remove the lower and front garnish moldings.
4. Remove the rear run.
5. Lower the window until the regulator rollers are accessible, and disconnect the front rollers from the channel.
6. Lower and tilt the glass to remove it.

INSTALLATION

1. Transfer the channel, using the tool shown in Fig. 15.
2. Position the glass in the quarter panel, and connect the front rollers.
3. Install the rear run, adjusting it as necessary.
4. Install the garnish mouldings, position the water shield, and install the trim panel.
5. Install the seat cushion and back

QUARTER WINDOW REGULATOR—MODEL 62
REMOVAL

1. Remove the rear seat cushion and back.
2. Remove the trim panel and position the water shield away from the access hole.
3. Disconnect the regulator from the glass channel rollers.
4. Raise the glass by hand and secure it in the raised position.
5. Remove the regulator retaining bolts, slide the regulator arm out of the equalizer and remove the regulator.

INSTALLATION

1. Position the regulator inside the quarter panel, engage the arm in the equalizer, and install the regulator retaining bolts snugly.
2. Position the rollers in the glass channel, lower the glass and connect the regulator.
3. Check the operation of the glass, adjust it if necessary, and tighten the retaining bolts.
4. Position the water shield, and install the trim panel.
5. Install the seat cushion and back.

QUARTER WINDOW REGULATOR—MODEL 63
REMOVAL

1. Remove the rear seat cushion and seat back.
2. Remove the quarter trim panel and watershield.
3. Remove the screws retaining the glass channel bracket to the lower glass channel and remove the glass channel bracket. Prop the window assembly in its up position.
4. Remove the four screws retaining the regulator assembly to the quarter panel and remove the regulator assembly.

INSTALLATION

1. Position the regulator assembly in the quarter panel and install the four regulator retaining screws.
2. Remove the prop used to hold the window up and install the glass channel bracket on the glass channel.
3. Install the quarter trim panel watershield and trim panel.
4. Install the rear seat back and cushion.

QUARTER WINDOW FRONT GUIDE—MODEL 63
REMOVAL

1. Remove the rear seat cushion and seat back.
2. Remove the quarter window handle, arm rest, the quarter trim panel, trim panel retainer, garnish moulding, and position the water shield away from the access hole.
3. Remove the quarter window front guide lower retaining bolts and the adjuster screw lock nut.
4. Turn the adjuster screw to its full in position.
5. With the quarter glass in the lowered position remove the quarter window front guide from the glass channel rollers.
6. Remove the quarter window front guide through the access hole with the window glass in the up position.

INSTALLATION

1. With the quarter glass in the up position, install the quarter window front guide into the glass channel rollers.
2. Install the quarter window front guide retaining bolts and adjuster screw lock nut snugly.
3. Check the operation of the glass, adjust it if necessary, and tighten the retaining bolts and adjuster screw lock nut.
4. Position the water shield and install the garnish moulding, trim panel retainer, quarter trim panel, regulator handle, and arm rest.
5. Install the rear seat back and seat cushion.

QUARTER WINDOW REAR GUIDE—MODEL 63
REMOVAL

1. Remove the rear seat cushion and seat back.
2. Remove the quarter window handle, arm rest, quarter trim panel, trim panel retainer and garnish moulding, and position the water shield away from the access hole.
3. Position the rear seat back panel cardboard away from the seat back panel.
4. Remove the quarter window rear guide retaining bolt and adjuster screw lock nut, and remove the rear guide.

INSTALLATION

1. Position the rear guide in the quarter and install the retaining bolt and adjuster screw lock nut snugly.
2. Check the operation of the glass, adjust it if necessary, and tighten the retaining bolt and adjuster screw lock nut.
3. Install the rear seat back panel card board.
4. Position the water shield, and install the garnish moulding, trim panel retainer, trim panel, regulator handle, and arm rest.
5. Install the rear seat back and seat cushion.

REAR QUARTER WINDOW GLASS—FAIRLANE, COMET—MODEL 76
REMOVAL

1. Remove the rear seat cushion, seat back and quarter trim panel.
2. Remove the quarter window upper stops.
3. Remove the lower glass channel bracket (Fig. 9) from the lower glass channel.
4. Remove the three quarter window guide panel retaining screws.

5. Raise the top assembly off the windshield header far enough to permit clearance between the window and roof side rails.

6. Remove the window from the quarter panel.

7. Remove the retaining screw from the weatherstrip and remove the weatherstrip from the window.

8. Remove the screws retaining the window top frame and remove the frame from the glass.

9. Using a tool such as shown in Fig. 15, remove the glass from the lower and side channel.

INSTALLATION

1. Using a tool such as shown in Fig. 15, install the lower and side channels on the glass.

2. Position the top frame on the glass assembly and install the frame retaining screws.

3. Position the quarter window weatherstrip on the window assembly and install the weatherstrip retaining screw.

4. Position the quarter window in the guide assembly and install the guide retaining screws snugly.

5. Install the lower glass channel bracket on the glass channel.

6. Install the window upper stops snugly.

7. Raise the top assembly and fasten the top hold-down clamps.

8. Align the window assembly to the door glass and top side rails. Adjust the upper and lower window stops and tighten all retaining screws.

9. Cycle the window assembly up and down to insure proper adjustment. Then, install the quarter trim panel, rear seat back and seat cushion.

REAR QUARTER WINDOW AND/OR WEATHERSTRIP MODEL 71
REMOVAL

1. Remove the spare tire cover and spare tire.

2. Remove the inside lower garnish moulding from the wheel well area.

3. Remove the quarter window inside front garnish moulding.

4. Remove the quarter window outside front moulding (Fig. 16).

5. Working from inside the car, loosen the weatherstrip from the window opening flange, and push the window, weatherstrip and moulding assembly out of the opening.

6. Remove the moulding and weatherstrip from the glass.

7. Using solvent, remove all old

sealer from the window opening flange, the window and the weatherstrip.

INSTALLATION

1. Apply a bead of sealer around the window opening flange.

2. Position the weatherstrip on the glass and install the outer moulding in the weatherstrip.

3. Install a draw cord in the weatherstrip, and apply Ru-Glyde to the weatherstrip surfaces that will contact the window opening flange.

4. Position the window assembly to the window opening and use the draw cord to pull the weatherstrip over the window opening flange.

5. Using a caulking gun, apply sealer between the outside of the glass and the weatherstrip.

6. Install the outside front moulding retaining screws (Fig. 16).

7. Install the inside quarter window front garnish mouldings.

8. Install the inside lower garnish moulding.

9. Check for water leaks, then clean the glass and mouldings.

10. Install the spare tire and cover.

WINDSHIELD—COMET, FALCON, FAIRLANE

Following is a generalized pro-

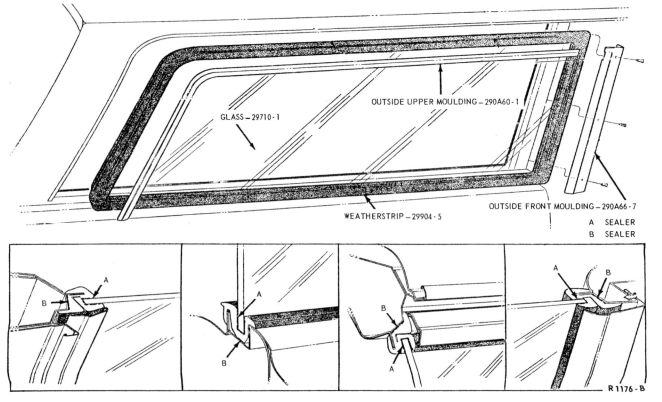

FIG. 16—Stationary Rear Quarter Window—Models 71

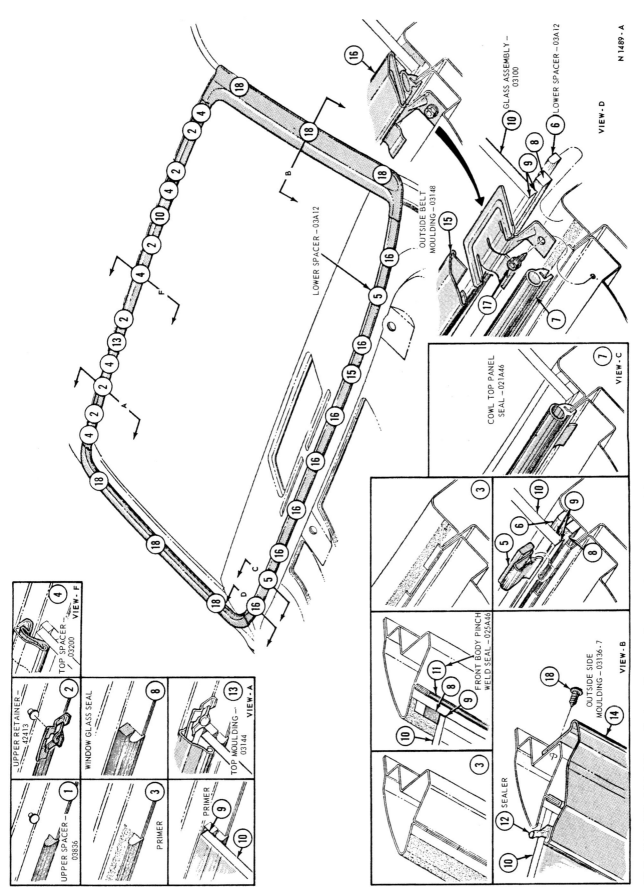

N 1489 - A

FIG. 17—Windshield Installation—Comet, Falcon, Fairlane Except Model 76

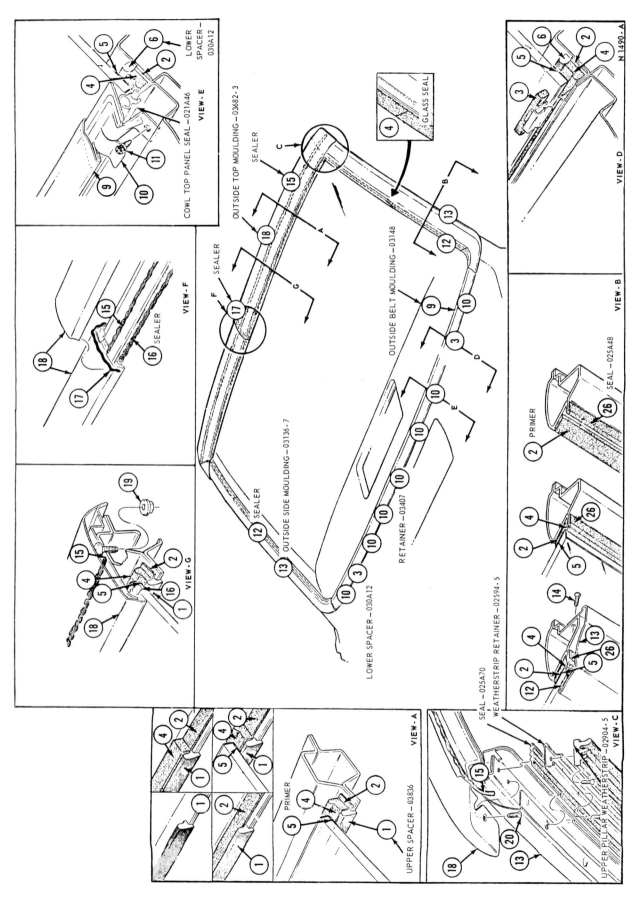

FIG. 18—Windshield Installation—Comet, Falcon, Fairlane—Model 76

cedure for windshield glass replacement. Refer to Figs. 17 and 18 for Comet, Falcon or Fairlane models. On convertible models, lower the top assembly.

REMOVAL

1. Model 76: Remove the pillar weatherstrips, weatherstrip retainer retaining screws and the weatherstrip retainers.

2. Remove the wiper arm and blade assemblies.

3. Remove the cowl top ventilator grille panel retaining screws and remove the cowl top ventilator grille panel.

4. Remove the outside top moulding retaining screws (Model 76) or unsnap the upper moulding retainers, (all other models), using tool T64P-42430 R or L and remove the outside top moulding.

5. Remove the outside side moulding retaining screws and remove the outside side mouldings.

6. Remove the outside lower moulding retainer retaining screws. Remove the outside lower moulding and retainers.

7. Remove the sun visor and bracket assemblies.

8. Remove the interior rear view

mirror. On models with the rear view mirror attached to the glass do not remove the mirror bracket from the glass.

9. Remove the interior garnish mouldings.

10. With the aid of an assistant, and using a length of piano wire inserted between the seal and the flange of the window opening, cut the seal around the perimeter of the glass.

11. Remove the windshield glass.

12. Remove the remaining butyl tape seal from the pinchweld flange of the window opening and remove the moulding retainers and spacers from the pinchweld flange.

INSTALLATION

1. Clean the pinchweld flange and prime the flange.

2. Install the spacers and moulding retainers on the pinchweld flange.

3. Temporarily position the glass in the opening. Mark the center of the glass and the cowl. Position suction cups on the outside of the glass to facilitate handling.

4. Remove the glass from the opening. Clean a one inch surface around the inside outer perimeter of the glass and prime this surface with the primer supplied in Kit

C4AZ-19562-A.

5. Mix two tubes of sealer as directed in Kit C4AZ-19562-A.

6. Position the sealer in a caulking gun and apply approximately a $\frac{5}{16}$-inch bead of sealer to the inside edge of the glass.

7. Apply approximately a $\frac{5}{16}$-inch bead of sealer to the pinchweld flange.

8. Position the glass in the center of the opening, using the locating marks as a guide.

9. Remove the suction cups.

10. Install the outside mouldings. Be sure that the cowl top panel seal is installed under the lower outside moulding.

11. Install the cowl top ventilator grille panel.

12. Install the windshield wiper arm and blade assemblies.

13. Install the interior garnish mouldings, rear view mirror and sun visors.

WINDSHIELD—MUSTANG MODEL 63, 65
REMOVAL

1. Using Tool T64P42430 R or L, remove the top left and right outside windshield mouldings (Fig. 19).

2. Using Tool T64P42430 R or L, remove the left and right wind-

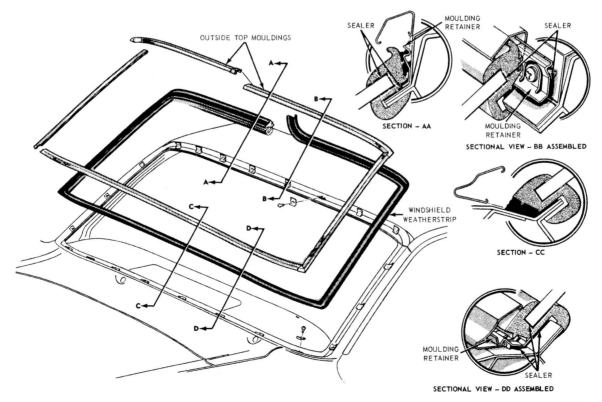

FIG. 19—Windshield Installation—Mustang Body Types 63, 65

shield outside side mouldings.

3. Remove the windshield wiper arm and blade assemblies.

4. Using Tool T64P42430 R or L, remove the windshield outside belt mouldings (Fig. 19).

5. Remove the windshield and weatherstrip assembly by pushing outward along the inner edges of the windshield.

INSTALLATION

1. Remove the weatherstrip from the glass.

2. Clean all old sealer from the weatherstrip and the body opening flange.

3. Using a caulking gun, apply sealer in the weatherstrip glass opening.

4. Position the weatherstrip on the glass and install a draw cord in the body opening groove of the weatherstrip.

5. Using a caulking gun, apply a bead of sealer all the way around the body opening outer flange.

6. Apply rubber lubricant to the weatherstrip surface that contacts the body opening flange.

7. Position the windshield and weatherstrip assembly in the windshield opening and, with a helper applying pressure from the outside,

use the draw cord to pull the lip of the weatherstrip over the window opening lower flange, each side flange and then over the upper flange.

8. Install the outside belt moulding (Fig. 19) by positioning it and snapping it over its clip retainers.

9. Install the outside side mouldings by snapping them over their clip retainers.

10. Install the top right and left outside side mouldings by snapping them over their clip retainers.

11. Clean the windshield and mouldings.

12. Install the windshield wiper arm and blade assemblies.

WINDSHIELD—MUSTANG MODEL 76
REMOVAL

1. Lower the convertible top.

2. Remove the rear view mirror.

3. Remove the four upper garnish moulding retaining screws and remove the upper garnish moulding.

4. Remove the sun visor bracket and pivot retaining screws and remove the sun visor assemblies.

5. Remove the front upper body pillar weatherstrips (Fig. 20). Note that these weatherstrips are pressed into their retainers.

6. Remove the front upper body pillar weatherstrip retainer retaining screws (four) and remove the retainers.

7. Remove the retaining screw and two retaining nuts from each left and right windshield outside top moulding and remove the mouldings (Fig. 20, View AA).

8. Remove the two retaining screws from each windshield outside side moulding and, using Tool T64P42430 R or L, remove the outside side mouldings.

9. Remove the windshield wiper arm and blade assemblies.

10. Using Tool T64P42430 R or L, remove the windshield outside belt moulding.

11. Remove the windshield and weatherstrip assembly by pushing outward along the inner edges of the windshield.

INSTALLATION

1. Remove the weatherstrip from the glass.

2. Clean all old sealer from the weatherstrip and the body opening flange.

3. Using a caulking gun, apply sealer in the weatherstrip glass opening.

4. Position the weatherstrip on the

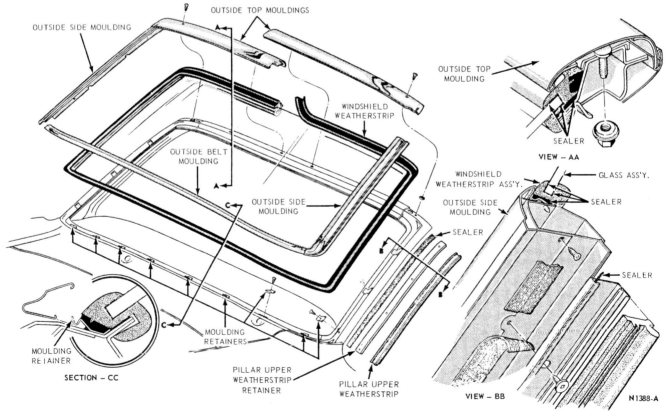

FIG. 20—Windshield Installation—Mustang Body Type 76

glass and install a draw cord in the body opening groove of the weatherstrip.

5. Using a caulking gun, apply a bead of sealer all the way around the body opening outer flange.

6. Apply rubber lubricant to the weatherstrip surfaces that contact the body opening flange.

7. Position the windshield and weatherstrip assembly in the windshield opening. With a helper applying pressure from the outside, use the draw cord to pull the lip of the weatherstrip over the window opening lower flange, each side flange and then over the upper flange.

8. Install the outside belt moulding (Fig. 20) by snapping the moulding over the retaining clips.

9. Install the outside side mouldings by snapping them over their retaining clips and install the retaining screws.

10. Position the left and right outside top mouldings and install the retaining screws and nuts.

11. Position the left and right front upper body pillar weatherstrip retainers (Fig. 20) and install the retaining screws.

12. Install the front upper body pillar weatherstrips by pressing them securely into their retainers.

13. Install the sun visor bracket and pivot assemblies.

14. Position the upper garnish moulding and install the garnish moulding retaining screws.

15. Install the rear view mirror.

16. Clean the windshield and mouldings.

17. Install the wiper arm and blade assemblies.

BACK WINDOW AND/OR WEATHERSTRIP—COMET, FALCON, FAIRLANE
REMOVAL

1. Using Tool T64-P42430-R or L, release the outside upper mouldings (Fig. 21), from their moulding retainers and remove the outside upper mouldings.

2. Using Tool T64-P42430-R or L, release the outside lower mouldings from their moulding retainers and remove the outside lower mouldings.

3. From inside the car, loosen the weatherstrip edges and then push out the back window and weatherstrip as an assembly.

4. Place the window asembly on a bench and remove the weatherstrip from the glass.

INSTALLATION

1. Clean the glass, weatherstrip and the body opening flange.

2. Using a sealer gun, apply sealer in the weatherstrip glass opening.

3. Position the weatherstrip on the glass, and then install the mouldings in the weatherstrip.

4. Insert the draw cord in the weatherstrip, and apply rubber lubricant to the weatherstrip surfaces that will contact the back window opening flange.

5. Using a sealer gun, apply a bead of sealer completely around the back window opening.

6. Position the window assembly in the body opening. With a helper applying hand pressure from the outside, use the draw cord to pull the lips of the weatherstrip over the window opening flanges.

7. Install the outside lower left and right mouldings.

8. Install the outside upper left and right mouldings.

9. Clean the window and mouldings.

BACK WINDOW—MUSTANG MODEL 65
REMOVAL

1. Using Tool T64P42430 R or L, remove the outside side mouldings and the outside upper corner mouldings.

2. Using Tool T64P42430 R or L,

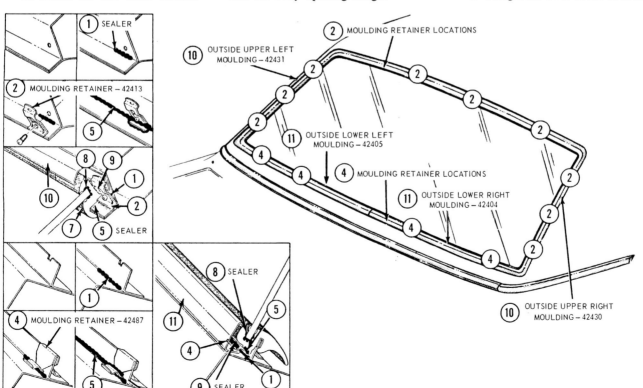

FIG. 21—Back Window Installation—Comet, Falcon, Fairlane

R 1245 - C

remove the outside upper moulding and the outside lower moulding.

3. Remove the back window and weatherstrip assembly by pushing outward along the inner edges of the glass.

4. Remove the weatherstrip from the glass.

INSTALLATION

1. Clean all old sealer from the weatherstrip and the body opening flange.

2. Using a caulking gun, apply sealer in the weatherstrip glass opening groove.

3. Position the weatherstrip on the glass and install a draw cord in the weatherstrip body opening groove.

4. Using a caulking gun, apply a bead of sealer all the way around the body opening flange.

5. Apply rubber lubricant to the weatherstrip surface that contacts the body opening flange.

6. Position the window and weatherstrip assembly in the body opening and, with a helper applying pressure from the outside, use the draw cord to pull the lip of the weatherstrip over the body opening flange.

7. Snap the outside lower mould-

ing into position over its retaining clips (Fig. 22).

8. Snap the outside upper moulding into position over its retaining clips (Fig. 22).

9. Snap the outside side mouldings into position over the retaining clips (Fig. 22).

10. Install the outside upper corner mouldings.

11. Clean the glass and mouldings.

BACK WINDOW—MUSTANG MODEL 63
REMOVAL

1. Remove the quarter trim upper front moulding retaining screws and remove the quarter trim upper front mouldings.

2. Remove the quarter trim upper rear moulding cap retaining screw and remove the cap. Remove the quarter trim upper left and right rear moulding retaining screws and remove the mouldings. (Fig. 23).

3. Remove the back window garnish moulding upper joint cover. Remove the back window upper left and right garnish moulding retaining screws and remove the mouldings (Fig. 23).

4. Remove the left and right vent

air extractor grille assembly (quarter trim upper front panels) retaining screws and remove the panels (Fig. 23).

5. Remove the back window lower front left and right trim panel retaining bolts and screws and remove the panels (Fig. 23).

6. Remove the quarter trim upper rear left and right panel retaining screws and remove the panels.

7. Using moulding removal Tool T64P-42006-A or B, remove the back window exterior mouldings in the following order: right upper moulding, right lower moulding, left upper moulding and left lower moulding (Fig. 24).

8. With an assistant applying pressure from the inside, remove the back window and weatherstrip assembly.

9. Remove the weatherstrip from the glass.

INSTALLATION

1. Clean excess old sealer from the body window opening.

2. Clean old sealer from the weatherstrip if the weatherstrip is to be re-used.

3. Position the weatherstrip on the glass and install a pull cord (⅛ inch sash cord) around the weatherstrip

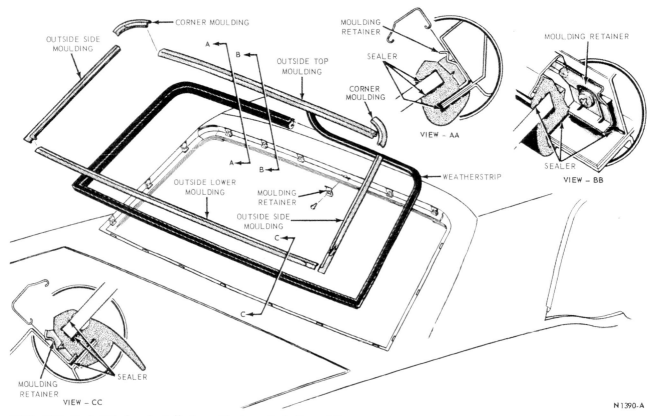

FIG. 22—Back Window Installation—Mustang Body Type 65

N1390-A

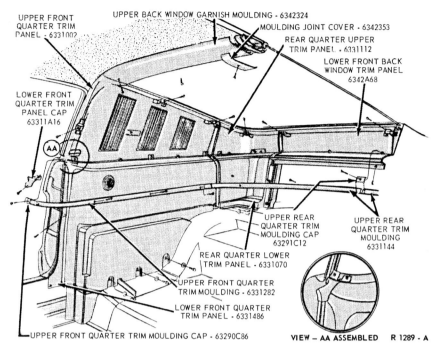

FIG. 23—Interior Moulding and Quarter Trim Panel Installation—Mustang Body Type 63

body opening groove.

4. With the aid of an assistant, position the glass and weatherstrip assembly in the body window opening. Use the pull cord to pull the lip of the weatherstrip over the pinch-weld while applying pressure to the glass from the outside.

5. Apply sealer between the weatherstrip and the outside pinch weld flange.

6. Apply sealer between the outer glass surface and the weatherstrip.

7. Snap the window exterior mouldings into place in the following order; left lower moulding, left upper moulding, right lower moulding and right upper moulding.

8. Install the upper rear left and right quarter trim panels.

9. Install the upper front left and right quarter trim panels.

10. Install the back window lower front trim panel.

11. Install the upper rear left and right quarter trim mouldings and moulding cap.

12. Install the upper front left and right quarter trim mouldings.

13. Install the back window upper left and right garnish mouldings and garnish moulding joint cover.

14. Clean the back window and mouldings.

INSIDE REAR VIEW MIRROR —BONDED TO WINDSHIELD REMOVAL

1. Clean both the inside and outside surfaces of the windshield in the area of the mirror mounting bracket.

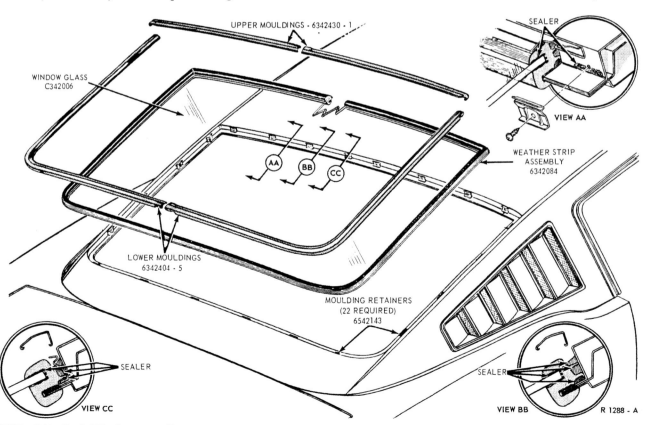

FIG. 24—Back Window Installation—Mustang Body Type 63

Inspect the windshield for stone chips and scratches.

2. Using welding putty or wet rags, insulate all chips or scratches within 12 inches of the mirror mounting bracket.

3. Apply heat to the bracket mounting area from outside the windshield with a standard 250 watt infrared bulb (heat lamp). Hold the lamp approximately 4 inches from the windshield, and rotate it in a small circle.

4. The mirror mounting bracket can be pulled off the windshield glass in approximately 8-10 minutes using the mirror as a handle.

5. Slowly remove the heat lamp. **Do not remove the insulating materials until the windshield has cooled to room temperature.**

6. Remove the mirror and arm from the bracket.

INSTALLATION

1. Locate and mark with a wax pencil the bracket location on the outside surface of the windshield (Fig. 25).

2. Use a good grade of Ethyl Alcohol to thoroughly clean the inside glass surface bracket mounting area and mounting bracket face. It is important that the mounting surfaces are properly cleaned before the resin is applied.

3. To mix the resin pour the entire contents of the small catalyst bottle ino the large epoxy bottle (Fig. 25).

4. Stir the contents for 3 to 5 minutes.

To guarantee the correct mixing ratio and resulting bond strength it is mandatory that the entire contents of both bottles are used and properly mixed. Under no circumstances should only portions of the epoxy or catalyst be used.

5. Apply the mixed resin to the bracket mounting surface. Level off the resin film as smoothly as possible.

6. Place the mounting bracket surface upward in a vise or in a small mound of permagum or any suitable holding material that will support the mounting bracket (Fig. 25). Hold a standard 250 watt infrared lamp about 5 to 6 inches from the mounting surface of the bracket for 2½ minutes.

7. Allow the bracket to cool for one minute. With light hand pressure apply the mounting surface of the bracket to the desired inside area of the windshield.

8. Secure the bracket to the windshield using a piece of tape about 5 inches long located just under the knob of the bracket. Apply another piece of tape in the vertical direction to firmly hold the mounting bracket in place on the windshield.

9. When the temperatures are above 67°F., the mirror and arm should not be mounted to the bracket for 8 hours, to allow the resin to properly adhere the bracket to the glass. However, the car may be used with the bracket taped in place one hour after installation.

When the temperatures are below 67°F., the mirror and arm should not be mounted to the bracket for 16 hours. However, the car can be used 2 hours after the bracket has been taped in place.

10. After the bracket has had time to adhere to the glass, remove the tape and install the mirror and arm to the bracket.

TAILGATE GLASS
REMOVAL

1. Open and temporarily support the tailgate.

2. Remove the tailgate cover panel retaining screws and remove the panel.

3. Remove the window regulator arm roller retaining pins, disconnect the arms from the rollers, and remove the rollers from the glass channel.

4. Remove the window from the tailgate.

INSTALLATION

1. With a glass remover tool, remove the glass lower retainer and channel, and weatherstrip.

2. Remove the weatherstrip from the glass lower retainer and channel assembly, and then clean the glass groove.

3. Position the weatherstrip into the glass lower channel. Install the weatherstrip and channel to the glass.

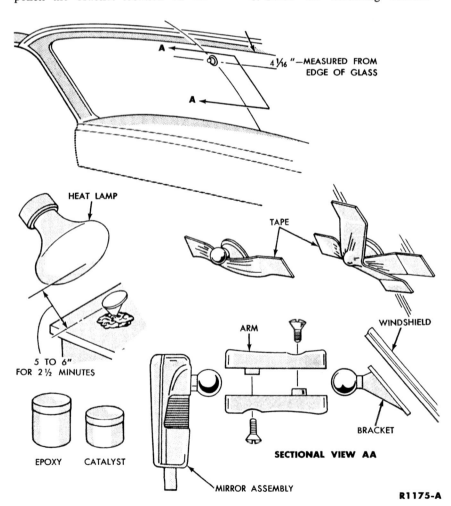

FIG. 25—Bonded Rear View Mirror Installation—Comet, Falcon, Fairlane

4. Slide the window assembly into the glass runs and connect the regulator arms and rollers to the glass lower channel.

5. Apply Lubriplate to the glass rollers.

6. Clean the old sealer from the tailgate cover panel and apply new sealer.

7. Install the tailgate cover panel to the tailgate.

8. Connect the tailgate hinge supports and remove the temporary support.

TAILGATE WINDOW REGULATOR—COMET, FAIRLANE
REMOVAL

If the tailgate window regulator mechanism should fail with the window in a partially closed or closed

position, the tailgate can be opened by removing the window side and upper runs (Fig. 26).

1. Open and temporarily support the tailgate.

2. Disconnect the tailgate hinge supports at the tail gate.

3. Remove the tailgate cover panel retaining screws and remove the panel.

4. Remove the window regulator arm roller retaining pins, disconnect the arms from the rollers, and remove the rollers from the glass channel.

5. Remove the tailgate window from the tailgate and scribe the regulator mounting location.

6. Remove the regulator retaining bolts and remove the regulator.

INSTALLATION

1. Place the regulator manual drive spline into the handle, align the regulator, and install the regulator retaining bolts.

Install the window assembly in the tailgate.

2. Clean the old sealer from the tailgate cover panel and apply new sealer.

3. Install the tailgate cover panel to the tailgate.

TAILGATE WINDOW REGULATOR—POWER
REMOVAL

If the tailgate window regulator mechanism should fail with the window in a partially closed or closed position, the tailgate can be

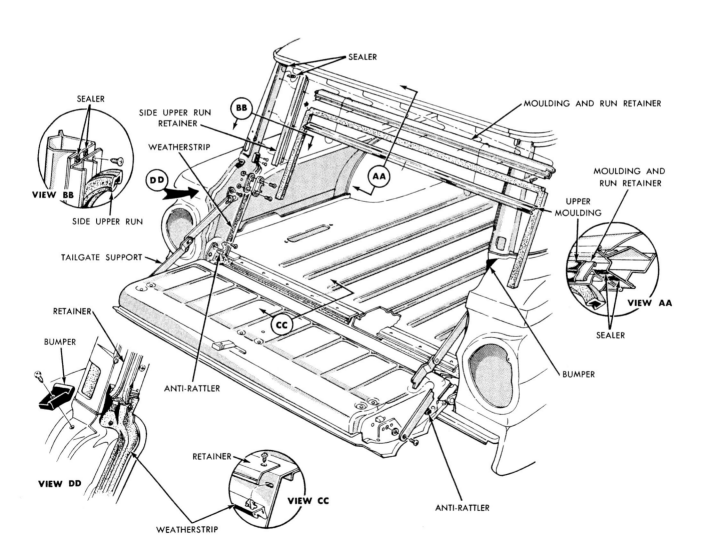

FIG. 26—Tailgate and Weatherstrip Installation—Typical

R1132-B

opened by removing the window side and upper runs (Fig. 26).

1. Open and temporarily support the tailgate.

2. Disconnect the tailgate hinge supports at the tailgate.

3. Remove the tailgate cover panel retaining screws and remove the panel.

4. Remove the window regulator arm roller retaining pins, disconnect the arms from the rollers, and remove the rollers from the glass channel.

5. Remove the window from the tailgate.

6. Disconnect the motor leads from the wiring harness in the tailgate.

7. Scribe the regulator mounting location, remove the regulator retaining bolts, and remove the regulator with the motor attached.

INSTALLATION

1. **Do not remove the electric regulator drive assembly for transfer to the new regulator until the regulator counterbalance spring is unloaded.** To unload the regulator counterbalance spring, place the spring in a vise so that the spring cannot unwind, disconnect the spring from the outer retaining tab, and then slowly loosen the vise jaws.

2. Remove the screws retaining the regulator drive assembly and the motor to the regulator and remove the drive assembly and motor.

3. Position the drive assembly and motor to the new regulator and install the retaining screws.

4. Drill out the rivets retaining the manual clutch and housing assembly to the regulator. Remove and discard the manual drive assembly. **The manual clutch and gear assembly should not be removed until the electric drive assembly is installed.**

5. Install the regulator assembly on the tailgate and align the regulator as required.

6. Connect the wiring harness to the motor and secure the harness in place with the retainer.

7. Install the window assembly into the tailgate.

8. Apply Lubriplate to the glass rollers.

9. Clean the old sealer from the tailgate cover panel and apply new sealer.

10. Install the tailgate cover panel to the tailgate.

11. Connect the tailgate hinge supports and remove the temporary support.

TAILGATE SWITCH AND LOCK CYLINDER—POWER
REMOVAL

1. Open and temporarily support the tailgate.

2. Disconnect the tailgate hinge supports at the tailgate.

3. Remove the tailgate cover panel retaining screws and remove the panel.

4. Remove the window regulator arm roller retaining pins, disconnect the arms from the rollers, and remove the rollers from the glass channel.

5. Remove the window from the tailgate.

6. Remove the regulator.

7. Remove the nuts retaining the lock and switch, and then remove the lock and lock cylinder from the tailgate (Fig. 27).

8. If the switch requires replacement, disconnect the switch wires from the tailgate wiring harness and remove the switch and wires.

9. To remove the lock cylinder, depress the lock cylinder retaining pin, insert the key and rotate the cylinder until the retaining pin drops, and then remove the lock cylinder.

INSTALLATION

1. To install the lock cylinder, insert the key in the lock cylinder and slide the cylinder into the retainer.

2. To install the switch assembly, route the wiring harness through the tailgate to the tailgate harness switch connector.

3. Place the lock assembly and gasket to the tailgate and position the switch to the lock assembly. It may be necessary to rotate the lock cylinder to align the switch and the lock. Install the retaining nuts.

4. Install the window regulator.

5. Install the tailgate window assembly into the tailgate.

6. Apply Lubriplate to the glass rollers.

7. Clean the old sealer from the tailgate cover panel and apply new sealer.

8. Install the tailgate cover panel to the tailgate.

9. Connect the tailgate hinge supports and remove the temporary support.

TAILGATE WINDOW HANDLE AND LOCK CYLINDER— MANUAL
REMOVAL

1. With the tailgate window in the closed position, unlock the tailgate handle, and rotate the handle assembly to reveal the mounting screws (Fig. 28).

2. Remove the handle mounting screws, and then remove the handle assembly and pad.

3. To remove the lock cylinder turn the key in the cylinder to align the cylinder locking pin with the access hole in the handle assembly. Depress the locking pin and remove the lock cylinder.

INSTALLATION

1. To replace the lock cylinder, transfer the O-rings, and then with the key in the cylinder, install the lock cylinder in the handle assembly.

2. If the window regulator has been replaced, it may be necessary to reposition the handle assembly so that it hangs in a vertical position, with the tailgate window in a closed position. To adjust the handle position, remove the snap ring and socket from the window regulator stem, and then install the socket with the notch at the top.

3. Install the pad and handle assembly.

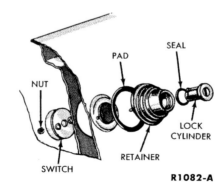

FIG. 27—Tailgate Switch and Lock Installation—Typical

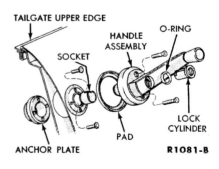

FIG. 28—Tailgate Window Regulator Handle Installation —Typical

DUAL-ACTION TAILGATE HINGES
REMOVAL AND INSTALLATION
Upper Left Hinge

1. Open the tailgate (horizontally, as a dropgate) and scribe a location mark around that part of hinge to be replaced.

2. Remove the hinge retainer screws.

3. Position the hinge to the scribe marks and install the retainer screws.

Lower Left Hinge

1. Open the tailgate (horizontally, as a dropgate) and position a support under the hinge side of the gate.

2. Remove the tailgate door check. Raise the tailgate partially and remove the torsion bar retainer link from the body.

3. Scribe the hinge location on the body and the tailgate. Remove the hinge retainer screws and remove the hinge.

4. Position the hinge to the body and tailgate scribe marks and install the hinge retainer screws.

5. Close the tailgate and check for proper lower hinge alignment. Adjust the hinge if necessary.

6. Open the tailgate partially and install the torsion bar retainer link to the body.

7. Install the tailgate door check.

DUAL-ACTION TAILGATE LOCKS
REMOVAL AND INSTALLATION
Right Lower Lock

1. Open the tailgate (side opening). Remove the tailgate trim panel, watershield and access panel.

2. Disconnect the linkage from the lock. Remove the three retaining screws and remove the lock.

3. Transfer the linkage retainer clips to the new lock. Position the lock in the gate and install the retainer screws.

4. Install the linkage to the lock. Install the access cover, watershield and trim panel.

Right Upper Lock

1. Open the tailgate (side opening). Remove the tailgate trim panel, watershield and access panel.

2. Engage the upper lock pawl to the closed position and raise the window partially out of the gate. Remove the regulator arms from the window regulator channel and remove the window assembly.

3. Disconnect the linkage at the upper lock. Remove the wire connector from the upper lock safety switch.

4. Remove the right guide upper retainer bolt. Remove the three screws retaining the lock and remove the lock assembly.

5. Transfer the linkage retainer clips and the safety switch to the new lock assembly.

6. Position the lock in the gate and install the lock retainer screws. Install the window guide upper retainer bolt.

7. Connect the wire connector to the switch and connect the linkage to the lock.

8. Position the window assembly in the gate and install the regulator arms to the regulator channel. Close the lock pawl to engage the switch and lower the window into the tailgate.

9. Install the tailgate access panel, watershield, and trim panel. Open the upper lock and close the tailgate. Check the lock alignment to the striker. Adjust the lock striker if necessary.

DUAL-ACTION TAILGATE TORSION BAR
REMOVAL

1. Remove the tailgate trim panel, watershield and access cover.

2. Move the tailgate glass out partially by closing the right upper lock pawl and turning the key in the tailgate cylinder.

3. Remove the lock control bellcrank assembly and window lower stop.

4. Loosen the window regulator motor harness to gain slack at the tailgate-to-body location.

5. Raise the tailgate partially and remove the torsion rod retainer link from the body (2 screws).

6. With an assistant, remove the left lower hinge pivot bolt. Unlock the right lower lock, remove one check cable retainer screw from each side and move the tailgate assembly away from the body opening. Place the tailgate on an appropriate stand approximately bumper high.

7. Remove the torsion bar retainer bracket and remove the torsion bar from the left side of the gate. (Fig. 29).

INSTALLATION

1. Place the torsion bar in its respective mounting position and install the torsion bar right retainer bracket.

2. With an assistant, position the tailgate assembly to the body opening. Engage the right lower lock to the striker plate. Install the left hinge pivot bolt and install the check cable retainer screws.

3. Install the torsion bar retainer link to the body.

4. Position the motor wiring harness in its original position.

5. Install the window lower stop and lock the bellcrank assembly.

6. Lower the window in the tailgate to where the top edge of the glass is even with the weatherstrip and adjust the lower stop if necessary.

7. Install the tailgate access cover, watershield and trim panel.

DECK LID HINGE OR TORSION BAR
REMOVAL

1. Prop the deck lid open.

2. Mark the hinge position on the lid and on the mounting bracket for reference when a new hinge is installed.

3. Using a tool T64K-44890-B pry the anchor end of the torsion bar out of its adjustment notch (Fig. 30). Lower the deck lid and from inside the luggage compartment remove the bar.

4. Position a cover under the hinge edge of the deck lid to prevent paint damage. Remove the hinge attaching bolt from the deck lid and from the mounting bracket, and remove the hinge.

INSTALLATION

1. Position the hinge, and partially tighten the mounting bolts.

2. Remove the protective cover and install the torsion bar, reversing the procedure in step 3 above. The farther rearward the anchor end is twisted, the greater the tension.

3. Remove the prop and check the lid position. After any necessary adjustment, tighten the hinge attaching bolts.

DECK LID LOCK

1. Unlock and open the deck lid.

2. Remove the bolts retaining the lock assembly and remove the lock.

3. Position the lock assembly to the deck lid and loosely install the retaining bolts.

4. Adjust the lock assembly and tighten the bolts.

DECK LID LOCK CYLINDER
REMOVAL

1. Open the deck lid and remove

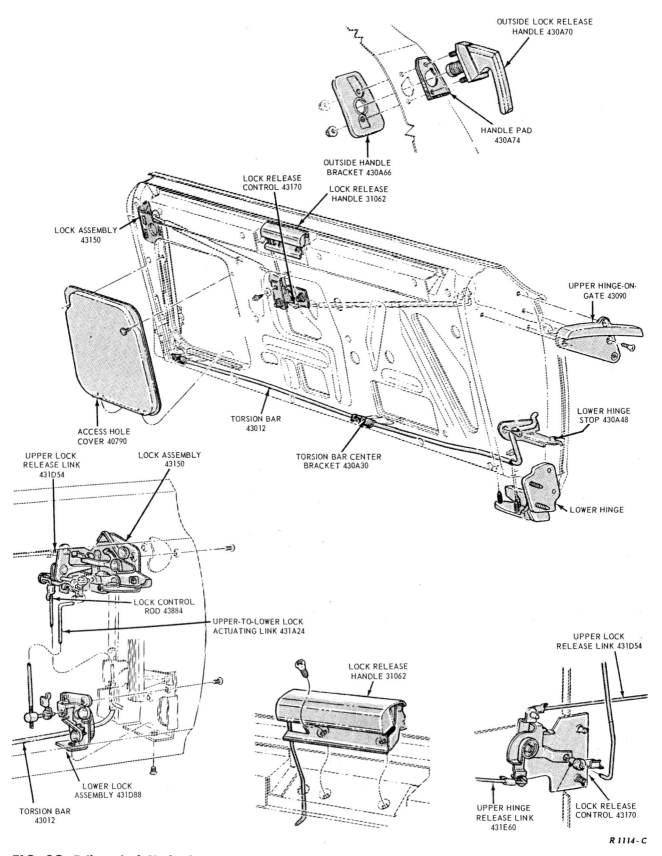

FIG. 29—Tailgate Lock Mechanism

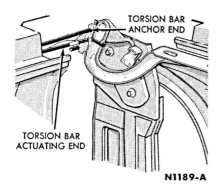

FIG. 30—Deck Lid Torsion Bar —Typical

the lock assembly and the door lock extension.

2. Remove the sleeve assembly retaining nut, lock washer, spacer, and sleeve and cylinder (Fig. 31).

3. To remove the lock cylinder from the sleeve assembly, turn the key in the cylinder ⅛ turn clockwise from the locked position, depress the cylinder retaining pin, and remove the key and cylinder.

INSTALLATION

1. To install the lock cylinder turn the key in the cylinder ⅛ turn clockwise from the locked position and insert the cylinder into the sleeve assembly.

2. Position the sleeve assembly spacer, and washer to the deck lid door and install the retaining nut.

3. Position the door lock extension, install the lock assembly and adjust it.

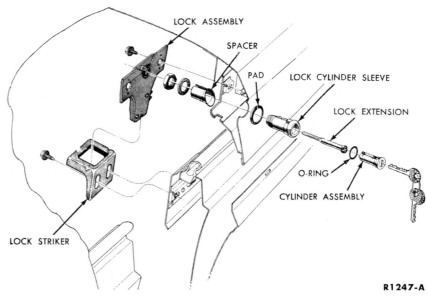

FIG. 31—Deck Lid Lock Installation—Typical

TRIM, SEATS, AND CONVERTIBLE TOP

GROUP 18

PART 18-1   **PAGE**

INTERIOR TRIM AND LANDAU
TOP COVER 18- 1

PART 18-2

SEATS 18-11

PART 18-3   **PAGE**

CONVERTIBLE TOP 18-19

PART 18-1

INTERIOR TRIM AND LANDAU TOP COVER

Section	Page	Section	Page
1 Door and Quarter Trim Panels	18- 1	4 Console	18- 9
2 Headlining	18- 3	5 Roof Outside Cover	18- 9
3 Instrument Panel Safety Cover	18- 7		

1 DOOR AND QUARTER TRIM PANELS

REMOVAL AND INSTALLATION

Basically, all door and quarter trim panels are retained in the same manner. In view of this, one removal and installation procedure will cover all models.

1. Remove the window regulator handle and the four inside handle retaining screws and remove the handles from their shafts.

2. Remove any screws retaining the trim panel to the inner panel, such as the arm rest retaining screws (Fig. 1).

3. With a putty knife, pry the trim panel retaining clips out of the inner panel at each side.

4. Bow the trim panel out of the retainers, and carefully loosen the water shield, if necessary.

5. Place a daub of sealer over each trim retaining clip hole to seal the retaining clips when they are pushed into the door. Also, apply this sealer around the window regulator shaft and other existing holes.

6. Fasten the water shield to the inner panel (Figs. 2 and 3).

7. Make sure that all the retaining clips are installed in the trim panel. Place the upper edge of the trim panel in the retainer, bow the trim panel, and then insert the lower edge into the retainer. Push the retaining clips into the holes in the door inner panel.

8. Install the arm rest retaining screws.

9. Place the friction plate against the trim panel and push the handle onto the shaft. Install the handle retaining screws.

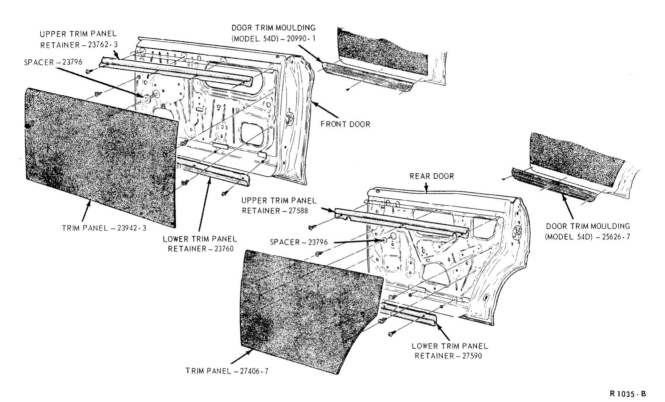

R 1035 - B

FIG. 1—Typical Door Trim Panel Installation

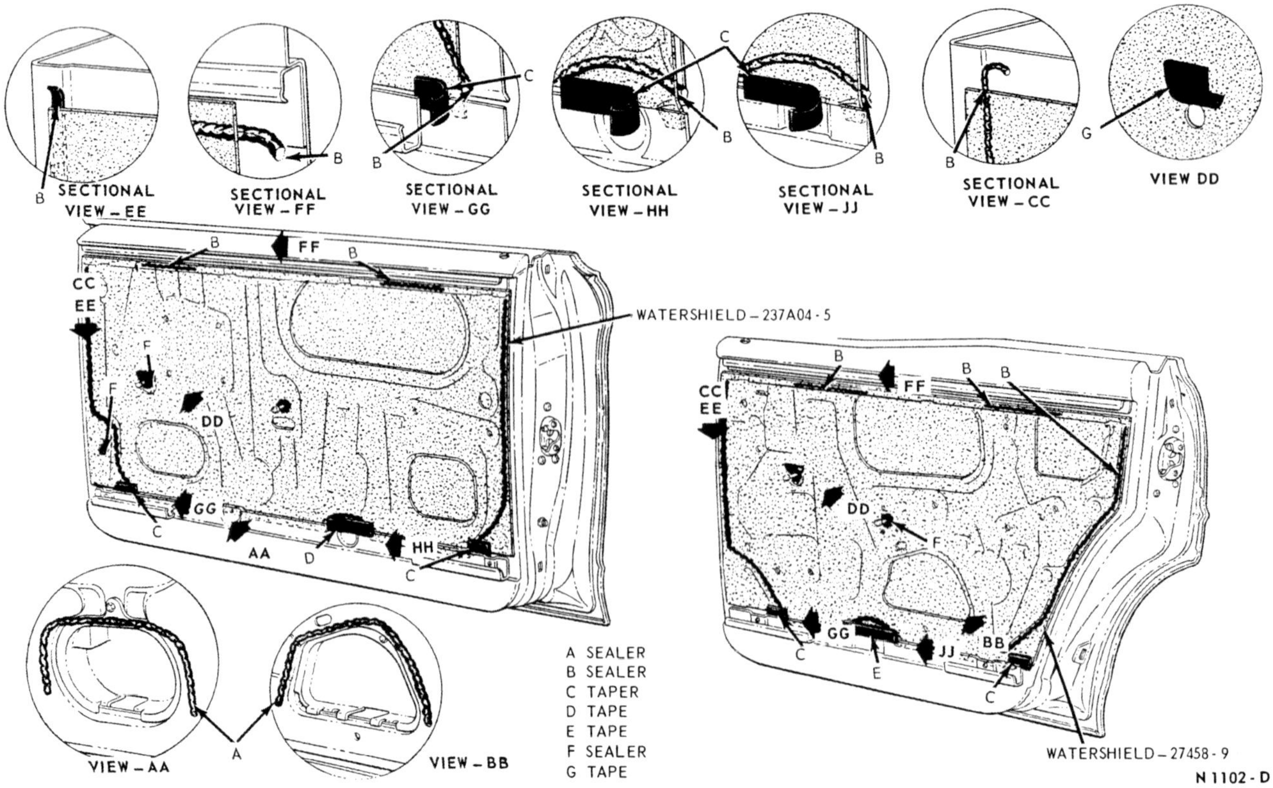

A SEALER
B SEALER
C TAPER
D TAPE
E TAPE
F SEALER
G TAPE

N 1102 - D

FIG. 2—Typical Door Trim Water Shields

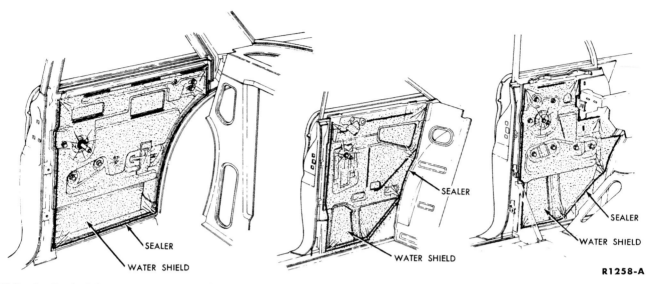

FIG. 3—Typical Quarter Trim Water Shields

2 HEADLINING

COMET—FALCON—FAIRLANE
REMOVAL

1. Remove the sun visors and rear view mirror.

2. Remove the windshield side and upper garnish mouldings.

3. Pull the door opening weatherstrips down far enough to provide access to the headlining perimeter.

4. Remove the rear seat cushion and seat back.

5. Remove the quarter trim panels.

6. Remove the rear package tray trim panel.

7. Remove the coat hooks and the dome light lens assemblies.

8. Unhook the headlining from the rear quarter retaining strips.

9. Cut the headlining loose around the back window.

10. Peel the headlining from around the windshield and door openings (Figs. 4 and 5).

11. Unhook the headlining support rods and remove the headlining assembly from the car.

INSTALLATION

1. Unpack and lay out the new headlining.

2. Transfer the support rods from the old headlining to the new one.

3. Position the headlining in the car and insert the support rod ends into their respective retaining holes in the roof side rails.

4. Measure and trim excess material from the headlining around the back window.

5. Apply trim cement around the back window flange and around the mating headlining edge. Tuck the headlining under the back window weatherstrip and pull out any wrinkles.

6. Apply trim cement around the rear quarter area and to the mating surface of the headlining. Hook the headlining material over the retaining strips and bend the retainer tabs down.

7. Apply trim cement to the roof header and to the mating surface around the front of the headlining.

8. Position the headlining to the roof header and pull out any wrinkles.

9. Apply trim cement around the door openings and mating surface of the headlining. Steam between the headlining panels as required to help remove any wrinkles and secure the headlining perimeter.

10. Trim the excess headlining material.

11. Install the package tray and quarter trim panels.

12. Install the coat hooks and dome light lens.

13. Install the windshield upper and side interior mouldings.

14. Install the windlace around the door openings.

15. Install the rear view mirror and sun visors.

16. Install the rear seat back and

rear seat cushion.

17. Clean the interior and headlining.

MUSTANG (MODEL 63)

1. Remove the sun visors and the inside rear view mirror.

2. Remove the roof headlining side front retainer from each A pillar (Fig. 6—View BB).

3. Remove 5 screws and remove the back window upper garnish moulding.

4. Remove 4 screws and remove the quarter trim upper front mouldings and caps (Fig. 7).

5. Remove 5 screws and remove the quarter trim upper front panel.

6. Remove the windlace from the door openings (Fig. 6).

7. Cut the headlining at the windshield weatherstrip and loosen the headlining.

8. Cut the headlining at the back window weatherstrip and loosen the headlining.

9. Pull the headlining from the door opening pinch weld, disconnect the bows, and remove the headlining.

10. Place the old and new headlinings on a clean surface and transfer the bows to the new headlining. The bows are color coded on one end for identification (Fig. 6).

11. Position the headlining in the car and install the roof bows in the side rails.

12. Apply trim cement (C2AZ-19C525-A) to the back side of the

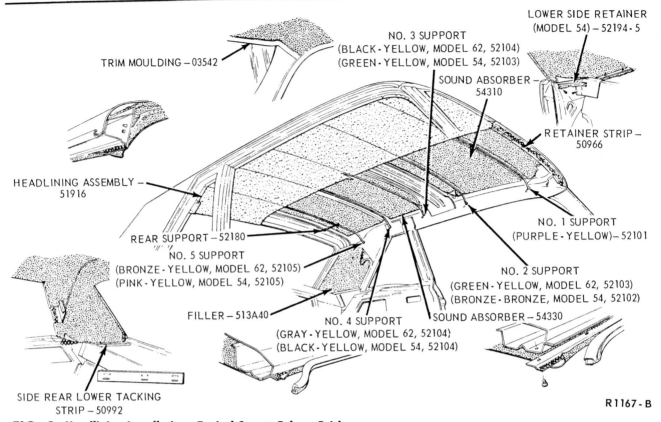

TRIM MOULDING – 03542

NO. 3 SUPPORT
(BLACK-YELLOW, MODEL 62, 52104)
(GREEN-YELLOW, MODEL 54, 52103)

LOWER SIDE RETAINER
(MODEL 54) – 52194-5

SOUND ABSORBER –
54310

RETAINER STRIP –
50966

HEADLINING ASSEMBLY –
51916

REAR SUPPORT – 52180

NO. 5 SUPPORT
(BRONZE-YELLOW, MODEL 62, 52105)
(PINK-YELLOW, MODEL 54, 52105)

FILLER – 513A40

NO. 4 SUPPORT
(GRAY-YELLOW, MODEL 62, 52104)
(BLACK-YELLOW, MODEL 54, 52104)

NO. 1 SUPPORT
(PURPLE-YELLOW) – 52101

NO. 2 SUPPORT
(GREEN-YELLOW, MODEL 62, 52103)
(BRONZE-BRONZE, MODEL 54, 52102)

SOUND ABSORBER – 54330

SIDE REAR LOWER TACKING
STRIP – 50992

R1167-B

FIG. 4—Headlining Installation—Typical Comet, Falcon, Fairlane

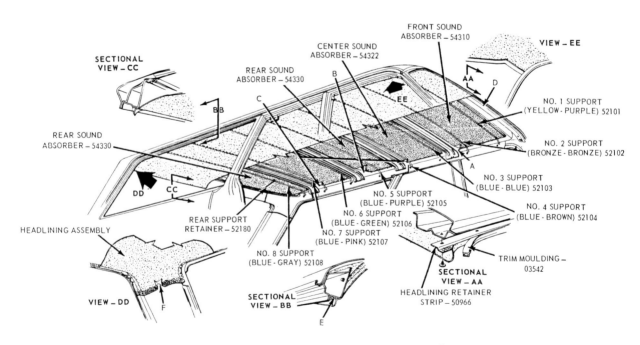

SECTIONAL
VIEW – CC

REAR SOUND
ABSORBER – 54330

REAR SOUND
ABSORBER – 54330

CENTER SOUND
ABSORBER – 54322

FRONT SOUND
ABSORBER – 54310

VIEW – EE

NO. 1 SUPPORT
(YELLOW-PURPLE) 52101

NO. 2 SUPPORT
(BRONZE-BRONZE) 52102

NO. 3 SUPPORT
(BLUE-BLUE) 52103

NO. 4 SUPPORT
(BLUE-BROWN) 52104

NO. 5 SUPPORT
(BLUE-PURPLE) 52105

NO. 6 SUPPORT
(BLUE-GREEN) 52106

NO. 7 SUPPORT
(BLUE-PINK) 52107

NO. 8 SUPPORT
(BLUE-GRAY) 52108

REAR SUPPORT
RETAINER – 52180

HEADLINING ASSEMBLY

VIEW – DD

SECTIONAL
VIEW – BB

TRIM MOULDING –
03542

SECTIONAL
VIEW – AA

HEADLINING RETAINER
STRIP – 50966

A - B - C - D - E - F ADHESIVE (C2AZ-19C525-A)

R1259-B

FIG. 5—Headlining Installation—Typical Station Wagon

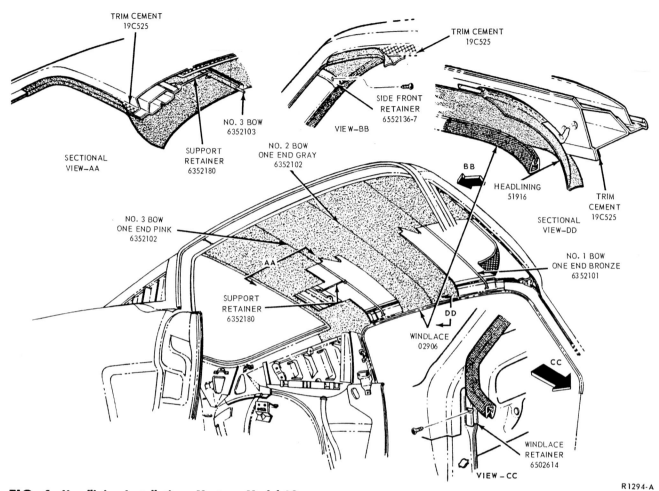

TRIM CEMENT
19C525

SECTIONAL
VIEW—AA

NO. 3 BOW
6352103

SUPPORT
RETAINER
6352180

NO. 3 BOW
ONE END PINK
6352102

SUPPORT
RETAINER
6352180

NO. 2 BOW
ONE END GRAY
6352102

VIEW—BB

TRIM CEMENT
19C525

SIDE FRONT
RETAINER
6552136-7

BB

HEADLINING
51916

SECTIONAL
VIEW—DD

TRIM
CEMENT
19C525

NO. 1 BOW
ONE END BRONZE
6352101

WINDLACE
02906

DD

CC

WINDLACE
RETAINER
6502614

VIEW – CC

R1294-A

FIG. 6—Headlining Installation—Mustang Model 63

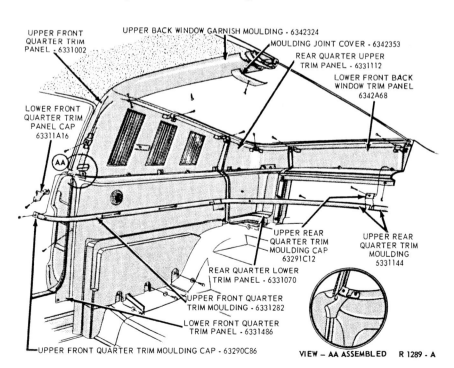

UPPER FRONT
QUARTER TRIM
PANEL - 6331002

UPPER BACK WINDOW GARNISH MOULDING - 6342324

MOULDING JOINT COVER - 6342353

REAR QUARTER UPPER
TRIM PANEL - 6331112

LOWER FRONT BACK
WINDOW TRIM PANEL
6342A68

LOWER FRONT
QUARTER TRIM
PANEL CAP
63311A16

AA

UPPER REAR
QUARTER TRIM
MOULDING CAP
63291C12

REAR QUARTER LOWER
TRIM PANEL - 6331070

UPPER FRONT QUARTER
TRIM MOULDING - 6331282

LOWER FRONT QUARTER
TRIM PANEL - 6331486

UPPER FRONT QUARTER TRIM MOULDING CAP - 63290C86

UPPER REAR
QUARTER TRIM
MOULDING
5331144

VIEW – AA ASSEMBLED   R 1289 - A

FIG. 7—Interior Mouldings and Quarter Trim Panel Installation

headlining at the back window opening.

13. Tuck the headlining under the back window weatherstrip. Smooth out any wrinkles or gathering and trim off any excess material.

14. Apply trim cement (C2AZ-19C525-A) to the back side of the headlining at the windshield opening.

15. Tuck the headlining under the windshield weatherstrip. Smooth out any wrinkles or gathering and trim off any excess material.

16. Apply trim cement (C2AZ-19C525-A) to the roof side rails at the door openings. Position the headlining to the side rails and trim off any excess material (Fig. 6).

17. Install the windlace in the door openings.

18. Install the roof headlining side front retainer at each A pillar.

19. Install the inside rear view mirror and sun visors.

20. Install the right and left quarter trim upper front panels (Fig. 7).

21. Install the quarter trim upper front mouldings and front caps.

22. Install the back window upper garnish moulding.

23. Clean all mouldings and remove any headlining scraps from the car.

MUSTANG (MODEL 65)

1. Remove the rear seat cushion and seat back and remove the quarter trim panels.

2. Remove 2 clips and retainers and remove the package tray.

3. Bend back the headlining lower rear side retaining strip tabs (Fig. 8).

4. Remove the coat hanger hooks.

5. Remove the sun visors.

6. Remove the headlining retainer from each A pillar (Fig. 8).

7. Remove 3 screws and remove the rear view mirror.

8. Remove the door opening windlace from each side of the body.

9. Cut the headlining along the edge of the windshield and back window weatherstrips.

10. Remove the headlining from the right and left sides in the package tray area. Then, remove the headlining from the roof side rails and remove it from the car.

11. Place the new and old headlining on a clean surface and transfer the headlining support wires in sequence to the new headlining. **The roof bows are color coded on one end. When ordering new roof bows, be sure to note the color code.**

12. Position the headlining in the car and install the rear support wire and 2 rear support retainers. Then, install the remaining support wires, working towards the front of the car.

13. Trim the headlining at the windshield header, leaving approximately ½ inch of material for tucking under the windshield header weatherstrip.

14. Apply trim cement to the windshield header and, starting from the center, cement the headlining to the header. Insert the remaining head-

lining material under the windshield header weatherstrip.

15. Trim the headlining at the rear window, leaving approximately ½ inch of material for tucking under the weatherstrip. Apply trim cement to the rear window upper rail and, starting from the center, cement the headlining to the upper rail. Insert the remaining material under the rear window weatherstrip.

16. Pull the headlining down at the sides to remove wrinkles. Cut the listings at each end to eliminate gathering of the material.

17. Apply trim cement to the left roof side rail over the door and quarter window. Pull the headlining down to remove wrinkles and cement it in place. Then, trim the headlining as necessary. Cement and trim the right side the same way.

18. Straighten the metal prongs (View AA—Fig. 8) at the package tray area; attach the headlining to the prongs and bend the prongs down as

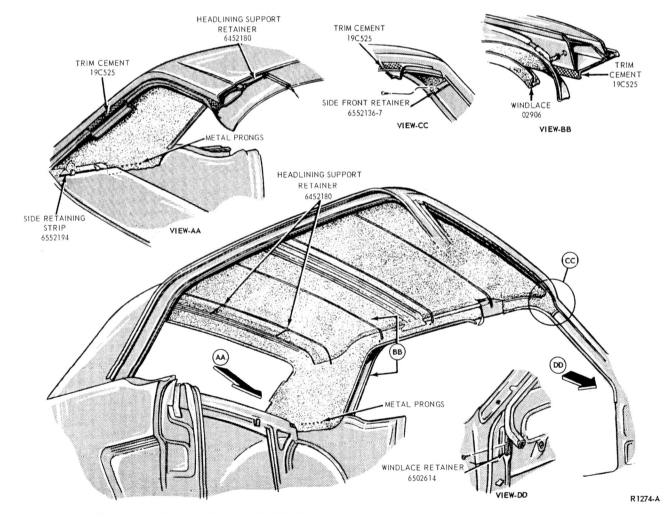

FIG. 8—Headlining Installation—Mustang Model 65

shown.

19. Roll the lower rear side retaining strips into the headlining and retain them by bending the tabs (View AA).

20. Install the right and left roof side windlace at the door and window openings.

21. Install the headlining retainer at the A pillar (View DD).

22. Install the rear view mirror, sun visors, and coat hooks.

23. Slide the package tray into position and install the retainers and clips. Then, install the quarter trim panels and rear seat back and cushion.

3 INSTRUMENT PANEL SAFETY COVER

REMOVAL AND INSTALLATION
COMET, FALCON, FAIRLANE

1. Open the glove box door. Remove the glove box liner retaining screws and remove the glove box liner.

2. Fairlane: Remove the radio control knobs and the control shaft retaining nuts.

3. Comet: Remove the radio speaker grill by prying upward to release the two retaining clips.

4. Remove the instrument cluster retaining screws.

5. Pull the instrument cluster out far enough to disconnect the speedometer cable, light sockets and wiring connectors from the instrument cluster. Remove the instrument cluster.

6. Remove the nuts retaining the safety cover to the instrument panel.

7. Pry up and remove the safety cover.

8. Position the new safety cover to the instrument panel (Figs. 9 and 10).

9. Install the safety cover retaining nuts.

10. Position the instrument cluster to the instrument panel. Connect the wiring connectors and the speedometer cable. Install the light sockets.

11. Install the instrument cluster retaining screws.

12. Comet: Position the radio speaker grille and snap the retainers in place.

13. Fairlane: Install the radio control shaft retaining nuts and the radio control knobs.

14. Position the glove box liner in place and install the glove box liner retaining screws.

MUSTANG

1. Remove the right and left side lower mouldings (Fig. 11) and the upper retaining mouldings.

2. Remove the radio speaker grille.

3. Remove 2 nuts retaining the cover above the radio (View DD), and pull the cover from the instrument panel.

4. Using solvent, clean the old cement from the instrument panel mounting surfaces.

5. Apply cement to the instrument panel mounting surface and cover. Position the cover on the instrument panel and install the 2 retaining nuts in the area over the radio.

6. Install the radio speaker grille, upper retaining mouldings, and lower mouldings.

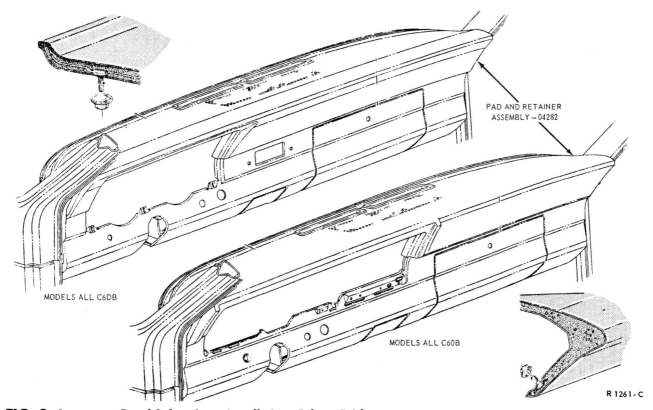

FIG. 9—Instrument Panel Safety Cover Installation—Falcon, Fairlane

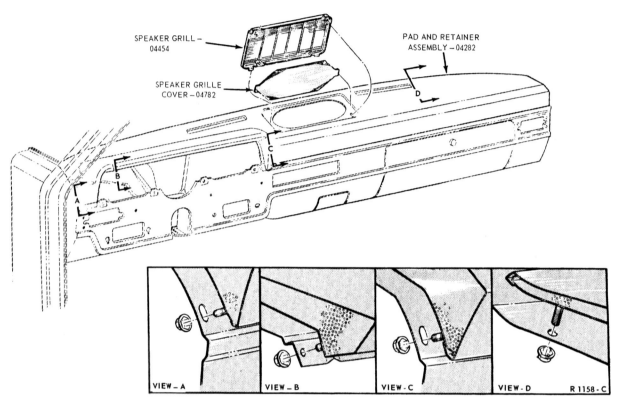

FIG. 10—Instrument Panel Safety Cover Installation—Comet

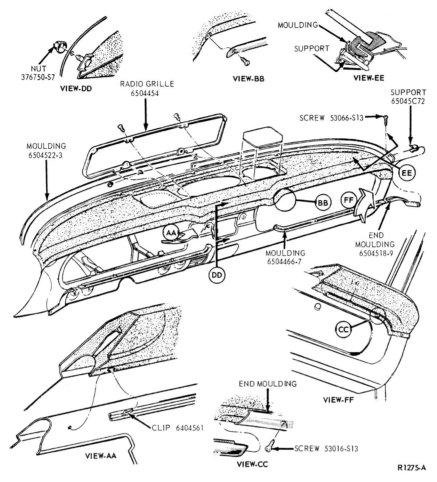

NUT
376750-S7
VIEW-DD

RADIO GRILLE
6504454

VIEW-BB

MOULDING
SUPPORT
VIEW-EE

MOULDING
6504522-3

SUPPORT
65045C72

SCREW 53066-S13

END
MOULDING
6504518-9

MOULDING
6504466-7

END MOULDING

CLIP 6404561

VIEW-AA

VIEW-CC

SCREW 53016-S13

VIEW-FF

R1275-A

FIG. 11—Instrument Panel Safety Cover Installation—Mustang

4 CONSOLE

REMOVAL AND INSTALLATION
MUSTANG

The Mustang has 2 optional consoles; one is used when air conditioning is installed and one is used without air conditioning. Models that are not equipped with air conditioning have a glove box at the front end of the console. Models equipped with air conditioning do not have the glove box.

1. Remove the knob or handle from the gear shift selector lever.

2. Remove 3 screws from each side of the console in the seat area.

3. Remove 2 screws from inside the glove box (if equipped).

4. Lift the console rear end up and remove the console from the car.

5. Position the console to the floor pan and install the attaching screws.

6. Install the gear shift lever knob or handle.

5 ROOF OUTSIDE COVER

COMET, FALCON, FAIRLANE
REMOVAL

1. Remove the rear seat cushion back and quarter trim panels.

2. Remove the quarter trim panel retainer mouldings and quarter window garnish mouldings.

3. Remove the package tray panel and loosen the headlining in the quarter area sufficiently to permit access to the side belt moulding retainer nuts (Fig. 12).

4. Remove the side and rear belt mouldings.

5. Remove the back window outside mouldings. Remove the back window and weatherstrip.

6. Remove the windshield wiper arm assemblies and remove the top cowl panel.

7. Remove the side, top and bottom windshield outside mouldings.

8. From within the vehicle remove the rear view mirror assembly, the windshield pillar cap mouldings and the plastic windshield header moulding.

9. Cut the windshield sealer as described in Part 17-3 and remove the windshield.

10. Remove the sealer from the windshield pinch weld flange and remove the moulding retainer clips.

11. Remove the drip rail moulding and then using a 0.128 to 0.132 inch diameter drill, remove the rivets from the drip rail cover retainers and discard the retainers.

12. Remove the staples from the front and back window opening that are retaining the cover and remove the cover from the roof.

13. Remove the old adhesive from the roof area with a scraper or use an appropriate cleaning solvent. **It is extremely important that the entire roof and drip rails are thoroughly cleaned.**

INSTALLATION

It is recommended that drive nails be substituted for the staples shown in Fig. 12.

Wherever possible, use the existing drive nail or screw holes. Therefore, each location should be identified on the pinch weld flange with a wax crayon.

Seal all unused holes with either C1AZ-19627-A Pressure Sensitized Tape or AB-19560-A caulking cord.

1. Carefully position the outside cover on the roof panel. (Fore and Aft center punch marks have been provided in the cover for centering purposes.)

2. With the cover properly positioned and temporarily secured, apply an even coating of C2AZ-19C-525-A adhesive to the roof panel and a like amount to the corresponding area of the roof outside cover assembly. For best results, secure limited sections at a time. **Make certain that the adhesive is not lumpy as it will be objectionable from an appearance standpoint.**

3. Using a 0.128 to 0.132 inch diameter drill, pierce the vinyl material at the existing staple or screw hole locations. Install drive nails in each of the holes.

4. Position both drip rail retainers and, using the same drill referred to above, pierce the vinyl at each of the holes. Install the Pop rivets from the underside of the drip rail except at the extreme rear hole in which case the rivet should be inserted from the retainer side.

5. Trim the excess cover material from around the entire perimeter.

6. Apply sealer C3AZ-19562-A

(for white tops) or sealer C3AZ-19562-B (for black tops) over the entire surface of the drip rail retainers. With the drip rail properly sealed, a minimum depth of 1/8 inch should be retained for adequate water drainage. **Place masking tape on the cover assembly for the entire length of the drip rail before applying sealer. After sealer has been applied, remove the tape.**

7. Install the drip rail mouldings.

8. Install the back belt center and side mouldings.

9. Reposition and secure the headlining.

10. Install the back window and outside window mouldings.

11. Install the quarter trim panel retainer mouldings and quarter window garnish mouldings.

12. Install the package tray panel, quarter panels, rear seat back and seat cushion.

13. Install the windshield.

14. Install the windshield interior garnish mouldings and sun visor assemblies.

15. Install the windshield exterior mouldings, retainers, and windshield wiper blade assemblies.

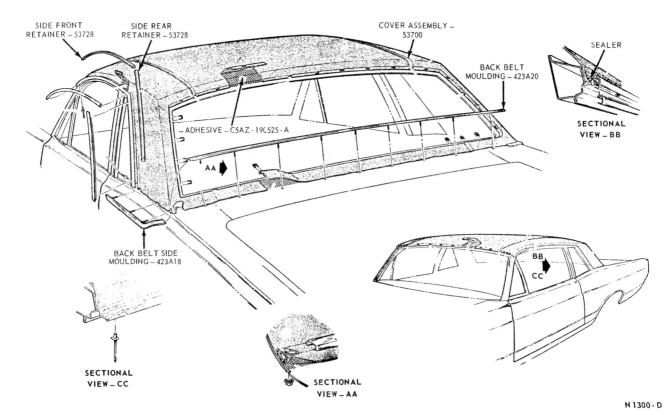

N 1300 - D

FIG. 12—Roof Outside Cover Installation—Comet, Falcon, Fairlane

PART 18-2   SEATS

Section	Page	Section	Page
1 Standard Seats—Removal and Installation	18-11	Front Seat Back Cover	18-13
Seat and Seat Track	18-11	Rear Seat Back Cover	18-13
Front Seat Cushion and Back	18-11	2 Bucket Seats—Removal and Installation	18-16
Rear Seat Cushion and Back	18-11	Seat and Seat Track	18-16
Front Seat Cushion Cover	18-11	Front Seat Cushion Cover	18-16
Rear Seat Cushion Cover	18-13	Front Seat Back Cover	18-16

1   STANDARD SEATS

REMOVAL AND INSTALLATION

SEAT AND SEAT TRACK

Work, other than that of minor nature, is more easily performed when the front seat assembly is removed from the car.

1. Remove the nuts retaining the seat tracks to the floor pan. If equipped with power seats, disconnect the seat wiring loom connector. Lift the seat assembly from the car (Fig. 1).

2. Disconnect and remove the release cable from the seat frame. Remove the seat tracks from the seat frame.

3. Transfer the seat adjusting lever knob and the retracting springs, if necessary, to the new track assembly.

4. Position the seat tracks on the seat frame and install the retaining bolts and release cable.

5. Position the seat assembly in the car and install the retaining bolts and nuts.

Release Cable Adjustment. Release cable maladjustment will affect only the right side of the seat. In case the latch retaining the track fails to release, turn the release cable turnbuckle or eye bolt enough turns to shorten the release cable travel sufficiently to release the track latch. If the latch fails to secure the seat travel, turn the release cable turnbuckle or eye bolt to lengthen the release cable enough to allow the latch to snap in the locking position.

FRONT SEAT CUSHION AND/OR BACK

1. Remove the front seat and seat track from the car if the cushion is to be replaced.

2. To replace the seat cushion, re-move the seat assembly from the seat track.

3. On cars with a solid seat back, remove the bolts and washers attaching the seat back to the seat cushion frame. Before being able to remove the attaching bolts it is necessary to remove the seat back and seat cushion trim from the bolts.

4. On cars with a split front seat back, remove the hairpin clip from the center seat back stud and the seat cushion stud. Before being able to remove the hair pin clips it is necessary to remove the pivot covers.

5. Position the seat back assembly on the seat. On cars with the split seat back, install the hairpin clip at the seat center bracket and the seat cushion stud and install the pivot covers.

6. On a car with a solid seat back, install the bolts and washers attaching the seat back to the seat and fasten the seat back and seat cushion cover trim with hog rings.

7. Position the seat cushion on the seat track and install the retaining bolts if removed.

8. Install the front seat and seat track in the car.

REAR SEAT CUSHION AND/OR BACK

1. Lift the rear seat cushion and pull it forward to remove it from the car.

2. Remove one rear seat arm rest (two-door sedans).

3. Remove 2 rear seat back attaching screws located at the bottom of the seat back.

4. Lift up on the seat back to disengage the seat from the upper hooks and remove the seat back from the car.

5. Position the seat back in the car and engage the seat with the upper hooks.

6. Install the seat back lower retaining screws and the removed arm rest. Then install the rear seat cushion.

FRONT SEAT CUSHION COVER

Fig. 2 shows a front seat cushion buildup. Seat cushions for all models are built up in basically the same manner. Therefore, when installing new seat cushion covers or pads, refer to Fig. 2 for the location of listing wires, hog rings, anti-squeak pads, and seat pad stack-up.

1. Remove the seat and seat track assembly.

2. On models with a solid seat back, remove the bolts and washers attaching the seat back to the seat cushion frame.

3. On models with a split seat back, remove the seat back outer support arm covers and remove the hairpin clips from the pivot pins.

4. On models with a split seat back, remove the retaining screw from the seat back center support trim cover and remove the seat back center pivot hair pin clips.

5. Remove the seat back assembly.

6. Remove the seat back stop plates from the seat cushion.

7. Remove the hog rings retaining the seat cushion cover and remove the cover (Fig. 2). Inspect the pad and replace it if necessary.

8. Transfer the listing wires to the new cover.

9. With the seat cushion assembly right side up, make sure that the pads are stacked properly and centered; then place the cover over the pads to hold them in position.

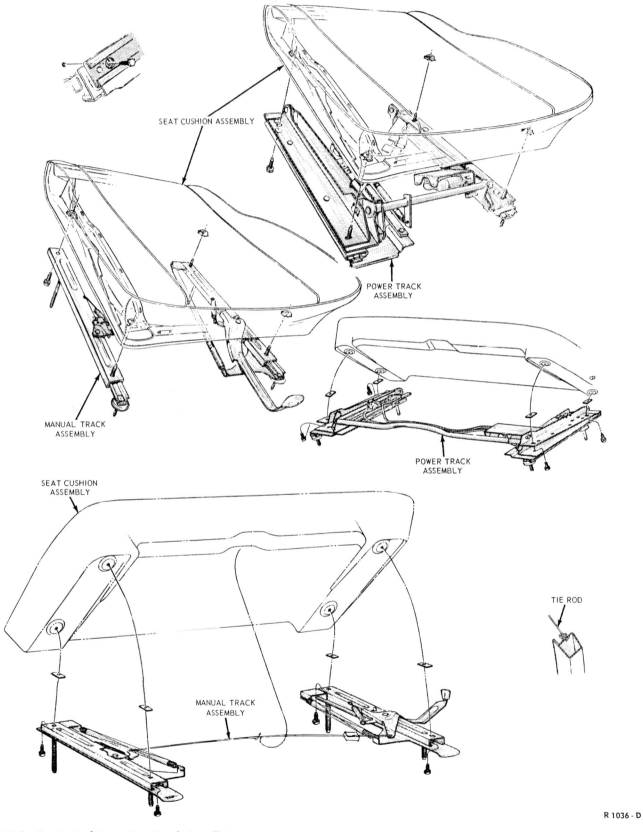

SEAT CUSHION ASSEMBLY

POWER TRACK
ASSEMBLY

MANUAL TRACK
ASSEMBLY

POWER TRACK
ASSEMBLY

SEAT CUSHION
ASSEMBLY

TIE ROD

MANUAL TRACK
ASSEMBLY

R 1036 - D

FIG. 1—Typical Front Seat Track Installation

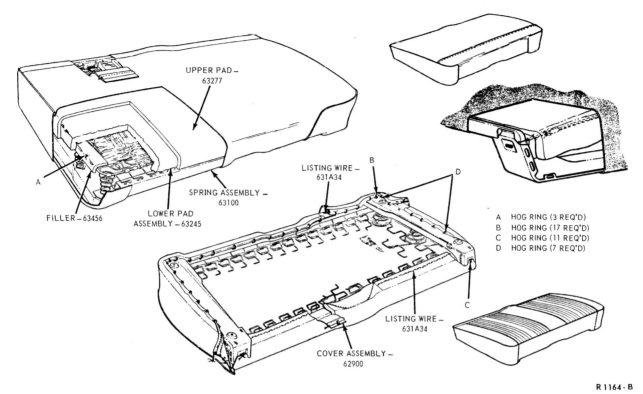

FIG. 2—Typical Front Seat Cushion Cover Installation

10. Carefully turn the seat assembly over so that the pads do not shift out of position.

11. After centering the cover and straightening the seams along the front edge of the cushion, fasten the cover to the front of the seat frame with hog rings. Make sure that the hog rings encircle the listing wire. Install 1 hog ring in each hole provided in the seat cushion frame.

12. At the rear of the seat assembly, pull the cover taut over the pads, and install hog rings at the seat frame.

13. Fasten the side of the cover to the seat frame side with hog rings through the holes provided (Fig. 2).

14. Install the seat back stop plates and the seat back.

15. Install the seat tracks to the cushion and the seat assembly in the car.

REAR SEAT CUSHION COVER

1. Remove the rear seat cushion from the car by lifting on the front of the seat and pulling it forward.

2. Remove the cushion cover hog rings and remove the cushion cover from the seat frame.

3. Inspect the pad and replace it if necessary.

4. Transfer the listing wire, if equipped, to the new cushion cover.

5. Position the new cushion cover on the seat frame and springs and attach it in place with hog rings (Fig. 3).

6. Install the seat cushion in the car.

FRONT SEAT BACK COVER

Repairs to seat backs are performed out of the car and are usually limited to replacement of torn or burned seat covers. In a few instances, the pads may be damaged and require replacement.

Figs. 4 and 5 show a front seat back build-up. Seat backs for all other models are built up in basically the same manner. Therefore, when installing new seat back covers or pads, refer to Figs. 4 and 5 for the location of listing wires, hog rings, anti-squeak pads, and seat pad stack-up.

1. Remove the seat back.

2. Remove the ash receptacle and ash receptacle retainer, if equipped.

3. Remove the hog rings retaining the seat back cover to the frame. Unhook the listing wires from the seat spring assembly tabs, and remove the cover (Figs. 4 and 5).

4. Transfer the listing wire to the new seat back cover.

5. Inspect the seat pad and spring assemblies, and repair or replace as necessary.

6. Carefully place the cover over the seat frame and pad assembly. Pull the cover taut over the pads, hook the listing wires on the seat spring assembly tabs and install the hog rings (Figs. 4 and 5).

7. Cut a hole in the cover for the ash receptacle retainer, if equipped, and install the receptacle assembly.

8. Install the seat back to the seat cushion.

REAR SEAT BACK COVER

1. Remove the rear seat back from the car.

2. Remove the hog rings retaining the seat back cover to the frame and remove the rear seat back cover.

3. Transfer the listing wires to the new cover.

4. Position the new cover on the pad and seat frame and secure it in place with hog rings (Fig. 6).

5. Install the rear seat back in the car.

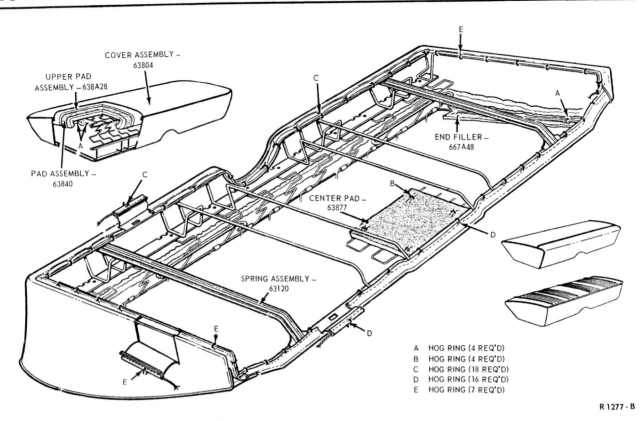

A HOG RING (4 REQ'D)
B HOG RING (4 REQ'D)
C HOG RING (18 REQ'D)
D HOG RING (16 REQ'D)
E HOG RING (7 REQ'D)

R 1277 - B

FIG. 3—Typical Rear Seat Cushion Cover Installation

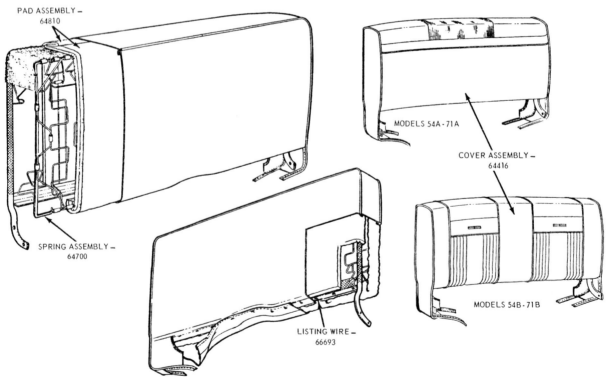

R 1278 - B

FIG. 4—Typical Front Seat Back Cover Installation—4-Door

A   HOG RING (1 REQ'D EACH LOWER CORNER)
B   ADHESIVE — C2AZ-19C525-A
C   TABS (ON SPRING ASSEMBLY)
D   HOG RING (3 REQ'D AT OUTER SIDE)
E   HOG RING (3 REQ'D AT INNER SIDE)

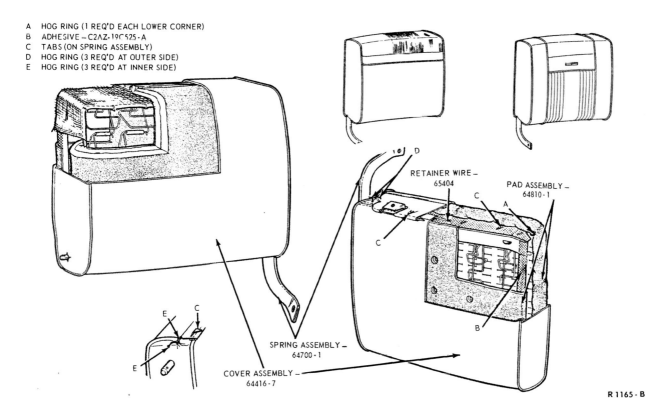

RETAINER WIRE —
65404

PAD ASSEMBLY —
64810-1

SPRING ASSEMBLY —
64700-1

COVER ASSEMBLY —
64416-7

R 1165-B

FIG. 5—Typical Front Seat Back Cover Installation—2-Door

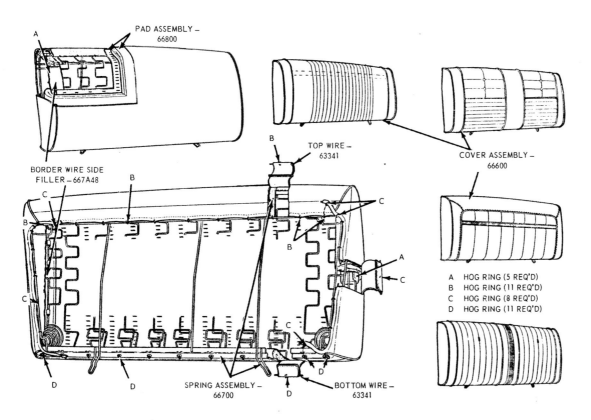

PAD ASSEMBLY —
66800

TOP WIRE —
63341

COVER ASSEMBLY —
66600

BORDER WIRE SIDE
FILLER — 667A48

A   HOG RING (5 REQ'D)
B   HOG RING (11 REQ'D)
C   HOG RING (8 REQ'D)
D   HOG RING (11 REQ'D)

SPRING ASSEMBLY —
66700

BOTTOM WIRE —
63341

R 1262-C

FIG. 6—Typical Rear Seat Back Cover Installation

2 BUCKET SEATS—MANUAL

The seat is mounted in the conventional manner on two seat tracks. The seat release is located at the lower front center of the seat, and is operated by pulling the lever side ways to release the seat tracks.

REMOVAL AND INSTALLATION

SEAT AND SEAT TRACK

The seat track assembly is easily replaced if the seat assembly is removed from the car.

1. Remove 4 floor pan plug buttons to gain access to the seat track retaining nuts (Mustang only).
2. From under the car, remove the seat track retaining stud nuts and washers. Remove the seat assembly from the car and place it on a clean work area.
3. Remove the screws which retain the seat track assembly to the seat cushion and remove the seat track assembly.
4. Disconnect the seat track brace and latch release rod from the track being replaced, and connect these parts to the new seat track.
5. Loosely install the track-to-floor retaining studs in the seat track.
6. Place the seat track assembly on the seat cushion, and install the retaining screws.
7. Place the seat assembly in the car and install the washers and nuts on the retaining studs.
8. Install the floor pan plug buttons (Mustang only).

FRONT SEAT CUSHION COVER

Repairs to seat cushions or seat backs are performed out of the car and are usually limited to replacement of torn or burned seat covers. In a few instances, the pads may be damaged and require replacement.

When installing a new seat cover or pad, refer to Figs. 7 and 8 for the location of listing wires, hog rings, anti-squeak pads, and seat pad stack-up.

Comet, Falcon (Model 76 Only)

1. Remove the seat and seat track assembly from the car and place it on a clean work area.
2. Remove the seat cushion from the seat track. From each side of the seat, remove the seat back retainer, and remove the seat back.
3. Remove the seat back scuff

plates and remove the hog rings retaining the seat cushion cover to the spring assembly. Separate the bottom cover from the seat cushion pad and remove the cushion cover.

4. Inspect the pad and spring assemblies, and repair or replace as necessary.
5. Transfer the listing wires to the new cover.
6. Place the new cover assembly over the pad and seat spring assembly and secure it to the front bolster wire with hog rings. Apply trim cement (C2AZ-19C525-A) to the bottom of the cushion cover and position the cover correctly to the seat cushion pad.
7. Secure each side bolster wire to the seat spring assembly with hog rings.
8. The front and side edges of the cover assembly can now be secured to the bottom of the spring assembly with hog rings as shown in Fig. 7.
9. Secure the rear edge of the cover assembly to the bottom of the spring assembly with hog rings.
10. Install the two scuff plates on the cushion.
11. Install the seat back side shield and seat tracks. Install the seat assembly.

Mustang

1. Remove the front seat and track from the car and remove the seat tracks from the seat.
2. Remove the front seat back shield and the seat back pivot side cover.
3. Remove the seat back pivot pin and remove the seat back from the seat cushion.
4. Remove the seat cushion scuff plate.
5. Remove the seat cushion cover and pad.
6. Position the seat cushion pad on the frame and install the hog rings (Fig. 8).
7. Position the cushion cover on the pad. Cement with trim cement (C2AZ-19C525-A) and retain with hog rings (Fig. 8).
8. Install the seat cushion scuff plate.
9. Position the seat back on the pivot and install the pivot pin.
10. Install the front seat back

shield and the seat back pivot side cover.

11. Install the seat on the seat tracks and install the seat and seat track in the car.

FRONT SEAT BACK COVER

1. Remove the seat and seat tracks from the car, if required, for accessibility to the seat side shield retaining screws.
2. Remove the right and left seat back side shields and remove the seat back retaining bolts or retainer pins and remove the seat back from the cushion.
3. Unsnap and remove the seat back rear cover (Figs. 7 and 8).
4. Remove the seat back upper moulding retaining screws and remove the mouldings.
5. Remove the seat back stop adjusting bolts and remove the hog rings retaining the cover to the frame.
6. Bend up the side retaining tabs (Fig. 7) and lift the cover off the tabs.
7. Remove any additional hog rings retaining the cover to the seat frame.
8. Position the trim cover off the side padding to gain access to the hog rings in the center of the seat back and remove the hog rings.
9. Position the new cover over the front center of the seat back and attach it with hog rings. Position the cover around the sides and top of the sponge padding, pulling the material tight. Then, turn the seat back face down.
10. Pull the trim cover tight and install hog rings at the top. Pull the cover tight and install hog rings at the bottom.
11. Pull the trim cover tight at the sides and position it over the side retaining tabs (Fig. 7). Bend the tabs down.
12. Position the rear cover on the seat back and snap it into place. Install the seat back stop adjusting bolts and nuts.
13. Install the seat back upper moulding.
14. Install the seat back on the cushion and install the seat back pivot covers.
15. Install the seat and seat track in the car.

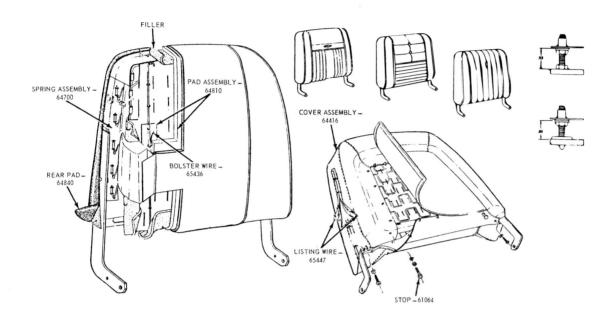

A   HOG RING (16 REQ'D)
B   HOG RING (3 REQ'D EACH BOLSTER)
C   HOG RING (6 REQ'D EACH BOLSTER)
D   HOG RING (5 REQ'D)
E   HOG RING (7 REQ'D)
F   HOG RING (5 REQ'D ALONG READ)
G   ADHESIVE—C2AZ-19C525-A

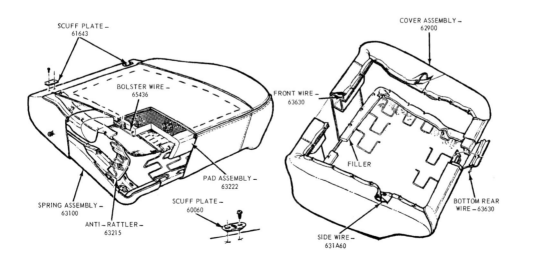

R 1098-C

FIG. 7—Typical Bucket Seat Back and Cushion Cover Installation—Comet, Falcon, Fairlane

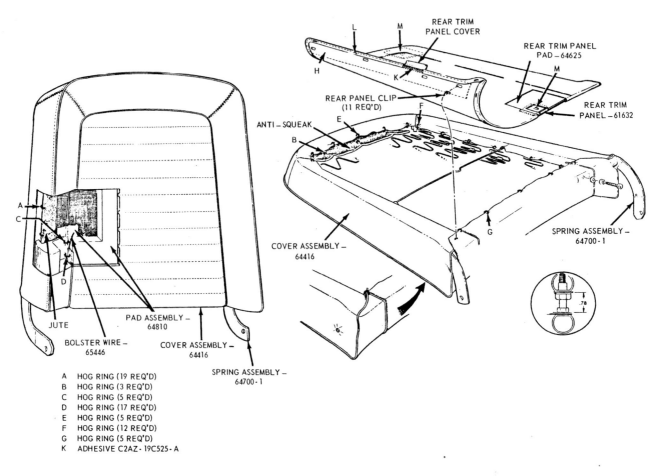

REAR TRIM PANEL COVER

REAR TRIM PANEL PAD – 64625

REAR TRIM PANEL – 61632

REAR PANEL CLIP (11 REQ'D)

ANTI – SQUEAK

COVER ASSEMBLY – 64416

SPRING ASSEMBLY – 64700-1

JUTE

PAD ASSEMBLY – 64810

BOLSTER WIRE – 65446

COVER ASSEMBLY – 64416

SPRING ASSEMBLY – 64700-1

.78

A   HOG RING (19 REQ'D)
B   HOG RING (3 REQ'D)
C   HOG RING (5 REQ'D)
D   HOG RING (17 REQ'D)
E   HOG RING (5 REQ'D)
F   HOG RING (12 REQ'D)
G   HOG RING (5 REQ'D)
K   ADHESIVE C2AZ- 19C525- A

A   HOG RING (15 REQ'D)
C   HOG RING (12 REQ'D)
B   HOG RING (4 REQ'D)
E   HOG RING (5 REQ'D)
F   HOG RING (12 REQ'D)
G   HOG RING (4 REQ'D)
H   ADHESIVE –C2AZ- 19C525- A

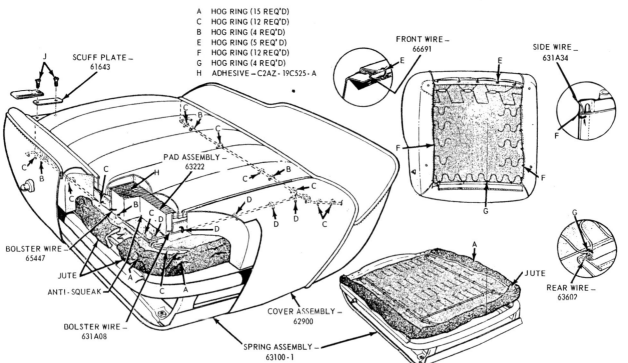

SCUFF PLATE – 61643

FRONT WIRE – 66691

SIDE WIRE – 631A34

PAD ASSEMBLY – 63222

BOLSTER WIRE – 65447

JUTE

ANTI-SQUEAK

BOLSTER WIRE – 631A08

COVER ASSEMBLY – 62900

SPRING ASSEMBLY – 63100-1

JUTE

REAR WIRE – 63602

R 1306 - A

FIG. 8–Typical Bucket Seat Back and Cushion Cover Installation–Mustang

PART 18-3 CONVERTIBLE TOP

Section	Page
1 Care of Top Fabric	18-19
2 Diagnosis and Testing—Power Top	18-19
Mechanical Checks	18-19
Electrical Tests	18-19
Hydraulic Tests	18-20
3 Adjustments and Light Repairs	18-21
Comet, Fairlane Top Adjustments	18-21
Mustang Top Adjustments	18-21
Side Rail Weatherstrips Adjustment	18-21
Lateral Adjustment	18-21
Intermediate Side Rail Adjustment	18-21
Balance Link Adjustment	18-21
Toggle Clamp Adjustment	18-21
Dowel Pin Adjustment	18-23
No. 2 Bow Adjustment	18-24
Hold-Down Side Clamps—Manual Top	18-24
4 Removal and Installation	18-24

Section	Page
Motor and Pump—Power Top	18-24
Lift Cylinder—Power Top	18-25
Counterbalance Cylinder—Mustang	
Manual Top	18-25
Back Curtain	18-25
Comet, Fairlane	18-25
Mustang	18-26
Back Curtain Zipper	18-26
Comet, Fairlane	18-26
Mustang	18-27
Convertible Top Fabric	18-27
Comet, Fairlane	18-27
Mustang	18-29
Roof Front Header Weatherstrip	18-33
Comet, Fairlane	18-33
Mustang	18-33

1 CARE OF TOP FABRIC

Proper care of the top material will reduce the possibility of water stains, mildew, or shrinkage. Do not stack the top if it is damp. Always use the convertible top vinyl boot to keep the top material clean, dry, and positioned when the top is stacked.

The rear window slide fastener should be lubricated at least once a year with stainless stick lubricant.

Use the top compartment behind the rear seat back only for storage of the top. The storage of other items not only interferes with the proper operation of the top, but may also damage or stain the top material.

The vinyl top may be washed each time the car is washed. Clean the material with FoMoCo Interior Trim Cleaner and a scrub brush. Be sure

to rinse the top thoroughly with clean water during and after washing.

Do not use a cleaning material that is not recommended for vinyl material because damage to the top may result.

The vinyl coating becomes tacky at approximately 180°F. Therefore, when making paint repairs, be sure to protect the top material from heat.

2 DIAGNOSIS AND TESTING—POWER TOP

Refer to Wiring Diagram Manual Form 7795P-66 for locations of wiring harnesses. Schematics are shown in Group 22 of this manual.

If the top cannot be lowered or raised satisfactorily, or if it fails to operate at all, and the trouble is not readily apparent, make the following mechanical, electrical, and hydraulic tests to find the cause of the trouble. **Always check the battery before making any of the following checks.**

Table 1 shows symptoms and possible causes of trouble.

MECHANICAL CHECKS

1. If the action of the top is slow, raise and lower it and look for bent or misaligned linkage.

2. If binding is noted when clamp-

ing the top at the header, check the alignment of the door and the quarter windows with the side rail weatherstrips. Also check the top sag adjustment and toggle clamp adjustment.

ELECTRICAL TESTS
BATTERY CHARGE

The battery charge should be determined before making any electrical checks because a partially discharged battery will cause slow motor and pump operation.

CURRENT DRAW

To check the current draw in the top operating circuit, disconnect the black wire at the circuit breaker (located on the starter relay), and con-

nect an ammeter in series in the circuit. Operate the top control switch and note the ammeter readings. The current draw should be 28 amperes maximum operating. Current in excess of 75 amperes indicates a frozen pump or cylinder or a mechanical obstruction. Low amperage with the motor running and no top movement indicates a defective pump or low fluid level in the reservoir.

TOP CONTROL SWITCH

1. Disconnect the wiring harness at the switch multiple connector located behind the instrument panel.

2. Connect one terminal of a test lamp to the black (feed) wire of the top control switch, and ground the

TABLE 1—Trouble Symptoms and Possible Causes

Possible Causes of Trouble Symptoms	Trouble Symptoms							
	Top Does Not Retract	Top Action Sluggish	Top Sides Operate Unevenly	Top Does Not Stack	Side Rail(s) Do Not Fit	Top Does Not Rise From Stack	Top Does Not Latch	Top Leaks
Top Control Switch	X					X		
Inadequate Battery Charge	X	X				X		
Motor and Pump	X	X				X		
Circuit Breaker	X					X		
Faulty Wiring	X	X				X		
Hydraulic Cylinder(s)	X	X	X			X		
Air in Hydraulic System	X	X				X		
Insufficient Hydraulic Fluid	X	X				X		
Top Lowered when Wet Causing Fabric to Shrink							X	
Toggle Clamp Adjustment①							X	X
Door Window Adjustment①					X			X
Quarter Window Adjustment①					X			X
Weatherstripping								X
Balance Link Bracket Adjustment				X	X			
Center Side Rail Adjustment (Mustang only)					X			

①The top should not be raised with the windows up.

other lead. If the test lamp does not light, there is an open or short circuit between the battery and the switch or a bad circuit breaker.

3. If there is voltage to the switch, connect a jumper wire between the black (feed) wire and the red wire, and then between the black wire and the yellow wire. If the top motor operates, the switch is faulty and must be replaced.

CIRCUIT BREAKER

If there is no voltage at the top control switch, connect a jumper wire across the terminals of the circuit breaker (located on the starter relay) and operate the switch. If the top motor operates, the circuit breaker is faulty and must be replaced. If there is no voltage at the circuit breaker, check the black wire from the circuit breaker to the starter relay.

SWITCH-TO-MOTOR WIRES

Disconnect the yellow and the red switch-to-motor leads at the junction block near the motor. Connect a 12-volt test lamp between the yellow wire and a ground and check by operating the top control switch to raise the top. Connect the test lamp between the red wire and a ground, and check by operating the switch to lower the top. If the test lamp does not light in either case, the wire from the junction block to the switch is open or shorted.

MOTOR

Check the operation of the motor by connecting first one motor lead, and then the other, directly to the battery positive terminal. If the motor operates in either case, but will not operate when hooked into the wiring harness, check the wiring harness again for short or open circuits. If the motor will not work when hooked directly to the battery, check the black (ground) wire from the motor. If the motor still does not work, it must be replaced.

HYDRAULIC TESTS

Faulty hydraulic system operation can be caused by lack of fluid, leaks, air in the system, obstructions or kinks in the hoses, or faulty operation of the cylinder or the pump.

FLUID LEVEL

1. Remove the rear seat and raise the top.
2. Place absorbent cloths below the filler plug.
3. Remove the filler plug, and check the fluid level. It should be level with the bottom edge of the hole.
4. If the level is low, check the system for leaks, adding automatic transmission fluid Type A, Suffix A as necessary.

LIFT CYLINDER

Remove the rear seat and the quarter trim panels, operate the top control switch, and check the operation of the lift cylinders for the following:

If the movement of the piston rods are sluggish or uneven, check the hoses from the pump to the cylinders for kinks.

If one piston rod moves slower than the other, the cylinder with the slower rod is defective and should be replaced.

If both rods move slowly, or do not move at all, disassemble and repair the pump.

3 ADJUSTMENTS AND LIGHT REPAIRS

Before aligning the top, visually determine if the trouble results from top misalignment and/or window misalignment. It may be necessary to align both the top and the windows because of the relationship between the two. Adjustments of the door and quarter windows must be checked and any necessary changes made before making top adjustments. These windows must be fully closed to insure proper top adjustment. Door window and quarter window adjustments are outlined in Part 17-3.

COMET, FAIRLANE TOP ADJUSTMENTS

Refer to Fig. 1 for the following Comet and Fairlane top adjustments:

1. Loosen screw and washer assemblies item A and adjust the bracket item B (part of top Assembly), inboard or outboard to obtain the 0.30-inch clearance dimension between the rear side rail and belt side moulding. The bracket must be adjusted and secured in the vertical position. Tighten the screw and washer assemblies (views H and J).

2. Loosen nut item C and rotate cam pin item D to obtain the 0.50-inch parallel dimension between the rails and door glass and between the rear rail and quarter glass. The cam pin must not be rotated more than 90° either side of the mean adjustment mark on the rail. Hold the cam pin item D and tighten the nut item C (views C and K).

If the dowel item E does not line up with the sun visor bracket dowel hole on a fore and aft line, the top cloth is to be removed from the No. 1 bow. Loosen two screws, item F and adjust the No. 1 bow fore or aft to position the dowel. Tighten the screws, item F. The top cloth is then retacked and cemented (views B and D).

3. Loosen the nut item G and adjust the dowel item E inboard or outboard to center the dowel into the sun visor bracket dowel hole. Tighten nut item G (view E).

4. Maintain a proper design relationship between the No. 1 bow and the header, loosen set screw item H

and rotate hook item J in or out. Tighten the set screw item H (view E).

5. If interference is encountered between the top cloth and top of the door glass frame when the door is opened, the No. 2 bow and/or No. 3 bow can be adjusted by loosening the nuts items K and L and raising the bows. After the adjustment, tighten the nuts items K and L (views F and G).

6. To maintain the correct design relationship between rails and glass, the set screw item W must be backed out (view A).

7. Operate the folding top assembly one complete cycle and recheck the alignment as indicated in steps 1 through 7.

8. With the top assembly in the down position, locate the strikers item M on the rail-folding top center side, opposite the clamp assembly item N. Secure the striker to the rail. Loosen two screws item P and adjust the clamp assembly up or down to insure proper hold-down effort on the striker. After adjustment, tighten screws item P (view L).

MUSTANG TOP ADJUSTMENTS
SIDE RAIL WEATHERSTRIPS ADJUSTMENT

The rear and center side rail weatherstrips are adjustable fore and aft to provide a good seal at the break joints. The front weatherstrip is not adjustable.

1. Lock the top assembly to the windshield header.

2. Trim the rear edge of the front top side rail weatherstrip flush with the rear end of the front side rail to obtain a water tight seal at point X (Fig. 2).

3. Adjust the rear side rail weatherstrip to provide a water tight seal at the joint (Fig. 2), and tighten the weatherstrip retaining nuts.

LATERAL ADJUSTMENT

This adjustment shifts the top assembly sidewise to obtain a good fit between the rear side rail and the quarter outside rear side belt moulding.

1. Loosen the screws which retain the main pivot bracket to its support (Fig. 3).

2. Shift the main pivot bracket toward either side as necessary to obtain the proper clearance (9/32 inch) between the rear side rail and the quarter outside rear side belt mouldings and tighten the retaining screws.

INTERMEDIATE SIDE RAIL ADJUSTMENT

This adjustment moves the top assembly to obtain a good fit between the top assembly and the side window glass line.

1. With the door glass properly adjusted, loosen the eccentric nut (View B, Fig. 4), and rotate the eccentric pin to obtain a 3/8-inch parallel dimension between the front door glass and the front and center side rails.

2. Hold the eccentric pin to prevent it from turning, and tighten the eccentric nut. **The main balance link marking and washer pointer is an average dimension of adjustment. Rotation of the eccentric will raise or lower the side rails to obtain the correct design-height dimension between the side rails and the glass.**

BALANCE LINK ADJUSTMENT

The balance link is retained to the intermediate side rail assembly with an eccentric pin (Fig. 4, View B). Rotation of the eccentric pin raises or lowers the side rail over the door glass area. Clearance between the glass frame and side rail is 3/8 inch constant.

TOGGLE CLAMP ADJUSTMENT

The toggle clamps that hold the No. 1 bow against the header can be adjusted to provide a good seal.

1. To determine which side is not sealing, check the weatherstrip between the No. 1 bow and the header with a 3 x 5-inch card. A reasonable pull must be felt as the card is pulled out. Both toggle clamps need not be adjusted unless necessary.

2. Release the toggle clamps (Fig. 5), loosen the Allen screw, and thread the toggle hook in or out until

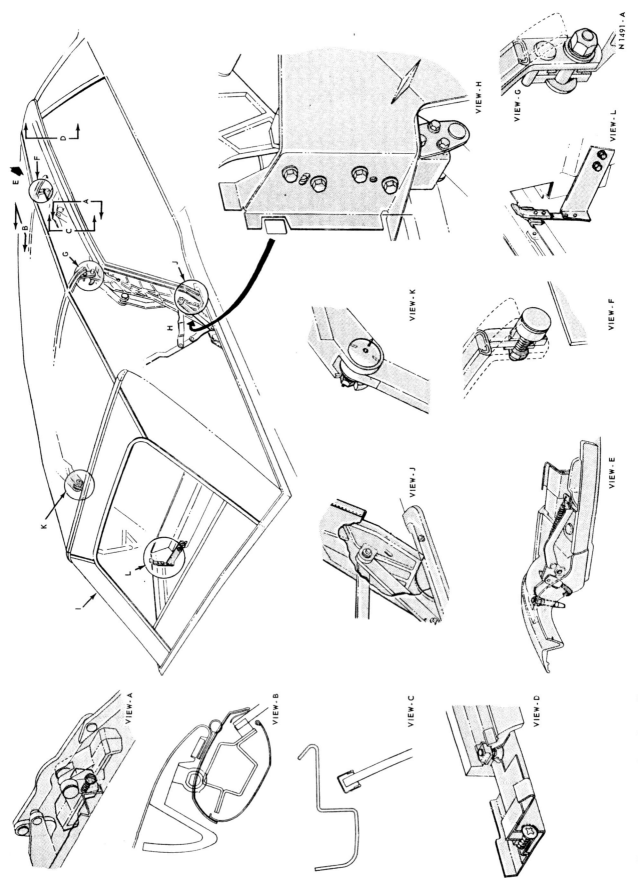

FIG. 1 —Comet, Fairlane Top Adjustments

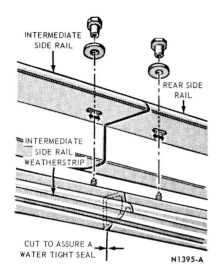

FIG. 2—Side Rail Weatherstrip Adjustment—Mustang

adequate sealing pressure is applied at the header weatherstrip. **Excessive tightening of the toggle hooks will distort the No. 1 bow and cause poor weatherstrip sealing.** Tighten the Allen screw after adjusting the clamp.

DOWEL PIN ADJUSTMENT

To obtain proper alignment of the

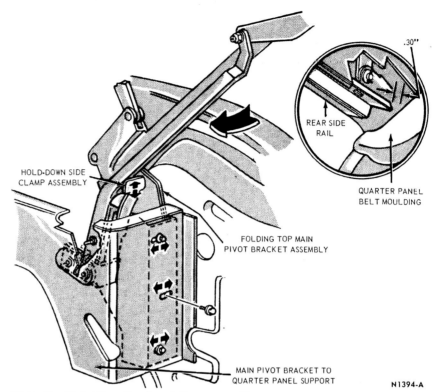

FIG. 3—Main Pivot Bracket Adjustment—Mustang

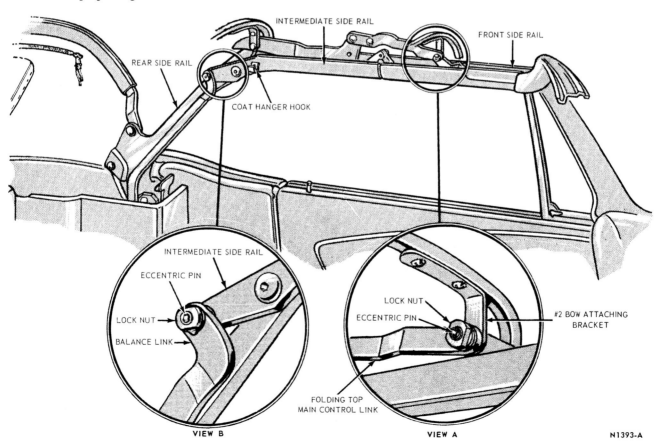

FIG. 4—Top Side Rail Adjustments—Mustang

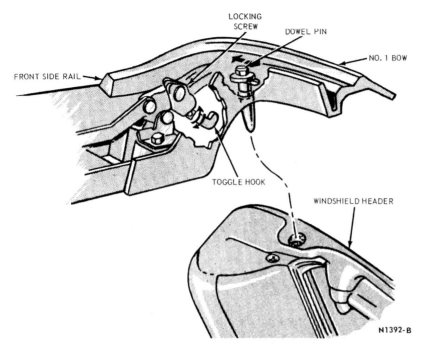

FIG. 5—Toggle Clamp Hook and Dowel Adjustment—Mustang

dowel pins with the dowel pin holes in the windshield header, loosen the dowel pin retaining nut (Fig. 5) and move the dowel pins inboard or outboard. Then, tighten the dowel retaining nut.

NO. 2 BOW ADJUSTMENT

Raise the top and lock it to the windshield header. Loosen the lock nut (View A—Fig. 4), and rotate the eccentric pin to raise or lower the top material along the door glass line. The specified clearance for the top material to door glass frame is ⅛ inch. Hold the eccentric and tighten the lock nut.

HOLD DOWN SIDE CLAMPS— MANUAL TOP

The hold down side clamp assemblies located on each quarter panel support mounting (Fig. 3), are adjustable up and down to retain the top assembly when in its fully stacked position.

---

4 REMOVAL AND INSTALLATION

MOTOR AND PUMP—POWER TOP

A pump repair kit and a reservoir repair kit are available for service.

REMOVAL

1. Operate the top to the fully raised position.
2. Open the deck lid and cover the luggage compartment floor.
3. Remove the two screws retaining the rear folding top compartment support wire retaining clips and remove the clips.
4. Disconnect the motor leads and the ground wire.
5. Remove the attaching nuts, and remove the motor and pump assembly from the floor pan. Do not lose the rubber grommets.
6. Vent the reservoir by removing the filler plug, and then install the filler plug. **The reservoir must be vented in order to equalize the pressure. This lessens the possibility of fluid spraying on the trim and paint when the hoses are disconnected.**
7. Place absorbent cloths beneath the hose connections, disconnect the hoses, and then plug the open fittings and lines.

DISASSEMBLY

1. Remove the filler plug, and drain the fluid from the reservoir

into a clean container.
2. Scribe lines on the reservoir and pump body so that these parts can be positioned properly upon assembly.
3. Remove the center bolt from the reservoir cover (Fig. 6).
4. Remove the reservoir cover and the O-ring seal from the pump.
5. Remove the mounting bolts that hold the valve body to the pump body.
6. Place a cloth under the assembly, and carefully remove the valve

body so that the check balls are not lost.
7. Remove the inner and outer rotors and the drive ball.

ASSEMBLY

Use all the parts contained in the pump repair kit when assembling the pump or reservoir.

1. Install the inner rotor on the armature shaft and position the drive ball.
2. Install the outer rotor over the inner rotor.

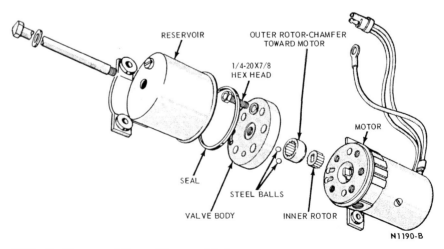

FIG. 6—Motor and Pump Disassembled

3. Place the check balls in the motor body channels.

4. Install the valve body on the motor body.

5. Install the five valve body mounting bolts.

6. Install the O-ring seal on the valve body.

7. Install a new seal on the center bolt, and install the reservoir cover on the valve body, using the line previously scribed as a guide.

8. Place the assembly in a horizontal position, fill the reservoir with automatic transmission fluid Type A, Suffix A to the level of the bottom of the filler plug hole. Install the filler plug and a new seal.

INSTALLATION

1. Remove the plugs from the lines and fittings, and connect the lines to the pump. Use cloths to absorb any fluid that leaks out of the lines or the pump.

2. Install the assembly on the floor pan, making sure that the rubber grommets are in proper position under the mounting brackets.

3. Connect the motor lead wires at the connector, and connect the ground wire.

4. Operate the top assembly two or three times to bleed any air from the system, and check the fluid level in the reservoir. The fluid level should not be less than ¼ inch below the filler plug opening. **The top must be up when the fluid level is checked.**

5. Position the retaining clips on the rear folding top compartment support wire and install the retaining screws.

6. Remove the covers from the luggage compartment floor and close the deck lid.

LIFT CYLINDER—POWER TOP

1. Remove the rear seats and quarter trim panel.

2. Remove the hairpin clip, washer, and clevis pin from the upper end of the cylinder.

3. Remove the mounting bolts, bracket, and bushings from the cylinder.

4. Pull the cylinder down; place absorbent cloths below the hose connections; disconnect the hydraulic lines, and remove the cylinder.

5. Install the hydraulic lines on the new cylinder and install the cylinder bushings, mounting bracket, and bolts.

6. Install the clevis pin, washer, and hairpin at the upper end of the cylinder.

7. Operate the top assembly two or three times to bleed any air from the system, and check the fluid level in the reservoir. The fluid level should not be less than ¼ inch below the filler plug opening. **The top must be up when the fluid level is checked.**

8. Install the quarter trim panel and rear seats.

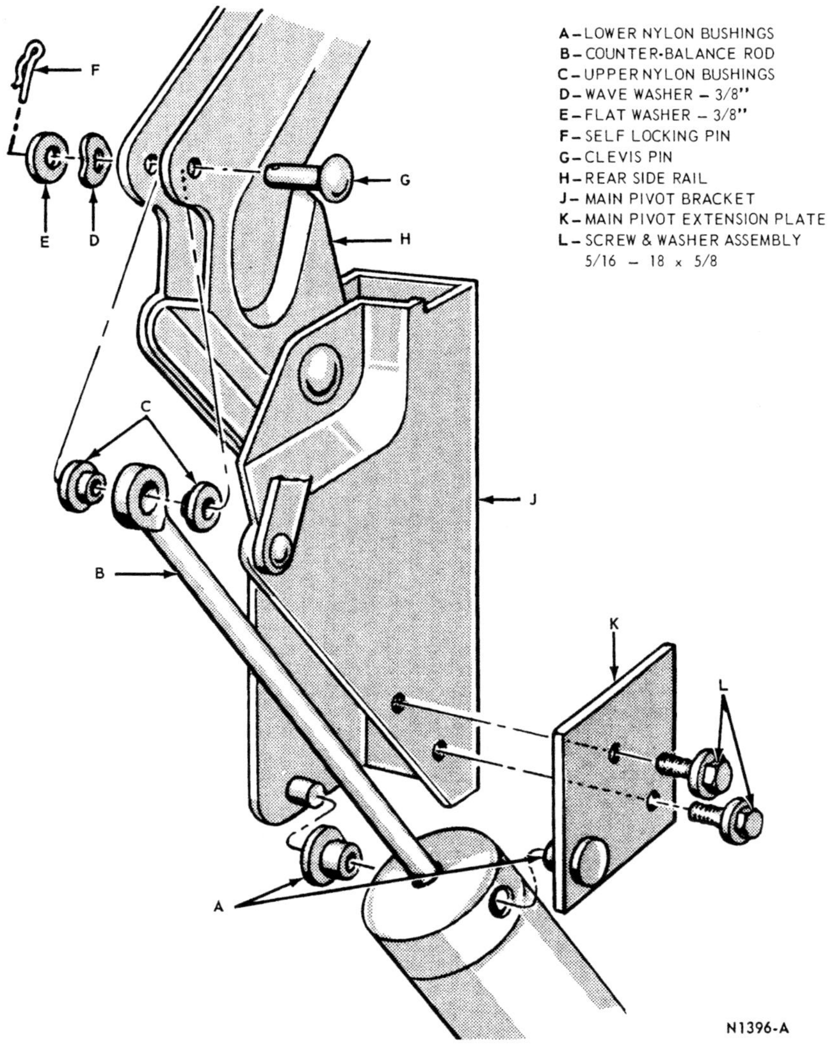

COUNTERBALANCE CYLINDER— MUSTANG MANUAL TOP
REMOVAL

1. Raise the top. **Do not attempt to remove the counterbalance cylinder with the top in the lowered (stacked) position.**

2. Remove the rear seat cushion and seat back.

3. Remove the quarter trim panels.

4. Remove the self locking pin F, Flat washer E, wave washers, and clevis pin G (Fig. 7). Disengage the counterbalance rod B from the rear side rail H (Fig. 7).

5. Remove the two bolts L and the main pivot extension plate K from the main pivot bracket J (Fig. 7), and remove the counterbalance spring assembly. Keep the upper and lower nylon bushings A and C for reuse if serviceable.

INSTALLATION

1. Position the counterbalance spring in place and install the main pivot bracket.

2. Install the counterbalance rod retaining pin and washers.

3. Install the quarter trim panel.

4. Install the rear seat back and seat cushion.

BACK CURTAIN
COMET, FAIRLANE

1. Unfasten the clamps that hold the top to the windshield header.

2. Remove the retainer pins retaining the folding top rear compartment trim to the tacking strips and

A — LOWER NYLON BUSHINGS
B — COUNTER-BALANCE ROD
C — UPPER NYLON BUSHINGS
D — WAVE WASHER — 3/8"
E — FLAT WASHER — 3/8"
F — SELF LOCKING PIN
G — CLEVIS PIN
H — REAR SIDE RAIL
J — MAIN PIVOT BRACKET
K — MAIN PIVOT EXTENSION PLATE
L — SCREW & WASHER ASSEMBLY
     5/16 — 18 x 5/8

N1396-A

FIG. 7—Counterbalance Cylinder Installation—Mustang

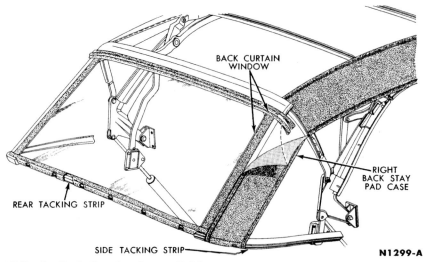

FIG. 8—Back Curtain—Comet, Fairlane

position the trim away from the tacking strips.

3. Remove the bolts and lock washers that retain the curtain tacking strip to the body panel.

4. Open the back curtain window slide fastener and remove the curtain assembly.

5. Pull the tacking strips from the curtain and remove the staples from the tacking strip (Fig. 8).

6. Remove the tacking strip lock screws from the tacking strips.

7. Properly position the curtain and staple it securely to the tacking strip.

8. Staple the side tacking strips to

the curtain.

9. Position the curtain assembly to the body panel, and loosely install the belt tacking strip retaining bolts and lock washers.

10. Close the curtain window slide fastener.

11. To adjust the curtain window tension and remove wrinkles, tighten or loosen the tacking strip retaining bolts as required. After adjusting the curtain, install and tighten the tacking strip lock screws until they bottom against the body panel.

12. Reposition the folding top rear compartment trim and install the retainer pins.

MUSTANG

1. Unhook the top from the windshield header and prop the top up to relieve tension.

2. Unzip the back curtain.

3. Remove 3 screws retaining each side of the top compartment trim at the quarter panel.

4. Remove 5 screws attaching the top compartment trim to the rear seat and remove the compartment trim tension springs (Fig. 9).

5. To assure the proper location of the back curtain assembly during installation, the following location marks should be made with tailor's crayon or equivalent:

Locate the center punch mark on the belt center tacking strip retainer (Fig. 13, View A-A). Transpose this center mark to the adjacent rear curtain and compartment trim materials.

Mark the rear curtain along the lower edge of the belt center tacking strip (Fig. 13, View BB and CC).

Mark the belt center tacking strip to indicate the rear window opening at both sides (Fig. 13, View BB).

6. Pull the top compartment trim back and remove 8 bolts retaining the back curtain and the center tacking strip.

7. Remove the staples from the webbing and the top quarter from the tacking strip. Remove the back window, top compartment trim, and the tacking strip, as an assembly, from the car.

8. Remove the back curtain from the tacking strip and position the new back curtain to the tacking strip. Cut out the bolt hole locations on the back curtain.

9. Position the back curtain assembly into the car and tack the webbing and quarter assembly to the tacking strip. Then, zip the back curtain shut.

10. Remove the prop from the top and secure the top to the windshield header.

11. Install and tighten the tacking strip attaching bolts.

12. Install the top compartment trim quarter and seat back retaining screws. Clean the top in the rear roof bow area with a suitable cleaner.

BACK CURTAIN ZIPPER

COMET, FAIRLANE

1. Unhook the top from the windshield header and prop the top up to relieve tension.

2. Unzip the back curtain.

3. Remove the retainer pins retaining the folding top rear compart-

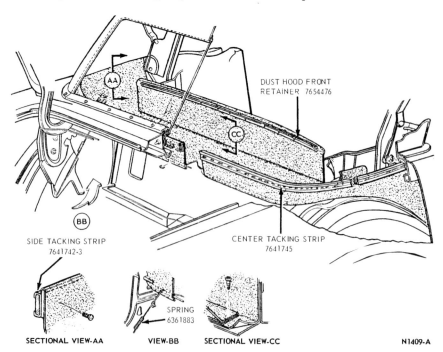

FIG. 9—Back Curtain Installation—Mustang

ment trim to the tacking strips and position the trim away from the tacking strips.

4. Remove the bolts and flat washers that retain the curtain tacking strip to the body panel, and remove the back curtain.

5. Mark the zipper location on the back curtain, then, remove the zipper from the back curtain and sew on a new zipper.

6. Remove the bolts and flat washers that retain the side belt tacking strips to the body.

7. Remove the rear bow binding end cap; slide out the binding insert and remove the staples and retainer.

8. Remove the staples retaining the top deck and quarter assembly to the rear bow.

9. Remove the staples retaining the top right and left back stay pad case assemblies to the rear roof bow.

10. Remove the staples retaining the zipper to the rear bow tacking strip and remove the zipper.

11. Position the upper half of the back curtain zipper to the center of the rear roof bow tacking strip. Staple or tack it securely to the tacking strip.

12. Staple the top left and right back stay pad case assemblies to the rear bow tacking strip. Seal the unused holes in the top material.

13. Staple the top deck and quarter assembly to the rear bow tacking strip.

14. Staple the binding in position, and install the binding end caps.

15. Position the side belt tacking strips to the body and install the retaining bolts.

16. Position the back curtain in the car and install the retaining bolts.

17. Zip the curtain shut and remove the prop from the top. Then, lock the top to the windshield header.

18. Tighten or loosen the tacking strip retaining bolts as required to adjust the curtain tension and remove wrinkles.

19. Reposition the folding top rear compartment trim and install the retainer pins.

MUSTANG

1. Unhook the top from the windshield header and prop the top up to relieve tension.

2. Unzip the back curtain.

3. Remove the rear roof bow retainer tips and pull the outside moulding from the rear bow.

4. Remove the staples retaining the top deck and quarter assembly to the rear roof bow tacking strip and

remove the retainer.

5. Mark the location of the right and left case assembly, at the roof bow, then, remove the staples retaining the right and left case assembly to the rear roof bow.

6. Mark the location of the zipper center at the rear roof bow with tailor's crayon. Then, pull the upper half of the back curtain zipper from the rear roof bow tacking strip.

7. Remove 3 screws retaining the top compartment trim to the belt front side tacking strip on each side. Remove 5 screws retaining the compartment trim to the seat back (Fig. 9). Remove the top compartment trim tension springs.

8. Pull the top compartment trim back and remove 8 bolts retaining the center tacking strip. Mark the zipper end locations on the top material with tailor's crayon.

9. Remove the staples from the webbing and the top quarter from the tacking strip. Remove the back curtain, well liner, and tacking strip as an assembly from the car.

10. Mark the location of the zipper on the back curtain, then, remove the zipper from the back curtain and sew on a new zipper.

11. Locate the center and position the upper half of the back curtain zipper to the center of the rear roof bow tacking strip and staple or tack it securely to the tacking strip.

12. Position the right and left case assemblies to the rear roof bow tacking strip and staple or tack them securely to the tacking strip.

13. Position the top deck and quarter assembly to the rear roof bow tacking strip and staple or tack it securely to the tacking strip, working from the center outward.

14. Staple or tack the rear roof bow retainer securely to the rear roof bow, then, insert the moulding in the retainer.

15. Install the right and left rear roof bow retainer tips (Fig. 13).

16. Position the back curtain in the car and tack the webbing and quarter assembly to the tacking strip.

17. Zip the curtain shut and remove the prop from the top, then, lock the top to the windshield header.

18. Install the center tacking strip bolts and tighten them until all wrinkles are removed from the back curtain and quarters. Then, install the top compartment trim retaining screws.

CONVERTIBLE TOP FABRIC

The convertible top consists of the

deck and two side quarters, bonded into one piece of material. The bonded seams eliminate the possibility of leaks and also separation, due to thread deterioration. In most cases it will be advantageous to replace the back curtain when replacing the top fabric.

COMET, FAIRLANE
Removal

1. Place a protective cover across the deck, cowl and hood to prevent scratching the finish when replacing the top.

2. Remove the rear seat cushion and seat back.

3. Raise the top to gain access to the underside of the front bow.

4. Remove the No. 1 bow weatherstrip retainer (Fig. 10) and the weatherstrip. Remove the windshield header seal.

5. Remove both front side rail weatherstrips and weatherstrip retainers.

6. Remove the two center side rail and the two rear side rail weatherstrips and weatherstrip retainers.

7. Remove the screw and washer that secures each end of the folding top compartment well to the pivot bracket supports (Fig. 10).

8. Remove the retainer pins retaining the folding top rear compartment trim to the tacking strips and position the trim away from the tacking strips.

9. Remove the tip (Fig. 10) from each end of the moulding on the rear bow. Carefully pull the moulding out of the retainer. Pry the moulding retainer off the bow.

10. To assure the proper location of the tacking strips in the new top assembly, back curtain assembly and/or compartment trim assembly, mark the following locations with tailor's crayon:

Locate and mark the center of the belt center tacking strip retainer. Transpose this center mark to the adjacent rear curtain and compartment trim materials.

Mark the rear curtain along the lower edge of the belt center tacking strip.

Mark the belt center tacking strip to indicate the rear window opening at both sides.

Mark the top deck quarters along the lower edge and at the ends of each belt side front tacking strip.

11. Remove the bolts that attach the top and back curtain tacking strips to the body.

12. Remove the staples that secure

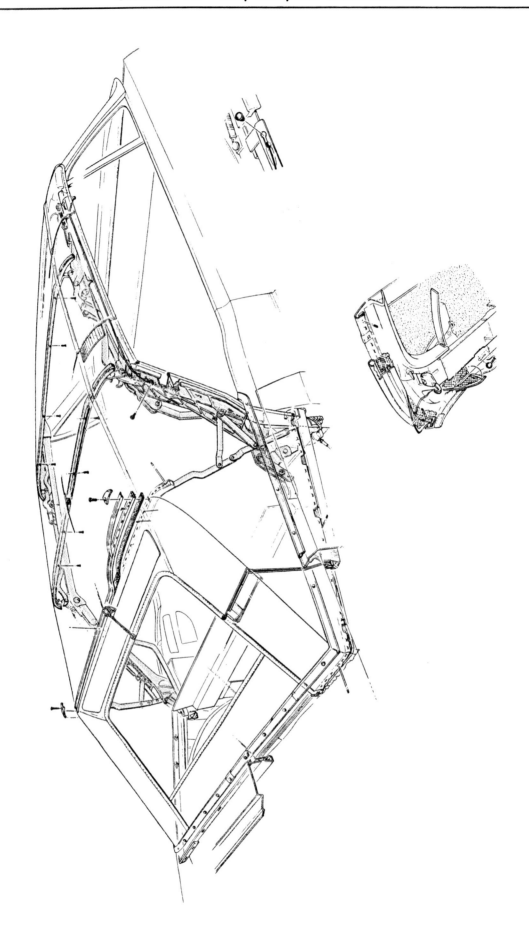

R 1263 - B

FIG. 10—Convertible Top Trim Installation—Comet, Fairlane

the top material to the rear bow.

13. Carefully pull the top material free from the underside of each side rail.

14. Remove the staples that secure the top material to the underside of the front bow.

15. Remove the retainer screws and carefully separate the top from the listings on the No. 2 and 3 bows. Remove the staples that secure the top back stay-pads.

16. Remove the staples that secure the upper end of the back curtain to the rear bow. Remove the curtain.

Installation

1. Remove the tacking strips from the old top and back curtain.

2. Staple them to the new top and back curtain in the same location as they were on the old top.

3. Center the dot on the back curtain with the V mark (center) on the rear bow and staple the upper half of the zipper to the bow. Separate the curtain from the upper half of the zipper.

4. Retack the top back stay pads. Fit the new top on the roof bows.

5. Working from the center outward, staple the top deck to the rear bow. Make sure that the rear section of the slits is stapled to the bow before drawing and stapling the front portion of the slits (Fig. 10).

6. Secure, and tighten the quarter deck tacking strips to the body.

7. Center the top material and pull it forward over the front bow to remove the wrinkles from the top deck and quarters and to align the listings with the No. 2 and 3 bows. While the material is pulled over the front bow, make a reference mark on the material at the leading edge of the bow with a piece of chalk. The mark should extend the entire length of the bow.

8. Raise the top high enough to gain access to the underside of the front bow.

9. Align the reference mark to the leading edge of the bow and staple the material in place. Install the windshield header seal.

10. Install the weatherstrip and the retainers on the No. 1 bow.

11. Secure the flaps to the underside of the side rail with trim cement. Trim the excess material from the flaps.

12. Install the rear, center and front weatherstrip and retainers on the side rails so that the end of the weatherstrips are in alignment with the side rail joints.

13. Install a piece of tape across the rear bow to cover the staples.

14. Install the moulding retainer, moulding and the two tips on the rear bow.

15. Secure the back curtain to the upper part of the zipper.

16. Secure the back curtain tacking strip in place with the attaching bolts. Tighten the bolts as required working from the center outward to remove all wrinkles.

17. Reposition the folding top rear compartment trim and install the retainer pins.

18. Secure each end of the trim to the pivot bracket supports with a metal screw and washer.

19. Install the rear seat back and cushion.

20. Install listing retainers in the No. 2 and 3 bow listings and install the screws.

21. Remove the protective covers from the deck and the hood.

22. Clean all chalk and reference marks from the top material.

MUSTANG

Removal

1. Protect the painted surfaces of the upper back panel, luggage compartment door and both quarter panels with suitable covers.

2. Fabricate two bow locating gauges to the dimensions shown in Fig. 11.

3. Remove the rear seat cushion and seat back.

4. Remove the top compartment trim side and front attaching screws (Fig. 12).

5. Disengage the 2 retaining springs from the rear compartment trim support wire (Fig. 12).

6. Lower the top and remove the weatherstrip retainer from the No. 1 bow.

7. Remove the front side weatherstrip attaching nuts from both front side rails and remove the weatherstrip assembly (Fig. 13).

8. Remove the windshield header seal assembly and the top material from the No. 1 bow (Fig. 13).

9. Remove the center and rear side rail weatherstrips (Fig. 2). Loosen the top quarter material flaps which are cemented to the front and rear side rails (each side).

10. Disengage the top material hold-down cables from the rear side rail attachment and pull the cables forward until each is removed from the retaining sleeve (Fig. 14).

11. Remove each side rail coat hook.

12. Raise the top and clamp the No. 1 bow to the header.

13. Install the two fabricated bow locating gauges as shown in Fig. 15.

14. Remove the No. 2 and No. 3 bow listing retainer screws and remove both retainers from the listings (Fig. 13).

15. Raise the compartment trim up sufficiently to remove all of the tacking strip attaching screws (Fig. 13).

16. Remove the No. 4 bow outside moulding end tips, moulding and moulding retainer (Fig. 13).

17. Detach the top material from the No. 4 bow. Peel the top material back to expose the No. 4 bow and mark the existing top back stay webbing location at the No. 4 bow and the tacking strip (Fig. 14).

18. Detach the upper end of the webbing from the No. 4 bow. Unzip the rear curtain window and remove the soft trim with tacking strips attached. Place the assembly on a bench.

19. Mark the No. 4 bow at both ends of the zipper elastic material and detach the upper half of the zipper assembly from the No. 4 bow.

20. To assure the proper location of the tacking strips in the new top assembly, back curtain window assembly and/or compartment trim assembly, proceed as follows:

a. Locate the center punch mark on the belt center tacking strip retainer (Fig. 13, View A-A). Transpose this center mark to the adjacent rear curtain and compartment trim materials.

b. Mark the rear curtain along the lower edge of the belt center tacking strip (Fig. 13, View BB and CC).

c. Mark the belt center tacking strip to indicate the rear window opening at both sides (Fig. 13, View BB).

d. Mark the top deck quarters along the lower edge and at the ends of each belt side front tacking strip (Fig. 13, View CC).

21. Carefully and without tearing the material, detach the trim material being replaced from the tacking strips.

22. Trim off the selvage edge of the **old top** deck quarter and/or back curtain material that extends below the tacking strips. **The selvage edge must only be cut from the old parts which are being replaced.**

Installation

1. Lay the new rear curtain window assembly on a clean bench with

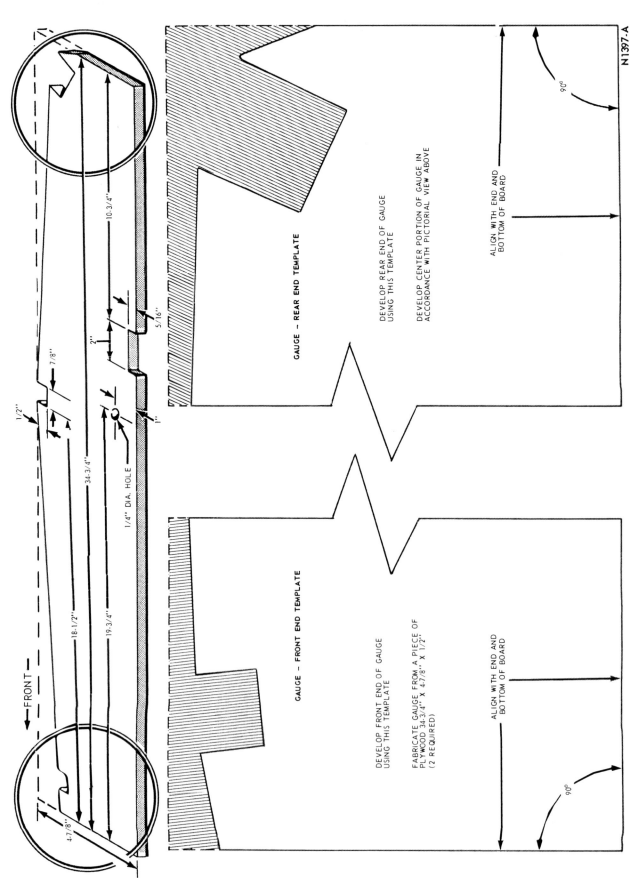

FIG. 11—Bow Locating Gauge Fabrication

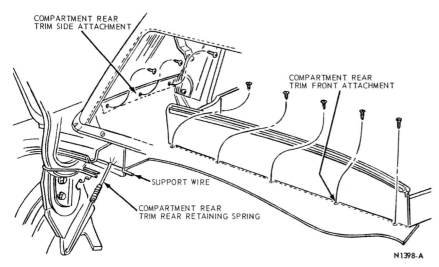

FIG. 12—Top Compartment Rear Trim Installation—Mustang

the interior surface up. Measure the width and mark the center of the back window at the top, above the zipper, and at the bottom, at the tacking strip area (Fig. 13).

2. Using the old rear curtain window assembly as a template, mark the new curtain to indicate the lower edge of the tacking strip. Also mark the tacking strip attaching hole loca-

tions. Carefully remove the old rear curtain window assembly and cut out the tacking strip attaching holes in the new curtain, only.

3. Using the old top assembly as a template, mark the new top quarter deck to indicate the lower edge of the tacking strip. Also mark the tacking strip attaching hole locations. Discard the old top. Cut out the

tacking strip holes in each quarter of the new top, only. **Do not trim off the selvage edge.**

4. Using the old compartment trim as a template, transpose the markings to the new compartment.

5. Align the belt center tacking strip with the compartment trim alignment marks and retain with staples. The edge of the material should be flush with the bottom of the tacking strip.

6. Align the belt center tacking strip with the rear curtain window aligning marks and retain it with staples.

7. Align the belt side front tacking strip with the aligning marks on the top deck quarter (both sides) and retain it with staples.

8. Position each top back stay webbing on the belt center tacking strip and retain it with staples (Fig. 14).

9. Align the top deck quarter to the belt center tacking strip, maintain proper rear curtain opening and retain it with staples (Fig. 13, View BB).

10. Carefully position the upper half of the zipper assembly on the No. 4 bow aligning the bow and ma-

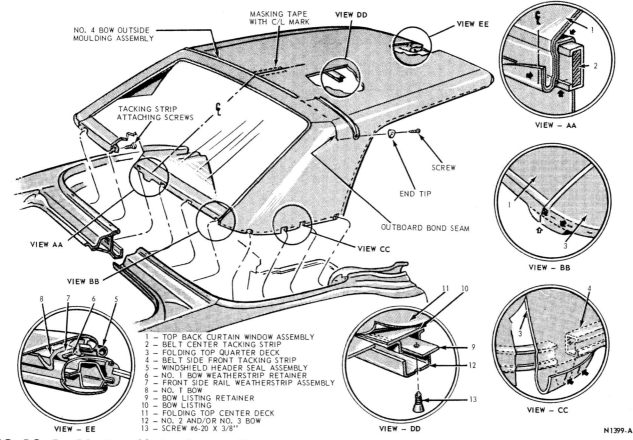

1 – TOP BACK CURTAIN WINDOW ASSEMBLY
2 – BELT CENTER TACKING STRIP
3 – FOLDING TOP QUARTER DECK
4 – BELT SIDE FRONT TACKING STRIP
5 – WINDSHIELD HEADER SEAL ASSEMBLY
6 – NO. 1 BOW WEATHERSTRIP RETAINER
7 – FRONT SIDE RAIL WEATHERSTRIP ASSEMBLY
8 – NO. 1 BOW
9 – BOW LISTING RETAINER
10 – BOW LISTING
11 – FOLDING TOP CENTER DECK
12 – NO. 2 AND/OR NO. 3 BOW
13 – SCREW #6-20 X 3/8''

FIG. 13—Top Trim Assembly Attachments—Mustang

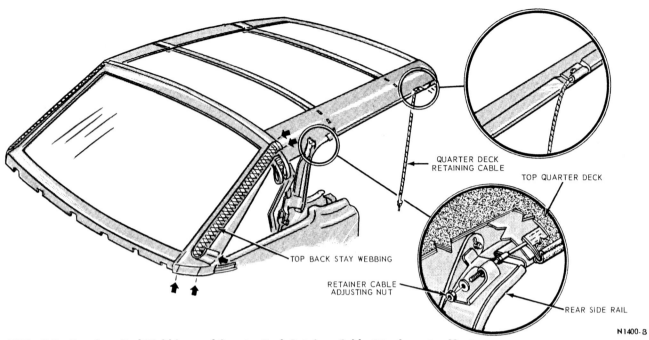

QUARTER DECK
RETAINING CABLE

TOP QUARTER DECK

TOP BACK STAY WEBBING

RETAINER CABLE
ADJUSTING NUT

REAR SIDE RAIL

N1400-8

FIG. 14—Top Stay Pad Webbing and Quarter Deck Retainer Cable Attachments—Mustang

terial center marks. The edge of the material should be flush with the front edge of the No. 4 bow tacking strip. Working from the center outboard, secure the assembly with staples. Both ends of the elastic strip should correspond with the marks on the No. 4 bow. Refer to Step 19 under Removal.

11. Position the rear curtain and top assembly on the stack and engage the zipper.

12. Position the top back stay webbing on the No. 4 bow aligning marks and secure it with staples (Fig. 14).

13. Install a piece of masking tape on the underside of the No. 4 bow at the centerline punch mark located in the bow. Mark the tape indicating

the centerline.

14. Measure and mark the center between the bond seams of the top center deck at the No. 4 bow on the underside of the material. Install a 6-inch piece of masking tape on the top material inner surface at the centerline of the No. 4 bow. Mark the centerline along the entire length of tape. (Refer to Fig. 13.)

15. With the bow locating gauge in place (refer to Step 13 under Removal and Fig. 15), install the belt center tacking strip attaching screws to approximately ¼ to ½-inch from the bottoming out position. Install the belt side front tacking strip attaching screws and tighten to within ¼ to ½-inch of bottoming.

16. Center the top material on

the No. 4 bow and pull it forward sufficiently to center the outboard bond seam on the No. 4 bow (Fig. 13). Secure the top material to the No. 4 bow with staples.

17. Install the two retainers in the No. 2 and No. 3 bow listings (Fig. 13).

18. Route the quarter deck retaining cables through the hold down sleeves in the top material and retain each cable at the rear (loosely) with the attaching nut and washer (Fig. 14).

19. Pull the top trim material forward over the No. 1 bow until the No. 2 and No. 3 bow listings (Fig. 13) are centered over their respective bows. While maintaining tension on the top trim, place a pencil mark on the outer surface of the trim material along the forward edge of the No. 1 bow.

20. Remove the two bow aligning gauges and reinstall the coat hooks (Fig. 4).

21. Fold the front edge of the top material back from the No. 1 bow. Disengage the No. 1 bow from the windshield header and prop it up about one foot above the header.

22. Apply an ample amount of trim cement C2AZ-19C525-A across the lower front surface of the No. 1 bow including the tacking strip and to the adjacent inner surface of the top material.

23. Lower the No. 1 bow onto the header but do not clamp it. With

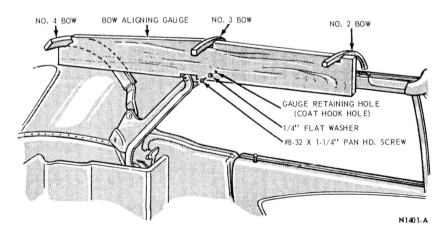

NO. 4 BOW   BOW ALIGNING GAUGE   NO. 3 BOW   NO. 2 BOW

GAUGE RETAINING HOLE
(COAT HOOK HOLE)

¼" FLAT WASHER

#8-32 X 1-1/4" PAN HD. SCREW

N1401-A

FIG. 15—Bow Locating Gauge Installation—Mustang

the top material properly centered on the No. 1 bow, start at the outer front corners and alternately pull the material forward to the pencil aligning mark. Make certain that all wrinkles are removed, and then fold and cement the material to the underside of the bow.

24. Position the windshield header seal assembly (Fig. 13) and secure the seal and top material with staples. Trim off excess top material.

25. Cement the front and rear flaps to each side rail. Pierce holes in the flaps for the weatherstrip attachments.

26. Install the front side rail weatherstrip and the No. 1 bow retainer.

27. Tighten the retainer cable adjustment nut at each rear side rail sufficiently to hold the top material tightly against the rail.

28. Install the intermediate and rear side rail weatherstrips. Adjust as required (Fig. 2).

29. With the No. 1 bow clamped to the header, tighten all belt tacking strip attaching screws securely.

30. Engage the compartment trim support wire to the luggage compartment door hinge bracket springs (Fig. 12).

31. Install the compartment trim to the belt side front tacking strip with the attaching screws (Fig. 12).

32. Install the compartment trim with the seat back support lower ledge attaching screws (Fig. 12).

33. Install the rear seat back and cushion.

34. Remove the interior centerline tape strips.

35. Install the No. 4 bow outside moulding retainer, insert the moulding and install the two end tips (Fig. 13).

ROOF FRONT HEADER WEATHERSTRIP
COMET, FAIRLANE

1. Release the toggle clamps and lower the top.

2. Remove the screws attaching the weatherstrip retainer to the No. 1 bow and remove the retainer.

3. Remove the nuts retaining the weatherstrip to the right and left front side rails and remove the weatherstrip assembly.

4. Position the weatherstrip assembly to the No. 1 bow and install the retainer and retaining screws.

5. Position the side rail sections of the weatherstrip and install the retaining nuts.

6. Raise the top and lock it to the windshield header.

MUSTANG

1. Release the toggle clamps and

partially lower the top.

2. Remove 12 screws attaching the weatherstrip retainer to the header and remove the retainer.

3. Remove 2 screws attaching the weatherstrip to the header at each corner (Fig. 16).

4. Remove 6 nuts and washers (3 each side) retaining the weatherstrip to the roof side rails and remove the weatherstrip.

5. Apply sealer to the header and roof side rails and place the new weatherstrip in position.

6. Install the weatherstrip retainer with 12 screws and the 2 weatherstrip attaching screws at each corner.

7. Install 3 nuts and washers attaching the weatherstrip to each side rail. Trim the weatherstrip for a watertight fit (Fig. 16).

8. Raise the top and lock it to the windshield header.

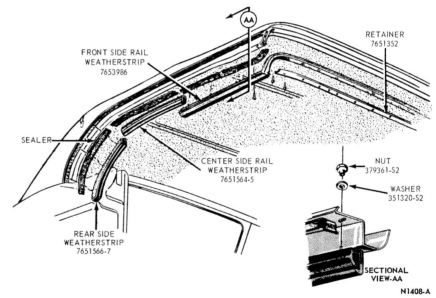

FIG. 16—Side Rail Weatherstrip—Mustang

MAINTENANCE SCHEDULE

GROUP 19

THOUSANDS OF MILES OR NUMBER OF MONTHS WHICHEVER OCCURS FIRST (Except Where Noted)	As Required	6	12	18	24	30	36	See Manual Page
ENGINE								
Change engine oil and filter ①		X	X	X	X	X	X	20- 1
Check engine oil level	At Fuel Stops							20- 1
Replace fuel filter							X	20- 1
Adjust carburetor—idle speed, idle mixture and fast (cold) idle speed (automatic choke only)	X							20- 1
Adjust accelerator pump lever	Seasonal							20- 5
Clean carburetor air cleaner and filter (paper type only)		X	X	X	X	X		20- 6
Replace carburetor air cleaner filter — Paper ①							X	20- 7
Replace carburetor air cleaner filter — Plastic ①			X		X		X	20- 7
Clean crankcase oil filler tube breather cap ①		X	X	X	X	X	X	20- 7
Clean emission system hoses, tubes, oil separator, fittings, carburetor spacer and replace emission control valve			X		X		X	20- 7
Replace thermactor air pump filter if so equipped			X		X		X	20- 8
Check engine accessory drive belts	X							20- 8
Lubricate exhaust control valve (390 CID only)	X							20- 9
Valve tappet adjustment (Conventional) Mustang 289—4V High Performance Engine			X		X		X	20- 9
Check ignition timing			X		X		X	20- 9
Check and adjust distributor points	X							20- 9
Check spark plugs	X							20-10
Replace engine coolant (or every two years)							X	20-10
Check engine coolant level	X							20-10
TRANSMISSION								
Adjust automatic transmission front (intermediate band)							X	20-10
Adjust automatic transmission rear (reverse) band if so equipped	X							20-10
Check transmission oil level		X	X	X	X	X	X	20-11
Check axle fluid level		X	X	X	X	X	X	20-11
Check clutch linkage adjustment	X							20-11
CHASSIS								
Lubricate transmission linkage	X							20-12
Lubricate front suspension ball joints							X	20-12
Lubricate universal joints							X	20-12
Lubricate power steering actuator valve and ball stud							X	20-12
Check steering gear pre-load	X							20-12
Check steering gear pre-load (Mustang only)		X						20-12
Check power steering reservoir fluid level		X	X	X	X	X	X	20-13
Check master cylinder fluid level		X	X	X	X	X	X	20-13
Check brake lines and lining and clean and repack wheel bearings						X		20-13
Check and adjust parking brake	X							20-15
Check tire pressure	X							20-16
Inspect and cross-switch wheels and tires	X							20-16
Check front wheel alignment and linkage	X							20-16
Check battery fluid level	X							20-19
Check air conditioning system	Annually at Beginning of A/C Season							20-19

①On engine items, more frequent intervals will be required if the vehicle is operated in **extremely dusty** areas for extended periods of idling or short runs which prevent the engine from reaching normal operating temperatures.

THOUSANDS OF MILES OR NUMBER OF MONTHS WHICHEVER OCCURS FIRST (Except Where Noted)	As Required	6	12	18	24	30	36	See Manual Page
BODY								
Lubricate hood latch	X							20-19
Lubricate hood hinge pivots	X							20-19
Lubricate hood auxiliary catch	X							20-19
Lubricate door lock cylinders		X	X	X	X	X	X	20-19
Lubricate luggage compartment lock cylinder		X	X	X	X	X	X	20-19
Lubricate door hinge and hinge check	X							20-19
Lubricate luggage compartment hinge pivots	X							20-19
Lubricate tailgate lock cylinders (Except Mustang)		X	X	X	X	X	X	20-19
Lubricate tailgate support and hinges (Except Mustang)	X							20-19
Lubricate fuel filler door hinges (Comet, Fairlane only)	X							20-20
Lube weatherstrip rubber seals and seat track	X							20-20
Clean body drain holes or examine dust valves for operation	X							20-20
Replace windshield wiper blades	X							20-20
Check convertible top operation (Except Falcon)	X							20-20
Check convertible top fluid level (Except Falcon)	X							20-20

MAINTENANCE OPERATIONS

GROUP 20

PART 20-1

MAINTENANCE OPERATIONS

Section	Page	Section	Page
1. Engine	20- 1	3. Chassis	20-12
2. Transmission	20-10	4. Body	20-19

1 ENGINE

CHANGE ENGINE OIL AND FILTER

1. Raise the car.

2. Remove the oil pan drain plug and allow the engine oil to drain into a container.

3. Place a drip pan under the filter. Unscrew the filter from the adapter fitting.

4. Coat the gasket on the filter with oil. Place the filter in position on the adapter fitting. Hand tighten the filter until the gasket contacts the adapter face, then advance it ½ turn.

5. Replace the oil pan drain plug and tighten it securely.

6. Refill the crankcase with the proper amount and grade of oil.

7. Lower the car.

8. Operate the engine at fast idle, and check for oil leaks. If oil leaks are evident, perform the necessary repairs to correct the leakage.

CHECK ENGINE OIL LEVEL

Check the oil level dipstick to be sure it indicates the correct quantity of oil in the crankcase. Be sure the oil is clean.

REPLACE FUEL FILTER

1. Remove the air cleaner.

2. Loosen the retaining clamp securing the fuel inlet hose to the fuel filter.

3. Unscrew the fuel filter from the carburetor and discard the gasket. Disconnect the fuel filter from the hose and discard the retaining clamp.

4. Install a new clamp on the inlet hose and connect the hose to the filter. Place a new gasket on the new fuel filter and screw the filter into the carburetor inlet port. Tighten the filter.

5. Position the fuel line hose clamp and crimp the clamp securely.

6. Start the engine and check for fuel leaks.

7. Install the air cleaner.

ADJUST CARBURETOR—IDLE SPEED, FAST (COLD) IDLE SPEED AND IDLE MIXTURE (AUTOMATIC CHOKE ONLY) AUTOMATIC CHOKE PLATE CLEARANCE (PULL-DOWN) AND FAST IDLE CAM LINKAGE ADJUSTMENT

Ford 1-V. The automatic choke fast idle cam linkage must be prop-

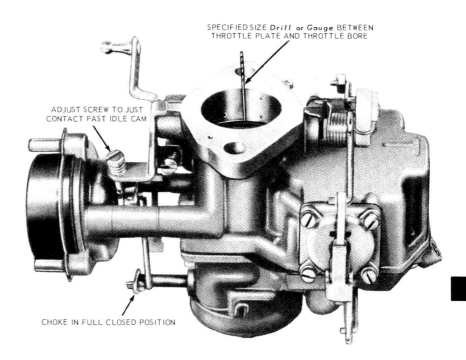

SPECIFIED SIZE *Drill* or *Gauge* BETWEEN THROTTLE PLATE AND THROTTLE BORE

ADJUST SCREW TO JUST CONTACT FAST IDLE CAM

CHOKE IN FULL CLOSED POSITION

B2413-B

FIG. 1—Fast Idle Cam Linkage Adjustment—Ford I-V

erly adjusted before performing the choke plate clearance (pull-down) adjustment, because the position of the pull-down rod is one of the determining factors affecting the throttle to choke opening relationship.

1. Insert a gauge pin or drill of the specified clearance (Part 10-8) thickness between the throttle plate and the side of the throttle bore. Hold the throttle plate against the gauge pin or drill (Fig. 1). Close the choke plate and turn the fast idle screw inward until it just contacts the fast idle cam.

2. Place a drill or gauge of the same thickness as the specified clearance (Part 10-8) between the choke plate and the upper body wall (Fig. 2). Close the choke plate on the drill or gauge and hold it securely.

3. Close the throttle until the fast idle screw touches the fast idle cam. Adjust the plastic nut to just contact the swivel on the choke lever assembly.

Ford 2-V and 4-V.

1. If the air cleaner, heater hose and mounting bracket have not been removed previously, remove them from the carburetor.

2. Position the fast idle (rpm) adjustment screw on the index mark of the fast idle cam (Fig. 3).

3. Turn the choke thermostatic spring housing cover 90° rich (counterclockwise) and check the clearance between the front of the choke plate and the air horn (Fig. 3). Adjust the clearance to specification (Part 10-8), if required. **Turn the fast idle cam lever adjusting screw clockwise (inward) to increase the clearance and counterclockwise (outward) to decrease the clearance. Make certain the fast idle screw remains on the index mark (kickdown step) of the fast idle cam during the adjustment procedure.**

4. Bend a specified size (Part 10-8) wire gauge (tool) at a 90° angle, approximately ⅛ inch from its end (Fig. 4).

5. Remove the choke thermostatic spring housing. Block the throttle about half-open so that the fast idle cam does not contact the fast idle adjustment screw.

6. Insert the bent end of the gauge between the lower edge of the piston slot and the upper edge of the right hand slot in the choke housing (Fig. 4), and pull the choke countershaft lever counterclockwise until the gauge is snug in

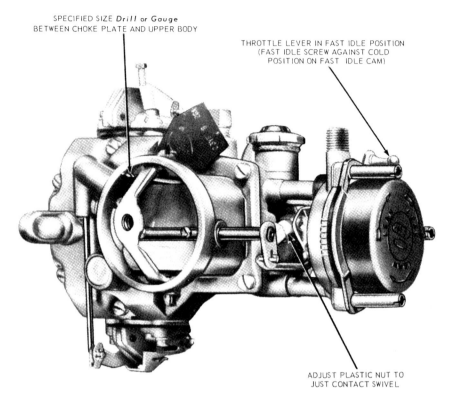

FIG. 2—Choke Plate Clearance (Pull-Down) Adjustment—Ford 1-V

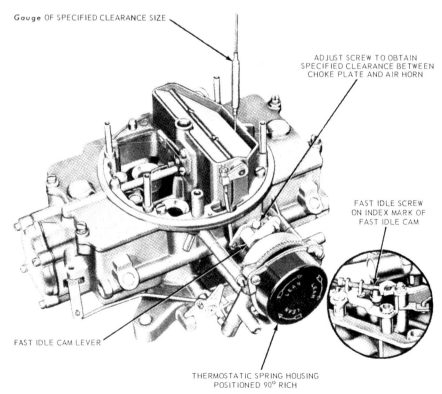

FIG. 3—Fast Idle Cam Linkage Adjustment—Ford 2-V and 4-V

the piston slot. Hold the wire gauge in place by exerting light pressure on the countershaft lever, and adjust the choke plate clevis (pull-down) adjusting nut to obtain the specified clearance (Part 10-8) between the front of the choke plate and the air horn (Fig. 4).

7. Install the choke thermostatic spring housing and gasket. Install the housing retainer and the retaining screws.

8. Set the choke thermostatic spring housing to the specified index mark. If no other carburetor adjustments are required, adjust the engine idle speed and idle fuel mixture, and the dashpot (if so equipped.)

MANUAL CHOKE PLATE CLEARANCE (PULL-DOWN) ADJUSTMENT—FORD 4-V

1. Remove the air cleaner assembly (Part 10-5) if it has not been previously removed.

2. Pull the choke cam and lever to the full choke position. Insert the specified size gauge or drill (Part 10-8) between the downward side of the choke plate and the air horn wall. The gauge or drill will open the choke plate against the

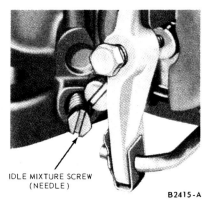

IDLE MIXTURE SCREW (NEEDLE)

B2415-A

FIG. 5—Idle Fuel Mixture Adjustment—Ford I-V

pull-down spring tension. Adjust the choke operating (pull-down) rod adjusting nut to just contact the plastic swivel.

3. If the choke plate clearance adjustment was performed with the carburetor installed on the car, install the air cleaner assembly (Part 10-5) if other carburetor adjustments are not required.

IDLE FUEL MIXTURE AND IDLE (HOT ENGINE) SPEED ADJUSTMENTS

It is of utmost importance that

the idle fuel system on 2-V and 4-V carburetors be balanced as closely as possible in order to obtain a satisfactory, stable, idle and fuel mixture adjustment. This is achieved by establishing initial idle speed and mixture adjustments before proceeding with the final idle speed and mixture adjustment, and the fast (cold engine) idle speed adjustment.

With the air cleaner removed, make the idle adjustments in the following sequence:

Initial Idle Speed and Fuel Mixture Adjustments. Refer to Figs. 5 and 6 for views of the Ford 1-V carburetor idle fuel mixture and idle (hot engine) speed adjustment screws.

The idle fuel mixture and idle (hot engine) speed adjustment screws for the Ford 2-V and 4-V carburetors are shown in Figs. 7 and 8.

1. Set the initial idle fuel mixture by turning the idle mixture screw(s) (needle) inward (clockwise) until lightly seated; then, turn the

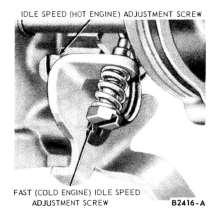

IDLE SPEED (HOT ENGINE) ADJUSTMENT SCREW

FAST (COLD ENGINE) IDLE SPEED ADJUSTMENT SCREW   B2416-A

FIG. 6—Idle Speed Adjustments —Ford I-V

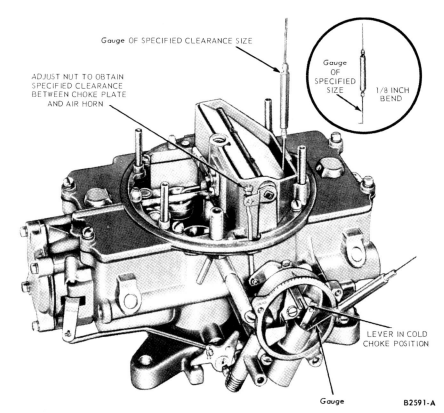

Gauge OF SPECIFIED CLEARANCE SIZE

ADJUST NUT TO OBTAIN SPECIFIED CLEARANCE BETWEEN CHOKE PLATE AND AIR HORN

Gauge OF SPECIFIED SIZE   1/8 INCH BEND

LEVER IN COLD CHOKE POSITION

Gauge   B2591-A

FIG. 4—Choke Plate Clearance (Pull-Down) Adjustment—(Typical) Ford 2-V and 4-V

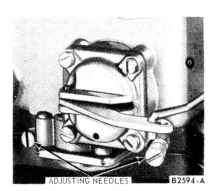

ADJUSTING NEEDLES   B2594-A

FIG. 7—Idle Fuel Mixture Adjustments—Typical for Ford 2-V or 4-V

screw(s) outward (counterclockwise) the specified turns (Part 10-8). **Do not turn the needle(s) tightly against their seat(s) as they may groove the end(s). If a needle is damaged, it must be replaced before a satisfactory fuel mixture can be obtained.**

2. Position the choke mechanism so that the choke plate is fully open. Seat the throttle plate in the throttle bore. **It may be necessary to back off on the dashpot (if so equipped) adjustment screw to seat the throttle plate in the throttle bore.** Set the idle speed adjustment screw to just make contact with the stop on the carburetor lower body, and turn the screw inward (clockwise) the specified (Part 10-8) turns.

Final Idle (Hot Engine) Speed and Mixture Adjustments. The engine idle speed is adjusted to settings for a hot engine and a cold engine (fast idle speed during choke operation). All final idle speed and mixture adjustments must be made on a hot, normalized engine.

Refer to Figs. 5, 6, 7 and 8 for views of the idle fuel mixture and idle (hot engine) speed screws for the various carburetor applications.

1. Operate the engine until engine temperatures are stabilized. **On a car with an air conditioner, operate the engine for twenty minutes before setting the engine idle speed. The engine idle speed is adjusted with the air conditioner operating.**

2. Position the transmission lever in neutral. Allow the throttle to drop back to the normal idle speed position. Attach a tachometer to the engine. Set the parking brake.

3. Turn on the headlamps. **It is necessary to place the alternator under a load condition in this manner in order to obtain the specified engine idle speed during the adjustment procedure.**

4. **On a car with a manual shift transmission, the engine idle speed is checked and adjusted with the gear shift lever in neutral position. On a car with an automatic transmission, the engine idle speed is checked and adjusted first with the transmission selector lever in the neutral position and adjusted with the transmission selector lever in the drive range position.** Adjust and check the engine idle speed. **Be sure the dashpot (if so equipped) is not interfering with the throttle lever. On an automatic choke equipped carburetor, make sure the fast idle screw is not contacting the**

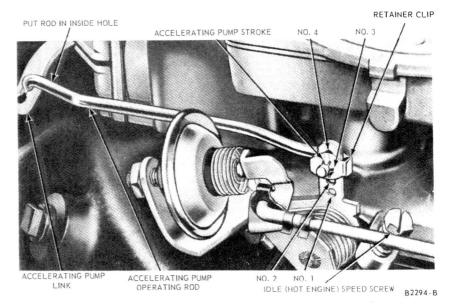

FIG. 8—Accelerating Pump Stroke and Idle (Hot Engine) Speed Adjustments—Typical for Ford 2-V and 4-V

fast idle cam. On a manual choke equipped carburetor, make sure the choke cam and lever is in the slow position, with the fast idle screw not contacting the cam.

On a carburetor equipped with a hot idle compensator, be sure the compensator is seated to allow for proper idle adjustment.

Adjust the engine idle speed to specifications (Part 10-8) by turning the engine idle speed screw (Figs. 6 or 8) inward to increase the speed or outward to decrease the speed.

5. Turn the idle mixture needle(s) (Figs. 5 or 7) inward until the engine rpm begins to drop, due to the lean mixture. **On a car equipped with a Thermactor exhaust emission system, turn the needle(s) outward ¼ turn. The outward adjustment of the idle fuel mixture needles is the final adjustment required.** On a car without the Thermactor system, turn the needle(s) outward until the engine rpm increases and begins to drop; then turn the idle mixture needle(s) inward for maximum rpm and engine smoothness. **On Ford 2-V and 4-V carburetors, the needles should be turned evenly and alternately approximately the same amount. The final setting may vary about ½ turn difference between needles.**

6. After the correct engine idle mixture has been obtained, **check the idle speed with the transmission selector lever in neutral and manually opening and closing the**

throttle. Adjust the idle speed to specification, if required.

If the car is equipped with an automatic transmission, position the selector lever in drive range to check and adjust the idle speed to specification (Part 10-8), if necessary.

The final engine idle speed may be varied to suit the conditions under which the car is to be operated.

7. Shut off the engine. Check the fast (cold engine) idle speed.

FAST (COLD ENGINE) IDLE SPEED ADJUSTMENT— AUTOMATIC CHOKE

On a Ford 1-V carburetor, the fast (cold engine) idle adjustment screw (Fig. 6) is located on the left side of the carburetor.

On a Ford 2-V and 4-V carburetor, the fast (cold engine) idle adjustment screw (Fig. 9) is located on the right side of the carburetor.

The fast idle adjusting screw contacts one edge of the fast idle cam. The cam permits a faster engine idle speed for smoother running when the engine is cold during choke operation. As the choke plate is moved through its range of travel from the closed to the open position, the fast idle cam pick-up lever rotates the fast idle cam. Each position on the fast idle cam permits a slower idle rpm as engine temperature rises and choking is reduced.

Make certain the idle (hot engine) speed and mixture is adjusted

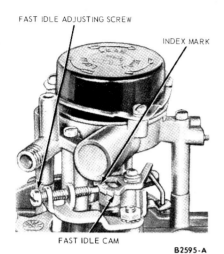

FAST IDLE ADJUSTING SCREW

INDEX MARK

FAST IDLE CAM

B2595-A

FIG. 9—Fast (Cold Engine) Idle Speed Adjustment—Ford 2-V and 4-V

to specification before attempting to set the fast idle speed.

1. With the engine operating temperature normalized (hot), air cleaner removed and the tachometer attached, manually rotate the fast idle cam until the fast idle adjusting screw rests adjacent to the shoulder of the highest step (screw aligned with arrow mark) on the cam.

2. Start the engine and turn the fast idle adjusting screw inward or outward as required to obtain the specified idle rpm (Part 10-8).

3. Place the transmission selector lever in neutral and turn off the engine. Switch off the headlamps and the air conditioner (if so equipped). Remove the tachometer.

4. If the car is equipped with an automatic transmission, check the anti-stall dashpot for proper adjustment.

FAST (COLD ENGINE) IDLE SPEED ADJUSTMENT— MANUAL CHOKE

The adjusting screw on the right side of the carburetor contacts one edge of the choke cam and lever (Fig. 10). The cam permits a faster engine idle speed for smoother running when the engine is cold during choke operation. As the choke cam and lever is moved through its range of travel from the open to the closed position, the fast idle pick-up lever rotates the throttle shaft.

1. Manually rotate the choke cam and lever until the fast idle adjusting screw rests on the index

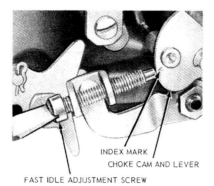

INDEX MARK
CHOKE CAM AND LEVER

FAST IDLE ADJUSTMENT SCREW

B2357-A

FIG. 10—Manual Choke Fast (Cold Engine) Idle Speed Adjustment

mark (arrow) on the cam (Fig. 10).

2. Turn the fast idle adjusting screw inward or outward (as required) so that the fast idle adjusting screw just contacts the fast idle cam at the index mark to obtain the specified fast idle rpm (Part 10-8).

3. If the car is equipped with an automatic transmission, check the dashpot for proper adjustment.

ANTI-STALL DASHPOT (AUTOMATIC TRANSMISSIONS) ADJUSTMENT

The anti-stall dashpot adjustment is made with the air cleaner removed (Part 10-5, Section 2) from the car.

Ford 1-V

1. Adjust the throttle position to the hot idle setting. Turn the dashpot adjusting screw outward until it is clear of the dashpot plunger assembly (Fig. 11).

2. Turn the dashpot adjusting screw inward until it initially contacts the dashpot plunger assembly; then, turn the adjusting screw inward (clockwise) the specified (Part 10-8) number of turns against the dashpot diaphragm plunger assembly.

3. Check the accelerating pump lever and stroke for proper adjustment, if required. Install the air cleaner (Part 10-5, Section 2).

Ford 2-V and 4-V

1. With the engine idle speed and mixture properly adjusted, and the engine at normal operating temperature, loosen the anti-stall dashpot lock nut (Fig. 12).

2. Hold the throttle in the closed position and depress the plunger with a screwdriver blade. Check the

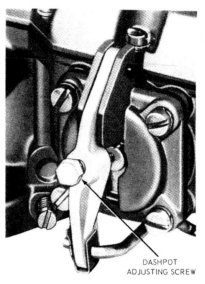

ADJUST THROTTLE TO HOT IDLE POSITION PRIOR TO ADJUSTING DASHPOT

DASHPOT ADJUSTING SCREW

B2417-A

FIG. 11—Anti-Stall Dashpot Adjustment—Ford I-V

clearance between the throttle lever and the plunger tip with a feeler gauge of the specified clearance dimension (Part 10-8). Turn the anti-stall dashpot in its bracket in a direction to provide the specified clearance between the tip of the plunger and the throttle lever. Tighten the lock nut to secure the adjustment.

3. Check the accelerating pump stroke for proper adjustment, if required. Install the air cleaner assembly (Part 10-5, Section 2).

Adjust Accelerating Pump Lever —Ford 1-V. The pump stroke is controlled by changing location of the roll pin in the lever stop hole

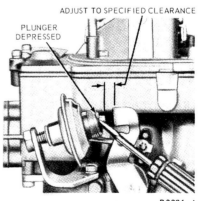

ADJUST TO SPECIFIED CLEARANCE
PLUNGER DEPRESSED

B2296-A

FIG. 12—Anti-Stall Dashpot Adjustment—Typical for Ford 2-V and 4-V

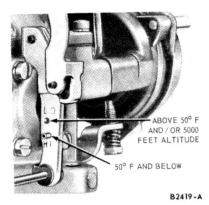

ABOVE 50° F
AND / OR 5000
FEET ALTITUDE

50° F AND BELOW

B2419-A

FIG. 13—Accelerating Pump Stroke Adjustment—Ford I-V

(Fig. 13).

1. For operation in ambient temperatures 50°F and below, place the roll pin in the lever hole marked HI (lower hole).

For best performance and economy at normal ambient temperatures and high altitude (above 50°F and/or above 5,000 feet altitude), place the roll pin in the LO (upper hole) of the lever.

2. Check the vent valve for proper adjustment.

Adjust Accelerating Pump Lever —Ford 2-V and 4-V. The primary throttle shaft lever (overtravel lever) has 4 holes and the accelerating pump link has 2 holes (Fig. 8) to control the accelerating pump stroke for various ambient temperatures and operating conditions of the engine.

The accelerating pump operating rod should be in the specified (Part 10-8) hole in the overtravel lever and the inboard hole (hole closest to the pump plunger) in the accelerating pump link (Fig. 8).

1. To release the rod from the retainer clip, press the tab end of the clip toward the rod; then, at the same time, press the rod away from the clip until it is disengaged.

2. Position the clip over the specified (Part 10-8) hole in the overtravel lever. Press the ends of the clip together and insert the operating rod through the clip and the overtravel lever. Release the clip to engage the rod.

VENT VALVE ADJUSTMENT— FORD 1-V

The vent valve adjustment is always performed after the accelerating pump adjustment has been completed.

1. With the air cleaner removed,

set the throttle linkage to the hot idle position. The groove in the vent valve rod should now be even with the open end of the vent (Fig. 14). Bend the arm on the vent valve rod actuating lever (where it contacts the accelerating pump lever) to align the groove with the edge of the bore.

2. Install the air cleaner (Part 10-5, Section 2).

CLEAN CARBURETOR AIR CLEANER AND FILTER

REMOVAL

1. Disconnect the crankcase ventilation system hose, if so equipped, from the air cleaner body.

2. Remove the wing nut retaining the air cleaner assembly to the carburetor. On cars equipped with a hot and cold air intake duct, remove the 2 wing-type screws that secure the air duct and thermostat assembly to the air cleaner.

3. Remove the air cleaner assembly, then remove the cover and lift the filter element out of the air cleaner body.

CLEANING FILTER ELEMENT

The polyeurethene filter element on a "closed" crankcase ventilation system equipped car cannot be cleaned; it must be replaced.

The cellulose fiber filter element used on an "open" crankcase ventilation system equipped car must never be cleaned with a solvent or cleaning solution. Also, oil must not be added to the surfaces of the filter element or air cleaner body.

There are two procedures that can be used to clean the air filter element. One method is performed with the use of compressed air. The other is performed by tapping the element on a smooth horizontal surface.

Compressed Air Method. Direct a stream of compressed air through the element in the direction opposite that of the intake air flow, that is from the inside outward. **Extreme care must be exercised to prevent rupture of the element material.**

Tapping Method. Hold the element in a vertical position and tap it lightly against a smooth, horizontal surface to shake the dust and dirt out. **Do not deform the element or damage the gasket surfaces by tapping too hard.** Rotate the filter after each tap until the entire outer surface has been cleaned.

Inspection. Hold the filter in front of a back-up light and carefully in-

NOTCH ON VENT VALVE ROD
TO ALIGN WITH EDGE OF HOLE,
WITH THROTTLE IN
HOT IDLE POSITION

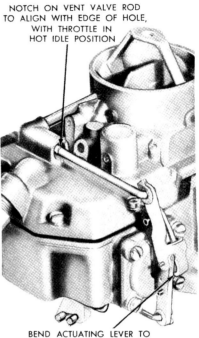

BEND ACTUATING LEVER TO
OBTAIN CORRECT ROD POSITION

B1810-B

FIG. 14—Vent Valve Adjustment

spect it for any splits or cracks. If the filter is split or cracked, replace it.

BODY AND COVER

Clean the air cleaner body and the cover with a solvent or compressed air. If the air cleaner contains an opening for the crankcase ventilation system air flow, probe the opening to assure removal of deposits. Wipe the air cleaner dry if a solvent is used. Inspect the air cleaner body and cover for distortion or damage at the gasket mating surfaces. Replace the cover or body if they are damaged beyond repair.

INSTALLATION

1. Install a new air cleaner mounting gasket on the carburetor, if required.

2. Position the air cleaner body on the carburetor, and make certain the body is properly seated on the gasket.

3. Connect the air inlet duct and valve assembly, if so equipped, to the air cleaner with the wing-type retaining screws. Tighten the screws.

4. Place the filter element on the the air cleaner body. **Make sure the filter is properly seated. If the word TOP is indicated on the filter element, make sure the word TOP faces up.** Install the cover and tighten the retaining wing nut.

5. Connect the crankcase vent

hose, if so equipped, to the air cleaner and tighten the retaining clamp.

REPLACE CARBURETOR AIR CLEANER FILTER

REMOVAL

1. Disconnect the crankcase ventilation system hose, if so equipped, from the air cleaner body.

2. Remove the wing nut retaining the air cleaner assembly to the carburetor. On cars equipped with a hot and cold air intake duct, remove the 2 wing-type screws that secure the air duct and thermostat assembly to the air cleaner.

3. Remove the air cleaner assembly, then remove the cover and lift the filter element out of the air cleaner body.

INSTALLATION

1. Install a new air cleaner mounting gasket on the carburetor if required.

2. Position the air cleaner body on the carburetor, and make certain the body is properly seated on the gasket.

3. Connect the air inlet duct and valve assembly, if so equipped, to the air cleaner with the wing-type retaining screws. Tighten the screws.

4. Place the filter element on the air cleaner body. **Make sure the filter is properly seated. If the word TOP is indicated on the filter element, make sure the word TOP faces up.** Install the cover and tighten the retaining wing nut.

5. Connect the crankcase vent hose, if so equipped, to the air cleaner and tighten the retaining clamp.

CLEAN CRANKCASE OIL FILLER BREATHER CAP

Remove the cap and wash it in a low-volatility, petroleum-base solvent. Probe the breather hole(s) to assure removal of any accumulated deposits. Shake the cap dry and install it. **Do not dry with compressed air as air pressure may damage the filter element.**

CLEAN EMISSION SYSTEM HOSES, TUBES, OIL SEPARATOR (427 C.I.D. ENGINE), FITTINGS, CARBURETOR SPACER AND REPLACE EMISSION CONTROL VALVE. REPLACE THERMACTOR AIR PUMP FILTER IF SO EQUIPPPED.

REMOVAL

170 and 200 Six

1. On a closed venilation system,

remove the inlet hose from the air cleaner and filler cap.

2. Remove the air cleaner.

3. Grasp the crankcase vent hose near the rocker arm cover grommet (Fig. 15) and pull to remove the regulator valve from the rocker arm cover.

4. Using hose clamp pliers, slide both hose clamps toward the center of the vent hose. Remove the regulator valve from the vent hose and remove the vent hose from the hose fitting in the intake manifold.

5. Remove the vent hose fitting from the intake manifold.

289 V-8

1. On a closed ventilation system, remove the ventilation system air intake hose from the air cleaner and the oil filler cap (Fig. 16).

2. Remove the air cleaner and intake duct assembly.

3. Using hose clamp pliers, slide both crankcase vent hose clamps toward the center of the vent hose. Slide the vent hose clamps away from the hot idle compensator (if so equipped).

4. Pull the regulator valve and fitting (elbow) out of the valve rocker arm cover mounting grommet.

CLEANING

Do not attempt to clean the crankcase ventilation regulator valve. It should be replaced at the specified mileage intervals.

Clean the crankcase ventilation system connection on the carburetor spacer by probing the inlet nipple with a flexible wire or bottle brush.

Clean the rubber hoses with low-volatility, petroleum-base solvent and dry with compressed air.

INSTALLATION

170 and 200 Six

1. Install the vent hose fitting in the intake manifold.

2. Position the hose clamps on the vent hose. Install the hose on the fitting in the intake manifold and the regulator valve in the hose. Using hose clamp pliers, slide the clamps into position.

3. Insert the regulator valve into the rocker arm cover mounting grommet.

4. Install the air cleaner.

5. On a closed ventilation system, connect the inlet hose to the air cleaner and the filler cap.

6. Operate the engine and check for leaks.

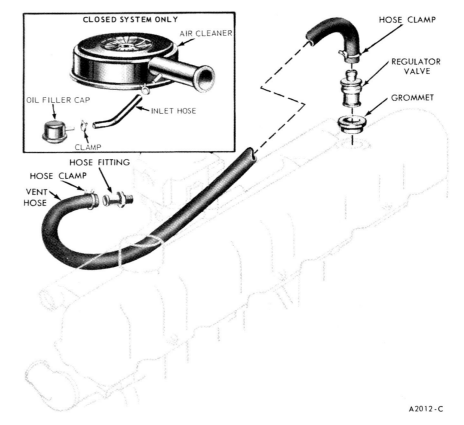

FIG. 15—Crankcase Vent System (Six)

A2012-C

289 V-8

1. Insert the regulator valve and fitting (elbow) into the valve rocker arm cover mounting grommet.

2. Position the hose clamps on the vent hose. Connect the vent hose to the carburetor spacer regulator valve and hot idle compensator (if so equipped). Using hose clamp pliers, slide the clamps into position.

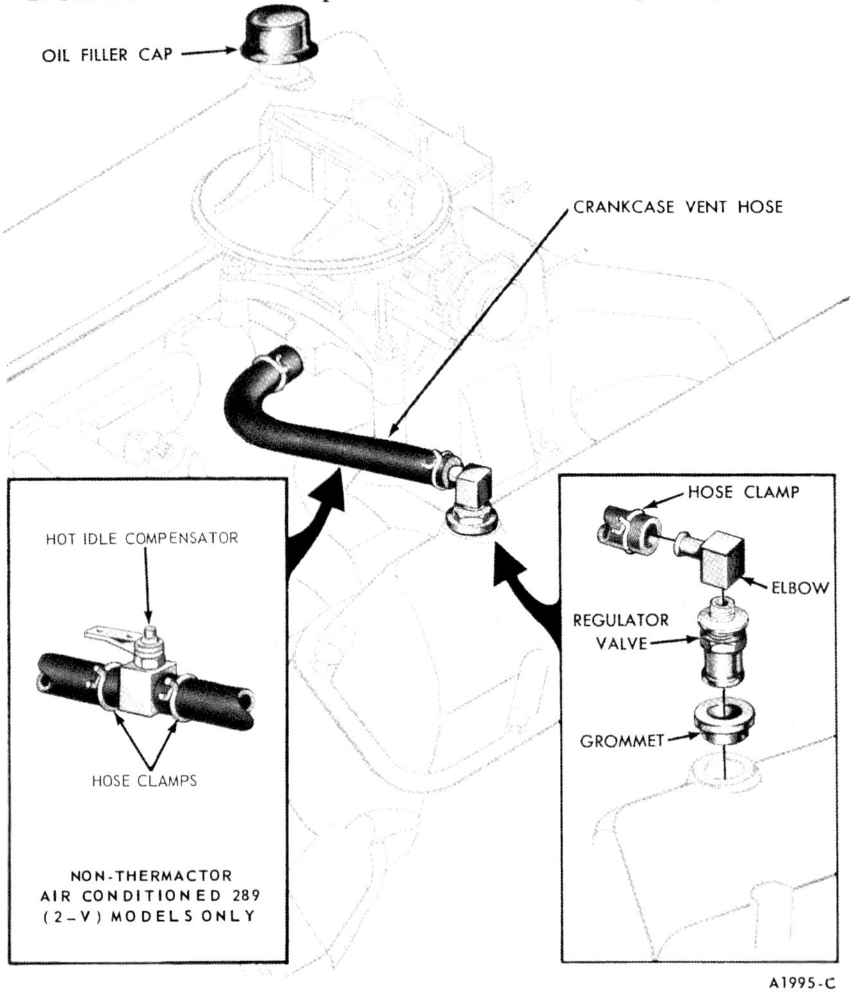

3. Install the air cleaner and intake duct assembly.

4. Install the ventilation system intake hose to the air cleaner and the oil filler cap.

5. Operate the engine and check for leaks.

REPLACE THERMACTOR AIR PUMP FILTER

1. Remove the wing nut (Fig. 17) and air horn assembly. Remove the filter element from the air horn assembly.

2. Wipe the air horn assembly and air cleaner with a clean, dirt-free cloth to remove any accumulated dirt or foreign matter. Under extremely dirty conditions it may be necessary to wash both the air horn and body in low-volatility mineral spirits. Be sure the parts are dry before installing them.

3. The filter element is not cleanable. Place a new filter element on the air horn assembly. Position the assembled air horn and filter element in the air cleaner body. **Be sure the tang is fitted in the slot (Fig. 17).** Install the wing nut.

CHECK ENGINE ACCESSORY DRIVE BELTS

BELT TENSION

Properly tensioned drive belts minimize noise and also prolong service life of the belt. Therefore, it is recommended that a belt tension gauge be used to check and adjust the belt tension. **Any belt that has operated for a minimum of 10 minutes is considered a used belt, and when adjusted, it must be adjusted to the reset tension shown in the specifications.**

1. Install the belt tension tool on the drive belt (Fig. 18) and check the tension following the instructions of the tool manufacturer.

Due to the inaccessibility of the alternator belt on a Comet equipped with air conditioning and power steering, a belt tension gauge cannot be used. Therefore, it must be tensioned by the deflection method. Deflection should not exceed ¼ inch when thumb pressure is applied.

2. If adjustment is necessary, loosen the alternator mounting and adjusting arm bolts. Move the alternator toward or away from the engine until the correct tension is obtained. Tighten the alternator adjusting arm and the mounting bolts. *Check the belt tension.*

DRIVE BELT REPLACEMENT

1. On a car with power steering,

OIL FILLER CAP →

CRANKCASE VENT HOSE

HOSE CLAMP
ELBOW
REGULATOR VALVE
GROMMET

HOT IDLE COMPENSATOR

HOSE CLAMPS

NON-THERMACTOR
AIR CONDITIONED 289
(2-V) MODELS ONLY

A1995-C

FIG. 16—Crankcase Vent System (V-8)

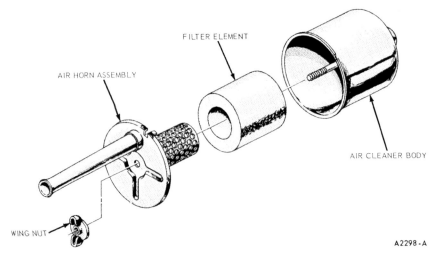

FILTER ELEMENT

AIR HORN ASSEMBLY

AIR CLEANER BODY

WING NUT

A2298-A

FIG. 17—Thermactor Exhaust Emission System Air Cleaner

loosen the power steering pump bracket at the water pump and remove the drive belt.

On a car with an air conditioner, remove the compressor drive belt.

2. Loosen the alternator mounting and adjusting arm bolts. Move the alternator toward the engine. Remove the belt(s) from the alternator and crankshaft pulleys, and lift them over the fan.

3. Place the belt(s) over the fan. Insert the belt(s) in the water pump pulley, crankshaft pulley and alternator or generator pulley grooves. Adjust the belt tension to specifications.

4. On a car with an air conditioner, install and adjust the compressor drive belt to specifications.

5. On a car with power steering, install the power steering pump drive belt and tighten the pump bracket to the water pump. Adjust the drive belt tension to specifications.

LUBRICATE EXHAUST CONTROL VALVE (390 CID ENGINE)

Lubricate the shaft bushings with FoMoCo Exhaust Gas Control Valve Solvent (COAA-19A501-A) or a penetrating oil and graphite mixture, while operating the valve manually until it operates with complete freedom.

VALVE TAPPET ADJUSTMENT (CONVENTIONAL) (289-4V)

1. Be sure the engine is at normal operating temperature before attempting to set the valve lash.

2. Remove the air cleaner.

3. Remove the valve rocker arm covers and gaskets.

4. With the engine idling, set the valve lash (Fig. 19) using a step-type feeler gauge only ("go" and "no go"). The final (hot) intake and exhaust valve lash settings are listed in the Specifications Section.

For example, to obtain the correct setting if the valve lash is 0.019 inch, use a step-type feeler gauge of 0.018 inch ("go") and 0.020 inch ("no go"). The "go" step should enter, and the "no go" step should not enter. The resultant setting will be to the required setting (0.019 inch).

5. Install the valve rocker arm cover gaskets and covers.

6. Install the air cleaner.

CHECK IGNITION TIMING

To check and adjust the timing with a Rotunda 13-07 power timing

Tool—T63L-8620-A

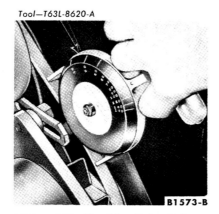

B1573-B

FIG. 18—Checking Drive Belt Tension

light, proceed as follows:

1. Remove the plug wire from the number 1 spark plug.

2. Install the spark plug adaptor on the spark plug.

3. Connect the plug wire to the spark plug adaptor.

4. Clamp the timing light spark plug lead to the spark plug adaptor.

5. Connect the timing light battery leads to the battery terminals.

6. Disconnect the distributor vacuum line (if so equipped).

7. If necessary, clean and mark the timing marks.

8. Operate the engine at the specified idle rpm and point the timing light at the timing pointer.

9. If the timing is incorrect, loosen the distributor hold down bolt and rotate the distributor until the desired initial advance is obtained.

10. Tighten the distributor hold down bolt and check the timing again.

11. Turn off the engine.

12. Remove the timing light and connect the vacuum line.

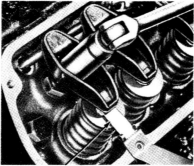

Step-Type Feeler Gauge   A2053-A

FIG. 19—Valve Lash Adjustment

CHECK DISTRIBUTOR POINTS AND ADJUST

Unsnap the distributor cap retaining clips, lift the distributor cap off the distributor housing, and position the cap out of the way (if necessary, remove the air cleaner and/or the high tension wire to gain access to the distributor).

Lift the rotor off the cam. Remove the dust cover (transistorized ignition).

INSPECTION

Replace the distributor point assembly if the contacts are badly burned or excessive metal transfer between the points is evident. Metal transfer is considered excessive when it equals or exceeds the gap setting.

REMOVAL

1. Remove the primary distributor-transistor lead and condenser wire (if equipped) from the breaker plate.

2. Remove the screw attaching the ground wire to the distributor point assembly.

3. Remove the screw nearest the distributor points, then remove the distributor point assembly.

INSTALLATION

1. When installing new distributor points, reverse the procedure for removal and make sure that the ground wire is attached to the distributor point assembly attaching screw which is furthest from the distributor points.

2. If the used points are serviceable, set the gap using a dwell meter as follows:

Connect the dwell meter following the manufacturer's instructions. **In a car equipped with transistor ignition, make sure that the dwell meter is connected to the tachometer block rather than the coil.**

Operate the engine at idle speed and note the reading on the dwell meter.

Stop the engine and adjust the gap (decreasing the gap increases the dwell). Now check the dwell again.

Repeat this procedure until specified dwell is obtained.

If new points are installed, set the gap to specifications using a feeler gauge.

3. Install the dust cover (transistorized ignition).

4. Install the rotor. Install the distributor cap on the distributor housing and snap the retaining clips in place.

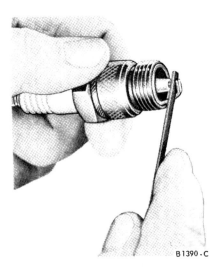

FIG. 20—Cleaning Plug Electrode

5. Install the air cleaner and/or the high tension lead if either was removed.

CHECK SPARK PLUGS

REMOVAL

1. Remove the wire from each spark plug by grasping, twisting and pulling the moulded cap of the wire only. **Do not pull on the wire because the wire connection inside the cap may become separated or the weather seal may be damaged.**

2. Clean the area around each spark plug port with compressed air, then remove the spark plugs.

3. Examine the firing ends of the spark plugs, noting the type of deposits and the degree of electrode erosion.

4. Clean the plugs on a sand blast cleaner, following the manufacturer's instructions. **Do not prolong the use of the abrasive blast as it will erode**

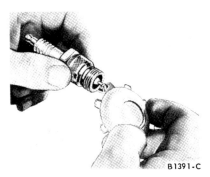

FIG. 21—Gapping Spark Plug

the insulator and electrodes.

5. Clean the electrode surfaces with a small file (Fig. 20). Dress the electrodes to secure flat parallel surfaces on both the center and side electrodes.

6. After cleaning, examine the plug carefully for cracked or broken insulators, badly pitted electrodes, and other signs of failure. Replace as required.

ADJUSTMENT

Set the spark plug gap to specifications by bending the ground electrode (Fig. 21).

INSTALLATION

1. Install the spark plugs and torque each plug to specifications.

When a new spark plug is installed in a new replacement cylinder head, torque the plug to 20-30 ft-lbs.

2. Connect the spark plug wires.

REPLACE ENGINE COOLANT

To drain the radiator, open the drain cock located at the bottom of the radiator. The cylinder block of a V-8 engine has a drain plug located on both sides of the block (Fig. 22). The six cylinder engines have one drain plug located at the right rear of the cylinder block.

FIG. 22—Typical Cylinder Block Drain Plug

To fill the cooling system, close the radiator drain cock and install the drain plugs in the block. Fill the system to just below the filler neck of the radiator supply tank. Disconnect the heater outlet hose at the water pump to bleed or release trapped air in the system. When the coolant begins to escape, connect the heater outlet hose. Operate the engine until normal operating temperature has been reached. **After the initial fill, the coolant level will drop approximately one quart after the engine has been operated about 20 minutes at 2000 rpm. This is due to the displacement of entrapped air. Add more coolant to fill the radiator supply tank.**

CHECK ENGINE COOLANT LEVEL

The coolant level should be kept one inch below the filler neck opening.

---

2 **TRANSMISSION**

ADJUST AUTOMATIC TRANSMISSION FRONT (INTERMEDIATE) BAND

C-4 TRANSMISSION

1. Clean all the dirt from the band adjusting screw area. Loosen the lock nut several turns.

2. With the tool shown in Fig. 23 tighten the adjusting screw until the tool handle clicks. The tool is a preset torque wrench which clicks and overruns when the torque on the adjusting screw reaches 10 ft-lbs.

3. **Back off the adjusting screw exactly 1½ turns.**

4. **Hold the adjusting screw from turning and torque the locknut to specification.**

C-6 TRANSMISSION

1. Raise the car on a hoist or jack stands.

2. Clean the threads of the intermediate band adjustment screw.

3. Loosen the adjustment screw lock nut.

4. Tighten the band adjustment

screw as shown in Fig. 24 until the wrench overruns, then back it off 1½ turns. Tighten the adjustment screw lock nut to specification being careful not to disturb the adjustment screw setting.

5. Lower the car.

ADJUST AUTOMATIC TRANSMISSION REAR (REVERSE) BAND

C-4 TRANSMISSION

1. Clean all the dirt from the ad-

justing screw area. Loosen the lock nut several turns.

2. With the tools shown in Fig. 25, tighten the adjusting screw until the tool handle clicks. The tool is a preset torque wrench which clicks and overruns when the torque on the adjusting screw reaches 10 ft-lbs.

3. **Back off the adjusting screw exactly 3 full turns.**

4. Hold the adjusting screw from turning and torque the lock nut to specification.

CHECK AUTOMATIC TRANSMISSION FLUID LEVEL

1. Make sure that the car is standing level. Then firmly apply the parking brake.

2. Run the engine at normal idle speed. If the transmission fluid is cold, run the engine at fast idle

Tool—T59P-77370-B or 7345

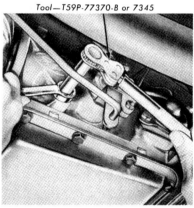

D1460-A

FIG. 23—Intermediate Band Adjustment

UNDERSIDE OF SPRING RETAINER

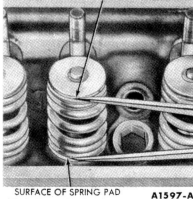

SURFACE OF SPRING PAD   A1597-A

FIG. 24—Adjusting Intermediate Band

Tool—T59P-77370-B or 7345

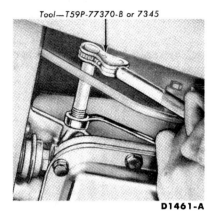

D1461-A

FIG. 25—Low-Reverse Band Adjustment

speed (about 1200 rpm) until the fluid reaches its normal operating temperature. When the fluid is warm, slow the engine down to normal idle speed.

3. Shift the selector lever through all positions, and place the lever at P. Do not turn off the engine during the fluid level checks.

4. Clean all dirt from the transmission fluid dipstick cap before removing the dipstick from the filler tube.

5. Pull the dipstick out of the tube, wipe it clean, and push it all the way back into the tube. Be sure it is properly seated.

6. Pull the dipstick out of the tube again, and check the fluid level. If necessary, add enough fluid to the transmission through the filler tube to raise the fluid level to the F (full) mark on the dipstick. **Do not overfill the transmission.**

CHECK MANUAL SHIFT TRANSMISSION OIL LEVEL

1. Remove the filler plug from the side of the case.

2. If lubricant does not flow from the filler hole, fill the case with the specified lubricant until it is level with the lower edge of the filler hole.

3. Install the filler plug.

CHECK REAR AXLE FLUID LEVEL

The lubricant level should be maintained at the lower edge of the filler plug hole with the specified lubricant.

CHECK CLUTCH LINKAGE ADJUSTMENT
MANUAL

1. Measure the total travel of the

pedal (Fig. 26). If the travel is not within specification, move the clutch pedal bumper and the bracket up or down until the travel is within specified limits. **Always check and adjust total travel before checking free travel.**

2. With the clutch pedal against its bumper (pedal release), measure the overall length of the spring. The overall length should be as specified in Part 5-4.

3. With the engine idling, depress the pedal just enough to take up the free travel and note the reading on the tape (Fig. 26). The difference between this reading and the reading where the pedal is released is the clutch pedal free travel. If the free travel is not within specification, adjust the clutch pedal to equalizer

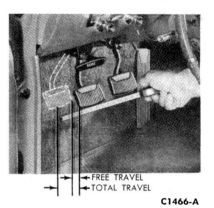

←FREE TRAVEL
←TOTAL TRAVEL

C1466-A

FIG. 26—Typical Clutch Pedal Free-Travel

rod. (Fig. 27). To increase the free travel loosen the rearward adjusting nut and tighten the forward nut. To reduce the free travel, loosen the forward nut and tighten the rearward nut. **Both nuts must be tightened against the trunnion after making the adjustment.**

4. As a final check, measure the pedal free travel with the transmission in neutral and the engine running at about 3000 rpm. If the free travel at this speed is not ½ inch, readjust the clutch pedal to equalizer rod to obtain the specified free travel. Otherwise, the release fingers may contact the release bearing continuously, resulting in premature bearing and clutch failure. Free travel must be exactly to specification.

INTERLOCK (OVERDRIVE MODELS ONLY)

Be sure that the clutch linkage is

correctly adjusted before adjusting the interlock mechanism (Fig. 28).

1. Place the gearshift lever in neutral position.

2. Loosen the adjustment lock nut on the interlock rod.

3. Disconnect the rod from the interlock lever.

4. Loosen the interlock pawl attaching screws. Move the interlock lever forward as far as possible to seat the interlock pawl on the first and reverse-speed shift lever. Tight-

en the two pawl attaching screws.

5. Adjust the length of the interlock rod so that it can be connected to the interlock lever while being held in the forward position. Connect the rod to the lever.

6. Shift the transmission into low and into neutral to check operation of the interlock. Readjust the interlock pawl for snug fit if necessary.

7. Use COAZ-19584-A lubricant as required for the interlock linkage.

LUBRICATE MANUAL TRANSMISSION SHIFT CONTROL AND LINKAGE

Clean and lubricate the shift linkage, trunnions and external shift mechanism (floor shift) as necessary. Use Lithium base grease (no Polythelene).

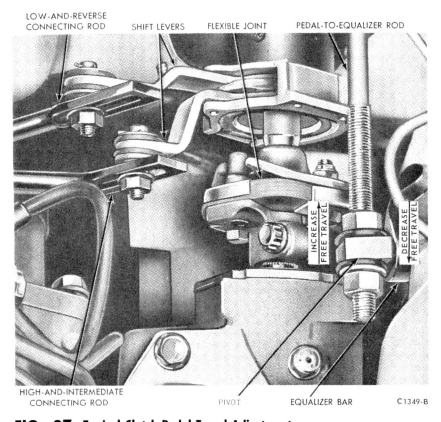

LOW-AND-REVERSE CONNECTING ROD   SHIFT LEVERS   FLEXIBLE JOINT   PEDAL-TO-EQUALIZER ROD

INCREASE FREE TRAVEL   DECREASE FREE TRAVEL

HIGH-AND-INTERMEDIATE CONNECTING ROD   PIVOT   EQUALIZER BAR   C1349-B

FIG. 27—Typical Clutch Pedal Travel Adjustment

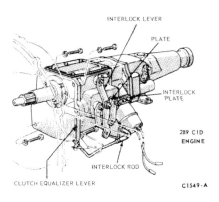

INTERLOCK LEVER

PLATE

INTERLOCK PLATE

289 CID ENGINE

CLUTCH EQUALIZER LEVER   INTERLOCK ROD   C1549-A

FIG. 28—Interlock Mechanism

---

3 CHASSIS

LUBRICATE AUTOMATIC TRANSMISSION KICKDOWN LINKAGE

Lubricate all pivot points in the kickdown linkage with the specified engine oil.

LUBRICATE FRONT SUSPENSION BALL JOINTS

Wipe any accumulated dirt from around the lubrication plugs.

Remove the plugs and install lubrication fittings. Lubricate the ball joints and remove the lubrication fittings. Install the plugs.

LUBRICATE UNIVERSAL JOINTS (FALCON AND COMET)

Wipe any accumulated dirt from around the lubrication plugs.

Remove the plugs and install

lubrication fittings.

Apply the specified lubricant. Remove the fittings and install the plugs.

LUBRICATE POWER STEERING ACTUATOR VALVE BALL STUD

Wipe the lubrication fitting clean and apply the specified lubricant.

CAUTION: Care should be exercised to stop the addition of lubricant when the boot seal begins to inflate or bulge.

CHECK STEERING GEAR PRELOAD

There are only two possible adjustments within the recirculating ball-type steering gear, and **these should be made in the following order to avoid damage or gear failure.**

1. Disconnect the Pitman arm

from the sector shaft.

2. Remove the steering wheel, spring and the centering cone from the shaft and note the relation of the shaft to the bearing.

3. If the shaft is not centered, attach a spring scale to it.

4. Center the shaft by pulling on the scale and note the reading.

5. If more than 20 lbs. pull is required to center the shaft, the steering column should be aligned as detailed in steering gear installation, before adjusting the preload and mesh load.

6. Loosen the nut which locks the sector adjusting screw (Fig. 29), and turn the adjusting screw counterclockwise.

7. Measure the worm bearing preload by attaching an in.-lb.

torque wrench to the steering wheel nut (Fig. 30). With the steering wheel off center, read the pull required to rotate the input shaft approximately 1½ turns either side of center. If the torque or preload is not within specification (Part 3-6), adjust as explained in the next step.

8. Loosen the steering shaft bearing adjuster lock nut, and tighten or back off the bearing adjuster (Fig. 29) to bring the preload within the specified limits.

9. Tighten the steering shaft bearing adjuster lock nut, and recheck the preload.

10. Turn the steering wheel slowly to either stop. **Turn gently against the stop to avoid possible damage to the ball return guides.** Then rotate the wheel 2¼ turns to center the ball nut.

11. Turn the sector adjusting screw clockwise until the specified pull (Part 3-6) is necessary to rotate the worm past its center high spot (Fig. 30). **No perceptible backlash is permissible at 30° on either side of center.**

12. While holding the sector adjusting screw, tighten the locknut to specification and recheck the backlash adjustment.

13. Connect the Pitman arm to the sector shaft and torque to specification.

CHECK POWER STEERING RESERVOIR FLUID LEVEL

Start the engine, turn the steering wheel all the way to the left and

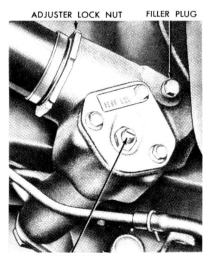

ADJUSTER LOCK NUT   FILLER PLUG

SECTOR SHAFT
ADJUSTING SCREW   G1071-B

FIG. 29—Typical Steering Gear Adjustments

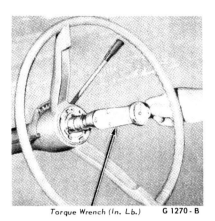

Torque Wrench (In. Lb.)   G 1270 - B

FIG. 30—Checking Pre-Load

right several times, and shut off the engine.

Check the fluid level in the reservoir. If the level is low, add enough fluid to raise the level to the bottom of the filler neck. **Do not overfill the reservoir.**

CHECK BRAKE MASTER CYLINDER FLUID LEVEL

1. Remove the filler cap from the master cylinder. The diaphragm which seals the master cylinder should come off with the cap.

2. Fill the reservoir to ⅜-inch from the top.

3. Install the filler cap, making sure that the diaphragm is properly seated in the cap.

CHECK BRAKE LINES AND LINING
DRUM BRAKES

Raise all four wheels. Remove one of the front brake drums, and inspect the drum and the linings (the wheel bearings should be inspected at this time and repacked if necessary). **Do not let oil or grease touch the drum or the linings.** If the linings are worn to within ⅟₃₂ inch of the rivet heads, replace or reline both sets (primary and secondary) on the front or rear wheels. **Under no circumstances replace one lining only, or one wheel set. Both front wheel sets or both rear wheel sets should be replaced whenever a respective lining or shoe is worn or damaged.** If the drum braking surface is excessively scored, refinish it. The condition of the remaining front linings is usually about the same as that of the one inspected. The rear brake linings may also need replacing at the same time.

FRONT WHEEL DISC BRAKES

Raise all four wheels. Remove one

of the front wheel and tire assemblies, and inspect the rotor, caliper, and linings (the wheel bearings should be inspected at this time and repacked if necessary). **Do not let oil or grease touch the drum or the linings.** If the linings are worn to within 0.030 inch of the surface of the shoe, replace both sets of shoe and lining assemblies (inboard and outboard) on the front wheels. **Under no circumstances replace one shoe and lining assembly only, or one wheel set. Both front wheel sets should be replaced whenever a respective shoe and lining is worn or damaged.**

If the rotor braking surface is excessively scored, distorted, warped, worn, or shows runout over 0.0013 inch, it should be replaced. If the caliper is cracked or otherwise damaged, it must be replaced as a unit.

With the parking brakes in the fully released position, check the brake cables. The cable adjustment should be just tight enough to remove the slack. **Excessive tightening may pull the brake shoes off their anchors.**

Check all brake lines for leakage or physical damage and replace or repair as required.

CLEAN AND PACK FRONT WHEEL BEARINGS
DRUM BRAKES

1. Raise the car until the wheel and tire clear the floor.

2. Remove the wheel cover or hub cap. Remove the grease cap from the hub. Remove the cotter pin, nut lock, adjusting nut, and flat washer from the spindle. Remove the outer bearing cone and roller assembly.

3. Pull the wheel, hub, and drum assembly off the wheel spindle.

4. Remove the grease retainer and the inner bearing cone and roller assembly from the hub with a drift.

5. Clean the lubricant off the inner and outer bearing cups with solvent and inspect the cups for scratches, pits, excessive wear, and other damage. If the cups are worn or damaged, remove them with a drift.

6. Soak a new grease retainer in light engine oil at least 30 minutes before installation. Thoroughly clean the inner and outer bearing cones and rollers with solvent, and dry them thoroughly. **Do not spin the bearings dry with compressed air.**

7. Inspect the cone and roller assemblies for wear or damage, and

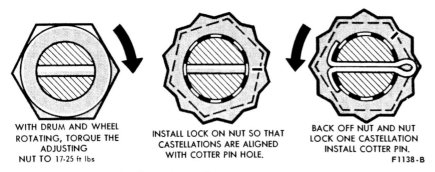

WITH DRUM AND WHEEL ROTATING, TORQUE THE ADJUSTING NUT TO 17-25 ft lbs

INSTALL LOCK ON NUT SO THAT CASTELLATIONS ARE ALIGNED WITH COTTER PIN HOLE.

BACK OFF NUT AND NUT LOCK ONE CASTELLATION INSTALL COTTER PIN.

F1138-B

FIG. 31—Front Wheel Bearing Adjustment

replace them if necessary. **The cone and roller assemblies and the bearing cups should be replaced as a unit if damage to either is encountered.**

8. Thoroughly clean the spindle and the inside of the hub with solvent to remove all old lubricant.

Cover the spindle with a clean cloth, and brush all loose dust and dirt from the brake assembly. **To prevent getting dirt on the spindle, carefully remove the cloth from the spindle.**

9. If the inner and/or outer bearing cup(s) were removed, install the replacement cup(s) in the hub. **Be sure to seat the cups properly in the hub.**

10. Pack the inside of the hub with specified wheel bearing grease. Add lubricant to the hub only until the grease is flush with the inside diameter of both bearing cups.

11. All old grease should be completely cleaned from the bearings before repacking them with new grease. Pack the bearing cone and roller assemblies with wheel bearing grease. A bearing packer is desirable for this operation. If a packer is not available, work as much lub-

ricant as possible between the rollers and cages. Lubricate the cone surfaces with grease.

12. Place the inner bearing cone and roller assembly in the inner cup, and install the new grease retainer. **Be sure that the retainer is properly seated.**

13. Install the wheel, hub, and drum assembly on the wheel spindle. **Keep the hub centered on the spindle to prevent damage to the grease retainer or the spindle threads.**

14. Install the outer bearing cone and roller assembly and the flat washer on the spindle; then, install the adjusting nut (Fig. 31).

15. Adjust the wheel bearings (Fig. 31) and install a new cotter pin. Bend the ends of the cotter pin around the castellations of the nut lock to prevent interference with the radio static collector in the grease cap. Install the grease cap.

16. Install the hub cap or wheel cover.

DISC BRAKES

1. Raise the car until the wheel and tire clear the floor.

2. Remove the wheel cover or

hub cap.

3. Remove the wheel and tire from the hub.

4. Remove 2 bolts attaching the caliper to the caliper bracket. Remove the caliper from the rotor and wire it to the underbody to prevent damage to the brake hose.

5. Remove the grease cap from the hub. Remove the cotter pin, nut lock, adjusting nut, and flat washer from the spindle. Remove the outer bearing cone and roller assembly (Fig. 32).

6. Pull the hub and rotor off the wheel spindle.

7. Remove the grease retainer and the inner bearing cone and roller assembly from the hub.

8. Clean the lubricant off the inner and outer bearing cups with solvent and inspect the cups for scratches, pits, excessive wear, and other damage. If the cups are worn or damaged, remove them with a drift.

9. Soak a new grease retainer in light engine oil at least 30 minutes before installation. Thoroughly clean the inner and outer bearing cones and rollers with solvent, and dry them thoroughly. **Do not spin the bearings with compressed air.**

Inspect the cone and roller assemblies for wear or damage, and replace them if necessary. **The cone and roller assemblies and the bearing cups should be replaced as a unit if damage to either is encountered.**

10. Thoroughly clean the spindle and the inside of the hub with solvent to remove all old lubricant.

Cover the spindle with a clean cloth, and brush all loose dust and dirt from the brake assembly. **To prevent getting dirt on the spindle, carefully remove the cloth from the spindle.**

11. If the inner and/or outer bearing cup(s) were removed, install the replacement cup(s). **Be sure to seat the cups properly in the hub.**

12. Pack the inside of the hub with specified wheel bearing grease. Add lubricant to the hub only until the grease is flush with the inside diameter of both bearing cups.

13. All old grease should be completely cleaned from the bearings before repacking them with new grease. Pack the bearing cone and roller assemblies with wheel bearing grease. A bearing packer is desirable for this operation. If a packer is not available, work as much lubri-

HUB AND ROTOR ASSEMBLY

ADJUSTING NUT

OUTER BEARING CUP

OUTER BEARING CONE AND ROLLER

GREASE CAP

COTTER PIN

NUT LOCK

WASHER

NUT

HUB BOLT

INNER BEARING CUP

GREASE RETAINER

INNER BEARING CONE AND ROLLER

WHEEL ASSEMBLY

F 1259 - A

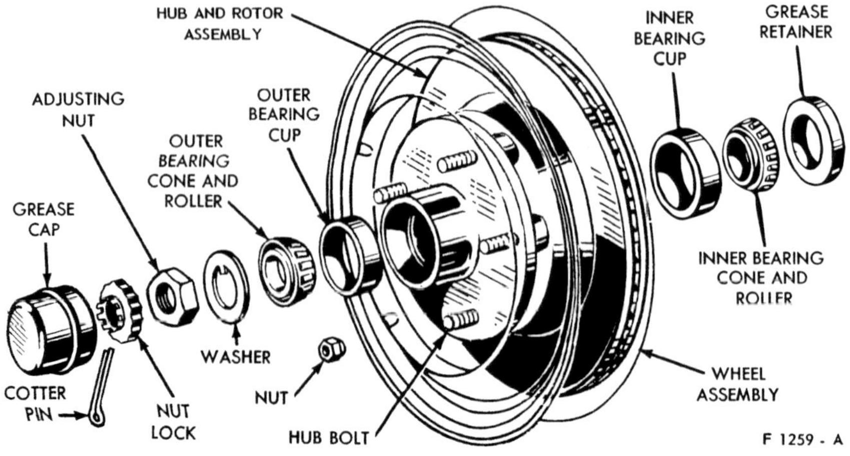

FIG. 32—Hub and Bearing—Disc Brakes

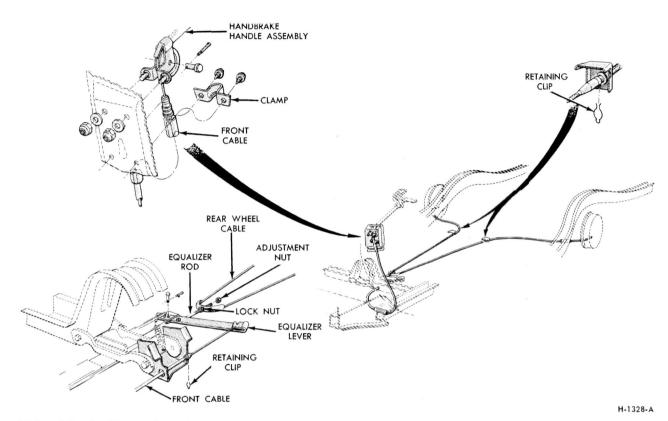

H-1328-A

FIG. 33—Parking Brake Linkage—Mustang

cant as possible between the rollers and cages. Lubricate the cone surfaces with grease.

14. Place the inner bearing cone and roller assembly in the inner cup, and install the new grease retainer. **Be sure that the retainer is properly seated.**

15. Install the hub and rotor on the wheel spindle. **Keep the hub centered on the spindle to prevent damage to the grease retainer or the spindle threads.**

16. Install the outer bearing cone and roller assembly and the flat washer on the spindle, then install the adjusting nut.

17. Position the caliper over the rotor and install the 2 attaching bolts.

18. Install the wheel and tire on the hub.

19. Adjust the wheel bearings, and install a new cotter pin. Bend the ends of the cotter pin around the castellations of the nut lock to prevent interference with the radio static collector in the grease cap. Install the grease cap.

20. Install the hub cap or wheel cover and lower the car.

CHECK AND ADJUST PARKING BRAKE LINKAGE, IF REQUIRED (MUSTANG)

Check the parking brake cables when the brakes are fully released. If the cables are loose, adjust them as follows:

1. Fully release the parking brake by turning the handle counter clockwise and pushing it inward.

2. Pull the parking brake handle outward to the third notch from its normal released position.

3. Raise the car.

4. Turn the locking adjustment nut forward against the equalizer (Fig. 33) until a moderate drag is felt when turning the rear wheels in the direction of forward rotation.

5. Release the parking brake, and make sure that the brake shoes return to the fully released position **and no drag is felt when** turning the rear wheels.

CHECK AND ADJUST PARKING BRAKE LINKAGE, IF REQUIRED (COMET, FALCON, FAIRLANE)

Check the parking brake cables when the brakes are fully released.

If the cables are loose, adjust them as follows:

1. Fully release the parking brake pedal.

2. Depress the parking brake pedal one notch from its normal released position.

3. Raise the car.

4. Loosen the equalizer locknut and turn the adjusting nut forward

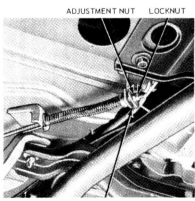

ADJUSTMENT NUT   LOCKNUT

EQUALIZER   H 1405-A

FIG. 34—Parking Brake Linkage Adjustment (Comet, Falcon, Fairlane)

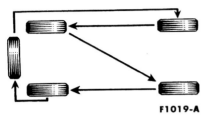

FIG. 35—Tire Cross-Switching Diagram

against the equalizer until a moderate drag is felt when turning the rear wheels (Fig. 34). Tighten the locknut.

5. Release the parking brake, and make sure that the brake shoes return to the fully released position.

CHECK TIRE PRESSURES

Check all tires for specified pressures (cold).

INSPECT AND CROSS-SWITCH WHEELS AND TIRES

Switch the tires according to Fig. 35.

Tighten the wheel nuts to specified torque.

CHECK FRONT WHEEL ALIGNMENT AND LINKAGE
FRONT WHEEL ALIGNMENT CHECKS

Do not check and adjust front wheel alignment without first making the following inspection for front end maladjustment, damage, or wear.

1. Check for specified air pressures in all four tires.

2. Raise the front of the car off the floor. Shake each front wheel grasping the upper and lower surfaces of the tire. Check the front suspension ball joints and mountings for looseness, wear, and damage. Check the brake backing plate mountings. Torque all loose nuts and bolts to specifications.

3. Check the steering gear mountings and all steering linkage connections for looseness. Torque all mountings to specifications. If any of the linkage is worn or bent, replace the parts.

4. Check the front wheel bearings. If any in-and-out free play is noticed, adjust the bearings to specification. Replace worn or damaged bearings.

5. Spin each front wheel with a wheel spinner, and check and balance each wheel as required.

6. Check the action of the shock absorbers. If the shock absorbers are not in good condition, the car may not settle in a normal, level position, and front wheel alignment may be affected.

Wheel Inspection. Wheel hub nuts should be inspected and tightened to specification at pre-delivery. Loose wheel hub nuts may cause shimmy and vibration. Elongated stud holes in the wheels may also result from loose hub nuts.

Keep the wheels and hubs clean. Stones wedged between the wheel and drum and lumps of mud or grease can unbalance a wheel and tire.

Check for damage that would affect the runout of the wheels. Wobble or shimmy caused by a damaged wheel will eventually damage the wheel bearings. Inspect the wheel rims for dents that could permit air to leak from the tires.

Check all the factors of front wheel alignment except the turning angle before making any adjustments. The turning angle should be checked only after caster, camber, and toe-in have been adjusted to specifications.

Equipment Installation. Equipment used for front wheel alignment inspection must be accurate. If portable equipment is being used, perform all inspection operations on a level floor.

Alignment height spacers (Figs. 37 and 38) are used to check caster and camber. The spacers should be omitted when checking toe-in.

1. Drive the car in a straight line far enough to establish the straight-ahead position of the front wheels, and then mark the steering wheel hub and the steering column collar (Fig. 36). **Do not adjust the steering wheel spoke position at this time.** If the front wheels are turned

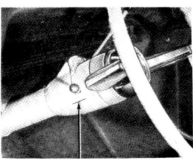

ALIGNMENT MARKS   F1267-B

FIG. 36—Typical Straight Ahead Position Marks

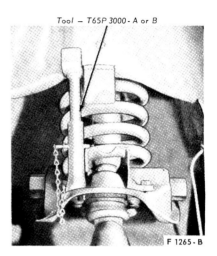

Tool – T65P 3000 - A or B

F 1265 - B

FIG. 37—Alignment Spacers— Front

at any time during the inspection, align the marks to bring the wheels back to the straight-ahead position.

2. With the car in position for the front end alignment inspection and adjustment, install the alignment spacers as follows to establish the curb height.

Insert the pin in the spacer hole marked for the model being checked (Mustang rear does not use the pin).

Raise the front of the car and position the alignment spacers between the suspension upper arm and the spring tower as shown in Fig. 37. The lower end of the spacer should be placed over the head of the ball joint front outside attaching rivet. Position the alignment spacers for the rear of the car between the rear axle and the side rail as shown in Fig. 38.

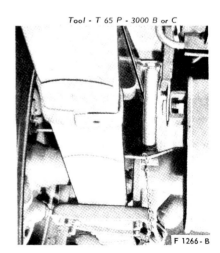

Tool - T 65 P - 3000 B or C

F 1266 - B

FIG. 38—Alignment Spacers— Rear

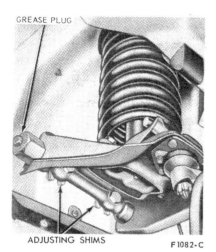

FIG. 39—Typical Upper Arm Assembly—Mustang and Falcon

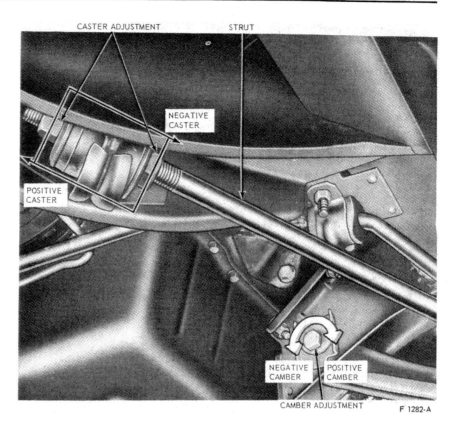

FIG. 40—Caster and Camber Adjustments—Comet, Falcon, Fairlane

3. Install the wheel alignment equipment on the car. Whichever type of equipment is used, follow the installation and inspection instructions provided by the equipment manufacturer.

Caster. Check the caster angle at each front wheel.

The caster is the forward or rearward tilt of the top of the wheel spindle. If the spindle tilts to the rear, caster is positive. The spindle tilts to the front, caster is negative. See Part 3-6 for the correct caster specifications. The maximum difference between both front wheel caster angles should not exceed ½°. However, a difference of not more than ¼° is preferred.

Camber. Check the camber angle at each front wheel.

Camber is the amount the front wheels are tilted at the top. If a wheel tilts outward, camber is positive. If a wheel tilts inward, camber is negative. Correct camber specifications are given in Part 3-6. The maximum difference between both front wheel camber angles should not exceed ½°. However, a difference of not more than ¼° is preferred.

Toe-In. Before attempting to check toe-in, remove all the alignment spacers. Toe-in should only be checked and adjusted after the caster and camber have been adjusted to specifications. Check the toe-in with the front wheels in the straight-ahead position. **Run the engine so that the power steering control valve will be in the center (neutral) position if so equipped.** Measure the distance between the extreme front and also between the extreme rear of both front wheels. The difference

between these two distances is the toe-in. Specifications are in Part 3-6.

Front Wheel Turning Angle. When the inside wheel is turned 20°, the turning angle of the outside wheel should be as specified in Part 3-6. The turning angle cannot be adjusted directly because it is a result of the combination of caster, camber, and toe-in adjustments and should therefore, be measured only after these adjustments have been made. If the turning angle does not measure to specifications, check the spindle or other suspension parts for a bent condition.

After front wheel alignment factors have been checked, make the necessary adjustments. **Do not attempt to adjust front wheel alignment by bending the suspension or steering parts.**

CASTER AND CAMBER ADJUSTMENTS (MUSTANG)

Be sure all required equipment is installed before adjusting caster and camber.

Caster and camber can be adjusted

by removing or installing shims between the inner shaft of the front suspension upper arm and the underbody (Fig. 39).

Both caster and camber adjustments can be made at the same time by loosening the nuts on the two bolts that fasten the inner shaft to the underbody. After the required shims have been removed or installed, torque the nuts to specification. Caster and camber adjusting shims are available in 1/32-inch and ⅛-inch thicknesses.

The 1/32-inch shims should be placed against the fender housing sheet metal or between the ⅛-inch shims.

CASTER

To adjust caster, remove or install shims at either the front bolt or the rear bolt (Fig. 39).

The removal of shims at the front bolt or the installation of shims at the rear bolt will cause the upper ball joint to move forward. The removal of shims at the rear bolt or the installation of shims at the front bolt will cause the ball joint to move rearward. A 1/32-inch change of shim thickness at either bolt will change the caster angle approximately ½°. The difference between the shim stack thickness at the two bolts should not exceed 1/16-inch (Fig. 28).

CAMBER

To adjust camber, remove or install equal shim thicknesses at both bolts.

The removal of equal shims at both bolts will move the upper ball joint inward. The installation of equal shims at both bolts will move the ball joint outward. A 1/16-inch change of shim thickness at both bolts will change the camber angle 1/3°. The total shim stack thickness at each bolt should not exceed 9/16 inch.

CASTER AND CAMBER ADJUSTMENTS (COMET, FALCON AND FAIRLANE)

Caster

Caster is controlled by the front suspension strut (Fig. 40). To obtain positive caster, loosen the strut front nut and tighten the strut rear nut against the bushing. To obtain negative caster, loosen the strut rear nut and tighten the strut front nut against the bushing.

Camber

Camber is controlled by the eccentric cam located at the lower arm attachment to the side rail (Fig. 40). To adjust the camber, loosen the eccentric bolt nut and rotate the bolt and eccentric clockwise from the high position to increase camber or counterclockwise to decrease camber.

After the caster and camber have been adjusted to specification, torque the lower arm eccentric bolt nut and the strut front nut to specification.

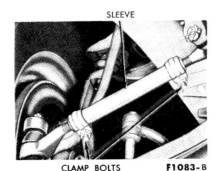

FIG. 41—Spindle Connecting Rod Sleeve

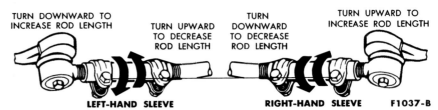

FIG. 42—Spindle Connecting Rod Adjustment

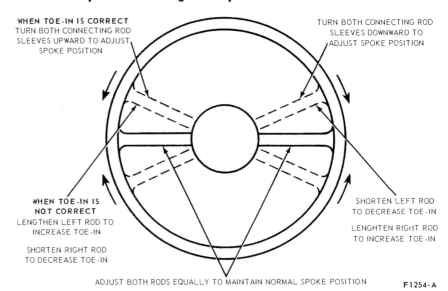

FIG. 43—Toe-in and Steering Wheel Spoke Adjustments—Falcon

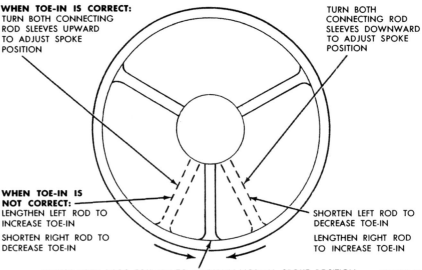

FIG. 44—Toe-in and Steering Wheel Spoke Adjustments—Mustang

TOE-IN AND STEERING WHEEL SPOKE POSITION ADJUSTMENTS

Check the steering wheel spoke position when the front wheels are in the straight-ahead position. If the spokes are not in their normal position, they can be properly adjusted while toe-in is being adjusted.

1. Loosen the two clamp bolts on each spindle connecting rod sleeve (Fig. 41).

2. Adjust toe-in. If the steering wheel spokes are in their normal position, lengthen or shorten both rods equally to obtain correct toe-in (Fig. 42). If the steering wheel spokes are not in their normal position, make the necessary rod adjustments to obtain correct toe-in and

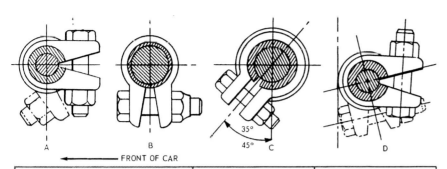

CAR	MANUAL STEERING		POWER STEERING	
	Right Side	Left Side	Right Side	Left Side
COMET – FALCON – FAIRLANE	D	A	D	A
MUSTANG	B	B	B	C

G 1379-A

FIG. 45—Spindle Connecting Rod Sleeve Clamp Position

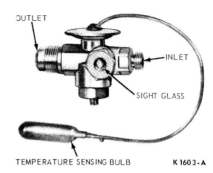

FIG. 46—Sight Glass

steering wheel spoke alignment.

3. Recheck toe-in and the steering wheel spoke position. If toe-in is correct and the steering wheel spokes are still not in their normal position, turn both connecting rod sleeves upward or downward the same number of turns to move the steering wheel spokes (Figs. 43 and 44).

4. When toe-in and the steering wheel spoke position are both correct, torque the clamp bolts on both connecting rod sleeves to specification.

The sleeve position should be as shown in Fig. 45 when the clamp bolts are tightened.

CHECK BATTERY FLUID LEVEL

The battery is mounted under the hood at the right front side of the engine compartment.

Keep the fluid in each battery cell up to the level of the ring in the bottom of the filler well. Generally, tap water may be added unless it has a high mineral content or has been stored in a metal container.

CHECK AIR CONDITIONING SYSTEM

A quick test of the refrigerant supply can be made by observing the flow of refrigerant through the sight glass (Fig. 46).

To check the refrigerant supply, place a large fan in front of the radiator to aid in cooling the engine. Set the servo control for maximum cooling and the blower on high. Operate the engine at 1300 rpm and observe the sight glass while the compressor is operating. There should be no bubbles in the sight glass after the start of the compressor. Bubbles will appear when the compressor starts but should clear after a few moments.

---

4 BODY

LUBRICATE HOOD LATCH

Spray Rotunda Polyethylene Grease (C4A2-19584-B) (Fig. 47) on all pivot points and on the striker plate as required to eliminate any binding condition. Operate the latch mechanism several times to be sure that the lubricant has effectively worked in.

LUBRICATE HOOD HINGE PIVOTS

Spray Rotunda Polyethylene Grease on the hinge pivot points as required. Open and close the hood several times to be sure that the hinge pivots do not bind.

LUBRICATE HOOD AUXILIARY CATCH

Spray Rotunda Polyethylene Grease on all pivot points as required to eliminate any binding conditions. Operate the catch several times to be sure that the lubri-

cant has effectively worked in.

LUBRICATE DOOR LOCK CYLINDERS

Use Rotunda Lock Lubricant (B4A-19587-A) through the key slot. Insert the key and operate the lock several times to be sure that the lubricant has effectively worked in.

LUBRICATE LUGGAGE COMPARTMENT LOCK CYLINDER

Apply Rotunda Lock Lubricant (B4A-19587-A) sparingly through the key slot. Insert the key and operate the lock several times to be sure that the lubricant has effectively worked in.

LUBRICATE DOOR HINGE AND HINGE CHECK

Spray Rotunda Polyethylene Grease on the hinge pivot points as required to eliminate any binding

condition. Open and close the door several times to be sure that the lubricant has effectively worked in.

LUBRICATE LUGGAGE COMPARTMENT HINGE PIVOTS

Spray Rotunda Polyethylene Grease on the hinge pivot points as required. Open and close the luggage compartment several times to be sure that the hinge pivots do not bind.

LUBRICATE TAILGATE LOCK CYLINDER

Use Rotunda Lock Lubricant (B4A-19587-A) sparingly through the key slot. Insert the key and operate the lock several times to be sure that the lubricant has effectively worked in.

LUBRICATE TAILGATE SUPPORT AND HINGES

Spray Rotunda Polyethylene Grease on all pivot and friction

points to eliminate any binding conditions. Operate the tailgate several times to be sure that the lubricant has effectively worked in.

LUBRICATE FUEL FILLER DOOR HINGES

Spray Rotunda Polyethylene Grease on the hinge pivot points as required to eliminate any binding condition. Open and close the door several times to be sure that the lubricant has effectively worked in.

LUBRICATE WEATHERSTRIP AND RUBBER SEALS

Use Silicone Lubricant (COAZ-19533-A-Jelly) or (COAZ-19533-B-Spray) as applicable, to lubricate door weatherstrips to eliminate weatherstrip squeaks and make doors easier to close.

LUBRICATE SEAT TRACK

Using the plastic spray extension, spray Rotunda Polyethylene Grease

(C4A2-19584-B) on the seat track slides, as required, for ease of operation.

CLEAN BODY DRAIN HOLES OR EXAMINE DUST VALVES FOR PROPER OPERATION

Make sure the drain holes in the doors, rocker panels and quarter panels are free from obstruction. Visually check the dust valves for proper sealing and draining operation.

REPLACE WINDSHIELD WIPER BLADES

Wiper blade replacement intervals will vary with the amount of use, type of weather, chemical reaction from road tars or salts and the age of the blades. Be sure that the windshield glass surface is not contaminated with oil, tree sap or other foreign substance which cannot be easily rubbed off.

Generally, if the wiper pattern

across the glass is still uneven and streaked after these tests, replace the blades.

CHECK CONVERTIBLE TOP OPERATION

If convertible top operation becomes sluggish or slow, check the hydraulic reservoir fluid level. Fluid level should be approximately ¼-inch from the filler opening. The proper fluid for all cars is specified in Group 21.

CHECK CONVERTIBLE TOP FLUID LEVEL

1. Remove the rear seat and raise the top.

2. Place absorbent cloths below the filler plug.

3. Remove the filler plug, and check the fluid level. It should be level with the bottom edge of the hole.

4. If the level is low, check the system for leaks, adding the specified hydraulic fluid as necessary.

USE TO LUBRICATE
- HOOD LATCH AND HINGE PIVOTS
- HOOD AUXILIARY CATCH
  DOOR PUSH BUTTONS AND STRIKER PLATES
- DOOR LOCK CYLINDERS
  DOOR HINGE AND HINGE CHECK
- LUGGAGE COMPARTMENT LOCK CYLINDER
- LUGGAGE COMPARTMENT HINGE PIVOTS
- TAILGATE LOCK CYLINDER
- TAILGATE SUPPORT AND HINGES
- FUEL FILLER DOOR HINGES
- SEAT TRACKS
- MANUAL VENT WINDOW GEAR BOX
- MANUAL WINDOW REGULATOR ASSEMBLY

M 1113-A

FIG. 47—Polyethylene Grease Can

LUBRICATION CHARTS AND SPECIFICATIONS

GROUP 21

LUBRICATION SPECIFICATIONS

ITEM	FORD PART NO.	PART NAME	FORD SPECIFICATIONS
Body Hinges	C4AZ-19584-A R-138-B	Lifetime Body Grease	ESB-M1C105-A
Brake Master Cylinder	B7AZ-19542-A R-103-A	Rotunda Heavy Duty Brake Fluid	SAE 70R3
Front Suspension Ball Joints and Steering Linkage	C1AZ-19590-B	FoMoCo Ball Joint Grease	M1C75-A
Front Wheel Bearings	C2AZ-19585-A	FoMoCo Wheel Bearing Grease	ESA-M1C60-A
Hood Latch & Safety Catch	C4AZ-19584-A R-138-B	Lifetime Body Grease	ESB-M1C105-A
Lock Cylinders	B4A-19587-A	Rotunda Lock Lubricant	ESB-M2C20-A
Rear Axle (except 390 CID 2V and 4V)	C1AZ-19580-E or F	FoMoCo Hypoid Gear Lube	ESW-M2C50-A
Rear Axle (Hi Performance Engines and 390 CID 2V and 4V)	C2AZ-19580-D	FoMoCo Hypoid Gear Lube	ESW-M2C57-A
Limited Slip Axles (use 4 oz. of additive per axle)	C1AA-19B546-A	Locking Differential Additive	ESW-M2C58-A
Steering Gear Housing (Manual or Power)	C3AZ-19578-A	Lifetime Steering Gear Grease	ESW-M1C87-A
Steering-Power (Pump Reservoir)	C1AZ-19582-A R-106-A	Rotunda Automatic Transmission Fluid	M2C33-D
Convertible Top Reservoir	C1AZ-19582-A R-106-A	Rotunda Automatic Transmission Fluid	M2C33-D
Transmission (Automatic)	C1AZ-19582-A R-106A	Rotunda Automatic Transmission Fluid	M2C33-D
Transmission (Manual Shift)	C3RZ-19C547-B	Rotunda Manual Transmission Lube	ESW-M2C83-A
Universal Joints	C1AZ-19586-B	FoMoCo Universal Lube	ESA-M1C57-A
Engine Crankcase Oil SAE 10W-20W-30 SAE 5W-10W-20 SAE 20W-30-40	C5AZ-19579-A, B or C R-10-A, B or C C5AZ-19579-D, E or F R-10-D, E or F C5AZ-19579-G, H or J R-10-G, H or J	Rotunda Motor Oil (MS Sequence tested SAE 10W-20W-30 above—10°F SAE 5W-10W-20 for substained temperatures below —10°F SAE 20W-30-40 for temperatures above +90°F)	ESE-M2C101-A
Engine Oil Filter	C1AZ-6731-A R1-A	Rotunda Oil Filter—6,000 mile type	

ENGINE CRANKCASE OILS

Use of SAE 10W-30 oil will provide the proper viscosity for all normal ranges of outside temperatures. For operation at sustained outside temperatures below −10° F. a 5W-20 oil should be used.

Oil Quality

Use only oils which have been tested and certified by the maker as satisfying automobile manufacturers specifications for Engine Operating Sequence Tests for Service M.S. The Ford Motor Company specification covering these tests is ESE M2C101-A. These tests are defined by ASTM committee D2 for Section G-IV of technical committee B and are published in the SAE Handbook.

These tests cover oil characteristics as follows:
Sequence I—Low Temperature Wear Prevention—(Cold Starts)
Sequence II—High-Speed—High Temperature Wear Prevention.
Sequence III—High Temperature Deposit Formation—(Varnish)
Sequence IV—Corrosion and Rust Prevention
Sequence V—Sludge Formation

If engine oils are used which do not meet these requirements, it will be necessary to change oil more frequently than every 6,000 miles.

If it is necessary to use an "MS" oil which is not certified by the marketer as having passed the Engine Operating Sequence Tests, the addition of Rotunda Oil Conditioner to the oil will satisfy the requirements. Rotunda 6,000 Mile Motor Oil meets these requirements.

Oil Filter

Use of the right oil filter is also essential to good engine life and operation. For 6,000-mile filter change intervals, filters must meet Ford Specification ES-COAE-6714-A.

The Genuine Rotunda Oil Filter meets this requirement.

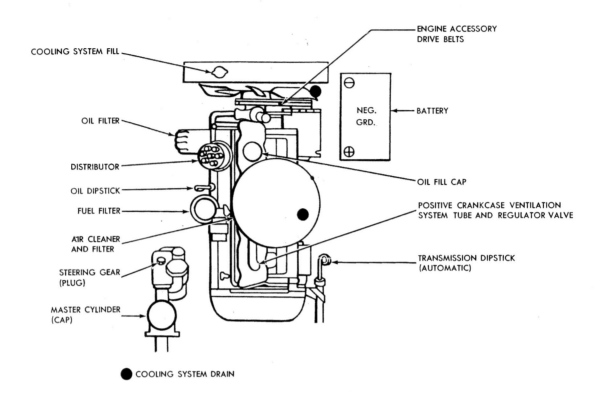

● COOLING SYSTEM DRAIN

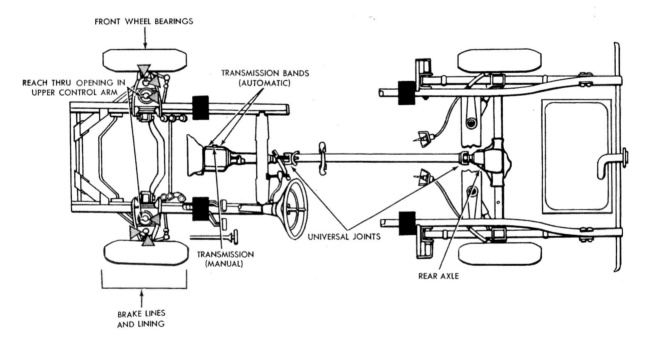

▲ FRONT SUSPENSION

Y1005-B

FIG. 1–Typical Lubrication Chart–6-Cylinder Engine

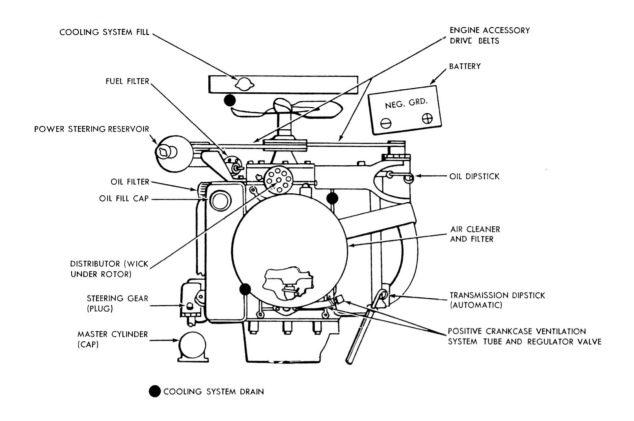

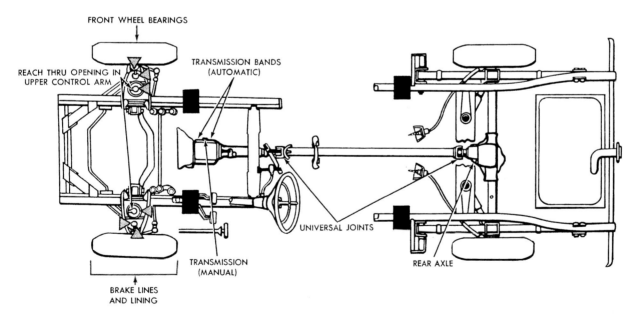

FIG. 2—Typical Lubrication Chart—V-8 Engine

SCHEMATICS

19 THRU	19K	BLUE-RED STRIPE			37A	37	BLACK-YELLOW STRIPE
	21	YELLOW		53B	53A	53	BLACK-BLUE STRIPE
	25	BLACK-ORANGE STRIPE	54C	54B	54A	54	GREEN-YELLOW STRIPE
						●	SPLICE

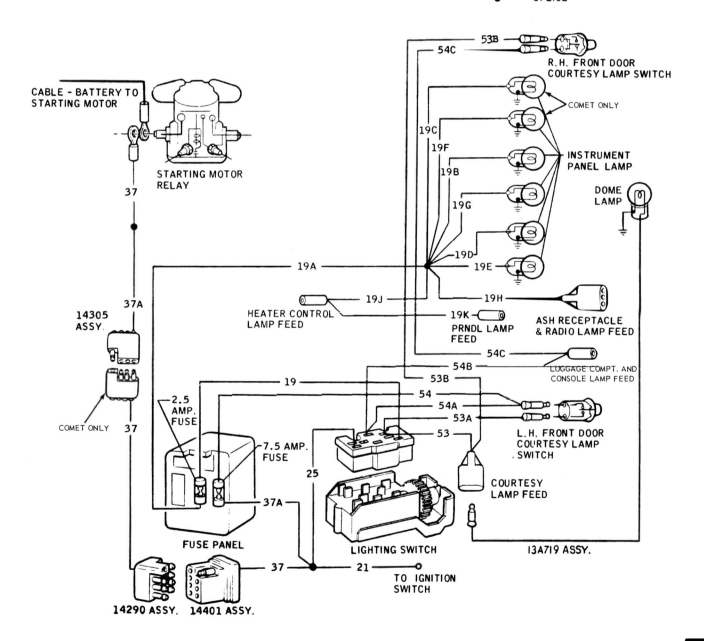

FIG. 1—Interior Lighting

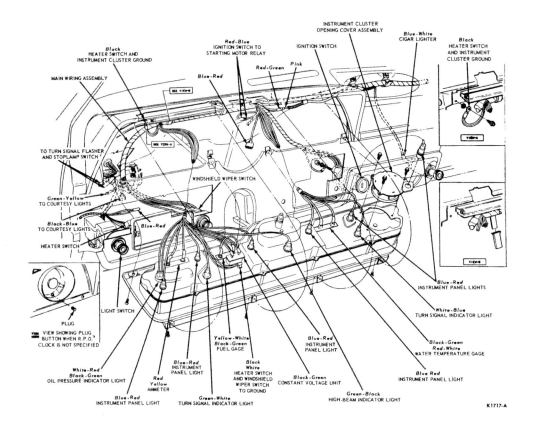

FIG. 2 – Comet Instrument Panel

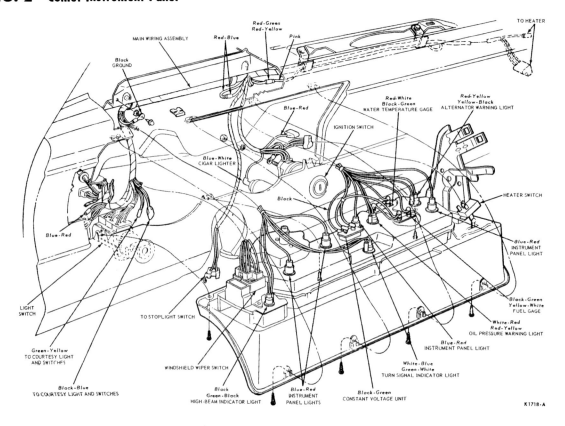

FIG. 3 – Falcon Instrument Panel

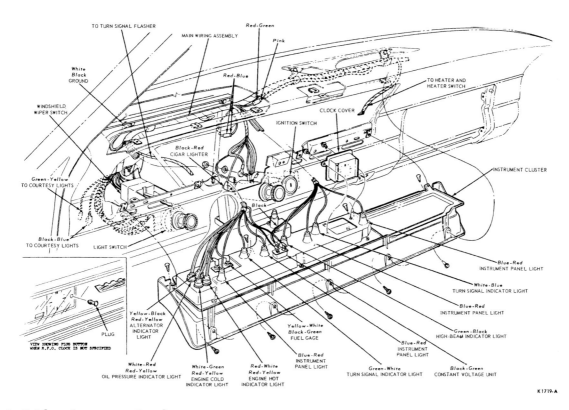

FIG. 4—Fairlane Instrument Panel

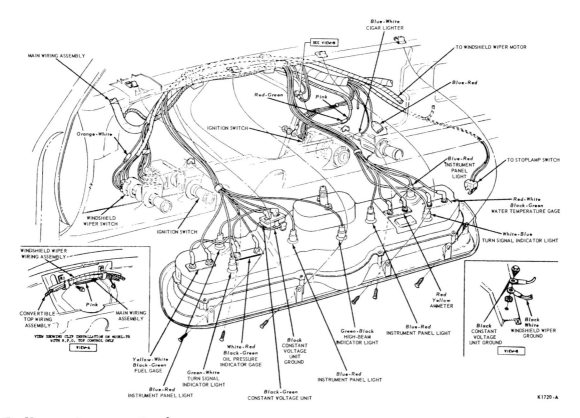

FIG. 5—Mustang Instrument Panel

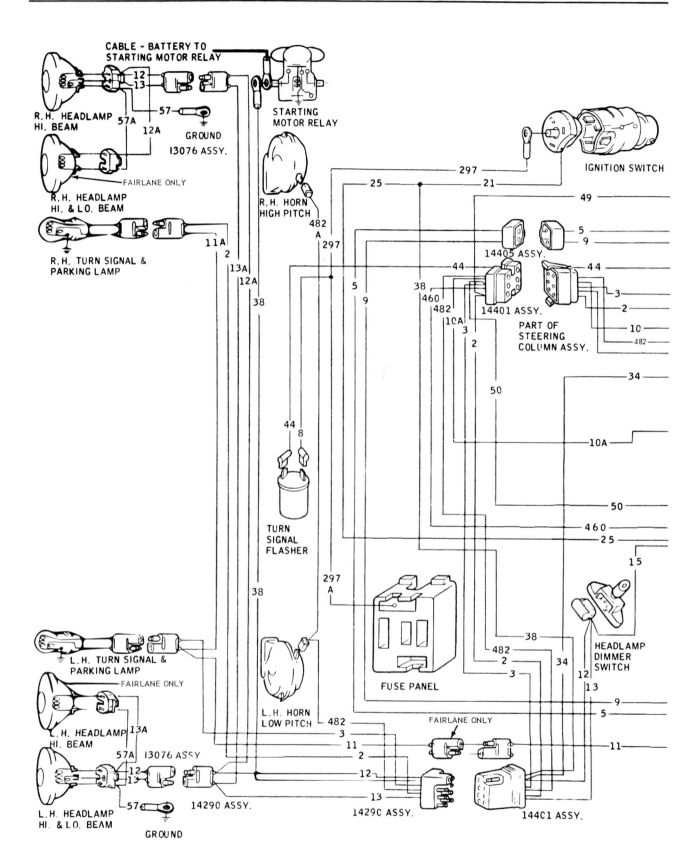

FIG. 6—Exterior Lighting, Turn Signals and Horns—Except Comet

K1722-A

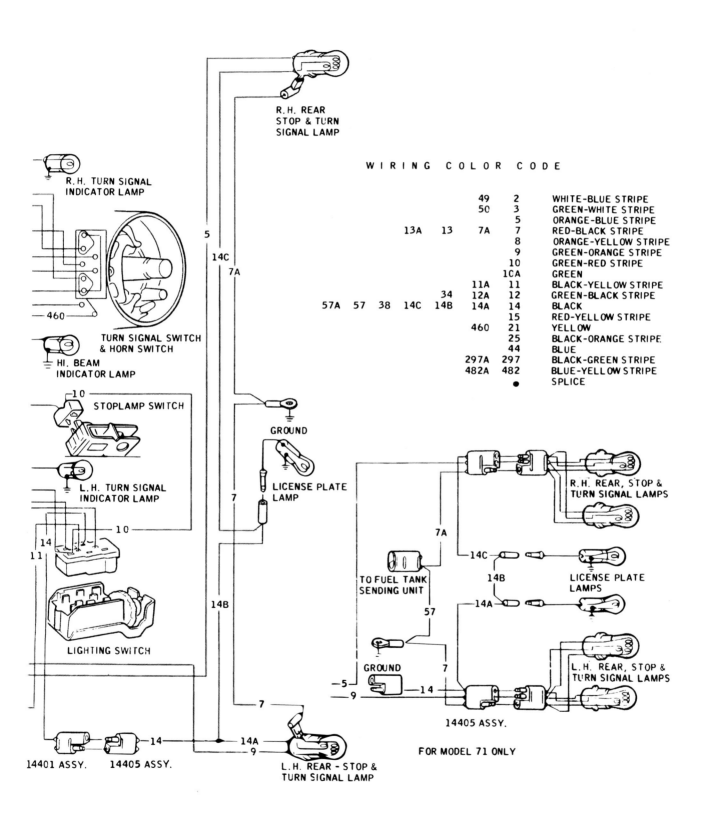

FIG. 6—Exterior Lighting, Turn Signals and Horns—Except Comet (Continued)

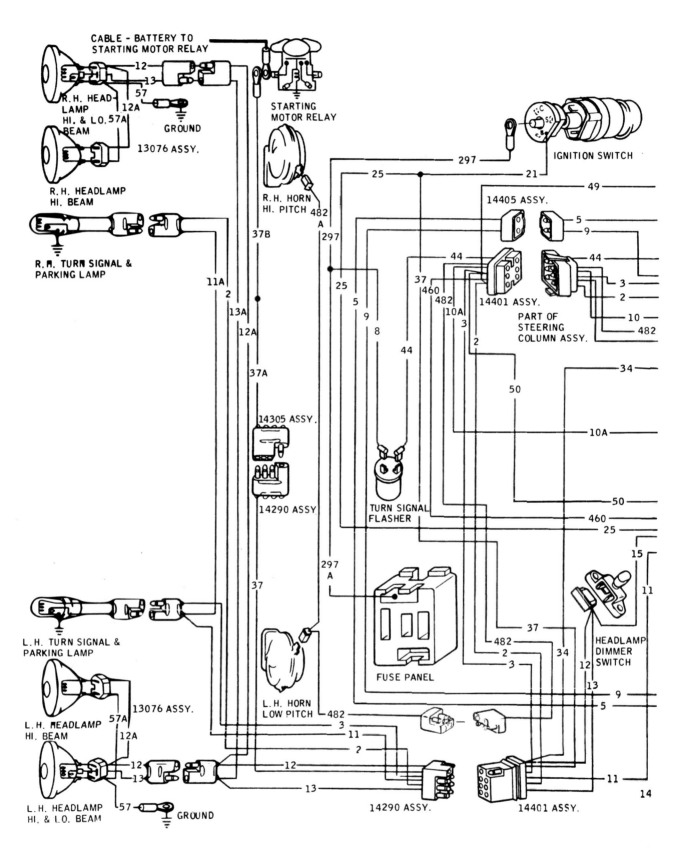

FIG. 7—Exterior Lighting, Turn Signals and Horns—Comet

K1723-A

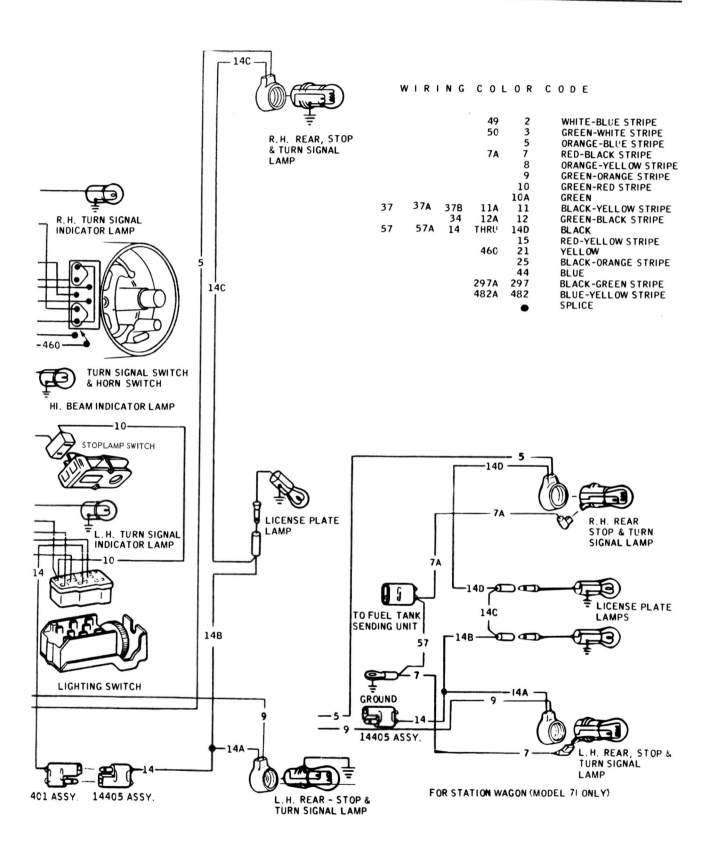

FIG. 7—Exterior Lighting, Turn Signals and Horns—Comet (Continued)

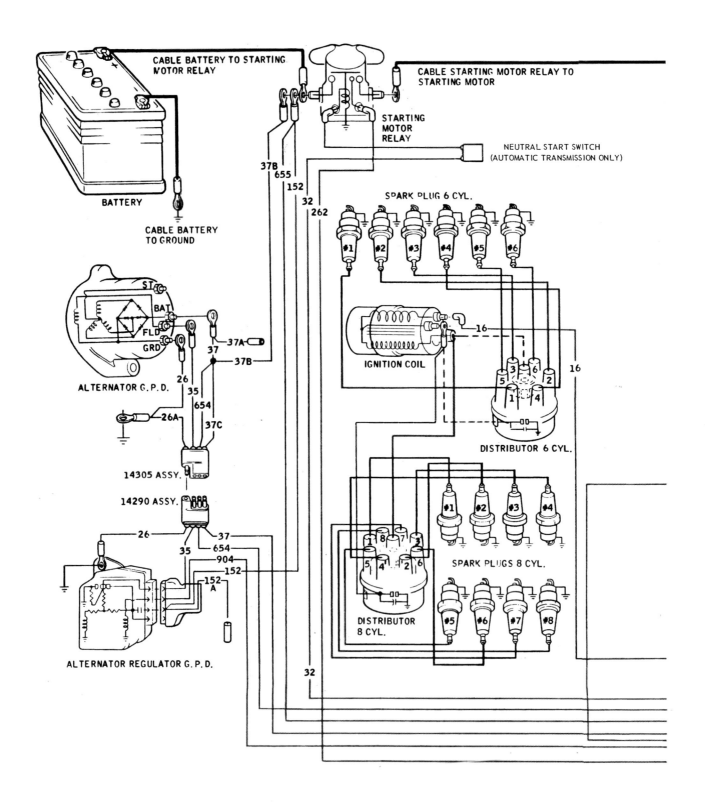

FIG. 8—Ignition, Starting, Charging and Gauges

K1724-A

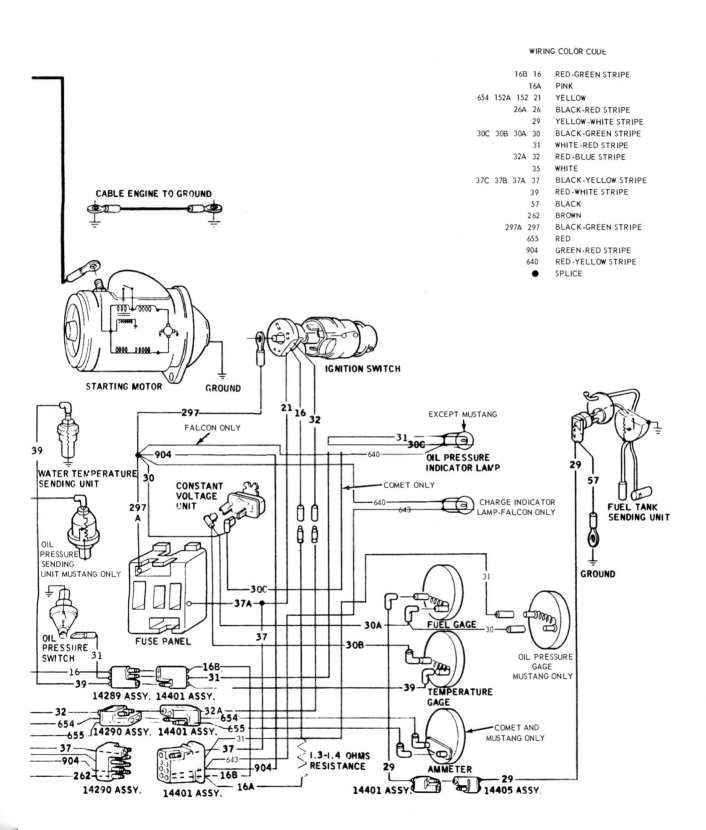

WIRING COLOR CODE

16B 16	RED-GREEN STRIPE	
16A	PINK	
654 152A 152 21	YELLOW	
26A 26	BLACK-RED STRIPE	
29	YELLOW-WHITE STRIPE	
30C 30B 30A 30	BLACK-GREEN STRIPE	
31	WHITE-RED STRIPE	
32A 32	RED-BLUE STRIPE	
35	WHITE	
37C 37B 37A 37	BLACK-YELLOW STRIPE	
39	RED-WHITE STRIPE	
57	BLACK	
262	BROWN	
297A 297	BLACK-GREEN STRIPE	
655	RED	
904	GREEN-RED STRIPE	
640	RED-YELLOW STRIPE	
●	SPLICE	

FIG. 8—Ignition, Starting, Charging and Gauges (Continued)

K1724-A

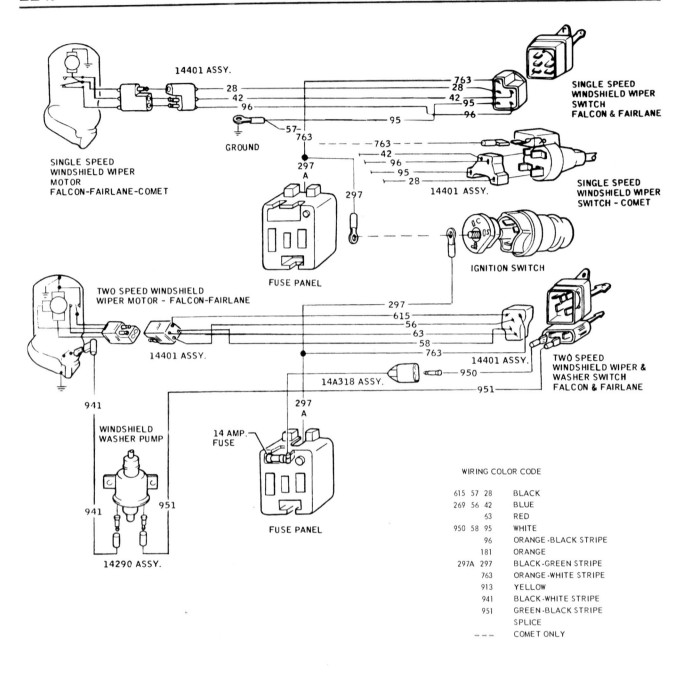

WIRING COLOR CODE

615	57	28	BLACK
269	56	42	BLUE
		63	RED
950	58	95	WHITE
		96	ORANGE-BLACK STRIPE
		181	ORANGE
297A		297	BLACK-GREEN STRIPE
		763	ORANGE-WHITE STRIPE
		913	YELLOW
		941	BLACK-WHITE STRIPE
		951	GREEN-BLACK STRIPE
			SPLICE
---			COMET ONLY

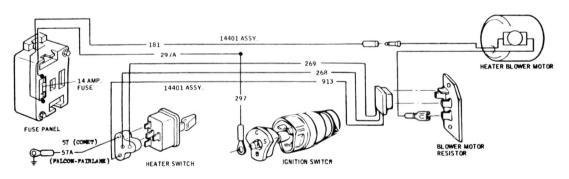

K1725-A

FIG. 9—Windshield Wipers and Heater

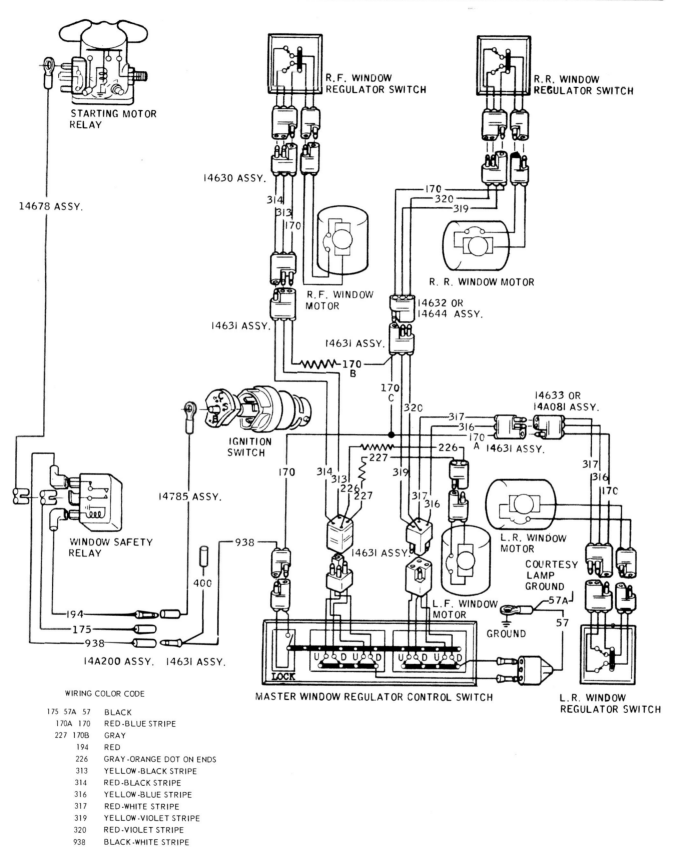

STARTING MOTOR RELAY

14678 ASSY.

R.F. WINDOW REGULATOR SWITCH

R.R. WINDOW REGULATOR SWITCH

14630 ASSY.

314
313
170

170
320
319

R. R. WINDOW MOTOR

R.F. WINDOW MOTOR

14631 ASSY.

14632 OR 14644 ASSY.

14631 ASSY.

170 B

170 C

320

14633 OR 14A081 ASSY.

317
316
170

226

317

316

170C

14631 ASSY.

IGNITION SWITCH

170

227

226
227

319

317
316

L.R. WINDOW MOTOR

COURTESY LAMP GROUND

14785 ASSY.

938

400

314
313

226
227

14631 ASSY.

317
316

L.F. WINDOW MOTOR

57A

GROUND

57

WINDOW SAFETY RELAY

194
175
938

14A200 ASSY.   14631 ASSY.

MASTER WINDOW REGULATOR CONTROL SWITCH

LOCK   U D D U D   U D D U D

L.R. WINDOW REGULATOR SWITCH

WIRING COLOR CODE

175 57A 57	BLACK
170A 170	RED-BLUE STRIPE
227 170B	GRAY
194	RED
226	GRAY-ORANGE DOT ON ENDS
313	YELLOW-BLACK STRIPE
314	RED-BLACK STRIPE
316	YELLOW-BLUE STRIPE
317	RED-WHITE STRIPE
319	YELLOW-VIOLET STRIPE
320	RED-VIOLET STRIPE
938	BLACK-WHITE STRIPE

K1727-A

FIG. 10— Comet Power Windows

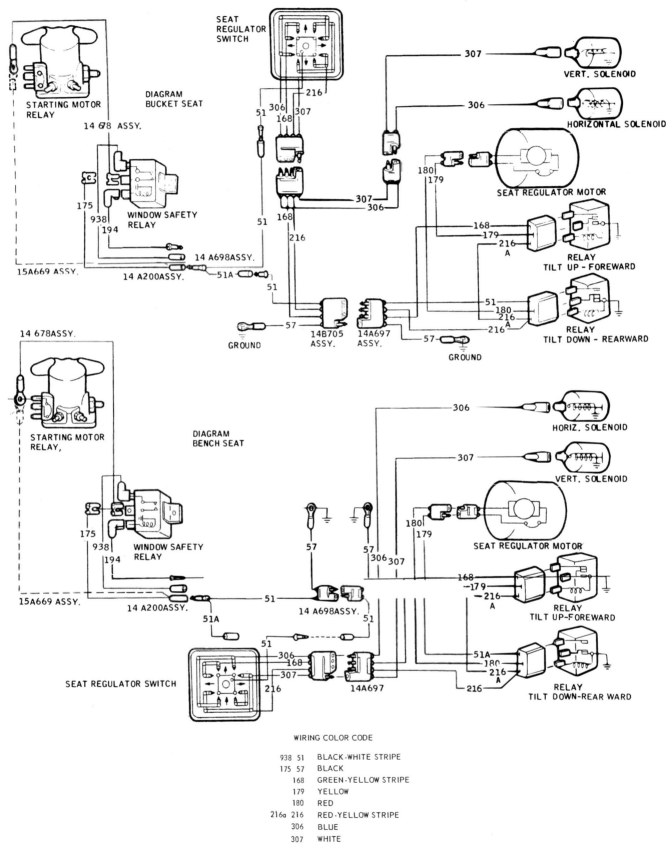

WIRING COLOR CODE

938	51	BLACK-WHITE STRIPE
175	57	BLACK
	168	GREEN-YELLOW STRIPE
	179	YELLOW
	180	RED
216a	216	RED-YELLOW STRIPE
	306	BLUE
	307	WHITE

K1728-A

FIG. 11 — Comet 4-Way Power Bench and Bucket Seat